iro

pan to
catch the
splash

PROCEDURES
IN
EXPERIMENTAL
PHYSICS

JOHN STRONG

Lost Technology Series
Reprinted by Lindsay Publications Inc.

Procedures
in
Experimental Physics

by

John Strong, Ph.D.
Special Research Associate
Harvard University

in collaboration with

H. Victor Neher, Ph.D.
Assistant Professor of Physics
California Institute of Technology

Albert E. Whitford, Ph.D.
Assistant Professor of Astronomy
Washburn Observatory, University of Wisconsin

C. Hawley Cartwright, Ph.D.
Instructor in Physics
Massachusetts Institute of Technology

and

Roger Hayward
Architect, Pasadena, California

ILLUSTRATED BY ROGER HAYWARD

Procedures in Experimental Physics

John Strong, Ph.D.

Copyright 1986 by Lindsay Publications, Inc., Bradley, IL
60915. Original copyright, 1938 by Prentice-Hall, Inc.
Published by Prentice-Hall, Inc,. New York.

ISBN 0-917914-56-2

7 8 9 0

Preface

IT is the purpose of this book to describe important procedures in experimental physics. Subjects of special interest and value to the authors in their own investigations have been selected for treatment. Many of the procedures and results of research appear here in print for the first time.

The ideal way to learn the procedures of experimental physics is by direct contact with them in the laboratory. Realizing this, we have endeavored to bridge the gap between laboratory demonstrations and experience on the one hand, and exposition on the other, by the liberal use of figures.

I am indebted to Mr. D. O. Hendrix for most of the procedures presented in Chapter II, and to Dr. R. M. Langer for the treatment of the unsteady flow of heat presented in Chapter XII.

I have drawn freely from many books and scientific periodicals. It is hoped that there are no lapses in my effort to acknowledge adequately the source of this material.

The assistance of my wife, of Mrs. Elizabeth H. Hayward, and of Mr. James T. Barkelew in the preparation of the manuscript is gratefully acknowledged, as is also the helpfulness and courtesy of the Prentice-Hall editors.

J. S.

WARNING

Remember that the materials and methods described here are from another era. Workers were less safety conscious then, and some methods may be downright dangerous. Be careful! Use good solid judgement in your work, and think ahead. Lindsay Publications, Inc. has not tested these methods and materials and does not endorse them. Our job is merely to pass along to you information from another era. Safety is your responsibility.

Write for a catalog or other unusual books available from:

Lindsay Publications, Inc.
PO Box 12
Bradley, IL 60915-0012

Contents

CHAPTER   PAGE

I. FUNDAMENTAL OPERATIONS IN LABORATORY GLASS BLOWING 1

Some physical properties of glass. Cutting tubes and bottles. Cleaning. Preheating. The rotation of the work. Bending tubes. Shrinking. Annealing. Pulling a point. Closing a tube. "Cutting" a tube in the fire. Preparations for making joints. Making a joint. Ring seals. Blowing bulbs. Constrictions. Correction of errors. Platinum seals. Tungsten-glass seals. Copper-to-glass seals. Kovar and Fernico. Porcelain-Pyrex seals.

II. LABORATORY OPTICAL WORK 29

Introduction. General procedure. Theory of grinding and polishing. Methods of polishing. Procedure for optical surfaces of 3 to 6 inches in diameter and larger. Cutting and roughing out the work. Biscuit cutter. Glass saws. Modified Draper machine. Support of the work. Grinding the curve in the work. Fine grinding. Pitch for tools. Polishing. Figuring. Cutting zones and transition zones. Interpretation of the action of polishing and figuring tools. Figuring tools for zones. Manner of figuring various zonal defects, and of making aspheric surfaces of revolution. Astigmatism. Optical testing. Newton's fringes. Haidinger's fringes. Eyepiece tests. Foucault knife-edge test. Zonal knife-edge testing. The Ronchi test. Hartmann's test. Lining up a system of mirrors. Two methods of generating optical surfaces. Working optical surfaces on the hand-lever machine. Relationship between two optical surfaces. Blocking. Quartz and calcite. Optical working of crystals. Polishing of metals. The Schmidt camera.

III. TECHNIQUE OF HIGH VACUUM 93

The law of ideal gases. The mean free path. Viscosity and heat conductivity. Pumping speeds. Conductance of vacuum pumping lines. Evacuation. Roughing pumps. Outgassing of glass and metals. Vapor pressure of waxes. Getters. Static and kinetic vacuum systems. Diffusion pumps. The use of oils as diffusion pump liquids. Oil diffusion pumps. Mercury traps. Virtual leaks. Oil traps. Construction of kinetic vacuum systems. Joints. Seals. Electrodes. Valves. Mechanical motion. Leaks. Vacuum gauges. The McLeod gauge. The ionization gauge. The Pirani gauge. The Langmuir gauge. The Knudsen gauge.

viii   CONTENTS

CHAPTER   PAGE

IV. COATING OF SURFACES: EVAPORATION AND
    SPUTTERING 151
    Burning-on method. Chemical silvering processes. Clean-
    ing. Brashear's process. Rochelle salt process. Lacquer-
    ing. Gold and copper. Sputtering. Clean dry surfaces
    and breath figures. Cleaning mirrors for aluminizing.
    Evaporation. Evaporation technique for aluminum.
    Vacuum equipment. Uniform films. Parabolizing a
    spherical mirror with aluminum. Partially reflecting films.

V. THE USE OF FUSED SILICA 188
   General remarks on fused quartz. Chemical properties.
   Physical properties. The use of quartz in the form of
   fibers. Equipment useful in making and working with
   quartz fibers. Making fibers. The care and preservation
   of small fibers. Some useful techniques in fiber work.
   Other uses of quartz.

VI. ELECTROMETERS AND ELECTROSCOPES . . . 217
    Definitions. General theory. Applications to electro-
    scopes. Applications to electrometers. Some types of
    electroscopes. Some types of electrometers. Some practi-
    cal considerations in the use of electrometers and electro-
    scopes. Steady deflection measurements. Limitations of
    various types of instruments. A comparison of various
    types of instruments. Useful techniques in electroscope
    and electrometer work. Insulators used in electrometer
    and electroscope work.

VII. GEIGER COUNTERS 259
     The point counter. The proportional counter. The
     "Zählrohr" or Geiger-Müller counter. Sensitivity of
     counters to ionizing particles. G-M tubes for special uses.
     Methods of measuring the number of counts. Coincidence
     circuits. High-voltage sources. Voltage regulators. Dis-
     cussion of probabilities and errors in Geiger counter work.

VIII. VACUUM THERMOPILES AND THE MEASUREMENT
      OF RADIANT ENERGY 305
      Construction and evacuation of a sensitive thermopile.
      Wires for the thermojunctions. Preparation of the alloy
      wires Construction of the junctions. Alternative meth-
      ods of constructing thermopiles. The use of sensitive
      thermopiles. Compensated thermopiles. Auxiliary appa-
      ratus. Relays. Construction of thermojunctions by evapo-
      ration and sputtering. Considerations in thermopile
      design. Sensitivity and minimum energy detectable.
      General summary of the work on thermopile design.

CONTENTS

CHAPTER   PAGE

IX. OPTICS: LIGHT SOURCES, FILTERS, AND OPTICAL
INSTRUMENTS 341

Divisions of the spectrum. Light sources. The ultraviolet. Prisms, lenses, and mirrors for the ultraviolet. Filters for the ultraviolet. Polarization of the ultraviolet. The infrared. Prisms, windows, lenses, and mirrors for the infrared. Reflection of crystals. Residual rays. Special absorbers for the near infrared. Visible spectrum. The Christiansen filter. Reflection of metals. Monochromators. Polarization. Engineering applications of polarized light. Quarter-, half-, and full-wave plates. Splitting of mica. Mica gauges. Magnification of lenses. Other properties of lenses. Properties of mirrors. Properties of prisms. Optical recording systems.

X. PHOTOELECTRIC CELLS AND AMPLIFIERS . . 396

Introduction. Limit of detection compared. Types of cells. Characteristics of emissive-type cells. The manufacture of cells. Vacuum and gas-filled cells. Photovoltaic cells. Amplification of photoelectric currents. Direct-current amplifiers. Experimental details. Other low-grid-current tubes. High-gain direct-current amplifiers. Alternating-current amplifiers. Fluctuation noises in vacuum-tube circuits. Applications of photoelectric cells. General remarks on photoelectric photometry. Spectrophotometry. Densitometers. Amplification of small galvanometer deflections. Thyratrons.

XI. PHOTOGRAPHY IN THE LABORATORY . . . 449

Comparison of the sensitivities of the eye with the photographic emulsion. Hurter and Driffield curves. Reciprocity law. The resolving power. Light sources. Filters. Focusing. Sensitizing. Gelatin shifts. Exposure. Development. Time and temperature development. Tray development. Desensitizing. Fixing. Washing and drying. Printing and enlarging papers. Intensifying and reducing. Some applications of photography. Photographic photometry.

XII. HEAT AND HIGH TEMPERATURE 493

Heat conduction. The steady state. Shape factors. Heat conduction. The nonsteady state. Heat transfer by free convection. Heat transfer by radiation. Low temperatures. Methods of obtaining high temperatures. Fixed temperatures. Thermostatic devices. Temperature measurement.

XIII. NOTES ON THE MATERIALS OF RESEARCH 531

Alkali metals. Alkali-earth metals. Mercury. Platinum metals. The refractory metals: Tungsten, molybdenum, tantalum, and so forth. Alloys. Wood. Waxes and cements. Lubrication. Soapstone.

CONTENTS

CHAPTER PAGE

XIV. NOTES ON THE CONSTRUCTION AND DESIGN OF
INSTRUMENTS AND APPARATUS 569
The cutting of metals. The lathe. Soft soldering. Hard
soldering. Spot welding. Instrument design. Vibrationless supports.

XV. MOLDING AND CASTING 593
The lost-wax method. Patterns for sand casting. Sand
casting. Cuttlebone casting.

CHAPTER I

Fundamental Operations in Laboratory Glass Blowing

THE fundamental operations in glass blowing for laboratory use are cutting, rotating, bending, blowing, and welding. By various combinations of these operations, apparatus is constructed from glass tubing and glass cane. It is the purpose of this chapter to describe how these operations are executed. Hard glass, such as Pyrex, is now used extensively for making laboratory apparatus. It is more difficult to manipulate than soft glass because it has a higher working temperature and thus congeals quickly when it is removed from the flame. However, less difficulty is experienced in annealing hard glass because of its low thermal expansion and high strength. Since this more than outweighs the greater skill required for manipulation, we will be concerned chiefly with hard glass in this chapter.[1]

An arrangement of a glass-blowing workbench is shown in Fig. 1. Cross-fires are shown for heating the glass to softness, a method that may be termed American, since German glass blowers ordinarily use a single-blast burner. Compared with the blast burner, cross-fires heat the glass more rapidly and uniformly. Either method may be used for most of the operations. However, some of them require a pointed flame, which is more easily obtained with a blast burner.

Here, where we treat of the American method, the hand torch, mounted as shown by the dotted lines in Fig. 1, is used to obtain the pointed flame. Natural or artificial gas

[1] Glass may be obtained from the Corning Glass Company, Corning, New York.

1

is used for fuel in the burners. Compressed air is used for working soft glass; but in order to obtain the higher temperature required to work hard glass, oxygen or a mixture of oxygen and air must be used. In an ordinary blast burner, however, acetylene can be used as fuel with compressed air.

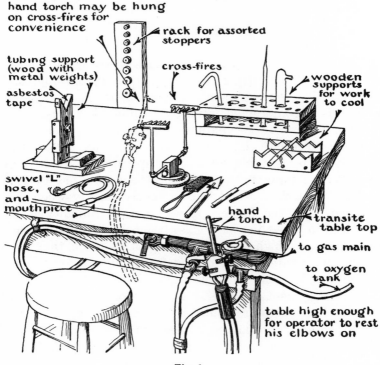

Fig. 1.

Accessory equipment includes a collection of corks of various sizes, some fitted with closed glass tubes to serve as handles for rotating the work, and others with open tubes for blowing. Pieces of rubber hose of various sizes fitted with closed glass tubes, to close up the ends of small tubes, are also included. A swivel L and mouthpiece device with a connecting rubber hose, shown in Fig. 1, is convenient for blowing rotated work that is large or otherwise awkward to bring to the mouth.   Forceps and molding tools used for spinning glass are shown in Fig. 2.   A file for cutting small tubes and a hot-wire device for cutting larger tubes are shown in Fig. 3.   To sharpen the corners of the file, the narrow sides are ground on an emery wheel.   When the file

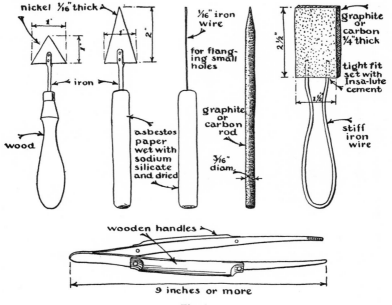

Fig. 2.

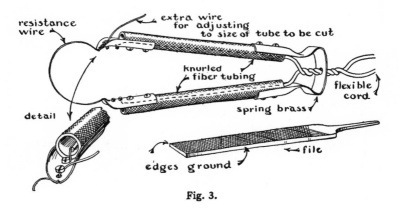

Fig. 3.

requires tempering, it is heated until it becomes a dull red
and plunged into cold mercury.

Pyrex tubes of various sizes, capillaries, and cane are kept
in stock for constructing apparatus. There should also be
a supply of other glasses, such as soda glass, lead glass, and

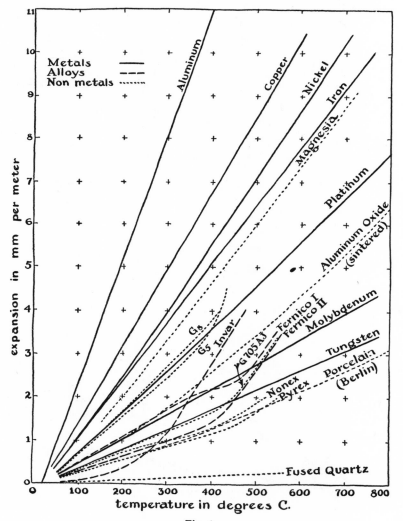

Fig. 4.

Nonex. These should be well labeled and kept apart from the main stock.

Some physical properties of glass. The thermal expansion of various glasses and metals is shown in Fig. 4 and Table I. Other characteristic temperatures of glass and quartz are given in Table II. The variation of viscosity

TABLE I

THERMAL EXPANSION COEFFICIENTS

Material	Expansion Coefficient ($\times 10^7$)
Lime glass (G8)................	92
Lead glass (G5)...............	90
Nonex (G702P)................	36
Porcelain (20° to 290° C.).......	41
Pyrex........................	32
Quartz glass (16° to 1000° C.)....	5.8
Copper.......................	162
Platinum.....................	91
Dumet:	
radial......................	80 to 100
axial......................	61 to 65
Fernico and Kovar:	
25° to 450° C................	47
25° to 500° C................	56
Molybdenum..................	56
Tungsten.....................	47

TABLE II

CHARACTERISTIC TEMPERATURES FOR GLASS AND QUARTZ

Material	Strain Point	Annealing Temperature	Working Temperature
Soft glass.........	389° C.	425° C.	....
Nonex............	486°	521°	....
Pyrex............	503°	550°	750° to 1100° C.
Quartz...........	1020°	1120°	1756° to 1800°

with temperature for a typical glass is shown in Fig. 5. The viscosities corresponding to important characteristic temperatures—annealing temperature, working temperature, and melting temperature—are indicated on the curve in Fig. 5. The significance of the first two temperatures is

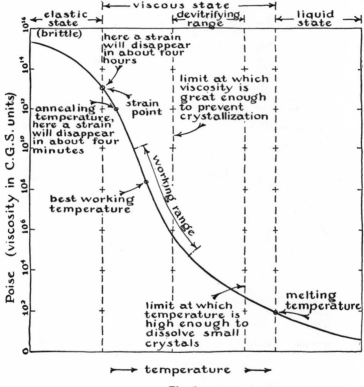

Fig. 5.

that internal strain is relieved in about 4 hours when glass is heated to the yield point, while only about 4 minutes are required at the annealing temperature. At the yield point the viscosity is about 10^{13} poise. At the annealing temperature it is about 10^{12} poise. In the working range of temperature the viscosity varies between the limits 10^5 and 10^{10} poise, with the optimum working viscosity about $10^{8.6}$ poise.

Glass is considered molten when the viscosity is less than 10^2 poise.

Cutting tubes and bottles. To cut small glass tubes (to $\frac{1}{2}$ inch in diameter) for the operations of glass blowing,

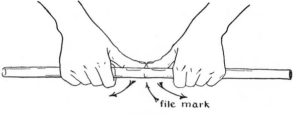

file mark

Fig. 6.

they are first scratch-marked with the sharp edge of a file, care being taken that the scratch, a few millimeters long, is accurately perpendicular to the tube.   A break is then made by a combined bending and pulling force as illustrated in Fig. 6.   Tubes can be broken at the scratch-mark by means of a stroke with the file as shown in Fig. 7.   This technique is suitable when the tube is hot or when it is to be cut near the end.

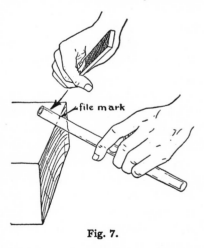

Tubes larger than $\frac{1}{2}$ inch in diameter require a different technique.   After being scratch-marked with the file, they may be cracked by applying the tip of a small piece of glass cane, made incandescent in the flame, to one end of the file mark. The crack thus produced

file mark

Fig. 7.

may or may not completely encircle the glass.   If not, it can be made to do so by leading it with repeated applications of the glowing cane tip, each application being just ahead of the end of the crack.

A tube or bottle of several inches in diameter is cut by first filing a narrow scratch-mark around its circumference. A piece of stiff paper or cardboard may be used to guide the file in making this mark. The wire of the device shown in Fig. 3 is adjusted to fit in the mark. The ends of the wire must not touch. An electric current is passed through the wire, heating it to a red heat for a few seconds, and water is applied to the scratch-mark and wire with a pad of wet cotton. This procedure will produce a clean crack around the circumference. Small irregularities in the crack may be removed by grinding on a brass plate with Carborundum grits, or after the glass has been softened in the flame they may be pulled off with forceps or cut off with shears.

Cleaning. Good welds cannot be made with contaminated glass. Therefore, the first operation after cutting should be cleaning. Sometimes washing with water is sufficient, but nitric acid may be substituted if necessary. In extreme cases, hot chromic acid "cleaning solution" may be required. Water used to rinse glass tubing is removed from the outside with a clean cloth and from the inside with a wad of cotton pulled through with a string or blown through with air. Or, if distilled water is used, the tube may be dried by drawing air through it with a water aspirator and by warming it gently at the same time.

Preheating. Glass tubing and especially large glass apparatus must be preheated carefully before they can be safely exposed to the local intense heat of the cross-fires or hand torch. By one procedure for preheating, the work is first exposed to the relatively cool flame of a Meker burner with the air shut off. As the glass temperature rises, more and more air is admitted to the Meker burner, giving a hotter and hotter flame, until finally, when the work is thoroughly heated, it is safe to expose it to the intense heat of the cross-fires or blast burner. By an alternative procedure the work is exposed to the heat of the cross-fires for a fraction of a second, after which it is quickly withdrawn to allow temperatures to equalize, and then after a few seconds another section of the work is exposed. This operation is repeated in such a way that the temperature of the work as a whole is uniformly elevated. The exposure to the flame is increased and the interval outside the flame decreased as the heating progresses, until the work is brought to a temperature at which it distills enough sodium vapor to make the flame yellow. This sodium test usually indicates a temperature at which it is safe to begin the operations of shrinking, blowing, molding, and so forth. Some things, such as tubes, require preheating only in the zone around the region to be worked.

The rotation of the work. Rotation of work is a fundamental operation. It should be executed uniformly and with good coördination of the two hands. Glass properly rotated in the flame becomes uniformly soft, and the effect of gravity on it is symmetrical.

The lower surfaces of hot glass cool more rapidly than the upper surfaces. For this reason it is also important to continue uniform rotation even after the work is removed from the flame.

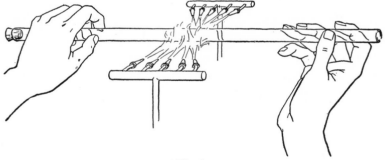

Fig. 8.

The beginner will have difficulty manipulating the work in the flame, particularly after the glass connecting the two parts on either side of the flame becomes soft, when he may "tie up" the work. To avoid this, he is advised to practice rotation with a model consisting of two glass tubes connected with fairly heavy cloth. He should be able to rotate these in the manner shown in Fig. 8, so that the cloth does not wrinkle or twist and is under neither compression nor tension. He is then ready to begin operations with the flame. The work is manipulated by the thumbs and forefingers so that, despite differences in diameter, the sections of the work on either side of the soft zone in the flame are rotated in synchronism, the motion consisting of a series of angular displacements of about 45°. The left hand always handles the heavier section of the glass, while the right manipulates the section beyond the soft zone. The right hand has the more delicate though lighter task, since it must rotate its section in phase and without undesired stretching or compression relative to the main section of the work. The hands are held as shown in Fig. 8 to facilitate the application of the right end of the work to the lips for blowing.

Bending tubes. A tube to be bent is heated in the crossfires with continued rotation until it is quite soft along a

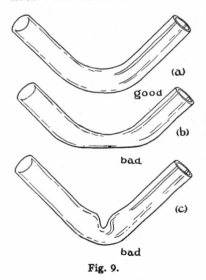

(a)

good

(b)

bad

(c)

bad

Fig. 9.

length equal to several diameters. It is then removed from the flame and bent to the desired angle with the apex down as shown in Fig. 9. As large tubes are difficult to heat uniformly, imperfections often occur. They are also present in small tubes, particularly in small, thin-walled tubes, that have been bent to a sharp angle. Imperfections are worked out in every case by local heating with a pointed flame. When one portion of the tubing wall is heated until it is soft, the general form of the bend is maintained by the portion on the opposite side of the axis of the tube. If the outside tends to flatten as shown in Fig. 9(b), it is corrected by blowing while the glass is soft. If the inside surface folds as shown at (c), it is locally heated with a sharp pointed flame and worked by alternating shrinking with blowing until it is uniform. These corrections are followed by a general heating to anneal the whole bend.

A glass coil is made on a mandrel. The mandrel is usually either a steel or brass tube covered with asbestos paper. The paper is applied wet, the ends being lapped and cemented with sodium silicate. After the paper is dry, this lap joint is sandpapered. One or more coats of stove polish or some other form of carbon will prevent the glass from adhering to the asbestos. Notches in the end of the tube secure the coil to the mandrel. The procedure is illustrated by Fig. 10.

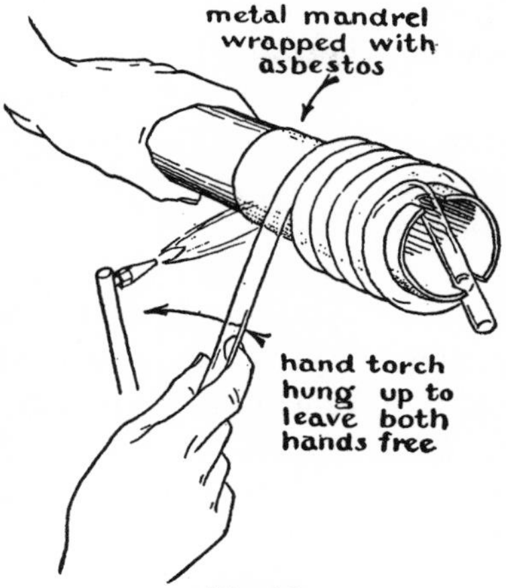

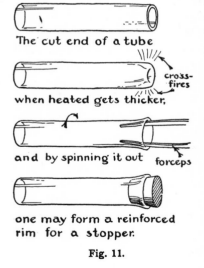

metal mandrel
wrapped with
asbestos

hand torch
hung up to
leave both
hands free

Fig. 10.

Shrinking. Since softened glass is a liquid, its surface tension tends to deform it in such a way that the total surface is decreased. Shrinking at elevated temperatures is restrained by the viscosity of the glass, and this restraint is greater at the lower limit of the working range. Shrinking may yield both desirable and undesirable changes in the work and it is controlled by the use of spinning tools and by blowing into the work. Fig. 11 shows the use of forceps to counteract the undesirable

The cut end of a tube

cross-fires

when heated gets thicker,

and by spinning it out   forceps

one may form a reinforced rim for a stopper.

Fig. 11.

tendency of the end of a tube to decrease its diameter by shrinking, while the desirable effect of increased wall thickness is achieved.

Annealing. The annealing of complicated and elaborate work is one of the most difficult operations in glass blowing. It is also an important one, since, if the work is not properly annealed, it may break in cooling or, what is worse, fail after it is put into operation. The purpose of annealing is to bring the glass from the working temperature to room temperature with the introduction of a minimum amount of strain. Annealing is properly executed when all parts of the work are maintained at a uniform temperature while the glass is gradually cooled. Large, complicated work should be annealed in a suitably regulated oven. Small work in which the wall thicknesses are uniform can be successfully annealed either with a Meker burner or in the cross-fires.

When the manipulations have been completed, the work is heated until it is above the annealing temperature. The temperature is then gradually lowered by applying the procedures of preheating in reverse order. It is important that the temperatures be kept uniform during the cooling by special extra applications of heat on those parts which tend to cool more rapidly, either because they are thinner or because they are subject to greater heat losses by radiation and convection. When the temperature is judged to be well below the strain point, the work may be set aside for final cooling in a place free from drafts.

Pulling a point. "Pulling a point" is a technical term used by glass blowers indicating that a tube is heated in the flame and drawn out as illustrated in Fig. 12 to give a "point," which is usually some 6 inches in length. The point may have several functions. It may serve as a handle for rotation or, with the tip removed, as a mouthpiece through which to blow; or it may afford a means of closing the work. Also, pulling a point is a preliminary to several other operations.

We will assume, for the purpose of our discussion here, that a section of tubing is required with points on both ends as an element of some apparatus under construction, and further-more that this is to be obtained from a longer stock tube. First, a point is pulled on the end of the stock tube. If it is long, the stock tube may be supported on the left by a

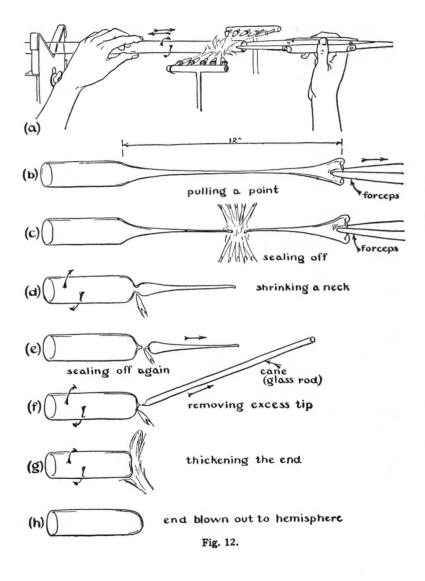

(a)

(b) pulling a point   forceps

12"

(c) sealing off   forceps

(d) shrinking a neck

(e) sealing off again   cane (glass rod)

(f) removing excess tip

(g) thickening the end

(h) end blown out to hemisphere

Fig. 12.

V-block as shown at (a) in Fig. 12. After preheating the tube by the second procedure outlined above, it is softened a few diameters back from the end. Then the glass is gathered together at the tip with forceps; the work is removed from the flame, and with continued rotation the soft glass is drawn out as shown at (b). The capillary section is fused in the middle as shown at (c), or, if the point is to serve as a mouthpiece, it may be cut and fire-glazed by momentary exposure to a flame.

The tubing is then heated until it is soft at a suitable distance back of the first point, and the desired section is drawn off, forming at the same time the, second point.

It is important to have the walls of the point symmetrical about the axis of the tube. Errors may be corrected by heating the shoulder of the point until it is soft and manipulating the glass from the end of the capillary. It is advisable to work the glass at a low temperature when making corrections.

Closing a tube. Pulling a point is the first operation in closing a tube as shown in Fig. 12(d) to (h). The point is removed with a sharp flame as shown at (d) and (e). Excess glass at the tip is removed with forceps or with a piece of cane (f), and the end is then heated to shrink it (g); then it is blown to the final hemispherical shape (h). The hand torch is usually used for this operation.

"Cutting" a tube in the fire. The first step in "cutting" a tube in the fire is to pull a point. Again the point is removed as described above, Fig. 12(d) and (e), and excess glass removed, Fig. 13(a). The end is then heated (b) and blown with a strong puff to yield a thin kidney-shaped bulb (c), which is broken off with the file or forceps as shown at (d). The edges are now heated to shrink them and thicken them to the size of the tubing elsewhere (e). The diameter is increased by a spinning process and the use of forceps as in (f) or flanging tool as in (g). If forceps are used, they are introduced and allowed to expand slowly as the glass is rotated in the fire. The end of the tube is then squared with the carbon plate (h).   If a flange is required, the end is spun out with the arrowhead spinning tool and squared with the carbon plate as shown at (h) and (i). Metal spinning tools are wet with beeswax to prevent sticking to soft glass.

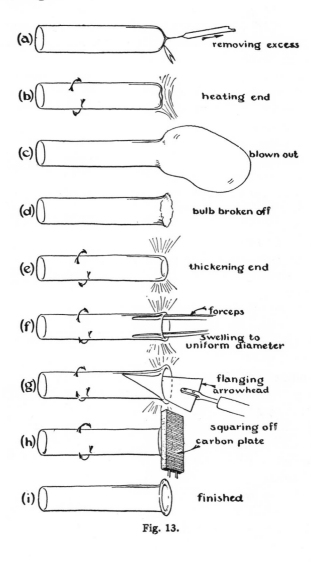

Fig. 13.

Fig. 14.

Preparations for making joints.
Thorough cleaning of the glass tube
and careful attention to the preliminaries of cutting, flanging,
or drawing and expanding it
facilitate the manipulations
in the flame. A common fault
in the beginner is that he thinks he can easily correct defi-
ciencies in these operations
after the work is in the flame.
It is significant that good
glass blowers do not handi-
cap themselves by carelessness with these preliminaries.

The elements that are to
be welded to form a joint
must have approximately the
same diameter and wall
thickness. If a large tube is
to be joined to a smaller one,
the large tube is first prepared as shown in Fig. 14(a)
by pulling a point on it and
then cutting off the point in
the flame where the shoulder
has the same diameter as the
small tube.

A capillary or thick-walled
tube is prepared as shown at
(b). It is heated to softness
and blown until it has the
proper wall thickness and
then pulled until it has the
same diameter as the tube
to which it is to be sealed.

A bulb or cylinder to which
a small tube is to be joined is

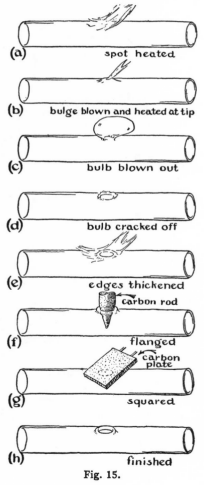

(a)   spot heated

(b)   bulge blown and heated at tip

(c)   bulb blown out

(d)   bulb cracked off

(e)   edges thickened

(f)   flanged   carbon rod

(g)   squared   carbon plate

(h)   finished

Fig. 15.

first preheated. A soft flame is then directed on the place selected for the joint until it is soft, and a slight bulge is blown as shown in Fig. 15(a). This bulge is strongly heated at its apex with the tip of a sharp flame as at (b). Then, after removing it from the flame, a small thin-walled bulb is blown as at (c). This is then broken off with the forceps or file. The edges of the hole thus made are softened with the flame, flanged with the carbon taper, and squared with the carbon plate as shown in Fig. 15(d) to (h).

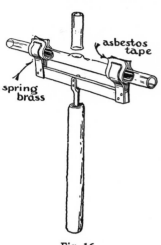

Fig. 16.

A straight tube is prepared for making T's by opening the side as described above. When several T's are to be made, a holder for the straight-through tube as shown in Fig. 16 is convenient. Y's are made by first bending a tube to an acute angle. This is then opened at the apex as shown in Fig. 17.

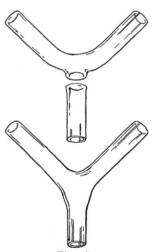

Fig. 17.

Making a joint. The elements are heated with rotation in a flame whose diameter is approximately the same as the diameter of the tubes. They are arranged facing each other, as shown in Fig. 18, with the axis of the joint perpendicular to that of the flame. When the tubes are thoroughly soft at their ends, they are removed from the flame and touched together at right angles as shown at (b). This contact is used as a hinge to steady the hands while the tubes are brought into exact register and pushed together (c). With continuous rotation, the joint is held in the flame until it shrinks to a uniform outside diameter (d). It is then withdrawn from the flame and blown out until it has a uniform

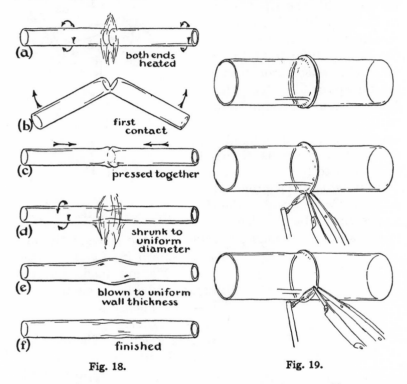

Fig. 18.   Fig. 19.

wall thickness (e), and stretched at once to a uniform outside diameter (f). Since it is necessary to blow a joint, obviously all openings except the one applied to the lips must be temporarily closed.

Large tubes that are to be joined must have flanges. When it is necessary to make a joint on apparatus which cannot be rotated, the squared ends of the elements of the joint are accurately fitted together and heated, a section of the circumference at a time. The welding of the flanges is effected with the heat of the hand torch and pressure applied with the forceps working around the circumference as shown in Fig. 19. After this the joint is locally heated, a small section of the circumference at a time, until it is soft, and the softened area is worked by alternate shrinking and blowing until the wall is smooth. Then the whole circumference is uniformly heated for final blowing, alignment, and annealing.

Ring seals. When a tube is inserted in a bulb or a larger tube, a ring seal joins the tubing wall to the edge of the aperture in the bulb or large tube. First, the glass around the

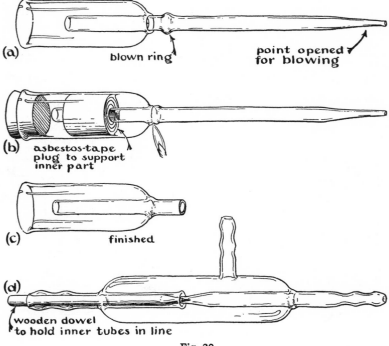

Fig. 20.

aperture is accurately molded with the carbon taper until it is slightly larger than the outside diameter of the small tube to be inserted. The small tube is prepared for the seal by heating a narrow zone around its circumference with a pointed flame and swelling it as shown in Fig. 20(a). This is accomplished by blowing and simultaneously applying a longitudinal compression. The small tube is then inserted and held exactly concentric with the larger tube by an improvised support, such as a roll of asbestos paper, as illustrated in Fig. 20(b). The place to be sealed is exposed to a pointed flame with continued rotation until the glass at the ring is soft. Then the weld is made by pushing the swelling of the smaller tube against the constricted opening of the larger tube. The work is removed from the flame, blown, and aligned, while at the same time the small tube is given a slight pull. Fig. 20 shows the construction of a water aspirator which requires two ring seals. A tapered wooden dowel which just slips into the first tube centers the second while it is being sealed. Ring seals require careful annealing.

Another procedure for ring seals, particularly suited for inserting a small tube through the side of a larger tube, is

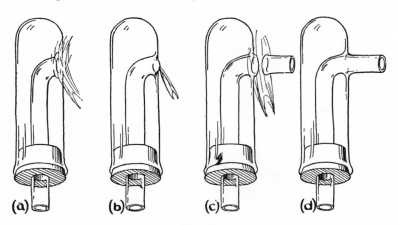

Fig. 21.

illustrated by Fig. 21. The inner section of the insert is flanged and molded to conform to the inside wall of the large tube and is supported in contact with it as shown at (a). The area of the outside wall of the large tube opposite the place where the section makes contact on the inside is then heated until the two tubes are sealed together. A bulge is blown and opened with a sharp flame at the center of this seal as shown at (b). The opening is molded and a small side tube is joined to the edges of it to form a continuation of the inner section as shown at (c) and (d).

Blowing bulbs. Difficulty may be experienced in making large bulbs (of 2 inches in diameter or larger), for which it is necessary to heat heavy masses of soft glass to a uniform temperature in the flame. Also, the work must be skillfully managed outside the flame to make the effects of air cooling symmetrical. Because of these difficulties it is advisable to use commercial balloon flasks for bulbs rather than to make them from tubing. Small bulbs, less than 1 inch in diameter, are not so difficult to make.

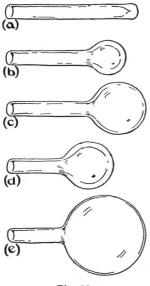

The first operation in making bulbs is to heat the end of a glass tube until the glass collects as shown in Fig. 22(a). As glass collects, it is alternately blown out and shrunk to distribute it uniformly until enough has collected for the final bulb. The collected glass is then heated to a uniform temperature and removed from the flame.

Fig. 22.

After the work has been rotated a few seconds about a horizontal axis, it is expanded by blowing through an appropriate mouthpiece. The blowing is gentle at first and stronger as the glass stiffens. The work is continuously rotated. However, if one portion of the surface tends to expand more rapidly than the other portions, it is turned down and cooled to restrain its expansion, since the under side of the work cools most rapidly.

To blow a bulb in the middle of a tube, the operation of collecting glass, as described above, is carried out in zones

until several adjacent ones are obtained as shown in
Fig. 23(a) to (c). Then, by blowing and shrinking, these are

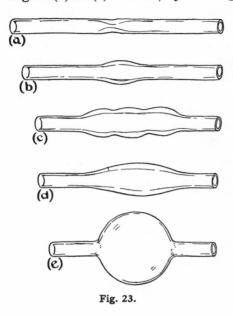

combined in a single
uniform zone (d). This
is well heated, removed
from the flame, allowed
to cool a moment, and
blown to the desired
form (e).

Constrictions. Two
types of constrictions
may be required. One,
useful for preventing
kinetic overflow of mer-
cury in a manometer
tube when the pressure
suddenly changes, has
a constricted inner wall
but uniform outside di-
ameter. The second
type, useful as a "seal-
off" for a vacuum system, has a uniform wall thickness. To
make either type, the glass tubing to be constricted is heated
and worked until the glass walls thicken. This operation is
essentially the same as the preliminary operation for blowing
a bulb in the middle of a tube as shown in Fig. 23(a). After
the walls have been thickened, the glass is removed from the
flame, and the tube is rotated and pulled instead of blown as
for a bulb. To get a constriction of the first type, the tube
is pulled until the outside diameter of the tube is uniform,
while to get a "seal-off" constriction the tube is pulled until
the wall thickness is uniform.

Correction of errors. Owing to errors of manipulation,
the walls of glass apparatus frequently are not uniform.
This lack of uniformity not only detracts from the workmanlike appearance of the finished apparatus but also increases
the difficulty of annealing, since the thick and thin portions

Fig. 23.

tend to cool at different rates, a circumstance which causes strain in the glass.

Excessive glass can be drawn off from a region in the walls of an apparatus by using a piece of cane as illustrated in Fig. 13(a). After the required amount of glass is drawn off, the region is worked by blowing and shrinking until the wall thickness becomes uniform. Also, if the wall of a region is too thin, glass can be added from a piece of cane and worked out smooth by blowing and shrinking. Holes may inadvertently appear in the work. They are closed by drawing their edges together with a piece of cane.

Platinum seals. Formerly, the only satisfactory method of making a metal-to-glass seal was by the use of platinum and soft glass. Such seals are rarely used now because of the high price of platinum. Also, hard glass, which seals directly to tungsten, is now used extensively for making laboratory apparatus. However, a platinum tube may be required to introduce pure hydrogen by diffusion into a glass apparatus. For this and other special purposes, platinum–soft glass seals are required.

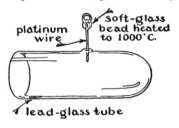

Fig. 24 shows a platinum electrode in a soft-glass tube. In making this platinum seal, a small bead of soft glass (either lead or soda glass) is first fused to the platinum wire. The bead and wire are heated to

finished seal
Fig. 24.

about 1000° C. to obtain a good glass-to-metal bond. Then the bead is sealed into the wall of the tube as shown in the illustration.

Tungsten-glass seals. Tungsten wires may be sealed through Pyrex if their diameters are less than 0.060 inch. Larger tungsten wires, to diameters of twice as much, are first sealed in a sleeve of Nonex glass, which in turn is sealed into the wall of glass apparatus. This latter operation is necessary, especially if the seal is to be exposed to the heat of a baking-out oven. Nonex glass has a lower softening temperature than Pyrex, and between the strain point and room temperature the total thermal expansion of Nonex is almost equal to the expansion of tungsten for the same temperature interval.

A tungsten wire is prepared for sealing through glass by heating it to a white heat in the gas flame. If this is not done, bubbles appear at the surface of the seal. The surface of the tungsten is cleaned for sealing by heating and touching it with a piece of potassium or sodium nitrite. The tungsten is then washed, and a short sleeve of Pyrex (or Nonex, depending on the size of the wire) tubing is fused to it as shown in Fig. 25(a). The intense heating required to shrink the glass should be started at one end of the sleeve, so that the shrinking progresses from that end. This avoids trapping air bubbles between the metal and the glass. The interface between glass and tungsten is red, because oxide on the surface of the tungsten dissolves in the glass and dyes it. After the sealing operation between glass and metal is finished, the sleeve is welded into the apparatus as shown at (b). In making metal-to-glass seals, it is important to cool the glass slowly to avoid excessive strain.

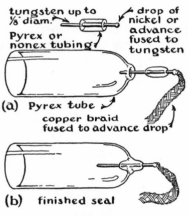

(a) Pyrex tube
copper braid
fused to advance drop

(b) finished seal

Fig. 25.

Tungsten wire is frequently fibrous, having longitudinal channels which may leak if it is sealed into a vacuum apparatus. To avoid such a possibility, the tip of the tungsten should always be closed by fusing nickel or advance wire over it. The nickel or advance tip also affords a place for attaching copper wires.   Copper can be fused to these tips, whereas it cannot be easily welded to tungsten directly.

Discharge tube electrodes are made from coiled aluminum wire of about $\frac{3}{32}$ inch in diameter and a tungsten-Pyrex seal as shown in Fig. 26.   The aluminum-wire projection of the coil is fused to make the connection to the tungsten wire. The tungsten wire with a nickel enlargement to secure it in

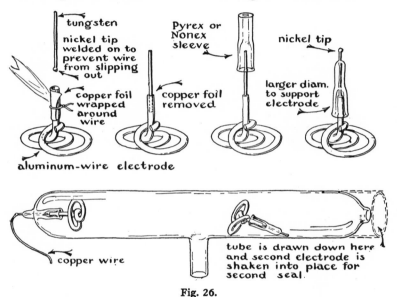

Fig. 26.

position is pushed into the fused aluminum.   The projection is wrapped with copper foil to preserve its form.   After the aluminum has solidified, the copper foil is removed.   A glass sleeve, shaped as illustrated, is then sealed to the tungsten.   This sleeve fits the aluminum projection and affords additional support for it.

Copper-to-glass seals.   It is possible to seal copper to Pyrex or soft glass by the technique developed by W. G. Housekeeper.[2]   The copper has a much larger coefficient of thermal expansion than either type of glass—it is the arrangement

[2] Housekeeper, W. G., *Elect. Engineering*, 42, 954 (1923)

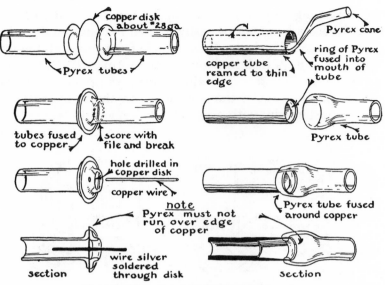

Fig. 27. Housekeeper glass-to-metal seals.

of the seal which prevents the glass from breaking. When the copper is thin, it is deformed to absorb differences between its expansion and that of the glass, a circumstance made possible by its high ductility and low yield point. The construction details of various seals developed by Housekeeper are shown in Figs. 27 and 28. For the constructions shown in Fig. 27 it is important to prevent the glass from passing over the rim of the copper.

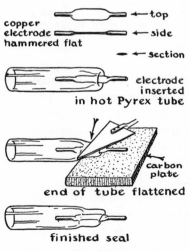

Fig. 28. Housekeeper seal.

The seal shown in Fig. 28 is made with a copper wire, which is hammered out to have thin sharp edges. Care is necessary in heating the Pyrex to avoid melting the copper.

Kovar and Fernico.[3] The rate of expansion of glasses increases near their softening temperatures, as Fig. 4 shows. On the other hand, the thermal expansion for most metals is nearly linear. However, the expansions of two new alloys, Kovar and Fernico, closely duplicate the expansion of some of the commercial glasses.[4] These alloys yield metal-to-glass seals which are unstrained under all annealing conditions, and they may be sealed to appropriate glasses without any of the special procedure required for Housekeeper seals. Large seals of 4 inches in diameter and ⅛ inch in wall thickness have been made between Kovar and 705 AJ glass. Such seals as the ones shown in Fig. 29 have made modern all-metal radio tubes possible.

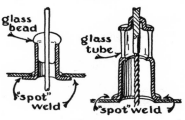

Fig. 29.

---

[3] The fundamental study of expansion properties of Fe-Ni-Co alloys, on which this kind of metal-to-glass seal is based, was made in the Westinghouse Research Laboratories by Howard Scott, Technical Publication 318, American Institute of Mining and Metallurgical Engineers (1930). These alloys are manufactured under U. S. Patent 1,942,260, held by the Westinghouse Electric and Manufacturing Company. Further information is contained in Scott, Howard, *Frank. Inst., J.*, *220*, 733 (1935); Burger, E. E., *Gen. El. Rev.*, *37*, 93 (1934); and Hull, A. W., and Burger, E. E., *Physics*, *5*, 384 (1934). The Westinghouse product, called Kovar, is obtainable from the Stupakoff Laboratories, 6627 Hamilton Avenue, Pittsburgh, Pennsylvania. Fernico is obtainable from the General Electric Company, Schenectady, New York.

[4] According to A. W. Hull, "Fernico is capable of existing at room temperature in either the gamma, face-centered phase, or in the alpha, body-centered phase. When annealed from 900° or more, it has the face-centered structure and the characteristic low expansion, and is stable in this condition at any temperature above −40° C. Exposure to liquid air temperature or mechanical strain will transform it into the alpha phase, which has a different expansion and is to be avoided."

According to Mr. Scott, "To obtain the desired low and reversible expansion characteristic of Kovar and Fernico, their composition is so adjusted that transformation from the gamma to alpha phase occurs between − 80 and − 180°C. Seals, however, cannot be cooled safely below − 40°C. because of the progressively increasing expansion between metal and glass on cooling below room temperature. Special compositions can be made which make possible cooling to somewhat lower temperatures."

These new alloys may be soft-soldered, copper-brazed, and spot-welded. It is not recommended that they be silver-soldered, however, as this tends to make them brittle. They oxidize much less than iron and therefore do not oxidize seriously at elevated temperatures. Nevertheless, care should be taken to avoid extended overheating during sealing. An important property of the alloys is that they are not attacked by mercury.

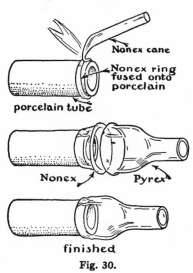

porcelain tube

Nonex   Pyrex

finished

Fig. 30.

Porcelain-Pyrex seals. Porcelain, particularly the grade known as Insulite,[5] may be sealed directly to Pyrex in small diameters (less than ½ inch), or it may be sealed to Pyrex in large diameters with an intermediary glass ring of Nonex as shown in Fig. 30.

---

[5] Insulite is obtainable from Stupakoff Laboratories, 6627 Hamilton Avenue, Pittsburgh, Pennsylvania.

CHAPTER II
Laboratory Optical Work

Introduction. In this chapter we will describe the technique of making the optical surfaces required for mirrors, prisms, interferometers, lenses, and so forth. The optical surfaces on these instruments are characterized by being much more accurate than ordinary machined and ground surfaces. In fact, optical tests sensitive to a few millionths of an inch are necessary to show their lack of true perfection. Since our concern here is with high-precision work, in which errors are usually less than a wave length of light, we do not include methods used for plate glass, cheap lenses, and other commercial work in which the tolerance is greater.

The technique described here is intended primarily to guide the research worker who finds it desirable or necessary to prepare his own optical surfaces.

In any case the task set before the' worker is that of generating an extremely accurate polished surface. Accordingly, we will first set down the general technique involved without detailed reference to what is being made. Later we will treat of special procedures.

General procedure. The glass or other material on which the optical surface is to be prepared is first roughly formed to the desired shape. For example, in the case of a lens, the first step will consist of cutting out a disk of glass. A prism will be first sawed or ground to rough dimensions from a larger block. The proposed surface itself is then generated more precisely by periods of grinding with suitable laps. The surface is ground first with coarse·grits of Carborundum to conform approximately to the specifications. Then finer and finer abrasives are used until at last the grinding is terminated with the finest emery flour. The grinding is periodically interrupted for testing with a straightedge, template, micrometer, or spherometer. After fine grinding, the surface is polished with a pitch lap and rouge. Finally it is brought as near to perfection as the specifications require by "figuring," that is, by local retouching with polishing tools. The figuring is guided by delicate optical tests.

Theory of grinding and polishing. Optical grinding and polishing are alike in that both require the use of a material which is harder than the glass. This material is used in the form of loose grits or fine powder. The two operations are unlike in that the grits and powder used for grinding are worked over the surface with a hard tool, ordinarily made either of glass or cast iron, whereas polishing tools are made from a soft base material. A polishing tool for preparing precise optical surfaces is usually composed of some combination of pitch and wax as the soft base material. Paper cloth and wood are often used for polishing tools in cases in which no great precision is demanded.

The grinding process depends upon the characteristic conchoidal fracture produced when an excessively high pressure is applied to a point in the surface of the glass.

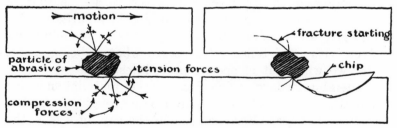

Fig. 1.

The pressure exerted on the surface by a single particle of abrasive or grit, as it is rolled about between the tool and the work, builds up stress beyond the strength of the glass, resulting in the removal of a chip. This is illustrated by Fig. 1. Carborundum and emery grits are ordinarily used. The efficiency of the process depends primarily on the sharpness of the grits. Carborundum grits break down faster than emery, although they are harder than emery. Fractured Carborundum grits have sharp edges and consequently they grind fast. Ellison[1] says that Carborundum grinds about six times as fast as emery. Carborundum is used for the first coarser grades of grits, and emery for the last finer grades. Natural emery (corundum) cuts about twice as fast as synthetic emery. The corundum produces a smoother surface than either Carborundum or synthetic emery and is, accordingly, best for the final grinding.

The hardness of various abrasives is indicated in Moh's extended hardness scale. (See Table I.)

TABLE I

HARDNESS SCALES

Moh's Scale of Hardness		Extended Moh's Scale	
Substance	Value	Substance	Value
Orthoclase...............	6	Orthoclase or periclase..	6
Quartz..................	7	Vitreous pure silica.....	7
Topaz..................	8	Quartz...............	8
Sapphire...............	9	Topaz...............	9
Diamond...............	10	Garnet...............	10
		Fused zirconia........	11
		Fused alumina........	12
		Silicon carbide........	13
		Boron carbide.........	14
		Diamond.............	15

Ridgway, R. R., Ballard, A. H., and Bailey, B. L., "Hardness Values of Electrochemical Products," a paper presented before the Electrochemical Society, May, 1933.

From a practical point of view, we may consider that the polishing operation is a planing process.[2] The grains of

[1] Ingalls, Albert G., editor, *Amateur Telescope Making*, page 74.   New York: Scientific American Publishing Company, 1935.

[2] For a more comprehensive treatment of the theory of polishing from a different point of view, see the following:

Lord Rayleigh, *Proc. Opt. Convention*, No. 1, page 73 (1905); and *Scientific Papers*, Vol. IV, page 542.   Cambridge: The University Press, 1903.

French, J. W., "The Working of Optical Parts," *Dictionary of Applied Science*, Vol. IV, page 326.   London: The Macmillan Company, 1923.

Finch, G. I., "The Beilby Layer," *Science Progress*, *31*, 609 (1937).

abrasive appear to fix themselves automatically in the soft material of the tool, usually pitch, so that their crystal surfaces are parallel to the direction of motion of the tool and parallel to the plane of its surface. Thus a complex scraper is formed. As this moves over the glass, the height of each abrasive particle is automatically adjusted in the soft backing so that it produces a fine smooth cut. The removed glass is washed away by the liquid lubricant, usually water. The planing action starts on the peaks of the "hills" that result from the fine grinding and produces a full polish there at the first stroke. Continued operation of the polishing tool removes additional glass, so that the hills become plateaus and are finally planed down to the level of the deepest valleys. The character of the surface on any particular plateau is not improved by continued polishing—it is to be regarded as fully polished from the first stroke. This is illustrated in Fig. 2. After the whole surface becomes uniformly polished, further working with the polishing tool removes additional glass. In constructing an experimental aspheric camera lens, as much as thirty thousandths of an inch of glass has been removed by polishing.

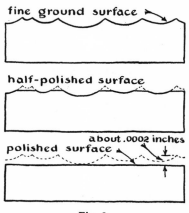

Fig. 2.

Methods of polishing. Glass can be successfully polished with almost any fine abrasive, provided a suitable soft and yielding backing is used. For some types of work—for example, for edging mirrors where irregularities in the surface do not matter—glass is polished with a wood tool charged with Carborundum or emery. Glass may be polished with rouge, either the red oxide or the magnetic black oxide, and also with charcoal or oxide of tin. However, for ordinary optical work rouge is the most satisfactory polishing material. Surfaces of glass, quartz, speculum metal, calcite, and fluorite are best polished with rouge on a wax or pitch tool. The action of various polishing agents depends on the type of backing, whether cloth, paper, or pitch is used, on the hardness of the material being polished, and on the method of lubrication. Some agents which are indifferent polishers when used with a wax or pitch tool and lubricated with water are quite effective when used dry on a paper lap. For paper polishing, oxide of tin (putty powder) is commonly used. Chromium oxide (Cr_2O_3) is recommended for polishing certain metals such as stainless steel which are "attacked" ' by rouge.

The material for the polishing tool may be a soft metal—copper, lead, or aluminum. Tools made of these metals are sometimes used for polishing thin specimens of minerals which are to be examined with the microscope. Levigated alumina is usually employed as abrasive for work of this type.

The polishing tools used in precision optical work are made of pitch or pitch and wax compounds, in contrast with cloth- or paper-faced tools used on some commercial products. Glass is polished with surprising rapidity on a cloth polisher, but it exhibits a peculiar grainy "lemon-peel" surface. This method of polishing is generally used in the manufacture of plate glass. Paper polishers in general produce a somewhat better surface than cloth but are seldom used except for the manufacture of inexpensive lenses, such as for cheap hand magnifiers and so forth. All polishing tools of a fibrous nature produce a "lemon-peel" surface.

Procedure for optical surfaces of 3 to 6 inches in diameter and larger. The technique which will form the nucleus of our first treatment is particularly suited to the making of surfaces of 3 to 6 inches in diameter or larger worked in glass or quartz. The procedures involved are fundamental and apply equally to mirrors, lenses, or prisms. The method treated here is used by D. O. Hendrix, a practicing

optician associated with Mount Wilson Observatory.[3]   This
procedure is different in some respects from that described

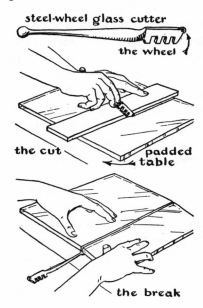

steel-wheel glass cutter

the wheel

the cut

padded table

the break

in the classic book on amateur telescope making by
Ingalls, Porter, and Ellison.[4]
For example, in their book
they recommend using the
tool underneath the work,
while here we treat primarily
of the method using the tool
on top of the work.

**Cutting and roughing out
the work.** The work, whether
it is a mirror, a lens, or a
prism, can often be cut to
rough shape from stock plate
glass with an ordinary wheel
cutter, the most common
form of glass cutter, which is
used for cutting all kinds of
polished glass in all ordinary
thicknesses.   The cutter is
drawn across the glass surface
once with sufficient pressure
definitely to mark the glass.
It should not be run back and
forth along the same line.
After the glass is "marked,"
it is broken by bending it
away from the cut, as shown,
for example, in Fig. 3.   The

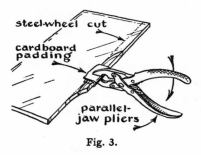

steel-wheel cut

cardboard padding

parallel-jaw pliers

Fig. 3.

parallel-jawed pliers, also illustrated in Fig. 3, are useful for
making narrow cuts.   The break may also be started by
lightly tapping the glass on the back side opposite the mark

[3] I am indebted to Mr. D. O. Hendrix for the procedures presented here.
[4] Ingalls, Albert G., editor, *Amateur Telescope Making*.   New York: Scien
tific American Publishing Company, 1935.

with the small knob provided on the handle of the wheel cutter.

The procedure for cutting thick plate glass is to lubricate the wheel cutter with turpentine or kerosene before the cut is made. After the glass is marked, the break is started with a blunt chisel. The chisel is held firmly against the back of the glass at a point directly opposite the mark and tapped sharply with a small hammer. The edge of the chisel should be parallel to the mark. It is well to have the glass supported, cutter-mark down, on a cloth or padded surface. When the break has started, it is led along the cut with the chisel. (See Fig. 4.)

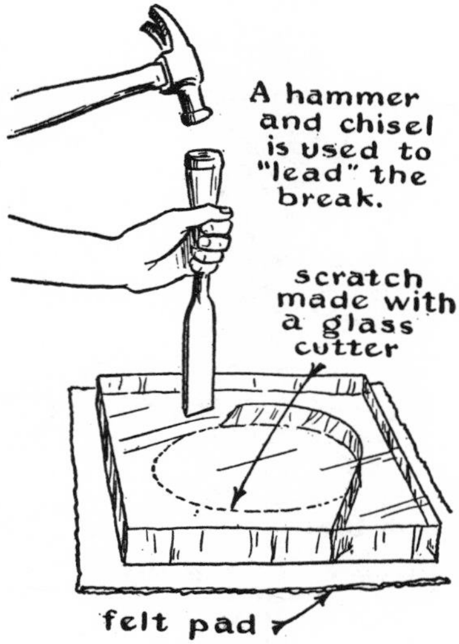

A hammer and chisel is used to "lead" the break.

scratch made with a glass cutter

felt pad

Fig. 4.

iron disk fed with Carborundum and water

pan to catch the splash

Fig. 5.

Very thin glass is best cut with a diamond point especially mounted and sharpened for this purpose.[5]

If a disk is desired, the glass is first cut square, and the corners are then cut to give a polygonal piece approximating the desired shape. The rough edges may be removed by holding the glass against a rotating flat disk of cast iron fed with a mixture of Carborundum and water. (See Fig. 5.) Also,

---

[5] Diamond glass cutters may be obtained from the Standard Diamond Tool Corporation, 64 West 48th Street, New York City. This company also sharpens diamond glass cutters.

the glass disk may be waxed onto a metal plate mounted in the headstock of a lathe. As it is rotated, the edges are ground with an iron tool, which is fed with Carborundum

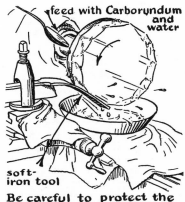

feed with Carborundum and water

soft-iron tool

Be careful to protect the lathe from the abrasive which will spatter from the vibrating tool.

Fig. 6.

and water as shown in Fig. 6. A light springy tool is recommended. Oilcloth should be used to protect the lathe so that abrasive does not get into its working parts or on its ways.

Biscuit cutter. A common method of cutting small disks (up to about 6 inches in diameter) from slabs of glass is by means of a "biscuit cutter," This is simply a thin-walled tube of iron or brass mounted in a drill press as shown in Fig. 7. The rotating tube is fed against the glass, Carborundum and water being applied with a spoon. Fig. 7 also shows a novel method of central feeding. To prevent chipping when the biscuit cutter goes through the glass, it is well to wax an auxiliary backing plate onto it with beeswax. Grade 60 or 90 Carborundum should be used except for fine cuts or cuts on delicate and fine work, in which case grade 120 Carborundum should be used. The cutter will cut more rapidly if instead of water a mixture of turpentine and cam-

brass "biscuit cutter"

glass waxed to an auxiliary glass plate

Fig. 7.

phor is used with the Carborundum. The proportions of the mixture should be 5 grams camphor to $\frac{1}{2}$ liter turpentine.

Diagonal mirrors, such as the Newtonian diagonal for a small telescope, may be cut out of a larger figured flat mirror with the biscuit cutter. The larger mirror is mounted in the drill press at an angle of 45° and cemented with beeswax on a backing of plate glass. It is cut in the manner shown in Fig. 8. Usually the front of the flat is also coated with a cover glass, stuck on with beeswax, to prevent scratching the figured surface with the abrasive. A mirror thus cut out may develop a slight turned-up edge. However, if the cut rim, which now has a rough ground surface, is polished with wood and Carborundum, the figure of the mirror will usually become flat again. (This is sometimes called the Twyman phenomenon.)

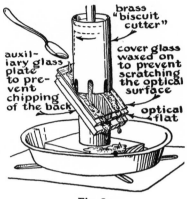

Fig. 8.

Glass saws. Strips and slabs of glass are cut from a thick piece of glass stock with saws. The simplest and easiest of these to set up is the so-called "mud saw," shown in Fig. 9(a). It consists of a rotating disk of soft sheet iron fed with a mixture of Carborundum and water. Sometimes sugar, syrup, talc, glycerin, or bentonite (particularly good) is added to this mixture to make the Carborundum adhere to the blade and to keep the grits from settling out in the reservoir pan. The usual construction allows one edge of the saw to dip into the "mud," or Carborundum mixture, which is held in a pan below the disk. The work to be slabbed is supported on a counterbalanced table and is held against the saw with a slight pressure.

A diamond saw forms an efficient slabbing cutter. The diamond saw shown at the bottom of Fig. 9 may be made as follows: The diamonds are pulverized as shown at (b) and charged into the nicks of a circular disk prepared as shown

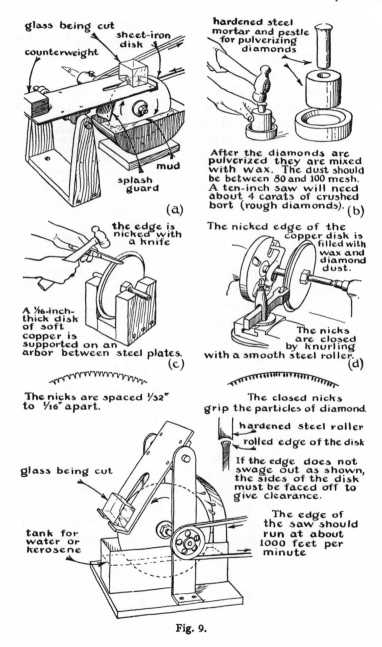

glass being cut
sheet-iron disk
counterweight
mud
splash guard
(a)

hardened steel mortar and pestle for pulverizing diamonds

After the diamonds are pulverized they are mixed with wax. The dust should be between 80 and 100 mesh. A ten-inch saw will need about 4 carats of crushed bort (rough diamonds). (b)

the edge is nicked with a knife

A ⅟₁₆-inch-thick disk of soft copper is supported on an arbor between steel plates.
(c)

The nicks are spaced ⅟₃₂″ to ⅟₁₆″ apart.

The nicked edge of the copper disk is filled with wax and diamond dust.

The nicks are closed by knurling with a smooth steel roller.
(d)

The closed nicks grip the particles of diamond.

hardened steel roller
rolled edge of the disk

If the edge does not swage out as shown, the sides of the disk must be faced off to give clearance.

glass being cut

tank for water or kerosene

The edge of the saw should run at about 1000 feet per minute

Fig. 9.

at (c). These nicks are rolled as shown at (d) to hold the diamond powder and give the saw clearance. In operation the saw blade is lubricated and washed with water or kerosene.

Modified Draper machine. Once the prism, lens, mirror, or other blank is cut out, the operations involved in grinding the curves and polishing and figuring them may be carried out either by hand or with a grinding and polishing machine. A machine like the one shown in Fig. 10, a so-called modified Draper machine, is suitable.

The tool is moved laterally by the modified Draper machine in a thin oval stroke across the face of the work. The amplitude of this stroke is controlled by adjustment of the throw of the crank. The stroke can be arranged by movement of an adjustable guide so that it is either diametral or chordal in respect to the work. The tool may be allowed to rotate freely, or it may be driven by a belt. Also, the tool may be loaded to increase its pressure, or it may be counterbalanced to decrease its pressure on the work. The table on which the work is mounted is power driven to rotate about 2 r.p.m.

Support of the work. It is very important to support the work properly, or it will develop astigmatism, the anathema of optical work.

The first requisite is to have the modified Draper machine table turned and lapped 0.001 to 0.003 inch concave, depending on the size. It is then covered with a layer of thin felt and oilcloth as shown at the bottom of Fig. 10. This supports the glass uniformly on its flat bottom side and effectively prevents flexure during all of the operations. When the second surface of a lens is being worked, the plane concave glass tool that was used in the fine grinding of the first face is used to support the work on the grinding table. The tool is first mounted on the table concave side up. Then it is covered with felt and the lens is laid on it.

The work is supported laterally on the table by three edge arcs, which should fit neatly to the edge of the blank without

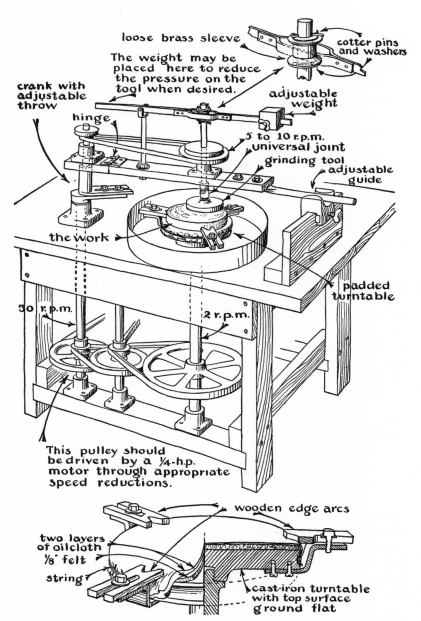

loose brass sleeve

cotter pins and washers

The weight may be placed here to reduce the pressure on the tool when desired.

crank with adjustable throw

adjustable weight

hinge

5 to 10 r.p.m.

universal joint

grinding tool

adjustable guide

the work

padded turntable

30 r.p.m.

2 r.p.m.

This pulley should be driven by a ¼-h.p. motor through appropriate speed reductions.

wooden edge arcs

two layers of oilcloth

⅛" felt

string

cast-iron turntable with top surface ground flat

Fig. 10. Note that the universal joint shown here is used only for rough grinding. For fine grinding and polishing, the tool is connected to the crossarm by a pivot and socket arrangement. See Figs. 16 to 20.

40

exerting any pressure on it except as is necessary to balance lateral forces produced by the action of the tool. The work is moved around in the edge supports from time to time during grinding and polishing to distribute the effect of these forces uniformly around the periphery of the mirror, to avoid the introduction of astigmatism.

The work, if it is a mirror or lens, is prepared by having its face and back fine-ground and made parallel with a rotating cast-iron lap used with loose grits as shown in Fig. 5. The edges are then ground round and lightly beveled. Finally, the edges are polished with a wood tool and fine Carborundum grains.

Grinding the curve in the work. Full-size grinding tools of tough metal such as copper, brass, or soft iron, when turned to a definite radius of curvature, will reproduce this radius in the glass. The soft metal surface becomes charged with abrasive and is not worn appreciably when it is used on a brittle material such as glass. On the other hand, cast-iron tools change slowly during grinding, and glass tools change at approximately the same rate as the work.

The traditional way of making a 6-inch mirror by hand is to use two equal disks of glass, one as the work and the other as a grinding tool. The grinding is accomplished as shown in Fig. 11 with the work mounted on a firm pedestal, the height of which is optional. The optician walks around it as he strokes the work with the tool. Pressure is applied to the center of the tool with the thumb of the right hand. The tool is rotated with the fingers in a counterclockwise direction as it is stroked across the right side of the work. When a chordal stroke is used, the upper disk becomes concave and the lower convex. By this means a certain amount of control is given the operator. He may continue grinding, increasing the curvature in the surfaces all the time, until the desired result is attained. If he wishes to decrease the curvature, he will place the tool below and stroke it with the work. Or he may periodically reverse the relative positions of the two disks if he wishes to hold the surfaces fairly flat or constant in radius of curvature. When it is desired to hold the curvature constant, a diametral rather than a chordal stroke is used.

On the modified Draper machine, the grinding of a mirror to a definite radius of curvature is effected with a small tool.

handle for the work

wood

wooden edge arcs

solid wood table

4″ pipe

concrete-filled tub

4 to 5 feet high

this grinds concave

the stroke

this grinds convex

heavy carpet or sponge rubber

As the operator strokes the work he slowly rotates the part in his hand as he walks slowly around the stand.

Fig. 11. Many workers will prefer to have the work at a lower level, 3 to 4 feet, than is shown here.   Note: The operator shown in this figure is left-handed.

Concave curves are cut in the glass with a $\frac{1}{3}$-size tool stroking the work across its center.   A convex curvature is generated by a sub-diameter tool stroked across a chord of the work.   Although a convex curvature will be generated if a full-size tool is stroked across the center of the work (diametral stroke), it becomes convex more rapidly when a chordal stroke is used.   The rate at which the curvature changes is proportional to the amplitude of the diametral stroke or the offset of the chordal stroke.

After the work has been roughed out to the proper radius of curvature with 90, or for extreme curves 60, Carborundum, the full-size tool is used to true up the surface. The stroke used here is a thin oval across the center of the work. The amplitude used is about one third to one sixth the diameter of the work. The grinding is continued with the full-size tool until the tool and work are spherical. This is indicated by the quality of the fit between the tool and the work, which can be tested with a pencil mark made on the work. This procedure may produce scratches. A circular template is often made of the required radius and the work is ground until it fits this template. Spherometers are also used to test the work for sphericity. When the work is spherical, the spherometer reading, d, the radius of curvature of the work, R, and the radius of the circle containing the spherometer legs, r, are related as follows:

$$d = \frac{r^2 + d^2}{2R}.$$

The spherical surfaces obtainable by grinding are so good, in fact, that opticians who worked before testing methods were developed as they are today hesitated to polish the grinding pits entirely away, since they formed a convenient "landmark" to which to refer the figure.

To grind deep curves like those required for an $f/1$ Schmidt camera, one puts a band around the edge of the mirror and covers its face with a layer of Carborundum grits. The band holds the grits on the mirror. As the work slowly rotates, a fast rotating sub-diameter cast-iron ring tool is reciprocated diametrically, or nearly so, across its surface in a thin oval stroke. The amplitude of the stroke is adjusted so that the ring tool comes to the edge of the work at the extremes of the stroke.

Final grinding in all cases should be carried out with a glass grinding tool. Glass is used rather than metal in order to have the tool change at approximately the same rate as the work, thus insuring a more perfect fit at all times between the tool and the work.   The tool may be a glass disk formed as a complement of the work; that is, if the work is a convex spherical surface of radius R, the tool will be a concave sphere of almost exactly the same radius.   Or the tool may be a plate of glass cemented to a metal backing.   It is well to cut the grinding tool with one or more decentered grooves as shown in Fig. 12 in order to prevent suction, facilitate the access of grinding compound to all parts of the tool, and insure that the tool grinds slightly faster than the work. These grooves may be cut into the glass with the diamond or mud saw.

center

grooves 1/32 to 1/16 inch deep cut with a mud saw or diamond saw

glass grinding tool

glass facets cemented to curved iron tool with hard pitch or sealing wax

grinding tool for large work

Fig. 12.

For large mirrors, glass disks or squares can be cemented to a convex or concave iron backing as is illustrated in Fig. 12.

The radius of curvature of the work, R, is determined by means of a spherometer or more simply by a template cut from metal.   The latter can be cut with a sharp steel point (sharpened like a brass turning tool) mounted on the end of a board of length R and pivoted at the other end on a nail.   For flats a good straightedge may be used as a template.

Fine grinding.   After the proper radius is attained and the work has been trued up with the full-size tool, the optician passes successively to grades 150, F, 400, and 600 Carborundum.   The full-size tool, loaded to a pressure of about 0.5 lb./square inch, is used.   For a 6-inch mirror about a teaspoonful of grits is applied at a time.   Each application of grits, applied with one or two spoonfuls of water, is allowed to grind until the gritty cutting sound, which is heard at first, has softened.   For a 6-inch mirror, grits are repeatedly added until the work has been ground a total time of 30 minutes (or 1 hour by hand). After a half-hour of grinding with one grade of Carborundum, the optician passes on to the next grade, and finally, after the 600 grade Carborundum, finishes with two grades of emery, $302\frac{1}{2}$ and $303\frac{1}{2}$. The work, the table of the machine, and the tool should be thoroughly washed after finishing with each grade of abrasive.

Carborundum grits as obtained commercially are well graded and do not need to be washed. However, the emeries must be washed each time they are used. The washing procedure is as follows: Put emery to a depth of 1 inch in a quart Mason jar, fill the jar with water, stir, and let settle for 10 seconds. Decant the suspended emery off to a second clean jar and discard the residue. After 10 seconds in the second jar, decant again, and repeat the operation a third time. After this, the settling time is increased to a minute to yield a residue which we will designate as residue A. The liquid over this is decanted into a clean jar, in which it is allowed to settle until it is clear, yielding residue B. The liquid over B is then put back over residue A, stirred, allowed to stand for 1 minute, and then added again to B. This is repeated several times to transfer a large fraction of the emery from A into B. Residue B, when mixed with an equal volume of powdered washed talc, is ready to be used for grinding. The talc serves as a lubricant and prevents sticking of the tool. The talc must be washed in the same manner as the emery was washed to free it of metallic iron.

The final grinding with the two grades of emery will yield a surface which exhibits specular reflection of white light at grazing incidence. At a steeper angle the reflected image is red. In fact, specular reflection of the red part of the spectrum up to a grazing angle of about 12° may be obtained. The maximum grazing angle of specular reflection affords a simple test of the quality of the fine-ground surface. A clear filament lamp should be used as a light source for this test, and when the surface gives a reflection at a grazing angle of about 12°, the work is ready to be polished.

When it is required to have the center of the mirror perforated, the necessary hole is usually cut with the "biscuit cutter" before the grinding is started. The plug is then fastened back in place with plaster of Paris. The plug is left in place until the figuring is finished.

Pitch for tools. Polishing pitch should have the following properties: It should flow slightly at ordinary room temperature; it should trim easily with a sharp knife; and, further, it should not lose its "temper" by evaporation of volatile oils. A compound which conforms to these specifications quite well is made up as follows:

    Coal tar (melting point 170° to 180° F.) . . . . 2 lbs.
    Pine tar (Mefford Chemical Company) . . . . 4 liquid oz.
    Beeswax . . . . 1½ oz.
    Venice turpentine . . . . not more than about 2 or 3 cc.

The tar is melted and the other ingredients are added in the order listed.

The function of the turpentine is to adjust the final "temper" of the pitch. More or less turpentine is added, depending on whether a hard or soft pitch is desired. Before adding the turpentine and after each addition, test the pitch for temper. The simple method of performing this test is to chew a small sample of the pitch after chilling it by pouring it out on a cold glass surface. At body temperature, so-called "soft" pitch can be chewed, while "hard" pitch cracks under the pressure of the teeth. Furthermore, hard-pitch tools stored face up will show evidence of flow in the sides of the groove in about a week. A soft tool exhibits flow after standing a day. Polishing pitch does not attain its final hardness on cooling but continues to harden for a day or more. This is a sort of "jelling" process, which must be taken into account.

After the correct mixing temper is attained, pitch is filtered to remove small sticks or other hard particles. The hot pitch is poured through a cheesecloth filter supported on an iron ring. Two layers of cheesecloth are adequate to hold back harmful impurities.

Polishing tools of 6 inches in diameter or less are made by simply pouring the melted pitch compound over a support to a depth of about $\frac{3}{8}$ inch. After the pitch has cooled, it is channeled by cutting it with a hot knife so that the surface is divided into a decentered system of square facets of uniform size. These facets are later trimmed in the manner shown in Fig. 13. Tools having bubbles in the pitch cause no trouble unless it happens that the bubbles occur in a definite zone on a full-size tool that is to be worked over the mirror or lens with a short stroke. In order to avoid a zone of bubbles, the pitch is cast by pouring it onto the support at one edge rather than at the center.

There are two methods of accommodating the tools to the different working conditions of summer and winter: By one, the formula is changed, the pitch being tempered with more turpentine for cooler weather; by the other, the size of the facets is changed. The facets are made smaller in cooler weather. When the formula given above is used, the facets should be about 1 inch square for temperatures above 75° F. and about $\frac{1}{2}$ to $\frac{3}{4}$ inch square for temperatures below 75° F.

If the polisher is to be used on soft or easily scratched material, such as speculum metal, it is advisable to use harder pitch and to have the facets narrow. The channels allow the pitch to flow evenly and also allow the rouge and water free access to all parts of the work. For speculum metal it is recommended that the facets be $\frac{1}{32}$ to $\frac{1}{16}$ inch wide and $\frac{3}{4}$ inch long.

To construct a polishing tool of relatively short radius, the pitch facets are first cast in a suitable mold in the form of sticks. (See Fig. 14.) These are then cut into squares and fastened to the metal tool as shown in Fig. 15.

After the tool has been faceted, it is warmed and pressed to the work, with soap in a 25 per cent glycerin solution as a lubricant on the work to prevent sticking. The pressing

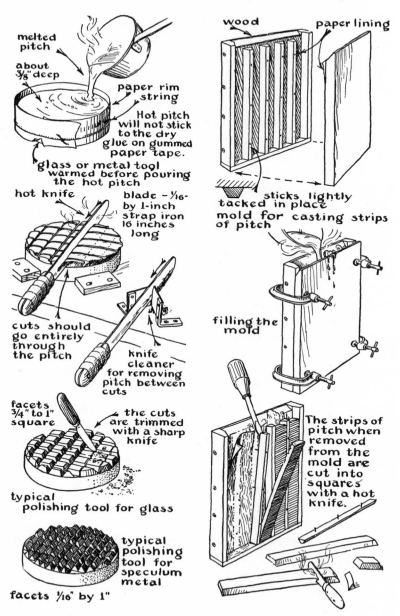

melted pitch

about ⅜" deep

paper rim
string

Hot pitch
will not stick
to the dry
glue on gummed
paper tape.

glass or metal tool
warmed before pouring
the hot pitch

hot knife

blade –1/16-
by 1-inch
strap iron
16 inches
long

cuts should
go entirely
through
the pitch

knife
cleaner
for removing
pitch between
cuts

facets
¾" to 1"
square

the cuts
are trimmed
with a sharp
knife

typical
polishing tool for glass

typical
polishing
tool for
speculum
metal

facets 1/16" by 1"

Fig. 13.

wood   paper lining

sticks lightly
tacked in place
mold for casting strips
of pitch

filling the
mold

The strips of
pitch when
removed
from the
mold are
cut into
squares
with a hot
knife.

Fig. 14.

operation is illustrated in Fig. 16.   The tool is gently warmed over a hot plate until the pitch is soft.   Then it is applied to the work, wet with a mixture of soap and glycerin, and left to cool.   This procedure yields an intimate contact between the tool and the work.   Tools for flats may be first turned in the lathe before they are pressed.   After pressing the pitch tool, it is advisable to wash it in cold water and also wash and dry the work to remove the soap and glycerin.

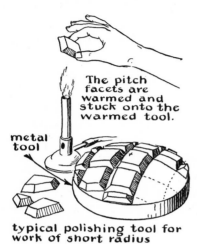

The pitch facets are warmed and stuck onto the warmed tool.

metal tool

typical polishing tool for work of short radius

Fig. 15.

Polishing.   Polishing is carried out on the table of the modified Draper machine in the same manner as grinding, except that the polishing tool is usually allowed free rotation.   Rouge and water is added to the work from time to time near the edge of the tool with an

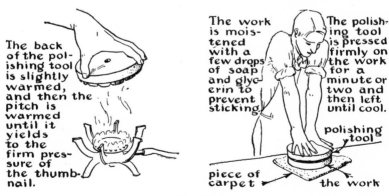

The back of the polishing tool is slightly warmed, and then the pitch is warmed until it yields to the firm pressure of the thumbnail.

The work is moistened with a few drops of soap and glycerin to prevent sticking.

The polishing tool is pressed firmly on the work for a minute or two and then left until cool.

polishing tool

piece of carpet

the work

Fig. 16.

eye dropper.   The rouge should be washed.   The washing procedure is the same as that described for washing emery or talc, except that the settling time is longer—up to one-half hour.

Hard facets in the tool may cause sharp zones to appear in the work during polishing. To avoid the effects of such surface inhomogeneities in the pitch and resultant irregularities in the cutting action of the tool, the work is "broken up"; that is, the tool is frequently (and irregularly) given a spin. The facets in the tool should form a decentered system. A diametral stroke is employed for polishing. A feature of the polishing machine which also contributes to breaking up the work is the incommensurable coupling obtained by the belt which connects the rotation of the work with the phase of the stroke. The stroke is varied from time to time from a long stroke of one fourth the diameter of the tool to a short stroke.

If the surface of a pitch polishing tool becomes so heavily charged with rouge that it appears hard and glassy, the polishing speed will be considerably reduced, and furthermore "sleeks" are liable to appear. Sleeking, or the appearance of groovelike marks on the polished surface, is probably caused by the formation of ball-shaped aggregates of rouge, wax, and perhaps glass, which plow out shallow channels in the surface. Beeswax-coated tools are particularly bothersome in this respect. One method of avoiding sleeks is to allow the tool to run nearly dry before each application of fresh rouge. The optician calls this "drying up each wet." This probably causes the surface of the tool to become quite warm, allowing the pitch surface to flow rather rapidly and to renew itself.

Large lenses and very soft materials are best polished by coating the surface of the polisher at regular periods with fresh pitch or beeswax. The polishing tool is to be coated at intervals of 1 to 3 hours. The beeswax is applied to the facets of the tool with a swab made of cheesecloth bound on a short stick. It is advisable to have the wax smoking hot and to apply as thin a coating as possible. In polishing speculum metal, which scratches rather easily, the fresh beeswax coating is to be charged with dry rouge. The rouge is applied to the facets with the tip of the finger.

When a full polish is achieved, that is, when the grinding pits are entirely removed, the work is ready for testing and figuring. A convenient and simple test for full polish is to focus sunlight on the glass surface with a lens. The focus of this lens does not heat the glass much, but light scattered by pits in the surface is quite conspicuous if the surface is not fully polished.

To avoid introducing astigmatism into the work during polishing, it is frequently rotated a fraction of a revolution with respect to the supporting table in order to distribute the effect of edge arcs symmetrically around its periphery.

Figuring. Figuring is the process whereby a polished surface has its shape altered by local working with polishing tools. For example, a spherical surface is made aspheric, or undesirable zones or astigmatism is removed.

Sometimes in figuring plane parallels or prisms the effect of inhomogeneities in physical properties of the glass can be corrected (in first approximation) by slight deviations from flatness in the surfaces.

The general procedure in figuring is one of trial and error. Testing is alternated with local polishing on those areas which are high in reference to a desired surface.

Cutting zones and transition zones. The behavior of the polishing tool depends on its size, character of faceting, shape, and the manner in which it is manipulated on the work. There is no way in which a tool may be manipulated so that it will remove glass from a surface uniformly. Rather, each manipulation, if carried out on a perfectly flat surface, tends to produce its own characteristic zones, which will be referred to as the cutting zones of the tool. Figs. 17 and 18 illustrate the cutting zones of some typical tools. These zones are defects in the mirror surface symmetrically positioned about the center of the work. The figuring procedure consists in testing the imperfect surface and working it with a suitable tool whose cutting zones will tend to cancel the zones revealed by the test.

Sharp zones are first "softened" with a large tool coated

with soft pitch. This procedure applies both to those zones remaining from polishing and to those which may appear during the figuring. The latter are usually transition zones resulting from imperfect cancellation of a smooth zone in the work by the cutting zone of the tool. This is illustrated by Fig. 20. After the sharp zones are softened with a soft pitch tool, the optician tests again to determine the figure. To carry the figuring farther, a satisfactory surface tangent to the "valleys" of the surface, lying wholly within the glass, is imagined, and the hills relative to this imagined surface are polished away with an appropriate tool and stroke. This cycle of testing, polishing in a manner such that the cutting zones improve the figure, testing, smoothing transition zones with a soft tool, testing, and so forth, is continued, until the necessary figure is attained.

Interpretation of the action of polishing and figuring tools. If we could assign quantitative values to all of the factors influencing the cutting action of any given tool and stroke, we could conceivably predict the cutting zone for it. However, we cannot do this; but we can describe the factors qualitatively as they are appraised in the minds of opticians.

First, the polishing tool cuts away the glass in proportion to the time the tool is passing over the glass.

Second, the tool cuts faster as the speed increases. The cutting or polishing rate is not, however, proportional to the speed at which the tool passes over the work.

Third, sections of the tool which overhang the work during a part of the stroke cut relatively faster than the sections which do not overhang the work.

Fourth, the facets of the tool which lead cut faster than following facets, because new rouge available to the leading facets is wiped away from the path of following facets.

Fifth, the tool cuts fastest where the pressure on it is greatest, everything else being equal. This accounts for the selective action of the full-size tool on high zones, which action is the basis of all figuring. It is important to give this factor careful consideration in working aspheric surfaces, in which the tool naturally works in a way that tends to return the surface to a sphere.

Figuring tools for zones. Figs. 17 and 18 show various-shaped tools and illustrate the zones which they would ordinarily produce in a true flat surface when worked with both long and short strokes. The stroke in each case is a thin oval across the center of the work. The use of an' oval stroke has an advantage over a straight reciprocating stroke in that the tool never comes to a complete stop.

It will be noted from Fig. 17 that the full-size tool makes the work more convex by an amount which increases with the length of the stroke. Intermediate-sized tools, as the $\frac{5}{6}$ size, hardly change the over-all curvature of the work when a long stroke is used, while a short stroke with this tool makes the work more concave. Smaller tools make the work more concave.

It will be further noted that the effect of the tool in changing the over-all curvature is (except for the case noted) greater than its effect in producing cutting zones. This change of curvature is generally inconsequential, except where one is making flats or striving for a radius of curvature specified to extreme precision.

Fig. 18 shows the action of ring and star polishing tools.

The behavior of tools on short radius curves may differ considerably from their behavior on flats. Figs. 17 and 18 refer to flats.

As testing methods are not very precise and the polishing methods even less so, it is well to approach the desired surface carefully and slowly, with periods of polishing interrupted frequently for testing. This allows one continually to change the "stratagem according to the tactical situation and nature of the terrain."

One should use a clock to time the work done with a given polishing tool. If a mirror is improved by a certain treatment of 20 minutes' duration and the test shows that about as much more work is required, it is advisable to continue the treatment for 10 or 15 minutes more and test again in

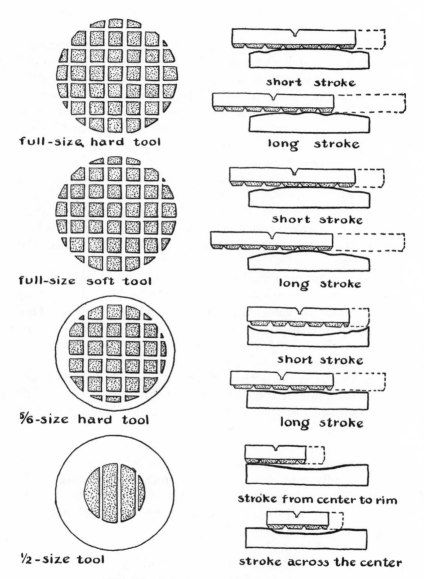

full-size hard tool

short stroke

long stroke

full-size soft tool

short stroke

long stroke

⅚-size hard tool

short stroke

long stroke

½-size tool

stroke from center to rim

stroke across the center

Fig. 17.   Cutting zones for various tools.

order not to overreach the desired result.   It must also be emphasized that tools may cut faster at first than later, so that the significance of the time factor should not be taken too seriously.   Also, the behavior of any given tool may be erratic.   It is best to try it for short periods at a time with frequent testing in order to be certain of its action.   Inas-

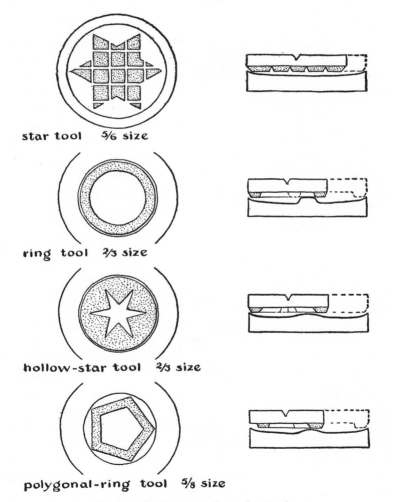

star tool   ⅚ size

ring tool   ⅔ size

hollow-star tool   ⅔ size

polygonal-ring tool   ⅝ size

Fig. 18.   Cutting zones for various tools.

much as the figuring procedure should not be hurried, beeswax-coated tools, which polish about three times as fast as uncoated tools, are not used for figuring. During the final stages of figuring, when delicate testing is required, the work should be allowed to stand on the testing support for sufficient time to allow complete equalization of temperatures.

A handle improvised from an old doorknob may be used to assure even pressure.

A piece of "marquisette" wet with soap and glycerin, and placed between the work and the tool will divide the pitch facets into tiny facets about ⅛ inch square.

Fig. 19.

Pressing the tool through coarse cloth (such as an onion sack) gives many small facets in addition to the large facets. This results in quick contact of the tool to the glass and smooth action of the figuring tool from the start. (See Fig. 19.)

To avoid astigmatism, the work should be occasionally rotated on the supporting table. In addition, with small tools it is important always to work the tool around the optical surface through an integral number of revolutions.

Hard tools tend to maintain a surface spherical or flat and are useful for generating flats or mirrors which are being worked to a specified radius. On the other hand, soft tools are recommended for working aspheric surfaces. Mirrors made by amateurs may exhibit a better figure than mirrors turned out by professional workers. The reason for this lies in the fact that amateurs usually use soft tools, which produce smooth flowing zones. On the other hand, professional opticians have the skill and knowledge to remove zones quickly with harder tools. In many cases, this rapid working produces faint transition zones, which show up under the most severe testing conditions. It is characteristic of the commercial optician that he will produce a figure as good as, but no better than, that which his specifications call for.

Manner of figuring various zonal defects, and of making aspheric surfaces of revolution. Focograms and exaggerated profile curves illustrating the manner of figuring various symmetrical defects are shown in Figs. 20, 21, 22, and 23.

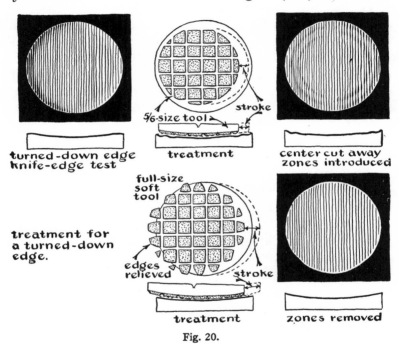

turned-down edge
knife-edge test

5/6-size tool   stroke

treatment

center cut away
zones introduced

treatment for
a turned-down
edge.

full-size
soft
tool

edges
relieved   stroke

treatment   zones removed

Fig. 20.

The interpretation of focograms is described in a later paragraph. At the upper left of Fig. 20 we see the focogram and exaggerated profile of a mirror with turned-down edge. This is corrected as follows: A ⅚-size tool and short stroke is used. Two cutting zones are produced. One zone is positioned where the leading edge of the tool comes to the extreme limit of the stroke, and the other is positioned where the trailing edge of the tool comes to the limit of the stroke. Besides making cutting zones, the tool has the further effect of making the figure more concave. The result is to change the full-line profile curve at the top left of the figure or the dotted profile curve at the top center to the profile exhibiting two sharp transition zones, as shown by the full curve at the top center and right. These transition zones are then smoothed off with a full-size soft tool with relieved edges (to avoid a turned-down edge), using a short stroke.

The treatment with a $\frac{5}{6}$-size tool, as described above, is suitable for removing a turned-down edge from a circular flat; since the final treatment with a soft tool makes the work more convex (see Fig. 17), one can, by the judicious balance of the work done with the two tools, balance the increase in concavity produced by the first by the increase in convexity produced by the second. Fig. 20 shows the procedure applied to a spherical surface.

The sketches at the top of Fig. 21 show how a turned-up edge is turned down with a full-size soft tool.

The second series of sketches of Fig. 21 shows two methods of figuring to remove an intermediary depressed zone. The profile of the full line at the left or the dotted line in the center is changed by the indicated treatment, shown in the center, to the full-line profile in the center or the dotted-line profile at the right. In turn, this is changed by the indicated treatment to the spherical curve represented by the full-line profile at the right. In the first treatment the existing dotted profile, center, is elevated at the center and has a turned-up edge in reference to the imagined curve represented by the full-line profile. This imagined curve is realized with a sub-diameter tool. At the right the full line represents the imagined surface which is realized by removing the narrow sharp transition zones with a full-size soft tool. Inasmuch as this treatment does not change the radius of the work, it is suitable for figuring flats.

By the alternate treatment, which decreases the concavity of the mirror, the cutting zones of the soft full-size tool change the intermediary depressed zone (depressed in reference to an imagined spherical surface) to two sharp

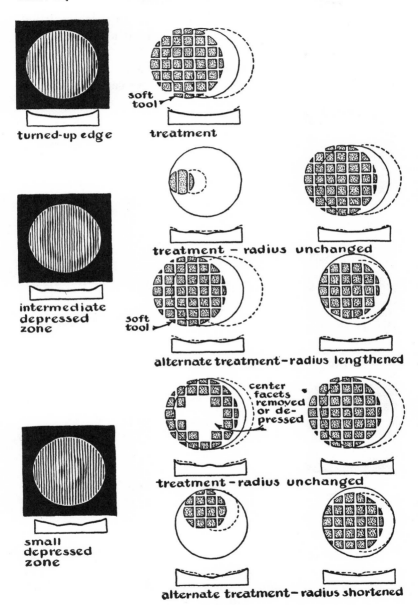

turned-up edge   treatment

soft tool

treatment – radius unchanged

intermediate depressed zone

soft tool

alternate treatment–radius lengthened

center facets removed or depressed

treatment–radius unchanged

small depressed zone

alternate treatment–radius shortened

Fig. 21.

elevated zones on a second imagined spherical surface. These elevated zones are then managed with a sub-diameter soft tool as illustrated.

Two treatments for a small depressed zone near the center of the work are illustrated in the bottom series of Fig. 21.

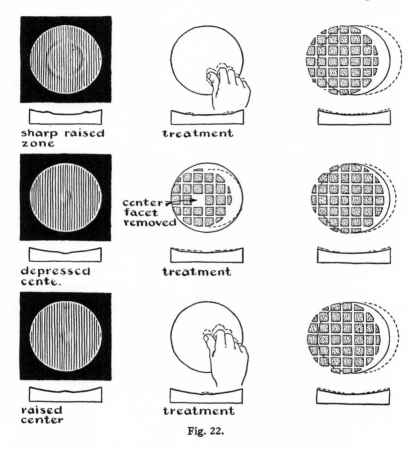

sharp raised zone   treatment

depressed cente.   center facet removed   treatment

raised center   treatment

Fig. 22.

By one, the first imagined surface lying wholly under the glass surface requires the removal of an outer layer represented by the difference between the dotted starting profile in the center and the full-line final profile in the center. The next imagined surface, now a spheric one, leaves several sharp zones to be removed by the usual treatment with a full-size soft tool.

The alternate treatment goes from the primary defective surface to one with an intermediary elevated zone relative to the desired spheric surface. A chordal stroke is used. The elevated zone is removed by a second larger-size tool.

In working on small zones in large mirrors or relatively large zones in small mirrors the optician has as possible figuring tools the thumb, the fingers, and the ball and heel of his hand.

Fig. 22 shows how a narrow elevated zone may be removed with the thumb and how a depression may be removed with tools from which a facet has been removed. The thumb is used with extreme caution, applied lightly for one revolution at first, and then, if necessary, for a few more complete revolutions. There is a danger of overcompensating for the elevated zone with the cutting zone of the thumb, because small polishing tools cut very rapidly.

In testing an optical surface which has been figured by the fingers, one must allow enough time for the heat developed by the friction of the fingers to be dissipated. Even for one revolution, this heating will produce a false zone, by expansion of the glass, which may be higher than the original zone.

The top of Fig. 23 shows how a spheric mirror can be parabolized with a star tool. The focogram at the top right gives the appearance of the parabolic surface when it is tested at the center of curvature. The focogram of a parabolic profile tested at the mean center of curvature exhibits the character of a soft raised intermediary zone.

The second series of Fig. 23 shows an alternate parabolizing procedure and focograms of the appearance of the figure of the mirror, as tested at the focus, before and after the use of the method. The advantage of testing a parabolic mirror at the focus is evident: The optician works toward a uniform distribution of light over the mirror face. The advantage of testing at the focus over testing at the center of

spherical mirror
tested at the
center of
curvature

method of correcting,
focal length decreases

parabolic
mirror tested at
the average
center of
curvature

spherical mirror
tested at the
focus, i.e., with
an optical flat

alternate method of
correcting, focal
length increases

parabolic
mirror tested
at the focus,
i.e., with an
optical flat

spherical convex
mirror tested
with a spherical
mirror or with a
paraboloid and flat

method of correcting

hyperbolic con-
vex mirror
tested with a
spherical mirror,
or paraboloid
and flat

spherical lens
tested with an
optical flat

method of correcting

hyperbolic lens
tested with
an optical flat

Fig. 23.

curvature is especially great when zones are being removed. Zones which are practically invisible if the mirror is examined at the center of curvature become quite conspicuous when it is tested at the focus.

The last two series of Fig. 23 show procedures that may be used for hyperbolizing.

Astigmatism. The correction of astigmatism is more difficult than the removal of central symmetric zones. Cylindrical defects and, in general, all defects which are not symmetrical about the center of the work produce astigmatism. These defects must be worked out by hand. The rule of procedure is the same as it is for zonal defects—namely, the polishing is done on the high portions of the surface. Transition zones are removed with a full-size tool in the regular manner. The simplicity of this rule must not, however, be allowed to obscure the fact that the correction of astigmatism is one of the most delicate operations required of the optician, and that aside from a knowledge of what is to be done it requires considerable manual dexterity. The tendency of tools to cut fastest near their periphery and especially where their edges come to rest is to be continually kept in mind. The complete removal of astigmatism in an optical surface is the apogee of good workmanship, while its avoidance is the result of experience.

Optical testing. There are many applications for optical tests besides their employment to guide figuring. For example, one may wish to know the figure of a finished spherical concave mirror, a flat, or perhaps a lens of unknown quality. Also, the testing methods described here can be used to test gratings. The Foucault knife-edge test is employed by the Schlieren-methode for photography of sound wave fronts.[6]

Newton's fringes. The simplest optical tests are interference tests using monochromatic light of wave length λ.

---

[6] Töpler, A., *Pogg. Ann.*, *131*, 33, 180 (1867).

Wood, R. W., *Physical Optics*, page 93. New York: The Macmillan Company, 1934.

The fringes manifest by a thin air film between optical surfaces are called Newton's fringes. They represent lines of equal optical separation of the surfaces. Between two adjacent fringes the optical thickness of the air film varies by an amount $\lambda/2$, and the fringes may be interpreted as contour lines for the surface of one glass referred to the surface of the other glass, which is usually a flat or spherical test surface.

The fringe system between two flats, if they are slightly inclined to each other and are illuminated with monochromatic light, is a series of parallel equispaced straight lines.

A cylindric surface of long radius of curvature in contact on a line with a flat gives straight fringes of unequal spacing.

A spherical convex or concave on a flat gives concentric circles.

Fig. 24 illustrates a box for testing optical surfaces in contact with a flat and the appearance of the fringes under different conditions.

The appearance of a convex spheric or cylindric surface on a flat is the same as the appearance of a concave surface. The difference in distance between the surfaces at one fringe and at the adjacent fringe is $\lambda/2$; but the sign of the difference, that is, whether the separation is increasing or decreasing, is not known. The following rule may be employed to differentiate between a concave and a convex surface. The exhibited curved fringes expand away from their center of curvature when the head is lowered or moved away from the normal to the flat if the surface is convex, while, if it is concave, they contract toward their center of curvature.

Newton's fringes are particularly suited to making a comparison between a "flat" of unknown quality and a master flat. Also, they may be employed for testing surfaces of a definite radius by pressing them against a master plate of the same radius but opposite curvature. In this case, white light rather than monochromatic light is generally used, and deviations from the master are determined by the residual color of the interference pattern.

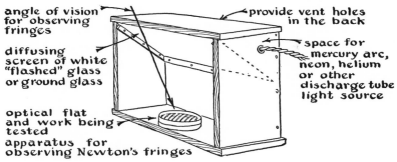

angle of vision
for observing
fringes

diffusing
screen of white
"flashed" glass
or ground glass

optical flat
and work being
tested
apparatus for
observing Newton's fringes

provide vent holes
in the back

space for
mercury arc,
neon, helium
or other
discharge tube
light source

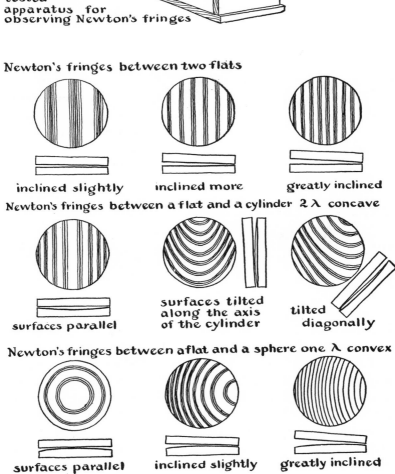

Newton's fringes between two flats

inclined slightly   inclined more   greatly inclined

Newton's fringes between a flat and a cylinder 2 λ concave

surfaces parallel   surfaces tilted
along the axis
of the cylinder   tilted
diagonally

Newton's fringes between a flat and a sphere one λ convex

surfaces parallel   inclined slightly   greatly inclined

Fig. 24.

When precision tests are made of a "flat" against a master flat and the fringes are observed at other than normal incidence, it is necessary to have the fringes running parallel to the plane of reflection, or they will be curved, even though the work is flat. Deviations of the fringes from a straight line are estimated by comparison with a stretched wire or thread.

Haidinger's fringes. Haidinger's fringes are excellent for testing the quality of plane parallels. Fig. 25 shows how

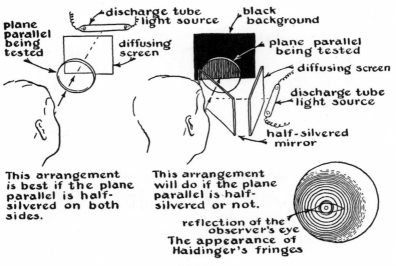

Fig. 25.

Haidinger's fringes are observed. The usual manner of observing Haidinger's fringes is shown at the right in Fig. 25, and the appearance of the fringes and their positioning in respect to the reflected image of the observer's eye are shown in the lower right of this figure. These fringes are arranged like the Newton's fringes produced by a sphere on a plane. They are different in that Newton's fringes are observed by focusing the eye on the thin air film between the plane and sphere, whereas Haidinger's fringes are observed at infinity either with the eye or with a telescope. Newton's fringes represent the locus of points of equal optical thickness, while Haidinger's fringes represent the locus of points where rays "from the eye" make equal inclination to the plane-parallel plate. The Haidinger fringes are observed at normal incidence, and the plane-parallel plate is moved laterally to apply the test to different areas of the work. A variation of thickness, from one end of a plane parallel to the other, results in the appearance or disappearance of fringes. If the plate gets thicker, fringes appear. The appearance and disappearance of one ring corresponds to $\lambda/2n$ change in thickness. For the most delicate testing, a telescope is used. A large field telescope equipped with a filar micrometer may be used to measure the diameter of the rings. With this telescope the appearance of about one tenth of a ring can be detected. For glass having an index of 1.5, one tenth of a ring represents a difference of thickness of 1.5×10^{-6} cm or approximately 0.5×10^{-6} inch.

Eyepiece tests. Another important means of examining the quality of image-forming systems of mirrors or lenses is to inspect an imaged pinhole light source. A high-power magnifier, such as a 14X Hastings triplet, is suitable for examining the image. This test is called the eyepiece test because it is essentially the test which is applied when one observes a star in the eyepiece of an astronomical telescope on a good night. The eyepiece test is the most sensitive optical test for astigmatism. The infrafocal and extra-focal images should be examined, as well as the focal image. It is advisable to record the results of this test by drawing rough distribution curves representing the light intensity along a horizontal diameter of the image. Fig. 26(a) illustrates eyepiece images for a good (though not perfect) spheric mirror tested at the center of curvature. Fig. 26(b) illustrates the eyepiece test for an overcorrected parabolic mirror tested at the center of curvature, and (c) illustrates the test applied to a mirror with very slight astigmatism.

Fig. 33 illustrates the eyepiece test in comparison with the Foucault, Ronchi, and Hartmann tests.

This was a very good spherical mirror 10 inches in diameter, f/16 It had a depressed central zone λ/40 deep, barely detectable with the Foucault Test.

appearance of the image of an artificial star (pinhole .0003" in diam.) as seen with a 20-power eyepiece

-0.10"	-0.05"	0.00"	+0.05"	+0.10" (a)
inside	focus	at focus	outside	focus

light-intensity curves

This was an overcorrected parabolic mirror 12 inches in diameter, f/8. The test was made at the center of curvature (f/16) and it therefore appeared to have a turned-down edge and a depressed center.

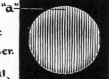

appearance of the image of an artificial star (pinhole and eyepiece same as above)

-0.10"	-0.05"	0.00"	+0.05"	+0.10" (b)
inside	focus	at focus of "a"	outside	focus

light-intensity curves

This is a typical astigmatic mirror. Astigmatism is only detectable in the Foucault Test when it is very marked.

appearance of the image of an artificial star

inside focus	focus in vertical plane	circle of confusion	focus in horizontal plane	outside focus (c)

Fig. 26. Eyepiece image test.

Foucault knife-edge test.   The Foucault knife-edge test is usually employed for the detection of central spherical aberration, particularly in testing work of fairly large aperture, such as lenses or mirrors used for astronomical telescopes.

The test is simplest as applied to a spherical concave surface of long radius.   A small hole is pierced in thin metal

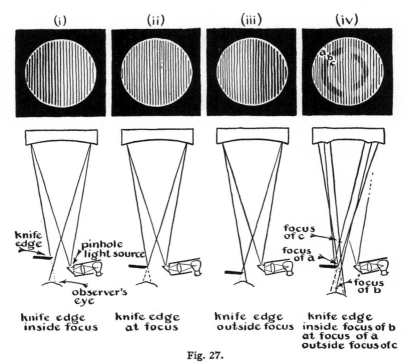

Fig. 27.

sheet with a sharp needle and illuminated by means of a lamp, together with a suitable optical system.[7]   This hole is located near the center of curvature of the mirror.   (See Fig. 27.)   Light from it is reflected by the mirror to form an image at an equal distance on the opposite side of the center

---

[7] Several layers of the thin metal sheet are laid together on an anvil, and a sharp needle is driven halfway through them.   They are then separated and the one with a suitable hole is selected.   Each pierced sheet has a small hole of a different size and all the holes are round.

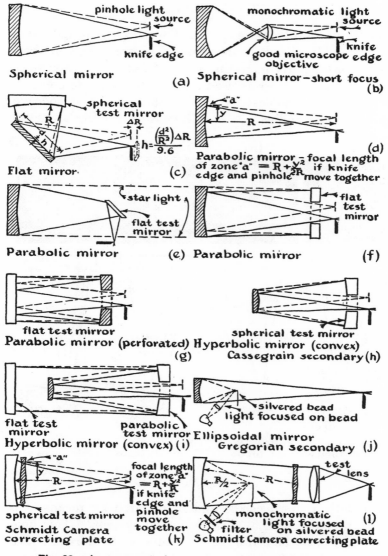

Fig. 28. Arrangements for carrying out the Foucault test:

(a) Testing of a spherical mirror at the center of curvature.
(b) Testing of a short-focus spherical mirror.
(c) Testing a flat with an auxiliary spherical mirror. If knife edge and pinhole move together, a lack of flatness represented by a sagittal distance h introduces astigmatism between the horizontal and vertical focus. The relation between h and ΔR is given.

(d) Zonal testing of a parabolic mirror at the center of curvature. R is the radius of curvature at the center.

(e) Testing of a parabolic mirror at the focus with starlight.

(f) Testing of a parabolic mirror at the focus with an auxiliary testing flat.

(g) Alternate procedure for testing a parabolic mirror with a flat.

(h) Testing of an hyperbolic mirror with a spherical testing mirror.

(i) Testing of an hyperbolic mirror with a parabolic mirror and flat.

(j) Testing of an elliptic mirror.

(k) and (l) Testing of a Schmidt lens.

---

of curvature. When the eye is placed behind this image so as to receive light from all parts of the mirror, the whole aperture will appear evenly illuminated. Then if an opaque screen, the so-called knife edge, is moved laterally across the focal point, the whole aperture will appear to darken evenly, that is, if the mirror is truly spherical, as in Fig. 27(ii). If the knife edge is moved across the cone of light a short distance inside the focus, its shadow, as it appears on the mirror, moves in the same direction as the knife edge, Fig. 27(i); if it is placed outside the focus, the shadow moves in the opposite direction, Fig. 27(iii). It is possible by this means to locate the focus of the mirror with great precision.

In the case of an imperfect mirror, such as the one shown in Fig. 27(iv), all rays do not converge to a single point, and if the knife edge intercepts the converging light rays as reflected from the mirror, the aperture will appear to be unequally illuminated; some rays are completely cut off by the knife edge, whereas others pass by it and so reach the eye. The mirror shown at the right has an intermediary raised zone. For the inside half of the zone (c) the focal length is shorter than it is for the outside half (b). With the knife edge advanced into the mean focus of the converging rays, those rays from the areas which have their center of curvature exactly at the position of the knife edge are attenuated; rays from (c) reach the eye without attenuation, while rays from (b) are cut off entirely by the knife edge. Accordingly, (c) and (b) appear very bright and dark respectively.

The appearance of the mirror with the knife edge and eye in the positions indicated is as if it were made of plaster and illuminated at grazing incidence with an imaginary light source.[8] Usually the pinhole source is on the right side of the center of curvature and the eye on the left. In this case, if the knife edge cuts the image from left to right, the observer, thinking of this imaginary light source as illuminating the plaster disk from the right, interprets its shadows in accordance with their apparent inclination. For a lens, the observer interprets the shadows by thinking of the illumination as coming from the left.

Various more complicated setups for making the Foucault test are shown in Figs. 28 and 29. In these two figures a

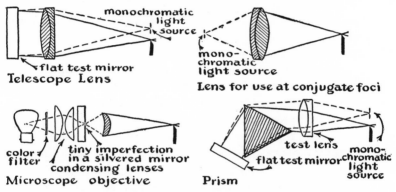

Fig. 29.   Foucault tests for achromats to be used to focus parallel light and diverging light.   Also, tests for a microscope objective and a prism.

test mirror or lens of unquestioned quality (or at least of known quality) is shown clear, while the tested mirror or lens is cross-hatched.

Zonal knife-edge testing.   Aspherical mirrors, such as paraboloidal ones, can be tested at their mean center of curvature without an auxiliary testing flat by measuring the radii of curvature of the glass at various zones.   The mirror is covered with a diaphragm of cardboard with holes opposite the zones to be tested.   The simplest diaphragm has holes at the center, at the edge, and at 0.707 of the radius, as

---

[8] See article on Foucault's shadows by E. Gaviola, in *Amateur Telescope Making, Advanced* (Albert G. Ingalls, editor), page 76.   New York: Scientific American Publishing Company, 1937.

illustrated in Fig. 30.   If the mirror is parabolic, the characteristic shadow shown in the upper right of Fig. 23 will appear when the mirror is viewed without the diaphragm. With the diaphragm, the measured difference in focus of the center and the zone at the rim will be $r^2/2R$, where R is the mean radius of curvature of the mirror and r the radius of the mirror.   This test is suitable for testing small mirrors to determine when a raised intermediary zone, as illustrated in Fig. 23, is carried sufficiently far to parabolize the mirror.

Diaphragms for very large parabolic mirrors, or mirrors of focal ratio of $f/4.5$ or greater, are constructed so that the radius of curvature of a large number of zones can be measured.   Ordinarily, mirrors of aperture $f/10$ or less need not be parabolized unless their diameter is greater than 24 inches.

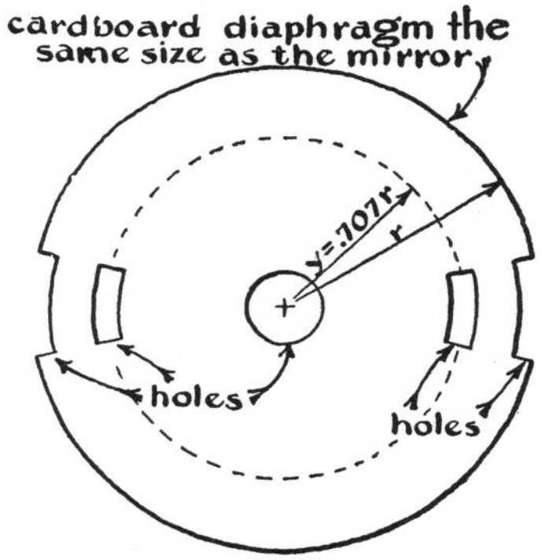

cardboard diaphragm the same size as the mirror.

$y = .707r$
r

holes

holes

Typical zonal diaphragm of a parabolic mirror
For this diaphragm, if the focal length of the center is R, the focal length of the intermediate zone should be $R + r^2/4R$, and the focal length of the rim should be $R + r^2/2R$.   Example — for a 6-inch mirror, $f = 4$ feet, the focus at the center will be 96 inches, at the intermediate zone $96" + 0.023"$, and at the rim $96" + 0.047."$ The dimension R (96) need not be precisely measured.

Fig. 30.

Another procedure for quantitative application of the knife-edge setup has been described by E. Gaviola.[9]   By this procedure the inclination of different zones is determined relative to a mean surface for the mirror by measuring the position of the knife edge which intersects the light rays reflected from these zones.

In any knife-edge setup, and especially where accurate quantitative zonal measurements are to be made, it is important to avoid parallax.   Although a setup like the one

[9] Gaviola, E., *J.O.S.A.*, *26*, 163 (1936).

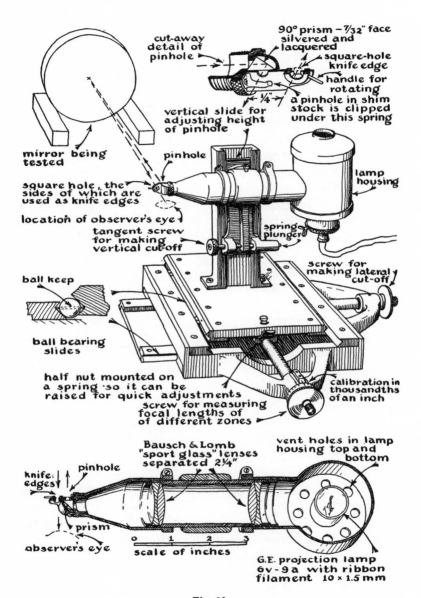

cut-away detail of pinhole

90° prism – 7/32" face silvered and lacquered

square-hole knife edge

handle for rotating

a pinhole in shim stock is clipped under this spring

vertical slide for adjusting height of pinhole

1/4"

pinhole

mirror being tested

lamp housing

square hole, the sides of which are used as knife edges

location of observer's eye

tangent screw for making vertical cut-off

spring plunger

screw for making lateral cut-off

ball keep

screw for making lateral cut-off

ball bearing slides

half nut mounted on a spring so it can be raised for quick adjustments

screw for measuring focal lengths of of different zones

calibration in thousandths of an inch

Bausch & Lomb "sport glass" lenses separated 2¼"

vent holes in lamp housing top and bottom

knife edges

pinhole

prism

observers eye

0   1   2   3

scale of inches

G.E. projection lamp 6v-9a with ribbon filament 10 × 1.5 mm

Fig. 31.

shown in Fig. 27, using a simple pinhole and knife, is suitable for qualitative tests on small mirrors of long radius, a more elaborate setup is usually required.

Parallax appears whenever a Foucault test is made on more than one mirror, such as a test on a parabolic mirror at its focus with an auxiliary flat. (See Fig. 28.) This parallax is due to the fact that a ray from the pinhole strikes the parabolic mirror at one point and is subsequently reflected, after returning from the flat, at a different point on the parabolic mirror. The displacement between these points on the paraboloid mirror is somewhat less than the displacement between the pinhole and the knife edge. Even so, the displacement may be sufficient to yield results that are quite misleading. As a result of parallax one does not get an indication of the character of the mirror at either of the two indicated points but rather a kind of average for the two points. This information is of little value and may be quite misleading if the effect of errors at one point of the parabolic mirror is compensated by opposite errors at the other.

A knife-edge testing device is illustrated in Fig. 31. Fig. 32 shows two attachments for it which may be used to

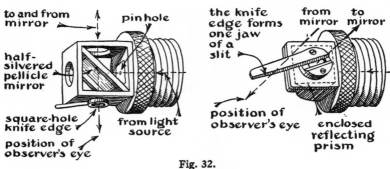

Fig. 32.

avoid parallax. The device at the left eliminates parallax by eliminating the displacement between the knife edge and the pinhole—a virtual image of the pinhole formed by means of a half-silvered pellicle mirror lies exactly on the knife

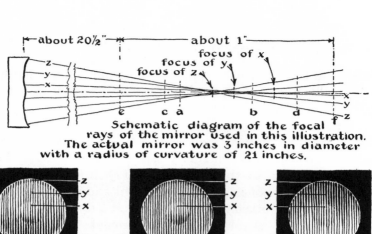

Schematic diagram of the focal
rays of the mirror used in this illustration.
The actual mirror was 3 inches in diameter
with a radius of curvature of 21 inches.

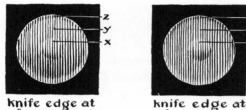

knife edge at
focus of z

knife edge at
focus of y

knife edge at
focus of x

Foucault Knife-Edge Test   (knife edge at the bottom)

shield placed over
mirror to help
identify zones

Eyepiece Test

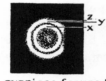

eyepiece focused
at a – inside focus

eyepiece focused
at b – outside focus

appearance of extra focal images

The screen used had
150 lines per inch.

Ronchi Test

screen inside focus (c)

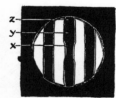

outside focus (d)

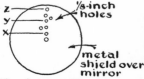

⅛-inch
holes

metal
shield over
mirror

HartmannTest

eyepiece inside focus (e)

outside focus (f)

Fig. 33. Comparison of Foucault, eyepiece, Ronchi, and Hartmann
tests of a defective mirror.

edge. A pellicle mirror is made by flowing lacquer on an inclined glass plate. After the lacquer is hard, it is stripped off the glass under water. The film of lacquer is then mounted on the flat surface of a brass frame and half-silvered by the evaporation process.

The device at the right uses a slit instead of a pinhole. This device avoids parallax by the simple expedient of removing it by half a revolution in azimuth from the testing diameter.

The Ronchi test. The Ronchi test will be treated here only briefly, since it is not widely employed and its interpretation is not simple.[10] A small light source illuminates the mirror through a ruled surface (about 100 lines per inch), and the image is also formed through another section of the same ruled surface. For comparison, the Foucault test of a defective mirror is shown at the top of Fig. 33. Below, we have the results of the eyepiece test and Ronchi test of the same mirror, and, at the bottom, the Hartmann test is illustrated. Fig. 34 shows a simple quick way of testing a léns with the Ronchi screen. A good lens gives straight Ronchi lines.

Hartmann's test. Hartmann's test is similar to the Ronchi test for a lens, illustrated in Fig. 34. A diaphragm, such as the one shown at the bottom left of Fig. 33, is prepared with several appropriately spaced holes. This diaphragm is placed directly in front of the mirror or lens. The Foucault test determines errors in the mirror by the lateral positioning, relative to their neighbors, of various rays as they pass through the focus; the Hartmann test determines the positions of these rays, relative to their neighbors, at points either inside the focus at (e) or outside of the focus at (f). The relative position of the holes in the plate and the appearance of the rays, as observed with the eyepiece at (e) and (f), are shown in the figure.[11]

---

[10] Anderson, J. A., and Porter, R. W., *Astrophys. J.*, *70*, 175 (1929).

[11] For further treatment of optical testing, see articles contained in *Amateur Telescope Making, Advanced*, and references cited therein.

The advantages of the Hartmann test over the others illustrated in Fig. 33 are that it is not necessary to locate the mean focus, and that the results of the test are easily recorded photographically, both of which features make it particularly useful for figuring lenses for the ultraviolet region of the spectrum.

Lining up a system of mirrors. In the more complicated testing setups shown in Figs. 28 and 29 it is often quite

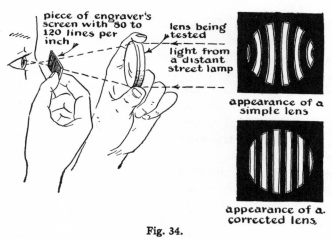

Fig. 34.

difficult to get the mirrors or lenses lined up. The appearance of coma in the eyepiece image, however, can be used to advantage for this. The coma of a system not properly lined up is quite strong and indicates clearly in what direction the mirrors are to be adjusted to get round images.

Some opticians put two white threads at right angles to each other across the face of one of the mirrors. When these threads and all of the secondary images of them viewed from the focus appear symmetrical, the system is in alignment.

Two methods of generating optical surfaces. As we have already pointed out, the optician's task is defined as the generation of accurate surfaces on mirrors, lenses, prisms, and so forth, which possess a high polish. This is ordinarily done by hand or with the modified Draper machine, as described before. Or it may be done with a high-speed hand-lever machine in the manner described below. The procedure with a modified Draper machine or by hand is slow, but it yields the most accurate results. The modified

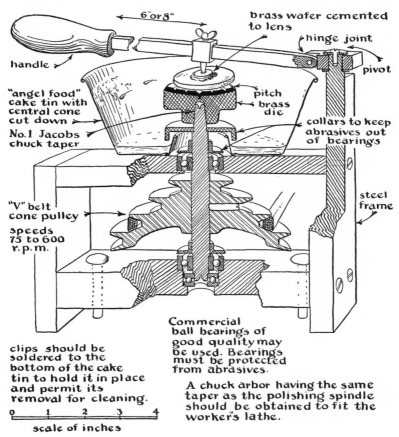

Fig. 35.

Draper machine illustrated in Fig. 10 uses a single crank and allows for counterbalancing of the tool, automatic control of the tool, slow smooth stroking, and easy placement of the work. In contrast with this, the hand-lever machine shown in Fig. 35 features high speed and simplicity. The spindle is run at about 100 to 600 r.p.m. Naturally, the heat thus generated, as well as the high speeds of cutting, makes work of the highest precision impossible.

Working optical surfaces on the hand-lever machine. The tool used with the hand-lever machine may be attached to a high-speed spindle as shown in Fig. 35, or the work may be attached with wax to the spindle and the tool applied above. In the former case, a socket for the pivot point of

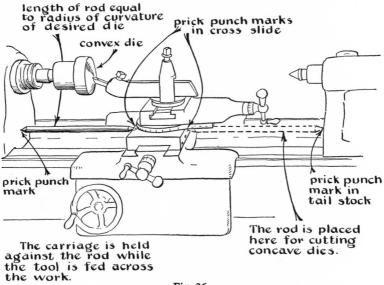

Fig. 36.

the hand lever is waxed to the work with a mixture of 2 parts coal-tar pitch to 1 part sieved wood ashes. When the tool is applied above, the socket is turned in the back of it.

The preliminary grinding may be accomplished on the hand-lever machine with a sub-diameter ring tool of iron, as with the Draper machine. When this ring tool is moved back and forth across the center of the spinning work with a short stroke so that there is no overhang of the tool, the surface is made concave. A long stroke with overhang gives a convex surface. The tool is pivoted and allowed to spin freely, and 90 Carborundum with water is fed on it to accomplish the grinding. The growth of the curve in the work is measured with templates. These are usually cut on a lathe from a thin sheet of brass or bronze.

The final grinding is done on the hand-lever machine with a spherical brass tool of the same diameter as the work. The spherical tool is made as follows: A brass male and female part are turned on the lathe to the same curvature in the manner illustrated by Fig. 36. These are then lapped together with Carborundum to generate complementary spherical surfaces. If a lathe is not available, they may be separately ground with the hand-lever machine to an approximate fit with a third metal ring tool and then lapped together. It is important to cut a cavity in the center of the one to be used as the grinding tool. The cavity should have a diameter of about one twentieth of the tool diameter.

After the proper curve is approached in the work by grinding with the ring tool, the spherical brass tool is substituted, and the final grinding is carried out with 90, F, and 600 Carborundum and $302\frac{1}{2}$ emery. During the grinding process the offset of the tool in respect to the work should never be so great that the tool and the work rotate in opposite directions.

Polishing is accomplished on the hand-lever machine with rouge on a pitch lap. The brass tool used for grinding may be warmed and coated with a layer of hard pitch or pure beeswax for polishing. While the wax is still warm, it is pressed to the proper shape with the already fine-ground work (wet with soap and glycerin solution) to give a layer of pitch about $\frac{1}{8}$ to $\frac{1}{4}$ inch in thickness. As for grinding, this lap is cut away in the center to form a cavity of one twentieth of the tool diameter. Also, the pitch is cut to form annular grooves. These grooves facilitate contact between the pitch and the work. The pitch lap should be frequently trimmed.

If the central cavity removed is too broad, the tendency is to polish the edges first, while if the central cavity is small and pitch is trimmed off the edges of the tool, it will polish the center first. Also, whether the polish progresses faster in the center of the work or near the edge depends on the offset. A little offset favors polishing the edges fast, and a big offset makes the progress of polishing greater in the center. One can easily keep track of the progress of the polishing by shining a strong light on the work and observing the "grayness" produced by the residual grinding pits.

It is difficult to balance all these factors, and in practice one should observe how the polish progresses. If the polish is not progressing satisfactorily, the offset can be altered or the tool trimmed accordingly.

Figuring aspheric lenses on the hand-lever machine is accomplished by polishing with sub-diameter tools and star or ring tools.

Small lenses are aligned on the spindle by tilting them while the blocking wax used to cement them in place is still warm. The spindle is turned slowly, and if an object, preferably a small light source, seen reflected in the surfaces does not describe an eccentric circle as the lens rotates, the alignment is complete.

After being centered on a brass tube mounted in the head-stock of the lathe, in the same manner as described above, the work is edged with an iron tool and grits. (See Fig. 6.)

Relationship between two optical surfaces. Although we have emphasized the phases of procedure which are important in generating the optical surface, we have not dealt extensively with the orientation of that surface with respect to the general form of the work or with respect to other optical surfaces. These are matters usually managed in an obvious manner. However, in the construction of prisms, especially right-angle prisms and plane parallels, the manner of getting proper relationship between the two flat surfaces involved is not so obvious. A half-hour of polishing on the Draper machine or a few minutes of polishing on the spindle machine will usually put enough polish on ground surfaces to allow their relationship to be tested on a spectrometer table or with other optical tests. Right-

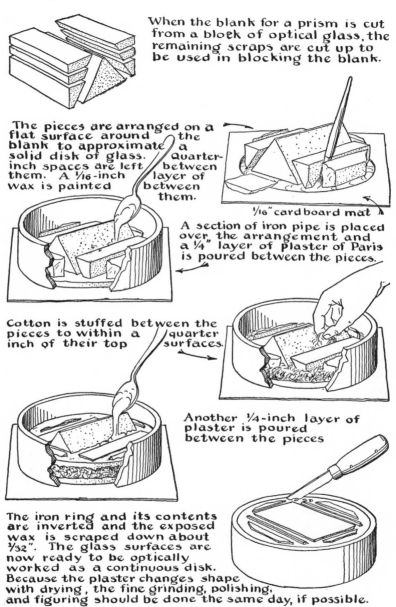

When the blank for a prism is cut from a block of optical glass, the remaining scraps are cut up to be used in blocking the blank.

The pieces are arranged on a flat surface around the blank to approximate a solid disk of glass. Quarter-inch spaces are left between them. A ¹⁄₁₆-inch layer of wax is painted between them.

¹⁄₁₆" cardboard mat

A section of iron pipe is placed over the arrangement and a ¼" layer of plaster of Paris is poured between the pieces.

Cotton is stuffed between the pieces to within a quarter inch of their top surfaces.

Another ¼-inch layer of plaster is poured between the pieces

The iron ring and its contents are inverted and the exposed wax is scraped down about ¹⁄₃₂". The glass surfaces are now ready to be optically worked as a continuous disk. Because the plaster changes shape with drying, the fine grinding, polishing, and figuring should be done the same day, if possible.

Fig. 37.

angle prisms are tested by employing their property of deviating a light beam exactly 180°. This test is sensitive to about 1 minute of angle when it is made with the naked eye, and if it is made using a telescope equipped with a Gauss eyepiece, it is sensitive to about 1 second of angle.

Plane parallels are ground to be flat and parallel to about $\frac{1}{20,000}$ of an inch. Good micrometers are used to test the glass for parallelism to this accuracy. The final optical precision is obtained by figuring. The test using Haidinger's fringes, described before, is used to guide the figuring. Plane parallels are usually made with circular faces to be cut up later into rectangles if necessary.

Blocking. Inasmuch as round glass surfaces are more easily figured than square or rectangular ones, it is advisable to mount a prism blank in a metal ring as shown in Fig. 37, together with auxiliary glasses having the same coefficient of expansion, to make up a circular array of glass surfaces. This circular array is held in the metal ring with plaster of Paris, and the ensemble is then worked as a single disk of glass. The parts may be immersed in a single thick layer of plaster, but it is best to imbed them in a double layer of plaster as shown in Fig. 37. A mixture of 3 parts plaster to 2 parts water is used. This gives an almost non-shrinking, although not very strong, cement. The work may be coated first with a thin layer of beeswax in cases where free lime or moisture in the plaster might attack the glass. After the plaster of Paris sets, its surface is shellacked to make it impervious to water. The grinding and figuring should be finished in one day. Otherwise, owing to "aging" of the plaster, the central and auxiliary surfaces will not maintain satisfactory alignment.

Quartz and calcite. When optical surfaces are generated on crystals, it is frequently required to orient the surfaces precisely with respect to the crystal axes. Fig. 38 illustrates the manner in which the optical axis of quartz is precisely located. The crystal is cut at each end with the mud or diamond saw, the cuts being made roughly perpendicular to

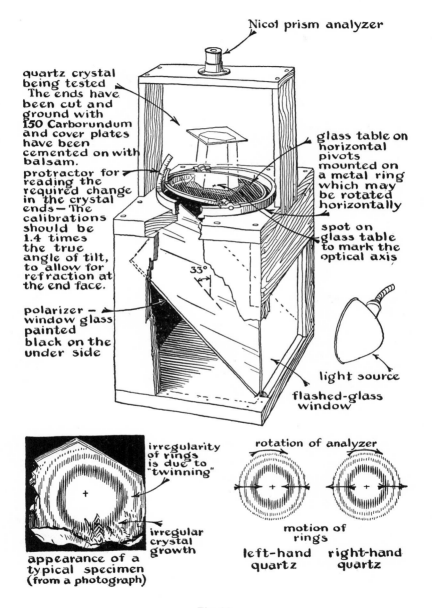

Nicol prism analyzer

quartz crystal
being tested
 The ends have
been cut and
ground with
150 Carborundum
and cover plates
have been
cemented on with
balsam.

protractor for
reading the
required change
in the crystal
ends — The
calibrations
should be
1.4 times
the true
angle of tilt,
to allow for
refraction at
the end face.

glass table on
horizontal
pivots
mounted on
a metal ring
which may
be rotated
horizontally

spot on
glass table
to mark the
optical axis

33°

polarizer —
window glass
painted
black on the
under side

light source

flashed-glass
window

irregularity
of rings
is due to
"twinning"

irregular
crystal
growth

appearance of a
typical specimen
(from a photograph)

rotation of analyzer

motion of
rings

left-hand
quartz

right-hand
quartz

Fig. 38.

the optical axis. These parallel saw cuts are then ground with the abrasives to grade 150 Carborundum and "artificially polished" by cementing cover glasses to the ground

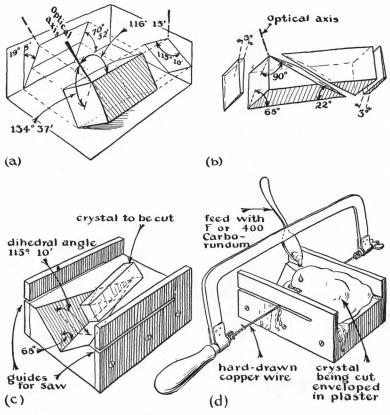

Fig. 39. Calcite:
(a) Orientation of axis.
(b) Cuts for making Nicols.
(c) and (d) Procedure for cutting calcite to make Nicols.

ends with balsam. Polarized light is used to determine the optical axis in the manner illustrated in the figure. The system of rings noted through the analyzer will remain stationary when the crystal is rotated about a vertical axis if the cuts are perpendicular to the optical axis. If the rings "wobble" as the crystal is rotated, the axis of rotation is to be tilted by means of the gimbals provided (or with wedges) until the fringes are stationary during rotation. The ends are then recut, taking account of refraction (see note on the figure), and the plate retested to check the result.

When properly cut quartz crystal is rotated in a clockwise direction, the rings close in toward the center if the crystal is left-handed quartz and move out if it is right-handed quartz.

An irregular piece of quartz can be roughly examined for striae by immersion in a tank filled with a solution composed of 80 per cent ethyl cinnamate and 20 per cent xylol (by volume). Iron oxide surface stains may be removed from the crystal by washing in oxalic acid solution.

The orientation of the principal axis of calcite is shown at the top of Fig. 39. To cut calcite for making Nicols, the crystal is oriented and mounted in a wooden form having the cutting plane defined by a preliminary saw cut. The cut through the crystal is made by hand by sawing through both plaster and crystal with a hard-drawn copper wire mounted in a scroll-saw frame and charged with Carborundum.

Optical working of crystals. Quartz is the optician's favorite medium. Both the fused and the crystal material are ground and polished by the same procedure as glass.

Calcite crystals, especially large ones, are expensive, and in addition they are soft and easily fractured. Accordingly calcite is always worked by hand with very light pressures. All but the smaller Carborundum grains tend to produce fractures in calcite, and therefore the series F-400-600 Carborundum and $302\frac{1}{2}$ and $303\frac{1}{2}$ emery is recommended for working it. If prisms with very thin edges are to be made, 400 Carborundum is used as the coarsest grit. A beeswax-coated pitch lap is satisfactory for polishing and figuring calcite. For figuring, calcite should be blocked with calcite of the same crystal orientation.

Rock salt is polished and figured on a hard-pitch tool pressed with a glass pressing lap.[12] The desired figure is

---

[12] Brashear, John A., *Proc. of Am. Assn. for Adv. of Science, 38,* 166 (1885).

obtained with an overcorrected pressing lap, as the figure
obtained on this material is usually convex with respect to
that established in the tool by the pressing lap. For example, in making flats, one would use a slightly concave
pressing lap ($\frac{1}{1000}$ of an inch in a 4-inch disk or 60-foot
radius of curvature). Rouge in saturated salt solution is
used to start the polishing. Fig. 40 shows the arrangement
of the pitch tool which is placed below the work, and a
chamois skin used for drying the work. The work is rubbed
against the lap until the rouge is almost dry. It is then

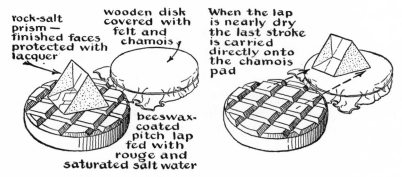

Fig. 40.

kept moist with the breath for the final strokes and is slipped
off the tool onto the chamois to be dried. This technique
should be practiced on test pieces before big work is undertaken. The first face of a prism or lens is lacquered or
waxed to prevent attacks by moisture while the second face
is being worked. The pitch tool is coated with beeswax.
Beeswax is useful for even softer materials than rock salt,
such as potassium chloride, potassium bromide, and even
potassium iodide.

Polishing of metals. Perhaps the most important metal
in optics is speculum metal. It is very hard, exhibits a
conchoidal fracture like glass, and is worked by the same
procedure, being ground with the same sequence of grits.
The polishing tool should have narrow facets. It is often

advantageous to do the final figuring of speculum surfaces with the metal face turned down to avoid scratching.

Stellite is also worked like glass except that longer grinding periods (two to three times that for glass) are required. Ordinarily pitch polishing tools are used with rouge or chromium oxide as polishing agent. One should try to "hold" the figure from the grinding stages until polishing is completed.

Hard steel is worked in the same manner as glass.

In grinding soft steel, a still softer metal, such as copper or lead, is used as a grinding tool.

Soft steel and hard-drawn copper are difficult to polish, but they can often be managed with a polishing tool coated with a mixture of paraffin and oxide of tin. As much oxide is added to the molten paraffin as it will take without crumbling. This mixture is applied hot with a swab to the pitch polishing lap.

If a metal tends to etch or discolor during polishing, it is advisable to try carbon as a polishing agent (charcoal ground in a ball mill and washed). Chromium oxide will often give a bright polish in cases where rouge would discolor the metal.

The very soft metals—silver, soft copper, gold, and so forth—cannot be easily surfaced by the ordinary optical methods. They become charged with the grits and refuse to grind. Silver circles are brightened by rubbing moistened cigarette ashes with the thumb back and forth in a direction parallel to the engraved lines.

The Schmidt camera. The Schmidt camera is an image-forming device which combines features not possessed by any lens system, and, while it has some disadvantages, it may well prove to be a natural solution to many more instrumental problems than those to which it has already been applied.[13]

The camera has had considerable application in astronomy, particularly meteor photography and survey work of

---

[13] Strömgren, B., "Das Schmidtsche Spiegelteleskop," *Vierteljahrschrift der Astronomischen Gesellschaft, 70,* 65 (1935).

Smiley, C. H., "The Schmidt Camera," *Popular Astronomy, 44,* 415 (1936).

large star fields. It has been applied to stellar spectrographs, and it is believed that it will have other applications in research where extreme speed, a long spectral range, and a large field are important. Two awkward features of the Schmidt camera are its curved focal plane and the inaccessibility of the plate or film holder. The curvature of the focal surface is $R/2$, where R is the radius of curvature of the primary mirror. The focal surface is convex toward the sphere.

The construction of a Schmidt camera is so difficult that it should not be undertaken except by one with considerable optical experience. The following is intended primarily as a description of it.

The scheme of the instrument is shown at the top of Fig. 41. It consists of a spherical primary mirror and a Schmidt lens, which corrects the primary mirror for spherical aberration. The lens is located at the center of curvature of the spherical mirror, and its deviation from flatness is so small that no great error of achromatism is produced by the dispersion of the index of refraction of the glass from which it is made. However, as an optical figuring job this deviation is great enough to make the construction of the lens difficult. This is because the curve deviates as much from any sphere as it does from flatness, so that all the construction difficulties of making aspheric surfaces are encountered.

The Schmidt lens may have several contours, as illustrated in Fig. 41. The variation of thickness may be obtained by putting the curves entirely on one side of the plate or on both sides. The variation in the thickness Δt of a plate of diameter $2r$, expressed as a function of the distance from the center of the plate y and the radius of curvature R of the primary spherical mirror, can be represented by any one of the family of curves

$$\Delta t = \frac{y^4 - ky^2r^2}{4(n-1)R^3},$$

where k may have any value between 0 and 4.

The characteristics of some of the curves are as follows: Where $k = 4$, the lens is too thick; where $k = 0$, the slope at the edge is so steep that the construction difficulties are great; where $k = 1.5$, the achromatism is best; where $k = 1$, the slopes are moderate, the color characteristics

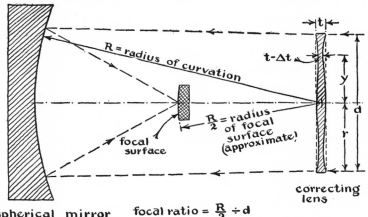

R = radius of curvature

$t-\Delta t$

$\frac{R}{2}$ = radius of focal surface (approximate!)

focal surface

correcting lens

spherical mirror   focal ratio = $\frac{R}{2} \div d$

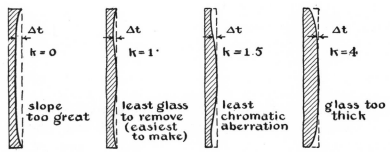

Δt

$k = 0$

slope too great

Δt

$k = 1 \cdot$

least glass to remove (easiest to make)

Δt

$k = 1.5$

least chromatic aberration

Δt

$k = 4$

glass too thick

These curves may be put on either or both sides of the lens provided the value of $(t - \Delta t)$ is maintained.

$$\Delta t = \frac{y^4 - k\,r^2 y^2}{4(n-1)R^3}$$

k = a constant between 0 and 4
n = index of refraction of lens material

Fig. 41.

are good, and the curve can be put half on one side of the plate and half on the other. In the case where $k = 1$, the curve requires the least glass to be removed.

The Schmidt lens is made of Uviol glass or even fused quartz if the camera is to be used for photography in the

ultraviolet spectrum. The Schmidt camera has been made
to numerical apertures as fast as $f/0.6$. Such a camera is
much faster than a camera using a lens of corresponding
aperture because there are fewer glass surfaces to penetrate,
and the light losses are correspondingly less.

The Schmidt plate is ground and polished with a special
ring tool. Each of the glass facets for grinding or pitch
facets for polishing is mounted on a separate spring as in

back of tool

face of tool

Phosphor bronze sectors
  These should be cut from
the sheet metal in the
same orientation with
respect to the rolling of the
metal in order to have
their "springiness" symmetrical.

For grinding, glass or tile
facets are cemented on
the spring tips. For polishing
pitch facets are used.

Fig. 42.

Fig. 42.   This or a similar flexible construction of a tool is
used since considerable deformability is required of it.

The curve $k = 1$ requires the thickness at the center to be
the same as that at the edge. This is indicated when a
straightedge laid across the work will touch the center but
not rock on it. The minimum thickness of the plate at
$y = 0.707\,r$ is determined from the thickness at the edge,
and the value of Δt calculated from the equation. The
intermediary zone is depressed by grinding until this minimum thickness corresponds with that required as measured
by a micrometer.

Figuring may be guided by several testing schemes shown
at the bottom of Fig. 28.

CHAPTER III

Technique of High Vacuum[1]

SOME of the equations from the kinetic theory are important in the design, construction, and operation of vacuum apparatus. Accordingly, we will begin our treatment of the technique of high vacuum with a discussion of them. The derivations of these equations are omitted, since we are interested only in their applications.

The laws of ideal gases. The laws of ideal gases are represented, mathematically, by Eqs. 1 and 2.

$$P_1 = \frac{w_1}{M_1} R \frac{T}{V}. \tag{1}$$

$$P_T = P_1 + P_2 + \ldots P_n. \tag{2}$$

P_1 represents the total pressure exerted on the walls of a vessel containing w_1 grams of a gas of molecular weight M_1, when this vessel has a volume V and is maintained at an absolute temperature T. If more than one gas is present, for example, if the vessel contains w_1 grams of one gas of molecular weight M_1, w_2 grams of a second gas of molecular

---

[1] This chapter is intended primarily to supplement the works on vacuum technique listed below:

Dunyoer, L., *Vacuum Practice.* New York: D. Van Nostrand and Company, 1926.

Dushman, S., *Frank. Inst., J.*, *211*, 689 (1931).

Dushman, S., *High Vacuum.* Schenectady: General Electric Company, 1922.

Goetz, A., *Physik und Technik des Hochvakuums.* Aktges. Braunschweig: Friedrich Vieweg und Sohn, 1926.

Kaye, G. W. C., *High Vacua.* New York: Longmans, Green and Company, 1927.

Newman, F. H., *The Production and Measurement of Low Pressures.* New York: D. Van Nostrand and Company, 1925.

weight M_2, and so forth, the partial pressure exerted by each gas is given by Eq. 1.

The total pressure, given by Eq. 2, is the sum of these partial pressures. The value of the constant R, the so-called universal gas constant, is independent of the molecular weight of the gas, but its value does depend on the units in which the pressure and volume are expressed. In vacuum work the pressure is usually expressed in millimeters of mercury[2] and the volume in cubic centimeters, in which case R has the value of 62,370.

Eqs. 1 and 2 are based on the assumptions, first, that the molecules are infinitely small and, second, that no inter-molecular forces exist. Neither assumption is valid for real gases. Nevertheless, the equations describe the behavior of real gases, especially hydrogen and helium, with sufficient accuracy for our purposes here. Although the equations break down at elevated pressures (pressures greater than 1 atmosphere), they become increasingly precise if the pressure is reduced. And, at pressures encountered in vacuum work, Eqs. 1 and 2 not only apply to the description of the behavior of gases but describe the behavior of many unsaturated vapors as well.

The mean free path. The mean free path is the average distance traversed by molecules between successive inter-molecular collisions. The magnitude of this quantity is determined by the size of the molecules and is given by the formula

$$\lambda = \frac{1}{\sqrt{2}\pi n \sigma^2}. \tag{3}$$

σ represents the molecular diameters and n the number of molecules per cubic centimeter. Values of the mean free

---

[2] P is usually expressed by physicists in millimeters of mercury pressure. Other units are the following:

1 millibar = 0.75 mm
1 Tor = 1 mm
1 micron = 10^{-3} mm

path for nitrogen calculated by Eq. 3, using 3.1×10^{-8} cm for the molecular diameters, are given in Table I.

TABLE I

MEAN FREE PATH OF NITROGEN AT $0°$ C.

Pressure in Millimeters of Mercury	Mean Free Path
760	8.5×10^{-6} cm
1	0.0065 cm
10^{-3}	6.5 cm
10^{-4}	65 cm
10^{-5}	6.5 m
10^{-6}	65 m
10^{-9}	65,000 m

Viscosity and heat conductivity.   The viscosity and heat conductivity of a gas, like the mean free path, depend on the molecular diameters.   As a result, we have the relationship between the mean free path and the viscosity η,

$$\eta = \tfrac{1}{3}\rho v_{av.}\lambda, \tag{4}$$

and the relationship between the viscosity and the thermal conductivity K,

$$K = \eta c_v \epsilon. \tag{5}$$

In these equations ρ is the gas density in grams per cubic centimeter; c_v is the heat capacity at constant volume of unit mass of the gas; and ϵ is a constant, being 2.5 for monatomic and 1.9 for diatomic gases. $v_{av.}$ is the average velocity of the molecules and is defined by the equation

$$v_{av.} = \sqrt{\frac{2.1 \times 10^8 T}{M}} \text{ cm/sec.} \tag{6}$$

The relationship between σ, λ, η, and K for various gases is illustrated in Table II.

TABLE II

Properties of Gases

Gas	Molecular Diameters ($\sigma \times 10^8$ cm)	Coefficient of Viscosity ($\eta \times 10^6$ cm)	Thermal Conductivity ($K \times 10^6$ cm)
Hydrogen.........	2.47	86	318
Nitrogen..........	3.50	166	52
Oxygen...........	3.39	187	56
Helium...........	2.18	189	339
Argon............	3.36	210	38.9

Kaye, G. W C., and Laby, T. H., *Tables of Physical and Chemical Constants and Some Mathematical Functions.* New York: Longmans, Green and Company, 1936.

Substituting PM/RT for ρ and Eq. 3 for λ in Eq. 4, we see that the pressure cancels. In other words, Eq. 4 predicts that the viscosity will be the same at reduced pressure as it is at ordinary pressures. The experimental verification of this prediction by Meyer and Maxwell was a triumph for the kinetic theory.[3] They measured the damping of a torsion pendulum in a bell jar at pressures varying from 1 atmosphere to about 10 mm of mercury. The damping produced by the viscosity of the air was found to be the same at all pressures.

Eq. 5 predicts that the heat conductivity is also independent of the pressure. This was established experimentally by Stefan.[4]

Eqs. 4 and 5 are derived from the assumption that the mean free path is small in comparison with the size of the apparatus. Table I shows the pressures at which this assumption becomes invalid.

If Meyer and Maxwell had reduced the pressure in their bell jar below about 10^{-1} mm, they would have observed a decrease in the damping effect on the torsion pendulum.

[3] Meyer, O., and Maxwell, James Clerk, *Pogg. Ann.*, *125*, 40, 546 (1865), *143*, 14 (1871).

[4] Stefan, J., *Akad. Wiss., Ber.*, *65*, 2. 45 (1872).

Likewise, if Stefan had extended his observations, he would have found a decrease in the heat conductivity towards 10^{-1} mm and its complete disappearance below about 10^{-4} mm.

Pumping speeds.   Consider that a vessel contains a gas at pressure P and opens through an aperture to a region where a high vacuum is maintained.   Further assume that this high vacuum is to be maintained at a pressure so much lower than P that it is essentially a perfect vacuum.   The volume of gas escaping through the aperture per unit time, dV/dt, measured at pressure P, is given by the formula

$$\frac{dV}{dt} = A\sqrt{1.32 \times 10^7 \frac{T}{M}} \text{ cm}^3/\text{sec.}, \tag{7}$$

where A is the area of the aperture.   The value of dV/dt for air ($M = 29$) at room temperature ($T = 300°$ Kelvin) is 11,700 cc/sec. cm², or 11.7 liters/sec. cm².   It is a noteworthy feature of this formula that dV/dt is independent of the pressure in the vessel.

A hypothetical aperture of unit area communicating with an essentially perfect vacuum may be regarded as a pump with a speed of 11.7 liters/sec.   Oil and mercury diffusion pumps have two characteristics in common with such an aperture.   They have pumping speeds of the same order of magnitude as the aperture, and their observed pumping speeds are roughly constant over a considerable pressure range.

The speed of a diffusion pump is, accordingly, expressed as the volume of gas passing through the throat of the pump measured at the pressure which obtains at the throat.   The speed factor of a pump is the ratio of its speed per unit area of the throat to the value 11.7 liters/sec.   A good oil diffusion pump has a speed factor of about 0.5 or 0.6.   The speed factor for mercury diffusion pumps[5] varies from 0.1 to 0.3.

---
[5] Ho, T. L., *Rev. Sci. Instruments, 3,* 133 (1932).

The pumping speed of diffusion pumps can be measured by means of a leak like the one shown in Fig. 1. Gas at atmospheric pressure is allowed to leak into the pumping line. The rate at which the gas is introduced is measured by the motion of a mercury pellet in the calibrated capillary tube. At the same time the pressure at the throat of the pump is determined with a vacuum manometer. The rate dV/dt at which gas passes through the pump is obtained by multiplying the volume which the mercury pellet sweeps through per unit time by the ratio of the pressure in the capillary (that is, the barometric pressure) to the pressure which obtains at the pump throat.

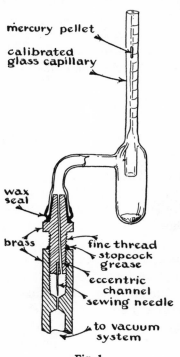

mercury pellet

calibrated glass capillary

wax seal

brass

fine thread stopcock grease

eccentric channel sewing needle

to vacuum system

Fig. 1.

Conductance of vacuum pumping lines. Ordinarily, a pump is connected to an apparatus by a tube or system of tubes which constitute the vacuum pumping line. The measured speed of the pump, which we will designate S_0, at one end of the vacuum line is greater than the effective pumping speed, S, at the other end of the line. Naturally, the difference between S_0 and S is small if the pumping tubes are short and have a large diameter. The difference between S^{-1} and S_0^{-1} determines the capacity of a vacuum line. The capacity is the reciprocal of W, the resistance of the vacuum line to the flow of gas. The relationship of the quantities S_0, S, and W is given by the formula

$$\frac{1}{S} = \frac{1}{S_0} + W. \tag{8}$$

W, in turn, is defined in terms of tube dimensions by Knudsen's formula,

$$W = 1.59 \times 10^{-5} \sqrt{\frac{273M}{T}} \left(\frac{l}{d^3} + \frac{4}{3d^2} \right) \frac{\text{sec.}}{\text{cm}^3}, \tag{9}$$

where l is the length of the pumping line and d is its diameter, both expressed in centimeters.[6] The first term in the parentheses represents the resistances of the line, while the second term represents the resistance of the two ends of the line (or the resistance of a sharp bend in the line). The second term is usually insignificant in comparison with the first and may be neglected. For example, W. Klose found that a straight pumping channel with four right-angle bends, one with four T-shaped enlargements, and a curved tube of equal diameter all exhibited essentially the same pumping speed.[7]

The coefficient of Eq. 9 becomes unity if 29, the molecular weight of air, is substituted for M, room temperature of $300°$ K. is substituted for T, and $8r^3$ is substituted for d^3, where r is the radius of the tube. It is further required that l' and r be expressed in millimeters and that W be expressed in sec./liter instead of sec./cm^3. After making these substitutions and neglecting the second term in the parentheses, Eq. 9 reduces to

$$W' = \frac{l'}{r^3} \frac{\text{sec.}}{\text{liter}}. \tag{10}$$

An an example of the application of Eq. 10, consider a pumping tube of 250 mm length and 5 mm radius. This gives a value of W' equal to 2 sec./liter. Substituting this value in Eq. 8, we see that the pumping speed S can never exceed $\frac{1}{2}$ liter/sec., even if a very fast pump is used, for which $1/S_0$ is practically zero.

Evacuation. The factors determining the rate at which an apparatus is evacuated are the volume of the apparatus, V,

[6] Knudsen, M., *Ann. d. Physik*, *28*, 75, 999 (1908). This formula applies when d is less than the mean free path.

[7] Klose, W., *Phys. Zeits.*, *31*, 503 (1930).

the effective speed of the system of pumps, S, and the limiting pressure which the pumps are capable of attaining, P_0. The method of evaluating the first factor, V, is obvious. The value of S may be calculated from the values of S_0 and W by Eqs. 8 and 10, or it may be measured by connecting the leak and gauge to the apparatus.

The value of P_0 is not easy to estimate, so it is necessary to measure it with a gauge. P_0 does not depend on the pumping speed of the pumps on tight systems which are outgassed. When the system is leaking or giving off gas, P_0 depends on the rate of leaking as well as the speed of the pumps. On a tight outgassed system the limiting pressure for mercury diffusion pumps equipped with a liquid air trap is 10^{-7} mm or less. For oil diffusion pumps without traps the limiting pressure varies from 10^{-5} to 10^{-6} mm, although lower values are occasionally reported. The vacuum attainable with mechanical pumps is usually 10^{-2} to 10^{-4} mm. The water aspirator is restricted to work at pressures above the vapor pressure of water, about 25 mm of mercury at room temperature.

The effect of outgassing on P_0 is illustrated by an experiment described by Dushman.[8] He found a limiting pressure of 0.033 bar for a Gaede rotary pump connected to a vacuum gauge when the connecting glass tube was giving off gas. When the glass tubing, however, was baked out until its surface was free of absorbed moisture and other gases, the limiting pressure was reduced to 0.0007 bar.

The rate at which the pressure is reduced in an apparatus, as determined by the pumping speed S, the volume V, and the limiting pressure P_0, is given by the equation

$$\frac{dP}{dt} = -\frac{S}{V}(P - P_0). \tag{11}$$

The integration of this equation yields

$$(t_2 - t_1) = \frac{V}{S} \log_e \left(\frac{P_1 - P_0}{P_2 - P_0} \right). \tag{12}$$

[8] Dushman, S.. *Phys. Rev.*, *5*, 225 (1915).

Eq. 12 is useful, for example, in predicting the time $(t_2 - t_1)$ required for a vacuum system to recover from a surge of gas which raises the pressure to the value P_1. In this case P_2 represents the working pressure required in the apparatus.

If P_2 and P_1 are much larger than P_0, then P_0 may be neglected, and Eq. 12 can be simplified to the form

$$\frac{P_2}{P_1} = e^{-\frac{S}{V}(t_2 - t_1)}.\tag{13}$$

Roughing pumps. The so-called roughing pumps are used to support diffusion pumps because the latter will

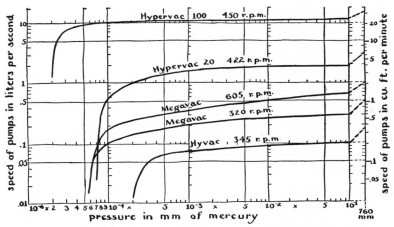

Fig. 2. Pumping speeds of mechanical pumps (data supplied by the Central Scientific Company, Chicago, Illinois).

operate efficiently only against a small differential of pressure at pressures less than a few tenths of a millimeter of mercury. Rotary mechanical pumps are ordinarily used.[9]   The pumping speeds of several rotary pumps at various pressures are given in Fig. 2.   Other types of pumps, such as the water

---

[9] The series High-vac, Mega-vac, and Hyper-vac is supplied by the Central Scientific Company, Chicago, Illinois.   The Leybold vacuum pumps are handled in this country by James G. Biddle Company, Philadelphia, Pennsylvania.   Extremely fast mechanical pumps are manufactured by the Kinney Manufacturing Company, 3541 Washington Street, Boston, Massachusetts.

aspirator, the Gaede rotary pump, and the Sprengel and Toepler pumps, are seldom used now. These pumps are adequately described in the literature.[10]

Outgassing of glass and metals. Outgassing removes gases adsorbed to the surface of glass and metal. It is necessary to outgas exposed glass and metal in order to obtain the highest degree of vacuum. Prolonged heating of glass at 150° to 200°C. in vacuum removes most of the gases adsorbed on the surface, while further heating to 300°C. removes the final monomolecular film of water and adsorbed gases. Gases liberated when the heating is carried above this temperature originate from the decomposition of the glass.[11]

In practice, lead-glass apparatus is outgassed by heating it in an oven or with a soft flame to a maximum temperature of 360°C. for a time varying from 10 minutes to an hour or more. Lime glass and hard glass are heated to 400° and 500°C. respectively. Higher temperatures are to be avoided, since the annealing or softening point of soft glass is only 425°C. and of hard glass 550°C.

Before a glass apparatus is sealed off from the pumps, the seal-off constriction is heated for a minute or two at a temperature just below the softening point of the glass.

When metals are strongly heated in a vacuum, they give off adsorbed gases as well as absorbed gases and gas arising from the decomposition of oxides near the surface. Gases under the surface layer of the metal, both dissolved gases and those held in chemical combination, are difficult to remove, even at elevated temperatures, unless the metal is fused. The metal oxides, with the exception of chromium oxide, are readily dissociated in vacuum at elevated temperatures. Metals which have been fused in vacuum are now available commercially.[12]

---

[10] See footnote 1, page 93.

[11] R. G. Sherwood's report on decomposition of glass: *Am. Chem. Soc., J., 40*, 1645 (1918); *Phys. Rev., 12*, 448 (1918).

[12] These metals may be obtained from the Eisler Corporation, Newark, New Jersey.

Surface gas on tungsten wire is liberated by a temperature of 1500°C. From 70 to 80 per cent of this gas is carbon monoxide, and the remainder is hydrogen and carbon dioxide.[13] The volume of surface gas evolved, measured at standard conditions, amounts to three or four times the volume of the tungsten wire. Sweetser studied the gas liberated by copper, nickel, Monel, and copper-coated nickel-iron alloy (Dumet). He found that these metals rarely gave off a volume of gas greater than the volume of the wire.[14]

Marshall and Norton have studied the gases given off by tungsten, molybdenum, and graphite.[15] After these materials have been outgassed by prolonged heating in vacuum at temperatures above 1800°C., they may be exposed to atmospheric pressure, and the gases which they then take up are readily removed by subsequent reheating to a moderate temperature in vacuum. However, they should not be touched with the fingers.

Many metals may be heated in hydrogen to remove surface contamination. At the same time dissolved gases near the surface of the metal are, in part, replaced by the hydrogen. This substitution is desirable, since hydrogen comes off readily when the metal is subsequently heated in vacuum either in a bake-out oven or by high-frequency induction.

Vapor pressure of waxes. Table III gives the results of Zabel's measurements of the relative vapor pressures of waxes used in vacuum work. The numbers given there represent the results of measurements taken with an ionization gauge.

The wax compounded from shellac and butyl phthalate (see Chapter XIII) should exhibit a low vapor pressure, judging from Table III.

[13] Langmuir, I., *Amer. Inst. Elect. Engin., Proc., 32,* 1921 (1913).
[14] S. P. Sweetser's results are reviewed in Dushman's *High Vacuum,* page 163.
[15] Norton, F. J., and Marshall, A. L., *Reprint No. 613,* General Electric Company (1932).

TABLE III

VAPOR PRESSURE OF MATERIAL RELATIVE TO THAT OF BRASS

Material	Ratio
Pyrex	0.7
Iron	3.5
Iron coated with rust	250
Picein	4
Beeswax and rosin	5.5
Glyptal*	8.5
DeKhotinsky (soft to hard)†	15 to 25
Glyptal lacquer (baked)	2
Butyl phthalate	5.4
Stopcock grease	7
Ramsay Fett	85

Zabel, R. M., *Rev. Sci. Instruments*, *4*, 233 (1933).

* Sager, T. P., and Kennedy, R. G., Jr., *Physics*, *1*, 352 (1931).

† Old formula. A new wax is now supplied by Central Scientific Company for which these values may not apply.

Getters. Ordinarily, in the laboratory, a diffusion pump is used to remove the residual gases which roughing pumps cannot remove, and the resulting high vacuum is maintained by continued pumping. There are, however, other methods of removing the residual gases in an apparatus which is sealed off at the pressure attainable with a roughing pump.[16] These methods involve the use of so-called getters, which not only remove the residual gases initially, but maintain the vacuum against the deteriorating effects of subsequent outgassing.

Getters may be grouped into three classes, depending on the manner in which they remove residual gases. Some depend on the physical adsorption of the residual gases on the refrigerated surface of a porous substance like charcoal or silica gel; others absorb the gas in the manner that hydrogen is absorbed by palladium black or tantalum; and still others combine with the residual gas chemically.

[16] Andrews, M. R., and Bacon, J. S., "Systematic Investigation of the Action of Getters in Sealed Tubes," *Am. Chem. Soc., J.*, *53*, 1674 (1931).

The high absorbing capacity of charcoal and silica gel is due in part to their large surfaces. The surface of charcoal, for example, is estimated to be as great as 2500 square meters per gram. Absorbent charcoal to be used for removing residual gas is itself first outgassed by heating it in the vacuum produced by the roughing pumps. It should not be heated above the softening temperature of Pyrex, because it will lose some of its absorption capacity owing to "crystallization" of the charcoal and attendant loss of surface area. After this outgassing the pumps are turned off to isolate the vacuum system, and the charcoal is cooled (preferably with liquid air) to develop its absorbing capacity. The absorbing power of charcoal for various gases at 0°C. and −185°C. (liquid air temperature) is given in Table IV.

TABLE IV

ABSORPTION CAPACITY OF COCONUT CHARCOAL: VOLUME OF GAS AT STANDARD
CONDITIONS OF TEMPERATURE AND PRESSURE ABSORBED BY
UNIT VOLUME OF CHARCOAL

Gas	0°C.	− 185°C.
Helium	2	15
Hydrogen	4	135
Argon	12	175
Nitrogen	15	155
Oxygen	18	230
Carbon dioxide	21	190

Dewar, Sir James, *Encyclopædia Britannica*, *16*, 751 (1911).

Of the metal getters, tantalum is of special interest. It absorbs hydrogen in large volumes—it may absorb as much as 740 times its own volume of gas at temperatures around 600°C. This absorbed gas is given off when the metal is heated in vacuum at temperatures greater than 800°C. At high temperatures, tantalum is one of the metals most easily outgassed. At elevated temperatures the residual gases, oxygen and nitrogen, are also removed by chemical combination with tantalum. Because of these properties, it is frequently used for radio-tube anodes. The metals columbium and zirconium behave in much the same way as tantalum. Tungsten and molybdenum, at temperatures above 1000°C., are effective getters.[17] Oxygen is removed by these metals by the formation of oxides which are volatile at temperatures above 1000°C. Hydrogen is dissociated by the high temperature and condenses as atomic hydrogen on the container walls, especially if they are cooled with liquid air.

The alkali metals react with nitrogen, oxygen, hydrogen, and mercury vapor. The absorption of nitrogen, oxygen, and hydrogen is especially strong when the alkali metal is the cathode of a glow discharge.

Barium, calcium, and magnesium are extensively used as getters, since they combine chemically with all residual gases (noble gases excepted). Barium is more active chemically than calcium. These metals are introduced by various ways into the vacuum tubes in which they are to serve as getters. Calcium may be introduced in the form of fresh filings. Barium may be introduced in the form of copper- or nickel-covered wire. Either metal may be formed directly in vacuum by reducing it at elevated temperatures from one of its compounds. Usually the introduced metal is vaporized and condensed on the walls of the sealed-off vacuum system, where it forms a mirror. The getter action of the metal is greater in the vapor phase, although the condensed mirror film, especially a film of barium, will react chemically with residual gases which may subsequently appear in the apparatus.

A metal film exhibits, in addition to the chemical action, a physical action which may be of considerable significance. This physical action, the adsorption of gases, is strong because the metal surface is clean. Dushman gives an elementary calculation illustrating this action.[18] A spherical

[17] Langmuir, I., Am. Chem. Soc., J., 37, 1139 (1915); Indust. and Engin. Chem., 1, 348 (1915).
[18] Dushman, S., Frank. Inst., J., 211, 737 (1931).

bulb 5 cm in radius containing residual gas at a pressure of about $\frac{1}{10}$ mm of mercury will be completely evacuated when sufficient gas is adsorbed on the inside surface of the bulb or on a clean metal film to form a monomolecular layer.

Water and many vapors may be effectively removed by a trap cooled in liquid air. The density of water vapor in a gas, after it is passed through a liquid air trap, is 10^{-23} mg/liter. The relative effectiveness of some of the more commonly used drying agents is shown in Table V.[19] Of

TABLE V

DRYING AGENTS

Drying Agent	Mg of Water per Liter of Gas Dried at 25 °C.
Trap at liquid air temperature........	1.6×10^{-23}
P_2O_5...............................	$< 2 \times 10^{-5}$
$Mg(ClO_4)_2$.........................	$< 5 \times 10^{-4}$
$Mg(ClO_4)_2 \cdot 3H_2O$................	$< 2 \times 10^{-3}$
H_2SO_4..............................	3×10^{-3}
95 per cent H_2SO_4..................	3×10^{-1}
$CaCl_2$ (gran.)......................	1.4 to 2.5×10^{-1}

National Research Council, *International Critical Tables*, Vol. III, page 385. New York: McGraw-Hill Book Company, 1928.

these, phosphorus pentoxide is the one most frequently used in vacuum work. It should be fused to reduce its vapor pressure and to prevent it from flying about when the system is evacuated.

Static and kinetic vacuum systems. Most of the vacuum systems used in physical research fall into two general classes. In the first class we have those systems which are required to be thoroughly outgassed and entirely free from leaks in order to obtain a high degree of vacuum. We will call systems of this type static vacuum systems, in contrast to

---

[19] A drying agent which has the advantage of being solid when it is saturated as well as when it is "dry" is magnesium perchlorate. This chemical is manufactured by the Arthur H. Thomas Company, Philadelphia, Pennsylvania.

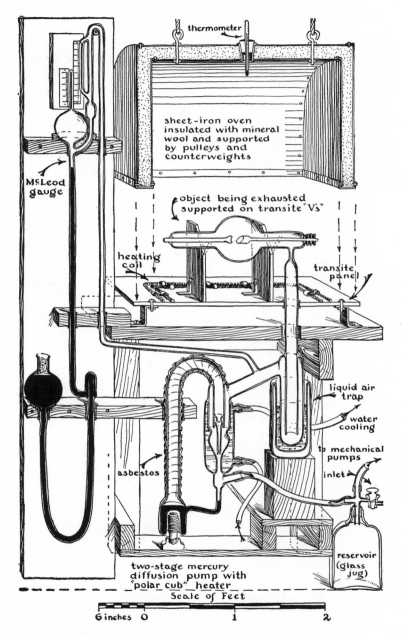

thermometer

sheet-iron oven
insulated with mineral
wool and supported
by pulleys and
counterweights

McLeod
gauge

object being exhausted
supported on transite "V's"

heating
coil

transite
panel

liquid air
trap

water
cooling

asbestos

to mechanical
pumps

inlet

reservoir
(glass
jug)

two-stage mercury
diffusion pump with
"polar cub" heater

Scale of Feet

6 inches   0   1   2

Fig. 3.

108

systems in which outgassing from glass on metal parts or in which even small leaks may be tolerated, owing to the use of extremely fast pumps.   We will designate systems of the latter type as kinetic vacuum systems.

Fig. 3 illustrates a typical static vacuum system.   It represents an X-ray tube being evacuated with a mercury diffusion pump of moderate speed.   Pressures as low as 10^{-9} mm (or even 10^{-10} mm) are obtained in some static vacuum systems.   Such extremely high vacuum is required for investigating the photoelectric effect, thermionic emission, and other physical phenomena for which the slightest contamination of a surface is to be avoided.   Static vacuum systems are not treated extensively here.   The reader who is especially interested in them is referred to the literature.

Kinetic vacuum systems are characterized by a limiting pressure of 10^{-5} to 10^{-6} mm obtained by the use of extremely fast pumps.   These pumps, as well as the apparatus which they exhaust, are usually made in the machine shop from ordinary brass and steel.   The metal is not outgassed as in static vacuum systems.

Kinetic vacuum systems are inferior to static systems, where surface contamination must be scrupulously avoided. They are, however, satisfactory for applications where the function of the vacuum is to allow the unhindered motion of molecular rays, electrons, ions, and light quanta.   For example, kinetic vacuum systems have been applied with success to the vacuum evaporation process for metalizing large telescope mirrors, to the maintenance of vacuum in high-voltage X-ray tubes, metal rectifier tubes, and oscillator tubes, and to the evacuation of spectrographs.

Fig. 4 shows a kinetic vacuum system for the metalization of glass mirrors.   There are two obstacles in the way of getting a high vacuum in such a system.   First, outgassing by heating is precluded on account of the use of wax seals and on account of the fact that the system may contain thick glass mirrors which cannot be safely heated.   Second, there is more chance of small leaks appearing than in a

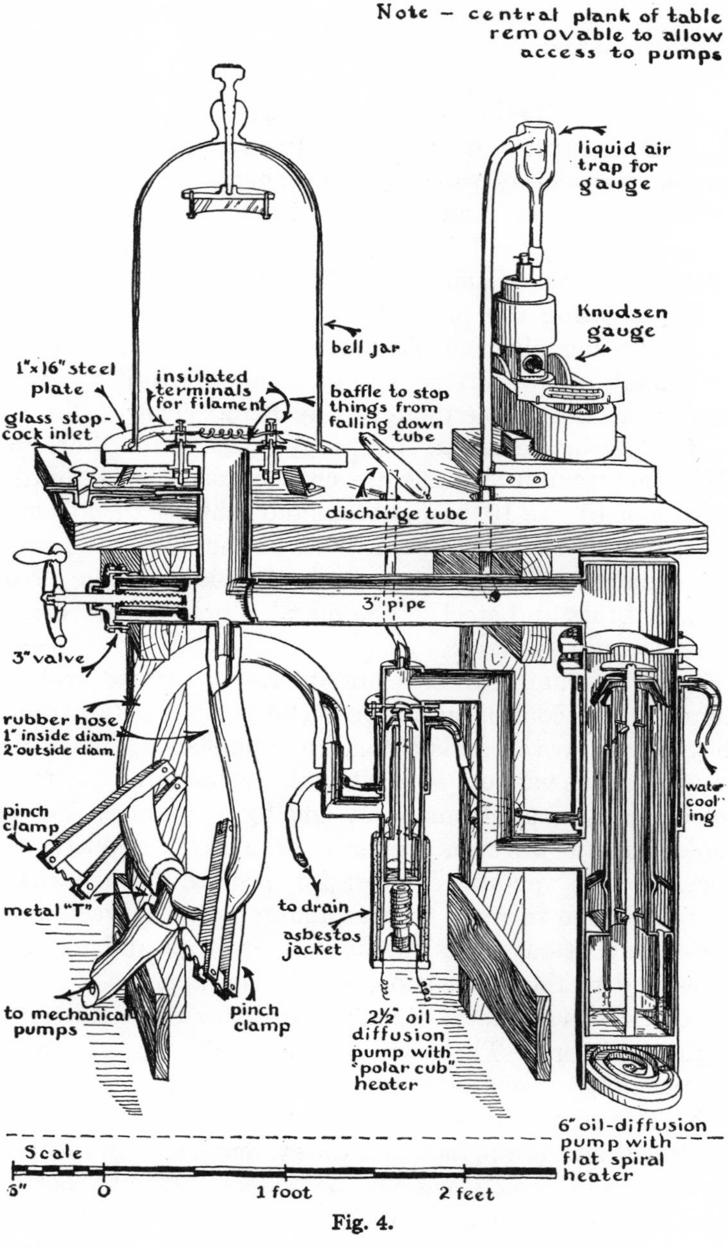

Note – central plank of table removable to allow access to pumps

liquid air trap for gauge

bell jar

Knudsen gauge

1"x16" steel plate

insulated terminals for filament

baffle to stop things from falling down tube

glass stop-cock inlet

discharge tube

3" pipe

3" valve

rubber hose 1" inside diam. 2" outside diam.

water cooling

pinch clamp

metal "T"

to drain

asbestos jacket

to mechanical pumps

pinch clamp

2½" oil diffusion pump with "polar cub" heater

Scale

3"   0   1 foot   2 feet

6" oil-diffusion pump with flat spiral heater

Fig. 4.

static vacuum system, since the system shown in Fig. 4 must be repeatedly opened.   The recent development of fast oil diffusion pumps, which give the degree of vacuum required in spite of these obstacles, has been mainly responsible for the modern extensive use of this type of flexible vacuum system.

Diffusion pumps. Diffusion pumps will operate only if the pressure is less than a few tenths of a millimeter of mercury, and they operate best with a "backing pressure" of a few hundredths of a millimeter of mercury.   The necessary "backing pressure" is obtained by mechanical pumps.   The operation of a mercury diffusion pump is illustrated in Fig. 5. The pump shown here illustrates Langmuir's practical adaptation of Gaede's discovery of the principle of diffusion pumping.[20]   The following explanation of its action applies as well to the action of oil diffusion pumps.

A stream of mercury vapor is obtained by heating liquid mercury in boiler B to a temperature of about 110°C. The vapor stream which effuses from the attached chimney is indicated by arrows. This stream forms a partition between chamber N and chamber M. The vapor finally condenses on the water-cooled walls of chamber N and returns under the influence of gravity to the boiler as a liquid. Gas molecules in chamber N which diffuse

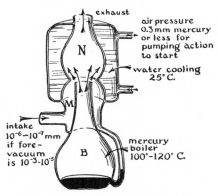

Fig. 5.   Diagrammatic sketch of Langmuir's diffusion pump.

into the vapor partition have a small chance of penetrating it and entering chamber M.   Rather, it is more probable that they will be carried by the stream back into chamber N. However, gas molecules in M which diffuse into the vapor

[20] Langmuir, I., *Phys. Rev.*, *8*, 48 (1916).
    Gaede, W., *Ann. d. Physik, 46,* 357 (1915).

partition are carried along by molecular bombardment into N, where they are removed by the mechanical pump.

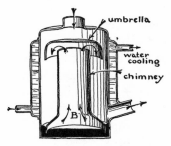

Fig. 6. Langmuir's umbrella pump.

The pressure in N must exceed that in M by a factor of the order of 100 if the rate of diffusion is to be the same in both directions across the vapor partition. Where N is evacuated by an auxiliary diffusion pump instead of the mechanical pump, pressures of 10^{-7} mm of mercury or lower can be obtained in a tight glass apparatus connected to M (provided mercury vapor is removed with a liquid air trap).

Mercury pumps have been studied by many investigators.[21] Figs. 6 to 12 are representative of the designs which have evolved as a result of these studies. We will not discuss these pumps in detail, as we are mainly interested in this chapter in kinetic vacuum systems and oil diffusion pumps. With oil pumps it is not uncommon to have pumping speeds of some tens or hundreds of liters per second, whereas

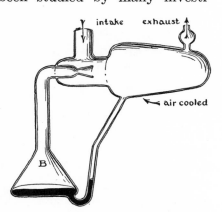

Fig. 7. Crawford's diffusion pump.

with mercury diffusion pumps the speeds are ordinarily only a fraction of a liter per second up to a few liters per second.

[21] Crawford, W. W., *Phys. Rev.*, 10, 558 (1917).

Klumb, H., *Zeits. f. techn. Physik*, 17, 201 (1936).

Molthan, W., *Zeits. f. techn. Physik*, 7, 377, 452 (1926).

Stintzing, H., *Zeits. f. techn. Physik*, 3, 369 (1922).

See the references to vacuum technique given in footnote 1, page 93, and other references cited herein. See also catalogues of E. Leybold Nachfolger.

Gaede, W., *Zeits. f. techn. Physik*, 4, 337 (1923).

Ho, T. L., *Rev. Sci. Instruments*, 3, 133 (1932); *Physics*, 2, 386 (1932).

The use of oils as diffusion pump liquids. There have been many attempts to find a substitute for mercury as a pumping medium, for the use of mercury has one considerable disadvantage, namely, its vapor pressure is so high that traps are required to prevent it from diffusing into the vacuum system and destroying the vacuum. These traps, having a high resistance to the flow of gas, choke the pump.

The only widely used substitutes for mercury are oils. The oils used for this purpose are either especially refined petroleum oils of the naphthene type as developed by C. R. Burch,[22] or they are organic compounds such as butyl phthalate as developed by Hickman and Sanford[23] of the Eastman Kodak Laboratories. Recently, Hickman has recommended a new synthetic organic oil called Octoil, which is claimed to be superior to butyl phthalate.[24] Oils of the type developed by Burch are manufactured under

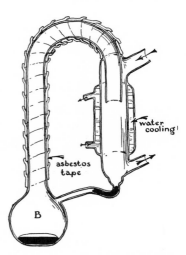

Fig. 8.   Down-jet diffusion pump.

Metropolitan Vickers' patents under the trade name of Apiezon oil.[25]   Similar oils are now available in this country which yield pressures below 10^{-6} mm of mercury.[26]

Oil pumps have the advantage over mercury pumps that they do not require traps except in certain applications.

[22] Burch, C. R., *Nature, 122*, 729 (1928); *Roy. Soc., Proc., 123*, 271 (1929).

[23] Hickman, K. C. D., and Sanford, C. R., *Rev. Sci. Instruments, 1*, 140 (1930).

[24] Hickman, K. C. D., *Frank. Inst., J., 221*, 215, 383 (1936).

[25] This oil may be obtained from the James G. Biddle Company, Philadelphia, Pennsylvania.

[26] Relative to pump oils see the following:

von Brandenstein, Maruscha, and Klumb, H., *Phys. Zeits., 33*, 88 (1932).

Klumb, H., and Glimm, H. O., *Phys. Zeits., 34*, 64 (1933).

These oils may be obtained from Litton Laboratories, Redwood City, California, and the Central Scientific Company, Chicago, Illinois.

Another advantage is that oil pumps may be fabricated either from steel or from brass and copper, whereas metal mercury pumps must be constructed of steel with welded joints.   Brass and copper pumps can be assembled with soft solder, except for the boiler and chimney, where it is advisable to use silver solder. Aside from the questions of traps and construction, the contrast between oil and mercury pumps is less distinct.   Oil pumps without traps do not give quite as low a limiting pressure as trapped mercury pumps, although their speed may be many times greater.   If traps are used, there is probably little difference between the limiting pressures attainable.   Oil pumps have the advantage that a baked-out total obstruction charcoal tube at room temperature is as effective as a liquid air trap.   However, the use of a total obstruction charcoal trap sacrifices the higher pumping speed of the oil pump.

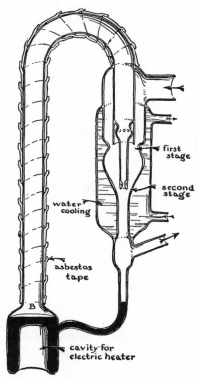

Fig. 9. Ruggles' and Kurth's two-stage mercury diffusion pump.

It is not advisable to use a single oil pump.   One should use at least two oil pumps in series.   The second pump serves to keep the oil in the first purified.   The limiting pressure is about tenfold lower when a second pump is used.   Because mercury pumps will operate against a slightly higher back pressure than oil pumps, there are many cases in which a single mercury diffusion pump is adequate.

Oil diffusion pumps. Oil diffusion pumps are like mercury diffusion pumps in several respects. They have the same functional elements—a boiler to vaporize the oil and a chimney for conducting the vapor to the jet. The two types of pumps are also similar in the way in which they function. The oil vapor is projected from the jet across the throat of the pump and condenses on the cooled walls which form the outer boundary of the throat; and the condensed oil drains from the condensing surface back into the boiler by gravity. The vapor jet may be arranged in several ways: It may be directed upward as in the up-jet mercury pump shown in Fig. 5, it may be directed downward as in the umbrella down-jet mercury pump shown in Fig. 6, or it may project laterally as shown in Fig. 7.

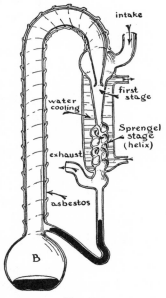

Fig. 10.

Although oil and mercury diffusion pumps have the same functional elements, they differ in the details of construction. The construction of oil diffusion pumps can be carried out in an ordinary machine shop. The important considerations for proper construction are outlined below:

1. The oil is decomposed slightly at the working temperatures of the boiler. This decomposition is accelerated by the higher temperature necessary when the cross section of the boiler is not large enough to afford an adequate surface from which to create vapor, or when the chimney and jet are not ample to deliver the required amount of vapor without an excessively high pressure drop.

2. Since oil has a low latent heat, the pump should be designed so that the heat required to maintain the working

temperature of the chimney and jet is supplied by conduction from the heater rather than by condensation of oil

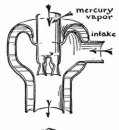

vapor. Naturally, copper is the best material for constructing the chimney on account of its large heat conductivity.

3. The decomposition of the oil is catalyzed by copper and brass and not by nickel. Accordingly, all parts of the pump exposed to the hot oil should be nickel-plated.[27]

Plan of Jets

4. The amount of oil decomposed in a given time is proportional to the amount of oil present in the boiler. It is, therefore, advisable to have only a shallow layer of oil in the boiler.

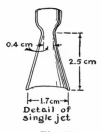

0.4 cm

2.5 cm

1.7cm

Detail of single jet

Fig. 11.

5. At least two single-jet pumps in series should be used. Multiple-jet pumps are not recommended because of the difficulty of regulating the flow of vapor to the various jets and of supplying the necessary amount of vapor required by them without an excessive boiler temperature.

6. Throat clearances narrower than $\frac{1}{8}$ inch are practical only for up-jet pumps. Condensed oil will bridge gaps of this narrowness in pumps of the down-jet type.

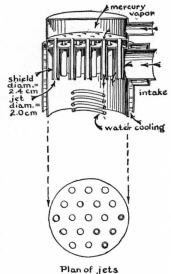

shield diam.= 2.4 cm

jet diam.= 2.0 cm

intake

water cooling

Plan of jets

Fig. 12.

7. Backward evaporation of the oil into the pumping line should be restrained by the use of baffles.

[27] Privately communicated: Charles V. Litton, Engineering Laboratories, Redwood City, California.

8. Cold oil is a better solvent for many gases and vapors than hot oil. Accordingly, the condensed oil should be returned to the boiler at the maximum temperature possible. Otherwise, a certain amount of the exhaust gases and vapors dissolve in the condensed oil and contaminate it.

9. The use of electric heat for the boiler is advisable, since it is subject to more delicate control than gas heat. A Calrod heater unit, such as used in electric stoves, can be re-coiled into a helix of 2 inches in outside diameter or as a flat spiral of smaller dimensions.

Figs. 13 to 18 illustrate several oil pumps which are currently popular.[28] The pump shown in Fig. 13, designed by Sloan, Thornton, and Jenkins, satisfies the requirements for good design outlined above and at the same time combines these features together with simplicity of construction. The following description of this pump is a quotation from a paper of Sloan, Thornton, and Jenkins.[29]

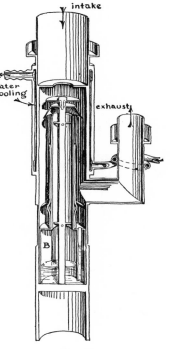

Fig. 13.

The Apiezon oil diffusion pump was originally developed by the Metropolitan Vickers Company in England for this very pur-

[28] References to pumps having interesting construction but not represented here include the following:

Copley, M. J., Simpson, O. C., Tenney, H. M., and Phipps, T. E., *Rev. Sci. Instruments*, *6*, 265, 361 (1935).

Esterman, I., and Byck, H. T., *Rev. Sci. Instruments*, *3*, 482 (1932).

Ho, T. L., *Rev. Sci. Instruments*, *3*, 133 (1932); *Physics*, *2*, 386 (1932).

[29] Sloan, D H., Thornton, R. L., and Jenkins, F. A., *Rev. Sci. Instruments*, *6*, 80 (1935).

pose of continuously exhausting radio tubes. The oil is sold commercially in this country.

Fig. 13 is typical of the simplified designs which have been widely adopted in this country. The outer shell 2″ in diameter consists of a water-jacketed brass cylinder with a copper plate silver-soldered into its bottom. In the cavity beneath the bottom plate is placed an electric heater which boils the Apiezon "B" oil at less than 200°C in the chamber above. The oil vapor rises through the copper chimney and is deflected downward by a spun copper umbrella. The $\frac{5}{16}$″ clearance between the edge of the umbrella and the condensing wall is not critical, although an optimum exists for any specified set of pressures. Around the chimney is a glass heat shield, and a metal baffle plate to retard the rise of oil vapor from the roof of the boiler, but these can be omitted without serious consequences. The two baffles above the umbrella prevent the escape of oil vapor directly into the region being evacuated. The convenient baffle system shown here reduces the speed of the pump to less than half, so that its overall speed is only thirty liters per second. This is more than sufficient for these oscillator tubes, since the connecting system reduces the speed to less than ten liters per second. A pressure in the oscillators of 10^{-5} mm is sufficient.

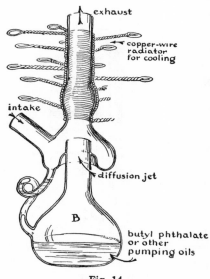

Fig. 14.

Incidentally, the same general design is also well suited to larger pumps of 4″ and 6″ diameter, for use with larger tubes. The speed of an oil pump can be greatly increased by enlarging the diameter of the overhead region which contains the baffles necessary to guard against escaping oil vapor.

A 2-inch pump of such construction will have a pumping speed of about 30 liters/sec., or a speed factor slightly greater than 50 per cent.

If such a high speed is not needed, an up-jet pump may serve. Fig. 14 shows Hickman and Sanford's all-glass design of an up-jet pump.

Fig. 15 shows an all-metal up-jet pump designed by Edwin McMillan.[30] With the boiler temperature adjusted to give maximum pumping speed, this pump will work at a rate of 4 liters/sec. against a backing pressure of $\frac{1}{2}$ mm of mercury. If the boiler temperature is too high, the action of the pump will be erratic, since returning condensed oil interferes with the vapor jet.

A design combining glass and metal construction, developed by Joseph E. Henderson,[31] is shown in Fig. 16. He reports this pump to be capable of working against a backing pressure of a few tenths of a millimeter pressure in contrast to the pressure of about $\frac{1}{100}$ mm required for oil pumps with a throat opening of $\frac{1}{8}$ inch or more. Pressures as low as 10^{-8} mm of mercury were obtained with it when it was operated with a charcoal trap.

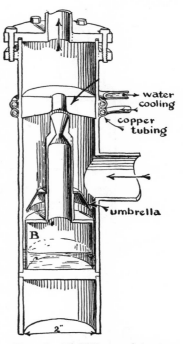

Fig. 15. McMillan up-jet pump. Hole in upper block (indicated by arrow) $\frac{1}{4}$ inch in diameter. Outside diameter of jet $\frac{9}{32}$ inch. Jet clearance $\frac{3}{32}$ inch. The necessary baffles above the jet are not shown.

---

[30] Privately communicated.
[31] Henderson, Joseph E., *Rev. Sci. Instruments, 6*, 66 (1935).

A pump designed by Zabel with a novel oil heater added by James A. Bearden[32] is shown in Fig. 17. The advantage of a pump of this design is that it quickly starts working after the heater is turned on.

More recently, K. C. D. Hickman and others have experimented with pumps in which the oil is continually purified.[33]

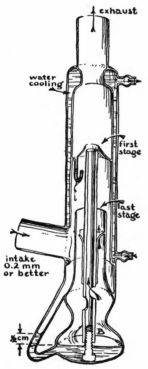

Pumps of this type are particularly suitable for work with gases and vapors which dissolve in the oil or decompose it. Fig. 18 shows a pump which incorporates some of the results of Hickman's investigations.

Mercury traps. Mercury vapor diffuses from a mercury diffusion pump into the exhausted vessel unless it is removed in a trap by condensation on a cold surface. Besides the inconvenience and expensive necessity of requiring a refrigerant, the use of traps has the more serious result of choking the pump. This is especially true for big mercury pumps of high speed. For example, a mercury pump with a speed of several hundred liters per second at its throat may have an effective speed beyond the trap of only several tens of liters per second.

Fig. 16.

The common trap designs for condensing mercury and water vapors are illustrated in Fig. 19. Type *A*, the simplest, is frequently used for trapping the vapors from a McLeod gauge. It is also useful in conjunction with an ionization or Pirani gauge for hunting leaks. Type *B*, the most

[32] Bearden, J. A., *Rev. Sci. Instruments*, *6*, 276 (1935).
Zabel, R. M., *Rev. Sci. Instruments*, *6*, 54 (1935).
[33] See footnote 24, page 113.

common type, may be conveniently constructed from metal and a simple glass tube as shown at B', or it may be

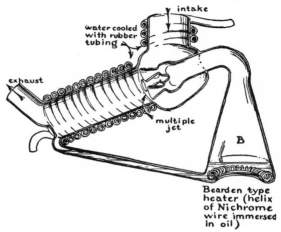

Fig. 17.

constructed as shown at B'' with a separator or baffle to cause the gas to circulate against the cold walls of the glass tube. Both types A and B are immersed in the refrigerant liquid. Types C, C', and C'' contain their own refrigerant, but because of inferior heat insulation these traps are less economical to keep cold.

As refrigerant liquids for trapping mercury and water vapor, either liquid air or dry ice in acetone may be used. The temperature of the former varies from $-190°$C. to $-183°$C., depending on the extent to which the nitrogen has been boiled out of the liquid air, leaving liquid oxygen.

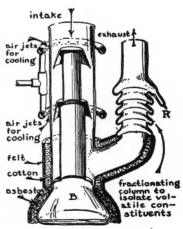

R— reservoir for removal of volatile components of oil formed in the boiler

Fig. 18.

The temperature of dry ice–acetone mixture is about $-78°C$. At the temperature of liquid air the vapor pressure of mercury is 1.7×10^{-27} mm, while at $-78°C$. it is 3.2×10^{-9} mm. For trapping water, liquid air temperatures are sufficiently low. However, since the vapor pressure of ice is about 10^{-3} mm at $-78°$, the dry ice–acetone mixture is not sufficiently cold to trap water vapor effectively. Accordingly, when this refrigerant is used for mercury, it is necessary at

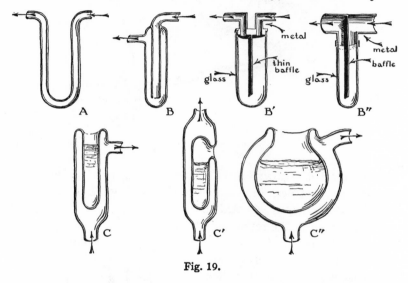

Fig. 19.

the same time to expose anhydrous phosphorus pentoxide in the vacuum in order to remove the water vapor.

The vapor pressure of the vacuum pump oils used in roughing pumps, according to Dushman, is 10^{-3} to 10^{-4} mm at ordinary temperatures, $\frac{1}{5}$ of this value at $0°C$., and negligibly small at the temperature of dry ice or liquid air.

Carbon dioxide is adequately trapped by traps cooled by liquid air, since its vapor pressure, at liquid air temperature, varies from 10^{-6} mm to 10^{-7} mm. Carbon monoxide, methane, ethane, and ethylene, having considerably higher vapor pressures, are not effectively trapped even by a liquid air trap.

Virtual leaks. Gases will condense when their partial pressure is above the vapor pressure corresponding to the trap temperature. (However, they will re-evaporate later when the pumps reduce the pressure to a sufficiently low value.) This condensation may give rise to a virtual leak if the trap is cooled too soon after the evacuation of a system is started. We use the term *virtual leak* because the system appears to have a leak, when it is, in fact, quite tight. As an example, consider a system with traps cooled with a dry ice–acetone mixture but with phosphorus pentoxide omitted. Some of the water vapor originally in the system, both in the air and from the walls where it is held adsorbed, will be condensed in the trap. As the evacuation of the system proceeds, the pressure will approach a limit of 10^{-3} mm, this being the pressure of the water vapor in the trap, and the system will exhibit all the "symptoms" of a leak. The same effect is encountered if liquid air is put on the system too soon. Some of the water vapor will condense on the upper regions of the trap walls, and as the liquid air level around the trap falls, owing to evaporation, the temperature of the water condensed as ice will rise until it begins to sublime, producing a virtual leak. On the one hand, these ice crystals are too cold to evaporate rapidly and be evacuated by the system (or colder regions of the trap), while, on the other hand, they are warm enough to degrade the vacuum. Likewise, gases like ethylene may condense in a trap cooled by liquid air and degrade the vacuum.

To avoid virtual leaks, the proper procedure is to keep the traps warm until a vacuum is obtained at which mercury begins to diffuse into the evacuated apparatus, that is, until a pressure of about 10^{-2} mm is obtained. Then the tip of the trap is cooled until the vacuum reaches its limit, P_0, and finally the trap is immersed in the liquid air to the full depth.

"Oil" traps. The vapor pressures of vacuum-pumping oils, such as Apiezon "B" oil, are very low, but gases produced by thermal decomposition of the oil may give rise to some deterioration of the vacuum and necessitate the use of traps.   For example, when Bearden evacuated an X-ray tube with the diffusion pump shown in Fig. 17, he found that a carbon deposit formed on the target of the tube.[34]   He found, also, that the filaments of the tube deteriorated at an excessive rate.   However, the use of a refrigerated trap greatly reduced these effects.   The trap he used was cooled with dry ice in alcohol.

The trap shown in Fig. 20 was designed by Hickman for diffusion pumps which use Octoil.[35]   According to him, it is sufficient to cool the trap with running water.   Electric re-frigerator units are sometimes used to trap vapors from oil pumps.   These are, naturally, justified only in large and permanent installations.

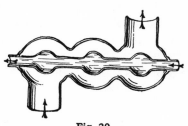

Fig. 20.

In ordinary experimental work, charcoal traps are satisfactory for use with oil diffusion pumps.   Several charcoal trap designs are shown in Fig. 21.   Of these, the total obstruction trap, A, is the most effective, although it has the highest resistance, W, for the gases passing through it. Becker and Jaycox suggested a trap of type A.   They found that a charcoal trap removed oil and condensable vapors to such a degree that an ionization gauge indicated a "pressure" as low as 10^{-8} mm of mercury.[36]   This has been confirmed by Joseph E. Henderson.[37]

When charcoal traps become charged with oil and vapors, it is necessary to bake them out.   Becker and Jaycox observed that condensed pump oils are decomposed by baking them in contact with charcoal, and that the decomposition products are gases.

[34] Bearden, J. A., *Rev. Sci. Instruments, 6*, 276 (1935).
[35] See footnote 24, page 113.
[36] Becker, J. A., and Jaycox, E. K., *Rev. Sci. Instruments, 2*, 773 (1931).
[37] Henderson, Joseph E., *Rev. Sci. Instruments, 6*, 66 (1935).

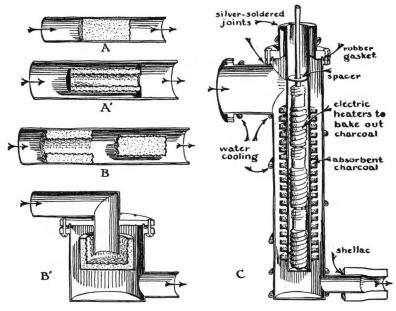

Fig. 21.

Construction of kinetic vacuum systems. Glass was formerly used extensively for the construction of vacuum apparatus, but now metal has replaced it for many uses. Glass as a construction material is characterized by its transparency, high electrical insulating quality, and by the fact that it is easily cleaned and may be baked out and sealed off to give a more or less permanent vacuum. Also, auxiliary parts can be welded to an apparatus without the use of any gaskets or sealing wax. These welds are easily tested for leaks with a spark.

Unfortunately, large and complicated apparatus is difficult to construct from glass. On the other hand, large vacuum systems made of metal are not fragile, and repairs and alterations on them can be easily made in the machine shop.

The metal most frequently used is yellow brass. A vacuum-tight apparatus can be made from plates and cylinders of this metal, screwed together and "painted" on the outside with beeswax and rosin mixture; or the plates, cylinders, and so forth, may be fitted together with rubber or lead fuse-wire gaskets. The brass parts may also be soft-soldered or silver-soldered, depending on the temperature resistance and strength required.

Steel apparatus may be soft-soldered, silver-soldered, brazed, or welded. Electric welding is quite satisfactory for vacuum work if it is done in two or three "passes" with shielded electrodes. It is generally less subject to leaks than gas welding, and it does not warp the work as much. Steel vacuum tanks, especially if they are rusty, are sometimes coated on the inside with Apiezon wax "W" to stop leaks as well as to offer a surface which does not give off gas.

Since metal vacuum walls outgas more than glass, small leaks are more difficult to find. It is a common procedure to coat the outside of metal apparatus with lacquer, which seals small leaks and at the same time gives a workmanlike appearance to the apparatus. Glyptal is heat resistant. For example, it may even be used for coating the outside surfaces of diffusion-pump boilers.

Many things are exposed in kinetic vacuum systems which one would not expose in static vacuum systems. Chief among them are rubber (especially as used for gaskets), waxed packing, beeswax and rosin mixture, Apiezon wax, and ordinary machined metal parts which are not outgassed.

Wood, paints and varnishes, porous cements, and rust should not be exposed even in a kinetic vacuum system.

Rubber hose may be used for connections, and with a pinch clamp it serves as a venting device. Rubber should not be exposed to high vacuum if pressures of the order of 10^{-6} or less are desired.

Joints. Two tubes of glass or metal may be butt-joined by slipping a wide rubber band over them. The rubber surface, including the junctions of the rubber to the tubes, is painted with several coats of shellac as shown in Fig. 22. This type of joint is easily disconnected. For small tubes, a short length of rubber hose makes a convenient connection. Rubber tape or strips of raw rubber may also be used. Inasmuch as rubber is somewhat permeable to some gases and gives off hydrogen sulphide and other vapors in vacuum, the

connected tubes should always fit together neatly to decrease the area of rubber exposed. The joint may be first wrapped with sheet aluminum and then with rubber.[38] This procedure decreases the area of rubber

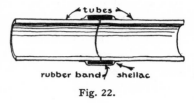

Fig. 22.

exposed. If any considerable area of rubber is exposed, it is advisable to boil it in a 15 per cent caustic solution (potassium hydroxide or sodium hydroxide) to dissolve free sulphur and remove talc from its surface. It is then washed with water and dried, either with alcohol or by a vacuum pump.

If rubber tubing becomes porous and checked with age, it should be painted on the outside with castor oil.

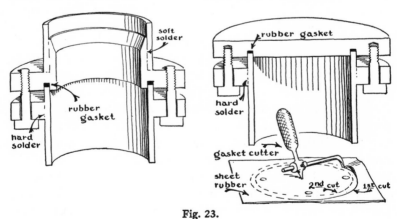

Fig. 23.

Two metal tubes may be joined with flanges which are sealed with a tongue and groove joint fitted with a rubber gasket as shown in Fig. 23. This construction is recom-

[38] The Central Scientific Company supplies a raw rubber tape for this. They recommend the use of a piece of thin aluminum sheeting with it.

mended where mechanical strength is desired and also where the joint must withstand moderate internal pressure. The tongue should have the same thickness as the groove to within a few thousandths of an inch, so that the rubber gasket will not extrude as the pressure for fitting the joint is applied. The gasket is cut from a sheet of packing with a cutter like the one shown. The rubber gasket is used dry, and if the tongue and groove have bright smooth surfaces, the joint is sure to be free from leaks. Furthermore, the joint exposes very little rubber surface to the vacuum system.

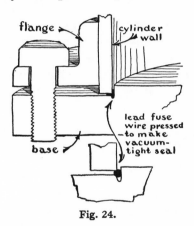

Fig. 24.

In another type of joint, shown in Fig. 24, a lead fuse wire can be used as a gasket instead of rubber. The gasket in this case is a loop of 20-ampere fuse wire, butt-welded by means of the heat from a match and a little soldering flux. The circumference of this loop is made slightly shorter than required and is stretched into the groove to make a snug fit. The pressure applied in the flange flows the lead into intimate contact with the two elements of the joint. Lead-wire joints can be used on systems to operate at elevated temperatures, since they will hold to higher temperatures than tongue and groove joints sealed with rubber. A lead gasket of this type is used on the 40-inch bell jar for aluminizing astronomical mirrors as shown in Fig. 13 of Chapter IV. This particular joint has been made more than a hundred times, and it has been consistently vacuum-tight. Aluminum wire holds to even higher temperatures.

Seals. It is frequently necessary to make a vacuum-tight seal between a glass bell jar and a metal base plate. Formerly, stopcock grease was used, applied to the foot of the bell jar. This type of seal was not always tight, and the grease frequently entered the apparatus and contaminated exposed surfaces. A better procedure is to use wax instead of stopcock grease. The bell jar is set on the base plate, both the foot of the bell jar and the base plate being clean and dry.

Beeswax and rosin mixture, smoking hot, is then applied with a medicine dropper to the outer edge of the bell-jar flange to effect the seal, as illustrated by Fig. 25. The bell jar can be removed from the base plate in the following manner: After scraping away the wax with a putty knife, loosen the jar by striking a sharp blow at the top with the palm of the hand or by driving a razor blade gently under the edge of the jar. If a metal bell jar is used, a recess may be provided so that the seal can be cracked by prying with a screw driver after as much of the wax as possible has been scraped away.

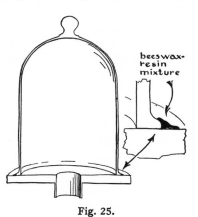

beeswax-resin mixture

Fig. 25.

Windows may be sealed over observation ports in a similar manner. The wax is applied with the medicine dropper, and the seal is effected without sensibly heating either the port or the window.

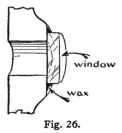

window

wax

Fig. 26.

Windows may be sealed with hard wax. It is necessary to heat both the port and the window to temperatures above 100°C. when hard waxes such as Apiezon "W," Picein, shellac, or DeKhotinsky wax are used. First the window and port are carefully cleaned, and then the window is clamped in the desired position. After being heated to the required temperature, the wax is applied to the outside edge of the window, from where it will be drawn between the window and the port by capillary force. The wax drawn under the window forms a thin bonding layer of large area, which exposes a minimum surface of wax to the vacuum. (See Fig. 26.)

Fig. 27 shows the procedure for sealing two glass tubes together with Picein wax to form a butt joint or telescope

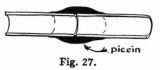

Fig. 27.

joint. The procedure here is to wrap a soft strip of Picein around the warmed glass tubes. This strip is molded from a stick of wax after it is thoroughly softened. The stick of wax is softened by alternately heating it in a Bunsen flame until its surface is liquid and withdrawing it to cool until its surface solidifies. When the strip is ready and while it is still soft it is wrapped around the warmed joint and molded as shown in Fig. 27. The wax will not stick to the fingers if they are damp. After the glass and wax are cool, a flame is applied to fuse the wax superficially and insure tangential contact to the tubing.

Electrodes. In the chapter on glass blowing, we discussed the construction details for leading electrical conductors into glass apparatus. In a kinetic vacuum system, electrodes are usually fastened through holes in a metal wall. Construction details are shown in Fig. 28 for high-current conductors and in Fig. 29 for high-potential conductors. The high-current conductor or electrode consists of a brass screw bolted into the vacuum wall, the head and

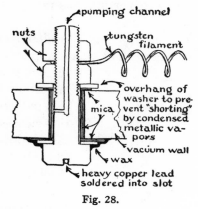

Fig. 28.

body of the screw being insulated from the metal vacuum wall with mica. After the insulation has been tested with a lamp, the whole assembly is made vacuum-tight by coating the screwhead, insulation, and the local area of the outside

surface of the vacuum wall with beeswax and rosin mixture
or with glyptal lacquer.   Beeswax and rosin mixture is used
if the operation temperature is about room temperature.
Glyptal, after baking to polymerize it, is used for operation
temperatures up to about 100°C.

The electrode just described does not have high insulating
qualities.   Where better insulation is needed, a capillary
glass tube is used in either of the ways shown in Fig. 29.
In either case the electrode is easily removable for cleaning
off condensed metallic vapors, for replacement of the glass,

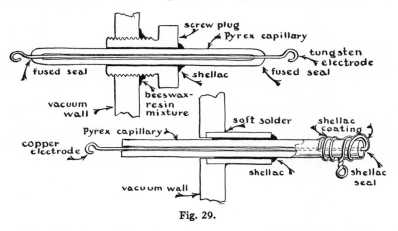

Fig. 29.

and so forth.   If the conductor wire is tungsten, it may be
sealed directly to the Pyrex capillary.   The capillary, with
its central conductor, is first sealed in a bored machine screw
with pure shellac or DeKhotinsky wax.   This is then screwed
through the walls of the vacuum system and made tight with
beeswax and rosin mixture applied on the outside.

Valves.   Valves are used on the low-vacuum side of diffusion pumps to prevent oil in the mechanical pumps from
flowing into the other parts of the apparatus.   Between the
diffusion pumps and the apparatus, large valves are useful
to allow by-passing the diffusion pumps.   For example, in
the vacuum system shown in Fig. 4, a large 4-inch valve
makes it possible to open up the main vacuum chamber

and re-evacuate it without destroying the vacuum in the diffusion pumps. Valves between various parts of a large vacuum system facilitate narrowing the search for leaks, since one part after another can be isolated.

The simplest valve for venting a vacuum system is a short length of rubber hose and a pinch clamp. Rubber vacuum hose is now available in sizes up to 1 inch in diameter.[39] This large hose may be used in short lengths on the high-vacuum side of the diffusion pump when the pumps have a high capacity and when a vacuum of only 10^{-4} is desired. Usually, however, it is advisable to confine the use of rubber hose to the low-vacuum side of the diffusion pumps.

Ordinary plumbing valves can be modified for use in high-vacuum work. The glands are repacked with twine soaked in Apiezon compound "Q," beeswax, stopcock grease, or universal wax. Since the rubber gaskets supplied in these valves are often too hard for vacuum work, it is necessary to replace them with softer rubber. It is advisable to make a new end for the valve so that the new gasket rubber can be retained in a groove. The outside of the valve may be painted with shellac or glyptal lacquer as insurance against leaks, it may be coated with Apiezon wax "W," or it may be tinned. DuMond and Rose have described valves equipped with a sylphon bellows as a substitute for a packing gland.[40] This is illustrated in Fig. 30. A packless valve of this type

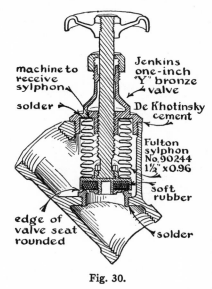

machine to receive sylphon

solder

Jenkins one-inch "Y" bronze valve

De Khotinsky cement

Fulton sylphon No. 90244 1½" x 0.96

soft rubber

edge of valve seat rounded

solder

Fig. 30.

[39] Small hose is obtainable from scientific supply houses. Large sizes of vacuum hose are sold by Central Scientific Company, Chicago, Illinois.

[40] DuMond, J. W. M., *Rev. Sci. Instruments*, *6*, 285 (1935).

Rose, John E., *Rev. Sci. Instruments*, *8*, 130 (1937).

manufactured by the Hoffman Company can be readily adapted to vacuum work as shown in Fig. 31.[41]

Ordinary stopcocks can be sealed with stopcock grease for use in a high-vacuum system. Stopcock grease is made by digesting 1 part pale crepe rubber cut in small pieces with 1 part Apiezon compound "M." This digestion is carried out in a balloon flask with prolonged mechanical stirring at an elevated temperature obtained by means of a water or steam bath.

When it is necessary to avoid grease on a stopcock, bankers' sealing wax, Apiezon wax "W," or Picein can be used.[42] Of these waxes, Picein

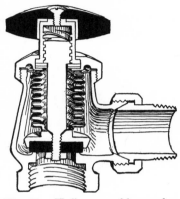

Fig. 31.   Hoffman packless valve.

exhibits the best body. With any one of them the valve is warmed until the wax becomes plastic each time that it is turned. (See Fig. 32.) Stopcocks may be lubricated with dry graphite and sealed with mercury.

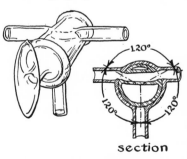

section

Fig. 32.   Zaikowsky stopcock.
U. S. Patent 2000552.

Mechanical motion. Mechanical motion can be introduced into a vacuum system through nonferrous vacuum walls with a magnet. An armature or bar magnet is fastened to the moving part inside the system and actuated by an electromagnet outside. The armature can be hermetically sealed in a glass tube to avoid outgassing.

[41] Hoffman Specialty Company, Waterbury, Connecticut.   Crane and Company are local agents.

[42] For a description of a greaseless valve using a silver bellows acting against a silver chloride seat, see Ramsperger, Herman C., *Rev. Sci. Instruments*, *2*, 738 (1931).

A metal bellows can be used to introduce the reciprocating or oscillating motion of a lever.[43]   When the end of the lever executes a circular motion, this motion can be transformed into rotation inside the vacuum.

Van de Graaf has developed the high-speed sealed shaft shown in Fig. 33.   The packing used is Apiezon grease "M" charged with graphite, and the pumping action of the right- and left-handed screws, cut on the shaft, prevents the extrusion of the packing compound.

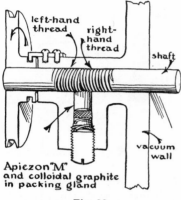

Apiezon "M" and colloidal graphite in packing gland

Fig. 33.

Mechanical motion can be introduced through an ordinary packing gland packed with cotton twine soaked in Apiezon compound "Q" as shown in Fig. 4.

Leaks.   In planning a metal vacuum system, a part of the construction cost should be set aside to provide suitable fittings, plugs, plates, and tie bolts.   The use of these makes it possible to pump air or hydrogen into separate compartments of the apparatus until the pressure is 50 or 100 lbs./square inch.   For detecting leaks the pumped-up compartment is submerged in water or painted with liquid-soap solution.   Hydrogen, which may be used instead of air to pump up the apparatus, has the advantage over air that it diffuses through small holes approximately four times faster.   When leaks are found, they may be repaired by welding or soldering or by merely peening the surface.   After the whole apparatus is put together, the outside of the system is coated with several layers of glyptal varnish, alternating the color of the varnish coats, say blue and red, to facilitate complete coverage with each one of them.   If possible, the coating is baked at a temperature of about 120°C.

[43] Brose, H. L., and Keyston, J. E., *Journ. Sci. Instruments*, 7, 19 (1930).

Leaks are usually found in a glass apparatus by passing the ungrounded high-potential electrode of a spark coil or high-frequency coil over the surface of the glass. When the electrode comes near the leaking channel, a spark jumps to it and causes residual gas inside the apparatus to become luminous. As a safety precaution, a spark gap of $\frac{1}{4}$ to $\frac{1}{2}$ inch should be connected in parallel with the electrode and the ground to prevent an excessive potential which might puncture the glass.

Leaks in metal apparatus which are not detected by immersing the apparatus in water or painting it with soap solution are more difficult to locate. In general, the procedure for finding them involves covering the walls of the apparatus with a liquid which solidifies, with water, or with a gas. In any case, while the search is in progress, the apparatus is maintained at the lowest pressure possible.

If a liquid covering is used, it is applied to local areas in progression until the offending region is located. As covering one may use a molten mixture of beeswax and resin, or it may be a thick solution of either shellac in alcohol or glyptal lacquer brushed on the walls, or it may be cellulose acetate solution sprayed on the walls. When a solution of shellac (or lacquer) is applied to the outside of a leaking channel, the solution is drawn into the channel by the vacuum. As the solvent evaporates from this solution into the vacuum chamber, the liquid in the channel congeals. Thus, the leaking channel is, in effect, filled with a solid shellac core. The amount of solvent passing into the vacuum through this core is negligible in cases where the procedure is suitable.

When the leak is covered with the solution, the vacuum usually improves at once. This improvement may be indicated by the disappearance of luminosity in a connected discharge tube and finally by sparking across an alternate gap. If an ionization or Pirani vacuum gauge is used, covering of the leak is indicated by motion of the spot of light on the scale of the instrument.

The general region in which leaks are located may be determined by temporarily covering the region with water. As the vapor pressure of water is only about $\frac{1}{30}$ of an atmosphere, the leak may be expected to be attenuated 30-fold when it is covered.

The third procedure for finding leaks involves covering general regions of the apparatus with gas, carbon dioxide for the top parts, since it is heavier than air, and illuminating gas for the bottom. Webster has described the use of a rubber "coffer dam" to facilitate the management of the gas.[44] Illuminating gas may be blown on various parts of the apparatus from a hose, or the surface may be gone over with a wad of cotton wet with ether. Evidence that the leak is admitting gas instead of air is a change in character of the luminescence in a discharge tube connected to the apparatus or a change in reading of a vacuum gauge separated from the apparatus by a liquid air trap.

There are two procedures for using a discharge tube with illuminating gas, carbon dioxide, or ether. By the first, the obtainable vacuum is necessarily so poor, on account of the leak, that a distinct discharge is obtained. When the leak is covered, the luminosity in the positive column changes from the brownish-red color characteristic of air to the bluish-green of carbon dioxide or to the white of gas and ether. By the second procedure, used when the leak is small and a lower pressure is attainable in the system, the luminosity in the discharge is feeble. Webster suggests connecting the discharge tube behind one of the diffusion pumps as shown in Fig. 4. The backing pumps are then shut off, preferably just behind the discharge tube connection. The diffusion pump compresses the gas which the leak may be admitting, resulting in a more brilliant luminescence in the discharge tube.

A liquid air trap may be connected between the apparatus and a vacuum when carbon dioxide or other condensable gases are used. With this arrangement, when the leak is

---

[44] Webster, D. L., *Rev. Sci. Instruments*, **5**, 42 (1934).

admitting carbon dioxide, the trap condenses this gas, thus preventing it from entering the gauge. At the same time air and other gases which do not condense in the trap are removed by the pumps. As a result, even though the pressure in the system may have increased, an improvement of the vacuum is indicated.

Obviously, a gauge which reads continuously (Knudsen, Pirani, or ionization gauge) is preferred to a McLeod gauge for hunting leaks. Relative rather than absolute readings of the pressure are sufficient for locating leaks. Thus, the Pirani and ionization gauges are satisfactory, although they do not give absolute pressure determinations.

Vacuum gauges. A vacuum gauge determines the pressure in an evacuated apparatus by a measurement of some physical property of the residual gases, such as viscosity, heat conductivity, and so forth. The measurement of the response of a gauge to the residual gas naturally becomes more delicate as the gas becomes more and more tenuous. Finally, below a certain pressure limit (which is characteristic of a given gauge) the gauge does not behave measurably different from what it would if the vacuum were perfect. For example, a discharge tube will give qualitative indications of pressure down to about 10^{-3} mm of mercury. Below this pressure the tube becomes nonluminous and nonconducting. The characteristic limits for some of the other gauges are as follows:

Ionization gauge....................	10^{-9} mm of mercury
Knudsen gauge.....................	10^{-6} mm of mercury
McLeod gauge.....................	10^{-6} mm of mercury
Pirani gauge......................	10^{-5} mm of mercury
Langmuir's viscosity gauge..........	10^{-5} mm of mercury

The operation of the McLeod gauge depends on a definite volume of residual gases being compressed, so that as the volume decreases, the pressure is increased to a value at which the hydrostatic head of mercury can be measured with an ordinary scale.

The ionization gauge measures with a galvanometer the positive ions that are formed in an electric field when the residual gas is bombarded with electrons. The Langmuir gauge depends on the measurement of viscosity, and the Pirani gauge on the measurement of heat conduction of the residual gas. The Knudsen absolute manometer measures the momentum transferred from a hot to a cold surface by the gas molecules.

Of the above gauges, only the McLeod and Knudsen are absolute manometers in the sense that their geometry and other measurable characteristics of construction and operation determine their response at a given pressure. The McLeod gauge is the simplest and most reliable for permanent gases, but it has the disadvantage of giving erratic response or no response at all to water vapor, carbon dioxide, ammonia, and pump oil vapors which adsorb on the walls of the gauge or condense to a liquid. This disadvantage is serious, inasmuch as water vapor, carbon dioxide, and so forth are often of importance in the last stages of obtaining a high vacuum. The Knudsen gauge responds to gases and vapors alike.

The response of an ionization gauge is difficult to predict from its construction details, and it must be calibrated with a McLeod gauge using permanent gases. Furthermore, before the pressure can be inferred, it is necessary to make corrections for the molecular weight of the gas and also for the possibility that the gas may be dissociated by the electron bombardment. Quantitative application of the gauge is unreliable to the degree to which these corrections are uncertain. Likewise, the response of the Pirani gauge depends on the molecular weight of the residual gas, and it must be calibrated with a McLeod gauge that uses permanent gases. The same is true for the viscosity gauge.

The McLeod gauge.[45] Although many improvements have been made in the McLeod gauge, they have seldom been applied. The gauge as ordinarily used today is essentially

---

[45] Gaede, W., *Ann. d. Physik*, *41*, 289 (1913).
Hickman, K. C. D., *J.O.S.A.*, *18*, 305 (1929).
Pfund, A. H., *Phys. Rev.*, *18*, 78 (1921).

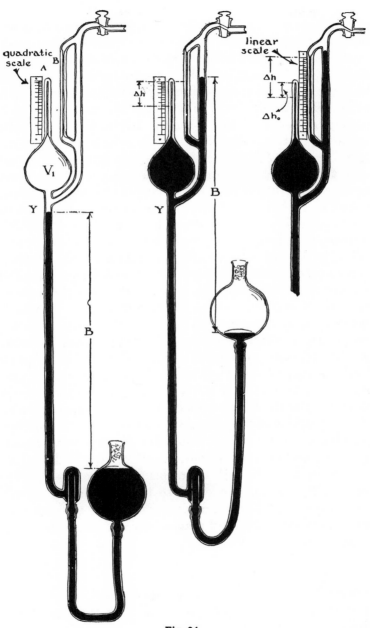

Fig. 34.

the same as it was originally. We will discuss here the simple form of the gauge illustrated in Fig. 34. It is made of glass as shown and is mounted on a vertical board. The difference in the heights of the mercury levels in the gauge and in the reservoir is approximately equal to the barometric pressure B. As the reservoir is raised, the mercury level in the gauge comes above the **Y**-branch, thus isolating a definite volume V_1 of the residual gas. This is isolated at the unknown pressure P_1, the pressure of the residual gas in the apparatus to which the gauge is connected. As the mercury reservoir is further raised, the isolated residual gas is compressed, and when its volume has been reduced to a volume V_2, the pressure is great enough to produce a sensible difference in the height of the mercury meniscus in the two capillaries, A and B. At the left, in Fig. 34, the mercury levels are shown at the beginning of a measurement, and at the right they are shown in two different positions corresponding to two methods of making readings. In one, if the meniscus in B is adjusted to the same height as the top of capillary A, the final volume, V_2, is equal to $\Delta h \cdot \sigma$, when σ is the cross-section area of the capillary. The decrease in volume from V_1 to V_2 is ordinarily of the order of one-hundred-thousandfold, with a corresponding increase of pressure in the capillary over that which obtained originally. The construction of the gauge with the comparison capillary B of identical bore with A eliminates the necessity of making corrections for surface tension. Referring to Eq. 1, we see that the product P_1V_1 is, in this case, a constant. The original product, P_1V_1, is equal to the final product, P_2V_2. From this we get the expression connecting the unknown pressure with the observed manometer difference, Δh:

$$P_1 = \frac{\sigma(\Delta h)^2}{V_1}. \tag{14}$$

V_1 and σ are constants of the gauge determined when it is constructed. σ is obtained by measuring the length of a known volume or weight of mercury in the capillary. V_1 is determined by filling the gauge with mercury. These original data may be recorded on the board to which the gauge is attached. Here they will not be lost. Values of P_1 determined by Eq. 14 are usually laid off on a nonlinear scale, which is mounted behind capillary A in order that pressures may be read directly.

The second procedure of making the observations on V_2 and P_2 is illustrated at the right in Fig. 34. The gas is compressed to a definite mark on capillary A at a distance Δh_0 from the top, so that the final volume, V_2, is the same for every measurement. The final pressure necessary to compress volume V_1 to V_2 is Δh, and the pressure P_1 in the system is determined by these quantities, according to the following equation:

$$P_1 = \frac{\sigma \Delta h_0}{V_1} \Delta h. \tag{15}$$

A linear pressure scale computed from this formula is ordinarily mounted behind capillary B.

The McLeod gauge is thoroughly reliable for the permanent gases from 10^{-1} mm to 10^{-4} mm of mercury. It is less reliable to 10^{-5} mm. Below this the indications are only qualitative, and at 10^{-6} the mercury often sticks in the top of capillary A.

The gauge is most reliable after it has been outgassed by gently warming it with a soft flame. Three gauges with different values of V_1 are necessary to cover adequately the complete pressure range from 10^{-1} to 10^{-6} mm. Many of the designs of McLeod gauges are more elaborate than the one shown in Fig. 34. For example, three bulbs may be mounted together with one reservoir, one for low pressures, one for intermediate pressures, and one for high pressures.

The McLeod gauge is fragile. If it breaks, not only is the gauge lost but what is often more serious, mercury may get into the vacuum system. In glass vacuum systems using mercury pumps this is not as serious as it may be in kinetic vacuum systems. These systems, fabricated of brass with soft-soldered joints, are attacked by mercury and the joints are destroyed.

Accidents with this gauge are usually caused by bringing the reservoir up too quickly. Then mercury in V_1 acquires enough momentum to shatter the bulb when the metal surface arrives at the opening of the capillary tube with no cushion of air to soften the shock.

Admitting air into the vacuum system is to be avoided when the mercury is not completely out of V_1. The admission of air will have the same result as carelessness in raising the reservoir.

Sometimes a mercury pellet will remain in capillary A when the reservoir is lowered. It can usually be brought down by tapping the capillary (after the mercury is all out of V_1). If this treatment fails, the capillary should be heated with a soft gas flame. In the latter case, a sheet of asbestos is placed behind the capillary to protect the calibration scale from the flame.

The capillary tubes used for the construction of McLeod gauges are seldom larger than 2 or 3 mm or smaller than $\frac{1}{2}$ mm bore. The volume of the bulb, V_1, ordinarily varies from 50 to 500 cc. Only pure distilled mercury should be used. Mercury is attacked by the sulphur present in rubber hose, so that dross is produced which adheres to the inside of the gauge and may become very annoying. A gauge contaminated with this sulphide may be cleaned out by the combined action of zinc dust and nitric acid. Rubber hose for use on a gauge should be cleaned before it is used by passing hot caustic potash solution back and forth through it for a quarter of an hour or so. The tubing should be thoroughly washed free of caustic and dried before use.

In cases where it is necessary to avoid contamination of the vacuum system with mercury vapor, a liquid air trap should be connected between the vacuum system and the gauge. For kinetic vacuum systems this precaution is often omitted. A stopcock between the gauge and the system which is kept closed when the gauge is not in use minimizes contamination.

The ionization gauge.[46] Ionization gauges are triodes mounted in a glass bulb connected to the apparatus in which the pressure is to be measured. They are electrically connected as shown in Fig. 35.

Electrons emitted from the filament are accelerated to the grid, and their momentum would carry them to the plate if an inverse field more than sufficient to prevent this

were not impressed between the grid and the plate. They therefore return to the grid and are finally collected on it. However, while they are between the grid and the plate, they bombard and ionize some of the molecules of the residual gas present there. These ions are collected on the plate and measured with a sensitive galvanometer. The ratio

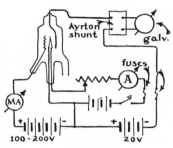

Fig. 35.

of this ion current to the current of bombarding electrons or grid current is proportional to the pressure at pressures below about 10^{-4} mm.

An ionization gauge may be made from an ordinary three-element radio tube equipped with a glass connection to the vacuum system. Such gauges are useful for the pressure range from 10^{-3} to 10^{-6} mm of mercury.

Fig. 36 shows the construction details of a gauge designed to have higher insulation of the plate than an ordinary radio tube. Measurements with it are possible to a pressure of 10^{-9} mm of mercury. The upper end of a glass bulb supports the plate assembly, while the lower end supports the combined grid and filament assembly. The grid is

[46] Buckley, O. E., *Nat. Acad. Sci.*, *Proc.*, *2*, 683 (1916).

Dushman, S., and Found, C. G., *Phys. Rev.*, *17*, 7 (1921).

Jaycox, E. K., and Weinhart, H. W., *Rev. Sci. Instruments*, *2*, 401 (1931).

Simon, H., *Zeits. f. techn. Physik*, *5*, 221 (1924).

made from a piece of nickel screen rolled to form a cylinder. This is bound mechanically to the central glass tube through the bottom by wrapping it with wire, and it is connected electrically to the grid electrode with one loose end of the wrapping wire. There are two filaments, but only one is used. The other is held in reserve to be used if the first is accidentally burned out. The filaments may be replaced by cutting the central tube at S.

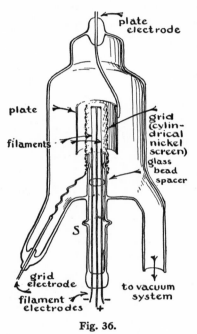

Fig. 36.

Expensive auxiliary electrical instruments are required for this gauge. They should be protected with Littelfuses as shown in the wiring diagram (Fig. 35).

The plate may be outgassed with high-frequency currents or by electron bombardment. In the latter case, an alternating potential of 500 volts is applied between the filaments and the plate. The amount of heat developed depends on the emission from the filament, and this is controlled by the filament current. Outgassing of the plate and glass walls of the gauge is necessary if quantitative measurements are to be made. However, for hunting leaks it is necessary only to outgas the plate once.

Dunnington has made a gauge using 30-mil helices of tungsten wire for both plate and grid. These helices are outgassed simply by passing a current through them for a few seconds. He found that such a gauge did not have a linear relationship between pressure and ratio of plate to grid currents. Once calibrated, however, it was found to be very reliable.

At a given pressure, the ratio of plate to grid current is different for different values of the grid current.   For this reason, it is necessary to adjúst the grid current to some definite value, usually in the range of 10 to 50 milliamperes.

The Pirani gauge.[47]   The Pirani gauge consists of a heated filament of platinum, tungsten, or some other metal with a high temperature coefficient of electrical resistance.   The filament is exposed to the residual gases and is cooled by them.   The temperature of the filament is determined by the heat conductivity of the residual gas, which, in turn, depends on the pressure.   The filament may be operated in several ways.   The most satisfactory method is to connect the filament to one arm of a Wheatstone bridge and heat it by a constant current as shown in Fig. 37.   If the bridge is balanced at one temperature of the filament, a change of its temperature caused by a change in the

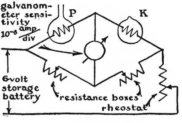

Fig. 37.

heat conductivity of the residual gases will unbalance it. Thus, the deflection of the bridge galvanometer indicates the pressure of the residual gases.

Ordinarily, the filament is mounted in a bulb fitted with a connecting tube and is balanced with an identical compensating filament mounted in an adjacent arm of the bridge. This auxiliary bulb is evacuated and sealed off at a very low pressure.   The use of an auxiliary bulb serves to make the gauge insensitive to variations in room temperature. Changes in the over-all temperature of one bulb are the same as changes in the other, so that the galvanometer does not

[47] DuMond, J. W. M., and Pickels, W. M., Jr., *Rev. Sci. Instruments*, *6*, 362 (1936).

Hale, C. F., *Am. Electrochem. Soc., Trans.*, *20*, 243 (1911).

von Pirani, M., *Deutsch. Phys. Gesell., Verh.*, *8*, 24 (1906).

Skellett, A. M., *J.O.S.A.*, *15*, 56 (1927).

Stanley, L. F., *Phys. Soc., Proc.*, *33*, 287 (1921).

respond to these changes but only to the changes produced
by the residual gas in the one bulb.

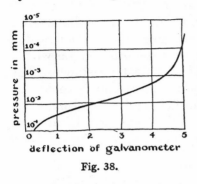

Fig. 38.

Fig. 38 shows a calibration
curve of a Pirani gauge manufactured by E. Leybold Nachfolger.   The pressure range
over which it is useful extends
from $\frac{1}{10}$ mm to 10^{-4} mm.

The construction of the Pirani gauge, together with the
theory of its use, is treated in
detail by several authors, who
should be consulted by anyone
planning to use the gauge for quantitative measurement. A
gauge useful for qualitative work, as for hunting leaks, can

be improvised from two
ordinary 20- to 40-watt vacuum tungsten lamps, one of
which is fitted with a connecting tube.   Fig. 39 shows
the construction details for
this gauge. The bridge galvanometer should have a
sensitivity of about 10^{-8}
ampere division. Sometimes
uncertain contact to the supporting wires may cause
variable heat loss from the
filament, and this should be
suspected if the gauge is
erratic.   Tapping will often
define the contact.

The Langmuir gauge.[48]
Langmuir's viscosity gauge is

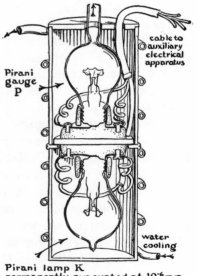

Fig. 39.

[48] Beckman, Arnold O., *J.O.S.A.*, *16*, 276 (1928).
Haber, F., and Kerschbaum, F., *Zeits. f. Elektrochem.*, *20*, 296 (1914).
Langmuir, I., *Am. Chem. Soc., J.*, *35*, 107 (1913).

made with a flattened quartz fiber about 50μ thick and from five to ten times as wide. This quartz ribbon is about 5 cm long and is mounted in one end of a glass tube about 25 mm in diameter, as shown in Fig. 40. When this ribbon is set vibrating in a high vac-uum, the amplitude changes very slowly because the damp-ing by the residual gas is almost negligible, and, owing to the low internal viscosity of fused quartz, the loss of vibrational energy from this source is also low. From atmospheric pressure down to a few milli-meters of mercury, the damp-ing produced by the molecules of the residual gas is nearly in-dependent of pressure. Over the transition range of pres-sure, where the damping varies from this constant value to zero, the time required for the amplitude of vibration to de-crease to half value is an index

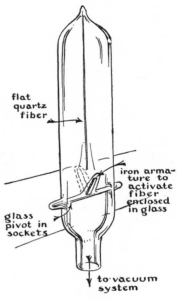

flat quartz fiber

iron arma-ture to activate fiber enclosed in glass

glass pivot in sockets

to vacuum system

Fig. 40.

of the pressure. Within this range the relation between the time, t, the pressure, P, and the molecular weight of the residual gas is given by the following formula:

$$P\sqrt{M} = \frac{a}{t} - b. \tag{16}$$

Here a and b are constants of the gauge. The value of the ratio b/a may be obtained by observing the damping time, t_0, for an essentially perfect vacuum, that is, a pressure of 10^{-6} mm or less. For this pressure the left side of Eq. 16 can be set equal to zero. The values of a and b are deter-mined from a second measurement of the time t_1 at a definite pressure P_1. This pressure is determined with a McLeod gauge. M is approximately 29 for air. The gauge may also be calibrated by subjecting it to saturated mercury vapor at a definite temperature at which the vapor pressure of mercury is known. The range over which the gauge is most useful lies between the pressures 2×10^{-2} and 5×10^{-5}.

A feature of this gauge is its small volume. Because there are no metal parts exposed, the gauge is suitable for measuring the pressure of corrosive gases like the halogens. This gauge, in conjunction with a McLeod gauge, may be used for measuring the molecular weight of an unknown gas at low pressures.

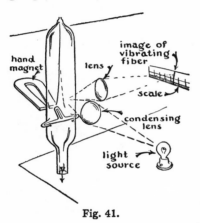

The flat quartz fibers may be obtained by drawing them out of the side rather than the end of a quartz tube or by following the technique given in Chapter V.

Figs. 40 and 41 show construction details and the method of mounting the fiber together with a pivoted glass tube, which contains an iron armature operated by an external electromagnet, to start the fiber vibrating. An optical arrangement for observing the amplitude of vibration is also shown. An image of the quartz fiber is projected on a scale with a simple lens.

Fig. 41.

The Knudsen gauge.[49]   Fig. 42 shows the Knudsen gauge as designed by DuMond. When this gauge is constructed according to the specifications outlined by him, it is claimed to have a definite sensitivity, so that no preliminary McLeod calibration for it is needed. The gauge shown here differs slightly from DuMond's design in that it is equipped with a permanent (Alnico) magnet for damping.

[49] DuMond, J. W. M., and Pickels, W. M., Jr., *Rev. Sci. Instruments, 6*, 362 (1936).

Knudsen, M., *Ann. d. Physik, 28*, 75 (1909).

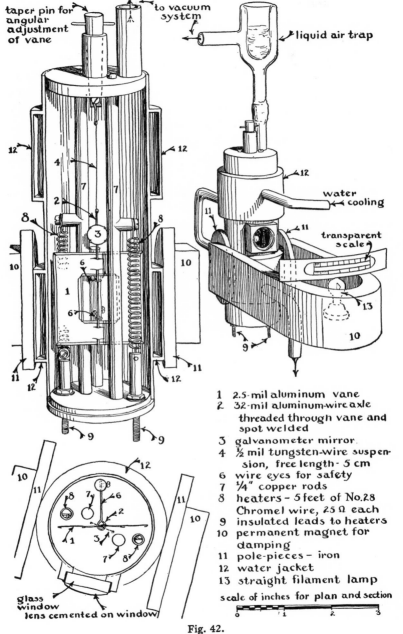

taper pin for angular adjustment of vane

to vacuum system

liquid air trap

water cooling

transparent scale

1 2.5-mil aluminum vane
2 32-mil aluminum-wire axle threaded through vane and spot welded
3 galvanometer mirror
4 ½ mil tungsten-wire suspension, free length- 5 cm
6 wire eyes for safety
7 ¼" copper rods
8 heaters - 5 feet of No.28 Chromel wire, 25 Ω each
9 insulated leads to heaters
10 permanent magnet for damping
11 pole-pieces - iron
12 water jacket
13 straight filament lamp

scale of inches for plan and section

0   1   2   3

glass window
lens cemented on window

Fig. 42.

149

Also, it has a special liquid air trap for determining what fraction of the pressure indication is produced by condensable vapors.

The Knudsen gauge is to be preferred to the McLeod gauge where it is important to avoid contaminating a vacuum system with mercury. No expensive auxiliary instruments are required with the Knudsen gauge, as with the ionization gauge. Furthermore, the filaments will not burn out and the suspension is not delicate.

It is advisable to modify DuMond's design so that all connections and supports fasten to one end plate. This facilitates making repairs. The metal case thus becomes, in effect, a water-cooled covering "bell jar" fitted with a window.

CHAPTER IV

Coating of Surfaces: Evaporation and Sputtering

GLASS, quartz, and other nonmetallic substances may be coated in the laboratory with thin films of metal by the following processes:

1. Burning on
2. Chemical deposition
3. Cathode sputtering
4. Evaporation

Each of these is characterized by certain restrictions and advantages. For example, the "burning-on" method is applicable only in cases where the glass can be heated; chemical silvering (and also coating with gold and copper from aqueous solution) cannot be applied to surfaces like rock salt which are attacked by water; sputtering is particularly suitable for preparing films of the platinum metals; and the evaporation process is suited to the application of aluminum films.

Although deposits can be produced on metals as well as nonmetals by these processes, electroplating (not treated here) is usually the most practical for coating metals.

Burning-on method. Glass may be coated with a thin film of metal by the burning-on process. The process is applicable for the noble metals, which are reduced by heating. The glass to be coated is covered with a layer of an oily solution of one of the metallic salts. When heat is applied, the oil burns away, and the salt is reduced, leaving a deposit of the metal. This deposit is formed in an adherent compact film by a final heating to the softening point of the glass.

A solution for depositing platinum[1] is made as follows: Evaporate 100 cc of a 10 per cent H_2PtCl_6 solution to dryness and dissolve it in a minimum quantity of absolute alcohol. Add this alcohol solution slowly to 6 cc of oil of lavender kept ice-cold. Finally, add some Burgundy pitch to give the mixture consistency, so that it will remain uniform when it is applied and the glass is slowly heated.

Solutions for gold, silver, and iridium are available commercially.

A platinum film burned onto porcelain may be electroplated with copper and soldered, thus affording a method of making a vacuum-tight seal between metal and porcelain.

Chemical silvering processes.[2] There are two widely used methods for chemical silvering. These are the Brashear method and the Rochelle salt method. The first is used to obtain thick coats on front-silvered mirrors which are to be frequently burnished, such as telescope mirrors. The Rochelle salt method, because its action is slower, is recommended for making partially silvered mirrors, such as interferometer plates, which require a uniform thin film with a specified ratio of reflection and transmission.

Cleaning. The silver film does not deposit well on contaminated surfaces. Therefore, fats and other surface contaminations must be cleaned off the glass, so that the colloidal particles of silver suspended in the silvering solution will adhere strongly to the glass to form a tenacious compact metallic film. Just as a greasy glass surface is difficult to wet with water, so a clean wet surface does not

---

[1] McKelvy, E. C., and Taylor, C. S., "Glass to Metal Joints," *Amer. Chem. Soc., J.*, *42*, 1364 (1920).

[2] Gardner, I. C., and Case, F. A., "The Making of Mirrors by the Deposition of Metal on Glass," *Bureau of Standards Circular No. 389.*

Ingalls, Albert G., editor, *Amateur Telescope Making.* New York: Scientific American Publishing Company, 1935.

"The Making of Reflecting Surfaces," a discussion held by the Physical Society of London and the Optical Society, November 26, 1920. London: The Fleetway Press, Ltd.

readily take up greases, fats, and other contamination. Accordingly, once a surface is clean, it will stay clean, if it is kept under distilled water until it is immersed in the silvering solution.

The first step in cleaning a mirror is to free the sides and back of it from rouge and all other contaminations. An ink eraser is ideal for the removal of such contaminations. The pumice or ground glass in the eraser has an abrasive action particularly suitable for this preliminary cleaning of non-optical surfaces. The polished face cannot be cleaned in this manner, but it is well to work the eraser well over the edge.

The mirror is next washed all over with soap and water, or Aerosol[3] and water. Aerosol is preferred to soap, since it may be washed off the face of the mirror without leaving any residue. If soap is used, it should be rinsed off with rain water or, better yet, with distilled water.

A mild and harmless abrasive action on the face of a mirror is sometimes necessary. This is obtained by rubbing it with a pad of wet cotton, to which some precipitated chalk is added. After a polished glass surface has been treated with chalk, the cleaning water should wet the whole mirror face and not draw back anywhere to leave dry areas. It may be necessary to repeat the chalk treatment several times.

The mirror is next rinsed with water and swabbed with concentrated nitric acid, a powerful oxidizing agent which removes organic matter adsorbed on the glass. The swab for applying the acid is made by wrapping absorbent cotton

[3] The compound Aerosol OT is manufactured by the Selden Division of the American Cyanamid and Chemical Corporation, Bridgeville (Pittsburgh), Pennsylvania.

Duncan, R. A., *Indust. and Engin. Chem.*, *26*, 24 (1934). This article gives a description of new detergents of which Aerosol is an example. These detergents have in common the constitution of sulphonated organic compounds of high molecular weight. They have a neutral reaction, and their advantage over soap for washing mirrors lies in the fact that they may be used in neutral, caustic, or even acid solutions. Unlike soap, they form soluble compounds with magnesium and calcium ions, which are common in tap water. The detergent Dreft, obtainable at grocery stores, is also suitable for washing mirrors.

on a glass rod and fastening it with cotton twine as shown in Fig. 1.   Care is exercised in using the swab to prevent the end of the rod from coming in contact with the mirror face. This nitric acid treatment should be carried out in the container in which the mirror is to be silvered to avoid possible contamination later with oil from the hands when the mirror is handled. ˙ If it is necessary to handle the mirror, it is advisable to use rubber gloves.

Cleaning solution (chromic and sulphuric acid mixture) may be used for cleaning glass, but it is not ordinarily

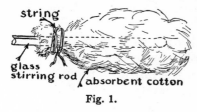

Fig. 1.

necessary. This solvent is very effective.   Even paraffin and carbonized organic material may be removed from glass in cases where the glass and the chromic acid solution can be heated together.

After being rinsed with tap water, the mirror is treated with a concentrated solution of stannous chloride.   This is removed after a few minutes by a very thorough rinsing. All chloride ions must be washed away, first with tap water and finally with distilled water.   The mirror can stand in the distilled water until the silvering begins.

It is important in silvering to clean carefully all the receptacles and graduates used.   A long stick with an ink eraser fastened to the end will be found helpful to remove water stains and other contaminations.

Brashear's process.[4]   The Brashear process is described graphically in Fig. 2.   The three formulas for the reducing solution given there afford different ways to effect the same end.   In the first formula the nitric acid slowly digests the table sugar, to yield the sugars dextrose and levulose. This requires time and so the solution must be aged before use.   In the second formula this aging is accelerated by boiling, and the solution can be used as soon as it is cool.

[4] Brashear, John A., *English Mechanic, 31*, 237 (1880).
Wadsworth, F. L. O., *Astrophys. J., 1*, 352 (1895).

Stock Solutions

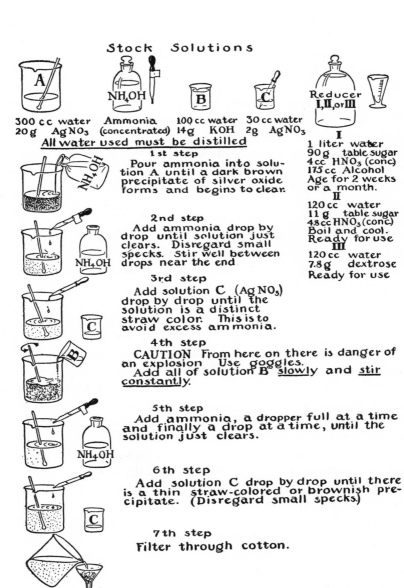

300 cc water   Ammonia   100 cc water   30 cc water
20 g $AgNO_3$ (concentrated)   14 g   KOH   2 g $AgNO_3$

All water used must be distilled

I
1 liter water
90 g   table sugar
4 cc HNO_3 (conc)
175 cc Alcohol
Age for 2 weeks
or a month.

II
120 cc   water
11 g   table sugar
48 cc HNO_3 (conc)
Boil and cool.
Ready for use

III
120 cc   water
7.8 g   dextrose
Ready for use

1st step
Pour ammonia into solution A until a dark brown precipitate of silver oxide forms and begins to clear.

2nd step
Add ammonia drop by drop until solution just clears. Disregard small specks. Stir well between drops near the end.

3rd step
Add solution C ($AgNO_3$) drop by drop until the solution is a distinct straw color. This is to avoid excess ammonia.

4th step
CAUTION From here on there is danger of an explosion. Use goggles.
Add all of solution B slowly and stir constantly.

5th step
Add ammonia, a dropper full at a time and finally a drop at a time, until the solution just clears.

6th step
Add solution C drop by drop until there is a thin straw-colored or brownish precipitate. (Disregard small specks.)

7th step
Filter through cotton.

last step
Add 120 cc of reducing solution and pour immediately over the mirror to be silvered.

Temperature $\begin{cases} 18°\text{C.} \\ 64°\text{F.} \end{cases}$

Fig. 2.

In the third formula dextrose is used directly. The alcohol is a preservative, and it is not required for the second and third solutions unless they are to be stored, in which case the same proportion of alcohol is used as called for in the first formula.

There is danger of an explosion after the fourth stage, indicated in Fig. 2. The formation of the explosive, fulminating silver, is not particularly favored by the low concentration of solutions and moderate temperatures that obtain here, but these relatively weak solutions will give fulminate on warm days if they are allowed to stand. This compound explodes on the slightest provocation when dry and sometimes when wet. Accordingly, all spent silver solutions should be rinsed down the sink at once. Goggles are recommended for safety.

As soon as the reducing reagent is added, the silvering solution is poured over the mirror. Filtering is optional. The distilled water in which the mirror has been standing may or may not be poured off first. Soon after the reducer is added, the solution becomes dark brown and then black. After this, it gradually develops a muddy brown appearance. At this stage the deposit of silver on the mirror is already continuous or should soon become so. The container for the mirror and solution may be tipped from time to time to stir the solution and allow inspection of the surface. When the silver film covers the whole surface and as soon as black specks begin to settle on it, a light swabbing with a cotton pad is recommended. This rubbing must be delicate at first, but it may be more vigorous as the silver becomes thicker, the surface being inspected from time to time for bloom. Usually when the solution begins to clear, it is nearly spent, and since the possibility of bloom becomes greater at this stage, it is best to pour off the solution and rinse the mirror with distilled water. For a full silver coat, Brashear's process requires, on the average, from 6 to 10 minutes.

If a bright light, such as the sun, is visible through the coat, it is too thin. In this case the mirror should be covered with distilled water, and the chemical solution for a second coat prepared.   Do not let the mirror dry between coats.

After a satisfactory coat is obtained, the rinsed mirror is rubbed with a pad of cotton until it is dry.   The silver is burnished with a burnishing pad (chamois skin tacked on a Shinola shoe-polishing pad) to "compact" the coat.   It is then polished with a similar chamois pad charged with optical rouge.   The rouge pad may also be used from time to time to burnish away tarnish which forms on the silver mirror.

Rochelle salt process.[5]   Two solutions are required for the Rochelle salt process.   Solution A is made as follows: 5 g of silver nitrate are dissolved in 300 cc of water and ammoniated, as in the Brashear process, so that the silver oxide precipitate formed at first is almost but not completely clear.   In case it inadvertently becomes clear, it must be back-titrated with a dilute solution of silver nitrate, so that the liquid finally presents a distinct straw color.   This is filtered and diluted with water to 500 cc.   Solution B is made as follows: 1 g of silver nitrate is dissolved in 500 cc of water.   It is then brought to a boil, and 0.83 g of Rochelle salt, dissolved in a little water, is added.   The boiling is continued until a gray precipitate is deposited.   The solution is filtered hot and diluted to 500 cc.   These solutions may be stored for a month or so if they are protected from light.

To silver a mirror, solutions A and B are mixed, volume for volume, and poured at once into the silvering vessel. The quantity of solutions given above is sufficient for a thick film on a glass surface of 200 cm^2 area.   The temperature recommended for silvering is 20°C. (68°F.).

Silver is deposited slowly by the Rochelle salt process; an hour may be required for a thick deposit to form.   Partial reflecting films are obtained as desired by withdrawing the glass from the solution at the appropriate time.   The progress of the deposition may be judged from auxiliary

---

[5] This treatment follows that given in Miller, Dayton Clarence, *Laboratory Physics*, page 269.   Boston: Ginn and Company, 1903.

glass plates, which are removed from time to time to determine the progress of the coating on the main plates.   Fig. 3 illustrates a simple test for determining when the silver film is half-reflecting (for 45° incidence).

Partial reflecting plates are washed with distilled water and dried.   Afterward they are polished by a light brushing with an eiderdown powder puff charged with optical rouge, as recommended by Pfund.

Silver films are protected from tarnishing by covers of filter paper that have been soaked with lead acetate solution

Light source should be directly over edge of mirror.

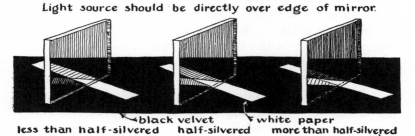

less than half-silvered   black velvet   white paper
                          half-silvered   more than half-silvered

Fig. 3.

and dried.   These covers are applied whenever the films are not actually in use.

Lacquering.   Another procedure for protecting the silver from tarnishing involves coating the film with a thin layer of colorless lacquer.   The layer of lacquer destroys some of the reflectivity of the mirror, and in addition it exhibits interference colors.   R. W. Wood has pointed out that a thin transparent film of lacquer on a good reflector should not show interference colors.[6]   The colors usually exhibited by a lacquer film are due to frilling.   This frilling can be observed directly only with the highest-power microscopes. Wood states that no frilling occurs and that there are, accordingly, no interference colors if collodion dissolved in chemically pure redistilled ether is used to lacquer the mirror.

---

[6] Wood, Robert W., *Physical Optics*, Third Edition.   New York: The Macmillan Company, 1934.

In order to obtain uniform lacquer films with the ether solution of collodion, it is necessary that the ether evaporate slowly.   The can illustrated in Fig. 4 is suggested for use in lacquering with an ether solution.

metal film can or candy box

edges of mirror may be pro-tected with a rubber band

holes just below edge of cover

1st Cover mirror with ether-collo-dion solution and close cover tightly.

2nd Pour out solution without opening container.

3rd Rotate con-tainer slowly while in a diagonal position until mirror is dry.

Fig. 4.

Gold and copper. A chemical process for depositing gold from solution is described by von Angerer.[7]   A process for copper is described by French.[8]

Sputtering. Although the sputtering phenomenon at the cathode of a glow discharge has been known for a long time,[9] the mechanism of the process is not fully understood even now.[10]   There are two current theories of sputtering. One of these holds that the emission of metal by the cathode is pure thermal evaporation due to high temperatures at-tained in areas of molecular dimensions.   These tempera-

[7] von Angerer, Ernst, Wien-Harms, *Handb. der Exp. Physik*, *1*, 375 (1926).

[8] French, E. A. H., *Optical Soc., Trans.*, *25*, 229 (1924).

[9] Grove discovered the sputtering phenomenon in 1852.   Grove, W. R., *Phil. Trans.*, *1* (1852).

[10] Compton, Karl T., and Langmuir, Irving, *Rev. Modern Physics*, *2*, 186 (1930).

Fruth, H. F., *Physics*, *2*, 286 (1932), gives a comprehensive bibliography of cathode sputtering.

Mierdel, G., Wien-Harms, *Handb. der Exp. Physik*, *13*, Part 3, page 400 et seq. (1929).

tures are produced by the energy of impinging ions. The other theory invokes a mechanism for transferring the energy of the gas ion into energy of a metal molecule which is similar to the mechanism by which the energy of a light quantum is transformed to energy of an emitted electron. However, in spite of its being incompletely explained, sputtering is understood empirically, and its practical application for obtaining metal films on glass is simple.

Sputtering can be carried out successfully under a wide variety of conditions. For example, the pressure of the glow discharge may range from 1 down to 10^{-2} mm. The cathode is naturally made of the metal to be sputtered, although its shape may vary considerably. The anode is usually aluminum or iron. The glow discharge is preferably produced by a direct potential, although an alternating potential can be used. The potential usually ranges above 1000 volts and frequently is as high as 20,000 volts. The residual gas in the sputtering chamber may be air, hydrogen, argon, or other gases. (The sputtering rate with helium is extremely low, and this gas is used for glow discharges where sputtering is to be avoided.) The surface to be sputtered is usually placed tangent to the boundary of the cathode dark space, although it may lie within or beyond it. The low pressure required can be obtained with a mechanical pump of small capacity on a tight system or with a faster mechanical or diffusion pump on a system equipped with a regulating leak.

A typical setup for the sputtering process is shown in Fig. 5. The sputtering chamber is usually a glass bell jar with a hole in the top for the cathode connection. It may be made from an old bottle with the bottom cut out and the base ground flat. It is best to have a glass plate for the base, although a metal one (preferably iron) will suffice. An aluminum plate can be used to cover any exposed metal parts which may give trouble by sputtering. It is advisable to heat all aluminum before it is used in order to drive off the machine oils which may be contained in it. Glass cylinders

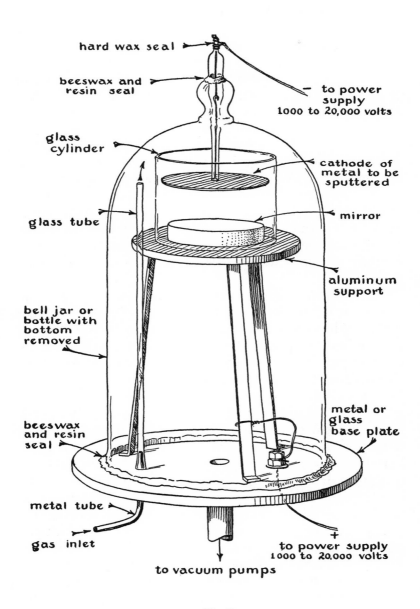

hard wax seal

beeswax and
resin seal

— to power
supply
1000 to 20,000 volts

glass
cylinder

cathode of
metal to be
sputtered

mirror

glass tube

aluminum
support

bell jar or
bottle with
bottom
removed

metal or
glass
base plate

beeswax
and resin
seal

metal tube

gas inlet

+
to power supply
1000 to 20,000 volts

to vacuum pumps

Fig. 5.

and plates, as shown in Fig. 5, are useful for confining the discharge. If these plates and cylinders are not used, the outgassing induced by the discharge may give rise to foreign substances deleterious to the film produced.

The cathode is fitted in the top of the bell jar as shown. It is pulled up against the square end of the depending glass tube by the connector wire. This wire is secured by wrapping it around the top end of the tube, where it is sealed with wax (Apiezon "W," shellac, or DeKhotinsky wax).

Batteries or motor-generator sets are ideal sources for the sputtering potential, but other sources of potential are often employed. An induction coil makes a convenient source of potential, giving partially rectified current. However, alternating current from a 10,000-volt neon-sign transformer can be used. It is advisable but not necessary to rectify the current from this transformer with a Kenetron rectifier.

The use of a milliammeter to measure the discharge current is advisable when making partially transmitting coats. When the sputtering equipment has been calibrated, this current serves as an index to determine proper exposure for obtaining a desired ratio of transmission and reflection. The sputtering rate can be controlled, for example, by adjusting the filament current of the Kenetron. The rate of sputtering increases a little more than linearly with the sputtering current, depending somewhat upon the conditions of temperature, pressure, and geometry which obtain. For work in which high reproducibility in the film thickness is required, it is advisable to use a fast pump and to wash the bell jar continuously with air or hydrogen. Inasmuch as the first part of the sputtering may be erratic and the discharge unsteady, it is well to cover the mirror with mica until sputtering has definitely started and become stable. This mica is mounted on pivots with an attached iron armature, so that it can be operated with the help of a magnet through the walls of the bell jar; or it may be operated by tipping the whole system.

The pressure for sputtering is usually adjusted so as to give a dark space of about the same length as the distance of the mirror from the cathode.

The cathode should be shaped so that the boundary of the dark space is roughly parallel to the mirror surface. For flat or nearly flat mirrors the cathode is made flat, while for strongly curved mirrors it should be correspondingly curved. A U-shaped sheet cathode can be used for coating the two sides of a plate at once, and a central wire cathode can be used to coat the inside of tubes, provided that their length is not much greater than their diameter. Conversely, a cylindrical cathode can be used for coating fibers on all sides at once and for coating the outside of tubes.

The gas admitted, when fast pumps are used, may be air, hydrogen, or argon. Hydrogen is preferred by some even

TABLE I

SPUTTERING RATES OF METALS

Observer	Gas	Rate of Sputtering in Descending Order
Crookes...........	air	Pd, Au, Ag, Pb, Sn, Pt, Cu, Cd, Ni, Ir, Fe, Al, Mg.
Kohlschütter......	N_2	Ag, Au, Pt, Pd, Cu, Ni.
Blechschmidt......	A	Cd, Ag, Pb, Au, Sb, Sn, Bi, Cu, Pt, Ni, Fe, W, Zn, Si, Al, Mg.
Güntherschulze....	H_2[a]	Bi 1470, Te 1200, As 1100, Tl 1080, Sb 890, Ag 740, Au 460, Pb 400, Zn 340, Cu 300, C 262, Sn 196, Fe 68, Ni 65, W 57, Co 56, Mo 56, Mn 38, Cd 32, Al 29, Cr 27, Ta 16, Mg 9.
Güntherschulze.....	O_2[a]	Zn 1030, Tl 650, Ag 614, Au 423, Pb 320, Cu 236, Sn 227, Fe 86, Mo 80, W 49, Ni 52, Cd 28.

Crookes, Sir W., *Roy. Soc., Proc.*, *50*, 88 (1891).

Kohlschütter, V., *Zeits. f. Elektrochem.*, *15*, 316 (1909); *Jahrb. Radioaktivitat*, *9*, 335 (1912).

Güntherschulze, A., *Zeits. f. Physik*, *36*, 563 (1926), *38*, 575 (1926).

[a] Numbers give rate of sputtering in milligrams per ampere hour under conditions of cathode fall of 770 volts and current density of about 7 milliamperes/cm².

though it has a very slow sputtering rate. The hydrogen may be obtained from a tank or from a gas electrolysis chamber. The relative sputtering rates for the various metals with different residual gases are given in Table I and Fig. 6.

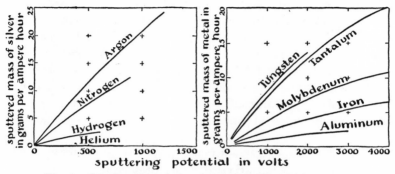

Fig. 6. Güntherschulze's measurements of sputtering rates.

E. O. Hulburt [11] has recently made a study of sputtering. He determined the rates of sputtering in a residual atmosphere of air at a pressure giving 5 cm dark space. The voltage he used was 1000 to 3000 volts and the current 50 milliamperes. The cathode was 5 cm in diameter and 2 to 4 cm from the surface coated. His results are given in Table II.

TABLE II

TIME TO OBTAIN METAL FILMS BY SPUTTERING

Metals	Time
Sb, Bi, Cd, Au, Pb, Pt, Ag, Sn, Zn.....	Opaque coating in 1 hour
Co, Cu, Ir, Fe, Ni, Se, Te.............	Opaque coating in 2 hours
Mo, Ta, W...........................	Opaque coating in several hours
Al, Be, C, Cr, Mg, Si................	Extremely low sputtering rate

Hulburt states that the use of mercury vapor enormously increases the sputtering rate of chromium, aluminum, and

[11] Hulburt, E. O., *Rev. Sci. Instruments.* 5. 85 (1934).

silicon. Optical films of these metals were produced in less than 15 hours in this vapor. Good but not entirely opaque optical films of beryllium were obtained after sputtering for 60 hours in hydrogen and mercury vapor.

Clean dry surfaces and breath figures. To get a surface both clean and dry as required for sputtering and evaporation is a great deal more difficult than to clean it for chemical silvering as described above. Most surfaces cleaned and then dried with absorbent cotton or a towel are found to condense the breath in a gray film. The reason is that in the drying process the glass surface becomes coated with a layer of contamination, which is probably a monomolecular film of fatty acid gathered from the cotton. Water condenses on such a film in tiny droplets, while on a really clean surface it condenses in an invisible uniform film.

Surfaces can be chemically cleaned and dried in a desiccator. Such surfaces give a continuous deposit when breathed on. Also, surfaces may be dried with linen without contaminating them, as Wm. B. Hardy has succeeded in doing. Hardy found it necessary, however, to use linen from which the oily compounds had been extracted with pure benzene.

However, a method to remove the contamination picked up from the towel when the mirror is dried is more practical than to depend upon successfully avoiding such contamination. This dry cleaning can be effected by the action of ions.

The study of this action of ions on the surface of glass started with Aitken and Lord Rayleigh.[12] They found that when the tip of a blowpipe flame was passed quickly over the surface of the glass, it cleaned the surface and produced a so-called breath figure; that is, if one breathed on the glass, the moisture condensed in a gray film of fine droplets, except that where the flame had traversed the surface, the moisture condensed in the form of a continuous "black" film. T. J. Baker and others have carried the study of breath figures

---

[12] Lord Rayleigh, *Scientific Papers*, Vol. 6, pages 26 and 127. Cambridge: University Press, 1920. Aitken, *Roy. Soc. Edin.*, *Proc.*, *94* (1893).

further.[13]   For example, Baker found that they were produced only by the hotter flames, which are rich in ions.
Among the interesting, phenomena revealed by his investigation was that breath figures could also be produced by
sparks, and that, curiously, they could be transferred from
one glass plate to another if the two plates were held together
but not quite in contact.   He also discovered that the black
area is a relatively good conductor of electricity and that the
coefficient of friction between glass and glass was very high
in the black area.   Fig. 7
illustrates a simple experiment for demonstrating this
difference in friction between glass which has been
flamed and that which has
not been flamed.

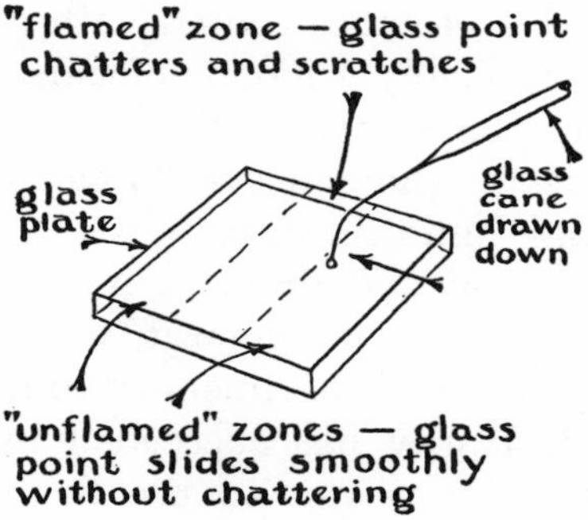

**"flamed" zone — glass point
chatters and scratches**

glass
plate

glass
cane
drawn
down

**"unflamed" zones — glass
point slides smoothly
without chattering**

Fig. 7.

A. C. F. Pollard[14] found it
easy to obtain good adherent
films of chemical silver on
glass by passing a blowpipe
over the surface of the glass
before immersion in the sil-
vering solution.   He also found that for a short time a freshly
fractured glass surface condenses moisture in a continuous
black film.

As a parallel to Pollard's discovery, it was found that aluminum coats prepared by evaporation in vacuum adhere so
tenaciously to areas that have been flamed that they cannot
be removed by stripping Scotch tape off the film, although
the tape removes the aluminum from regions not traversed
by the flame.[15]   Also, the black type of condensation, as
well as good adhesion of an aluminum film, occurs after a
glass surface is exposed to sparks at atmospheric pressure or
to a glow discharge at reduced pressure.   The explanation

[13] Baker, T. J., *Phil. Mag.*, *44*, 752 (1922).
[14] "The Making of Reflecting Surfaces," a discussion held by the Physical
Society of London and the Optical Society, November 26, 1920.
[15] Strong, J., *Rev. Sci. Instruments*, *6*, 97 (1935).

of all these phenomena is that the ions of the hotter flames, sparks, or glow discharges clean the surface of the glass.

The practices adopted to effect a final cleaning of a glass surface are either to expose it to the brush discharge from the electrode of a high-frequency transformer at atmospheric pressure or to expose the glass to a glow discharge in an evaporation chamber while it is being evacuated.

Cleaning mirrors for aluminizing. When aluminum is deposited on a glass surface which is not adequately cleaned, the adhesion will be inferior to that exhibited by a coat on a properly cleaned surface. In most cases the mirror will look good at first but will develop countless tiny blisters after standing a day or so.

The first phases of the cleaning procedure for aluminizing are like those for chemical silvering. The preliminary cleaning with the rubber eraser is carried out with particular

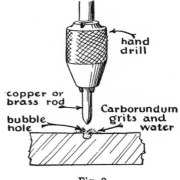

Fig. 8.

thoroughness. Small bubble holes in the face of the mirror that contain rouge and pitch from the figuring should be ground out with emery as shown in Fig. 8. If the rouge and pitch in small bubble holes is not removed, the towel used for drying the mirror may pick up some of the pitch and spread it over the surface of the mirror face in layers too thick to be removed by electrical cleaning.

After the glass has been cleaned and rinsed as described above for silvering, it is dried with clean cotton towels. It is well to use old cotton towels, because after many launderings they become more absorbent and contain less fatty substances than absorbent cotton. Care is exercised to avoid contaminating the freshly laundered towel by touching it with the hands in the areas to be used to dry the mirror face.

Finally, the glass is exposed to a glow discharge during the evacuation.

Evaporation. The evaporation method for producing thin films on glass, quartz, and so forth, is simple both in its mechanism and in its practical application. A small piece of the metal (or nonmetal, for that matter) is simply heated in a high vacuum until its vapor pressure is about 10^{-2} mm of mercury or greater, whereupon it emits molecular rays in all directions. The degree of vacuum required for successfully carrying out the process is such that the mean free path of the molecules is larger than the diameter of the vacuum container. Therefore molecular rays propagate from their source without disturbance until they impinge on the walls of the vacuum or some object within them. The mirror surface to be coated is exposed to these molecular rays, which condense on it to form the desired film. An interesting feature of the condensed film is that it apparently exhibits the same degree of polish as the underlying glass and so requires no subsequent burnishing, as does chemical silvering. Also, this film forms without material heating of the mirror.

Although the evaporation method was known by 1912, it remained obscure, for some reason, long after it should have become a practical "tool" in the laboratory.[16] Among the items which have influenced its recent rather extensive applications are the development of a bare tungsten heater technique,[17] the adaptability of the process to nonmetals and for the application of aluminum,[18] and the development of high-speed vacuum pumps. (See Chapter III.)

Whether or not a particular material is suited to giving films by the evaporation process is determined by the thermal stability and vapor pressure of the material and the practicality of bringing the material to the evaporation temperature in vacuum.

---

[16] Pringsheim, P., and Pohl, R., *Deutsch. Phys. Gesell.*, *Verh.*, *14*, 506 (1912).
[17] Ritschl, R., *Zeits. f. Physik*, *69*, 578 (1931).
[18] Strong, J., *Astrophys. J.*, *83*, 401 (1936).

Tungsten heaters useful for bringing some of the metals to the evaporation temperature are shown in Figs. 12 and 15 to 20.   The evaporation temperatures of the metals are given in Table III.

TABLE III

Evaporation Temperature[a] of Different Metals

Material	Evaporation Temperature $T°$ Absolute[a]	Material	Evaporation Temperature $T°$ Absolute[a]
Hg	320	Pb	1000
Cs	433	Sn	1148
Rb	450	Cr	1190
K	480	Ag	1319
Cd	541	Au	1445
Na	565	Al	1461
Zn	623	Cu	1542
Mg	712	Fe	1694
Sr	811	Ni	1717
Li	821	Pt	2332
Ca	878	Mo	2755
Ba	905	C	2795
Bi	913	W	3505
Sb	973		

[a] Temperature at which vapor pressure equals 10^{-2} mm of mercury.

Baur, E., and Brunner, R., *Helv. chim. Acta.*, *17*, 959 (1934).

Espe, W., and Knoll, M., *Werkstoffkunde der Hochvakuumtechnik*, page 358. Berlin: Julius Springer, 1936.

Knoll, M., Ollendorff, F., and Rompe, E., *Gasentladungs-Tabellen*. Berlin: Julius Springer, 1935.

Landolt-Börnstein, *Phys. Chem. Tabellen*, Fifth Edition. Berlin: Julius Springer, 1923–1936.

Leitgebel, W., *Metallwirtschaft*, *14*, 267 (1935).

Most of the metals melt first before they evaporate, the molten metal being kept from falling out of the coil by surface tension.

Other metals, like magnesium, sublime.   Of these, some sublime very slowly, because the metal will not fuse to the tungsten wire in vacuum.   Chromium affords an example. The evaporation of such a metal is managed as follows: It is first brought to fusion temperature in the tungsten coil in an atmosphere of hydrogen or helium.   These gases facilitate heat transfer between tungsten and the chromium or other metal, and, in addition, they restrain evaporation of the metal.   (See Fig. 9.)   After intimate contact with the tungsten wire is established, the metal will then sublime

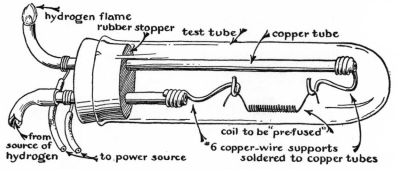

hydrogen flame
rubber stopper   test tube   copper tube

coil to be "pre-fused"
from source of hydrogen
to power source
*6 copper-wire supports soldered to copper tubes

Fig. 9.   Arrangement for pre-fusion of metal to tungsten coil.

faster in the vacuum, because the heat is transmitted to it more effectively.   An alternate way of attaining the same end is to electroplate the chromium or other metal onto the tungsten coil.[19]   The metals best managed by the above procedures include, besides chromium, the platinum metals and beryllium.

Frequently, it is desirable to prefuse a metal which otherwise sublimes, in order to free it from included impurities.

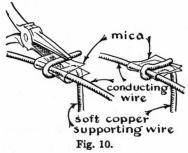

mica
conducting wire
soft copper supporting wire
Fig. 10.

Such metals as calcium, magnesium, and cadmium can be prefused in helium to outgas them and to prepare them for evaporation.

A great many metals react with the tungsten coil, as, for example, iron, nickel, beryllium, chromium, the platinum

---

[19] This electroplating technique is apparently one which has been frequently used.   Note the following references on its application to platinum and chromium respectively:

Strong, J., *Phys. Rev.*, *39*, 1012 (1932).

Williams, Robley C., *Phys. Rev.*, *41*, 255 (1932).

metals, and aluminum. In spite of this, it is possible to evaporate them for the preparation of small laboratory mirrors.

Fig. 10 shows a neat simple insulated support for wires in vacuum.

Evaporation technique for aluminum. The technique for evaporation of aluminum from tungsten coils is of special interest, since this metal is important for surfacing where high ultraviolet and high visible reflectivity are desired in combination with freedom from tarnishing.

Pringsheim and Pohl discovered that several metals (including aluminum) could be evaporated in vacuum and condensed on a glass surface to form a polished reflecting film. They used a magnesia crucible from which to distill the metal.[20] R. Ritschl, in 1928, in making an application of the evaporation method to the preparation of half-silvered interferometer mirrors, heated the silver in a bare tungsten coil.[21] This change in technique has the advantage that the tungsten does not evaporate or outgas so much in a vacuum as does the magnesia crucible.

Following this, Cartwright and Strong developed a simple apparatus for carrying out the evaporation process in the laboratory and made a survey of its applicability to different metals.[22] The usual technique, in which the metal to be evaporated was heated in a helix of tungsten wire, was found successful, except with the metals aluminum and beryllium, which dissolved the tungsten coil.

Other attempts were made to develop this technique of evaporating aluminum.[23] Experiments were carried out with crucibles of graphite, pure fused magnesia, and alumina (sapphire), as well as with sintered and fused crucibles of thorium oxide. These experiments showed that heating in a crucible was apparently impractical, since either the metal

---

[20] See footnote 16.

[21] See footnote 17.

[22] Cartwright, C. Hawley, and Strong, J., *Rev. Sci. Instruments*, *2, 189* (1931).

[23] Cartwright, C. Hawley, *Rev. Sci. Instruments*, *3*, 302 (1932).

reacted chemically with the material of the crucible or the latter evaporated when the aluminum was heated.

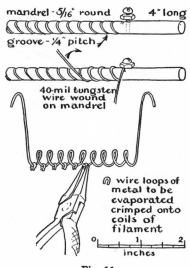

Fig. 11.

The discovery that tungsten has a limited solubility in molten aluminum led to the bare tungsten method of evaporation—the most practiced of all the methods.[24]

A chemical analysis of the tungsten alloy that is formed when aluminum is fused on a tungsten coil showed the solubility of tungsten in aluminum to be about 3 per cent by volume. Accordingly, the burning out of the tungsten wire may be avoided by the simple expedient of making it of relatively large diameter and arranging the charge so that the solubility of the molten aluminum for tungsten can be satisfied without dangerously reducing the diameter of the wire.

It might be expected that some of the dissolved tungsten would boil away, especially since its spectrum has been observed during evaporation.[25] In order to test this point, a coil was weighed before and after evaporating several charges of aluminum. Instead of a loss in weight, an increase was observed, indicating that some aluminum had

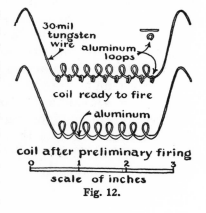

Fig. 12.

[24] Strong, J., *Phys. Rev.*, *43*, 498 (1933).
[25] Gaviola, E., and Strong, J., *Phys. Rev.*, *48*, 136 (1935).

diffused into the tungsten. However, extended heating in vacuum at a very high temperature decreased the weight, until, within the experimental error, it became the same as in the beginning. A chemical analysis of the condensed metal film was made to test whether or not tungsten is evaporated. The analysis gave no definite indication of tungsten. A concentration of 0.03 per cent by weight was

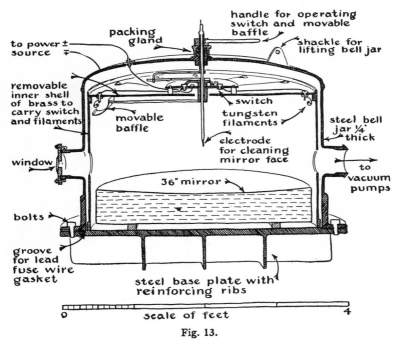

Fig. 13.

detectable. The tungsten which is dissolved thus appears to be almost completely precipitated back onto the coil as the evaporation proceeds. Although it may not be deposited back in exactly the same place, it does compensate in a large measure for the decrease in diameter of the tungsten wire.

The arrangement used at first for aluminizing mirrors at the California Institute of Technology is shown in Figs. 11 and 12. It is in the form of a helix, consisting of 10 turns of 30-mil tungsten wire, $\frac{5}{16}$ of an inch in diameter and pitched

4 turns to the inch. A **U**-shaped piece of aluminum wire 1 mm in diameter and about 10 mm in total length is clamped to each turn as is shown in Fig. 11. A potential of 20 volts applied to the coil in vacuum for 4 seconds prefuses these pieces as shown in Fig. 12. At this stage, surface tension keeps the molten aluminum from dropping. This prefusion also serves to free the metal from oxide and other impurities. It is customary to make a separate run in order to effect this fusing of the aluminum to the tungsten

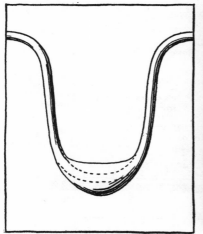

Fig. 14.

wires. In the 40-inch tank (see Fig. 13), however, the coils are covered by a baffle during the preliminary firing. The aluminum is finally distilled from the coils by applying the same voltage to each coil for about 15 seconds.

Actually, the aluminum does not evaporate from the fused metal but from the adjacent tungsten wire. This is clearly shown by the "self-photograph" of the filament reproduced in Fig. 14. This "self-photograph" was recorded on glass with the molecular rays of aluminum passing through a pinhole.

A recently developed evaporation source allows a much

higher rate of evaporation of aluminum with less tendency to burn out or drop molten aluminum. The new source uses three or four 20-mil tungsten wires twisted together as shown in Fig. 15. The metal charge, applied as illustrated in Fig. 11, flows out to fill the space between the wires when heat is applied. The aluminum covers the tungsten completely, so that a minimum "ratio" of heat radiation to molecular radiation of aluminum is achieved.

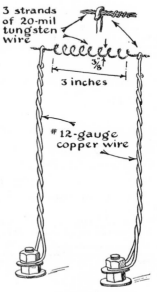

Fig. 15.

Fig. 16 shows the form by which the new source is applied to the evaporation of gold. When the gold melts in the "cup," it is drawn out to coat the tungsten and it fills up the spaces between wires from one end to the other.

For evaporation of silver and copper the source should be made from tantalum or molybdenum rather than tungsten, as the latter metal is not easily wet with silver and copper.

For evaporation of the platinum metals, a unit similar to the one shown in Fig. 15 is made up of three 20-mil tungsten wires and one platinum metal wire of the same diameter.

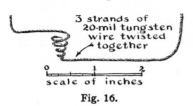

Fig. 16.

The "ratio" of heat to metal radiated is a minimum. Furthermore, the awkward process of electroplating the platinum on the filament is avoided. The evaporation should proceed slowly, even from this source, because if too much current is applied, the evaporation is no longer smooth, and globules of metal are discharged from the source.

Chromium is easily evaporated from a source like the one shown in Fig. 16.   A piece of the metal is put in the "cup" and is preheated in an atmosphere of hydrogen or helium to fuse it and distribute it over the tungsten.   Various other evaporation sources are illustrated in Figs. 17 to 20.

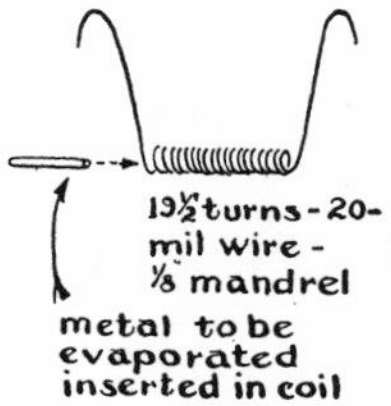

19½ turns - 20-mil wire - ⅛ mandrel
metal to be evaporated inserted in coil

Fig. 17.

Vacuum equipment.   The evaporation process is carried out in a vacuum of 10^{-3} mm of mercury or better.   For small mirrors the necessary vacuum may be obtained with a kinetic pumping system such as the one shown in the previous chapter.

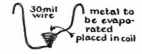

30-mil wire
metal to be evaporated placed in coil

Fig. 18.

The 40-inch tank, Fig. 13, shows the type of equipment used at the California Institute of Technology for larger mirrors. Still larger systems have been used.[26]

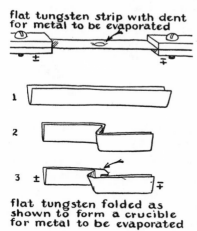

flat tungsten strip with dent for metal to be evaporated

flat tungsten folded as shown to form a crucible for metal to be evaporated

Fig. 19.

The cleaning electrode shown in Fig. 13 allows the vacuum vessel, containing the mirror, to be filled with a glow discharge during the preliminary evacuation with the roughing pumps; and this discharge effects the final cleaning of the mirror face.

It is recommended that the aluminum be evaporated soon after a nonconducting vacuum has been reached, in

[26] Strong, J., *Astrophys. J.*, *83*, 401 (1936).
Metal tanks of seamless steel are available from the Eclipse Fuel Engineering Company (Los Angeles agent, James H. Knopf) in the same form as bell jars. After the foot is machined, they are suitable for sealing to a base plate to form a good vacuum container for evaporation.   It is advisable to clean the tank inside and out by sand blasting and to coat it inside with Apiezon wax "W" and outside with Glyptal lacquer.

order to obtain maximum tenacity between the aluminum film and the glass. Also, this procedure yields harder films.

Uniform films. In order to obtain a uniform coat on large mirrors, aluminum is evaporated from several tungsten sources suitably arranged, rather than from one movable source.

The evaporation of polonium in a high vacuum from a point source has been investigated by Bonét-Maury.[27] This metal was chosen on account of its radioactivity. He found that the condensation on a plane surface is proportional to the inverse square of the distance from the source, and to the cosine of the angle between the normal to the surface and the line connecting the surface with the source. We may assume that the same is true of other metals which have a low vapor pressure at room temperature.

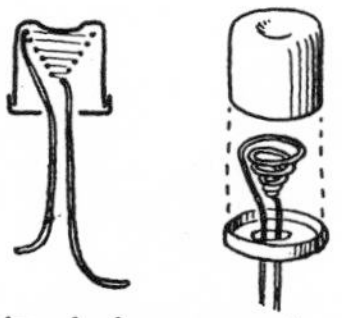

tantalum cap to enclose coil may be used for evaporating oxides or the dent in the top used for metals

Fig. 20.

Starting with this assumption, we may consider the distribution of the film thickness τ produced by various experimental arrangements. In the case of evaporation to the inside surface of a sphere of radius ρ from a point source of vapor at its center, the situation is very simple. We get a uniform film of which the thickness τ_0 is

$$\tau_0 = \frac{m}{4\pi\partial\rho^2}. \tag{1}$$

Here m is the mass of metal evaporated and ∂ is its density.

The film thickness at P on a plane surface at the normal distance ρ from a point source of evaporation is

$$\tau_P = \frac{m}{4\pi\partial r^2}\cos\theta = \tau_0\left(\frac{\rho}{r}\right)^3. \tag{2}$$

Here τ_0 is the thickness at P, r is the distance from the source to P, and θ is the inclination of the surface P to the molecular rays emitted by the source which impinge on it there.

[27] Bonét-Maury, P., *Ann. de Physique*, *11*, 253 (1929).

The film thickness produced on a plane surface by a circular array of vapor sources can be determined by applying the above formula to each of the sources. (See Fig. 21.) If there are N coils spaced uniformly around a circle at a distance ρ from the surface to be coated, the film thickness

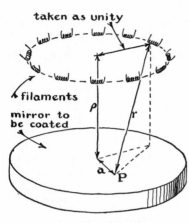

taken as unity

filaments

mirror to be coated

Fig. 21.

on the surface at P, which is at a distance a from the intersection of the axis of the circle with the face of the mirror, is given by the expression

$$\tau_P = \frac{M\rho}{4\pi\partial N} \sum_1^N \frac{1}{r_i^3}. \tag{3}$$

Here M is the total mass of metal evaporated, and r is the distance from P to the coil represented by the summation index i.

Dr. Edward M. Thorndike made the same calculation, assuming a continuous circular source. The thickness is given in this case by

$$\tau_P = \frac{M\rho}{8\pi^2\partial} \int_0^{2\pi} \frac{d\theta}{r^3}. \tag{4}$$

Here the point source at distance r from the point P is replaced by a line source represented by the angle element $d\theta$ at distance r, as before. This calculation involves the integration

$$\int_0^{2\pi} \frac{d\theta}{r^3} = \int_0^{2\pi} \frac{d\theta}{(1 + a^2 + \rho^2 - 2a \cos\theta)^{3/2}} =$$

$$\frac{4}{[(a-1)^2 + \rho^2]\sqrt{(a+1)^2 + \rho^2}} E\left(\frac{2\sqrt{a}}{\sqrt{(a+1)^2 + \rho^2}}\right), \tag{5}$$

in which E represents the elliptic function.[28] Values of this integral calculated by Thorndike are given in Table IV.

[28] Bierens de Haan, David, *Nouvelles tables d'integrales definies*, Table 67, Eq. 3, page 102. Leyden: P. Engels, 1867.

TABLE IV

VALUES OF $\int_0^{2\pi} \dfrac{d\theta}{r^3}$ FOR VARIOUS PARAMETERS

a	$\rho = \frac{1}{2}$	$\rho = 1$	$\rho = 1.1$	$\rho = 1.2$	$\rho = 2$	$\rho = 4$
0.00	4.50	2.22	1.91	1.65	.560	.090
0.25	4.82	2.24	1.93	1.65	.555	.090
0.50	3.96	2.29	1.93	1.63	.540	.088
0.75	7.74	2.28	1.89	1.57	.515	.085
0.80	....	2.27	....	....	....	....
0.90	....	2.22	....	....	....	....
1.00	8.28	2.11	1.74	1.45	.480	.082
1.50	3.40	1.38	1.09	1.02	.385	.072
2.00	1.20	0.74	0.67	0.61	.285	.068
3.00	0.28	0.24	0.23	0.22	.145	.050

For convenience, the radius of the circular source is here taken as unity. We see from this table that for $\rho = 1$ the film is quite uniform as far out from the center as $a = 1$. This case was realized in the 40-inch aluminizing tank by a circular array of twelve of the standard coils (see Fig. 12) spaced around a circle 36 inches in diameter, 18 inches above the face of the astronomical reflector to be coated (Fig. 22). Tests of transmission of a film produced with partially loaded coils confirmed the calculation, since the coat exhibited the expected uniformity.

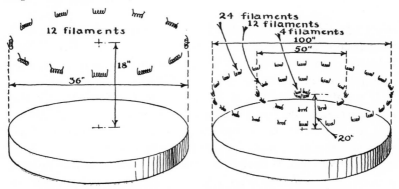

Fig. 22. Arrangements of evaporation coils for large mirrors.

In a larger 108-inch tank it was not convenient to use a similar array of coils spaced 50 inches from the face of the mirror. Instead, three arrays were used, each about 20 inches from the mirror. The arrangement is shown in Fig. 22. From the expressions developed above, as well as from actual tests, it was found that four coils in the center, twelve on a circle of 50 inches in diameter, and twenty-four on a circle of 100 inches in diameter gave the proper loading. This arrangement produced a uniform film of proper thickness on a 100-inch mirror, the film being just a little thicker than that required to be opaque to sunlight. It is desirable to have this thickness (about 1000 Å), since much thicker films are more easily scratched, while thinner ones may in time become transparent as a result of the gradual growth of thickness of the oxide layer which forms on the aluminum coat.

Parabolizing a spherical mirror with aluminum. As soon as the technique for the attainment of uniform films was perfected, it became possible to prepare nonuniform films, with the thickness of the film varying in just the manner required to parabolize a spherical mirror. The difference τ between the circle and parabola illustrated in Fig. 23 is given to close approximation by the expression

$$\tau = y^2(y_0^2 - y^2)\frac{1}{8R^3}, \tag{6}$$

where y is the ordinate and R is the radius of curvature of the circle. y_0 represents the ordinate where the two curves intersect. The difference is zero at $y = 0$ and at $y = y_0$ and has a maximum at $y = y_0/\sqrt{2}$.

If a spherical mirror of diameter $2y_0$ (represented by the surface generated by rotation of the circle in Fig. 23 about the X axis) is to be transformed to a paraboloidal surface (the surface generated by rotation of the parabola), it is evident from Eq. 6 that it is necessary to add to the sphere a zone of aluminum which has its maximum thickness at

$y = y_0/\sqrt{2}$, tapering off on either side of this as required by the equation.

The maximum thickness of aluminum, $\tau_{max.}$, required depends naturally upon the radius of curvature of the

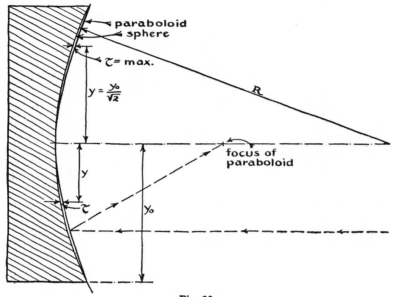

Fig. 23.

sphere, R. The connection between $\tau_{max.}$, R, and y_0 is given by the expression

$$\tau_{max.} = \frac{y_0^4}{32R^3}, \qquad (7)$$

or, in terms of its f value,

$$\tau_{max.} = \frac{y_0}{2048f^3}. \qquad (8)$$

Inasmuch as it is possible to put down films of aluminum to 1μ thickness and greater, it is possible to parabolize a 12-inch mirror $f/6$, which requires a maximum thickness of only 0.34μ of aluminum. This is not an uncommon example encountered in astronomical mirrors.

The correct procedure for applying such a parabolizing film is first to compute the thickness and distribution of the aluminum film produced by a point source positioned opposite the center of the mirror as shown in Fig. 24. This

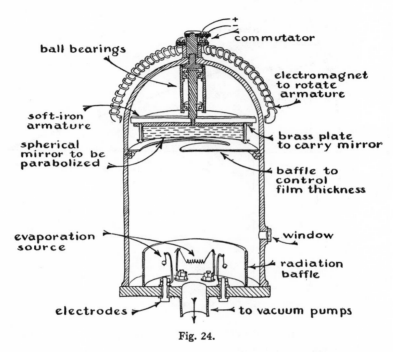

Fig. 24.

can be done by the use of the formula given below for the thickness of aluminum τ produced at a distance y from the center of the mirror.

$$\tau = \frac{my}{34d^3}. \tag{9}$$

Here m is the total mass of aluminum evaporated, in grams, and d is the distance between the source and the point in question on the mirror face.

A baffle of the shape illustrated by Fig. 25 is then cut from thin sheet brass and placed directly in front of the mirror as shown in Fig. 24. This baffle can be rotated, or, what is more convenient, it may be fixed and the mirror rotated as shown in Fig. 24. The baffle is so designed as to modify the thickness which would otherwise be obtained (given by Eq. 9), so that it will conform with that required by Eq. 6. The baffle will have zero angular opening at the center and edge and a maximum opening very near to $y = y_0/\sqrt{2}$. It is to be remembered that the effect of the baffle in a given zone is to decrease the thickness by a factor which is the ratio of

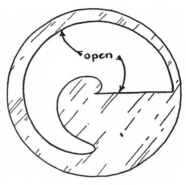

Fig. 25.

the quantities, 360° minus the angular opening of the baffle opposite the particular zone in question, to 360°. In order to avoid astigmatism, the mirror is rotated a great many times during the deposition.

It is necessary, for some reason not yet clearly demonstrated, to evaporate slightly more aluminum than the simple theory outlined above predicts. The procedure in this case is to deposit some metal (about the theoretical amount) and then test the mirror. On the basis of the Foucault test, an additional amount is evaporated, and so on until the required figure is obtained. If too much metal is added, the coat can be washed off with caustic soda. Usually the mirror can be finished on the second attempt.

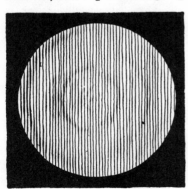

Fig. 26.   Starting sphere tested at the center of curvature.

When several mirrors, all alike, are to be parabolized, this preliminary testing may be done once for all.

Figs. 26, 27, and 28 show focograms of a mirror parabolized by this method. It was originally a sphere true to $\frac{1}{20}$ of a

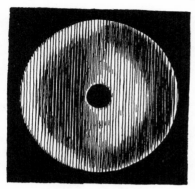

wave length of green light, as the first focogram (Fig. 26), taken at its center of curvature, shows. This sphere was $152\frac{1}{4}$ inches in radius of curvature. $2y_0$ was $12\frac{3}{8}$ inches. The next focogram, Fig. 27, shows it at its mean focus when tested with parallel light with the aid of a testing flat, obviously in need of parabolizing to give a good knife-edge cutoff. After it was para-bolized with a coat of alumi-

Fig. 27.   Sphere tested at its mean focus.

num, it appeared as shown in the third focogram, Fig. 28. Here, again, it exhibits a true figure of revolution, this time a parabola true to less than $\frac{1}{20}$ of a wave length of green light.

Mirrors imperfectly figured by conventional methods can be improved by this procedure. In this case the baffle design is determined by a preliminary quantitative survey of the mirror with a knife-edge testing outfit. (See Chapter II.)

It is possible to apply a thin film of aluminum to a convex sphere and transform it to a hyperbolic figure of revolution for use as the secondary mirror in a Cassegrain telescope.

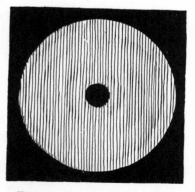

Fig. 28.   Sphere after paraboliz-ing with an aluminum film.   Tested at the focus.

The formula for the difference between the hyperbola, or any conic of eccentricity ϵ, and the sphere tangent to it at the center and touching it at the radius distance y_0 is

$$\tau = \frac{\epsilon^2 y^2 (y_0^2 - y^2)}{8R^3}.$$ (10)

Eq. 6 for the parabola is Eq. 10 when $\epsilon = 1$. To obtain a hyperbola, it is necessary to have the aluminum thick at center and edge with a minimum at $y = y_0/\sqrt{2}$. The baffle to effect this is just the inverse of the one shown in Fig. 25, being open where the other is opaque and vice versa. The further details of the process are described in a paper by Strong and Gaviola and in the paper of Gaviola on the quantitative use of the knife-edge test.[29]

Partially reflecting films. Partially reflecting films of silver and aluminum are useful for dividing a beam of light in many optical instruments such as color cameras and interferometers.

Figs. 29 and 30 show the reflection and transmission characteristics of silver and aluminum films obtained by the

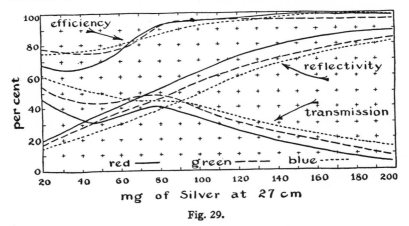

Fig. 29.

evaporation of various amounts of metal. The curves illustrate the color characteristics of the films and their efficiencies. They also indicate approximately the amount of metal to be evaporated to obtain any desired ratio of reflection to transmission. The curves for silver refer to

[29] Strong, J., and Gaviola, E., *J.O.S.A.*, *26*, 153 (1936).
Gaviola, E., *J.O.S.A.*, *26*, 163 (1936).

fresh deposits, whereas the curves for aluminum apply to films about 6 months old, which have more or less attained their equilibrium optical characteristics.

The reproducibility with which any given film can be prepared from the information given in Figs. 29 and 30 is

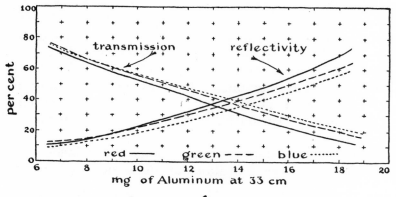

Fig. 30.

unfortunately not very great. The variations to be expected are greater in the case of aluminum.

The films from which the curves in Figs. 29 and 30 were obtained were evaporated with a vacuum of 1 to 5 × 10^{-5} mm, the mirror distance being 33 cm in the case of aluminum and 27 cm in the case of silver. A source like the

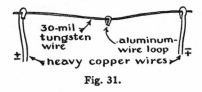

Fig. 31.

one shown in Fig. 17 was used for silver. The metal was in the form of a 40-mil wire. A straight, horizontal 30-mil tungsten wire served as the evaporation source for aluminum as shown in Fig. 31. The metal was a weighed U-shaped piece of wire pinched onto the center of the tungsten wire.

Silver films have a greater efficiency than aluminum films, and they are, accordingly, best for coating Farby and Perot interferometer plates. They may be protected from the tarnishing gases in the atmosphere by a thin layer of calcium fluoride or quartz.

The calcium fluoride (or quartz) films should be about $\frac{1}{4}$ of a fringe in thickness.   If a copper sheet is placed close to the evaporation source, it is possible to count the fringes as they are formed on this sheet by the evaporated calcium fluoride (or quartz).   The square of the ratio of the distance of the copper to that of the silver gives the ratio of film thickness of calcium fluoride (or quartz) evaporated onto these two surfaces.   The evaporation of calcium fluoride (or quartz) is stopped after an appropriate number of fringes have appeared on the copper.

A thin film of aluminum on the silver will oxidize to a protecting layer of aluminum oxide on exposure to the air. The proper amount of aluminum to be evaporated is about one-sixteenth the amount required to give a half-transmitting coat.   Accordingly, the proper amount of aluminum may be gauged by means of an auxiliary glass plate positioned at one-fourth the silver film distance from the evaporation source.   The proper amount of aluminum is evaporated when the film on the auxiliary glass plate appears to be about half-transmitting.

When a half-silvered mirror on glass is cemented with balsam to a second glass surface, the ratio of transmission to reflection is increased by about 5 per cent.

CHAPTER V

The Use of Fused Silica

BY

H. V. NEHER

General remarks on fused quartz. Formerly made only in rod and tube form, fused quartz[1] is now often employed as a substitute for glass in chemical ware, and most of the common pieces used in chemistry are now obtainable in this material. Such articles as flasks, beakers, dishes, plates, and so forth, are in fairly common use.

Apparatus made from fused quartz has two chief advantages over that made from glass. The low thermal expansion coefficient eliminates all fear of breakage due to rapid temperature changes. A hot piece of quartz plunged into water suffers no ill effects. Also, its relatively high melting point makes possible the study of reactions which would be more difficult with glass.

As will be pointed out later, many of its properties make it valuable in instruments of various kinds and when constancy is a prime requisite. One particularly valuable property of fused quartz is its extremely low loss of energy due to internal friction when stresses are applied. The loss amounts to only 10^{-3} of that in the best of the metals. Another property of value lies in its constancy of length. It not only has an extremely small thermal expansion coefficient, but returns to its original length after having been heated or cooled.

The chief disadvantage of fused quartz is its high cost,

---

[1] Fused quartz is obtainable from the Thermal Syndicate and the General Electric Company. Each carries a large stock of quartz products and will make special pieces on demand.

due mainly to the fact that it has a high melting point and demands special methods for its manufacture. The fact that it fuses with difficulty makes the working of tubing greater than an inch in diameter more or less impractical in the laboratory. Although an oxyhydrogen flame becomes useful when working large pieces of quartz, small pieces can be worked easily with an oxy–natural gas flame. An ordinary Bunsen burner flame using natural gas is hot enough to soften small pieces.

A very useful property discovered by C. V. Boys[2] in 1889, and discussed in detail later, is that fused quartz can be drawn into fine fibers which have remarkable strength. Fibers of any size down to 1μ (0.0001 cm) diameter or less can be easily and rapidly produced. No other vitreous material can in any way approach fused quartz in performance when made into these fine fibers.

Chemical properties. Fused silica at room temperature is inactive to practically all chemicals except hydrofluoric acid and the alkalies. However, at high temperatures it reacts with most metallic salts, forming silicates. This is due to the fact that silicon dioxide is an acid in the general sense of the term, and as such reacts vigorously at high temperatures with metallic oxides which are bases. The noble metals do not form silicates, and a quartz fiber covered with gold may be heated until the gold evaporates, without harming the fiber.

Physical properties. *Thermal properties.* The coefficient of thermal expansion of fused quartz rod under no stress has been measured with considerable accuracy.[3] The mean values near room temperature, defined by $\alpha = (1/l)(\Delta l/t_2 - t_1)$, are given in Table I. For comparison, steel has a coefficient of $10.1 \times 10^{-6}°C.^{-1}$, or 25 times as large, while for Invar α is about $0.9 \times 10^{-6}°C.^{-1}$. The coefficient of thermal expansion has not been measured for various sizes of fibers under varying amounts of strain.

---

[2] Boys, C. V., *Roy. Soc., Phil. Trans.*, *143*, 159 (1889).
[3] Kaye, G. W. C., *Phil. Mag.*, *20*, 718 (1910).

TABLE I

The Mean Values of the Coefficient of Thermal Expansion of Fused Quartz Near Room
Temperature, Defined by $\alpha = (1/l)(\Delta l/t_2 - t_1)$

Temperature (°C.)	α ($\times 10^{-6}$ °C.$^{-1}$)
− 40 to 0	0.31
0 to 30	0.42
30 to 100	0.52
100 to 150	0.58

The coefficient of thermal hysteresis of fused quartz is less than for any other known material. If a substance of length l is heated from a temperature t_1 to a temperature t_2 and allowed to cool to t_1, then $(1/l)(\Delta l/t_2 - t_1)$, where Δl is the residual difference in length, is a measure of the thermal hysteresis. For quartz, this quantity is -1 to -5×10^{-9}°C.$^{-1}$; that is, it contracts more than it expands. In comparison, Invar has a similar coefficient of -100×10^{-9}°C.$^{-1}$. This property makes fused quartz particularly valuable when it is necessary to maintain dimensions accurately.[4]

If fused quartz is held at a temperature above 1200°C. for some time, crystallization gradually takes place, beginning at the surface and working inward. As the temperature is raised, the crystallization becomes more rapid until a temperature is reached at which the crystals melt. When quartz is worked locally in a flame, a milky surface will form between the soft quartz and the cool portion. This is probably due to condensation of evaporated quartz and does no harm to the material except in appearance.

Elastic properties. The normal coefficient of elasticity, or the reciprocal of Young's modulus for quartz rod at room

---

[4] For a discussion of the behavior of metals and quartz used as standards of length the reader is referred to Glazebrook, Sir Richard Tetley, editor, *Dictionary of Applied Physics*, Volume III, pages 471–475. New York: The Macmillan Company, 1922–1923.

temperature, was measured first by Boys. This coefficient is defined by

$$\frac{1}{Y} = \frac{1}{l}\frac{\Delta l}{\Delta S_n},$$

where Y is Young's modulus and S_n is the normal stress. Boys found the value $Y = 5.2 \times 10^{11}$ dynes cm^{-2}, which is very near the most recently determined values for fibers from 50μ to 100μ in diameter. Young's modulus varies with the size of the fiber, becoming greater as the size of the fiber diminishes. This variation can be expressed by

$$Y = \frac{27 \times 10^{11}}{d} + 5.9 \times 10^{11} \quad \text{dynes cm}^{-2},$$

where d is the diameter of the fiber in microns. This relation fails to hold, giving values too large, for fibers less than 10μ in diameter. Experimental values of Y for various sizes of fibers are given in Table II. The increase in modulus of elasticity with decrease in size is due to the importance of the surface layer for the smaller fibers, which has a different elastic constant.

TABLE II

Breaking Strength, Young's Modulus, Y, Modulus of Rigidity, Z, and $\Delta l / l$ for Failure for Different Sizes of Quartz Fibers

Diameter (μ)	Breaking Strength ($\times 10^{11}$)	Y ($\times 10^{11}$)	Z ($\times 10^{11}$)	$\dfrac{\Delta l}{l}$ for Failure
1.5	0.90	..	..	..
2.0	0.80	..	..	..
3.0	0.65	11.1	6.6	0.059
4.0	0.55	10.3	6.1	0.054
5.0	0.48	9.8	5.8	0.049
7.0	0.39	9.0	5.3	0.043
10.0	0.30	8.5	4.8	0.035
15.0	0.23	7.9	4.2	0.029
20.0	0.17	7.6	3.9	0.022
30.0	0.145	7.1	3.5	0.020

Data taken from Reinkober, O., *Phys. Zeits.*, *38*, 112 (1937).

These are mean values; values of individual fibers may be as much as 20 per cent higher or lower than those given. Units are in dynes cm^{-2}.

The tangential coefficient of elasticity, or the reciprocal of the rigidity modulus, for solid rod of radius r and length l, is defined as

$$\frac{1}{Z} = \frac{1}{2l}\frac{\Delta(\phi r)}{\Delta S_t},$$

where S_t is the tangential stress and ϕ is the angle of twist of the rod. For a uniform solid round rod $S_t = (L/r)/(\pi r^2)$, where L is the applied torque and r is the radius. Z has a minimum value of 3×10^{11} dynes cm^{-2} but depends, as does Y, on the size of the fiber, as shown in Table II.

Two other elastic quantities are very often useful. The first indicates how much a fiber can be stretched before it breaks, that is,

$$\left(\frac{\Delta l}{l}\right)_{\text{for failure}} = \frac{(S_n)_f}{Y},$$

where $(S_n)_f$ is the normal stress for failure. Values of $\Delta l/l$ for failure are given in Table II. These apply only to fresh, clean fibers or those which have been kept perfectly clean and dry. (See below as to how to preserve fibers.) As far as is known, no other material approaches this factor. For the best nickel-vanadium steels the ratio is about 0.01. A comparison of Young's modulus for each material shows that quartz fiber compares favorably in strength with the strongest materials known.

The second quantity indicates how much a fiber can be twisted without failure, that is,

$$\left(\frac{r\phi}{l}\right)_{\text{for failure}} = \frac{(S_t)_f}{Z} \cong 0.05$$

for fibers up to 20μ in diameter, where $(S_t)_f$ is the tangential stress for failure. This ratio also increases as the size of the fiber decreases. Thus, a fiber 5μ in diameter can be twisted through at least 20 revolutions per centimeter of length before it fails. It should be remarked that the elastic limits for both normal and tangential stresses are coincident with the point of failure.

Another property of quartz which enhances its value for electrometer and other suspensions is its low internal viscosity. If a fiber is twisted through an angle ϕ, then the shearing stress is not strictly a constant but depends on time, thus:

$$S_t = Z \frac{\phi r}{2l} + \frac{\eta}{2} \frac{d}{dt}\left(\frac{\phi r}{l}\right).$$

The coefficient η is a measure of the internal friction, or viscosity. Some representative values[5] are given in Table III.

TABLE III

VISCOSITY OF VARIOUS SOLIDS

Material	Viscosity ($\times 10^9$ poises)
Silver..................	12.5
Gold....................	17.0
Nickel..................	1.65
Platinum...............	1.75
Tungsten...............	9.37
Zinc....................	411.0
Quartz.................	0.001 (approx.)

If a fiber of length l and radius r is allowed to oscillate in a vacuum with a body of moment of inertia I suspended from the lower end, and if T is the period and λ the logarithmic decrement of the vibration, the coefficient of viscosity in poises is given by

$$\eta = \frac{8Il\lambda}{\pi r^4 T}.$$

If such a torsion pendulum has a period of 2 seconds, it will lose about 10 per cent of its amplitude in 24 hours.

Thus η, as defined above, should be as small as possible if the internal losses are to be kept at a minimum.

---

[5] Honda, K., *Phil. Mag.*, *42*, 115 (1921).
Iida, K., *Bull. Earthquake Res. Inst. of Tokyo University*, *13*, 665 (1935).

Thermal-elastic properties. Both Young's modulus and
the rigidity modulus for fused quartz depend on temperature. Each becomes greater with moderate increase in
temperature. Boys[6] gives the coefficient of Y as 1.3×10^{-4}°C.$^{-1}$, and for Z it is the same. For very accurate work
any instrument using quartz fiber should be calibrated at
more than one temperature.

Hardness. Fused silica has a hardness of 7 on the 1 to 10
scale. It is thus harder than glass and also harder than
most of the metals.

Surface tension of molten silica. If a fiber is heated until
the quartz becomes quite soft, it will tend either to shrink
and enlarge at the point of heating or to pull apart, depending on the tension. We may define the surface tension as the
force per unit of circumference tending to pull the fiber together. This varies with the temperature, but an average
value will be 250 dynes cm^{-1}. In comparison, glass has a
surface tension of 140 to 160 dynes cm^{-1}.

Electrical properties. When fused quartz is clean and dry,
it is probably the best electrical insulator known. For
this reason it is useful in such apparatus as electroscopes and
electrometers, in which leakage must be reduced to a minimum. If used in the open air, quartz covered with the wax
known as ceresin is still better than amber as an insulator.
Care should be taken that the ceresin is that distilled from
the natural mineral and not the synthetic material very often
sold. When it is applied, the temperature of both the quartz
and the ceresin should be from 80° to 100°C. for the first
dip. Thicker coatings can be applied by allowing the
quartz to cool before dipping again.

The absorption of electrical charge, or "soak-in," is extremely low, being less than 10 per cent of that for amber.

The use of quartz in the form of fibers. The remarkable
property of retaining and even increasing its strength as it is
drawn into fine fibers makes the number of applications of

---

[6] Glazebrook, Sir Richard Tetley, editor, *Dictionary of Applied Physics,*
Volume III, page 699. New York: The Macmillan Company, 1922–1923.

quartz to fine instruments many and varied. Few scientists, it seems, have realized and appreciated its values. Stronger than any of the metals used for suspensions, with the exception of tungsten, it has the advantage that it can be made according to the specific requirements. Although some practice is necessary to acquire the proper skill, its acquisition would seem eminently worth while, considering the results that can be obtained.

Equipment useful in making and working with quartz fibers. A description of the torch burning natural gas and oxygen used by the author of this chapter will be given. If other gases are used, it may be necessary to modify the technique given below to meet the specific conditions.

The torch is made from a piece of brass tubing bent into the shape shown in Fig. 1 and having one end threaded for

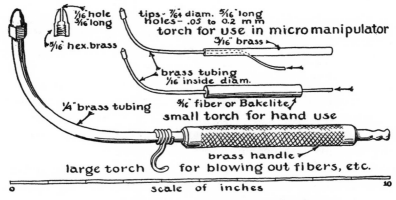

Fig. 1.   Large and small torches for working fused quartz.

removable tips. The best size of opening for quartz work is about 2 mm in diameter. Other sizes of tips from 1 to 3 mm in diameter will be found useful. To produce the necessary long steady flame, the length of the hole in the tip should be at least five times its diameter. The oxygen and gas are mixed at some distance from the torch. An ordinary T is sufficient for this mixing. It is necessary to have a ready means of control for both the gas and the oxygen.

If the latter is under high pressure, a reduction valve in conjunction with a needle valve gives the best regulation. A combination of needle valves and **T** which has been found to give satisfactory service is shown in Fig. 2.

In using such a torch, care should be taken in lighting to turn the gas on first, light it, and then gradually turn the oxygen on until the proper flame is produced. To extinguish the flame, turn the oxygen off slowly and then the gas. Disregard of this procedure may result in a backfire into the line but usually does little damage except to sensitive nerves.

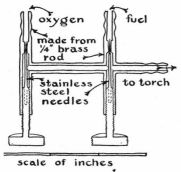

scale of inches

Fig. 2.   Combination of needle valves and mixer.

The described torch is a useful adjunct to any laboratory, especially when supplied with tips of various sizes. It is ideal for working Pyrex glass as well as quartz. When quartz fibers are being made, the torch is held by a clamp so that the flame is vertical.

Indispensable in the working of small pieces of quartz is a small torch shown in Fig. 1, identical with the larger one except for size, and using the same gases, which are controlled by separate fine needle valves. The best metal tubing for this torch is brass or copper $\frac{1}{16}$ inch in internal diameter. The gases are led from the mixer to the torch by $\frac{1}{16}$-inch rubber tubing. Small volumes throughout are important, or much time will be wasted in waiting for a change of gas mixture to arrive at the tip. The tips should be interchangeable and should have openings of from 0.05 to 0.2 mm in diameter. A slight modification of design (illustrated) permits the torch to be mounted and manipulated by mechanical means. The usefulness of this small torch will become apparent later.

In measuring the sizes of fibers, an ordinary microscope equipped with a scale in the eyepiece and having a magnification of from 300 to 1000 is very useful.   With some experience the sizes of fibers can be judged to within 20 to 50 per

cent by the amount of scattered light, the way they weave in the air, and so forth, but in many cases the diameter is important, and an accurate means of determining their size is invaluable.

After blowing out a fine fiber, two places are marked, and the position of the intervening portion is thus determined by small tabs.   Dennison's No. 251 tabs are recommended.

In many instances one works with fibers from a few

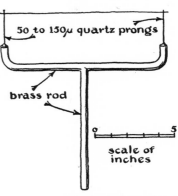

Fig. 3.   A simple fork used for holding fibers while they are being mounted.

centimeters to 10 or even 20 cm in length.   In these cases the fibers are mounted on a two-pronged fork.   This is easily made as shown in the sketch, Fig. 3.   The end of

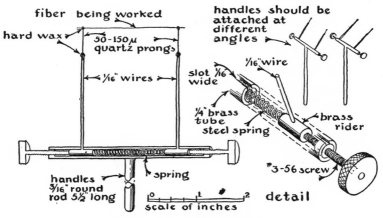

Fig. 4.   Adjustable prong fork.

each prong is drilled, and a piece of quartz (50μ to 150μ) is put in with hard wax.   The reason for the quartz tips is to allow some freedom to the fiber, since the quartz tips will bend if the fiber is pulled one way or the other. Rigid supports result in many more broken fibers. The fiber is fastened to the tips with a small piece of hard wax.

In cases in which one fiber is melted to another, each will shrink, and the quartz will gather at the junction. It is necessary then to have two forks, each with movable prongs.

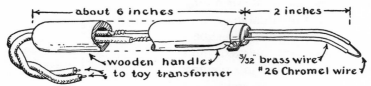

Fig. 5.   Hot-wire holder.

The fork designed according to Fig. 4 has proved very satisfactory. If the handles are attached at different angles, the two forks can be worked together more easily.

A hot wire mounted as in Fig. 5 has many uses and is especially valuable in melting small pieces of wax. The resistance wire can be any one of several, such as platinum, German silver, Chromel, Nichrome, and so forth. It should be 24–26 B and S gauge. A toy transformer with variable voltage of from 1 to 6 volts is convenient for controlling the temperature. A foot switch is very useful, since both hands may be occupied when the heat is wanted.

In testing for conductivity of quartz fibers which have a coating of metal, a probe (see Fig. 6) with a fine platinum

Fig. 6.   Platinum probe for testing conductivity of metal-covered fibers.

wire tip finds a use. For such testing high voltages should not be used, since the resulting sparking will remove the metal from the fiber around the point of contact. Several volts applied through a 100,000-ohm resistance and a low-sensitivity galvanometer will be found satisfactory for qualitative work.

Waxes are indispensable in fastening fibers either temporarily or permanently. For general use Dennison's hard red wax, DeKhotinsky wax, or flake shellac is recommended. If the wax is holding in place two or more fibers which are to have a metal evaporated or sputtered onto them, one of the latter two waxes should be used and heated until polymerization takes place, resulting in a material either difficult or impossible to melt. Otherwise the heat developed during the process of depositing the metal may cause the wax to soften and the fibers to be displaced.

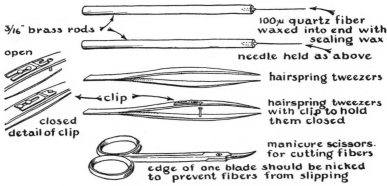

Fig. 7. Various instruments useful in fiber work.

In case it is necessary to hold a fiber temporarily and to maintain its desirable qualities, a wax must be used which, when heated, will completely disappear and not react in any way with the quartz. None of the products sold as waxes serve the purpose. An organic chemical which has the desired properties is diphenylcarbazide. It usually comes in powdered form and should be as pure as possible and especially free from inorganic materials.

In handling small pieces of wax, holding fibers, bending quartz fibers, and so forth, a piece of quartz 100μ in diameter and 2 to 3 cm long, waxed into the end of a metal rod, is very useful. (See Fig. 7.) It will also be found that a needle mounted in the end of a metal rod has many uses. It is recommended that several such quartz and needle holders be available.

When working with small objects, tweezers of various sizes are very convenient. These can be obtained from jeweler's supply houses or from most houses supplying scientific apparatus. For very fine work, watch-hairspring tweezers such as #3C made by Dumont & Fils, Switzerland, are recommended. Also valuable in cutting fibers are small scissors. These may be a good grade of manicure scissors or dissecting scissors used in biological work. A nick should be made in one blade to prevent large fibers from slipping. If the scissors are guided by mechanical means, small fibers (up to 40μ) can be cut off as little as 0.01 mm at a time under a microscope.

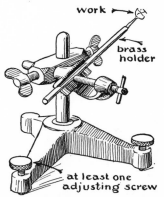

Fig. 8. Support for holding work or fixing the position of fibers.

In most fiber work it is necessary to fix the position of the fiber with some accuracy. Small tripods with adjustable feet, together with clamps and rods, as shown in Fig. 8, will serve to hold the various forks, needles, and so forth, used in the process of mounting the fibers. It is very difficult to hold a fiber still enough by hand, and it is always best to take advantage of mechanical devices wherever possible.

Very small fibers (1μ and less) can be easily seen by scattered light against a black background. Black velvet is one of the best. If the diameter of a fiber is to be measured under the microscope, a light background is needed; the scattered light against black gives a false impression of the size, since the actual outlines of the object cannot be seen.

To put a conducting coat of metal on quartz, any one of several methods can be used. The simplest, and one which is satisfactory for fibers down to 20μ in diameter, is to bake

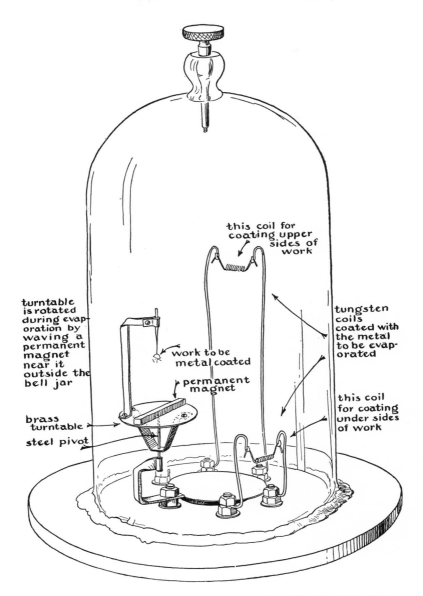

this coil for coating upper sides of work

tungsten coils coated with the metal to be evaporated

turntable is rotated during evaporation by waving a permanent magnet near it outside the bell jar

work to be metal coated

permanent magnet

this coil for coating under sides of work

brass turntable

steel pivot

Fig. 9. This arrangement allows the evaporated metal to be deposited on all sides of the work.

the metal on, using any of the good china paints. Most of the noble metals—for example, platinum, gold, iridium, and so forth—can be obtained in this form. The paint is made by dissolving one of the metal salts in an organic liquid. China painters use this on their dishes and fire them to 700°C. The organic material disappears, and the metal compound decomposes, leaving behind a uniform coating of the metal. The thickness for each coat may vary from 0.05μ to 0.15μ, depending on the thickness of the original paint. Very adherent, electrically conducting coatings can be applied to glazed porcelain, glass, quartz, and so forth. The hot wire, held under small pieces of quartz fibers covered with these solutions, will bake them in a few seconds. If an attempt is made to treat small fibers in this way, it will be found that the solution collects into small drops along the fiber, and a disconnected coating results when it is baked.

Sputtering or evaporating the metal on are the most satisfactory methods and have the advantage that conducting coats can be applied to fibers of any size. In general it is desirable to arrange to coat the fibers on all sides. Evaporation is the easier and simpler of the two methods. (See Chapter III.) A suitable apparatus for this is shown in Fig. 9.

In working quartz it is absolutely necessary to use dark glasses to protect the eyes. Besides the brilliant glow, which in itself is bad for the eyes, the light is very rich in ultraviolet, which is especially harmful and may cause blindness through long exposure. The glasses should be gray in color, preferably, and have a transmission of from 10 to 20 per cent. Ordinary glass will cut out the ultraviolet, so that inexpensive dark glasses will suffice.

The writer has used for some time a set of three micromanipulators. Each has a three-jointed arm, which allows complete freedom in determining the position of the fiber. For fine adjustment, micrometer screws with divided heads give accurate motion in three mutually perpendicular directions. The accompanying illustration, Fig. 10, shows one of the three manipulators.

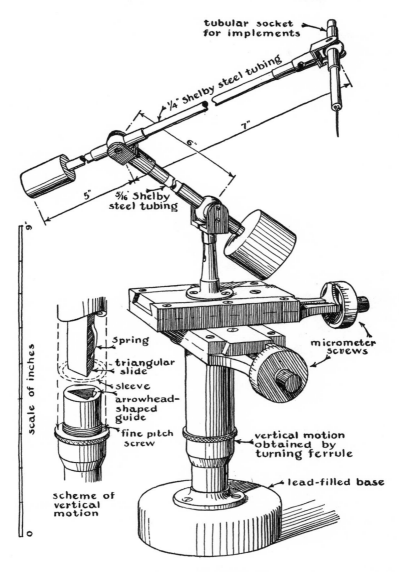

tubular socket
for implements

¼" Shelby steel tubing

7"

6"

5"

9"

scale of inches

0

5⁄16" Shelby
steel tubing

Spring

triangular
slide

sleeve

arrowhead-
shaped
guide

fine pitch
screw

scheme of
vertical
motion

micrometer
screws

vertical motion
obtained by
turning ferrule

lead-filled base

Fig. 10.　Micromanipulator.

Although much of the simpler fiber work can be done with
the unaided eye or with a magnifying glass, for fine work in
which accuracy is important and ease of working is desired
a binocular microscope with a magnification of 15 to 20 can
be strongly recommended.   Such a microscope not only
gives stereoscopic vision but when used properly results in
little, if any, eyestrain.   A scale in one eyepiece allows

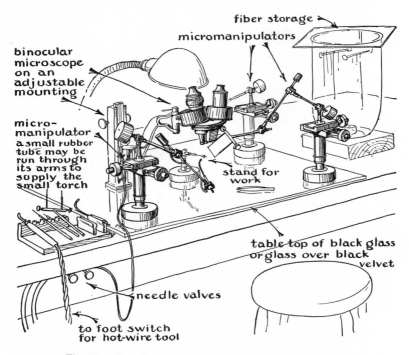

Fig. 11.   Complete assembly for working quartz fibers.

measurements to be made.   Lighting from several directions is desirable to provide proper illumination on the work
in all positions.

A complete setup of the major equipment used by the
writer in quartz fiber work is illustrated in Fig. 11.   The
black glass base permits the fine fiber to be seen easily by
scattered light.   When the actual outlines of large fibers

are to be seen, a piece of white paper is placed on the glass base and used as a background.

Making fibers.   A convenient size of stock quartz rod is 3 to 4 mm in diameter.   Smaller rod than this is apt to break when the larger fibers are being drawn and is not easily held in the hands.   Larger rod becomes more difficult to melt.

The first step in making a fine fiber is to draw one from 50μ to 100μ in diameter.   (See Fig. 12.)   Two pieces of stock

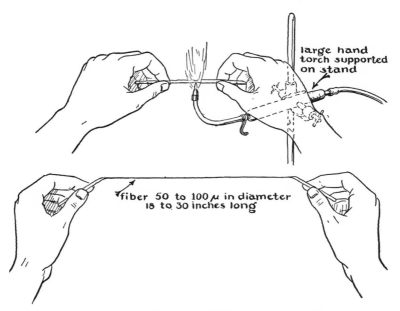

Fig. 12.   The first step in making a small fiber is to draw a larger one.   A very hot flame is used.

quartz of convenient length are held in the hands.   The oxygen-gas flame is adjusted to maximum heat; that is, both the oxygen and gas are increased, especially the oxygen, until a hissing flame results, and the small cone just over the opening in the torch tip has shortened until its height is perhaps two or three times its width.   The hottest portion of the flame is just above this small cone.   The ends of the quartz rod are melted together and then pulled apart a short distance, so that the connecting soft quartz is perhaps 1 mm in diameter.   This portion, when held in the hottest part of the flame, will become quite soft.   The quartz rods are then quickly removed from the flame, and at the same time the two pieces held in the hands are separated rapidly to a distance of several feet. The hotter the narrow section of quartz and the faster the drawing, the smaller will be the resulting fiber. Fibers down to 20μ can be drawn in this manner.

To make a smaller fiber from the larger one, the procedure is as follows: Break the connecting fiber produced in the above drawing process so that a section of 8 to 10 inches is left on each piece of quartz stock.   This section should be stiff enough to support itself in a vertical position. Now adjust the flame by turning the oxygen partially off, so that a steady flame about 15 to 20 inches long is produced.   The cone above the tip will lengthen to several inches.   Holding

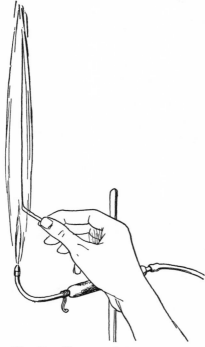

Fig. 13.   The second step in making a small fiber is to blow out the larger fiber by holding it in a long, vertical, relatively cool flame.

the quartz stock so that the attached fiber is vertical, move it into the vertical flame as illustrated in Fig. 13.   The whole length of the fiber will glow uniformly.   If the temperature of the flame and the size of the fiber are right, the fiber will gradually begin to lengthen, slowly at first and then more rapidly as it becomes smaller.   Finally, the upper section of the original fiber will go quickly toward the ceiling.

As soon as this happens, the lower end should be removed from the flame. A careful examination will reveal a fine fiber joining the two ends of the original, perhaps 3 to 6 feet long. Sections of it can be seen in scattered light. Place a small tab on one part of the fine fiber with one hand while holding the stock quartz (to which the other end of the fiber is attached) in the other. The position of the intervening portion is now determined, so that other tabs can be stuck on and suitable lengths removed. Each end of each length will thus have a small tab attached. These fibers are then stored in a clean container in which the air is kept dry. (See Fig. 14.)

The size of the resulting small fiber will depend on a number of factors. Chief among these are the size of the original fiber, the temperature and size of the flame, and the time intervening between the disappearance of the top of the original fiber and the removal of the lower end. Some practice is necessary to secure fibers of a desired size. It will be found that fibers produced in the above manner are straight and of quite uniform diameter for some distance on each side of the center.

A few cautions are necessary if good fibers are to be had. The basis of all of these is cleanliness. Much of the dust on objects around a laboratory and floating in the air is inorganic. If a fiber is heated where a piece of dust has settled, the metallic salts form silicates and in general completely spoil the surface, and for that reason the fiber also, at the point of contact. It is a general rule that no part of a fiber which ultimately is to have any stress applied should ever touch anything except those materials which are softer than the quartz and will not react with it. This may seem to be a stringent requirement, but in reality the fiber can always be handled by its ends, which are eventually discarded.

If the original large fiber shows any bright spots when put into the flame, it should be discarded. In general, this is the best test for dust that can be applied. Dust will immediately show itself by causing a bright spot, and the fiber can be discarded forthwith; if there is no dust on the fiber, it will not be harmed by heating. This test can be made with fibers from 10μ to 100μ with an ordinary Bunsen burner. For smaller ones the small torch using a pure gas flame should be used. In each case the fiber should be under some tension to keep it straight.

If the size of the fiber is to be measured with the microscope, it is usually sufficient to take a sample from each end and take the mean diameter. The sample is placed on a piece of glass, which in turn is placed on the microscope stage and viewed by transmitted light. To find the fiber in the microscope the following procedure is valuable in saving time: Have plenty of light passing through the optical system. Raise the objective until it is several times the working distance from the object. Remove the ocular. Move the glass on which the fiber is lying until, by looking down the microscope tube, the reduced image of the fiber is seen. Adjust the position of the fiber until its image appears approximately in the middle of the objective. Now move the objective down until the image begins to spread. When it appears to cover the objective completely, the object is near the focus, and on replacing the ocular, the image should be in the field of view.

After working with fibers for a while, one can judge their size by the amount of scattered light, the amount of weaving in the air, how much a fiber of a given length sags under its own weight, the radius of curvature when hung over a needle with a tab on one end, and so forth. These methods are good to from 20 to 50 per cent, except for fibers below 1μ to 2μ.

Another method for drawing fibers has been described by Boys.[7] It consists in pulling the two pieces of quartz apart very rapidly by means of a projected arrow. Long fibers down to 10μ of very uniform diameter can be produced in this fashion. The hotter the quartz and the faster the arrow is shot, the finer will be the fiber.

---

[7] *Ibid.*, Volume III, page 696.

The care and preservation of small fibers. When a fiber has its two ends marked with tabs, it should be hung in a clean, dry container. A crosspiece at the top of the container, on which are small pieces of soft wax or beeswax, serves as a hanger. The top tab is pressed into the wax, and the lower tab keeps the fiber from weaving around and touching things.

The container should be 10 to 12 inches deep, airtight, and preferably made from glass. It should be clean and contain a good drying agent —either phosphorous pentoxide or anhydrous potassium hydroxide. A convenient container is made from an inverted bell jar with a plate-glass top as shown in Fig. 14. Fibers deteriorate in moist atmospheres, but can be preserved for months with no change in breaking strength if kept clean and dry.

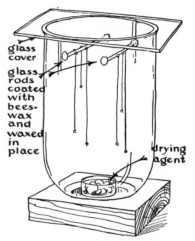

Fig. 14. Preserving quartz fibers.

Some useful techniques in fiber work. *Straightening.* Fibers from 10μ to 500μ can be quickly and easily straightened by hanging a weight on the lower end and running a Bunsen burner flame up and down the piece several times. The weight should be somewhat less than that necessary to elongate the fiber appreciably under the heat of the flame. A small Dennison tab is sufficient for fibers 10μ to 50μ and a $\frac{1}{2}$-inch tab for those between 50μ and 500μ. For fibers from 4μ to 10μ a small Dennison tab should be cut in two and the small torch burning pure gas used for heat.

Bending. Fibers from 40μ on up are best bent by hanging a weight such as a tab at one end, holding the fiber at the proper angle, and applying the heat locally with a small torch burning oxygen and gas. The piece between the flame and the tab will fall to a vertical position as shown in Fig. 15.

Fibers between 1μ and 40μ are best bent over another piece of quartz. A weight such as part or all of a small tab or a small piece of wax bends the fiber over the larger piece of quartz (100μ or less). A pure gas flame applied with the small torch at the contact of the two fibers will bend the

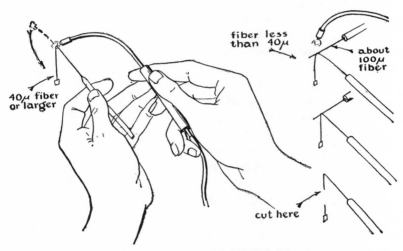

Fig. 15.   Bending large and small fibers.

smaller one over the larger. The flame should not be applied longer than is necessary, or the two pieces of quartz are apt to stick together.

Drawing and shrinking. If one end of a fiber is attached to a screw-controlled sliding mechanism, such as the movable prong fork described earlier, a portion of it may be readily drawn down to any desired size by applying a flame with the small torch and gradually screwing out one prong.

Soft quartz has a high surface tension, and fibers tend to shrink when heated. The heating is done with the small torch. It is necessary to have a properly adjusted flame. A compromise must be made between a hot flame with swiftly rushing gases, which readily melts and blows the fibers apart, and a cooler flame, which will not soften the quartz sufficiently. The ideal is reached when the tendency to blow away is overcome by the tendency to pull together due to surface tension. The fiber is heated in a slackened condition, and as the shrinkage proceeds it is fed by the movable prongs. A torch tip with a hole about 0.1 mm in diameter is perhaps the best. With some practice a fiber may be locally enlarged to many times its previous diameter. (See Fig. 16.)

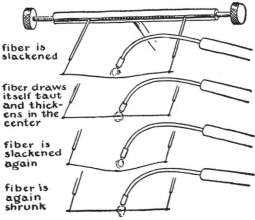

fiber is slackened

fiber draws itself taut and thickens in the center

fiber is slackened again

fiber is again shrunk

Fig. 16. Shrinking a small fiber.

Joining one fiber to another. When the above technique has been learned, the joining of two fibers crossing one another becomes simple. Each shrinks to the common junction, forming a joint which is stronger than any other portion. For this work it is necessary to use two of the forks with movable prongs, gradually feeding in the quartz as the joint grows in size.

Joining a fiber to a larger piece of quartz. If the larger piece is too large to melt locally with the small torch, a "teat" is put on at the proper place with a larger torch and then drawn down to a fine point. The fiber, mounted on the fork, is placed next to this teat, and heat is applied to the teat. Upon softening, the larger piece of quartz draws the small fiber in by surface tension. Straightening of the fiber near the junction is done by heating with the small torch burning pure gas when the fiber is under a slight tension.

With care, fibers as small as 1μ in diameter can be melted to other fibers or larger pieces of quartz.

Drawing an oval fiber.   The tip of each piece of the stock quartz is heated in the oxygen-gas flame so that only the

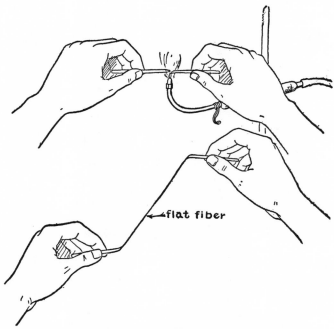

Fig. 17.   Making a flat fiber.

very end becomes soft.   With the axes of the two pieces held parallel, the ends are brought together and immediately separated at right angles to the axes of the stock quartz, and at the same time they are removed from the flame. (See Fig. 17.)   Only flat fibers larger than 30μ to 40μ can be produced in this fashion.   They are useful in vibration types of pressure gauges in which the motion is to be limited to one plane.

Drawing flat tubing. In some cases quartz is useful in making the Bourdon type of pressure gauge. If a long piece of flat tubing is made into a spiral and a mirror and scale are used to measure the change in angle, such a gauge becomes an accurate means of measuring moderate pressures. One way to produce long pieces of elliptically shaped thin-walled tubing is to use two large torches as cross-fires and to heat $\frac{1}{2}$- to $\frac{3}{4}$-inch quartz tubing without rotation. Heating should continue until the walls nearest the flame are quite soft. The tubing is removed from the flame and rapidly pulled to 3 or 4 feet. If heating has not been sufficient, the elongated occluded bubbles will cause the resultant tubing to be brittle. It is, in fact, a good procedure to work the heated section by alternately enlarging and contracting it with internal pressure before drawing. The oval tubing is bent into the desired shape with a moderately hot flame.

Making electrometer suspensions. Quartz fibers make ideal suspensions for electrometers. The most satisfactory way

Fig. 18.   Design of quartz fiber support used in the Dolezalek and Compton electrometers.   The whole is made from fused quartz, upon which is deposited a coating of metal, for example, gold or platinum.

of making the suspensions consists in joining the ends of the fiber to two larger pieces of quartz by melting them together with a small torch. In many cases these larger pieces are bent into small hooks, and then the whole is made conducting by evaporating or sputtering gold or some other metal on it as represented in Fig. 18.   In cases in which hooks cannot be used, the larger quartz is left straight and is cemented into place with a hard wax such as DeKhotinsky's. Contact is made by attaching a fine wire to the quartz with hard wax before the fiber is coated with the metal. The wire is later soldered to the metal pieces of the electrometer.

The method of soldering the metal-coated fibers does not produce a suspension as permanent as with the methods described above. The gold is apt to amalgamate with the solder and result in a poor contact between the main portion of the fiber and the solder.

Another method of fastening fibers to metal parts and at the same time making an electrical contact is to use colloidal graphite. A small drop is placed at the proper point, and in a short while the water will evaporate, leaving a strong conducting joint.

Quartz is very convenient for making various types of electroscopes. It is not only good for the moving parts but is used uncoated for insulation.[8]

Mounting cross hairs in optical instruments. Fibers made from quartz surpass any other material for cross hairs. Owing to the refraction of the light by the fiber, it appears black as seen in a bright field. Its essential smoothness, freedom from dust, uniformity of size, straightness, and the fact that it can be drawn to any desired diameter make it especially valuable.

The mounting is first prepared by melting hard wax onto it at the desired points. The fiber is mounted on a fork and

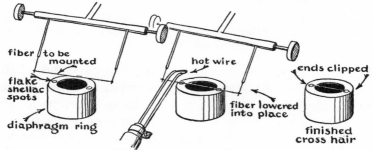

Fig. 19.   Steps in mounting cross hairs for microscope and telescope eyepieces.

lowered into position. A hot wire brought near the wax where the stretched fiber rests will allow the fiber to sink in and become firmly attached. The various steps are illustrated in Fig. 19.

Torsion balance. For objects weighing less than 1 mg the torsion balance becomes very useful. It is not difficult

---

[8] See Chapter VI, "Electrometers and Electroscopes."

to make a balance having a sensitivity of 10^{-7} to 10^{-9} g/div. without the use of mirrors or microscopes. A simple calculation will show the size of fiber necessary for the specific requirements. The crossarm should be statically balanced. The amount of twist of the fiber is conveniently read from a divided head.

The balance may be calibrated by weighing on an analytical balance a long section of fine wire such as 40 B and S

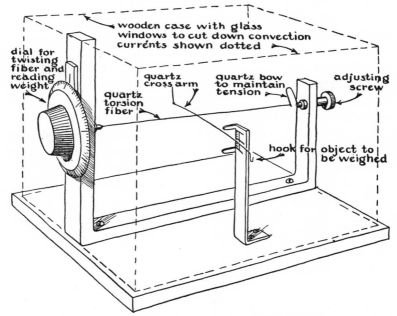

Fig. 20.   Simple design of a quartz microbalance.

gauge copper, 2-mil nickel, or smaller if needed, and cutting from this piece samples of a given length. Usually ten samples will give a probable error of less than 1 per cent in the calibration. If the tension in the torsion fiber is kept constant with a quartz bow, it can be assumed with much accuracy that the twist is proportional to the weight. Since $\phi r/l$ is the surface strain, where r is the radius of the torsion fiber, ϕ the angle of twist in radians, and l the length twisted, and since the maximum value of this is about 0.05, the maximum load which the balance can handle is easily computed. A simple design of such a torsion balance is shown in Fig. 20.

If all the joints are made of fused quartz, there need be no fear of a changing "zero," since the limit of elasticity coincides with the breaking point.

Other uses of quartz. Quartz rod or fiber is often used as a carrier of light—visible, ultraviolet, or infrared. Internal reflections keep the light inside the quartz and permit it to be led around corners, provided the corners are not too sharp.

In many cases in which accuracy in maintaining shape or position is important, quartz finds a use. All metals change their dimensions with time, especially when under strain. This change can be lessened by thorough annealing, which consists in subjecting the metal alternately to temperatures above and below room temperature. In extreme cases this treatment may take days or weeks. Annealed fused quartz does not suffer from changes in dimensions, since the flow under strain is less than 10^{-3} of that for metals.

Fused quartz is finding increasing uses in lamps of various kinds in which the transmission of ultraviolet light is important. For the same reason many photoelectric cells are made from quartz.

Although the above does not pretend to be an exhaustive list of the uses to which fused silica can be put, it is hoped that the reader will gain some idea of the usefulness of this material.

CHAPTER VI

Electrometers and Electroscopes

BY

H. V. NEHER

Definitions. It is not always clear just what distinguishes an electrometer from an electroscope, and there seems to be some confusion in the literature. For purposes of this discussion the following distinction will be made: An electroscope is an electrostatic measuring device in which only one potential difference is needed for its operation. Electrometers, on the other hand, need auxiliary potentials for their operation. The familiar gold-leaf electroscope and the quadrant electrometer are respective examples.

General theory.[1] Expressed in terms of Maxwell's coefficients, the electrostatic energy of any system of conductors at potentials V_1, V_2, ... V_n is given by[2]

$$W = \tfrac{1}{2}(c_{11}V_1{}^2 + 2c_{12}V_1V_2 + \ldots) = \tfrac{1}{2}\Sigma QV, \tag{1}$$

where the coefficients of capacity, c_{11}, c_{12}, c_{13}, and so forth, are given by

$$\left. \begin{aligned} Q_1 &= c_{11}V_1 + c_{12}V_2 + \ldots c_{1n}V_n, \\ &\vdots \\ Q_n &= c_{n1}V_1 + c_{n2}V_2 + \ldots c_{nn}V_n, \end{aligned} \right\} \tag{2}$$

the Q's being the charges on the conductors. The coefficients have the properties that $c_{ij} = c_{ji}$. c_{11} is the charge which is on conductor 1 when all the other bodies are grounded and

---

[1] This treatment follows, in general, that given by Hoffmann, G., in *Handbuch der Exp. Physik*, X, 42 (1928). Wein, W., and Harms, F., editors; Leipzig.

[2] Jeans, J. H., *Mathematical Theory of Electricity and Magnetism*, Fifth Edition, page 95. New York: The Macmillan Company

1 has a potential of unity. Similarly c_{12} is the charge induced on 1 when all the other bodies are grounded and unit potential is placed on 2.

If the c's are functions of a coördinate ξ and the V's are kept constant, then the force or torque tending to increase ξ is

$$\frac{\partial W}{\partial \xi} = \frac{1}{2}\left(\frac{\partial c_{11}}{\partial \xi}V_1{}^2 + 2\frac{\partial c_{12}}{\partial \xi}V_1 V_2 + \ \ldots\ \right). \tag{3}$$

In all instruments this electrical force or torque is balanced by some restoring force. If we know how the c's and the restoring force depend on ξ, then with the help of Eq. 3 we can solve for the voltage sensitivity.

Since most electroscopes and electrometers are used to measure electric charge, it is the charge sensitivity in which we are interested, although the voltage sensitivity is the more easily measured.

Referring back to Eq. 2, let i be the moving system. The charge sensitivity, S_Q, is given by

$$\frac{1}{S_Q} = \frac{\partial Q_i}{\partial \xi} = c_{i1}\frac{\partial V_1}{\partial \xi} + V_1\frac{\partial c_{i1}}{\partial \xi} + \ \ldots, \tag{4}$$

since both the c's and the V's are, in general, each functions of the coördinate.

Applications to electroscopes. The above theory when applied to electroscopes becomes very simple. In this instance we have but two conductors, usually one completely surrounding the other. Let the case be grounded. Then Eq. 1 becomes merely $W = \frac{1}{2}cV^2$, where c is the capacity of the electroscope system to the case. c must be a function of the displacement and in most instances can be considered a linear function, that is, $c = c_0 + b\xi$. For this case Eq. 3 becomes $\partial W/\partial \xi = \frac{1}{2}bV^2$. If this is balanced by a force proportional to the displacement, then $k\xi = \frac{1}{2}bV^2$, and the voltage sensitivity is

$$S_V = \frac{1}{\dfrac{\partial V}{\partial \xi}} = \frac{bV}{k}. \tag{5}$$

From Eq. 4, the charge sensitivity, S_Q, is given by

$$\frac{1}{S_Q} = c\frac{\partial V}{\partial \xi} + V\frac{\partial c}{\partial \xi}. \tag{6}$$

Now $\partial V/\partial \xi$ is given by Eq. 5, and $\partial c/\partial \xi = b$ if c is a linear function of ξ. Therefore

$$S_Q = \frac{bV}{ck + V^2b^2}. \tag{7}$$

For most electroscopes, b^2V^2 is small compared with ck, so that we can usually write

$$S_Q = \frac{bV}{ck} = \frac{S_V}{c}. \tag{8}$$

This last relationship between the voltage and charge sensitivities is the usual assumption made when working with electroscopes.

However, b^2V^2 need not be small compared with ck, and it is interesting to see what follows in such a case. It will be seen that Eq. 7 has a maximum value when $V_0^2b^2 = ck$, and under these conditions

$$(S_Q)_{\text{max.}} = \frac{1}{2}(ck)^{-1/2} = \frac{1}{2V_0b}.$$

The effective capacity has increased to

$$c_{\text{eff.}} = \frac{\dfrac{\partial Q}{\partial \xi}}{\dfrac{\partial V}{\partial \xi}} = 2c.$$

Any further increase in the voltage sensitivity results in a more rapidly increasing capacity and a decrease in charge sensitivity.

These conditions more aptly apply to electrometers and will be discussed in that connection in the following section.

Applications to electrometers. All electrometers can be considered as made from three conductors, two of which are stationary and usually similar, while the third is movable. All three are connected electrically to the outside of the instrument. We shall assume in the following discussion that the charge or potential to be measured is applied to the movable system, while the two stationary parts are maintained at equal and opposite potentials. This arrangement is not necessary, and in general the following discussion holds equally well for the case when the charge or potential to be measured is applied to a stationary part and the moving system is kept at the high potential. It is further assumed that the electrical and mechanical zeros of the instrument coincide. This last condition is fulfilled if, while the movable system is grounded with equal and opposite potentials applied to the stationary parts, no deflection takes place.

Of the twenty-seven terms in Eq. 3, twenty-five are small or zero, as compared with the remaining two under the above conditions. If the moving part is symmetrical with respect to the stationary parts, then these two terms are equal, and Eq. 3 becomes

$$\frac{\partial W}{\partial \xi} = V_1 V_3 \frac{\partial c_{13}}{\partial \xi},$$

where c_{13} is the capacity between the moving system and one of the stationary parts, which is at a potential V_1, while V_3 is the potential of the moving system.

Case I. In general, c_{13} will be a complicated function of ξ. This is especially true in the case of most string electrometers, but with the Hoffmann and Dolezalek the dependence of the capacity on the displacement is approximately linear. For these instruments $c_{13} = c_{13}{}^0 + b\theta$, and the torque becomes

$$L = V_1 V_3 b. \tag{9}$$

In equilibrium, $L = k\theta$, where k is the torsion constant of the suspension. It will be noticed that Eq. 9 is symmetrical in V_1 and V_3, so that the sensitivity is the same whether the stationary or the moving parts are at the fixed potential. Assuming that the stationary parts are kept at a fixed potential, the voltage sensitivity is

$$S_V = \frac{V_1 b}{k}. \tag{10}$$

The charge on the moving system, 3, becomes

$$Q_3 = c_{13}V_1 + c_{23}V_2 + c_{33}V_3.$$

Now the moving system is connected to a suspension which in turn is connected to an external capacity. Let the sum of these two capacities be denoted by c_e. If a charge q is placed on the system, then $Q_3 = q - V_3c_e$, and we have

$$q = c_{13}V_1 + c_{23}V_2 + (c_e + c_{33})V_3$$

and

$$\frac{1}{S_q} = \frac{\partial q}{\partial \theta} = c_{13}\frac{\partial V_1}{\partial \theta} + V_1\frac{\partial c_{13}}{\partial \theta} + c_{23}\frac{\partial V_2}{\partial \theta} + V_2\frac{\partial c_{23}}{\partial \theta} + (c_e + c_{33})\frac{\partial V_3}{\partial \theta} + V_3\frac{\partial c_{33}}{\partial \theta}.$$

Now c_{33}, to the desired approximation, is not dependent on θ, and $\partial c_{13}/\partial \theta = -\partial c_{23}/\partial \theta = b$. Also $V_2 = -V_1$ and $\partial V_1/\partial \theta = \partial V_2/\partial \theta = 0$. The charge sensitivity becomes

$$S_q = \frac{V_1 b}{2V_1^2 b^2 + (c_e + c_{33})k}.$$

$(c_e + c_{33})$ may be lumped into one quantity c, which is the electrostatic capacity of the electrometer and external system when the stationary pieces are grounded. Hence

$$S_q = \frac{V_1 b}{2V_1^2 b^2 + ck}. \tag{11}$$

This has a maximum value at $V_0 = (1/b)(ck/2)^{1/2}$, and this is the value of V_1 which should, if possible, be used on the binants or the quadrants,

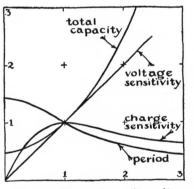

Fig. 1. The total capacity, voltage sensitivity, charge sensitivity, and period (ordinates) of an ideal electrometer in terms of their values at the optimum value of the plate potential. The plate potential is measured along the abscissa, and its optimum value is taken as unity. See W. W. Hansen, *R.S.I.*, 7, 182 (1936).

as the case may be, if high charge sensitivity is wanted. This makes $(S_q)_{\max.} = \frac{1}{2}(2ck)^{-1/2} = 1/(4V_0b)$. Any further increase in V_1 will increase the voltage sensitivity but will decrease the charge sensitivity. The behavior of the total capacity, voltage sensitivity, charge sensitivity, and period, as the auxiliary potentials are changed, is shown in Fig. 1.

Experimentally, the proper value of V_1 is easily determined, as will be seen from what follows. The effective capacity is

$$c_{\text{eff.}} = \frac{\partial Q}{\partial \theta} \cdot \frac{1}{\dfrac{\partial V}{\partial \theta}} = 2c$$

at the optimum value of V_1. The procedure is as follows: Determine the electrostatic capacity of the suspension and

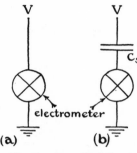

moving system, together with any permanently connected capacity such as an ion chamber. Call this total c. Compare the deflection of the electrometer when a potential V is applied with that obtained when the same potential is applied through a known capacity c_s as shown in Fig. 2. Then when the ratio of the deflections in the two cases is

Fig. 2. A method for determining the effective capacity of an electrometer in terms of a standard capacity, c_s.

$$\frac{\theta_1}{\theta_2} = \frac{2c + c_s}{c_s},$$

V_1 has the proper value.

The period may also be computed. When there is no net charge on the electrometer and when potentials are on the binants or quadrants, let the system be deflected through an angle θ by some external means and then allowed to vibrate. By Eq. 11,

$$2V_1 b + c\frac{\partial V_3}{\partial \theta} = 0,$$

and

$$V_3 = -\frac{2V_1 b}{c}\theta.$$

The electrical torque from Eq. 9 is therefore

$$L = -\frac{2V_1^2 b^2}{c}\theta.$$

Now the resultant torque is

$$- \frac{2V_1^2 b^2 \theta}{c} - k\theta,$$

the equation of motion becomes

$$I \frac{d^2\theta}{dt^2} = - \left(\frac{2V_1^2 b^2}{c} + k \right)\theta,$$

and the period is

$$T = 2\pi \sqrt{\frac{I}{\dfrac{2V_1^2 b^2}{c} + k}},$$

where I is the moment of inertia of the moving system. Now at the optimum value of V_1, $2V_1^2 b^2 = ck$, and hence the corresponding period is

$$T = 2\pi \sqrt{\frac{I}{2k}}. \tag{12}$$

In other words the period has become 40 per cent less than when no potentials are applied. The maximum charge sensitivity in terms of the period, capacity, and moment of inertia of the system becomes

$$(S_q)_{\text{max.}} = \frac{T}{2\pi}(cI)^{-1/2}. \tag{13}$$

Case II. If the coefficients c_{13} and c_{23} are quadratic functions of the displacement, that is, if

$$c_{13} = c_{13}{}^0 + b\theta + g\theta^2,$$

the values of the voltage and charge sensitivities are as follows:

$$S_V = \frac{V_1 b}{k - 2gV_1 V_3},$$

or

$$S_V = \frac{V_1 b}{k} \left(1 + \frac{2g\theta}{b} \right),$$

and

$$S_q = \frac{V_1(b + 2g\theta)}{2V_1^2(b + 2g\theta)^2 + ck}.$$

The optimum value of V_1 is given by

$$V_0 = \frac{1}{b + 2g\theta}\left(\frac{ck}{2}\right)^{1/2}$$

and

$$(S_q)_{max.} = \tfrac{1}{2}(2ck)^{-1/2}.$$

This last is just what was obtained when the dependence of the capacity between the moving and stationary parts was a linear function of the displacement.

The effective capacity at the maximum charge sensitivity is the same as in the simpler case, namely, twice the pure electrostatic capacity.

The total torque may be written as

$$L = -\left(k + \frac{2V_1^2b^2}{c}\right)\theta - \frac{6V_1^2bg\theta^2}{c}.$$

If g is positive, then the electrometer has what is known as positive control, while if g is negative, it has negative control. In the latter case the net torque may become zero at some point of the deflection, in which case the instrument becomes unstable. This frequently occurs when the sensitivity is high and is especially true with string electrometers, limiting the useful range to deflections near the midpoint. The period becomes longer if g is negative and will become longer the greater the amplitude of vibration.

It will be seen from the characteristics of the instrument in Case II that they are not so desirable as those in Case I, since they depend on the amount of displacement. However, there may be other advantages which make instruments of the second type more desirable, such as portability, ease of operation, and so forth. It should be borne in mind also that the above theory contains many simplifying assumptions, and the actual behavior of the instrument in some cases may be quite different. The chief differences are due to (1) a more complicated dependence of the capacity, between the stationary and moving parts, on the displacement and (2) air damping of the moving system. It is important to realize that where electrical charge is to be measured, there is an optimum value of the potential applied to the stationary parts for which the charge sensitivity has either an optimum or a maximum value, and that there is experimentally an easy way to test for such a condition.

Some types of electroscopes. The familiar gold-leaf electroscope is made either with a vertical stationary metal piece and a single strip of gold leaf fastened near the top, or with two gold leaves mutually repelling each other as shown in Fig. 3. The lead-in is insulated from the metal box with an amber or sulphur bushing. The capacity will be from 3 to 5 cm and the potential necessary to give a 45° deflection will be from 300 to 500 volts. When the leaf is observed with a microscope or a telescope, it becomes a quantitative instrument and will serve many purposes where high charge sensitivity is not important. The technique of mounting the gold leaves will be discussed at the end of this chapter.

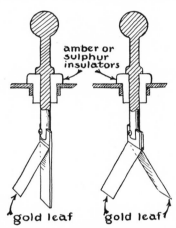

Fig. 3. Two types of gold-leaf electroscopes.

The Wilson tilted electroscope, designed by C. T. R. Wilson[3] and G. W. C. Kaye,[4] is a hybrid of the electroscope and the electrometer. The narrow gold leaf in Fig. 4(a) hangs normally in a downward position, and is observed by means of a microscope with a micrometer ocular. A potential of about 200 volts is applied to the plate. This plate is adjustable; that is, it can be moved in or out along the axis of its support. The proximity of the plate and the

[3] Wilson, C. T. R., *Cambridge Phil. Soc., Proc., 12*, 135 (1903).

[4] Kaye, G. W. C., *Phys. Soc., Proc., 23*, 209 (1911).

This instrument is made by Cambridge Scientific Instrument Company, Ltd., Cambridge, England.

potential applied to it give an electrostatic control which tends to neutralize the effect of gravity on the leaf.

Three cases in general may be cited for the voltage sensitivity as shown in Fig. 4(b): Case I, where there is little electrostatic control and the voltage sensitivity is linear over the entire scale; Case II, where the leaf is stable over the whole range but the electrostatic control is almost sufficient to neutralize the effect of gravity over part of the

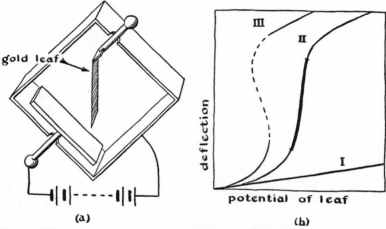

Fig. 4.   Schematic diagram of the Wilson tilted electrometer and some typical sensitivity curves.

range; Case III, where there is an unstable region and consequently two "zeros." Case II is the most useful, and if deflections are taken over the same regions of the scale, there is no trouble about nonlinearity.

The Wilson tilted electroscope, while it may find a use in some types of work, has been largely displaced by more modern instruments, such as quadrant and string electrometers.

The Wülf bifilar electroscope[5] has frequently been used in cosmic-ray work. It is well suited for a portable instru-

[5] This instrument can be obtained from E. Leybold's Nachfolger A. G. Köln-Bayental, Bonner Strasse 500, Germany.

ment but must be read in a fixed position. As is the case with most electroscopes, not only the reading but also the calibration is affected by tilting the instrument. It is usually enclosed in an airtight ionization chamber, in which the gas pressure is often increased to increase the number of ions formed by a given radiation. The charge is renewed on the electroscope either by a mechanical arm working through an airtight bushing in the wall or, what is better, by an internal arm operated by an electromagnet.

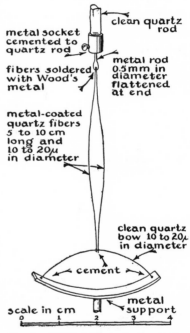

The construction of the electroscope proper is shown in Fig. 5. A clean quartz rod is cemented into the metal piece which holds a short 0.5-mm rod by means of a set-screw. The small rod is flattened at the lower end. Two metal-coated straight quartz fibers from 5 to 10 cm long and from 10μ to 20μ in diameter are cemented or soldered (with Wood's metal) to the flattened piece. The lower ends of the two fibers are cemented side by side

Fig. 5. Wülf bifilar electroscope.

to an insulating quartz bow made from 10μ to 20μ fiber. It is essential that the fibers, when uncharged, hang parallel to each other. Means of straightening quartz fiber will be found in Chapter V. If shellac is used as a cement, there will be sufficient conductivity from the metal to the fibers. The potential of 200 to 400 volts is applied to the upper metal support. If the fibers are 20μ in diameter and 8 cm long, a spread of 3 mm will be produced by about 300 volts. The capacity will be in the neighborhood of 1 cm.

The plane of motion of the fibers should be perpendicular to the optical axis of the microscope, the necessary adjustment being made by rotating the piece held by the setscrew.

It is possible to increase the sensitivity of the Wülf electroscope either by increasing the magnification of the microscope or by decreasing the diameter of the fibers. However, this is limited by the fact that the collecting potential for the ions should not drop too low, depending on the nature of the gas and its pressure. It is customary to have a collecting potential of not less than 100 volts.

From Eq. 8 the charge sensitivity is

$$S_Q = \frac{S_V}{c},$$

and if n is the average number of ions per second collected from each cubic centimeter of the gas, then

$$n = \frac{c}{ev} S_V \frac{d\xi}{dt},$$

where v is the volume of the ion chamber and e is the charge on the ions. The capacity c will vary with the spread of the fibers. The determination of c for different displacements amounts to the determination of b in $c = c_0 + b\xi$.

Regener's electroscope is a single-fiber type shown in Fig. 6. The conducting quartz fiber or Wollaston wire is mounted near a metal piece and is held taut by a fine bow. The whole is supported by a quartz insulator, and the charge is renewed in a way similar to that used with the Wülf type.

Lauritsen has used a small quartz-fiber electroscope with much success not only in small pocket dose-meters for

metal-coated quartz
supporting bow

clean quartz
supporting
rod

metal socket
cemented to
quartz rod

metal-
coated
quartz
fiber or
Wollaston
wire

metal

quartz bow
same as
above

Fig. 6. Regener's electroscope.

X-ray work but also in measuring radiations found in nuclear investigations.   Its outstanding feature is its simplicity. A wire is flattened at one end and bent over at right angles. A 5μ (0.005-mm) metal-coated quartz fiber about 6 mm long is cemented to this flat piece with shellac or colloidal graphite, making an angle with the wire support as shown in Fig. 7. A short piece of the same size fiber is cemented to the end of the longer fiber, at right angles to the plane of the wire and to the first fiber.   This added piece is to form an index for viewing with a microscope.   The wire support is mounted in an amber insulator, which in turn is mounted on the end

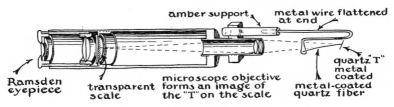

Fig. 7.   Lauritsen's electroscope.

of the microscope.   When the electroscope is used inside an ionization chamber, contact is made by a movable arm to the base of the metal support.

In order to obtain reliable readings on cosmic rays in airplanes, a torsion type of electroscope was developed in 1932. It was necessary to have a self-recording instrument of high sensitivity, the readings of which would not be affected by tilt or vibration of the plane.   As far as tilt is concerned, this effect on the readings can be reduced to less than 0.001 of the total deflection for a tilt of 90°.   As for vibration, satisfactory readings have been obtained with the electroscope mounted within 3 feet of the engine in a pursuit airplane.

A drawing of the electroscope is reproduced in Fig. 8. It is made entirely of fused quartz.   The torsion fiber is stretched until its length is increased about 1 per cent. The crossarm is bent at right angles at one end and, in case high magnification is used, it is drawn down to a convenient size.   A short bit of fiber serves as a fiducial mark.   The shapes of the stationary parts combine to give a linear scale over most of the range of discharge. A piece of platinum cemented to the quartz with a polymerizing cement is the point at which a new charge is placed on the system. With a very small oxygen-gas flame all joints are fused together so that the whole system becomes essentially one piece of

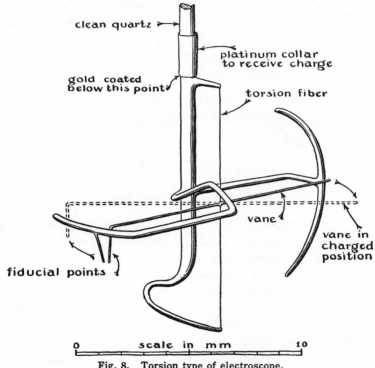

clean quartz

platinum collar to receive charge

gold coated below this point

torsion fiber

vane

vane in charged position

fiducial points

0   scale in mm   10

Fig. 8.   Torsion type of electroscope.

quartz. The system from the platinum down is covered with a conducting layer of gold. The vane is balanced by cutting off one end. For many applications this balancing need not be done with great care and, in fact, becomes rather delicate if a very fine torsion fiber is used. If too much is cut off, mass can be added by applying some thin gold china paint[6] and heating it with a hot wire.

[6] See Chapter V.

In general it will be necessary to put a permanent twist in the torsion fiber. This can be done by forcing the vane beyond the stop through the desired angle, relieving the tension by pushing on the bow at the bottom, and heating the fiber at each end with a small pure gas flame. This will soften the quartz just enough. The twist, of course, must be put in before the system is covered with its conducting coating of metal. The following illustration gives some idea of how much twist is needed: With a torsion fiber 5μ in diameter and 12 mm long and a crossarm or vane 18 mm long, if a 30° twist is put in the fiber, the deflection will begin at about 200 volts and the sensitivity will be about 2×10^{-3} radian/volt. The electrostatic capacity will be about 0.5 cm and the charge sensitivity about 1.2 radians/statcoulomb.

Assuming a rigidity modulus of 5×10^{11} dynes cm^{-2}, the torsion constant comes out 1×10^{-2} dyne cm radian^{-1} under the above specifications, and b (see Eq. 5) has a value of

$$b = \frac{S_V k}{V} = 0.6 \times 10^{-2} \text{ cm radian}^{-1}$$

with $V = 1$ statvolt. Since b is a geometrical quantity, it will not depend on the size of the torsion fiber. The above relation may be used to get an approximation to the sensitivity for other values of the torsion constant k.

If a very fine torsion fiber is used, in order to keep the collecting voltage up it may be necessary to twist the torsion fiber around one or more times. If the crossarm is not larger than 20μ in diameter, this can be done manually after the conducting coat has been put on by using a needle and forcing the ends through, between the torsion fiber and the main quartz support.

Some types of electrometers. The Dolezalek quadrant electrometer[7] is perhaps the most common type and the most useful. The general plan of the instrument is shown in

---

[7] This instrument is made by many firms, including the Cambridge Scientific Instrument Company, Ltd., Cambridge, England, the Cambridge and Paul Instrument Company, Ltd., and E. Leybold's Nachfolger A. G. Köln-Bayental, Bonner Strasse 500, Germany.

Fig. 9. It consists of a cylindrical box, or "pillbox," divided into four equal and insulated quadrants. Opposite quadrants are connected together. There are two ways of using quadrant electrometers. One is to keep the needle at the high potential with respect to ground and apply the

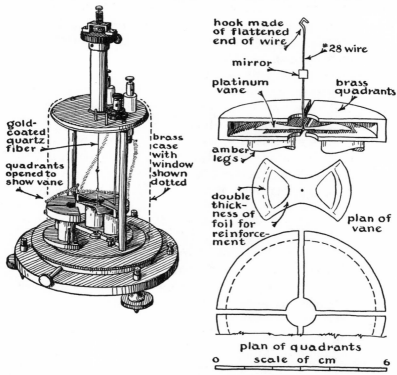

Fig. 9.   Dolezalek quadrant electrometer.

charge to be measured to one pair of quadrants while the other pair is grounded. The other way is to maintain one pair of quadrants at the potential $+V$ and the other at $-V$ and place the charge to be measured on the needle. The first method is illustrated in Fig. 10(a). V will usually be from 50 to 150 volts, depending on the desired sensitivity.

For the second case the battery connections can be those shown in Fig. 10(b), where the main batteries furnish only a potential and slight adjustments are made by a potentiometer as shown. Or the main batteries may be placed across the high resistances R and R, and adjustments are made with the potentiometer R', as represented in Fig. 10(c). The former circuit has the advantage that the life of the high-voltage batteries is essentially their shelf life, while the chief advantage of the second is that $|+V_1|$ always equals $|-V_1|$ and that the mechanical and electrical zeros remain together once they are made to coincide. However, modern "B" batteries maintain a remarkably constant potential at no current over long periods of time and have a very low temperature coefficient, so that in many cases the first circuit can be used.

An approximation can be made to the value b for the Dolezalek electrometer in terms of the geometry of the instrument. It will be seen that the vane is of such shape that the capacity between the vane and the box, as a deflection takes place, varies linearly with the change of angle. Let θ

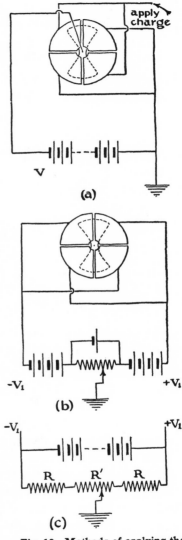

Fig. 10. Methods of applying the fixed potentials to the quadrant electrometer.

be the deflection, R the radius of the vane, h the distance of the vane from one side of the box, and d the depth of the box.

Then b is the increase of capacity between the vane and the conductor into which it moves per unit of angle, or

$$b = \frac{R^2 d}{8\pi h(d - h)}.$$

Since there is an equal and opposite vane on the other side, the total electrical torque, by Eq. 9, is

$$L = \frac{V_1 V_3 R^2 d}{4\pi h(d - h)},$$

which at equilibrium is equal to $k\theta$.   The voltage sensitivity is then

$$S_V = \frac{V_1 R^2 d}{4\pi hk(d - h)}, \tag{14}$$

and the charge sensitivity is

$$S_q = \frac{2\pi V_1 R^2 hd(d - h)}{(V_1 R^2 d)^2 + 8\pi^2 ckh^2(d - h)^2}. \tag{15}$$

At the optimum value of V_1,

$$V_0 = \frac{4\pi h(d - h)}{R^2 d}\left(\frac{ck}{2}\right)^{1/2}$$

and the maximum charge sensitivity becomes

$$(S_q)_{\text{max.}} = \tfrac{1}{2}(2ck)^{-1/2}.$$

The effective capacity at this sensitivity is, of course, $2c$, where c is the total electrostatic capacity on which the charge q is placed.

Eqs. 14 and 15 predict a constant voltage and charge sensitivity for given values of the potential on the quadrants or on the needle and for given geometrical conditions. Actually, however, this is not the case, for it will be found that as the potential on the quadrants or on the needle, as the case may be, is increased, the period gradually lengthens, and a value is finally reached at which the vane becomes unstable at a certain point of the scale.   This behavior is due to the occurrence of nonlinear terms in the expression for the capacity between the vane and the quadrants.   By careful adjustment the importance of these terms can be diminished but never eliminated.

In setting up the Dolezalek electrometer, the vane should not be too close to either the top or the bottom of the box, since small variations due to changes in temperature and so forth will change the characteristics. Also, irregularities in the vane may make important nonlinear terms in the capacity between the vane and the quadrants. Although the maximum charge sensitivity is not affected by this distance, the optimum voltage and the voltage sensitivity are affected.

The instrument is leveled until the piece holding the vane is in the center of the circular hole in the top of the box. A grounding switch, which may be manually or magnetically operated, must be provided. Care should be exercised not to introduce variable thermal e.m.f.'s.

The torsion head should be adjusted so that each half of the vane lies as nearly as possible symmetrically between two quadrants. With the vane grounded, small values of $+V$ and $-V$ are applied to the quadrants. Adjustment is made to the torsion head in the appropriate direction, so that whether a potential is on the quadrants or not, no motion of the vane takes place. After the full values of $\pm V$ are placed on the quadrants, slight adjustments can be made with the potentiometer as shown in Figs. 10(b) and 10(c). This procedure is generally known as bringing the mechanical and electrical zeros together, and must be done with all forms of electrometers.

In operation, the actual useful working value of the charge sensitivity will be about

$$S_q = 1.3 \times 10^4 \text{ div./statcoulomb}$$
$$= 0.4 \times 10^{14} \text{ div./coulomb}$$
$$= 0.6 \times 10^{-5} \text{ div./electron.}$$

The corresponding voltage sensitivity will probably lie in the range $S_V = 1000 \text{ to } 1500 \text{ div./volt,}$

while the optimum value of the voltage applied to the quadrants will probably be between 50 and 100 volts on each side of ground, or if the high potential is placed on the needle, it will usually be between 100 and 200 volts, depending, among other things, on the size of the torsion fiber.

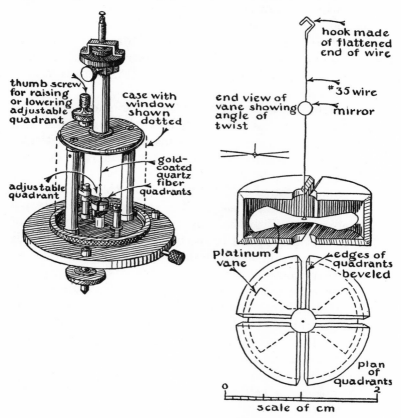

Fig. 11.   Compton adjustable quadrant electrometer.

It is assumed in the above that a scale with 1-mm divisions is used at the customary distance of 1 m.

The Compton electrometer[8] was introduced in 1919 by the two Compton brothers.[9]   It is of the quadrant type but is so

---

[8] This instrument is made by the Rubicon Company, 29 North Sixth Street, Philadelphia, and by the Cambridge Scientific Instrument Company, Ltd., Cambridge, England.

[9] Compton, A. H. and K. T., *Phys. Rev.*, *14*, 85 (1919).

arranged that one quadrant can be raised or lowered with respect to the other three. Further dissymmetry is introduced by giving the vane an initial tilt. By proper adjustment of this movable quadrant the time consumed by the needle in returning to its initial position after a deflection may be lengthened (negative control) or shortened (positive control). The design of the instrument is shown in Fig. 11. The dissymmetry introduces additional nonlinear terms

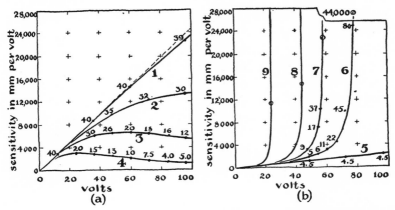

Fig. 12. Typical curves of the Compton electrometer showing the effect of various degrees of positive (a) and negative (b) control on the voltage sensitivity. The curves in (b) were taken with a much stiffer fiber than those in (a).

into the change of capacity as the needle moves, and an electrostatic torque is introduced which either opposes the torque of the suspension (negative control) or aids it (positive control). In the extreme case the action of the suspension can be more than completely neutralized, so that an unstable instrument results. This means that the voltage sensitivity can be made extremely high. Fig. 12(a) illustrates the relationship between the voltage sensitivity and the voltage on the needle for different degrees of positive control, while Fig. 12(b) shows the same relationship for various degrees of negative control. In this latter case a stiffer suspension was used. The circles on curves 6, 7, 8, 9 represent the highest sensitivity at which the zero of the instrument is sufficiently stable to allow satisfactory measurements to be made. The small figures above the curves of Figs. 12(a) and 12(b) represent the time required in each case for the needle to return to within 1 mm of the rest position after a deflection of 50 mm. Because of the small restoring torque and high air damping, the motion of the suspended system is aperiodic.

Where extremely small potentials are to be measured and where the demand on charge sensitivity is not too great, the Compton electrometer is very suitable. However, the same voltage sensitivity could be achieved with the usual quadrant electrometer by putting in a suspension fine enough to give the same time of return to zero, provided that the moving system were equally as light as that in the Compton. In fact, it will be noted from the curves that with neither positive nor negative control, shown by the straight line of Fig. 12(a), but with a fine fiber, voltage sensitivities can be obtained equal to those with a stiff fiber and large negative control. This high voltage sensitivity is not always useful when measuring electric charges, which is the main purpose of electrometers, for not only does the instrument become very sluggish, but drifts become bad. Also, for a given time of return from a given deflection the charge sensitivity has a maximum value.[10] Wolf[11] states that the maximum usable charge sensitivity of the Compton electrometer is 2×10^{14} div./coulomb, which occurs at a voltage sensitivity of 5000 div./volt.

The Hoffmann electrometer[12] combines the highest charge sensitivity of any commercial instrument with stability, that is, lack of drift, and ease of working. Great care has been exercised to eliminate contact potentials, thermal e.m.f.'s, and air currents. To achieve the elimination of air currents, heavy copper pieces surround the movable

[10] Pockman, L. T., *Rev. Sci. Instruments, 7,* 242 (1936).

[11] Wolf, F., *Ann. d. Physik, 18,* 373 (1933).

[12] Hoffmann, G., *Phys. Zeits., 13,* 480, 1029 (1912).

Hoffmann electrometers are made by E. Leybold's Nachfolger A. G. Köln-Bayental, Bonner Strasse 500, Germany.

system to insure that thermal gradients are kept at a minimum. A decided advantage is gained also by evacuating the case to a few millimeters of mercury, thus making the instrument "deadbeat."

The instrument operates upon essentially the same principle as the quadrant electrometer. The chief difference is

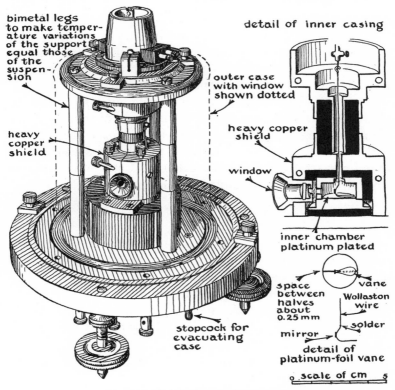

Fig. 13. The Hoffmann electrometer.

that a half vane is used for the movable system, so that, instead of quadrants, only two conductors, or binants, are necessary. Fig. 13 represents the relationships of the essential parts. The platinum needle and mirror together weigh approximately 5 mg, and the suspension is a 3μ (0.0003-cm) Wollaston wire.

To achieve a sensitivity independent of temperature, it is necessary to keep the vane or needle at the same distance from the binants.   This is accomplished by inserting into the supports of the upper part of the electrometer case, which in turn supports the suspension, a metal of such coefficient of thermal expansion that the over-all expansion completely neutralizes the change of length of the torsion fiber with temperature.

Contact and thermal electromotive forces are kept at a minimum by making everything from or plating it with platinum.   Also, insulation is protected by metal, so that possible spurious charges cannot affect the system.

Since the Hoffmann electrometer combines so many desirable features, it may be well to list some of them.   These characteristics must be combined in any other instrument with which it is intended to push the charge sensitivity to that limit set by Brownian motion, and still have freedom from drift and a reasonable working period.

1. The moment of inertia of the moving system must be small.   (See Eq. 13.)

2. The suspension must be made of material which has a small coefficient of internal friction; that is, the needle must return to zero after a deflection.

3. Air currents must be kept at a minimum.   This means that the moving system must be surrounded with heavy copper pieces.   The suspension should be closely surrounded by metal pieces as well.

4. The case must be evacuated to keep the working time within a reasonable limit.

5. Temperature compensation is needed if the distance between the vane and the stationary parts is to remain constant.

6. Thermal and contact electromotive forces must be eliminated.

In addition to the above, it is usually desirable to have the scale approximately linear.

Two additional features of the Hoffmann electrometer are (1) an electromagnetic grounding switch and (2) an induction ring for inducing a charge on the movable system.

To facilitate making the necessary electrical connections, a control mechanism is supplied with the instrument when it is purchased. Although not absolutely necessary, the control mechanism is a great aid, since the proper connections are made and broken at the right time by only one operation.

The latest model of the Hoffmann electrometer[13] combines all the desirable features of the earlier models but permits greater accessibility to the essential parts. Also the adjustments are much more easily made; for example, in the older types the instrument had to be exhausted after adjusting the binants, while in the new design this adjustment is made through a sylphon from the outside.

String electrometers are divided into two main divisions: (1) those with a fiber supported only at one end and (2) those in which the fiber is kept taut by a fine spring. The latter are the most common and, as far as is known, are the only ones on the market.

Electrometers of the first class are easily made and are often very satisfactory when high sensitivity is not needed.

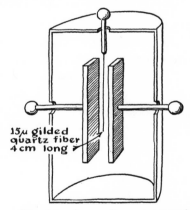

Fig. 14. An easily constructed quartz-fiber electrometer in which the fiber is supported only at one end.

The two plates can be flat and the fiber hung down between them as shown in Fig. 14. There should be an adjustment either on the plates or on the fiber or on both to bring the mechanical and electrical zeros together. Some adjustment may be made by tipping the instrument in the appropriate

[13] Zipprich, B., *Phys. Zeits.*, *37*, 35 (1936).

direction. A microscope must be provided to read the deflection. With the plates 1 cm apart, the fiber should be

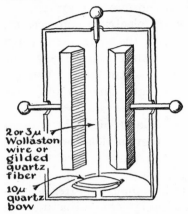

2 or 3μ
Wollaston
wire or
gilded
quartz
fiber

10μ
quartz
bow

Fig. 15.   Schematic diagram of the Wülf string electrometer.

about 25μ in diameter and 4 cm long if the potential on the plates is not to exceed 100 volts.

Of the second type, that designed by Wülf[14] is, perhaps, typical. It is shown diagrammatically in Fig. 15. The fiber is usually a Wollaston wire . 2μ in diameter, kept taut by a quartz-fiber bow. Screw adjustments permit movement of the plates with respect to the fiber as well as change in the tension of the fiber.

With all string electrometers the deflection is not a linear function of the applied charge or voltage at high sensitivity. It frequently happens that at high sensitivities the fiber leaves the field of view of the microscope as it reaches a position where instability occurs.

The chief advantages of string electrometers are (1) portability, (2) ease of adjustment, and (3) short working time.

The Perucca electrometer[15] is similar to the string electrometer, except that the part between the plates consists of

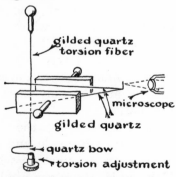

gilded quartz
torsion fiber

microscope

gilded quartz

quartz bow
torsion adjustment

Fig. 16.   Principle of operation of the Perucca electrometer.

[14] Wülf, Th., *Phys. Zeits.*, *15*, 250, 611 (1914).
    This instrument is made by E. Leybold's Nachfolger A. G. Köln-Bayental, Bonner Strasse 500, Germany.
    [15] Perucca, E., *Zeits. f. Instrumentenk.*, *47*, 524 (1927).
    This instrument is obtainable from E. Leybold's Nachfolger A. G. Köln-Bayental, Bonner Strasse 500, Germany.

two conducting quartz fibers supported on a torsion fiber as shown in Fig. 16. The two movable fibers are brought together at one end, and a small index, which is viewed with a microscope, is provided. The charge and voltage sensitivities are each greater than can be obtained with a string electrometer. Not only is it more sensitive, but it also combines all the advantages of the latter instrument.

The Lindemann electrometer[16] was developed primarily for use with photoelectric cells mounted on telescopes in measuring light from stars. Such use requires that the sensitivity and position of the moving system be independent of

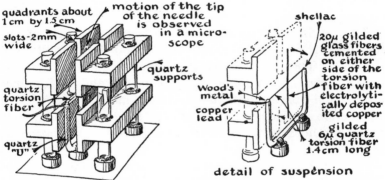

detail of suspension

The whole instrument is enclosed in a metal box 4.5cm, by 2.8cm, by 3cm high, with windows top and bottom.

Fig. 17. Arrangement of quadrants and movable system in the Lindemann electrometer.

tilt. The first is accomplished by making all parts very rigid and the second by using for the moving system a light needle mounted on a stretched torsion fiber. Since a mirror and scale would be cumbersome for such uses, the deflection of the needle is read with a microscope with a micrometer ocular. The whole electrometer weighs but 80 g. The quadrants and needle mountings are represented in Fig. 17.

16 Lindemann, F. A. and A. F., and Kerley, T. C., *Phil. Mag.*, *47*, 577 (1924).
This instrument is obtainable from the Cambridge Scientific Instrument Company, Ltd., Cambridge, England.

The principle on which the instrument works is similar to the quadrant electrometer. The quadrants are 1.5 cm broad and 1 cm high, with a slot 2 mm wide, into which the needle may pass, cut in each. These plates are mounted 5 mm apart on quartz rods. The torsion-fiber mounting and needle are placed between the plates so that the junction of the needle and torsion fiber is symmetrically located with respect to the four plates. The whole is mounted in an aluminum box with suitable connections. Through a glass window in one side of the box the motion of the end of the needle is observed with a microscope. A window directly opposite on the other side of the case permits light to enter.

The needle may be balanced so that a rotation of the instrument through 90° makes less than 0.06 mm motion of the end. The needle is usually about 1 cm long, and the torsion fiber is 6μ in diameter. The needle and torsion fiber are covered with a conducting coating of metal, and a suitable connection is made to the outside of the case. The quartz frame for holding the torsion fiber serves as insulation as well.

Electrical connections are the same as for any quadrant electrometer. Instability occurs at a potential of about 100 volts. At 3 volts below this unstable value the deflection will reach 99 per cent of its final value in 1 second. The voltage sensitivity under these conditions is 0.76 mm/volt motion of the end of the needle. With a suitable microscope a workable sensitivity of 500 div./volt can be obtained. The electrostatic capacity is about 2 cm.

The instrument may conveniently be used with a leak to measure currents of from 10^{-10} to 10^{-14} ampere. When not too great demands are to be met, this quite inexpensive electrometer will meet many needs, especially where portability is a requirement.

For a discussion of circuits, sensitivities, and limitations of the vacuum-tube electrometer, which uses specially constructed vacuum tubes, see Chapter X.

Some practical considerations in the use of electrometers and electroscopes. *Useful sensitivity in X-ray work.* Electrometers are frequently used with an ion chamber in X-ray work. As is well known, ions are formed not only by the X-ray beam but by (1) cosmic rays, (2) local radiation from radioactive matter in the surroundings, and (3) radioactive contamination on the inner walls of the ion chamber. Of these, (3) can be reduced to a small value in comparison with the others by two effective means. The inner walls can be painted with a mixture of collodion and lampblack, each of which is quite free from radioactive materials. The thickness should be about 0.05 mm to stop all the α particles. The other method is to maintain a fine wire grid at a suitable potential to drive the ions formed by the α particles back into the walls. Since in general (3) is due to particles which will have a range of less than 5 cm at normal air pressure, the range can be kept within the grid by a gas of high molecular weight or increased pressure, or both. Even rubbing Carborundum paper on the walls of the chamber will often help considerably in lowering the emission. As for (1), cosmic rays could be reduced to an extremely low value by going into a mine 100 to 200 feet below the surface of the ground, while (2) could be made negligible with 4 inches of surrounding lead. However, since it is not practical to go to such trouble, in most cases it is necessary to make the best of the situation.

Since the error of a result which depends on the difference or sum of two readings is[17]

$$\epsilon = (\epsilon_1^2 + \epsilon_2^2)^{1/2}, \tag{16}$$

where ϵ_1 and ϵ_2 are the errors of the two readings, it is hopeless to try to push the sensitivity of the measuring device beyond a certain point, and the only hope of increasing accuracy is by a longer period of observation. It is easily seen that the optimum useful value of the sensitivity is

---

[17] For a further discussion of probabilities and errors involved when a measurement depends on the effects of a finite number of particles, see page 298.

reached when the deflection due to background only and the deflection due to the X-ray beam only are equal for the same time of observation.

If the ratio of background to beam readings is to be made as small as possible, it is obvious that the volume also should be made as small as possible, since the background reading goes up with the volume.

Example. Assume an ion chamber of 1000 cm^3. Cosmic rays will contribute about 3 ions/cm^3/sec./atmosphere of air at sea level. Local radiation will be from 3 to 5 I (ions cm^{-3} sec.$^{-1}$ atmosphere^{-1} of air), while the background may vary over wide limits; from 0.1 to 10 ions cm^{-3} sec.$^{-1}$ atmosphere^{-1} of air will probably include the extreme cases. Since the α-particle paths will usually end in the gas, an increase of pressure will not change the number of ions formed by the α particles, but the ionization due to local radiation and cosmic rays will go up as the pressure increases. Let us assume $7I$ as due to electrons and $5I$ as due to α particles. The average path length of the electrons is about 10 cm, and at 60 ions/cm of path this corresponds to about 12 electrons/sec. crossing the chamber. In order to have a mean relative error of ϵ_1, then according to the laws of probability, $1/\epsilon_1^2$ particles must cross the chamber. Let ϵ_1 be 0.03, or 3 per cent; then 10^3 particles must be counted. This will take 80 seconds on the above assumptions. These 10^3 electrons will form 6×10^5 ions. Hence if we assume the same fluctuations in the ions from the beam, then according to Eq. 16, to have an average error of 4 per cent in a reading, we must time for at least a minute, and the sensitivity of the electrometer need not be greater than 10^{-5} div./ion if we estimate to 0.1 div.

As for the α particles from the walls, their effect may be considered as follows: Supposing they amount to $5I$, which is not an uncommon value, then there will be 5000 ions/sec. formed. Now an α particle will form, on the average, about 10,000 ions in the gas. Hence there is 0.5 α particle/sec. emitted by the walls. Now if ϵ_1 is the mean absolute error in a given reading and ϵ_2 in another reading, the mean relative error ϵ_r in the sum will be

$$\epsilon_r = \frac{(\epsilon_1^2 + \epsilon_2^2)^{1/2}}{\theta_1 + \theta_2}, \tag{17}$$

where θ is the deflection of the instrument. If N_1 is the number of particles per second of one kind of particle and I_1 the number of ions formed per particle, then it can be shown from Eq. 17 that the mean relative error of the sum is

$$\epsilon_r = \left(\frac{N_1 I_1^2 + N_2 I_2^2}{t(N_1 I_1 + N_2 I_2)^2}\right)^{1/2} = \left(\frac{(4.3 + 50) \times 10^6}{t(0.72 + 0.50)^2 \times 10^8}\right)^{1/2} = \frac{0.6}{t^{1/2}}$$

under the above assumptions if the subscript 1 refers to the electrons and 2 refers to the α particles.   It is then necessary to count for 400 seconds to gain an accuracy of 4 per cent. In this time 5×10^6 ions will have been collected.   In order to read this to 4 per cent we need a sensitivity no greater than 10^{-6} div./ion.

The above calculations have been made to show (1) the importance of eliminating α particles as much as possible and (2) that when this is done completely, the sensitivity of the electrometer has a limit beyond which there is no gain.

If charges are to be collected where there is very little background, such as in photoelectric work, then there is no reason why the sensitivity cannot be pushed to the maximum.   In all cases, if possible, an electrometer or an electroscope suitable to the accuracy required should be chosen.

Useful sensitivity in cosmic-ray work.   In case the instrument is subject only to cosmic rays and no shielding is used, the ionization is due to random electrons and "X" particles, which ionize the gas the same as electrons.   When this is so, the mean relative error is $N^{-1/2}$, where N is the total number of particles, the effects of which are measured.   If there are n high-energy particles/cm²/sec., and if the mean relative error is ϵ_r for one reading, then we must observe for a time

$$t = \frac{1}{\epsilon_r{}^2 \pi n R^2},$$

where

$$\frac{1}{\epsilon_r{}^2} = N,$$

for a spherical ionization chamber, and if σ is the specific ionization, since the average path length is $\frac{4}{3}R$, the total number of ions collected in the time will be

$$\nu = \frac{4}{3} \frac{\sigma R}{\epsilon_r{}^2},$$

and this must give a deflection which can be read with no larger relative error than ϵ_r. If $\sigma = 60$ ions cm^{-1}, $R = 10$ cm, and $\epsilon_r = 0.01$, then $\nu = 8 \times 10^6$ ions, and we need a sensitivity of about 3×10^{-6} div./ion. Now $n \cong 0.02$ electron/cm^2/sec. at sea level. Hence the minimum time of observation should be 30 minutes, and for each observation the mean error will be 1 per cent. This calculation, of course, neglects the error introduced by the background radiation.

Frequently, however, the ionization chamber is surrounded with shields made of iron or lead. These do two things: (1) In general, they lessen the intensity of the radiation, and (2) they introduce new radiations. All the particles passing through the ionization chamber are no longer randomly distributed in time, for, in addition, there now exist showers, consisting of from two to several hundred electrons, which come all at the same time from some region of the shield. These introduce larger fluctuations than would otherwise exist, and the time of observation for the size of ion chamber assumed above may be from two to four times as long for the same error, and a correspondingly less sensitivity of the measuring instrument will serve the purpose.

Steady deflection measurements. In some cases it may be desired to use the constant deflection instead of the drift method. This may be done by using the electrometer to measure the drop in potential across a fixed resistance as shown in Fig. 18. Assume that it is desired to measure a constant ion source I. Let the capacity to ground of the external system be c_1 and of the electrometer c_2, and let the drop in potential be measured across R_1. Then

$$i_1 + i_2 = I', \ i_1 = \frac{V}{R_1}, \ i_2 = \frac{dQ_2}{dt} = c_2\frac{dV}{dt},$$

$$I = \frac{dQ_1}{dt} + I' = C_1\frac{dV_1}{dt} + I', \ V = i_1 R_1.$$

The equation for the potential across the electrometer is then

$$V = \left[I - (c_1 + c_2)\frac{dV}{dt}\right]R_1.$$

Solving and putting in the boundary condition that when $t = 0$, $V = 0$,

$$V = IR_1\left[1 - e^{-\frac{t}{(c_1 + c_2)R_1}}\right].$$

Thus the potential across the electrometer rises exponentially. If we say arbitrarily that we shall wait until the deflection is 99 per cent of the ultimate deflection, then we must wait a time $t = 4.6 \ R_1c$, where $c = c_1 + c_2$. The deflection will be approximately VS_V after this time. Had we measured I by the drift method, we should have the same deflection in a time R_1c, the difference, of course, being due to the fact that in the second case the drift is constant, while in the first case the drift begins at the same rate, that is, as if $R_1 = \infty$, but gradually slows down, becoming very slow toward the last.

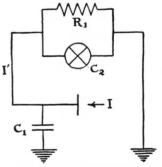

Fig. 18. Measuring an ion current I by determining the potential drop across a resistance R_1 by means of an electrometer, c_2.

It is therefore much more satisfactory to use the drift method for measuring feeble currents, while larger currents are conveniently measured by the steady deflection method. The drift method can be used in measuring large currents also by inserting a capacity of the appropriate value to lengthen the time of drift.

Limitations of various types of instruments. Limitation on the charge sensitivity of electroscopes and electrometers has already been pointed out. For the former the maximum charge sensitivity is

$$(S_Q)_{\text{max.}} = \frac{1}{2}(ck)^{-1/2} = \frac{1}{2V_0b},$$

and for the latter

$$(S_q)_{\text{max.}} = \frac{1}{2}(2ck)^{-1/2} = \frac{1}{4V_0b}.$$

The capacity of an electroscope which has no external lead will depend on the particular design, but for the Wülf or torsion type it will lie between 0.4 and 1 cm. That of an electrometer with its added external capacity will probably be between 20 and 100 cm. The restoring constant, k, of the suspension can be reduced in each to a point where the sluggishness of the motion makes the instrument tedious to work with, or in the case of most electroscopes, where the collecting potential becomes too small to collect most of the ions. Since an electrometer case can be evacuated, it is possible to adjust the pressure until the motion of the vane or needle becomes critically damped.

If the electrometer case is not evacuated, the working period may become excessively long when high sensitivities are desired. Much can be achieved by making the needle or vane small and light, as is done in the Lindemann and Perucca electrometers, and as is inherently the case with string electrometers.

Limitations imposed by drift. The amount of drift during a reading is often the limiting factor in electrometers. This frequently becomes bothersome long before the maximum sensitivity has been reached. One of the chief reasons for the drift is that the mechanical and electrical zeros gradually

drift apart.   The deflection caused by the zeros being different may be many times the actual amount they are apart.
Drift, among other causes, is due to (1) fluctuations in
battery voltage and (2) nonelastic changes of strain in the
suspension.   If the drift were constant, proper allowances
could be made, but there are so many factors which depend
in a different way upon changes of voltages, temperature,
humidity, and so forth, that it is often very difficult, if not
impossible, to eliminate completely or take account of the
drift.   This is especially true with vacuum-tube electrometers, even though balanced circuits are used.

Limitations on the amount of useful magnification.   Two
methods are in general use for determining the amount of
deflection in an electroscope or electrometer: (1) Microscope
with micrometer ocular and (2) mirror and scale.   For the
Lindemann electrometer and most electroscopes the microscope is used.   The limitation as far as magnification is concerned amounts to a limitation of resolution.   Magnification
can continue until the position of a diffraction band cannot
be located to within 0.1 div. in the eyepiece.   Beyond this,
nothing is gained.   With a numerical aperture of 1 and an
image distance of 20 cm the shortest useful focal length is
about 3 mm with a 100-div. scale in the eyepiece 1 cm long.

If a mirror and scale are used, there is a certain minimum
mirror size which will allow sufficient resolution.   With a
1 mm div. scale at the customary distance of 1 m, it is
necessary to have a mirror at least 2 mm in diameter to read
to 0.1 div. on the scale.

In all cases, whether in resolution, amount of drift, fluctuations, or the like, it *should always be possible to estimate to
0.1 of the smallest division* on the scale, and in general it is
*useless to push the sensitivity of any instrument beyond the
point where 0.1 div. loses its significance.*

Limitations imposed by Brownian motion.   It is part of
the classical theory of the equipartition of energy that all
bodies have a mean thermal energy of $\frac{1}{2}KT$ for each degree
of freedom, where K is Boltzmann's constant and T the

absolute temperature. This Brownian motion of the instrument is evidenced by random fluctuations about the point of equilibrium. It is evident that before a superimposed steady deflection can be detected, it must be at least as large as this mean Brownian deflection.

The mechanical energy of a moving system with a restoring force proportional to the .displacement is $\frac{1}{2}k\xi^2$, where k is the restoring force (or torque) per unit of displacement. If $\Delta\xi$ is the mean Brownian deflection, then the k corresponding to this is given by

$$\tfrac{1}{2}k(\Delta\xi)^2 = \tfrac{1}{2}KT,$$

or

$$k = \frac{KT}{(\Delta\xi)^2}.$$

Now with the electroscope the maximum charge sensitivity is reached when $S_Q = \frac{1}{2}(ck)^{-1/2}$. Consequently, the corresponding charge sensitivity is

$$S_Q = \frac{\Delta\xi}{2(KTc)^{1/2}},$$

if the deflection is equal to the mean Brownian deflection. At room temperature the maximum charge sensitivity is thus limited for electroscopes to

$$(S_Q)_{\text{max.}} = \frac{1.2 \times 10^{-4}}{c^{1/2}} \text{ div./electron,}$$

where c is in centimeters. For electrometers the expression becomes

$$(S_q)_{\text{max.}} = \frac{0.8 \times 10^{-4}}{c^{1/2}} \text{ div./electron.}$$

It is obvious that the electrostatic capacity of the instrument should be as small as possible if it is intended to push the charge sensitivity to the limit. Inherently the capacity of the electroscope is much less than that of the electrometer. This not only makes it possible to have a higher charge sensitivity for the same torsion constant but allows it to be used.

It is interesting to compare the above limit with that obtainable with a Geiger counter.   In some applications the number of counts and the number of unit charges collected are comparable.   The mean error with a Geiger counter in a single count of N particles distributed at random is $N^{1/2}$, so that if it is desired to have a mean relative error of 1 per cent, it is necessary to count $1/(0.01)^2$ or 10^4 particles.   With an electroscope having a capacity of 0.5 cm, it is necessary to collect 8×10^4 electrons to have the same mean error if the deflection can be read to 0.1 div.   This is, of course, disregarding the backgrounds in each case.

A comparison of various types of instruments.   Probably the most sensitive electrometer on the market is the Hoffmann.   The maximum sensitivity which can be reached with this instrument is approximately 5×10^{15} div./coulomb. Drift has been eliminated to such an extent that sufficient time can elapse to detect an average of 1 electron/sec. For ease of working, however, it is advisable to keep the charge sensitivity in the neighborhood of 1×10^{15} div./coulomb.   Much is gained in the Hoffmann by evacuating the case, thereby not only shortening the working time but greatly eliminating the effects of convection currents.

The vacuum-tube electrometer has gained much favor in the past few years.   It has the advantage that it can be used in places where it would be inconvenient or impossible to use the conventional type of electrometer.   The sensitivity can be made comparable to that of the Hoffmann, although it is very much inferior as far as drifts are concerned.   Ordinary precautions consist in having large storage batteries for plate and filament supply which are kept at as constant a temperature as possible, with all leads well shielded.   Resistances must also be kept constant.   Although with the proper circuit and circuit constants the effects of voltage fluctuations are reduced to a minimum, it is still not possible to eliminate the drift, and it is usually necessary to wait several hours after the connections are made for conditions to become only approximately steady.

When possible, an instrument should be chosen for the problem at hand. Frequently it is desirable to use an electroscope in place of the electrometer. The advantages to be gained may be listed as follows: (1) Freedom from external changes of temperature and humidity, (2) freedom from changes in battery potentials and resistances, (3) freedom from drifts, (4) need for only one potential, (5) ease of setting up and operating, (6) portability, and (7) low cost. The disadvantages are that (1) except with the torsion type the sensitivity is not as high as with the ordinary electrometer, (2) the sensitivity is not readily varied, and (3) it is not convenient to use a null method of reading.

In Table I are listed the approximate characteristics of some instruments. The values of charge sensitivities listed are not the maximum attainable but represent those that

TABLE I

COMPARISON OF CHARACTERISTICS OF VARIOUS INSTRUMENTS

Type	S_V	S_q ($\times 10^{14}$)	Working Period (seconds)
Wülf bifilar................	0.5	0.002	0.1
Wilson tilted...............	100	0.1	....
Neher torsion..............	100	2	1
Dolezalek quadrant..........	1000	0.4	60
Compton...................	5000	2	40
Lindemann.................	500	0.5	1
Wülf string................	500	0.2	1
Perucca...................	2000	1	10
Hoffmann vacuum..........	10,000	10	10
Vacuum tube...............	10,000	5	....

Units of voltage sensitivity, S_V, are divisions per volt which correspond to the maximum usable charge sensitivity, S_q, expressed in divisions per coulomb. Values of S_q are for no added external capacity.

can be reached and worked without great difficulty. The values of the voltage sensitivities are those which correspond to these values of the charge sensitivities. In some cases the voltage sensitivity can be made much higher, in particular with the Compton, with which it is possible to reach 50,000 div./volt. The working period represents approximately the time for the deflection to become zero after the net charge is removed.

Useful techniques in electroscope and electrometer work. *Mounting gold leaves.* Gold leaf usually comes in sheets about 8 cm square, the leaves being separated by sheets of tissue paper. The leaf will be found quite uniform and thin enough so that objects can be distinguished through it when it is held before the eye. The thickness is usually about 0.08μ. The leaf is cut to the desired size by placing it

between sheets of tissue paper and using a razor blade. The paper separating the gold leaf will be found satisfactory for the purpose. The cutting should be done on a flat base, such as cardboard. If the razor blade is sharp, the cut will be clean and the gold will not adhere to the paper. The leaf can be moved around from one sheet

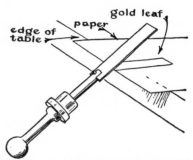

Fig. 19.   **Mounting the leaf on a gold-leaf electroscope.**

of paper to another by means of clean needles, mounted so that they can be handled with ease. It can also be picked up with clean fine-pointed tweezers. If the leaf touches anything which has a film of organic substance on the surface, it will easily adhere with only slight pressure. Once the leaf has stuck, it will usually tear before coming loose. It is safest to handle it as little as possible. When mounting the foil on the single-leaf type of electroscope, it is cut to size and then transferred to a piece of paper, such as typing paper, and placed so that one end of the leaf is near one edge of the paper. The edge of the paper is allowed to overhang the table about $\frac{1}{4}$ inch. Some alcohol-dissolved shellac is spread across that part of the metal piece from which the leaf is to hang. The edge of this shellac must be perpendicular to the edge of the metal support, in order that the leaf, when mounted, will deflect in a plane perpendicular to the plane of this support. The metal piece must be clean, or the leaf is apt to adhere to it.   The metal support is brought into position as shown in Fig. 19 and then lowered gradually.   The paper will bend and the leaf will adhere to the shellac.

The above operations should be carried out in a room in which the motion of the air is at a minimum.   It is often advisable to wear a mask or deflector over the nose to avoid blowing the leaf about.

Preparation of Wollaston wire.[18]   The Hoffmann and many string electrometers use a fine platinum suspension known as Wollaston wire.   It may be obtained in various sizes from 1.5μ to 5μ.   To produce such a fine wire of uniform size, the following process of manufacture is used.   Upon a much larger platinum wire is electroplated a uniform layer of silver.   The combination is then drawn down until the fine thread of platinum in the middle is of the proper size.   The silver is etched off with acid.   Since the resulting platinum wire is quite delicate, special care must be used in the etching as well as in subsequent handling.

In order to avoid small bubbles collecting on the wire and interfering with the etching, or in some cases breaking the fine wire, a special solution of chemically pure nitric acid in distilled water at a density of 1.10 g cm^{-3} is used.   To insure uniform etching, the wire should be thoroughly cleaned before it is immersed in the acid.   As an aid to handling after etching, a bead two to three times the diameter of the silver wire is formed on one end with a small oxygen flame before the silver is etched off.   A section of wire is then cut off, perhaps an inch longer than the necessary suspension.   The solution is placed in a tall vessel, such as a graduate, and the straightened silver wire is supported in it vertically.   The suspension should be left in for a longer rather than a shorter time, since the platinum is not damaged by the solution.

---

[18] Wollaston wire is obtainable from Hartmann and Braun, A. G., Frankfurt am Main, Germany, and Baker and Company, Philadelphia.

It is necessary that all the silver be etched off, or the suspension may be ruined in the annealing process.   The small bead marks the lower end as the suspension is drawn from the solution.   Before soldering it into place, it may be desirable to mount the suspension on a "wishbone," the distance between the two prongs being somewhat greater than the length of the mounted suspension.   If quartz fibers 20μ to 30μ in diameter are mounted in the tips of the prongs and the Wollaston wire is fastened to these with a hard wax, there will be much less chance of breakage.

Either before or after mounting, the suspension should be placed in a horizontal position and annealed with a small gas flame.   In still air the flame is passed beneath at such a distance that the platinum is heated to a bright red color. If all the silver has been etched off, the suspension will appear a uniform brightness throughout its length.   The annealing is necessary, if the wire is to be used in an electrometer, to relieve the strains which resulted from the drawing.

In soldering the suspension in place, a c.p. solution of zinc chloride is a good flux.   The heat is best applied with a small soldering iron, not directly at the point at which the suspension touches the solder but at a short distance away, relying upon the conductivity of the metal support.   It is best to work under a magnifying glass or, better still, a binocular microscope.   The joint should be rigidly inspected to see that the platinum is actually embedded in the solder and not just held by the solidified flux.

Insulators used in electrometer and electroscope work. The insulator ordinarily used in electrometers is amber. The amber now on the market is usually a manufactured product which has as good insulation properties as the natural amber and has the advantage of being obtainable in a variety of sizes.   Amber has a high volume resistivity, and the surface resistance of clean amber is also high.   If the surface is contaminated, the best remedy is to remove some of the amber with a clean tool by turning it in a lathe.   If this is not convenient, the amber may be covered with a thin coat of ceresin, as will be described later.

The best insulator known is clean, dry, fused quartz. By clean quartz is meant quartz which has not touched anything since being heated to the softening point, and by dry quartz is meant quartz either in a good vacuum or in a gas dried by phosphorus pentoxide. Fused quartz is also superior to other insulators in that the soak-in is far less. Under comparable conditions amber has at least ten times the soak-in possessed by quartz.

Ceresin is a natural wax which has remarkable electrical insulation properties.[19] It is about the same hardness as ordinary paraffin, each at 20°C. However, it has a somewhat higher melting point than either paraffin or the artificial ceresin, being liquid at 65°C. Its insulation properties have been measured by Curtiss[20] of the Bureau of Standards. He gives the surface resistivity as greater than 10^{17} ohm cm even at 90 per cent humidity. One of its main uses in the laboratory is to improve the surface resistance of other insulators. If the solid insulator and the ceresin are each heated to around 100°C. and a light coating of ceresin applied, the surface leakage will usually be found greatly reduced, sometimes by a factor of 100.

---

[19] Natural ceresin is distilled from the mineral ozokorite. An artificial ceresin, which is inferior to the natural product, is also on the market. In ordering, the natural product should be specified.

[20] Curtiss, L. F., *Bulletin of the Bureau of Standards*, 1915.

CHAPTER VII

Geiger Counters

BY

H. V. NEHER

THE Geiger counter is an ion-magnifying device which is sensitive to individual ionizing particles. The resultant flow of charge, except for the so-called proportional counter, is practically independent of the number of ions formed by the original particle. Thus, in most Geiger counters an α particle forms from 10^2 to 10^3 times as many initial ions as a β particle; yet each gives rise to a pulse of nearly the same size, and each is usually registered as one particle.

These counters have now reached a practical state of high development as a means of studying feeble radiations, such as those found in cosmic rays and artificial or natural radioactivity. The mechanism of the gaseous discharge in the counters is, however, not well known.

The point counter. The original design of Geiger[1] consisted of a pointed wire surrounded by, and insulated from, a metal cylinder as shown diagrammatically in Fig. 1. A high potential of 1500 to 5000 volts is applied across the counter, through a high resistance R (about 10^9 ohms). The cylinder is made

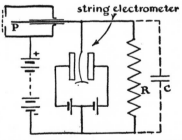

Fig. 1. The original point counter and circuit used by Geiger.

[1] Geiger, H., *Verh. d. D. Phys. Ges.*, *15*, 534 (1913); *Phys. Zeits.*, *14*, 1129 (1913).

positive with respect to the point P. The pulse is observed by means of a string electrometer.

Briefly, the action of the counter may be described as follows: The electric field immediately around the point is high enough so that at the pressure of the gas used any ion entering the space builds up by collision a large number of ions, which in turn build up more ions, until the quantity of charge which finally flows reaches the order of 10^{-8} coulomb, depending, of course, among other quantities, upon the applied potential. This charge, collecting on the distributed capacity, which may be represented by C, causes the potential across the counter to drop to a point at which the discharge can no longer be maintained, and the charge leaks off across the resistance R. The circuit then returns to its normally sensitive condition and is ready for a second count. The charge which builds up on C causes a drop in potential across R which is read by the electrometer.

The proportional counter. The counter just discussed operates on a trigger principle, and the size of the pulse is

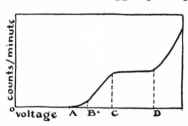

Fig. 2. Characteristic curve for the proportional Geiger counter. In the region from A to B the size of the pulse is proportional to the original ionization. In the region C to D the size of the pulse is practically independent of the amount of initial ionization.

practically independent of the ionization of the initial particle, responding alike to α or β particles. However, Geiger and Klemperer[2] have found that if a small metal sphere is fastened to the point and made positive with respect to the cylinder, instead of negative as in Geiger's original design, over a limited range of voltage, that is, within the range A

[2] Geiger, H., and Klemperer, O., *Zeits. f. Physik, 49*, 753 (1928). See also the following:

Franz, H., *Zeits. f. Physik, 63*, 370 (1930).

Klarmann, H., *Zeits. f. Physik, 87*, 411 (1934).

Duncanson, W. E., and Miller, H., *Roy. Soc., Proc., A, 146*, 396 (1934).

Haxel, O., *Phys. Zeits., 36*, 804 (1935).

to *B* in Fig. 2, the pulse is approximately proportional to the
original ionization of the particle.   This circumstance makes
it possible to distinguish between heavy particles, such as
α rays, protons, and deuterons, and the much lighter particles, electrons.   Since γ rays show themselves by the electrons liberated from the material they pass through, it is
also possible to count individual heavy particles in the presence of strong X-ray and γ radiation.

A design of proportional counter which has been used by
a number of workers is shown in Fig. 3.   The cylinder is

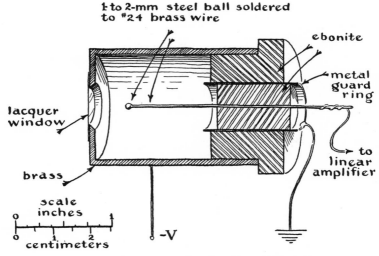

Fig. 3.   Typical construction of a proportional counter.

maintained at a constant negative voltage with respect to
the ball and wire.   A steel ball from 1 to 2 mm in diameter
will give good results, but the metal of which it is made is
unimportant.   The wire or rod supporting the ball may be
made of almost any convenient metal, and is usually about
one half the diameter of the ball.   When a heavily ionizing
particle enters the sensitive region surrounding the ball,
negative charges are collected.   The effect is amplified by
a linear amplifier.   Since the amount of charge collected is

proportional to the initial ionization, a means is here provided of distinguishing between heavy particles and electrons. A thin cellophane, lacquer, or mica window over the opening permits suitable gases to be used at reduced pressures. The threshold potential will probably lie between 1500 and 5000 volts, depending on the kind of gas used, its pressure, and the geometry of the counter.

Brubaker and Pollard[3] have studied the effects of various gases, using different kinds of heavy particles. Their recommendations are to use argon at pressures greater than 50 cm of mercury if there is a background of γ radiation, while for α-particle or proton-scattering experiments, where γ rays are not serious, hydrogen, nitrogen, or air between 2 and 10 cm of mercury pressure can be used.

If the potential on the above counter, with the small sphere in place of the point, is raised, a region C to D in Fig. 2 is reached where the effect of all particles is practically the same and the number of counts per unit time becomes almost independent of the applied voltage for a constant radiation. The length of this "plateau" depends primarily upon the distributed capacity and the resistance across the counter. When the point D is reached, the number of counts for a given radiation begins to increase, and any further increase in voltage soon sets up a steady gaseous discharge.

Since the sensitive portion in a point counter is limited to a small region in the immediate neighborhood of the point, it is useful primarily in experiments in which only a small solid angle is to be studied at a time, such as in problems on scattering.

The "Zählrohr" or Geiger-Müller counter. When it becomes necessary to have a large area sensitive to ionizing particles, the point counter no longer can be used, and its place is taken by the Zählrohr or Geiger-Müller[4] counter (hereafter designated as the G-M counter). It has become particularly useful in the study of cosmic rays, for it is possi-

---

[3] Brubaker, G., and Pollard, E., *Rev. Sci. Instruments*, *8*, 254 (1937).

[4] Geiger, H., and Müller, W., *Phys. Zeits.*, *29*, 839 (1928).

ble to use tubes of large cross-sectional area and thus have an accuracy comparable to that obtained with ionization chambers for the same time of observation. The advantages to be gained over the ionization-chamber method are that, by properly combining two or more G-M counters, (1) particles incident only from limited angles can be counted, and (2) background radiation due to contamination on the counter walls and radioactivity of the surroundings may be eliminated.

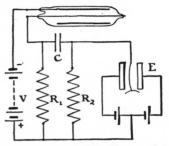

$C = 30 \text{ cm}$ $R_1 = 10^9 \text{ohms}$ $R_2 = 2 \times 10^7 \text{ohms}$

Fig. 4. A method for studying qualitatively the action of a Geiger-Müller counter, using a string electrometer as the detector.

Behavior of the G-M counter. Some of the properties of the counter may be studied by the arrangement shown in Fig. 4. The string electrometer, E, will be suitable, provided the counter is small, that is, the number of counts per minute is not more than 10 to 20. The circuit constants should be approximately as follows: $R_1 = 10^9$ ohms, $C = 30$ cm, and $R_2 = 20 \times 10^6$ ohms. The tube is made negative with respect to the wire.

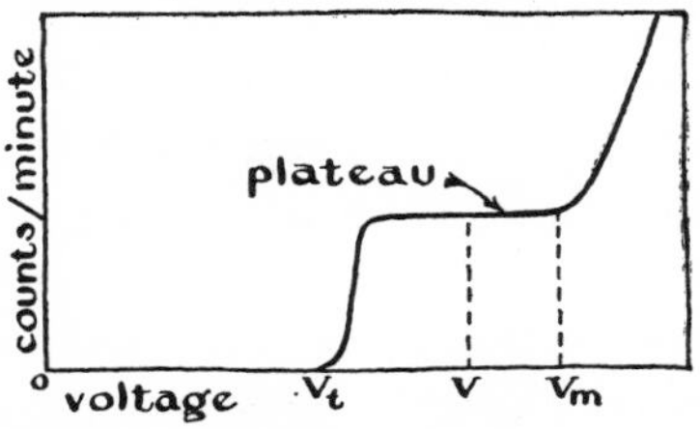

As illustrated in Fig. 5, when the potential, V, is raised, no effect will be noticed on the electrometer until a certain potential, known as the "threshold" voltage, V_t, is reached, when a small increase in potential will cause the number of counts per unit time to rise quite abruptly to a certain value.[5] Any further increase in the potential will cause

Fig. 5. Characteristic curve of a Geiger-Müller counter.

---

[5] The abruptness of this rise depends, to a large extent, on the ratio of the length to the diameter of the metal tube and on the position of the central wire. Owing to the end effects, the part of the tube which first becomes sensitive is that near the center. As the potential is raised, this active region moves out toward the ends, and soon practically the whole length becomes sensitive.

very little change in the counting until a potential V_m, which may be called the maximum operating potential of the counter, is reached. A small increase from here on will cause a sudden increase in counts, which soon goes over into a glow discharge. The "plateau" for a good counter and proper circuit constants may be 200 to 300 volts or even longer. This fact permits quantitative results to be obtained with G-M counters without elaborate means of regulating the voltage supply. The tube is usually operated at some intermediate voltage, V.

Although both positive and negative particles are present in the tube, the actual multiplying agents are probably the electrons. The electric field is higher than necessary for the electrons to form ions by collision, while it is probably not high enough for the positive or negative ions to do so. The electrons rushing toward the wire form new positive ions and electrons, the current building up according to the law $i = i_0 e^{\alpha x}$, where α is the number of new pairs of ions formed per centimeter of path and is called the Townsend coefficient. Probably negative ions are also formed by the attachment of electrons to the molecules. In the ionization process light is given off, liberating new electrons from the metal tube, and these, in turn, form other ions as they rush toward the wire. This photoelectric process has been found by Christoph and Hanle[6] and by Locher[7] to be important in the mechanism of the discharge. The process of accumulative ionization continues until the potential difference between the cylinder and the wire has dropped to a point where ionization by collision can no longer occur. The po-

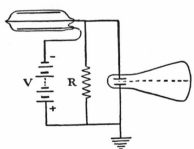

Fig. 6. The action of a counter is best studied with a cathode-ray oscillograph.

[6] Christoph, W., and Hanle, W., *Phys. Zeits.*, *34*, 641 (1933).
[7] Locher, G. L., *Frank. Inst., J.*, *216*, 553 (1933).

tential recovers itself according to the time constant R_1C of the circuit, C being the distributed capacity as well as the capacity of the coupling condenser.

The best way, however, to study the action of a G-M counter is to connect it directly to the two deflecting plates of a cathode-ray oscillograph as shown in Fig. 6.   The other pair of oscillograph plates is connected to a linear sweep circuit whose frequency can be varied.   If R is about 10^9 ohms, then as the potential V is raised, a point is reached at which deflections of the electron beam will occur at random intervals of time, indicating that the G-M tube has started to count.   As V is raised farther, the average number of pulses per unit time remains the same, but the magnitude, as shown by the oscillograph, increases by nearly the same amount that V increases.   By such means it can be shown that the potential to which the voltage falls during a discharge is not far below the threshold, the actual amount being roughly proportional to the difference between the applied voltage and the threshold potential.

The character of the discharge should be that shown in Fig. 7(a), where V_T is the threshold voltage.   Counters

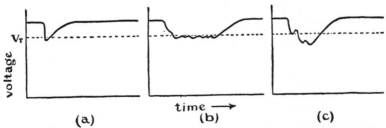

Fig. 7.   Three typical discharges of a G-M counter as seen with the oscillograph.   (a) represents the shape of discharge shown by a *fast* counter; (b) and (c) are representative of *slow* counters.   The width of the pulse in (a) may be made as short as 10^{-6} second; that for (b) or (c) may be as long as 0.2 second for a very slow counter.

may be divided into two main classes, "fast" counters and "slow" counters.   The drop in potential across the counter is extremely rapid for a fast counter, while the recovery time depends upon the product of R and the distributed capacity

of the circuit.   If the counter is a slow one, the breakdown
will be much less rapid, and the potential may remain near
the threshold for a relatively long time, as much as 0.2 second
in some cases, as represented in Fig. 7(b).   When a radioactive source is brought up, the time spent by the counter in
a continuous discharge state near the threshold may increase, so that the counter in a recording circuit would appear
to be insensitive to radioactivity or even to have a negative
sensitivity.   In some cases the shape of the discharge is that
shown in Fig. 7(c), where the breakdown is rapid at first
but the counter fails to recover immediately, the potential
fluctuating over wide ranges until recovery finally sets in.

Fast counters will retain the shape of discharge curve
shown in Fig. 7(a) when the resistance R is decreased to as
low as 10^5 ohms.   The length of the pulse in this case will be
about 10^{-5} second.   The best counters will still extinguish
themselves when R is made as low as 4000 ohms.   The width
of the pulse on the oscillograph in this case cannot easily be
measured, but it should be less than 10^{-6} second if C is
about 25 micro-microfarads.

Counters with this short time constant have important
applications when high counting rates are to be measured or
when the number of accidentals in a coincidence circuit is to
be kept at a minimum.   In fact, it is usually necessary to use
only two G-M counters in a coincidence circuit, for, as will
be shown later, if each of the two counters counts on the
average 3 times a second, then with a pulse of time width 10^{-5}
second there will be an average of only 16 accidentals per
day.

A complete explanation of the action of these counters
cannot be given, but it appears that the chief agents causing
the pulse are electrons and not negative ions, since the latter
have much too low a mobility to be collected in these short
times.   In a slow counter there is a delaying action of
some sort, and charges are collected over a relatively long
period of time.   It seems probable that negative ions as well
as electrons are collected at the central wire in this case.

As will be discussed presently, the surface of the cylinder has a vital effect upon the action of the counter. Among the possible physical properties which might be altered by treatment and affect the counter action could be mentioned (1) the work function of the surface, which would affect its photoelectric properties, and (2) the electrical resistance of the surface of the metal cylinder. At the present time, as already mentioned, very little is known of counter action.

Something can be said, however, as to the treatment which will give counters the very desirable characteristic of furnishing an extremely short pulse. This treatment, which will be discussed later, is not always necessary. In fact, counters with copper cylinders which have never been treated have worked well with 10^5 ohms across them. There is, at present, no rule by which it can be predicted whether or not a counter will have this short reaction time. The proper procedure is to try the counter in a circuit such as that shown in Fig. 13. If it fails to work, then an oscillograph would show that when a potential slightly above the threshold is reached, the counter will discharge once and then remain in a continuously conducting state.

Construction of G-M counters. The simplest method of making a G-M tube is to take a copper or brass tube of a

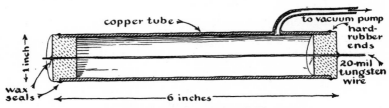

Fig. 8.   Simple construction of a G-M counter.

length at least five times the diameter, insert a hard-rubber plug in each end, and pass through the plugs, coaxial with the cylinder, a straight wire 0.1 to 0.2 mm in diameter. (See Fig. 8.) The wire can be made of many metals, but tungsten or copper will give good results. The whole must be made tight and the gas pressure reduced to from 3 to 6 cm of mercury. The gas may be air or a mixture of air and one of the noble gases, particularly argon.

A counter made in this fashion may work satisfactorily for a while, but it is not suited for constant operation over long periods of time. Even though the tube could be made perfectly tight, which is difficult, it still suffers from the defect of having a high temperature coefficient. Curtiss[8] has shown that with a tube having hard-rubber ends, the count goes down as the temperature increases, indicating an increase in the density of the gas, probably due to the outgassing of the hard rubber. This temperature coefficient can, in practice, be completely eliminated by sealing the

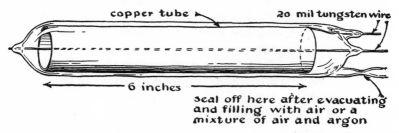

Fig. 9. Typical construction of a copper-in-glass counter. Following this general design, counters have been made from 0.5 cm to 10 cm in diameter.

metal tube inside a glass tube and making metal-glass seals to the tungsten wires. The construction details of a counter of this latter design are shown in Fig. 9. Satisfactory counters of this copper-in-glass type have been made from 0.5 cm to 10 cm in diameter.

After the counter is assembled, a concentrated solution of nitric acid (12 to 16 normal) should be admitted and allowed to attack the copper vigorously for 10 to 20 seconds. The acid is then removed and the counter washed thoroughly with distilled water. Under this treatment the copper will turn a dark, almost black color, which probably is due to a thin layer of CuO. The tube is then dried, evacuated, and the desired amount of gas admitted.

[8] Curtiss, L. F., *Bureau of Standards, J. of Research, 10,* 229 (1933).

The kind and amount of gas used determine to some extent the action of the counter. For many purposes air admitted to a pressure of 3 to 6 cm of mercury results in a very satisfactory counter. A mixture of argon and 10 to 20 per cent air for the same total pressure will have a threshold perhaps 40 per cent lower than air alone. There seems to be little choice, however, between the mixture of air and argon and air only. The counter will not work with pure argon. The threshold potential for a counter, 2.5 cm in diameter with a 10-mil wire, filled with 5 cm of mercury pressure of argon and 1 cm of air, will be about 800 volts. The same counter filled with air to the same total pressure will have a threshold of about 1200 volts.

Counters made according to the above directions will, in general, be of the *slow* type, that is, the collection time for the ions will be of the order of 0.1 to 0.01 second. Such counters are quite satisfactory for many purposes where short reaction times are not necessary. They may be used in the conventional Geiger circuit shown in Fig. 12, or if it is desired to eliminate the high resistance, a radio tube may be used to help the counter recover itself as shown in Figs. 14 and 15.

In case it is desired to make a *fast* counter, that is, one in which the collection time of the ions is of the order of 10^{-5} second, a different treatment of the copper cylinder is necessary. The treatment to be described is one of several known to produce a fast counter. A counter so treated will have the following characteristics: (1) The threshold potential will be as low or lower than for the same size counter filled with a mixture of argon and air at the same pressure. (2) The length of the plateau will be at least 30 per cent of the threshold potential. (3) The counter will function in the circuit shown in Fig. 13 with only 100,000 ohms in series with the high potential, instead of the 10^9 ohms necessary for a slow counter. (4) The efficiency is high. By amplifying the pulses, the efficiency of a $2\frac{3}{4}$-inch counter was found to be 100 per cent at a counting rate of 30,000 per minute within the limits of experimental error, which may be taken to be 1 per cent.

The procedure to make a *fast* counter is as follows:

1. Starting with a copper-in-glass counter with a tungsten wire, clean the copper thoroughly with about 6 normal nitric acid. (A water aspirator is indispensable for admitting and removing solutions.) Such a concentration of acid will leave the copper very bright.

2. After rinsing well, introduce a solution of 0.1 normal nitric acid. This will remove any copper compounds formed by the stronger acid.

3. Rinse thoroughly (at least 10 times) with distilled water and dry.

4. With dry air inside, heat the whole counter in a large flame until the copper turns a uniform brownish-black color.

5. Seal the counter off temporarily and then heat for several hours at about 400°C. Upon cooling, the copper cylinder will be coated with the bright red oxide, Cu_2O.

6. Evacuate and admit dry NO_2 gas to a pressure of 1 atmosphere. (This gas can be made by the action of 16 normal nitric acid on copper. It may be dried by passing through $CaCl_2$ and P_2O_5.)

7. Heat the counter with the NO_2 until the Cu_2O turns a dark velvety color. Pump out the NO_2.

8. Admit argon (commercial, 99 per cent pure is satisfactory), which has been bubbled through xylene, to a pressure of 6 to 10 cm of mercury pressure. The counter should be tried at this point. For a 1-inch counter the threshold should be 600 to 800 volts for 8 cm of mercury pressure. If the counter does not work properly, the gas should be pumped out and more argon, which has been bubbled through the xylene, admitted.

9. When the counter is found to work satisfactorily, it may be sealed off.

Although all the above steps may not be necessary in all cases, yet this procedure has been found to give very

satisfactory counters having reaction times of 10^{-5} second
or better. The characteristics of the counters also seem to
be permanent. The photoelectric properties as well as the
electrical resistance of the surface are probably radically
changed by this treatment.

The use of a cathode-ray oscillograph is indispensable in
the proper study of the action of a counter, and its use
cannot be too strongly recommended.

The above treatment is limited to copper-in-glass counters,
and no method as yet has been found to be applicable to
counters in general.

Sensitivity of counters to ionizing particles. If a set of
three identical counters are arranged one above the other,
with their axes parallel and hori-
zontal, and are connected to a circuit (see page 290) which responds
only to coincidences between the
three counters, then if the middle
one is moved out of line, as shown
in Fig. 10(a), the counting rate
will begin to fall and, except for
accidentals, which produce a
small effect, the rate becomes
zero when the middle one has
been moved far enough so that a
single particle cannot pass
through all three. (The count-

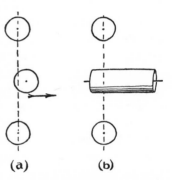

(a)   (b)

Fig. 10.   Testing the sensitivity of different regions of a
counter.

ing, when the three are in a line, is due, of course, to cosmic-
ray particles passing through the three counters.) Comparing this rate with the rate due to double coincidences between
the two outside counters, Street and Woodward[9] have shown
that for counters 3.82 cm in diameter the effective diameter
is the same as the geometrical diameter. Similarly, by rotating the middle counter 90°, as shown in Fig. 10(b), and moving it parallel to its axis, the sensitivity along the counter can
be obtained. With the conditions under which they were

⁹ Street, J. C., and Woodward, R. H., *Phys. Rev.*, *46*, 1032 (1934).

operating and with a counter whose geometrical length was 13 cm, the effective length was found to be 10.5 cm. The difference is probably dependent on the geometry of the arrangement as well as the potentials used.

A set of G-M tubes arranged in a vertical line and connected to count coincidences provides a means of determining the efficiency of a counter. If the middle counter were 100 per cent efficient, that is, if it responded to all cosmic-ray particles passing through the outside counters, then, if proper allowance were made for the accidentals, there should be as many counts when the middle one is turned off as when it is turned on. (The counter should not actually be removed, since the amount of absorbing matter will then be changed.) By comparing the rates in the two cases, an actual measure of the efficiency can be obtained. A good counter should be at least 95 per cent efficient. It is important that the efficiency for counters in a coincidence circuit be high, or the number of counts will be greatly reduced. If the efficiency of each of n counters is ϵ, the number of coincidences will be only ϵ^n of the number which would be counted if they were 100 per cent efficient.

G-M tubes for special uses. The tube illustrated in Fig. 9 answers very well the needs for work on cosmic rays, since the radiation readily penetrates the thin walls. For other types of radiation special constructions are necessary or are more efficient. A few of these will be discussed briefly.

For β-ray measurements, a point counter, as discussed on page 259, can be used at atmospheric pressure, in which case no trouble is experienced by the particles in entering the counter. In case the cylindrical counter is preferred, there are two alternatives: (1) Construct a thin window in the counter, usually at one end, or (2) if the β-ray source can be placed in a large chamber where the pressure can be reduced to the operating pressure of the counter, the metal cathode of the counter can be made of very thin material. As an illustration of this latter method Smythe and Hemmendinger[10]

---

[10] Smythe, W. R., and Hemmendinger, A., *Phys. Rev.*, *51*, 178 (1937).

have measured the activity of the potassium 40 isotope by using a counter with an aluminum wall 0.0254 mm thick and letting air at 5.6 cm of mercury pressure into the whole apparatus after the sample of potassium had been collected.

The above procedure for β rays applies equally well to α rays or other heavy charged particles, except that in general the windows must be made of thinner material, owing to the high energy loss of these particles in passing through matter. However, the proportional counter (see page 260) or the linear amplifier of Wynn-Williams,[11] as developed by Dunning,[12] is usually preferable in detecting these heavy particles, since the effects of other ionizing agents are negligible.

For the detection of γ rays it is desirable to increase as much as possible the number of secondary electrons emitted from the walls of the metal tube under the action of the radiation. As pointed out by Evans and Mugele,[13] this sensitivity can be increased by (1) making the cathode material from one of the heavy elements, such as platinum, which increases the absorption of the γ rays in the walls and produces more secondary electrons, and (2) increasing the surface area of the metal forming the cylinder either by grooving or by using a fine mesh screen. By these two devices it is possible to increase the count by a factor of two over that given by a plain copper electrode. The usefulness of a counter for measuring radiations is illustrated by the work of Pohl and Faessler,[14] who have shown that the intensity of a certain AgK_β radiation required only a few minutes to get a measurable response with a G-M counter, whereas it was necessary to expose Laue X-ray film to the same radiation for 100 hours.

When light of the proper frequency falls upon the inside of the metal tube of a counter, photoelectrons are liberated. Such a G-M photoelectric cell becomes a means of detecting

[11] Wynn-Williams, C. E., *Roy. Soc., Proc., A, 131*, 391 (1931).

[12] Dunning, John R., *Rev. Sci. Instruments, 5,* 387 (1934).

[13] Evans, R. D., and Mugele, R. A., *Rev. Sci. Instruments, 7*, 441 (1936).

[14] Pohl, M., and Faessler, A., *Zeits. f. Physik, 102*, 562 (1936).

very feeble radiations.   The metal used for the cylinder in the ordinary counter has its photoelectric threshold below the region of transmission by the glass and hence does not respond to the light falling upon it.   For metals of this nature the tube may be made to respond to radiations from 1800 Å up to the threshold of the metal by cementing a quartz window on one end of the glass tube as shown in Fig. 11.   The central wire of tungsten should be large enough

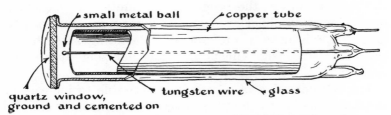

Fig. 11.   A counter which may be used for photoelectric work.

to support itself well from one end.   The free end should terminate in a small ball to eliminate point discharges.

The whole tube surrounding the metal cylinder could be made from quartz, and quartz-glass graded seals used where the wires are to be taken through.

The spectral sensitivity characteristics of counters having aluminum, zinc, cadmium, iron, and copper cathodes have been determined by Kreuchen[15] in the region 4000 Å to 2540 Å.   He found that they correspond in all cases for the same metals when used in ordinary photoelectric cells. Using the three metals zinc, cadmium, and copper in the bulk state, Kreuchen[16] also found that the sensitivity was increased by activating with hydrogen, but that these metals when evaporated showed no increase when treated with hydrogen.   The photoelectric yield of the activated bulk metal and the evaporated metal was the same.

Very little work has so far been done with cathodes of metals that are sensitive in the visible.   Locher[17] was one

[15] Kreuchen, K. H., *Zeits. f. Physik*, *94*, 549 (1935).
[16] Kreuchen, K. H., *Zeits. f. Physik*, *97*, 625 (1935).
[17] Locher, G. L., *Phys. Rev.*, *42*, 525 (1932).

of the first to work on this problem, producing counters with cylinders of various metals. He tested the sensitivities in the ultraviolet and in the visible, both of the pure metals and metals coated with dyes and other foreign substances. Kolin[18] has succeeded in evaporating sodium, magnesium, and calcium onto the metal cylinder and has attained high sensitivities in the visible. Christoph[19] has done the most extensive investigation of the problem so far. Using an evaporated coating of calcium, he has determined the characteristic of the counter for ultraviolet and visible light and finds that consistent behavior can be obtained after the counter has had a chance to age.

It appears that photoelectric G-M counters are less reliable than the photoelectric cell at the present time, but, owing to the sensitivity attainable, the former may offer a fruitful field of research.

Methods of measuring the number of counts. The string electrometer has been applied successfully by Rutherford and others[20] in counting particles up to an average of 1000 per minute by recording the motion of the fiber on a photographic film. This method has the advantage of simplicity but is limited to relatively low counts because of the response of the electrometer. It also has the disadvantage that the reading cannot be obtained immediately. The usual method today is to take advantage of the amplifying action of various kinds of vacuum and gas tubes, which eventually operate a mechanical recorder.

The conventional circuit for such a recorder in its simplest form is shown in Fig. 12. The bias on the grid of the first tube is such that the plate current is only partially stopped. The bias on the second tube is such that it almost completely blocks the plate current. When an ionizing particle passes through the counter, the wire collects a negative charge, which causes the grid of T_1 to go negative. The plate poten-

[18] Kolin, A., *Rev. Sci. Instruments*, 6, 230 (1935).

[19] Christoph, W., *Ann. d. Physik*, 23, 47 (1935).

[20] Rutherford, Ernest; Chadwick, James; and Ellis, C. D., *Radiation from Radioactive Substances*, page 52. New York: The Macmillan Company, 1930.

tial of T_1 rises, thus causing the grid on T_2 to go positive. T_2 then passes current, and if the quantity of charge is sufficient, the mechanical recorder[21] K will be actuated.

The value that R must have for the counter to function properly will depend on the counter.   For a very slow counter, that is, one which requires a long time for the charges to be collected, it may be necessary for R_1 to be as

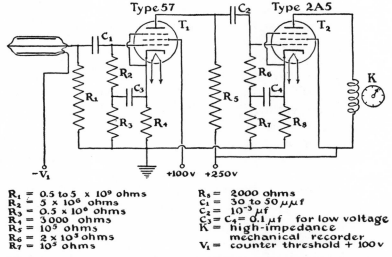

R_1 = 0.5 to 5 x 10^9 ohms	R_8 = 2000 ohms
R_2 = 5 x 10^6 ohms	C_1 = 30 to 50 $\mu\mu$f
R_3 = 0.5 x 10^6 ohms	C_2 = 10^{-3} μf
R_4 = 3000 ohms	$C_3 = C_4 = 0.1 \mu$f for low voltage
R_5 = 10^5 ohms	K = high-impedance
R_6 = 2 x 10^3 ohms	mechanical recorder
R_7 = 10^5 ohms	V_1 = counter threshold + 100 v

Fig. 12.   A conventional circuit for recording the pulses delivered by a G-M counter.

high as 5×10^9 ohms.   If the counter is a fast one, that is, if it is capable of giving a pulse of short duration, then R_1 may be as low as 10^5 ohms, and in some cases may be dropped to 4×10^3 ohms.   For these short reaction times, the duration of the pulse passed on to the second tube is too short for a vacuum-type tube, such as the 2A5, to pass sufficient quantity of electricity to actuate the mechanical recorder, and it is necessary to use either a pulse-lengthening device such as the multivibrator circuit to be described later, or

---

[21] Mechanical recorders of various resistances are manufactured by the Central Scientific Company, Chicago, Illinois.

a gas tube, for example, the 885. A circuit that is self-biasing throughout and designed for a fast counter using the 885 is shown in Fig. 13. The action of the second half of this circuit will be described later.

Almost any counter can be made to count by using a vacuum tube such as the type 57 or 6C6[22] to help the G-M counter extinguish itself. By so doing, it is possible to

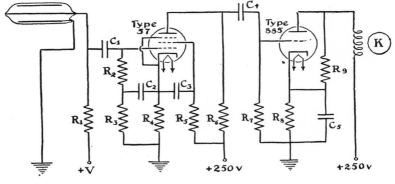

$R_1 = R_2 = R_3 = R_6 = R_7 = 10^5$ ohms
$R_4 = 2000$ ohms
$R_5 = 4 \times 10^5$ ohms
$R_8 = 10^4$ ohms
$R_9 = 7.5 \times 10^4$ ohms
$C_1 = 50 \mu\mu f$
$C_2 = C_3 = 0.1 \mu f$

$C_4 = 10^{-4} \mu f$
$C_5 = 0.2$ to $1.0 \mu f$
K = high-impedance mechanical recorder
V = counter threshold plus 100 volts

Fig. 13. A circuit designed for use with a *fast* counter. The resistance in series with the counter is much lower than in the conventional circuit. Because of the short pulse, a trigger-type tube is used to actuate the recorder.

eliminate such a high resistance as is used in the conventional circuit as well as greatly to increase the efficiency at high counting rates. There are several types of circuits by which this may be accomplished. The first[23] is shown in Fig. 14. The cylinder of the counter is connected directly to the grid of the first tube, while the potential which is applied to the wire is also connected to the plate of the tube through a

[22] The grid potential–plate current characteristic of these tubes makes them very desirable for this type of work. A negative $4\frac{1}{2}$ volts on the control grid are sufficient to block a potential of 1500 volts on the plate if 45 volts are used on the screen grid.

[23] Neher, H. V., and Harper, W. W., *Phys. Rev.*, *49*, 940 (1936).

resistance R_2. The coupling to the next tube is made by the usual condenser, except that in this case the pulse delivered is large enough to permit a small capacity C of the order of 10^{-5} microfarad to be used instead of 10^{-3} to 10^{-4} microfarad, as is used for the coupling condenser in the conventional circuit.

The action of the circuit can be explained briefly as follows: The vacuum tube is biased close to the point at which very little plate current flows. The full potential of V_1 is then across both the tube and the counter. When an ionizing

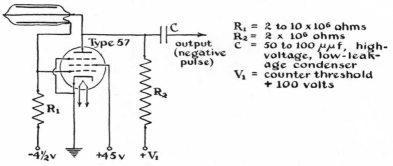

Fig. 14.   A circuit for use with a slow or fast counter using low resistances. The radio tube helps the G-M counter extinguish itself.

particle passes through the counter, positive charges collected by the cylinder cause the grid to go less negative. A current flows, causing a drop in potential across R_2. When this drop becomes. sufficient, the discharge in the counter will be extinguished, and the circuit recovers itself. This recovery is very rapid because of the low values of capacity and resistance. With such a circuit it has been found possible to count random pulses of 10^5 per minute with apparently few being missed.

The pulse delivered to a second tube will be negative, which means that the plate current in this tube must flow continuously except when a pulse occurs. If it is desired to operate a power tube, then, in order to conserve power, it is best to use another tube such as a type 27 inserted between

T_1 and T_2 to reverse the direction of the pulse. The negative pulse delivered by this circuit is, however, just what is
wanted on the mixing tubes in case two or more counters
are connected to count coincidences.

Another method[24] of using a vacuum tube to help the
G-M counter to recover itself is shown in Fig. 15. It will

be noticed that no bias is used
on the grid, so that there is
normally a drop of only a few
volts through the tube. Thus
the cathode, grid resistance,
screen voltage supply, and so
forth, are all at a high positive
potential. This puts a high
positive potential on the wire
of the G-M counter. If this
potential is above the threshold value, then when an ionizing particle passes through
the counter, a negative charge
collects on the grid, blocking
off the current in the tube.
This allows the cathode, grid,
and so forth, to drop rapidly
toward ground potential. As
soon as the potential across
the counter drops below the
threshold value and the negative charges have flowed off
across R_1, however, the grid

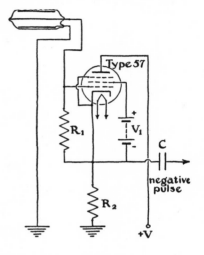

$R_1 = 5 \times 10^6$ ohms
$R_2 = 10^6$ ohms
$V_1 = 45$ volts
$V =$ counter threshold + 100 V
$C = 50$ to 100 $\mu\mu$f

Fig. 15. Second method of using
a radio tube to help the counter
extinguish itself. Since there is no
bias on the grid of the tube, practically the full voltage, V, is across R_2
and hence also across the counter.

again takes control, and the circuit rapidly recovers itself
and is ready for another count.

It will be observed that the pulse taken from the circuit of
Fig. 15 is negative. If a positive pulse is desired, a resistance of perhaps 2×10^5 ohms may be placed in the plate
circuit and a positive pulse to the next stage taken off as

---

[24] Neher, H. V., and Pickering, W. H., *Phys. Rev.*, *53*, 316 (1938).

shown in Fig. 16.   If, in addition, it is desired to eliminate the screen supply battery, a bleeder may be used as is also shown in Fig. 16.   When this resistance is placed between the high-voltage supply and the cathode, there is a definite end to the plateau, owing to the fact that the potential across the counter cannot drop below a certain value, which is determined by the ratio R_4/R_2. Consequently, if the high voltage is raised to such a point that this minimum value is above the threshold, the counter will not extinguish itself.

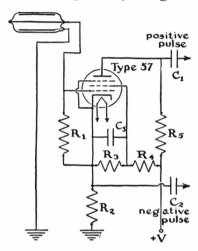

positive pulse

Type 57

C_1

R_1

C_3

R_5

R_3 R_4

R_2 negative pulse

C_2

+V

$R_1 = 5 \times 10^6$ ohms
$R_2 = 10^6$ ohms
$R_3 = 0.2 \times 10^6$ ohms
$R_4 = 0.5 \times 10^6$ ohms
$R_5 = 0.2 \times 10^6$ ohms
$C_1 = C_2 = 50$ to $100 \mu\mu f$
$C_3 = 0.1 \mu f$
$V =$ counter threshold $+ 100v$

Fig. 16.   Self-biasing arrangement for the screen grid of the circuit in Fig. 15.   A positive pulse may also be taken off when the resistance R_5 is inserted.

The advantages of this circuit over the preceding one are as follows: (1) The cylinder of the counter is grounded, which means that shielding is unnecessary and insulation less troublesome.   (2) For large counters the reaction time is less, since only the capacity of the wire, which is small, plays a part.   (3) Either a positive or a negative pulse may be taken off.   (4) The potential across the radio tube is not so large. The disadvantages are as follows: (1) An insulated filament supply must be used.   (2) The high-voltage supply must be able to stand from 0.5 to 1 milliampere of current continuously.

This latter circuit has been applied to some large counters for cosmic-ray work.   Since the number of counts for a given solid angle subtended by counters counting coincidences goes up with the area of the counters, there is a de-

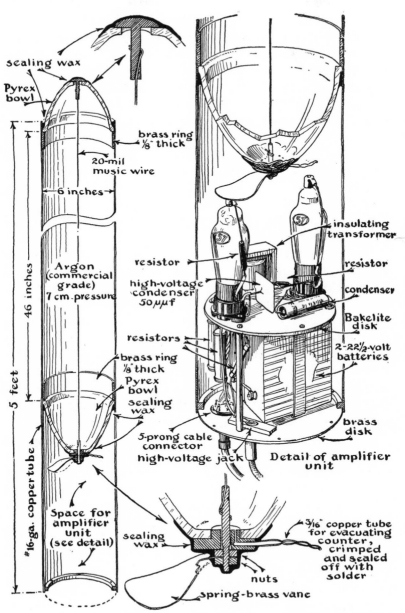

sealing wax

Pyrex
bowl

brass ring
⅛" thick

20-mil
music wire

6 inches

Argon
(commercial
grade)
7 cm. pressure

46 inches

5 feet

#16-ga. copper tube

brass ring
⅛" thick
Pyrex
bowl
sealing
wax

resistor

high-voltage
condenser
50μμf

resistors

5-prong cable
connector
high-voltage jack

insulating
transformer

resistor

condenser

Bakelite
disk

2-22½-volt
batteries

brass
disk

Detail of amplifier
unit

Space for
amplifier
unit
(see detail)

sealing
wax

nuts

3/16" copper tube
for evacuating
counter, crimped
and sealed
off with
solder

spring-brass vane

Fig. 17.   Design of some large counters using the circuit shown in Fig. 15.

cided advantage in increasing the size of the counter tubes. In this instance, copper tubes 5 feet long with a $\frac{1}{16}$-inch wall were employed. Some 12 inches of space were used at one end to mount two of the radio tubes. The arrangement is shown in Fig. 17. The Pyrex bowls which seal the ends are commercial transmitting station lead-in bowls, with the edges ground to fit inside the 6-inch tubing. Commercial argon, 99 per cent pure, was used at a pressure of 7 cm of mercury. The counting rate of each counter, which is due to cosmic rays and radioactivity in the counter and surroundings, was about 100 per second. The resolving time was 2×10^{-5} second with the constants shown in Fig. 15. This means that with three counters separated in a horizontal plane the accidentals were about 5 per hour.

Because of the short duration of the pulse in the preceding circuits, it is sometimes difficult to operate a mechanical recorder by using an amplifying tube such as that shown in Fig. 12. It is much more satisfactory to use a gas-filled trigger-type tube, such as the argon type 884, 885, or a mercury-vapor thyratron.[25] The former are quite inexpensive, have a short de-ionization time, and are preferable to the latter. One of the most satisfactory methods for using this tube has been devised by Pickering.[26] It is shown in Fig. 13 and in Fig. 18B, in which the second type of extinguishing circuit described above feeds the recorder circuit. The grid of the 885 is self-biased to a little beyond the point at which it can keep control. When the positive pulse from circuit A causes the gas discharge to take place in the 885, current flows through the recorder K, causing it to record a count. As the current continues to flow, C_2

---

[25] Each of these tubes has a very low plate resistance when in the conducting state. If the grid is sufficiently negative, no plate current will flow, but as soon as the grid potential is raised beyond a certain point, a gaseous discharge occurs, and the grid loses complete control. If a resistance is in series with the plate, the drop in potential inside the tube becomes approximately the ionization potential of the gas, or about 17 volts in the case of the argon tubes. The discharge can be stopped by dropping the plate potential below the ionization potential of the gas for a few microseconds.

[26] Pickering, W. H., *Rev. Sci. Instruments, 9,* 180 (1938).

charges up, and the potential of the cathode approaches
that of the plate.   However, the grid has remained near
ground potential,. so that the effective bias becomes very
large. When it becomes large enough, and the drop of potential across the tube becomes sufficiently small, the gaseous
discharge ceases, and the circuit returns to its normal state.

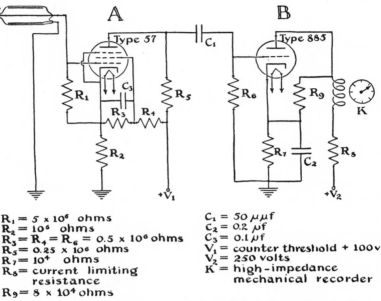

R₁ = 5 × 10⁶ ohms
R₂ = 10⁶ ohms
R₃ = R₄ = R₆ = 0.5 × 10⁶ ohms
R₅ = 0.25 × 10⁶ ohms
R₇ = 10⁴ ohms
R₈ = current limiting
       resistance
R₉ = 8 × 10⁴ ohms

C₁ = 50 μμf
C₂ = 0.2 μf
C₃ = 0.1 μf
V₁ = counter threshold + 100v
V₂ = 250 volts
K = high-impedance
       mechanical recorder

Fig. 18.   The circuit of Fig. 16 feeds a self-biased recording circuit.

The value of C_2 can be varied to suit the impedance of the
recorder K.   For the shortest resolving time, C_2 should be
made as small as possible.   The resistance R_8 may or may
not be necessary, depending on the impedance of the recorder.   In any case the instantaneous current through the
885 should not exceed 0.3 ampere.   The resolving time of
the circuit is usually shorter than that of the mechanical
recorder.

Another method of producing a pulse of much longer
duration than the initial pulse and so operating a mechanical
recorder is with the so-called multivibrator circuit.   This

circuit will give a square wave form in the output, the voltage swing of the plate being nearly the full potential applied. The length of the pulse on the output is independent of the length of pulse on the input, provided the latter is shorter than the natural pulse length delivered by the circuit.

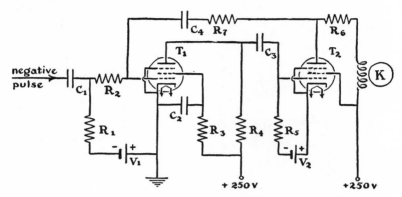

Medium Power Output	Large Power Output
T_1 = Type 6C6	T_1 = Type 6A4
T_2 = Type 41	T_2 = Type 6L6
$R_1 = R_2 = R_5 = 10^5$ ohms	$R_1 = R_2 = 10^5$ ohms
$R_3 = 0.5 \times 10^6$ ohms	$R_3 = 10^4$ ohms
$R_4 = 6 \times 10^4$ ohms	$R_4 = 10^4$ ohms
$R_6 = 0$ to 1.5×10^4 ohms	$R_5 = 5 \times 10^4$ ohms
depending on recorder K	$R_6 = 0$ to 1000 ohms
$R_7 = 10^6$ ohms	depending on recorder K
$C_1 = 10^{-3}$ to $10^{-4}\mu$fd	$R_7 = 10^6$ ohms
$C_2 = C_3 = 0.1\ \mu$fd, 400 volt	$C_1 = 10^{-3}$ to $10^{-4}\ \mu$fd
$C_4 = 10^{-2}$ to $10^{-4}\mu$fd (see text)	$C_2 = 0$
K = high-impedance	$C_3 = 0.5\mu$fd, 400 volt
mechanical recorder	$C_4 = 10^{-2}$ to $10^{-4}\ \mu$fd (see text)
$V_1 = 3$ volts	K = low-impedance
$V_2 = 60$ volts	mechanical recorder
	$V_1 = 11$ volts
	$V_2 = 45$ volts

Fig. 19. Multivibrator circuit.

This natural pulse length is determined chiefly by the feedback capacity C_4, Fig. 19.   The quantity of electricity which flows during a pulse is quite sufficient to operate a Cenco recorder of either the high- or low-impedance type.   If the 6L6 is used in the second stage, as much as 0.3 to 0.4 ampere can be delivered for any predetermined time up to say 0.1 second, provided the impedance of the output circuit is sufficiently low.   In case this type of circuit is desired, instead of using a thyratron such as the type 885, the arrangement in Fig. 19 may be substituted directly for the two tubes in Fig. 13.   It has many applications where a non-linear, constant pulse size output is desired.   By adjusting the grid voltage on the second tube the circuit can be made nonsensitive to input pulses less than a certain size.   For all pulses with a voltage swing beyond this limiting value, the size of pulse in the output will be constant, provided the pulse length in the input is less than the natural pulse length of the output.

The behavior of the circuit may be described briefly as follows: T_1 is biased so that it acts as a linear amplifier. T_2 is biased to just beyond the cutoff.   When a negative pulse arrives at C_1, T_1 passes a positive pulse onto T_2, and owing to the large condenser C_3, the grid of T_2 follows closely the plate of T_1 and hence goes positive by an amount depending on R_4 and the type of tube T_2.   As the plate of T_2 drops in voltage, a negative pulse is passed back onto the grid of T_1, causing T_2 to become still more conducting. This process continues until the plate of the second tube has dropped to within a few volts of the potential of its cathode. The grid of T_1 is now far below the potential of its cathode, and the charge on C_4 must leak off across R_2.   While this is occurring, T_2 is still highly conducting.   When the grid of T_1 returns to a point where the first tube again begins to conduct current, the plate of T_2 is allowed to rise in potential, and this in turn causes T_1 to be still more conducting.   The process is just the reverse of the initial stages of building up the pulse.   The make and break of the current in the plate circuit of the second tube is extremely rapid, each appearing to consume less than 10^{-6} second, provided there is a pure resistance load.   The time during which the plate current in T_2 remains at its constant value can be determined by C_4. As an illustration, when $C_4 = 2 \times 10^{-4}$ microfarad in either of the circuits shown in Fig. 19, the length of pulse in the output is about 5×10^{-4} second when a pulse the length of which is 10^{-5} second is fed to the input.

When the bias of T_2 is lessened, there comes a point when the circuit will become unstable and oscillate. Just before this point is reached, the sensitivity becomes extremely high. The point at which oscillations begin depends on C_4—the larger C_4, the greater must be the bias voltage on T_2. Using a type 6C6 and a type 41, with $C_4 = 0.5 \times 10^{-4}$ microfarad and the other constants those given in Fig. 19, a 0.007-volt pulse input of 10^{-5} second duration results in a full voltage swing of the plate. This is a voltage amplification of about 2.5×10^4. For an output pulse of longer duration, for example, 10^{-2} second, C_4 must be about 10^{-3} microfarad. In this case, for stable operation, T_2 must be biased such that a 3- to 4-volt pulse is needed on the input.

The circuit is adaptable for use with either a *fast* or *slow* G-M counter. If used with a fast counter, the negative pulse from the wire of the counter can be fed onto the grid of T_1 directly or through the condenser C_1. In case a slow counter is used, Getting[27] has pointed out that such a multivibrator circuit can be made to extinguish the counter in a way similar to the action of the circuits in Figs. 14 and 15. For such operation the wire of the counter is connected directly to the grid of T_1 with $R_2 = 0$ and $R_1 = 4 \times 10^6$ ohms. The cylinder of the counter has a negative potential applied equal to the threshold voltage plus 100 volts. The value of C_4 is adjusted to the reaction time of the individual counter as well as the reaction time of the recorder. A value of 3×10^{-4} microfarad is an average. The length of the plateau, however, is limited to the voltage swing of the output tube.

If the counts per unit time become too large, the mechanical recorder will miss an appreciable number. It is shown on page 299 that if any device can respond to only those impulses separated by a time interval greater than τ, then

[27] Getting, I. A., *Phys. Rev.*, *53*, 103 (1938).

the relative number of pulses missed, if they are spaced at random in time, is τN, where N is the average number of pulses per unit time. To overcome this difficulty, Wynn-Williams[28] has devised a scale-of-two circuit which cuts down the number of pulses by a factor of just two. It consists of two tubes such as the type 885, each tube being discharged by every other pulse. If another scale-of-two circuit is connected to one of the tubes of the first circuit, each tube of the second will respond alternately to half of the original pulses. Thus, one tube of the second circuit responds to only one fourth of the original number of pulses. This process of adding more scale-of-two circuits may be continued indefinitely, with one tube of the final circuit counting 2^{-n} of the original pulses, where n is the number of scale-of-two circuits.

A diagram of a modified[29] set of two of these scale-of-two circuits is shown in Fig. 20. The action is as follows: Let tubes 3 and 6 have a gaseous discharge. This state of affairs can be obtained by first closing S_1 and then S_2. The current through tubes 3 and 6 will cause a drop in potential across R_2 and R_4, which will bias tubes 2 and 5 so that they will not glow when S_2 is closed. The ratio of the plate potential to the grid potential for the grid to keep control is about 10 to 1 for the type 885 tube. However, to secure consistent action it is best to have this ratio somewhat lower. Ratios from 5 to 1 to 8 to 1 are recommended. Let a negative pulse be delivered to tube 1. A positive pulse will be passed on to tubes 2 and 3. Tube 2 will then become conducting, the drop in potential from plate to cathode becoming the ionization potential of the argon, or about 17 volts. The discharge of tube 2 thus causes a sudden drop in potential across R_8 which is passed on through C_4 to the plate of tube 3. But since tube 3 was conducting, R_9 already had a large drop in potential across it, and the additional pulse passed on

[28] Wynn-Williams, C. E., *Roy. Soc., Proc., 136*, 312 (1932).
[29] Shepherd, William G., and Haxby, Robert O., *Rev. Sci. Instruments, 7*, 425 (1936).

through C_4 makes the plate of tube 3 go negative with respect to the cathode.   The discharge is extinguished, and its grid then takes control.   Tube 2 is now glowing, and tube 3 is in the nonconducting state.   When a second negative pulse arrives at C_1, the above procedure is just the same except

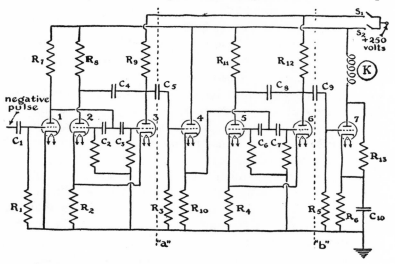

$R_1 = R_3 = R_5 = R_7 = R_{10} = 10^5$ ohms
$R_2 = R_4 = 600$ to 1000 ohms
$R_8 = R_9 = R_{11} = R_{12} = 5000$ ohms
$R_6 = 10^4$ ohms
$R_{13} = 7.5 \times 10^4$ ohms
All grid resistors $= 10^5$ ohms
Tubes 1, 4, = Type 56
Tubes 2, 3, 5, 6, 7, = Type 885

$C_1 = 0.005\,\mu f$
$C_2 = C_3 = 0.0005\,\mu f$
$C_4 = 0.02\,\mu f$
$C_5 = C_6 = C_7 = C_9 = 0.001\,\mu f$
$C_8 = 0.05\,\mu f$
$C_{10} = 0.2$ to $1.0\,\mu f$
K = high-impedance mechanical recorder

The unit between "a" and "b" may be considered a "scale of two" unit. Any number of such units may be added.

Fig. 20.   Modified Wynn-Williams scale-of-four working into the recording unit B of Fig. 18.

that the tubes are reversed.   It is obvious, then, that C_5 will receive a positive pulse only when tube 3 is made nonconducting, which will be just half the number of times a negative pulse arrives at C_1.

The unit from "a" to "b" of Fig. 20 is the same as the unit composed of tubes 1, 2, and 3, except for a slight difference in circuit constants and in the action of tube 4.   This latter

tube is inverted, so that it passes on a positive pulse as well
as responds to a positive pulse but is relatively insensitive
to negative pulses.   The number of pulses which appear at
C_9 is then only one fourth of the number impressed on C_1.
The unit from (a) to (b) may be considered a scale-of-two
unit, and any number may be added.   The final output is
made to actuate a self-biased recording circuit as shown in
Fig. 18B.

Tubes 1 and 4 act as one-way valves, keeping negative
pulses from passing through.   This makes for more consistent action, since a large negative potential applied to the
grid of an 885 will sometimes cause it to extinguish.   To
maintain stability, it is necessary to have the time constant
of the plate circuit greater than that of the grid circuit.

Still another method is available for counting impulses
delivered at a high rate.   By using a circuit somewhat
similar to the scale-of-two, Hunt[30] has devised a scheme to
obtain a pulsating direct current derived from charging and
discharging condensers by means of type 885 tubes.   A
micro- or milliammeter gives a reading proportional to the
average rate of arrival of the pulses.   By choosing the proper
capacities and resistances, this direct-frequency meter can
be used in counting random pulses up to 10^5 per minute.
The apparatus is conveniently calibrated with a beat-
frequency oscillator.

Coincident circuits.   In cosmic-ray work especially, it is
desirable to record only simultaneous discharges of two or
more counters.   Several means have been devised for accomplishing this, but the one now in almost universal use
is that of Rossi.[31]   It may be applied to any number of
counters.   The circuit is shown in Fig. 21.   The principle of
operation is as follows: The plates of all tubes are connected in parallel across a high resistance R_4 and a source
of potential.   The grid of each tube is normally at the same
potential as the cathode, so that the drop in potential

[30] Hunt, Frederick V., *Rev. Sci. Instruments, 6*, 43 (1935).

[31] Rossi, B., *Nature, 125*, 636 (1930).

across any one in the static condition is small compared with
the drop across R_4.   Under these conditions, if a negative
pulse arrives at C_1, tube T_1 will instantaneously have a much
higher resistance.   However, since T_2 and T_3 are in parallel
with T_1, there will be very little effect on the current through
R_4, and hence the drop in potential across R_4 will be practically unaltered.   The same holds if two tubes are affected,
say T_1 and T_2, for even though these suddenly assume a high
resistance due to their grids simultaneously being made more

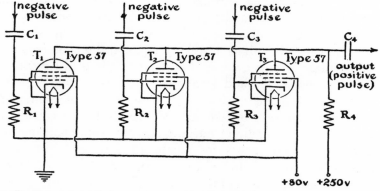

$R_1 = R_2 = R_3 = 2.5 \times 10^5$ ohms $R_4 = 1 \times 10^5$ ohms
$C_1 = C_2 = C_3 = 50$ to $100\ \mu\mu f$ $C_4 = 0.001\ \mu f$

Fig. 21.   Coincidence circuit of Rossi.   Any number of tubes may be used
in this parallel arrangement.

negative, the third one still has a low resistance compared
with R_4, and the resultant effect passed on through C_4 will
still be small.   However, if all three grids go more negative
simultaneously, then the potential at C_4 rises, and a positive
pulse is passed to the output.

With the circuit constants given in Fig. 21 the direct-
current resistance of each of the 57 or 6C6 tubes is 4000 ohms.
The maximum possible voltage change to the output when
one tube only receives a negative pulse is 0.8 volt, and when
two tubes only are so affected, the maximum possible change
is 2.8 volts.   However, when the grids of all three tubes go
negative simultaneously, the maximum change can be as

large as several hundred volts. By suitable adjustment of C_4, or of the grid potential on the first tube in the output, it is easy to rule out completely the singles and doubles and record only the triples.

For cosmic-ray work in which doubles, triples, quadruples, or any other number of coincidences are to be recorded, the

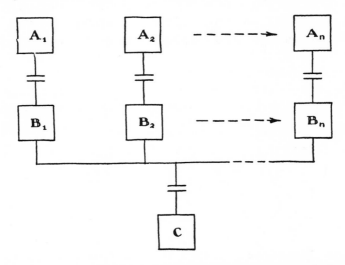

$A_1 = A_2 = A_n =$ G-M tube connected with vacuum tube as shown in Figs. 13, 14 or 15
$B_1 = B_2 = B_n =$ Amplifying tube such as shown in Fig. 21
$C =$ Suitable mixing tube such as is shown in Fig. 18B

Fig. 22. Schematic diagram for any number of G-M counters arranged to count coincidences.

following assembly, shown diagrammatically in Fig. 22, can be recommended:

1. Use the required number of high-speed counting circuits shown in Figs. 13, 14, or 15.

2. Connect the outputs through a capacity to the grids of the coincidence tubes shown in Fig. 21.

3. Use the output of this coincident circuit to operate the circuit shown in Fig. 18B.

High-voltage sources. Although batteries furnish an ideal source of high potential for counters, the expense involved usually prohibits their use. High-voltage direct-current generators can also be used, but the actual power required for the operation of a counter is so small that here again the expense is unjustified. The simplest and most practical method is to rectify alternating current after the potential has been increased with a transformer to the desired voltage, and then smooth the pulsating output with a condenser or, if much current is to be drawn, with one or more condensers and chokes.

In most cases half-wave rectification is sufficient, since the actual current drain for a Geiger counter is usually small.

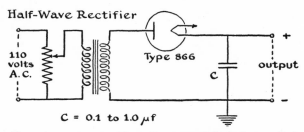

Fig. 23. For many purposes where the current drain is small, half-wave rectification is sufficient.

A simple, inexpensive rectifier is shown in Fig. 23, where a type 866 mercury-vapor tube[32] allows the condenser, C, to charge up to the peak voltage supplied by the transformer. It is necessary to have a filament transformer capable of withstanding the required potential if the negative side is grounded. The condenser C also has across it the full output potential. Its capacity need be no larger than 0.1 microfarad if only current to supply the counter is drawn. The amount of ripple for a current I can be computed approximately from

$$\Delta V = \frac{I}{Cn}, \quad \text{or} \quad \frac{\Delta V}{V} = \frac{1}{RCn},$$

[32] The type 866 mercury-vapor rectifier is an inexpensive tube which has ample current-carrying capacity and is rated for an inverse peak voltage of 7500. It requires a filament supply of 2.5 volts and 5 amperes.

Full-Wave Rectifier

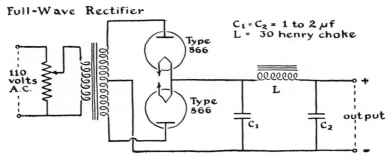

Fig. 24. If power is to be supplied, it is best to use full-wave rectification with a suitable filter.

where ΔV is the fluctuation in the voltage output, R the resistance across the output, and n the number of pulses supplied to the condenser, C, per second.

In case it is desired to draw much current from the output, it is best to rectify both halves of the alternating-current wave. Two 866 tubes may be used as shown in Fig. 24. In this case a transformer with a center-tapped secondary winding and one insulated filament transformer are necessary. The filter consists of two condensers of capacity of 1 to 2 microfarads and a 30-henry choke. The output of such a rectifier and filter unit will have less than a 1 per cent ripple for 60-cycle current when the current drain does not exceed 10 milliamperes.

If a rectified voltage is wanted which is greater than the peak potential supplied by the transformer, a voltage-doubling circuit such as shown in Fig. 25 may be used. The

Voltage Doubler

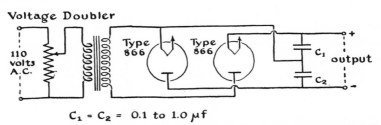

$C_1 = C_2 = 0.1$ to $1.0\ \mu f$

Fig. 25. The above arrangement will double the peak voltage supplied by the transformer. Two separate filament supplies must be used.

voltage output will be double the peak voltage available from the transformer. The circuit shown employs two type 866 mercury-vapor tubes.

If it is desired to regulate the output voltage, a voltage regulator such as will be described later can be used. These devices will also take out the ripple, provided the minimum at any time does not fall below the stabilized voltage.

Voltage regulators. Frequently it is desirable to maintain a constant voltage, for example, when working with a pro-portional Geiger counter. Several schemes[33] have been devised for accomplishing this, but one of the simplest is that shown in Fig. 26. The action is as follows: As the input potential is raised, no current flows through the 57, owing to the negative bias, until the output potential reaches a point where the grid is at about -3 volts with respect to the cathode. As the input potential is raised still farther, the output potential at first goes up slightly, and then, because of the drop in potential across R_4, reaches a maximum and finally falls. If g_m is the mutual conductance of the tube, the change of output voltage V_o with input V_i can be expressed as

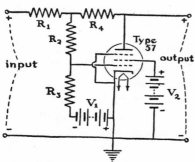

$R_1 = 0.2$ to 2×10^6 ohms
$R_2 = 4$ to 20×10^6 ohms
$R_3 = 2 \times 10^6$ ohms
$R_4 = 1$ to 2×10^4 ohms
$V_1 = 90$ volts
$V_2 = 45$ volts

Fig. 26. Simple type of voltage stabilizer which is suitable for potentials up to 4000 volts. If it is desired to stabilize voltages higher than this, a pentode designed for higher potentials must be used.

[33] See the following:
Ashworth, J. A., and Muzon, J. C., *Rev. Sci. Instruments, 8,* 127 (1937).
Evans, R. D., *Rev. Sci. Instruments, 5,* 371 (1934).
Gingrich, N. S., *Rev. Sci. Instruments, 7,* 207 (1936).
Richards, L. A., *Rev. Sci. Instruments, 4,* 479 (1933).
Street, J. E., and Johnson, T. H., *Frank. Inst., J., 214,* 155 (1932).
Webster, H. C., *Cambridge Phil. Soc., Proc., 28,* 121 (1931–1932).

$$\frac{\partial V_o}{\partial V_i} = \frac{R_2 + R_3 - R_3 R_4 g_m}{R_1 + R_2 + R_3 + R_1 R_3 g_m}.$$

If $R_4 = 0$, $R_1 = 2 \times 10^6$ ohms, $R_2 = 20 \times 10^6$ ohms, $R_3 = 2 \times 10^6$ ohms, $V_1 = 90$ volts, and $V_2 = 45$ volts, the regulation is about 1 per cent; that is, the change of output voltage is only 0.01 of the change of the input voltage. With $R_4 = 15,000$ ohms, and the other quantities the same as before, the maximum occurs experimentally at about 2000 volts input and 1000 volts output, and there is less than 1 volt change in the output when the input voltage is changed

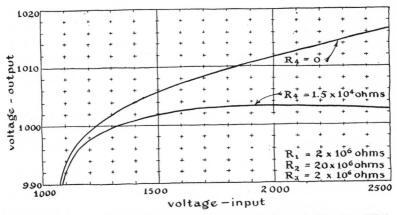

Fig. 27. Typical performance curve for the circuit shown in Fig. 26. With $R_4 = 0$, the regulation is about 1 per cent.

from 1500 to 2500 volts. Experimental results using the above circuit constants are shown in Fig. 27. As R_4 is increased, the maximum becomes sharper and moves down to lower voltages.

If it is desired to draw current from the output and still maintain a constant voltage supply, the above circuit is not satisfactory when more than a fraction of a milliampere of current is used. It is possible, by using the constant current characteristic of another pentode in conjunction with the above circuit, to keep a constant voltage output when the current is changed from 0 to 1 milliampere.

The circuit is shown in Fig. 28.   The action may be described as follows: As the input voltage is raised, a point is reached where T_1 becomes conducting, depending upon the ratio of R_2 to R_3.   Until this time, T_2 has been in a highly

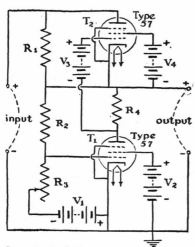

conducting state, with a direct-current resistance probably less than 1000 ohms, because of the $+45$ volts on the grid.   As soon as T_1 becomes conducting, the drop in potential across R_4 becomes approximately $V_3 + 3$ volts and tends to remain at this constant value.   As the input voltage is still further raised, T_2 continues to carry current but acts as a constant current device, and the voltage is stabilized by the action of T_1, as in the previous circuit.   If now current is drawn from the output, the immediate tendency is for the grid of T_1 to go more negative with respect to the cathode.   This makes T_1 less conducting, resulting in a less negative potential on the grid of T_2.   Thus T_2 becomes more conducting to supply the current delivered to the output.

R_1 = 2 x 10⁶ ohms
R_2 = 2 x 10⁶ ohms, wire wound
R_3 = variable, wire wound
R_4 = 10⁵ ohms
V_1 = 90 volts
V_2 = V_3 = V_4 = 45 volts

Fig. 28.   The above combination of two type 57 tubes permits excellent voltage stabilization for current drains up to 1 milliampere.   Drifts may be as low as 0.1 volt per hour in the output.   Potentials from several hundred to several thousand volts can be stabilized with this circuit using the type 57 tubes.

The performance of the circuit is illustrated in Fig. 29, where the circuit constants were those in Fig. 28 and $R_3 = 2 \times 10^5$ ohms.   The mutual interaction of the two tubes makes for a much more constant voltage regulation at all times than could be had with one tube.   Experimentally there was less than 0.1 volt change in the output of 1039.5

volts when the input changed from 1050 to 2500 volts.   A change from 0 to 1 milliampere drain at any input voltage above the stabilized value changes the output voltage by less than 0.2 volt.   When more current than this is drawn, the constant voltage characteristic of the circuit gradually disappears.

None of the resistances or potentials in the circuit are critical except V_1 and the ratio of R_2 to R_3.   For constancy, R_2 and R_3 should be wire wound and kept at the same temperature.   If V_1 is supplied by new "B" batteries of the dry-cell type, very satisfactory results will be obtained,

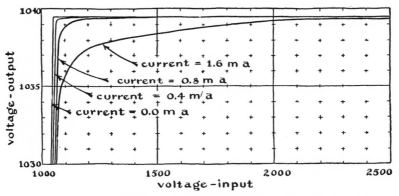

Fig. 29. Typical performance curves for the circuit shown in Fig. 28.   At no current drain there is less than 0.1 volt change in the output of 1039.5 volts when the input changes from 1050 to 2500 volts.

since their temperature coefficient is exceedingly small. The heater supply of T_2 is not at all critical, and a change of 50 per cent in the power input changes the output voltage of the circuit less than 0.1 volt.   However, a change of 50 per cent in the power input to the heater of T_1 changes the output voltage by about 5 volts in 1000.   Extended tests showed that after the first half hour, drifts may amount in the extreme cases to 1 volt per hour but may be as small as 0.1 volt per hour.

It will be noted that the output voltage is within a few volts of the input voltage until the constant voltage region begins, and that thereafter the power dissipation is in a radio tube and not in resistances.   By changing R_3 (Fig. 28) it is possible to achieve equal performance of the circuit from several hundred to several thousand volts.

This type of constant voltage device is a valuable aid in eliminating the ripple from rectified alternating current.   A condenser of low capacity can be used in the filter, and these circuits will take out the remainder of the ripple, provided the lowest potential reached is not below the stabilized voltage.

Although the type 57 and similar tubes are rated by the manufacturer at about 250 volts on the plate, much higher voltages than this may be applied if the wattage dissipation is kept low.   The limiting factor is usually sparking over in the base of the tube.   Almost all of the tubes of this type will stand 2000 volts on the plate, and many of them will not break down under 4000 to 5000 volts.

Discussion of probabilities and errors in Geiger counter work.   *Time between individual particles.*   If the particles are all independent of one another, they arrive at random, and the laws of probability can be applied.   Assuming a constant source of radiation, the probability of finding a time interval between t and $t + dt$ is given by[34]

$$P_t dt = \frac{1}{\bar{t}} e^{-\frac{t}{\bar{t}}} dt, \tag{1}$$

where $\bar{t}$ is the average value of the time interval.   Then the probability of finding a time interval between t_1 and t_2 is given by

$$\int_{t_1}^{t_2} P_t dt = e^{-\frac{t_2}{\bar{t}}} - e^{-\frac{t_1}{\bar{t}}}. \tag{2}$$

In particular, if we want to know the probability of finding a time interval equal to or less than the average time interval $\bar{t}$, we get $(1 - 1/e) = 0.632$, and the probability of finding a time interval between $\bar{t}$ and infinity is 0.368.   In

[34] See: *Handbuch der Exp. Physik*, XV, 786 (1928).   Wein, W., and Harms, F., editors, Leipzig (1928).

the case of a mechanical recorder which will not respond to pulses separated by a time less than τ, it is possible to find the average number of counts missed as follows: Let the average time between pulses, $\bar{t}$, be large compared with τ. Then Eq. 2 gives the probability of finding a time interval less than τ. To the first order of approximation this probability is $\tau/\bar{t}$. Thus, if N is the total number of particles counted, the mean error in the count will be $N\tau/\bar{t}$, and the mean relative error will be $\tau/\bar{t}$.

Number of particles in a given time. If the number of particles from a constant source of radiation is counted for a certain length of time and compared with the number counted again for the same length of time, the two values will, in general, be different. The relative error of a single set of counts will, of course, decrease as the number of counts is increased.

If $\bar{n}$ is the average number of particles arriving in a certain time, as determined by a long period of counting, and n is the actual number arriving in this time, the probability of finding this number n is given by Poisson's law[35]

$$P_n = \frac{(\bar{n})^n e^{-\bar{n}}}{n!}. \tag{3}$$

Thus, if by counting a large number of particles, it is found that on the average there are 100 per minute from a certain source, then the probability that in this same time 100 will actually be counted is 0.04, and the probability of 50 being counted is only about 10^{-8}. There is a certain probability of any number being counted, but obviously

$$\sum_0^\infty P_n = 1.$$

Error in a single count of n particles. If the mean or root mean square error, ϵ_m, is defined by

$$\epsilon_m{}^2 = \sum_0^\infty (n - \bar{n})^2 P_n,$$

---

[35] Bateman, H., *Phil. Mag.*, *20*, 704 (1910).

then application to Poisson's law gives

$$\epsilon_m = (\bar{n})^{1/2}, \tag{4}$$

and the probable error[36] is $0.67\epsilon_m = 0.67\,n^{1/2}$, since for large values, n differs from $\bar{n}$ by only a small amount. The mean relative error, therefore, is ϵ_m/n, or $n^{-1/2}$. In order to have a probable error of 1 per cent in a single set of counts, it is, therefore, necessary to count 4300 particles; and to have a probable error of 0.1 per cent, 4.5×10^5 particles must be counted.

Error introduced by background. If a single' counter is used to measure the activity of a source of radiation which is comparable with the natural count of the counter due to background, it is important to know the effect of the background upon the accuracy of the measurements.

If the error of one set of counts is ϵ_1, and the error in another set of counts is ϵ_2, then the error of the sum or difference will be

$$\epsilon = (\epsilon_1^2 + \epsilon_2^2)^{1/2}. \tag{5}$$

Consequently, if there are N_1 counts due to a certain radiation plus the background and N_2 counts due to the background only, the mean error of the difference. which is the effect of the source being measured, is $(N_1 + N_2)^{1/2}$, so that the relative mean error is $(N_1 + N_2)^{1/2}/(N_1 - N_2)$, and the relative probable error becomes[37]

$$\frac{\epsilon_p}{N_1 - N_2} = 0.67\frac{(N_1 + N_2)^{1/2}}{(N_1 - N_2)}. \tag{6}$$

As an example, if the counting when the source to be measured is present is twice what it is when only the background is being measured, then it is necessary to count $6 \times 4500 = 27,000$ counts with the source present to reduce the probable error of the difference to 1 per cent. This is six times as many counts as would be needed if no background were present. The counting time will be three times as long.

---

[36] See any book on errors for the relation between mean and probable errors.
[37] See also Evans, R. D., and Mugele, R. A., *Rev. Sci. Instruments*, **7**, 441 (1936).

In addition, half of this number must be counted when only the background is present, so that altogether $9 \times 4500 = 40,500$ counts must be made, which will take six times as long as if there were no background.

Errors due to accidentals in counting coincidences. If two counters are used to count coincidences between them, it will be found that even when the counters are separated by great distances in a horizontal direction, so that cosmic rays do not contribute to the coincidences, there remains a background of counts. These "accidentals" must usually be taken into account, especially when the real coincidences become of the same order of magnitude.

In a coincidence circuit using two tubes, if a pulse arrives at one amplifying tube within a certain time τ either before or after a similar pulse arrives at the other tube, where τ is the resolving time, a coincidence will be recorded. There is a certain probability that two unrelated pulses will thus be recorded as a coincidence, which, of course, is spurious.

Let the time widths of the pulses from each counter be equal. Then the resolving time will be defined as that time width of a pulse which will just respond as a coincidence when the peak of another similar pulse falls without a time 2τ of the first.

Let there be an average of N_1 pulses per second from one counter and an average of 1 per second from another counter. Then the probability that one will fall within a time width of one of the N_1 pulses will be $2\tau N_1$; and if there are 2 per second on the average from the one counter, then the number of accidentals will be $2(2\tau N_1)$, and so forth; and for N_2 per second the number of accidentals will be on the average

$$A_{12} = 2\tau N_1 N_2. \tag{7}$$

For the case of three counters connected to count triple coincidences, it is easily shown that the number of accidentals per second is given by

$$A_{123} = 3\tau^2 N_1 N_2 N_3, \tag{8}$$

when the counters are all separated in such a way that there are no real coincidences between any of the counters. The generalization of Eq. 8 for any number of counters n connected to count coincidences is

$$A_{12 \ldots n} = n\tau^{n-1}N^n, \tag{9}$$

where it is assumed that N and τ are the same for all counters. This last equation provides a ready means of determining the resolving time of the counter circuit. It is necessary only to separate the counters in a horizontal plane to such distances that the number of real coincidences between any two due to cosmic rays coming in near the horizon is small compared with the true accidentals, and to record the accidentals as well as the counting rate of one of the n similar counters.

In case the τ's and N's are all different, then, as Eckart and Shonka[38] have shown, the generalized expression becomes:

$$A_{12 \ldots n} = N_1 N_2 \ldots N_n \tau_1 \tau_2 \ldots \tau_n \left(\frac{1}{\tau_1} + \frac{1}{\tau_2} + \ldots \frac{1}{\tau_n} \right).$$

Consistency of data. To check whether or not a counter set is operating properly, it is usually desirable to compute the probable error of the final result in two different ways. If these agree in general to within the required limits, then it may be assumed that the counters have been working consistently and that instrumental fluctuations have been negligible.

Let the mean error in a single determination of N_1 counts be ϵ_1, the mean error in another determination of N_2 counts be ϵ_2, and so forth. Then by an extension of Eq. 5 the mean error of the result of n determinations is

$$\epsilon_m = (\epsilon_1^2 + \epsilon_2^2 + \ldots \epsilon_n^2)^{1/2},$$

or, by Eq. 4,

$$\epsilon_m = (N_1 + N_2 + \ldots N_n)^{1/2},$$

and the probable error is

$$\epsilon_p = 0.67(N_1 + N_2 + \ldots N_n)^{1/2}.$$

[38] Eckart, Carl, and Shonka, Francis R., *Phys. Rev.*, *53*, 752 (1938).

On the other hand, if N_1, N_2, and so forth, are taken over equal periods of time, the average value for this period of time will be

$$N_{av.} = \frac{N_1 + N_2 + \ldots N_n}{n}.$$

Let the residuals $(N - N_1)$, $(N - N_2)$, $\ldots (N - N_n)$ be denoted by r. Then the probable error of the result will be

$$\epsilon_p' = 0.67\left(\frac{\Sigma r^2}{n(n-1)}\right)^{1/2}.$$

If there are instrumental fluctuations entering, then ϵ_p' is usually greater than ϵ_p. If ϵ_p' is approximately equal to ϵ_p, it can be safely assumed that the counters are working consistently, for there is an even chance that the actual error will be greater than that computed, 1 chance in 4.6 that it will be greater than twice that computed, and only 1 chance in 22 that it will be greater than three times that computed.

TABLE I

Test on the Consistent Behavior of Two G-M Counters Counting Coincidences. N is the Number of Counts per Hour Taken with an Automatic Camera, and r the Deviation from the Mean or the Residual

N	r	r^2	N	r	r^2
3349	+ 5	25	3392	+ 38	1444
3333	− 21	441	3318	− 36	1296
3429	+ 75	5625	3232	− 122	14,884
3278	− 76	5776	3383	+ 29	841
3404	+ 50	2500	3292	− 62	3844
3308	− 46	2116	3500	+ 146	21,316
3292	− 62	3844	3340	− 14	196
3339	− 15	225	3481	+ 127	16,129
3373	+ 19	361	3295	− 59	3481
3350	− 4	16	3395	+ 41	1681

$$\Sigma N = 67,083 \quad \Sigma r^2 = 86,021$$
$$N_{av.} = 3354.1$$

Numerical example. The data shown in Table I were found with two large G-M counters counting coincidences, by taking readings every hour with an automatic camera. The probable error computed from the residuals is therefore

$$\epsilon_p' = 0.67\left(\frac{\Sigma r^2}{n(n-1)}\right)^{1/2} = 10.1,$$

and the number of counts per hour with the probable error is

3354.1 ± 10.1.

Computed from the number of counts, the probable error in 67,083 is $0.67(67,083)^{1/2} = 174$, and the number of counts per hour with the probable error can be written

3354.1 ± 8.7.

It will be noticed that the probable errors computed in these two ways are nearly equal, although that computed from the residuals of each hourly reading is somewhat larger.   However, there is no systematic trend in the data, there being nearly equal positive and negative residuals. An application of Chauvenet's[39] criterion to these data shows that a single residual must be larger than 150 in order to be rejected.   No residual in the example should, therefore, be discarded.   Consequently it may be concluded that there are no appreciable instrumental fluctuations entering into the result.

---

[39] Palmer, Albert de Forest, *Theory of Measurements*, page 127.   New York: McGraw-Hill Book Company, 1912.

CHAPTER VIII

Vacuum Thermopiles and the Measurement of Radiant Energy

BY

C. HAWLEY CARTWRIGHT AND JOHN STRONG

A RADIOMETRIC instrument consists of a blackened receiver, which is heated by the radiant energy to be measured. The instrument is provided with some physical means for measuring the rise in temperature of the receiver produced by the radiant energy. For the most delicate measurements the means employed must be responsive to a rise of temperature of the order of a few millionths of a degree.

In comparison with other methods of measuring light intensity, a radiometric instrument is characterized by the direct and simple way in which the response depends on the intensity of the light; the relation between these two quantities is linear. Also, the instrument is generally characterized by equal sensitivity for all wave lengths.

For measuring the intensity of radiant energy at wave lengths less than 1μ, radiometric instruments are more reliable but less sensitive than other instruments such as photoelectric or photographic photometers. Accordingly, a radiometric instrument is frequently used as a reference instrument for the calibration of photoelectric and photographic photometers. In infrared spectroscopy, however, the radiometric instrument is the most sensitive instrument now available.

When a radiometric instrument is giving its full response to a beam of light incident on the receiver, the rate at which the heat is lost by the receiver is in equilibrium with the rate at which heat is absorbed from the light beam, Φ_a. Inasmuch as the heat lost by the receiver is proportional to the produced rise in temperature, ΔT, we can write

$$\Phi_a = L_1 \Delta T + L_2 \Delta T + L_3 \Delta T + L_4 \Delta T, \tag{1}$$

where the L's represent the heat losses in unit time per unit temperature change. Thus, L_1 represents the loss of heat by radiation from the receiver, L_2 the loss by air conduction, L_3 the loss by conduction through members touching the receiver, and L_4 any other means of losing heat, such as, in the case of a thermopile, Peltier heat loss. Obviously, it is desirable to have the L's small, and for this reason the energy is to be concentrated onto a small receiver to reduce L_1. Furthermore, the receiver is usually mounted in a high vacuum in order to make L_2 vanish.

The response of the instrument is determined by the magnitude of ΔT, and different radiometric instruments are characterized by the manner in which ΔT is measured.

A thermopile measures ΔT by means of one or more thermoelectric junctions attached to the receiver.[1]

A microradiometer measures ΔT in the same manner as a thermopile.[2] In this instrument, however, the thermo-

---

[1] Brackett, F. S., and McAlister, E. D., *Rev. Sci. Instruments, 1,* 191 (1930).
Burger, H. C., and van Cittert, P. H., *Zeits. f. Physik, 66,* 210 (1930).
Coblentz, W. W., *Bureau of Standards, Bull., 11,* 131 (1914).
Firestone, F. A., *Rev. Sci. Instruments, 1,* 630 (1930).
Johansen, E. S., *Ann. d. Physik, 33,* 517 (1910); *Phys. Zeits., 14,* 998 (1913).
Lebedew, P., *Ann. d. Physik, 9,* 209 (1902).
Moll, W. J. H., *Inaug. Dissertation Utrecht* (1907); *Arch. Neerland, 13,* 100 (1908).
Moll, W. J. H., and Burger, H. C., *Zeits. f. Physik, 32,* 575 (1925); *Phil. Mag., 50,* 618 to 631 (1925).
Paschen, F., *Ann. d. Physik, 33,* 736 (1910).
Pettit, Edison, and Nicholson, Seth B., *Astrophys. J., 56,* 327 (1922).
Pfund, A. H., *Phys. Zeits., 13,* 870 (1912).
Rubens, H., *Zeits. f. Instrumentenk., 18,* 65 (1898).
[2] Boys, C. V., *Roy. Soc., Proc., 42,* 189 (1887), *44,* 96 (1888), *47,* 480 (1890); *Roy. Soc., Phil. Trans., 180A,* 169 (1889).
Coblentz, W. W., *Bureau of Standards, Bull., 2,* 479 (1906).
Paschen, F., *Ann. d. Physik, 48,* 272 (1893).

junctions and receiver are attached to the moving system of a galvanometer coil, which is suspended on a fine quartz fiber. The superiority of the microradiometer over a thermopile lies in the fact that, because no outside lead wires are required, energy losses in electrical resistance are diminished. However, the combination of the thermopile and galvanometer makes an instrument which is awkward to use in a spectrometer, because it must be protected from vibration in its operating position.

A bolometer consists of a blackened thin metal strip with electrical connections.[3] This strip forms the receiver for the radiations. It is connected as one arm of a balanced Wheatstone bridge. The change in the electrical resistance of the strip, as measured by a sensitive bridge galvanometer, is a measure of ΔT.

A radiometer consists of a system composed of a receiver and a mirror which is mounted in a partially evacuated case. The system is suspended by a fine quartz fiber. The back of the receiver is thermally insulated from the front, so that when a beam of light falls on the receiver, the front is heated more than the back.[4]

The radiometer is most sensitive at a gas pressure of about 0.06 mm of mercury. The gas molecules which strike the side of the receiver which is warmed by the radiations leave it with a greater velocity than those which strike the opposite and cooler side, and therefore a net backward recoil is exerted. This results in a deflection of the system until the recoil torque is balanced by the torque arising from

[3] Langley, S. P., *Am. Acad.*, *Proc.*, *16*, 342 (1881); *Annals of the Astrophysical Obs.*, *4*, 45 (1904), *5*, 75 (1905).

Leimbach, G., *Ann. d. Physik*, *33*, 308 (1910).

[4] Abbott, C. G., *Astrophys. J.*, *69*, 293 (1929).

Coblentz, W. W., *Bureau of Standards*, *Bull.*, *4*, 391 (1908), *9*, 15 (1913).

Crookes, Sir William, *Roy. Soc.*, *Phil. Trans.*, *11*, 166, 325 (1876).

Sandvik, O., *J.O.S.A.*, *12*, 355 (1926).

Hettner, G., *Zeits. f. Physik*, *27*, 12 (1924).

Nichols, E. F., *Phys. Rev.*, *4*, 297 (1897).

Smith, S., *Nat. Acad. Sci.*, *Proc.*, *16*, 373 (1930).

Tear, J. D., *Phys. Rev.*, *23*, 641 (1924).

torsion of the quartz fiber. The deflection of the system, as indicated by the mirror, is a measure of the temperature difference, ΔT, between the front and back surfaces of the receiver.

Anyone interested in radiometers will find some of the important papers on this subject listed in the footnotes. One of the features of the radiometer is its constant sensitivity. This reproducibility of the deflection is due partly to the use of a quartz suspension but mostly to the fact that the required pressure (0.06 mm of mercury) is one that is easily maintained permanently in a closed-off system. The radiometer has been used successfully in the microphotometer. The application of the radiometer to the microphotometer places but little demand on flexibility.

When maximum sensitivity is desired for very delicate measurements, the problem arises of choosing which type of radiometric instrument will be most sensitive, and further, which design of a given type will be most sensitive.

There are conflicting reports on the ultimate sensitivities obtainable with the different types of radiometric instruments. The thermopile is certainly almost as sensitive as any other radiometric instrument, and although other instruments might be made slightly more sensitive than vacuum thermopiles, they are usually more difficult to construct and use.[5] Accordingly, in our treatment here, the construction details of radiometric instruments other than the thermopile will be omitted. Vacuum thermopiles are widely used by experimenters in infrared spectroscopy, possibly more often than all other types of radiometric instruments taken together.

Construction and evacuation of a sensitive thermopile. The construction of a vacuum thermopile of the type shown in Fig. 1 will be described here.[6] This thermopile has two

---

[5] Cartwright, C. H., *Physics*, *1*, 211 (1931).

Klumb, Hans, *Zeits. f. techn. Physik*, *17*, 279 (1936).

[6] We wish to acknowledge the contributions to this design of Professor Firestone and Mr. Paul Weyrich, of the University of Michigan.

independent junctions and receivers. Four external leads are provided, so that these junctions either can be used separately or can be connected together in series or in oppo-

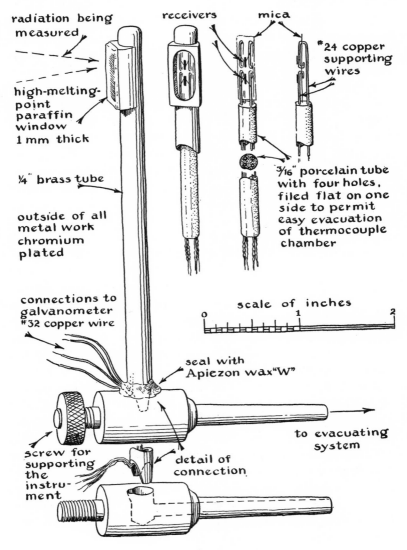

radiation being measured

receivers

mica

#24 copper supporting wires

high-melting-point paraffin window 1 mm thick

¼" brass tube

outside of all metal work chromium plated

3/16" porcelain tube with four holes, filed flat on one side to permit easy evacuation of thermocouple chamber

connections to galvanometer #32 copper wire

scale of inches

0   1   2

seal with Apiezon wax "W"

to evacuating system

screw for supporting the instrument

detail of connection

Fig. 1.

sition.   The thermopile is made compensating by connecting the junctions in opposition.   The receivers are rectangular and are placed end to end—an arrangement especially suited to spectroscopic investigations.   For special problems the shape of the receivers as well as other features of the design can, of course, be altered.

A crystalline quartz window is attached with Apiezon wax "W."   This wax is also used to seal the other joints. Apiezon wax "W" is easy to apply and has an extremely low

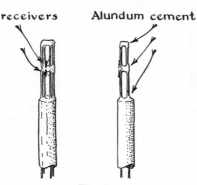

Fig. 2.

vapor pressure—a valuable feature for maintaining a permanent high vacuum.

A porcelain rod of $\frac{3}{16}$ inch in diameter containing four holes holds the relatively heavy copper wires on which the thermojunctions are mounted.   The projecting copper wires are fastened together by mica as shown in Fig. 1 or by Alundum cement as shown in Fig. 2 so that they will not vibrate.   Four flexible and insulated copper leads are soldered to these heavier copper wires, as shown in Fig. 1, and these are brought outside the housing through one of the wax seals.

Fig. 3 shows one method for maintaining a high vacuum of better than 10^{-4} mm of mercury in a thermopile.   The Pyrex tube shown here is filled with activated charcoal. The charcoal tube is evacuated and baked for several hours to outgas it before the stopcock is closed to isolate the system from the pumps.   At first the vacuum will be maintained at better than 10^{-4} mm of mercury for only a few hours.   However, each time the thermopile is re-evacuated the vacuum lasts longer, so that after about five evacuations, if the system is tight, the vacuum will remain good for a month or so.   The vacuum is tested by measuring the sensitivity of the thermopile under some convenient standard condition, such as that of exposing the thermopile to a 60-watt lamp placed 10 inches away and measuring the response of the junction with a relatively insensitive galvanometer. The degree of vacuum obtaining in a thermopile should not be tested with a spark, since electrostatic forces may destroy the junctions.

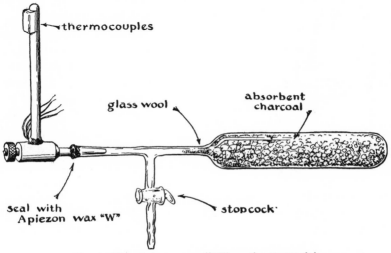

Fig. 3. (Use Apiezon wax "W" on the stopcock.)

Wires for the thermojunctions. One thermoelectric wire is made of pure bismuth, and the other is an alloy of bismuth and 5 per cent tin. The selection of this combination of wires to form thermojunctions has been made after a consideration of the Wiedemann-Franz coefficients, as well as of the thermoelectric powers of various possible combinations, including such metals as tellurium and the other bismuth alloys.[7]

The resistance of each thermoelectric wire should be at least 10 ohms, and the wire should not be longer than 3 mm. A bismuth wire 3 mm long with a resistance of 10 ohms has

[7] Cartwright, C. H., *Zeits. f. Physik, 92*, 153 (1934); *Ann. d. Physik, 18*, 656 (1933).

a diameter of about 24μ. The bismuth-tin alloy wire should have about 20 per cent more electrical resistance than the pure bismuth wire, because of the influence of the Wiedemann-Franz coefficient. However, owing to the greater specific electrical resistance of the bismuth alloy wire, its diameter will be about 7μ greater than the diameter of the pure bismuth wire.

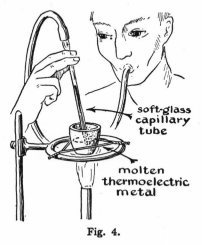

Preparation of the alloy wires. Thermoelectric wires can be purchased from the Baker Company, Newark, New Jersey, or they may be prepared by the Taylor process. To make the wires by the Taylor process, the thermoelectric metal is melted and sucked up into a thin-wall capillary tube of soft glass. (See Fig. 4.) This tube, containing the metal as a core, is heated in a small electric furnace and drawn out in the manner shown in Fig. 5. The

Fig. 4.

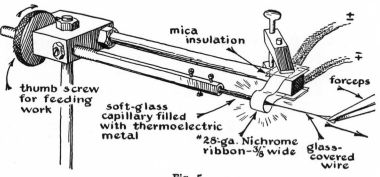

Fig. 5.

diameter of the wires produced in the composite drawn fibers is controlled by the temperature of the furnace and the speed of drawing. When the temperature of the furnace is properly regulated, the wires obtained are single crystals which can be bent and straightened repeatedly without breaking. Wires which are brittle should be discarded.

The glass is removed from the composite fibers with hydrofluoric acid, which dissolves the soft glass readily but scarcely corrodes or etches the metal. The hydrofluoric acid, usually diluted with a little water to suppress fuming, is conveniently held either in a shallow dish which has been coated with paraffin or simply in a groove melted in a block of paraffin. The wires are withdrawn from the acid with metal forceps and washed in a weak solution of Aerosol.[8] (Avoid letting the acid come in contact with the fingers.) The wires must be freed from all glass or difficulty in cutting and soldering will be encountered. About 5 minutes in the acid is required.

The good wires are mounted in flat cigar boxes, one for each of the metals. The electrical resistance of each wire should be measured and its resistance per unit length noted on a small label attached opposite the wire. After an assortment of wire sizes has been collected and measured, one is prepared to proceed with the construction of junctions of prescribed characteristics.

Construction of the junctions. A microscope of about 10-power magnification facilitates the manipulation and soldering of the thermoelectric wires. An erecting binocular type giving stereoscopic vision is ideal.

Fig. 6 illustrates the manner of soldering the thermoelectric wires to the copper supporting wires with a hot tinned sewing needle. The hot-wire device used for heating the needle is electrically heated, the heat being regulated by a resistance. The temperature of the tip of the sewing needle

---

[8] Aerosol or the detergent Dreft, the latter of which is sold in grocery stores, has many uses around the laboratory. Besides its usefulness in washing glass, aluminum mirrors, and so forth, it can be added to water to decrease its surface tension and increase wetting power. This is advisable for washing thermocouple wires, as the solution wets the wires and dissolves the hydrofluoric acid. Also, for coating the receivers, the solution with added Dreft has less "attraction" due to surface tension, and accordingly there is less danger of destroying the work when the brush with its blackening material is applied.

can be further controlled by varying the point of contact between the hot wire and the tip of the needle.

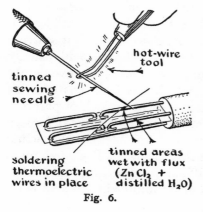

soldering
thermoelectric
wires in place

hot-wire
tool

tinned
sewing
needle

tinned areas
wet with flux
(Zn Cl₂ +
distilled H₂O)

Fig. 6.

Wood's metal is used for soldering. A solution of pure zinc chloride in distilled water is used as flux. After the soldering is completed, the excess zinc chloride should be carefully removed with a small brush wet with distilled water.

When the thermoelectric wires, which are selected for size so that each will be about 3 mm long, are soldered to the tinned copper supports, they are then "cut" to the proper length by touching them with the hot tinned needle as shown in Fig. 7. This not only "cuts" the wires but tins their ends at the same time. Difficulty with this operation will be encountered unless all of the glass has been dissolved off the wires.

These thermoelectric wires are now manipulated with a cold needle so that their ends are in contact. A little flux is added to their junction, and the soldering is effected by heat radiated from the hot-wire device. (See Fig. 8.) The junction is to be carefully watched. The instant to withdraw the heat is indicated by a slight jerk of the

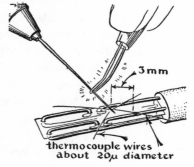

3 mm

thermocouple wires
about 20μ diameter

cutting thermoelectric wires

Fig. 7.

tips of the wires due to surface tension of the fused metal. If the resistance is too great, each wire is shortened by heating the Wood's metal at the base of the wire. Molten Wood's metal pulls in the thermocouple wire by surface tension.

The needle is used to heat the Wood's metal.   In this way, it is easy to construct two junctions with only a fraction of an ohm difference in their electrical resistances; and, if the

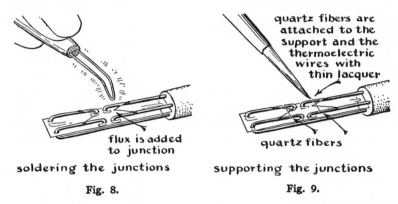

flux is added
to junction

soldering the junctions

Fig. 8.

quartz fibers are
attached to the
support and the
thermoelectric
wires with
thin lacquer

quartz fibers

supporting the junctions

Fig. 9.

wires used have been taken from the same stock piece of bismuth or alloy wire, the sensitivities of the junction will match closely.

Ruggedness in the final thermopile is obtained by the use of fine quartz fibers to support the thermoelectric wires and attached receivers.   The quartz fibers are fastened to the copper supporting wires by thin lacquer as illustrated in Fig. 9.

The receivers are made of thin gold foil of about 0.5μ thickness.   This is considerably thicker than sign painters'

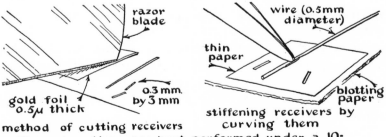

razor
blade

gold foil
0.5μ thick

0.3 mm.
by 3 mm

method of cutting receivers

wire (0.5mm
diameter)

thin
paper

blotting
paper

stiffening receivers by
curving them

These operations are best performed under a 10-power microscope.

Fig. 10.

gold leaf.[9] The receivers are cut to size (3 mm by 0.3 mm is a convenient size for spectroscopy) on the stage of the 10X microscope by means of a razor blade as shown in Fig. 10. The receivers are strengthened mechanically by giving them a cylindrical curvature in the following manner: The receiver is placed on a sheet of thin fine-grade paper mounted on blotting paper, and a rod of about 0.5 mm in diameter is pressed against it. (See Fig. 10.) Gold is particularly suitable for receivers because it is easily soldered.

A tiny bit of Wood's metal fused to the junction by radiation and wetted with flux facilitates attaching the receiver.

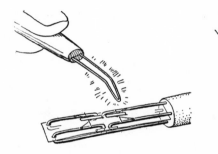

the receivers are coated with lampblack mixed with water that contains a trace of glue

soldering receivers in place

Fig. 11.

blackening the receivers

Fig. 12.

The gold receiver is laid in contact with the thermojunction and soldered by heating it with radiation from the hot-wire device. (See Fig. 11.) A slight jerk of the receiver indicates when the heater should be withdrawn.

After the receivers are soldered in place, they are blackened with lampblack or other blackening material with the aid of a very small amount of glue as a binder. This mixture is applied to the receiver with a small camel's-hair brush as shown in Fig. 12.

---

[9] Gold leaf of the required thickness is prepared by evaporating a proper amount of gold in vacuum (see Chapter IV) from a tungsten coil onto a glass plate. The film is then washed off the glass with a stream of water.

Finally, two quartz fibers are fastened over each receiver for added ruggedness.   The fibers are so fine and at the same time such poor heat conductors that the ruggedness gained by their use more than compensates for the negligible heat leakage which they introduce.   Fig. 13 illustrates the method of securing the receivers and shows the completed thermopile.

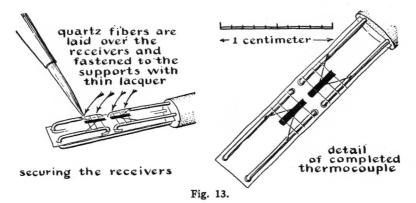

quartz fibers are laid over the receivers and fastened to the supports with thin lacquer

←— 1 centimeter —→

securing the receivers

detail of completed thermocouple

Fig. 13.

Alternative methods of constructing thermopiles.   Some experimenters prefer to make the housing for a thermopile from blown glass.   Fig. 14 shows a popular type of glass housing.   Fig. 15 shows how the junctions are manipulated in the field of the binocular microscope.

TABLE I

MATERIALS FOR THERMOPILE WINDOWS

Window Material	Spectral Region for Investigation
Crystalline quartz.................	Ultraviolet to 3.5μ
Fluorite..........................	Ultraviolet to 9μ
NaCl............................	Ultraviolet to 17μ
KCl.............................	Ultraviolet to 21μ
KBr.............................	Ultraviolet to 30μ
KI..............................	Ultraviolet to 35μ
High-melting-point paraffin.........	20μ to ∞
Crystalline quartz.................	45μ to ∞

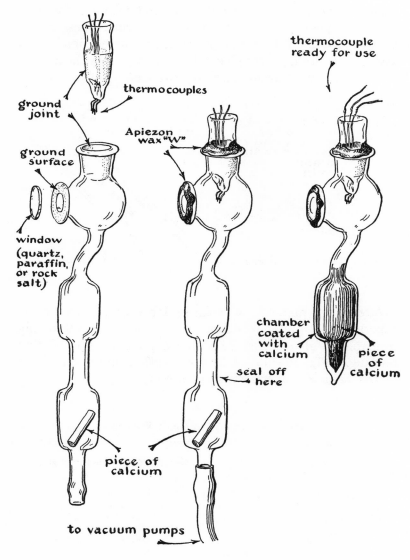

thermocouple
ready for use

thermocouples

ground
joint

Apiezon
wax "W"

ground
surface

window
(quartz,
paraffin,
or rock
salt)

chamber
coated
with
calcium

piece
of
calcium

seal off
here

piece of
calcium

to vacuum pumps

Fig. 14.

The selection of the proper window material for the thermopile is governed by the spectral region in which it is to be used. The appropriate choice can be made from the data given in Table I.

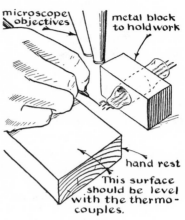

microscope objectives
metal block to hold work
hand rest
This surface should be level with the thermo-couples.

Fig. 15.

High-melting-point paraffin for use in the far infrared, listed in Table I, should not be confused with ordinary low-melting-point paraffin. High-melting-point paraffin is a crystalline material that does not deform when it is subjected to small stresses. In order to obtain strength and at the same time have the paraffin window very thin, it is advisable to make the window cylindrical. Fig. 16 illustrates a method of using a tube of paraffin turned out in the lathe. It is sufficient to have the cylindrical paraffin window only 1 mm thick. Inasmuch as the thermopile cannot be seen through

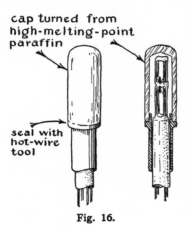

cap turned from high-melting-point paraffin
seal with hot-wire tool

Fig. 16.

the paraffin window, it is necessary to adjust the receivers to the focal point of the radiations with the help of the galvanometer.

Although the Taylor process for preparing thermoelectric wires is recommended, it is possible to obtain wires by the process used by Professor A. H. Pfund, whereby the molten metal is spashed on a plate of glass. One may either select small wires, that are accident-ally formed, or cut wires with a razor blade from the thin foil that is also formed. Wires obtained by this method have the disadvantage that, owing to fluctuations in their size, it is difficult to make matched junctions with them.

An alternate method of joining the thermocouple wires and attaching the receivers involves welding the thermoelectric wires together by means of a condenser discharge. The details of this procedure are given in the paper cited below.[10]

The receiver may be waxed to the welded thermojunction with Apiezon wax "W." This method of attaching the receiver yields almost the same sensitivity as soldering.

It is easier to construct a multiple-junction thermopile if one large receiver is waxed to the junctions than to undertake the delicate task of soldering separate small receivers to each junction. The electrical insulation between the junctions of a multiple-junction thermopile can be effected by coating each junction with lacquer before applying the wax used for holding the receivers.

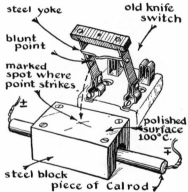

steel yoke
old knife switch
blunt point
marked spot where point strikes
polished surface 100°C.
steel block
piece of Calrod

The thermoelectric wires to be welded are placed on the marked spot and the blunt point is pressed down on them.

Fig. 17.

Some experimenters construct thermocouples in an order almost opposite to that described. The junction is formed, the receiver is fastened to the junction, and, finally, the thermocouple is soldered to the supporting wires.[11] This procedure is especially suited to the construction of a thermocouple with a small circular receiver, such as may be required for stellar radiometry. For a stellar thermocouple the junction may be soldered with a larger bit of Wood's metal so that there is formed at the junction a small sphere

[10] Cartwright, C. H., Rev. Sci. Instruments, 3, 73 (1932).
[11] Firestone, F. A., Rev. Sci. Instruments, 1, 630 (1930).

of metal, which is then compressed to form a flat receiver of circular shape and of the desired diameter.

Professor Pfund constructs thermocouples by compressing the thermoelectric wires together on a plate of polished steel that is heated to about 100°C.[12]   The receiver can be joined to the junction in the same manner.   A special device made from a knife switch is used for the manipulation as shown in Fig. 17.

For most applications lampblack is suitable for coating the receiver, but in special cases it may be preferable to use a selective absorbing material for "blackening" the receiver.[13] Thus, a thermopile used for investigation in the far infra-red spectrum between 52μ and 152μ might have receivers "blackened" with powdered glass.   For work in the visible and ultraviolet spectrum an electrolytic deposit of platinum black is particularly suitable.

The loss of heat by the radiation from a receiver is determined primarily by the emission of the receiver in the spectral region around 10μ (the region in which the maximum emission from a black body at room temperature occurs). The emissive power of platinum black in the region around 10μ is weak (about 20 per cent of that of a black body). Thus, the use of platinum black has the effect of reducing the heat loss L_1, so that the receiver is effectively only one fifth as great as if the receiver were coated with a material that is black for the heat spectrum as well as for the visible spectrum.   Besides increasing the sensitivity, this has the further advantage of reducing the theoretical number of junctions required for the best design.   Unblackened silver is suggested for receivers to be used in the ultraviolet region.

Fig. 3 illustrates the use of active charcoal for maintaining a high vacuum in the thermopile.   An alternate method

. [12] Pfund, A. H., "Radiation Thermopiles," *Rev. Sci. Instruments*, *8*, 417 (1937).

[13] Woltersdorff, W., *Zeits. f. Physik*, *91*, 230 (1934).

Forsythe, W. E., *Measurement of Radiant Energy*, page 210.   New York: McGraw-Hill Book Company, 1937.

Pfund, A. H., *J.O.S.A.*, *23*, 375 (1933), *23*, 270 (1933).

Strong, J., *Rev. Sci. Instruments*, *3*, 65 (1932).

involves the use of calcium as a getter. This method has
been used by Dr. Pettit of the Mount Wilson Observatory
and is quite satisfactory. Its use amounts to replacing the
active charcoal in the thermopile in Fig. 3 with fresh calcium
filings. These calcium filings are baked out while the tube
is connected to the pump. Later, from time to time when
the sensitivity of the thermopile falls off, owing to a decay
of the vacuum, maximum sensitivity can be re-established
simply by reheating the calcium.

The use of sensitive thermopiles. As ordinarily used, the
radiant energy focused on the active receiving surface of the
thermopile is interrupted periodically to isolate the effect
of this radiation from the effect of other radiations falling on
the receiver. The excursion of the galvanometer resulting
from interrupting the measured beam is ascribed to changes
in the temperature of the junctions produced by the radiant
energy. Considering that delicate measurements may produce a change in temperature of only $10^{-6}°C$., it is necessary
to interrupt the light rather accurately to compensate for
the first-order drifts which arise owing to a constant warming or cooling of the surroundings of the entire thermopile.
As a result, just as much time is required for controlling the
zero position of the galvanometer as for determining the
deflection produced by the energy being measured.

It is evident that care is required in selecting the best
position for the shutter in an optical system. For example,
it is required that the change in the radiant energy falling on
the thermopile due to closing the shutter should be the same
as the change produced by removing the source of the radiations without changing the position of any object "seen"
by the thermopile. Otherwise, the variation of radiation
from closing the shutter may falsify the measurement. The
shutter is to be put before the entrance slit of the spectrometer rather than after the exit slit in order to minimize this possibility.

Compensated thermopiles. While first-order drifts in
the galvanometer can be eliminated even for an uncom-

pensated thermopile by properly timing the exposures of the
thermopile to the radiant energy, second-order drifts (due
to a change in rate of the drift) can be eliminated only by
the use of a compensated thermopile. In practice, it is
difficult to construct a compensating receiver that will effect
the elimination of more than 90 per cent of the galvanometer
drift, but further compensation can be achieved by shunting
an electrical resistance across the most sensitive of the
junctions, either the active or the compensating ones.   The
junctions to be shunted and the value of the shunt resistance
are determined experimentally.   When the shunt resistance
has the proper value, severe temperature changes of the
surroundings of the thermopile housing produce a minimum
deflection of the galvanometer.   If care has been taken in
constructing a compensated thermopile, the shunting resistance will be great enough so that the sensitivity of the
thermopile is not appreciably impaired.   One method of
testing the compensation is to hold a hot soldering iron a few
centimeters in front of the thermopile.   When, for example,
a particular thermopile of the type shown in Fig. 1 was
compensated, the galvanometer drift was diminished to a
twentieth part of the original drift, and it was reduced
further a hundredfold by the shunting resistance.

Ordinarily, the energy to be measured is concentrated on
one receiver; the compensating receiver then acts as an external resistance in the galvanometer circuit, and therefore
the deflections are somewhat diminished.   In most cases the
reduction of first- and second-order drifts justifies compensation and the attendant smaller deflections.

By another procedure the image of the exit slit of the
spectrometer covers both receivers, while a shutter in front
of the entrance slit of the spectrometer obscures first the
aperture of the half of the slit focused on one receiver and
then the half focused on the other receiver.[14]   Thus the
area of each of the two receivers is half the area of the slit.
Theoretically, this scheme is expected to yield about 40

[14] Badger, R. M., *J.O.S.A.*, *15*, 370 (1927).

per cent more sensitivity than the ordinary compensated thermopile which has the area of the active receiver, as well as that of the compensating one, each equal to the area of the slit.   In order to realize this 40 per cent gain in another but less desirable way, the mirror used for concentrating the radiant energy may be tilted periodically, so that the image of the exit slit of the spectrometer covers first one receiver and then the other.

Auxiliary apparatus.   Ordinarily a galvanometer having a period of about 7 seconds and a low resistance of about 10 to 15 ohms is used with a thermopile.   For making delicate measurements, the wires leading from the thermopile to the galvanometer should be shielded, so that alternating currents will not be induced in them by stray electromagnetic fields.   When the wires are not properly shielded, induced alternating currents are, in a sense, rectified by the thermopile, especially by an uncompensated thermopile, and give a spurious galvanometer deflection.

A simple method of measuring the galvanometer response is to observe a well-illuminated scale with a telescope.   The galvanometer should be arranged so that the scale is at a distance of about 5 m.   A telescope of about 32-power magnification, placed as close as possible to the galvanometer, should be used.   With a galvanometer mirror 10 mm in diameter, it should be possible to see the millimeter divisions so clearly on a scale at a distance of 5 m that deflections on the scale can be estimated to a small fraction of a millimeter.

A lack of definition is often erroneously attributed to the galvanometer mirror, but it is usually due to the use of optically imperfect glass for the galvanometer window. However, there is a limit to the definition attainable, because of the finite size of the galvanometer mirror and the effect of diffraction.   A simple rule is that the scale distance as measured in meters must not be greater than the diameter of the galvanometer mirror as measured in millimeters.   Thus, for a scale distance of 5 m, the galvanometer should be at least 5 mm in diameter. About $\frac{1}{20}$ mm deflection at a distance of 5 m corresponds to the unavoidable natural fluctuations in the position of the galvanometer due to Brownian motion.

The accuracy with which the position of a cross hair on a millimeter scale can be estimated is much greater than

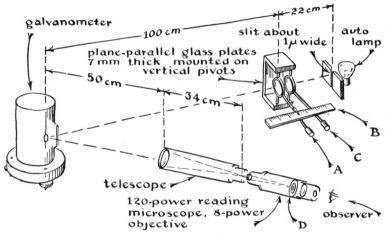

A — lever for adjusting parallel plate to compensate for the galvanometer deflection

B — tangent scale — The position of lever A read on this scale is proportional to the galvanometer deflection.

C — lever for adjusting "zero"

D — reticule in microscope — suggested form

image of slit in reading position

Fig. 18.

might at first be supposed. A standard laboratory experiment for students at the University of Berlin is to estimate the positions of extra marks made on a millimeter scale. All of the extra marks are made on a ruling engine, so that their positions are accurately known. Although the lines are all about $\frac{1}{10}$ mm wide, the student is asked to estimate the position of each extra line to $\frac{1}{100}$ mm. In estimating these positions, a student seldom makes an error of $\frac{1}{10}$ mm, and an experienced observer will have a probable error for a single reading of about 0.03 mm. Accordingly, it is significant to estimate galvanometer readings to $\frac{1}{20}$ mm.

Fig. 18 shows an ingenious and accurate arrangement used by Professor Czerny for determining the magnitude of small galvanometer deflections.[15]

Relays. A convenient method of reading galvanometer deflections is to use an optical amplifier. Also, when it is desirable to record radiometric measurements photographically, the primary deflections should be amplified by means of some type of relay, and the deflections of a secondary galvanometer recorded on moving photographic paper.

The Moll and Burger thermo-relay may be used for amplifying galvanometer deflections until Brownian motion becomes conspicuous.[16]   Other amplifiers include the barrier-layer photocell amplifier described by Barnes and Matossi[17] and the thermopile with two triangular-shaped receivers described by Cartwright.[18]

The Barnes and Matossi type of relay is made by dividing the active surface of a barrier-layer photocell by scratching along a diameter so as to make two contiguous semicircular areas of active surface. The arrangement of this amplifier is illustrated in Fig. 17, Chapter X. Leeds and Northrup produce an amplifying galvanometer and photocell combination of this type.[19]

The above methods of amplifying galvanometer deflections also magnify the drift of the primary galvanometer. This is undesirable. Pfund and Hardy have devised a resonance radiometer, which tends to "ignore" drift and separate it from the response to the measured radiation.[20]

[15] Czerny, M., *Zeits. f. Physik, 90*, 468 (1934).
Czerny, M., Heins, H., and Woltersdorff, W., *Zeits. f. Physik, 95*, 262 (1935).
[16] Moll, W. J. H., *Phil. Mag., 50*, 624 (1925). The Moll and Burger thermo-relay is sold by Kipp and Sonen, Delft, Holland.
[17] Barnes, R. B., and Matossi, R., *Zeits. f. Physik, 76*, 24 (1932).
[18] Cartwright, C. H., *Rev. Sci. Instruments, 3*, 221 (1932).
[19] Leeds and Northrup Company, Philadelphia, Pennsylvania.
[20] Hardy, J. D., *Rev. Sci. Instruments, 1*, 429 (1929), *5*, 120 (1934).
Pfund, A. H., *Science, 2*, 69 (1929).

Their scheme is somewhat elaborate and requires the use of a tuned pendulum shutter, in addition to two identical galvanometers. However, the instrument has advantages, especially when the thermopile is not adequately protected from extraneous thermal effects. Pfund describes the resonance radiometer briefly as follows:

If primary and secondary galvanometers are underdamped and adjusted to the same period, then, by interrupting the radiation falling on the thermopile with a periodicity corresponding to that of the galvanometers, a condition of resonance is set up. As a class, resonating systems are characterized by high sensitivity for "tuned" periodic disturbances and by indifference to random disturbances.

This indifference to random disturbances unfortunately does not include Brownian motions of the primary galvanometer. Hardy has measured the effect of the Brownian motion on the resonance radiometer and has found that the fluctuations in the deflection of the secondary galvanometer are magnified in accord with theoretical predictions for fluctuations due to Brownian motion.[21] Nevertheless, Hardy feels that delicate measurement to the limit set by these effects is definitely facilitated by the use of the resonance radiometer. The slowness of the resonance radiometer (it takes about 90 seconds to make a measurement) is one of its disadvantages.

Firestone[22] has made an ingenious variation from the Pfund scheme. It depends on charging and discharging a condenser through the secondary galvanometer with a circuit controlled by the amplified thermocouple current. A photocell amplifier is used. Naturally, as the output galvanometer circuit has infinite ohmic resistance, owing to the condenser in the circuit, no net current can flow, and consequently all deflections are excursions about an unchanging zero position.

We have emphasized the importance of using a compensated thermopile to diminish galvanometer drifts as well

[21] See also Van Lear. G. A.. Jr.. *Rev. Sci. Instruments, 4,* 21 (1933).
[22] Firestone, F. A., *Rev. Sci. Instruments, 3,* 163 (1932).

as to make the circuit electrically insensitive to high-frequency electromagnetic radiations. For the most delicate measurements, it is also necessary to have the galvanometer

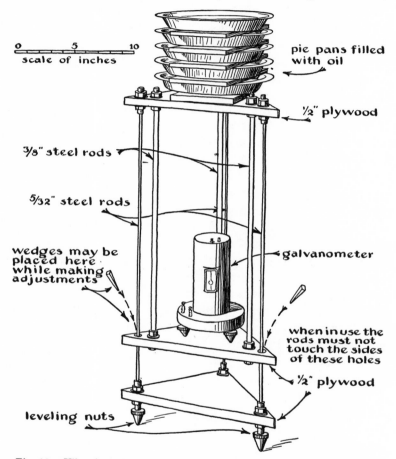

pie pans filled with oil

scale of inches

0 5 10

½" plywood

⅜" steel rods

5/32" steel rods

galvanometer

wedges may be placed here while making adjustments

when in use the rods must not touch the sides of these holes

½" plywood

leveling nuts

Fig. 19. Vibrationless support for a galvanometer. The plywood triangle, on which the galvanometer stands, should be loaded with lead weights until the natural oscillations have a period of about 2 seconds.

free from mechanical vibrations. This can be accomplished by the use of a vibrationless support such as the type shown in Fig. 19. The description of this vibrationless support is given in Chapter XIV.

Construction of thermojunctions by evaporation and sputtering. There are other applications of thermopiles and thermocouples, such as their use for vacuum manometers, for measuring alternating currents, for measuring sound intensities, for magnifying deflections of a spot of light in thermo-relays, and for total-radiation pyrometers. We cannot go into all these applications in detail, but the present chapter and the references cited should serve to guide an experimenter in these fields. The construction of thermopiles by evaporation and sputtering, however, warrants a description.

Thermopiles made from films of the thermoelectrically active metals, produced by evaporation or sputtering, can be constructed having a very low heat capacity, so low, in fact, that they will respond to the adiabatic heating produced by separate sound waves of 5000 cycles frequency.[23]

One of the metal films used is bismuth and the other is antimony. The foundation on which the metal films are deposited must be extremely thin and strong. For this purpose, glass, mica, or lacquer films are used.

When a soft-glass tube is fused at one end and strongly blown out with air pressure so as to expand and explode a thin bulb, the shattered bulb wall yields fine ribbons of glass about 1 or 2 mm wide and 1 or 2 cm long. These ribbons are of such a thickness as to give interference colors and make a suitable foundation for evaporated thermocouples.

When a mica sheet is rolled upon a stick of about 2 mm in diameter so that one of the principal directions is parallel to the stick, it is subject to shearing forces. These forces produce cleavages, so that when the sheet is subsequently split, bands from 1 to 0.1 mm wide are obtained which, judging from their interference colors, are as thin as or thinner than 1μ.[24]

Films for use as a thermopile base, or for many other

---

[23] Harris, L., and Johnson, E. A., *Rev. Sci. Instruments*, 5, 153 (1934).

[24] This is the technique described in Burger, H. C., and van Cittert, P. H., *Zeits. f. Physik*, 66, 210 (1930).

purposes, may be made by dropping a thinned solution of lacquer onto the surface of a bowl of dust-free distilled water.[25] Surface tension causes the drop to spread out, forming a liquid film on the water over about half the area of the water surface. The lacquer soon becomes solid as the solvent evaporates. Fig. 20 shows how these films are taken off the water on a metal frame. They are allowed to dry after the peripheral area of the film is pulled back anywhere that it is in contact with the main stretched area. The thickness of film desired is controlled by varying the dilution of the lacquer before it is dropped on the water.

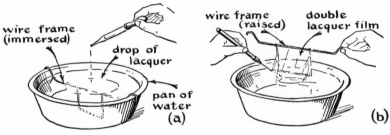

Fig. 20.

Extremely thin uniform films are formed on water cooled to 0°C. Films as thin as 5×10^{-6} cm are obtainable. Double films formed on a frame as illustrated in Fig. 20 are stronger than single films of double thickness, owing to the fact that, in the case of double films, weak areas in one film are seldom opposite weak areas in the second film.

When the thermoelectric metal is deposited on the foundation film by evaporation, the heat of condensation of the metal vapor, as well as the heat radiated by the filament and absorbed by the film, tends to elevate the temperature of the foundation. It is necessary to prevent the temperature of the film from rising to a point at which it might be

[25] Harris, L., and Johnson, E. A., *Rev. Sci. Instruments*, *4*, 454 (1933). They use methyl and ethyl acetate solvent for 2 parts cellulose acetate and 1 part glyptal lacquer at 0° C. to get the strongest films.

Czerny, M., and Mollet, P., *Zeits. f. Physik*, *108*, 85 (1937).

destructive: The films are mounted in the evaporation chamber in contact with mercury or, better yet, in contact with a copper cooling block.

Following the procedure described by Burger and van Cittert[26] bismuth and antimony are used for the thermojunctions, the bismuth being evaporated to form a strip about 1μ thick, while the antimony is evaporated to form a strip of half this thickness. The proper weight of metal to be evaporated is determined by a simple calculation using Eq. 2 in Chapter IV. The area coated with the metal is defined by templates. The bismuth strip, which is evaporated first, is deposited a little beyond the point which is to be the center of the junction, say 0.2 mm or so. Then, the evaporated antimony strip is allowed to overlap the center by an equal amount. The area where the strips overlap forms the junction. The junction is then coated by evaporation with bismuth black, antimony black, or zinc black over a prescribed area, which is defined by baffles.

To form an area to which electrical contact may be established, gold is sputtered or evaporated at appropriate points on the metal films. The connector wires may then be soldered to the gold.

The bismuth crystals formed in the strip by condensation of vapors have their axes perpendicular to the base. This crystal orientation results in a thermoelectromotive force against antimony of 75 microvolts/°C. The optimum crystal orientation, so far unattainable by evaporation, gives a thermoelectromotive force of about twice this value.

Evaporated thermojunctions are especially useful for making the Moll and Burger type thermo-relay. Burger and van Cittert were able to obtain a sensitivity about two and one-half times as great as that obtained with the ordinary rolled Moll and Burger element.

Considerations in thermopile design. The thermopile shown in Fig. 1 and described above can be adapted to meet most of the needs of an experimenter interested in making

[26] Burger, H. C., and van Cittert, P. H., *Zeits. f. Physik*, *66*, 210 (1930).

radiometric measurements. Some experimenters, especially those intending to make extremely delicate measurements, will be interested in the theory for the design of
thermopiles. For example, the experimenter designing a
vacuum thermopile of a given area has several decisions to
make. He must decide which metals to select for the
thermocouple wires and determine whether to make few or
many junctions. Also, he must decide on the material to
be used for coating the receivers. Or, he may wish to design a thermopile to operate at atmospheric pressure.

The equations expressing the theoretical dependence of the
galvanometer response on the number of junctions, area of
receiver, characteristics of thermoelectric wires, and so forth,
have been completely developed.[27] Calculations based on
this theory require a knowledge of the characteristics of the
thermoelectric wires, namely, their thermoelectric power,
electrical conductivity, and heat conductivity. The calculations also require a knowledge of the optical properties of
receiving surfaces, such as their emissivity and reflectivity
for various wave lengths. With this information, it is
possible to design the thermopile which will give optimum
response under the obtaining conditions.

The characteristic sensitivity of a thermopile determines
its response and, in the theory, this quantity Q is defined as
follows:

$$Q = \frac{\sqrt{I^2 R}}{\Phi}. \tag{2}$$

Φ is the radiant energy falling on the receivers in unit time,
I is the current in the galvanometer-thermopile circuit, and
R is the total resistance in this circuit. Q is in effect like
an efficiency—the efficiency with which the radiant energy
to be measured is converted into galvanometer deflections.

The expression for Q for an uncompensated vacuum thermopile of n junctions in terms of the quantities on which it
depends is

---

[27] Cartwright, C. H., *Zeits. f. Physik, 92*, 153 (1934).

$$Q = \frac{I\sqrt{R}}{\Phi} = \frac{nP}{\sqrt{R_t + R_g + R_e}} \left[4\sigma\epsilon A T^3 + \frac{n^2 T}{R_t}(\sqrt{W_1} + \sqrt{W_2})^2 + \frac{n^2 P^2 T}{R} \right]^{-1}, \quad (3)$$

where I is the thermoelectric current in the thermopile-galvanometer circuit, R is the total electrical resistance of the circuit, made up of the thermopile resistance R_t, the galvanometer resistance R_g, and any external resistance R_e. P is the combined thermoelectric power of the thermoelectric wires, expressed in volts per degree centigrade. σ is the Stefan-Boltzmann radiation constant, A the area of the receiver, T the absolute temperature of the receiver, and ϵ its effective radiating power. W_1 and W_2 are the Wiedemann-Franz coefficients of the two thermocouple wires.

The quantity in the brackets represents the total heat losses of the receiver. The middle term in the brackets represents heat loss by conduction through the wires, and the third term represents heat loss due to the Peltier effect. Ordinarily the influence of Peltier heat on the design may be neglected.

The first term in the brackets represents the heat lost by radiation and gas conduction. Where the receiver is not in a high vacuum, gas conduction has the same effect on thermopile design as increasing the magnitude of ϵ and, as we have pointed out before, the use of a receiver with a small emissivity for heat radiation, ϵ, has the effect on thermopile design of decreasing the quantity ϵA.

Fig. 21 illustrates for a vacuum thermopile the way in which Q depends on the values of ϵA, the number of junctions, and the total electrical resistance in the thermopile circuit. With ϵ taken as unity the curves are constructed for $A = 1 \text{ mm}^2$ and $A = 3 \text{ mm}^2$. Furthermore, these curves are for thermoelectric wires made of pure bismuth and wires of bismuth plus 5 per cent tin having a thermoelectric power of 120 microvolts/°C. and Wiedemann-Franz coefficients of 3×10^{-8} watt ohm/°C.^{2} and 4.2×10^{-8} watt ohm/°C.^{2} respectively.   The full curves are for thermopiles having one, two, three, and four junctions, and the dotted

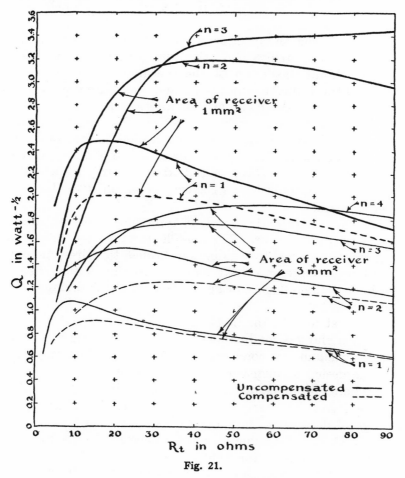

Fig. 21.

curves are for compensated thermopiles having one and two active and compensating junctions respectively.

It is desirable, from a practical point of view, to have a minimum number of junctions to build. The information given in Fig. 21 facilitates making the compromise between this practical consideration, on the one hand, and the desire to have a maximum sensitivity on the other. From curves in this figure, it is apparent that the energy should be concentrated onto a receiver which is as small as possible.

By reference to Eq. 3 we see that when the third term in the brackets is small in comparison with the first and second terms, the sensitivity, Q, appears to be proportional to the thermoelectric power, P. This is not always the case in practice, and a thermoelectric metal should not be chosen on the basis of the thermoelectric power alone. As a matter of fact, most metals with a high thermoelectric power have an unfavorable Wiedemann-Franz coefficient, which may, in the end, make them even less desirable than metals such as the bismuth alloys, which are convenient to manage.[28]

Sensitivity and minimum energy detectable. When the quantity Q, given by Eq. 2, is combined with the current sensitivity, $d\theta/dI$, and the total resistance of the circuit, R, it yields the composite sensitivity, S, of a thermopile and critically damped galvanometer according to the formula

$$S = \frac{\theta}{\Phi} = \frac{\frac{d\theta}{dI}Q}{\sqrt{R}}. \tag{4}$$

Here θ is the deflection of the galvanometer caused by the radiant energy Φ falling on the receiver in unit time.

It has been customary to compare the sensitivities, S, of the various radiometric instruments. This has led to some confusion in the literature. Actually, in making the most delicate radiometric measurements, we are not interested primarily in the value of S (which can be made as large as desired by the use of an amplifier) but rather in the accuracy with which the radiant energy can be measured in a given

[28] Cartwright, C. H., *Ann. d. Physik, 18,* 656 (1933). The Wiedemann-Franz coefficient, W, of any metal can be determined by using the empirical formula

$$W = 2.32 \times 10^{-8} + 3 \times 10^{-1}\frac{\rho}{T} \text{ watt ohm/}°C.^2,$$

where ρ is the specific electrical resistivity and T the absolute temperature. For good conductors ρ is small, so that W is the same for all these substances.

time, or, what amounts to the same thing, in the smallest
intensity of radiant energy that can be measured in a given
time with a given accuracy.   The magnitude of this smallest
deflection is influenced by disturbances acting on the instruments.

We will designate this smallest deflection that can be
measured by a single reading in a time t_0, and with a mean
relative error g, by the symbol $\theta_{\min}$.   Until 1926 it was
considered that the elimination of the disturbances on which
the value of $\theta_{\min}$. depends was simply a matter of refining
experimental technique. Ising was the first to point out
that our experimental technique is already advanced far
enough so that in many cases $\theta_{\min}$. is determined by the
ever-present Brownian motion fluctuations.[29]   If we
consider the thermopile system isolated from all disturbances except those produced by Brownian motion of the
galvanometer, then the value of $\theta_{\min}$. is easy to determine.
According to the principle of the equipartition of energy,
every object with one degree of freedom, such as the moving
system of our galvanometer, will possess a definite amount of
kinetic and potential energy.   The average value of the
kinetic energy or potential energy at 19°C. is

$$\tfrac{1}{2}kT = 2 \times 10^{-21} \text{ watt sec.} \tag{5}$$

The average deflection due to the potential energy is involved in the expression

$$\text{Potential energy} = \tfrac{1}{2}K\overline{\theta^2} = \tfrac{1}{2}kT, \tag{6}$$

where K is the torsional constant of the suspension and k is
Boltzmann's constant. When a reading is taken, the
fluctuations of θ give rise to an uncertainty amounting to
$\sqrt{kT/K}$.   Therefore, in order to have a probable error of g,
a single deflection must be at least $1/g$ times the average
fluctuation, or

$$\theta_{\min.} = \frac{1}{g}\sqrt{\frac{kT}{K}}. \tag{7}$$

---

[29] Ising, G., *Phil. Mag.*, *1*, 827 (1926).

It can be shown that this expression is a general one applicable to any radiometric instrument. Combining Eq. 7 with Eq. 4, we get an expression for the least energy that can be measured:

$$\Phi_{\min.} = \frac{6.6 \times 10^{-11}}{Sg\sqrt{k}} \text{ watt.} \tag{8}$$

In comparing the $\Phi_{\min.}$ of different radiometric instruments, it is necessary to specify not only the accuracy factor g, but also the time t, to be taken for measuring a deflection. In the case of a galvanometer, this is because the value of $d\theta/dI$ depends on t_0. The value of S also depends on t_0 for other radiometric instruments. It is not correct to assume, as is usually done, that the value of $\Phi_{\min.}$ varies with the square of the period of the deflecting device. As a matter of fact, in the case of a thermopile and critically damped galvanometer, the value of $\Phi_{\min.}$ is proportional to the square root of the period time of the galvanometer.[30]

The $\Phi_{\min.}$ of a thermopile and galvanometer can be expressed in terms of the factor g, the Q of the thermopile, and the period of the galvanometer, as follows:

$$\Phi_{\min.} = \frac{1.1 \times 10^{-10}}{gQ\sqrt{t_0}} \text{ watt.} \tag{9}$$

With the values of Q given by the curves in Fig. 12 it is therefore possible to estimate the minimum energy falling on the receiver in unit time that can be measured with a proposed apparatus. It is to be observed that the sensitivity of the galvanometer does not enter Eq. 9. Eq. 9, however, does imply that the deflections are measured either directly or with the help of an amplifying device to the limit set by Brownian motion.

General summary of the work on thermopile design. The remainder of this chapter will be devoted to a summary of the results of experimental and theoretical investigations made by one of the authors, C. Hawley Cartwright, on the

---

[30] Cartwright, C. H., *Physics*, *1*, 211 (1931).
Czerny, M., *Ann. d. Physik*, *12*, 993 (1932).

relative merits of the different radiometric instruments, and in addition will present some general (although not necessarily final) conclusions resulting from these studies.

Vacuum microradiometers can be made which will measure less energy, $\Phi_{min.}$, than the best vacuum thermopiles used with a separate galvanometer. This advantage is not sufficient to offset the practical advantage of greater flexibility of the thermopile with separate galvanometer.

Vacuum bolometers and vacuum thermopiles have at present practically the same limit, Φ_{min}. If a material with better characteristics than nickel were available for the construction of the bolometer strip, this situation would be altered.

Radiometers will not respond to as small energies, $\Phi_{min.}$, as thermopiles. The direct comparisons made by the author, especially in Berlin and Brussels, between vacuum thermopiles and radiometers yield results in favor of vacuum thermopiles. Radiometers are usually much more sensitive than thermopile and galvanometer combinations, owing to the use of a much lighter moving system than is possible with a galvanometer. Brownian motions are, however, increased, so that they more than offset the advantage of the larger primary deflections.

A question of considerable importance and one which bears on the above conclusions is the following: Why is there often considerable variation in the sensitivity of vacuum thermopiles, in fact, sufficiently large variations to be responsible for many of the publications that have appeared on improving thermopiles? The answer is that many vacuum thermopiles are not constructed with the maximum possible sensitivity, for the following reasons:

1. The sensitivity of a thermopile depends on the skill exercised in its construction.

2. For the most part, thermopiles have been constructed without first calculating the proper design or, if this is done, without dependable information on the physical properties of the materials used.

3. A sufficiently high vacuum is not always used. A properly designed and constructed thermopile should be about twenty times more sensitive in high vacuum than in air, and, on increasing the vacuum from 10^{-3} to 10^{-6} mm of mercury, the sensitivity should be doubled.

4. The thermoelectric power of the bismuth and bismuth-alloy wires is often less than 120 microvolts/°C. Slight impurities can greatly influence the thermoelectric power of bismuth by influence on crystal orientation, and so forth. For example, the thermoelectric power of pure bismuth relative to copper changes from 57 to 107.7 microvolts/°C. for different crystal orientations.[31]

5. The influence of deviations of the properties of bismuth, and especially bismuth alloys, from the predictions of the Wiedemann-Franz law is generally neglected, with the result that thermoelectric wires with a resistance which is too small are used so that the sensitivity falls on the left-hand steep part of the curves corresponding to those shown in Fig. 21.

Actually, the ultimate attainable sensitivity for a thermopile is limited by the unfavorable departure from the Wiedemann-Franz law of the thermoelectric metals that possess a high thermoelectric power. However, if this were not the case, it is interesting to note that the thermoelectric power itself would limit the sensitivity. From Eq. 3 we see that for a thermoelectric power of 250 microvolts/°C. the heat loss due to the Peltier effect is equal to the heat loss due to conduction through the wires. Although the possibility exists of finding better thermoelectric metals than bismuth and the alloy of bismuth and 5 per cent tin, it seems rather improbable that much progress will be made in this direction.

It is well to keep in mind that although tin has ten times less specific electrical resistance than bismuth, an alloy of bismuth and 5 per cent tin has twice the specific electrical resistance of pure bismuth. This should be considered when better thermoelectric metals are being sought. Bismuth

---

[31] Bridgman, P. W., *Am. Acad., Proc., 63*, 347 (1927–1928).

itself is an unusually favorable metal for thermopiles, not only because it has a relatively high thermoelectric power, but also because it is a pure metal element having a small specific electrical resistance and does not depart greatly from the Wiedemann-Franz law.

In order to improve the sensitivity of thermopiles, there is the possibility of using them at low temperatures, where Q can be increased, owing to a greater thermoelectric power, a more favorable Wiedemann-Franz ratio, and less radiation loss from the receivers. However, liquid-air thermopiles have several practical disadvantages.[32]

[32] Cartwright, C. H., *Rev. Sci. Instruments*, *4*, 382 (1933).

CHAPTER IX

Optics: Light Sources, Filters, and Optical Instruments

Divisions of the spectrum. The electromagnetic spectrum divides naturally into the region for which the eye is sensitive, the infrared region, with frequencies below those which we perceive as red, and the ultraviolet region, with frequencies higher than those which we perceive as violet. These regions are defined roughly by the wave lengths given in Table I. In the text we will use microns for expressing wave length in the infrared and Ångströms for expressing wave length in the visible and ultraviolet. The visible region includes less than one octave of frequency, while the so-called infrared region embraces at least nine octaves and the ultraviolet embraces five or six octaves.

Light sources. *The sun.* The sun naturally comes first in consideration of light sources. Its use is recommended

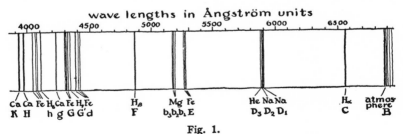

Fig. 1.

for many experiments because of its brightness and because in the Fraunhofer lines it contains numerous convenient wave-length landmarks. The Fraunhofer lines, which are conspicuous in the spectrum exhibited by a good pocket spectroscope, are shown in Fig. 1.

341

OPTICS

The energy distribution in the solar spectrum, as observed through the atmosphere, is closely approximated by that of a black body at 5400°K. The luminous efficiency of the

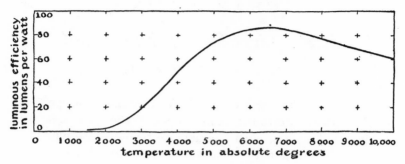

Fig. 2.

sun is about 80 lumens/watt. As will be seen in Fig. 2, this is nearly as high an efficiency as it is possible to attain with a heated body.

TABLE I

DIVISIONS OF THE ELECTROMAGNETIC SPECTRUM

Spectral Region	Wave-Length Limits
Extreme ultraviolet............	500 Å to 2000 Å
Ultraviolet....................	2000 Å to 4000 Å
Visible { Violet.................	4000 Å to 4460 Å
Indigo.................	4460 Å to 4640 Å
Blue..................	4640 Å to 5000 Å
Green.................	5000 Å to 5780 Å
Yellow................	5780 Å to 5920 Å
Orange................	5920 Å to 6200 Å
Red...................	6200 Å to 7200 Å
Near infrared.................	0.72μ to 20μ
Intermediate infrared...........	20μ to 40μ
Far infrared..................	40μ to 400μ

A heliostat or coelostat is required if a beam of sunlight is to be maintained in a fixed direction in the laboratory. Heliostats are obtainable from scientific supply companies.

Their mirrors, which are usually silvered on the back, should be recoated on the front surface with aluminum if it is desired to obtain in the reflected sunlight the full range of solar spectrum down to the atmospheric cutoff at approximately 3000 Å.

The details of construction for a home-made coelostat are shown in Figs. 3 and 4.　This coelostat may be driven by

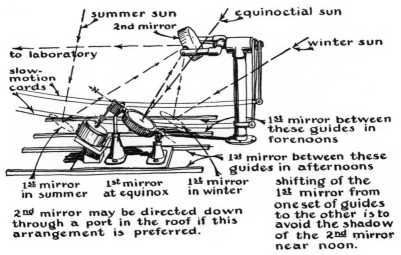

Fig. 3.

the works of an alarm clock as shown; it may also be driven by a Telechron clock.　The secondary mirror of the coelostat has controls operated by cords for making adjustments.

Tungsten lamps.　Tungsten lamps are the most convenient laboratory source of white light.　Their efficiency is about 11 lumens/watt for the nitrogen-coiled filament type.

The differences of spectral energy distribution of various tungsten-filament lamps are illustrated in Fig. 6, Chapter XI.　The spectrum of emission of the filament is limited in the ultraviolet and infrared by the transmission of glass. With glass bulbs $\frac{1}{4}$ mm in thickness, the spectrum extends from about 3100 Å in the ultraviolet to 3μ in the infrared.

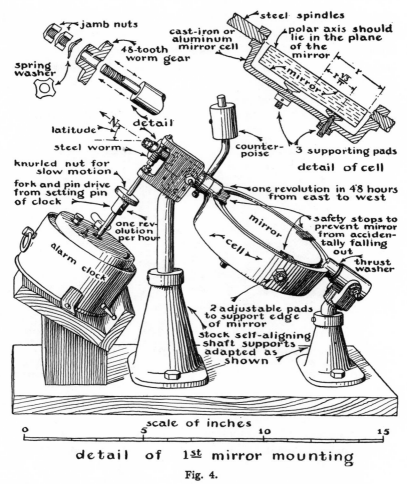

jamb nuts

spring washer

48-tooth worm gear

cast-iron or aluminum mirror cell

steel spindles

polar axis should lie in the plane of the mirror

mirror

r√3

r

latitude

detail

steel worm

knurled nut for slow motion

counter-poise

3 supporting pads

detail of cell

fork and pin drive from setting pin of clock

one revolution in 48 hours from east to west

alarm clock

one revolution per hour

mirror

cell

safety stops to prevent mirror from accidentally falling out

thrust washer

2 adjustable pads to support edge of mirror

stock self-aligning shaft supports adapted as shown

scale of inches

0   5   10   15

detail of 1st mirror mounting

Fig. 4.

Two tungsten lights convenient for many purposes in the laboratory are shown in Fig. 5. The one shown on the left is a projection lamp. It requires 6 volts and 18 amperes. An autotransformer or high-capacity storage battery serves as power source. The battery is, of course, preferred when constancy and steadiness of the emission are important.[1] The

---

[1] The autotransformer is as satisfactory as the battery when it is energized by the output of a Raytheon voltage regulator.

lamp shown at the right has a straight filament. It is useful as a galvanometer lamp. Both of these lamps are obtainable commercially.[2]

A trade-mark on the end of a tungsten lamp bulb, when it interferes with the light emission of the filament, may be removed by polishing with rouge and felt or with wet crocus cloth.

A lamp[3] with a quartz bulb for absorption spectra is shown in Fig. 6. The bulb contains argon at $1\frac{1}{2}$ atmospheres pressure. The tungsten operates at about 3100°C.

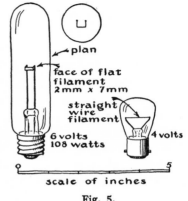

plan

face of flat filament 2mm x 7mm

straight wire filament

6 volts 108 watts

4 volts

scale of inches

Fig. 5.

and gives a continuous emission spectrum extending into the ultraviolet to 2500 Å. At the operating temperature, the vapor pressure of tungsten is appreciable, and it would normally blacken the quartz part of the bulb. However, vertical convection currents of argon gas carry the evaporated tungsten molecules upward from the filament, so that they are not deposited on the quartz but rather on the upper glass part of the bulb, where they do not impair the usefulness of the lamp.

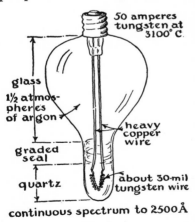

50 amperes tungsten at 3100° C

glass

1½ atmospheres of argon

heavy copper wire

graded seal

quartz

about 30-mil tungsten wire

continuous spectrum to 2500Å

Fig. 6.

Welsbach mantle.[4] This refractory mantle was formerly used extensively for house

[2] These lamps may be obtained from the General Electric Company, Nela Park, Cleveland, Ohio.

[3] This lamp is supplied by the Philips Laboratory, Eindhoven, Holland.

[4] Ives, H. E., Kingsbury, E. F., and Karrer, E., "A Physical Study of the Welsbach Mantle," *Frank. Inst., J., 186*, 401, 585 (1918).

illumination and is now used in gasoline lamps. It is brought to incandescence in the outer hot surface zone of a Bunsen burner type of flame, where it assumes a temperature nearly as high as the Bunsen flame temperature. The mantle is composed of thorium oxide with 0.75 to 2.5 per cent cerium oxide added to increase its visible emissivity. This addition of cerium oxide plays much the same role as the sensitizer for a photographic plate; that is, it introduces an absorption band in a desired spectral region without materially affecting the optical properties elsewhere. The effect of the cerium oxide is to make the emission in the green 30 per cent greater than that of a black body at 1800°C., whereas the emissions in the red and blue correspond closely to 1800°C. color temperature.[5] The near infrared emissivity is less than 1 per cent from 0.7μ to about 6μ, and the incapacity of the mantle to radiate heat in this important region accounts for its high temperature. For the spectrum beyond 10μ the mantle again has an emissivity greater than 75 per cent. The mantle is an excellent laboratory source for those long wave-length infrared radiations.[6]

Barnes suggests heating the mantle with a sharp oxygen flame striking it at a grazing angle.[7] This gives it a higher temperature, and also the elongated heated section produced is properly shaped for illuminating the slit of a spectrometer. More recently, Pfund has devised an arrangement to combine both electric and flame heating, allowing the attainment of even higher temperatures.[8]

Nernst glower. Nernst filaments are composed of zirconium dioxide powder with about 15 per cent yttrium oxide powder.[9] For operation on alternating current, flexible platinum lead wires are later cemented to each end

[5] Forsythe, W. E., *J. O. S. A.*, *7*, 1115 (1923).

[6] Rubens, H., *Deutsch. Phys. Gesell., Verh.*, *7*, 346 (1905); *Ann. d. Physik*, *18*, 725, (1905), *20*, 593 (1906); *Phys. Zeits.*, *6*, 790 (1905), *7*, 186 (1909).

[7] Barnes, R. B., *Rev. Sci. Instruments*, *5*, 237 (1934).

[8] Pfund, A. H., *J. O. S. A.*, *26*, 439 (1936).

[9] Nernst, W., and Bose, E., *Phys. Zeits.*, *1*, 289 (1900).

Nernst glowers are obtainable from Stupakoff Laboratories, 6627 Hamilton Avenue, Pittsburgh, Pennsylvania.

of the refractory tube with a mixture of the oxide powders and zirconium chloride as a binder. For operation on direct current, the manner of attaching the electrodes is more complicated. The Nernst lamp normally operates at around 2000°K. Its spectrum extends well into the ultraviolet and infrared. However, beyond 15μ its emission is said to be inferior to the emission of the Globar heater.

At one time the Nernst glower offered great promise for commercial lighting, owing to a luminous efficiency of 6 lumens/watt as compared with 3 lumens/watt for the carbon filament. However, the modern incandescent lamp with a coiled tungsten filament in an atmosphere of nitrogen, having an efficiency of 11 lumens/watt, entirely changed matters. The use of the Nernst light is now confined to the laboratory. Here its usefulness depends upon the fact that it is operated in air and has a convenient form (cylinder 0.4 to 0.6 mm in diameter and 1 to 2 cm long) for focusing on the slit of a spectrometer. Griffith has described details of construction for making Nernst filaments.[10]

Since the Nernst lamp has a negative temperature coefficient of resistance, it must be stabilized with external resistance or, better, with a ballast lamp having an iron-wire filament mounted in hydrogen.[11] The iron wire of this lamp runs at a faint red glow;

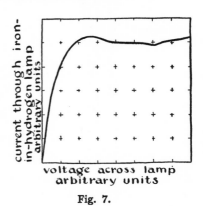

Fig. 7.

its remarkable current-stabilizing effect in an atmosphere of hydrogen at 30 to 100 millimeters pressure is shown in Fig. 7. Such a ballast lamp consumes 10 or 15 per cent of the total power needed for operating the Nernst filament.

[10] Griffith, H. D., *Phil. Mag., VI, 50,* 263 (1925).

[11] For the theory of the hydrogen ballast lamp, see Busch, H., *Ann. d. Physik, 64,* 401 (1921).

Globars. The Globar is a rod of bonded silicon carbide about $\frac{5}{16}$ inch in diameter and about 10 inches long. The ends fit into aluminum cup electrodes. A potential of 100 volts across the rod brings it to an orange or yellow heat. It can be operated in air at a temperature above 1000°C., although at temperatures around 2000°C. the carbide dissociates and carbon is vaporized or oxidized, leaving silicon, or, in the presence of air, silicon dioxide. A protective layer of thorium dioxide sintered to the outside of the Globar with thorium chloride as binder will allow of temperatures in excess of 2000°C.[12] A suitable mounting for the Globar is shown in Fig. 8.

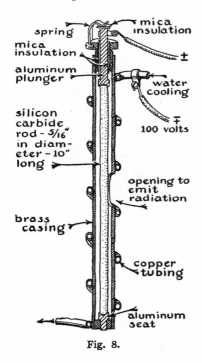

Carbon arcs. The carbon arc is useful as a laboratory light source. Ordinarily, the positive carbon is mounted horizontally. An 8-mm positive carbon is consumed at the same rate as a 6-mm vertical negative carbon. Accordingly, if carbons of this size are used, they may be fed into the arc automatically by clockwork.

The carbon arc requires at least 40 volts to operate it. Higher voltage increases the size of the positive crater without materially affecting its surface temperature.

The character of the light emission from the ordinary carbon arc may be influenced by the addition of metallic salts as cores in the carbons. (Magnesium fluoride is often used to get a white arc.) The spectral distribution of the

Fig. 8.

---

[12] I am indebted to C. H. Cartwright for this information.

carbon arc with cored carbons is illustrated in Fig. 9. This is a curve of galvanometer deflections against wave length, as determined with a quartz monochromator (shown in Fig. 32) and cesium oxide photocell. (See Chapter X.) The slit widths were the same for all wave lengths. This curve does not correct for the transmission of the image-forming lens (shown in Fig. 5, Chapter XI) which was used to focus the light. Without this lens the spectrum would have extended well into the ultraviolet.

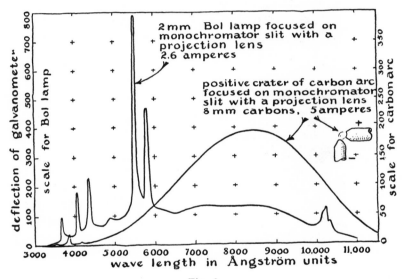

Fig. 9.

The ordinary carbon arc has a crater brightness of about 13,000 candles/cm² and an efficiency of about 35 lumens/watt. The Sperry Gyroscope Company has produced an arc that uses special shields to confine the current to a definite boundary around the rotating crater.[13] This arc is about six times as bright as the ordinary arc.

Lummer has succeeded in obtaining extreme temperatures in the carbon arc by operating it in an inert atmosphere

[13] Benford, F., *Trans. Soc. Motion Picture Eng.*, *24*, 71 (1926).

under high pressure. Under a pressure of 22 atmospheres he was able to obtain temperatures of 7600°K., considerably in excess of the solar surface temperature. The surface brightness reported for this temperature was 280,000 candles/cm². The attainment of such temperatures and brightness is difficult.

A technique of measuring. For the preliminary study of a spectrum plate, a technique of measuring and recording data which is neat and avoids confusion is illustrated in Fig. 10. This procedure employs an enlarged print of the original spectrum plate to identify the iron or other reference lines appearing in the eyepiece of the comparator. To facilitate this identification, the wave lengths of the iron lines are written in the margin of the print. Also, the print serves as a permanent record of the appearance of the spectrum as well as a record of the data of measurement.

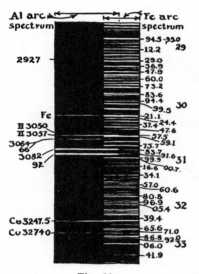

Fig. 10.

First, the wave lengths of conspicuous iron comparison lines, which are to be used as reference lines in the measurement, are written in the margin. The original plate has the same appearance in the eyepiece of the comparator as the enlarged print; thus it easily serves to identify the comparison lines. After the wave length of each unknown line is determined by interpolation, it is recorded on the clear margin of the print as shown at the left in Fig. 10. Notes may also be added in this margin when the wave lengths are later identified by reference to Kayser's tables.[14]

[14] Kayser, H., *Tabelle der Hauptlinien der Linienspektra aller Elemente.* Berlin: Julius Springer, 1926.

Iron arcs.   The iron arc is used in the laboratory by the spectroscopist as a source of ultraviolet light and also as a standard comparison source.   Its spectrum has been thoroughly studied, and the wave lengths of the lines, as well as the influence of pole and pressure effects on them, are well known.[15]

An iron arc developed by Pfund[16] suitable for use in the laboratory is shown in Fig. 11.   An iron oxide bead is placed on the lower electrode for stabilizing the arc.   If the

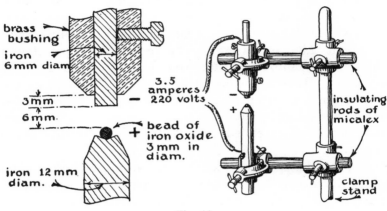

Fig. 11.

upper electrode is a graphite rod, the arc is even more stable than it is with an iron electrode.[17]   The arc can be started by rubbing a carbon across the gap.

Low-pressure mercury arcs.   The low-pressure mercury arc is a convenient laboratory light source.[18]   It gives several strong lines in the visible, ultraviolet, and near infrared

---

[15] See the following:

Babcock, Harold D., *Astrophys. J.*, *66*, 256 (1927), *67*, 240 (1928).

St. John, Chas. E., and Babcock, Harold D., *Astrophys. J.*, *46*, 138 (1917), *53*, 260 (1921).

[16] Pfund, A. H., *Astrophys. J.*, *27*, 298 (1908).

[17] The National Carbon Company produces a spectroscopic grade of pure graphite.   The pure carbon arc exhibits only one line in the visible or the ultraviolet spectrum.   This line is 2478 Å.

[18] For a description of a simple, home-made, low-pressure arc, see Pfund, A. H., *Astrophys. J.*, *27*, 299 (1908).

spectra. These lines are far enough apart to be separated with filters. (See Table XI.)

The ultraviolet spectrum of the arc in a fused quartz tube extends to about 2000 Å. The energy at the extreme short wave-length limit produces ozone in the air. The ozone formation, however, becomes weaker and weaker as the lamp is burned, owing to changes in the transmission limit of the quartz. Finally the ozone formation practically ceases. Baly has found that such changed quartz will emit a green phosphorescence and will regain its original transparency if it is heated in the blast burner.[19]

The Cooper-Hewitt type of mercury light has a brightness of about 2.3 candles/cm². The ordinary Cooper-Hewitt illuminating lamp has a tube 4 feet long and about 1 inch in diameter. It is a convenient light source for many experiments when an extended source is desired, as for observing Haidinger's and Newton's fringes. To get uniform illumination over an extended area, drafting linen is hung below the lamp.

In glass the Cooper-Hewitt lamp does not, of course, emit all of the ultraviolet spectrum. Recently this arc has been put on the market, made with a tube of Corex red-purple glass which suppresses the visible radiation (except 4046) and transmits the near ultraviolet. In this form it is excellent for therapeutic use.

The commercial hot quartz vacuum arc is much more brilliant (350 candles/cm²) than the Cooper-Hewitt lamp discussed above. The ordinary hot quartz lamp is not of a convenient form for use in the laboratory, but it is now available in the form of a vertical straight quartz tube constructed especially for laboratory use.[20] These laboratory arcs are equipped with rectifiers, so that they may be operated on either alternating or direct current.

---

[19] Baly, E. C. C., *Spectroscopy*. New York: Longmans, Green and Company, 1927.

[20] This lamp and the one discussed above are obtainable from the Cooper-Hewitt Electric Company, Hoboken, New Jersey.

High-pressure mercury arcs. Harries and Hippel[21] have described a high-pressure mercury lamp which is now commercially available.[22] This is illustrated by Fig. 12. The lamp is mounted in a nearly light-tight case—a very convenient construction for use in the laboratory. The lamp is made of uviol glass or quartz, with or without added cadmium to obtain the red cadmium 6438 Å line. Schott glass filters are also supplied for isolating the yellow, green, blue, violet, or ultraviolet lines.

The spectrum of the high-pressure lamp exhibits considerable continuous background. Accordingly, the spectral

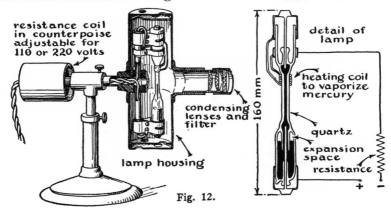

Fig. 12.

purity obtainable with it by the use of filters is not as great as it is with the low-pressure arc. The emission, however, is very steady, especially when the lamp is operated on storage batteries.

Cornelius Bol of Stanford University (formerly of the Philips Laboratory, Eindhoven, Holland) has developed a so-called super-high-pressure mercury arc.[23] The discharge

[21] Harries, W., and Hippel, A. v., *Phys. Zeits.*, *33*, 81 (1932).

[22] This lamp is obtainable from Schott und Gen., Jena, Germany. Their agent in this country is Fish-Schurman Corporation, 250 East 43rd Street, New York.

[23] Bol, C., *Das Licht*, *5*, 84 (1935); *Ingenieur*, *50*, 91 (1935).

Barnes, B. T., and Forsythe, W. E., *J. O. S. A.*, *27*, 83 (1937).

Dushman, S., *J. O. S. A.*, *27*, 1 (1937). A bibliography of high-efficiency light sources is given.

which produces the high pressure is started, however, by argon at a pressure of 2 or 3 cm of mercury. The operating potential for the lamp is around 500 volts. Heat generated by the argon discharge volatilizes the liquid mercury exposed in the lamp until a pressure of mercury gas of about 200 atmospheres is attained. On account of the high ultimate pressure, the lamp must be made of a thick-walled capillary tube as shown in Fig. 13. The tungsten electrodes project beyond the reserve mercury in order to guide the discharge down the central part of the tube. In the center, temperatures of 8600°C. and brightness values several times greater

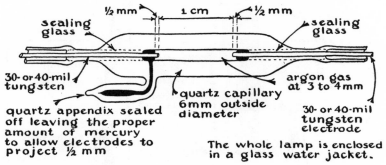

Fig. 13.

than the brightness of molten tungsten are attained. For example, a lamp operating on 640 volts at a pressure of 200 atmospheres has a brightness of 180,000 candles/cm^2 and a luminous efficiency of 79 lumens/watt. The emission of a Bol lamp is shown in Fig. 9. (See also Table II.)

The inside surface of the quartz capillary probably attains a temperature in excess of the critical temperature of mercury, so that no liquid mercury can condense. The mercury-gas envelope around the hot central core of the arc absorbs the resonance line emitted in the core, and at the obtaining pressure and temperature the resonance line is so broad that its absorption extends over the major part of the ultraviolet spectrum (to 2700 Å).

The electrodes are sealed in the Bol lamp with a new

glass. A lamp of convenient size for use in the laboratory has the electrodes spaced 1 cm apart. It is first filled with 2 cm pressure of gaseous argon and then with liquid mercury until the 30-mil tungsten wires project about $\frac{1}{2}$ mm beyond the mercury at each end. A 640-volt transformer is suitable for operating the light. It is connected in series with the arc and a suitable choke coil. When the arc is shorted out, the choke will draw about 3.4 amperes from the transformer.[24]

A "cold," low-pressure mercury-vapor lamp is shown in Fig. 14.[25] This lamp employs a few millimeters pressure of hydrogen, argon, or one of the other noble gases as a starting gas. Heat developed by the discharge in the noble gas soon distills mercury vapor from small globules of the liquid metal.

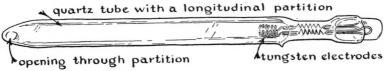

quartz tube with a longitudinal partition

opening through partition   tungsten electrodes

Fig. 14.

The potential for operating the lamp is obtained from a sign transformer or from a storage battery and spark coil. This lamp is only about one tenth as brilliant in the visible as the Harries and Hippel lamp, but its emission at 2536 Å is many-fold greater. In fact, about 80 per cent of its total emission is in the resonance line.

The resonance line from the mercury lamp shown in Fig. 14 is so strong that the mercury vapors, rising from a globule of liquid mercury held in the hand, cast a strong shadow on a fluorescent screen.[26] With a 3-mm Corex red-purple filter to suppress the visible spectrum, this lamp is ideal for exciting the fluorescence of minerals.

This type of mercury light is very useful in the laboratory.

---

[24] The Bol lamp must be operated surrounded with a stream of cooling water.

[25] This lamp is obtainable from the Reed and Miller Company, 16 South Raymond Street, Pasadena, California.

[26] See Leighton, W. G., and Leighton, P. A., *Jour. of Chem. Ed.*, *12*, 139 (1935).

When neon is used instead of argon as the starting gas, this single source yields a series of strong lines well distributed over the spectral range from 2536 Å to 10,140 Å. The gap in the mercury spectrum between 6907 Å and 10,140 Å is filled by a series of neon lines around 8300 Å.[27]

Filters for use with the various mercury arcs to yield monochromatic light are discussed in a later section.

Other gaseous discharges. Commercial sodium arcs are now available. They are confined in a special glass container that is not attacked by the metal vapor.[28] These arcs operate inside a clear Dewar flask and afford a large-area source of monochromatic light which is particularly suited to many laboratory tests and demonstrations. The characteristics of this and the Bol lamp are given in Table II.

TABLE II

CHARACTERISTICS OF SUPER-HIGH-PRESSURE MERCURY LAMP AND SODIUM LAMP

Item	Sodium Lamp	Mercury Lamp
Pressure (atmospheres).................	10^{-5}	200
Current density........................	0.4	280
Cross section (cm²).....................	1.43	0.0075
Candles/cm²...........................	10 to 20	1.8×10^5
Vapor temperature (°C.)................	280	8600
Light output (lumens/watt).............	68	78

Heller, G., *Philips Techn. Rev.*, *1*, 2 (1936).

Mercury lamp: 1400 watts and water cooled, 1.3 amperes, 2 mm cross section.

Sodium lamp: 100 watts in a clear Dewar flask.

Pyrex is not attacked by sodium as readily as are soft glasses, and by fusing borax or boric acid to the inside surface, its resistance to the alkali metal can be further in-

---

[27] For wide monochromator slits, the tungsten lamp is a much richer light source in this region than the argon discharge.

[28] Buttolph, L. J., *Am. Illum. Eng. Soc., Trans., 30*, 147 (1935). For similar lamps using other metallic vapors, see Alterthum, H., and Reger, M., *Das Licht, 3*, 69 (1933).

creased.[29] Magnesia crystals are not attacked by vapors of the alkali metal, and they may be used for experiments in which sodium, at higher temperatures and pressures, is to be confined behind windows transparent to both the ultraviolet spectrum and the infrared spectrum.[30]

The ultraviolet spectrum obtained from a hydrogen discharge tube is continuous, extending from the short wavelength emission limit of incandescent tungsten toward shorter wave lengths to the limit of transmission of quartz. This hydrogen continuum is most effectively excited by sources of the type developed by Duffendack and Manley, Smith and Fowler, Munch, and Jacobi.[31] These sources excite the spectrum with thermoelectrons emitted from a hot cathode.

Capillary discharge tubes filled with many different elementary gases are now available commercially.[32]

Sparks. To obtain the spark spectrum characteristic of the materials composing the electrodes, it is necessary to use a condenser of sufficient capacity to give an explosively noisy

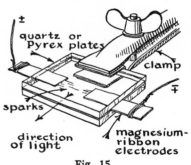

Fig. 15.

spark. Either a transformer or an induction coil can be used as the source of potential. A spark between magnesium electrodes, especially if it is confined between glass

[29] See Chapter XIV.

[30] Brice, R. T., *Rev. Sci. Instruments, 8,* 209 (1937).
Strong, J., and Brice, R. T., *J. O. S. A., 25,* 207 (1935).

[31] Duffendack, O. S., and Manley, J. H., *J. O. S. A., 24,* 222 (1934).
Duffendack, O. S., and Thomson, K. B., *J. O. S. A., 23,* 101 (1933).
Herzberg, G., *Ann. d. Physik, 84,* 553 (1926).
Jacobi, G., *Zeits. f. techn. Physik, 17,* 382 (1936).
Lau, E., and Reichenheim, O., *Zeits. f. Physik, 73,* 31 (1931).
Lawrence, E. O., and Edlefsen, N. E., *Rev. Sci. Instruments, 1,* 45 (1930).
Munch, R. H., *Am. Chem. Soc., J., 57,* 1863 (1935).
Smith, A. E., and Fowler, R. D., *J. O. S. A., 26,* 79 (1936).

[32] These tubes may be obtained from the Central Scientific Company, Chicago, Illinois, and A. D. Mackay, 198 Broadway, New York City.

plates, is very brilliant. Such a light source, shown in
Fig. 15, is useful for shadow photographs of bullets in motion,
and so forth, and for the photography of sound waves by the
Schlieren-methode.[33] The duration of the illumination from
the magnesium spark can be made extremely short.

Flames. Flames such as the Bunsen flame, which are
almost colorless, give characteristic emission spectra when
volatile metallic vapors are introduced. The metals most
commonly used to obtain monochromatic or nearly monochromatic light are given in Table III.

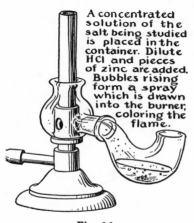

A concentrated solution of the salt being studied is placed in the container. Dilute HCl and pieces of zinc are added. Bubbles rising form a spray which is drawn into the burner, coloring the flame.

Fig. 16.

Sodium light may be ob-
tained by wrapping asbes-
tos, soaked in sodium chloride, around the tip of the
Bunsen burner tube. An-
other method of introducing
the salts into the flame is illustrated by the device shown
in Fig. 16. A neodymium filter may be used to absorb the
emission of sodium vapor and
at the same time transmit the
red emission lines from po-
tassium or lithium vapors. To obtain the metallic thallium
spectrum, a bead of the metal, fused in a platinum-wire loop,
is touched to the edge of the Bunsen flame. The bead is
introduced just far enough to obtain the desired rate of evaporation. If the bead is held too far inside the flame, it boils
away rapidly. Inasmuch as thallium is a poisonous metal, a
high concentration of the vapors in the room should not be
allowed. Also, sodium, potassium, and lithium vapors may
be introduced into a Meker burner flame by placing a small
globule of fused sodium chloride, potassium chloride, or
lithium chloride on the grill of the Meker burner.

[33] Wood, R. W., *Physical Optics*, page 93. New York: The Macmillan
Company, 1934.

The ultraviolet. The portion of the ultraviolet spectrum treated here will be limited to the wave-length range 2000Å to 4000 Å.[34]   In the long-wave half of this region between 4000 Å and 3000 Å many substances are transparent, including mica, celluloid, diamond, Canada balsam, ether, glycerin,

TABLE III

FLAME SPECTRA

Vapor	Wave Length of Emission Lines
Sodium..................	5890 Å, 5896 Å
Potassium................	7665 Å, 7699 Å
Lithium..................	6708 Å
Thallium.................	5350 Å

acetone, turpentine, xylene, and in thin layers, many ordinary glasses. (See Table IV.)   For the entire region from 4000 Å to 2000 Å the list of materials is not so great.   It includes rock salt, potassium chloride, fluorite, magnesia, lithium fluoride, alum, gypsum, sugar, calc-spar, water, ethyl alcohol, glacial acetic acid, liquid ammonia, fused and crystalline quartz, and cellophane. (For the transmission of cellophane see Table V.)

Prisms, lenses, and mirrors for the ultraviolet. Only a few of the substances mentioned above are suitable for making prisms and lenses.   Fluorite and quartz make excellent prisms.   They can be combined to make achromatic lenses.   But the scarcity of fluorite of good optical quality in large sizes makes these achromats very expensive.   A combination of quartz and rock salt is sometimes used for making achromats.   Recently, synthetic alkali halides and magnesium oxide have become available in large pieces, and these, together with other synthetic substances, will no doubt become important for constructing ultraviolet optics.

---

[34] For a general treatment of ultraviolet radiations, see Luckiesch, M., Holladay, L. L., and Taylor, A. H., *Frank. Inst., J., 196*, 353 (1923).

The optical constants of some of these materials for the visible spectrum are given in Table VI.

Concave aluminized mirrors are now used for ultraviolet optical systems. They have the same focus for ultraviolet as for visible light, and therefore they can be adjusted visually.

TABLE IV

TRANSMISSIONS OF GLASS (5 MM THICKNESS) IN THE ULTRAVIOLET

Wave Length (Å)	Bausch and Lomb Condenser Glass (%)	Schott Glass BK-7 (%)	Vita Glass (%)	Schott Uviol (%)
3300	82	83	86	93
3200	55	68	78	86
3150	35	56	72	81
3100	20	42	64	74
3050	..	24	54	66
3000	..	..	45	59

TABLE V

SPECTRAL CHARACTERISTICS OF CELLOPHANE—PER CENT TRANSMISSION AT INDICATED LINE

Standard Colorless Cellophane

Type	2334	2800	3132	3342	3663	4078	4359	4600	5200	5400	5800	6500
P. T.	60	69	73	79	84	86	87	88	90	90	90	90
M. T.	10	43	84	82	84	90	90	90	90	90	90	90

Standard Plain-Colored Cellophane

Type	2537	2800	3132	3342	3663	4078	4359	4600	5200	5400	5800	6500
Red	0	0	0	0	0	0	0	0	0	2	18	86
Dark green	9	31	28	20	7	0	6	14	47	44	22	12
Dark blue	25	39	38	38	51	71	78	66	43	29	12	7

This table was supplied by E. I. duPont de Nemours and Company, Wilmington, Delaware.

TABLE VI

INDEX OF REFRACTION OF SYNTHETIC MATERIALS

Material	C 6563	D 5893	e 5461	F 4861	g 4358
Fused quartz......	1.4567	1.4587	1.4604	1.4634	1.4669
CaF₂.............	1.4325	1.4338	1.4349	1.4369	1.4395
LiF.............	1.3906	1.3922	1.3930	1.3943	1.397
KCl.............	1.4870	1.4901	1.4929	1.4981	1.5043
KBr.............	1.5544	1.5590	1.5631	1.5709	1.5806
KI.............	1.6569	1.6655	1.6721	1.6853	1.7025
MgO.............	1.7337	1.7378	1.7412	1.7475	1.7550
Plexiglas.........	1.4856	1.4881	1.4902	1.4938	1.4992
Lucite...........	1.4916	1.4945	1.4967	1.5008	1.5064

Filters for the ultraviolet. Thin metal films are among the most interesting filters for the ultraviolet. The transmission band exhibited by silver and the alkali metals is associated with a gap lying between the region where the reflection is ascribed to the effect of free electrons (on the long wave-length side of the gap), and the region where reflection is ascribed to bound electrons (on the short wavelength side). In silver, this gap at 3160 Å is approximately 100 Å wide. It is much wider than this for the alkali metal films.

Potassium films may be used as a filter for isolating ultraviolet radiations. The full transmission of potassium in the ultraviolet begins at 3000 Å for films of a thickness just sufficient to be opaque in the visible to sunlight. R. W. Wood has studied this phenomenon and describes how these films can be formed on a quartz-glass bulb cooled to liquid air temperatures.[35] Unfortunately, films prepared as he describes are only permanent at temperatures considerably below room temperature. O'Bryan, however, has shown how potassium may be deposited between quartz-glass plates to give films permanent even at the elevated temperature of

[35] Wood, R. W., *Phys. Rev.*, *44*, 353 (1933).

boiling water.[36] The transmission of these thicker films begins at about 3350 Å, becomes about 25 per cent at 2500 Å, and decreases to a little below this value as the wave length 2000 Å is approached. The transmission of such a potassium film is illustrated by Fig. 17.

Fig. 17. Transmission of a potassium film.[36]

Bromine vapor can also be used as a filter. It is transparent to the ultraviolet rays. A layer of saturated bromine vapor 5 cm thick at room temperature is opaque to blue light and nearly opaque to green light, as one can readily see by interposing a bottle containing a little liquid bromine

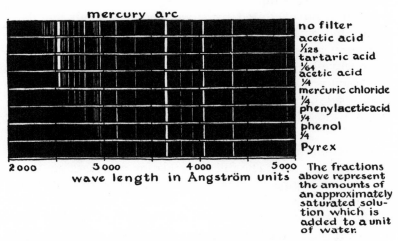

Fig. 18. Transmission spectra of various materials. After Williamson, R. C., *Phys. Rev.*, *21*, 111 (1923).

between a mercury lamp and a pocket spectroscope. The ultraviolet transmission of bromine begins at 3800 Å, and the vapor is quite transparent to the spectrum from wave length 3500 Å down to at least 2345 Å.

[36] O'Bryan, H. M., *Rev. Sci. Instruments*, *6*, 328 (1935).

A 5-mm layer of a solution of nitrosodimethylanalin (10 mg to 100 cc water) has about the same transparency as the bromine vapor.[37]

A filter of 14 g pure, iron-free nickel sulphate crystals and 10 g pure cobalt sulphate crystals dissolved in 100 cc distilled water is opaque to the visible spectrum but transparent

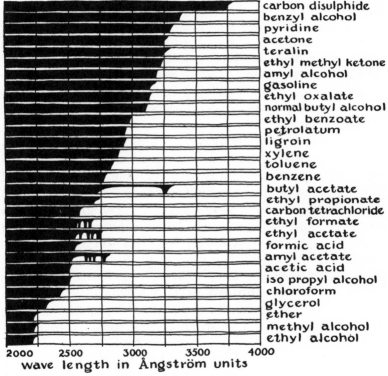

carbon disulphide
benzyl alcohol
pyridine
acetone
teralin
ethyl methyl ketone
amyl alcohol
gasoline
ethyl oxalate
normal butyl alcohol
ethyl benzoate
petrolatum
ligroin
xylene
toluene
benzene
butyl acetate
ethyl propionate
carbon tetrachloride
ethyl formate
ethyl acetate
formic acid
amyl acetate
acetic acid
iso propyl alcohol
chloroform
glycerol
ether
methyl alcohol
ethyl alcohol

wave length in Ångström units

Fig. 19. Transmission of various liquids. After Brode, W. R., *J. Phys. Chem.*, *30*, 56 (1926).

in the ultraviolet below 3300 Å. In layers 3 cm thick this filter transmits 3.5 per cent of the 3342 Å mercury line and 96 per cent of 3126 Å line, and it is transparent as far down in the ultraviolet as 2300 Å.[38]

[37] Wood, R. W., *Phil. Mag.*, *5*, 257 (1903).
[38] Bäckström, H. L. J., *Naturwiss.*, *21*, 251 (1933).

The ultraviolet transmission limit for mica is at about 2800 Å for 0.01 mm thickness. Mica of this thickness is completely opaque at wave lengths below 2600 Å.

The transmissions in the ultraviolet of some other materials are illustrated in Figs. 18 and 19.

Polarization of the ultraviolet. The new sheet polarizers[39] made of herapathite are opaque to ultraviolet light. (See Fig. 38.) Although the calcite of Nicol prisms is transparent to 2000 Å, the Canada balsam used for cementing them is not transparent in the ultraviolet at wave lengths below about 3000 Å. For cementing optical surfaces to be used in the ultraviolet, glycerin, castor oil, or dextrose sugar should be used. A Wollaston prism may be used to polarize light in the ultraviolet when its parts are properly cemented.

The infrared. The infrared spectrum extends from 7600 Å, or 0.76μ, to about 400μ. A thermopile or radiometer is generally used for measuring infrared radiation. As the operation of these instruments depends on thermal effects produced by the radiation, the infrared spectrum is often referred to as the heat spectrum. The infrared radiations are emitted by heated bodies. Ordinarily, heated bodies are used as laboratory sources for the infrared spectrum.

It is convenient to divide the heat spectrum into three regions: The near infrared, from 1.1μ to 20μ; the intermediate infrared, from 20μ to 40μ; and the far infrared, from 40μ to 400μ. The spectroscopic significance of the near infrared is that the characteristic frequencies of gases which fall in this region generally arise from molecular oscillations, whereas the characteristic frequencies which fall in the visible and ultraviolet regions arise in general from electronic oscillations. On the other hand, in the far infrared the characteristic frequencies of gases arise from molecular rotation and molecular bending. In the case of crystals the characteristic frequencies in the near infrared

[39] Land, E. H., *Frank. Inst., J.*, *224*, 269 (1937).
Freundlich, H., *Chemistry and Industry*, *56*, 698 (1937).

are generally interatomic oscillations within the chemical radicals that exist as units in the crystal, while frequencies in the far infrared are due to oscillations of the positive ions (or radicals) of the crystals relative to the negative ones.

The intermediate infrared spectral region from 20μ to 40μ was formerly closed to investigation on account of the lack of transparent substances to be used for making windows and prisms. There are now available, however, a transparent paraffin of high melting point,[40] and large synthetic crystals of the alkali halides which are transparent in the range 20μ to 40μ.[41]

Prisms, windows, lenses, and mirrors for the infrared. The important prism materials for the infrared are listed in Table VII. These materials are not ordinarily combined to

TABLE VII

Transmission of Materials for Infrared Radiations

Material	Useful Transmission Limit in the Infrared (μ)
Glass.................	2.2
Quartz.................	3.5
CaF_2	8.5
NaCl.................	15
KCl.................	21
KBr.................	29

form achromatic lenses for focusing the infrared rays; mirrors which are much more satisfactory are used. Even spherical mirrors are useful for the less exacting work, since the slits in infrared spectroscopy can never be set as fine as

[40] Kellner, L., geb. Sperling, *Zeits. f. Physik*, *56*, 215 (1929). The paraffin in question is Kurlbaum, M. P., 68° to 72°C.

[41] Bridgman, P. W., *Am. Acad.*, *Proc.*, *60*, 307 (1925), *64*, 19 (1929).

Korth, K., *Zeits. f. Physik*, *84*, 677 (1933).

Kyropoulos, S., *Zeit. f. anorg. allgem. Chem.*, *154*, 308 (1926).

Ramsperger, H., and Melvin, E. H., *J. O. S. A.*, *15*, 359 (1927).

Stober, F., *Zeits. f. Krist.*, *61*, 299 (1925).

Strong, J., *Phys. Rev.*, *36*, 1663 (1930).

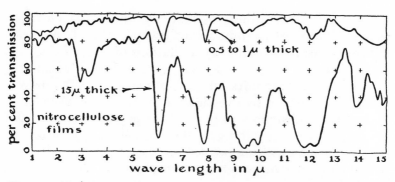

Fig. 20.　After Barnes, R. B., and Bonner, L. G., *J.O.S.A.*, *26*, 433 (1936).

they can in the other spectral regions, in which photography can be applied.[42]

Materials useful for windows on absorption cells and vacuum radiometric devices are listed in Table I, Chapter VIII. (See also Figs. 20, 21, 22.) Of these materials the high-melting-point paraffin is of special interest, since it is one of the few materials opaque to the near infrared spectrum and transparent to the long wave lengths. Soot is another such material. Although it is quite opaque in the visible, soot is translucent for the heat spectrum.

The reflection of most metals such as silver, speculum, and aluminum is high in the infrared. The reflectivity for wave

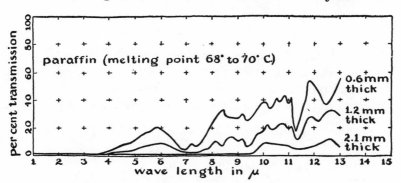

Fig. 21.. After Barnes, R. B., and Bonner, L. G., *J.O.S.A.*, *26*, 433 (1936).

[42] Strong, J., *Phys. Rev.*, *37*, 1661 (1931).

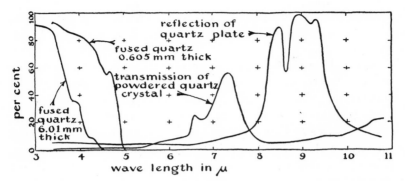

Fig. 22. Infrared transmission and reflection of quartz. After A. H. Pfund.

lengths longer than about 10μ can be calculated from the electrical conductivity of the metal by the expression

$$R_\lambda = 1 - 0.365\sqrt{\rho/\lambda}, \tag{1}$$

where ρ is in ohms mm^2/m and λ is in microns.

Reflection of crystals. Residual rays. Crystals exhibit so-called bands of "metallic" reflection at certain wave lengths where the reflection coefficient, usually of the order of 5 per cent, approaches 100 per cent. This property of crystals was first observed by E. F. Nichols.[43] The bands of high reflectivity exhibited by quartz, for example, are shown in Fig. 23.

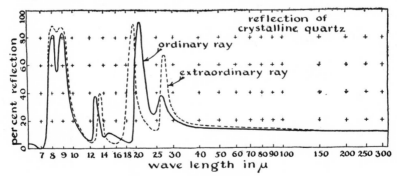

Fig. 23.   After H. Rubens.

[43] Nichols, E. F., *Ann. d. Physik*, *60*, 401 (1897); *Phys. Rev.*, *4*, 297 (1897). Rubens, H., and Nichols, E. F., *Ann. d. Physik*, *60*, 418 (1897); *Phys. Rev.*, *4*, 314 (1897).

Quartz (for the ordinary ray) exhibits two strong bands, one at 8.9μ and one at 20.8μ. Rock salt has only one band, at 52μ.

Multiple reflections from crystals are employed to isolate narrow bands of monochromatic radiation from the heat spectrum. For example, if the spectrum from a heated body is reflected once from a rock-salt crystal surface, the energy at wave lengths about 52μ are reflected while those radiations elsewhere, especially in the short-wave spectrum, where the reflection is nonmetallic, are attenuated about

TABLE VIII

Number of Reflections	Crystal Mirrors	Filter (3 mm paraffin in each case)	Wave Length (μ)	Frequency ($\sim$/cm)	Energy (cm of deflection; scale at 3 m)
4	Quartz	1 cm KCl	20.7	483	44
3 1	Fluorite Metal	5 mm KCl	23	435	18
2 2	Fluorite Calcite	3 mm KBr	27.3	366	42
4	Calcite	None	29.4	340	95
3 1	Fluorite Metal	0.4 mm quartz 1.2 mm KBr	32.8	305	2.6
3 1	Aragonite Metal	0.4 mm quartz	41	244	1.6
4	NaCl	2 mm quartz	52	192	5.2
4	KCl	2 mm quartz	63	159	2
4	KBr	2 mm quartz	83	120	1.6
4	KI	2 mm quartz	94	106	1
4	TlBr	2 mm quartz	117	85	1.7
4	TlI	2 mm quartz	152	66	1

twenty times. In spite of this attenuation by a single reflection, the energy in the 52μ band may still be much less than the integrated energy reflected at other wave lengths. After a second reflection, however, the short-wave spectrum is again attenuated about twenty times, or four hundred times altogether, while the energy in the band of waves around 52μ is little affected. Accordingly, after four or five reflections the only radiations remaining, the so-called residual rays, are those of the 52μ band.

The use of these successive reflections is a standard procedure for obtaining monochromatic bands of radiation in the far infrared. The crystals used for obtaining various wave lengths are listed in Table VIII. We shall describe the apparatus used for obtaining residual rays in a later part of this chapter.

Special absorbers for the near infrared. Water is transparent from wave lengths greater than 0.2μ in the ultraviolet throughout the visible spectrum. (See Fig. 24.)

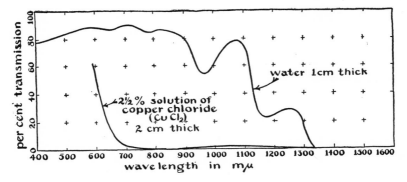

Fig. 24.

However, it is opaque in the heat spectrum for all rays beyond the limits λ_0 for thickness τ_0, as given in Table IX.

A water filter is often used to absorb the heat rays that are emitted when a carbon arc, the sun, or a tungsten lamp is used as a light source. The use of a water filter prevents the cracking of lantern slides with heat, burning of photo-

TABLE IX

TRANSMISSION LIMITS OF WATER IN THE INFRARED FOR THE
SOLAR SPECTRUM

τ_0	λ_0 in μ
1 mm	2.4
1 cm	1.5
10 cm	1.2
10 m	0.9
100 m	0.6

Fowle, F. E., *Smithsonian Miscellaneous Collections, 68*, 49 (1917).
Schmidt, W., *Meterolog. Zeitsch., 25*, 321 (1908).

graphic film, overheating of microscope objectives, or excessive heating of polarizing Nicols.

The addition of cupric salts to water results in increased
absorption of the infrared. The absorption for the infrared
is illustrated in Fig. 24 for a 2-cm cell containing cupric
chloride.[44]

Manufactured glass filters such as Aklo glass and the
Schott filters BG17 and BG19 are designed to remove the heat

TABLE X

TRANSMISSION OF AKLO HEAT-RESISTING GLASS (2 MM THICKNESS) FOR THE
LIGHT OF A VACUUM MAZDA LAMP (2360°K.)

Filter	Total Radiation (%)	Visible Radiation (%)
Extra Light Shade No. 395..............	40	83
Light Shade No. 396...................	21	75
Medium Shade No. 397.................	11	64
Dark Shade No. 398...................	4	42

Glass Color Filters, Corning Glass Works, Corning, New York.

[44] Absorption of water: Nicholson, Seth B., and Pettit, Edison, *Astrophys. J.,
56*, 295 (1922).
Absorption of cupric chloride solution: Coblentz, W. W., *Bureau of Standards Scientific Paper No. 168.*

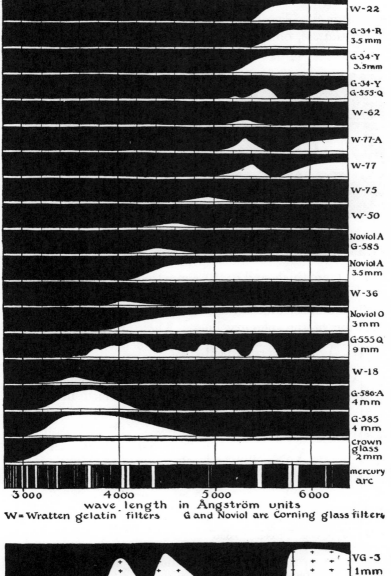

W-22
G-34-R 3.5 mm
G-34-Y 3.5 mm
G-34-Y G-555-Q
W-62
W-77-A
W-77
W-75
W-50
Noviol A G-585
Noviol A 3.5 mm
W-36
Noviol O 3 mm
G-555 Q 9 mm
W-18
G-586-A 4 mm
G-585 4 mm
crown glass 2 mm
mercury arc

3 000   4 000   5 000   6 000
wave length in Ångström units
W = Wratten gelatin filters   G and Noviol are Corning glass filters

VG-3 1mm

4,000   5 000   6 000   7 000
wave length in Ångström units

Fig. 25.   Transmission of glass and Wratten filters.

spectrum.[45] (See Table X and also *Jena Colored Optical Filter Glasses*, obtainable from Fish-Schurman Corporation, 250 East 43rd Street, New York City.) The transmission of

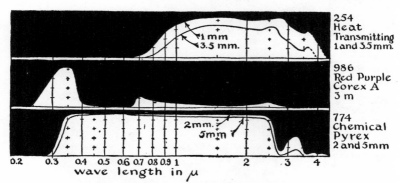

Fig. 26. From *Glass Color Filters*, Corning Glass Works, Corning, New York.

BG17, 1 mm thick, and BG19, 4 mm thick, is about the same as that of 2 cm of a nearly saturated copper sulphate solution.

Visible spectrum. Glass and gelatin filters are used for isolation of the mercury lines. They are easier to handle and much more permanent than water solutions. The transmissions of some of the glass and gelatin filters commercially available in this country are illustrated in Figs. 25 and 26. A list of the filter combinations for the separation of various spectrum lines is given in Table XI.

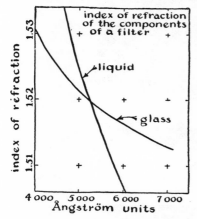

Fig. 27. After McAlister. (See footnote 46.)

The Christiansen filter. The Christiansen filter consists of a mass of solid particles immersed in a liquid medium, as,

[45] Heat-absorbing glass is manufactured by the Corning Glass Company, Corning, New York. BG17 and BG19, manufactured by Schott und Gen., are handled in this country by the Fish-Schurman Company, New York City.

for example, particles of borosilicate glass immersed in carbon disulphide and benzene.[46]   Fig. 27 shows the dispersion for a borosilicate crown glass and for a 10 per cent solution (by

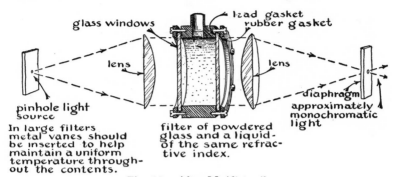

Fig. 28.   After McAlister.[46]

volume) of carbon disulphide in benzene (both anhydrous) at 20°C.   The filter composed of these two transmits freely the color for which the indices of refraction of the liquid and solid phases are identical, that is, where the two lines in Fig. 27 cross.   For this color the medium is optically homogeneous.   The filter is a nonhomogeneous optical medium for all other wave lengths. Accordingly, they are scattered.   By means of the arrangement shown in Fig. 28, the scattered waves are isolated from the freely transmitted color.   The individual transmissions of five filters are shown in Fig. 29.   These filters were 18 mm thick and were made up from borosilicate glass using different concentrations of carbon disulphide in benzene.

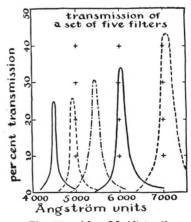

Fig. 29.   After McAlister.[46]

[46] Christiansen, C., *Ann. Physik u. Chemie*, *23*, 298 (1884), *24*, 439 (1885). McAlister, E. D., *Smithsonian Misc. Coll.*, *93*, No. 7 (1935).

One limitation of the Christiansen filter lies in its lack of complete opacity to wave lengths on either side of the transmitted band.

TABLE XI

Filters for Isolating Mercury Lines

Radiation	Corning Glass	Eastman Wratten	Liquid Filters
Infrared or 10,140	G554EK, 6 to 8mm	88 as used by R. W. Wood or 89A	Cobalt blue glass and saturated solution of potassium dichromate
5769 to 5790	G34R, 3 to 4 mm	22 Hg yellow	Chrysoidine and eosin
5461	G555Q, 8 to 10 mm, and G34Y, 3 to 4 mm	62 Hg green or 77 Hg special or 77 A. Hg special for interferometry	Neodymium ammonium nitrate and potassium dichromate
4359	Noviol A, 3 mm, and G585, 3 to 5 mm	50 Hg blue	Cobalt blue glass and quinine sulphate
4047 to 4078	G586A, 3 to 5 mm, and Noviol 0, 3 to 4 mm	36 Hg violet	Methyl violet and quinine sulphate
3650 3656 3663	G586AW, 8 to 10 mm	18 ultraviolet	Methyl violet and acid green

Buttolph, L. J., *Engineering Bulletin 104-B*, Cooper-Hewitt Company.

This limitation is a serious one. For example, when the filter is to be used in conjunction with a highly selective receiver, such as a photocell, the response of the receiver for rays weakly transmitted by the filter but for which the receiver is exceptionally sensitive (or for which the emission of the source is especially strong) may seriously interfere with the interpretation of the results obtained. Another limitation of this filter is its sensitivity to temperature changes. The filter cannot be used effectively in an intense beam of light such as sunlight, owing to temperature gradients set up in the cell.

However, the dependence of the transmitted wave length upon temperature may be put to use. F. Weigert and collaborators have found, for example, that a cell made of particles of crown glass immersed in liquid methyl benzoate transmitted red light at 18°C. (64°F.) and blue light at 50°C. (122°F.).[47]

A very interesting Christiansen filter effect is exhibited by the infrared transmission of thin powder films.[48] Their maximum of transmission occurs at the wave length at which the index of the powder is unity or equal to the index of the surrounding medium. For magnesia this transmission maximum in air is at 12.2μ, and if the filter is immersed in carbon tetrachloride, the maximum shifts to wave length 9μ, at which both the carbon tetrachloride and the magnesia have the same index.

Reflection of metals. Of the metals useful in the visible spectrum for reflection of light, the three most important are aluminum, speculum, and silver. Their reflectivities are shown in Fig. 30. It is to be noted that aluminum is

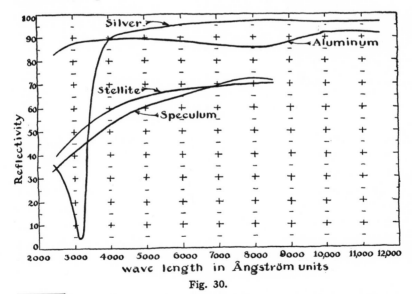

Fig. 30.

[47] Weigert, F., Staude, H., Elvegard, E., and Shidei, J., *Zeits. f. phys. Chem.*, *Abt. B*, *2*, 149 (1923), *9*, 329 (1930).

[48] Barnes, R. B., and Bonner, L. G., *Phys. Rev.*, *49*, 732 (1936).

superior to newly deposited silver for all wave lengths less than 4100 Å. In the visible spectrum the use of aluminum instead of silver is recommended. Although new silver has a better reflectivity in the visible spectrum than aluminum, it soon tarnishes.

The apparatus shown in Fig. 31 was used for the above reflectivity measurements. This apparatus measures the

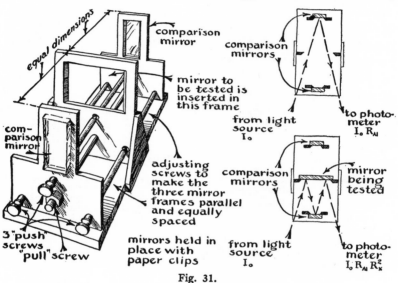

Fig. 31.

square of the absolute reflectivity directly (putting the comparison mirror in both the numerator and denominator, so to speak).

Monochromators. The best method of isolating a narrow wave-length band of high spectral purity from a source of white light is to use a double monochromator, that is, two single monochromators built together. High spectral purity is often desirable for highly selective effects, such as, for example, the determination of the long wave-length limit of the photoelectric effect, or in any other case when the slight spectral impurity that one might have with a single mono-chromator would vitiate the results of the measurement. A step can be made in the direction of high spectral purity by the use of filters in series with a single monochromator. These filters are, however, usually less efficient than a single monochromator. The transmission of a single monochromator is about 45 per cent.

The monochromator may have achromatic lenses, but these are very expensive if they are constructed of materials

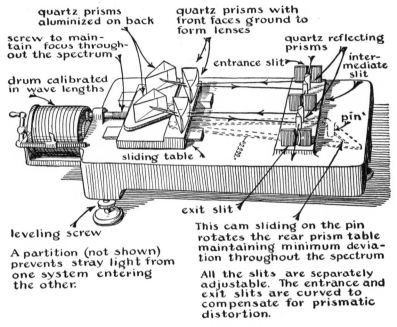

quartz prisms aluminized on back

quartz prisms with front faces ground to form lenses

screw to maintain focus throughout the spectrum

quartz reflecting prisms

entrance slit

intermediate slit

drum calibrated in wave lengths

pin

sliding table

exit slit

leveling screw

This cam sliding on the pin rotates the rear prism table maintaining minimum deviation throughout the spectrum

A partition (not shown) prevents stray light from one system entering the other.

All the slits are separately adjustable. The entrance and exit slits are curved to compensate for prismatic distortion.

Fig. 32. Hilger-Müller double monochromator.

which will function in the ultraviolet. Generally, monochromators employ quartz lenses. These are brought to focus with a mechanism operated by the wave-length drum. Fig. 32 shows how this is accomplished in the Hilger-Müller double monochromator by the use of a cam bar mounted on the prism table. As the prism table and lens system move as a unit toward the slit system, the lenses are brought into focus for shorter and shorter wave lengths. The cam bar is so·constructed that it causes the wave lengths to fall on the exit slits for which the lenses are in focus.

Use of mirrors in monochromators. Parabolic mirrors are often used in monochromators, because an optical system using mirrors is achromatic. However, mirrors have the distinct disadvantage as compared with lenses that the parallel collimated beam is returned in the direction of the entrance slit, a direction which precludes a neat simple arrangement of the other optical parts. To use a mirror on

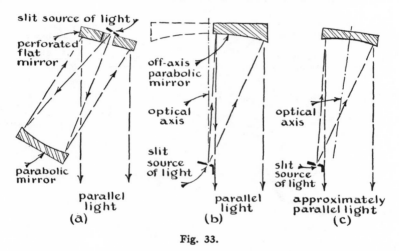

Fig. 33.

its optical axis requires either an auxiliary flat as in the Pfund[49] arrangement shown in Fig. 33(a) or an off-axis mirror as shown in Fig. 33(b). One way to make such an off-axis mirror is to construct a large ordinary paraboloidal mirror and cut out the desired mirror from one side of it.

A mirror system composed of spherical mirrors like the one shown in Fig. 33(c) may be used. This, of course, introduces large distortions in the wave front. It is possible, however, by proper orientation of a similarly imperfect

[49] Pfund, A. H., *J. O. S. A.*, *14*, 337 (1927). For a grating spectrometer application of Pfund's scheme see Randall, H. M., *Rev. Sci. Instruments*, *3*, 196 (1932).

Hardy, J. D., *Phys. Rev.*, *38*, 2162 (1931).

mirror to compensate in a measure for the distortions produced by the collimator and to obtain better definition than would be possible éven if a perfect telescope were used. The proper arrangement of the telescope system for achieving this compensation is shown in Fig. 34, with the regular Wadsworth arrangement.[50]

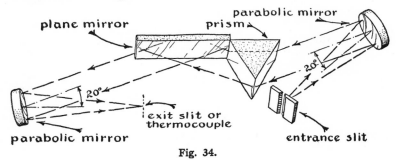

Fig. 34.

The optical train in monochromators is usually either the Littrow arrangement or the Wadsworth arrangement, both of which use the prism at minimum deviation. These arrangements are shown in Fig. 35.[51]

Water monochromator. An ultraviolet monochromator with improvised optics, devised by Harrison,[52] is shown in Fig. 36. The optical parts consist of a water prism and a spherical aluminized mirror. This monochromator is very simple, and optically it is good enough for isolating the stronger mercury lines (as the illustration of the produced spectrum shows). It has a relatively high aperture, $f/6$. The dispersions of crystal quartz, fused quartz, and water are related as 25:21:19 at 3000 Å. Since water is more transparent to the ultraviolet than quartz, this monochromator can be used for isolating wave lengths as short as 1820 Å.

[50] Czerny, M., and Turner, A. F., *Zeits. f. Physik, 61*, 792 (1930).
Czerny, M., and Plettig, V., *Zeits. f. Physik, 63*, 590 (1930).
[51] Littrow, O., *Am. J. Sci., 35*, 413 (1862).
Wadsworth, F. L. O., *Phil. Mag., 38*, 137 (1894); *Astrophys. J., 2*, 264 (1895).
[52] Harrison, George R., *Rev. Sci. Instruments, 5*, 149 (1934).

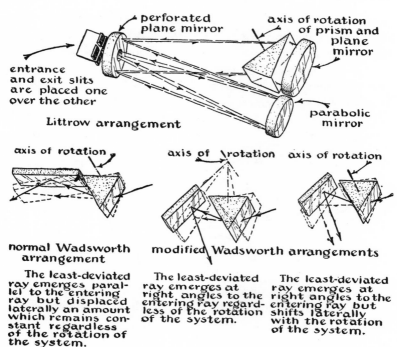

perforated
plane mirror

axis of rotation
of prism and
plane
mirror

entrance
and exit slits
are placed one
over the other

Littrow arrangement

parabolic
mirror

axis of rotation

axis of rotation

axis of rotation

normal Wadsworth
arrangement

modified Wadsworth arrangements

The least-deviated ray emerges parallel to the entering ray but displaced laterally an amount which remains constant regardless of the rotation of the system.

The least-deviated ray emerges at right angles to the entering ray regardless of the rotation of the system.

The least-deviated ray emerges at right angles to the entering ray but shifts laterally with the rotation of the system.

Fig. 35.

Focal isolation. Fig. 37 shows the method of focal isolation invented by Wood to isolate the far infrared radiations from a Welsbach burner.[53] When the first lens is positioned in relation to the light source at a distance equal to twice its focal length for the far infrared rays, where the index of refraction is 2.25, the near infrared rays emerging from the lens are divergent. An opaque spot at the center of the quartz lens prevents the direct transmission of the median near infrared rays through the aperture provided at the focus of the far infrared rays. Usually two lenses are arranged in series of effect complete separation of the far infrared rays.

A focal isolation method has been applied to the isolation

[49] Rubens, H., and Wood, R. W., *Phil. Mag.*, *21*, 249 (1911).

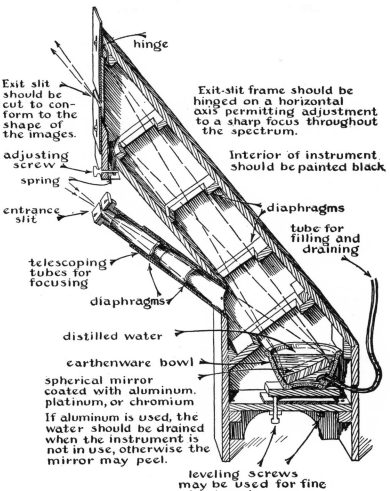

hinge

Exit slit
should be
cut to con-
form to the
shape of
the images.

Exit-slit frame should be
hinged on a horizontal
axis permitting adjustment
to a sharp focus throughout
the spectrum.

adjusting
screw

Interior of instrument
should be painted black

spring

entrance
slit

diaphragms

tube for
filling and
draining

telescoping
tubes for
focusing

diaphragms

distilled water

earthenware bowl

spherical mirror
coated with aluminum,
platinum, or chromium

If aluminum is used, the
water should be drained
when the instrument is
not in use, otherwise the
mirror may peel.

leveling screws
may be used for fine
adjustments

A drawing from a
photograph of part
of the mercury-arc
spectrum taken with
an instrument similar
to that above, but
using an oblique slit

2537   2804   3125   3650   4358

wave length in Ångström units

Fig. 36.

of the 1940 A group of aluminum lines with a quartz lens.[54] And, while there is for quartz no such diversity of index in this part of the spectrum as there is in the infrared, yet these lines are separated from the rest of the aluminum spectrum with a spectral purity of 0.98. The intensity obtained is sevenfold greater than that obtainable from a quartz monochromator. This focal isolation method has also been applied to the 2030 Å to 2140 Å group of zinc lines.

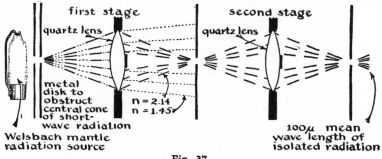

Fig. 37.

Residual-ray isolation. Apparatus using the residual-ray method for the isolation of wave lengths in the infrared is illustrated in Fig 38.[55] The apparatus shown at the top of this figure employs four crystal reflections, while the one at the bottom, placed at the focus of an image-forming mirror, uses only two crystal reflections.

When the two-crystal apparatus is equipped for 6.7μ (crystals of calcite) it is useful for measuring humidity, since this region of the spectrum is very sensitive to moisture in the radiation path. On the other hand, with either quartz, Carborundum, or potassium chromate crystals, which give bands of radiation at 8.7μ, 12μ, and 11.6μ, respectively, the instrument is useful as a radiation pyrometer insensitive both to water vapor and to light smoke or haze. In the region from 8μ to 13μ there is very little absorption by the

[54] Forbes, Geo. S., Heidt, Lawrence J., and Spooner, Lawrence W., *Rev. Sci. Instruments, 5*, 253 (1934).

[55] Strong, J., *Phys. Rev., 37*, 1565 (1931), *38*, 1818 (1931).

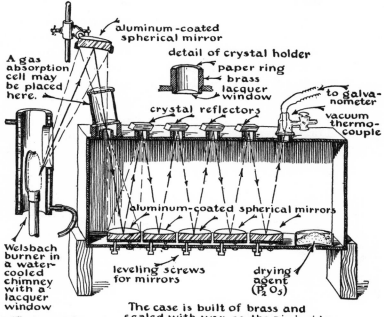

aluminum-coated
spherical mirror

A gas
absorption
cell may
be placed
here.

detail of crystal holder

paper ring
brass
lacquer
window

crystal reflectors

to galva-
nometer

vacuum
thermo-
couple

aluminum-coated spherical mirrors

Welsbach
burner in
a water-
cooled
chimney
with a
lacquer
window

leveling screws
for mirrors

drying
agent
(P_2O_5)

That radiation
should be used
which is emitted
almost tangentially.

The case is built of brass and
sealed with wax so the air inside
may be kept dry. The case should
be insulated with felt, which is
not shown.

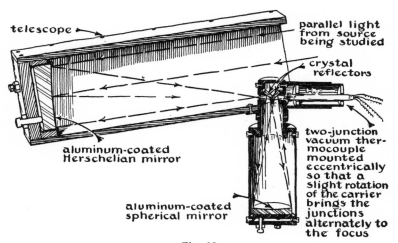

telescope

parallel light
from source
being studied

crystal
reflectors

aluminum-coated
Herschelian mirror

two-junction
vacuum ther-
mocouple
mounted
eccentrically
so that a
slight rotation
of the carrier
brings the
junctions
alternately to
the focus

aluminum-coated
spherical mirror

Fig. 38.

water in the air even when it is humid; in this region of the spectrum the entire thickness of the atmosphere exhibits a transmission comparable to the transmission of the atmosphere for green and yellow light ($T = 85$ per cent).

Polarization. There are now new polarizers available for use in the visible spectrum, but they are not as efficient as Nicol prisms.[56] The transmission of these polarizers, shown in Fig. 39, does not yield as high efficiency as that of a Nicol prism. For plane-polarized light of proper azimuth a Nicol prism transmits about 80 per cent. Two Nicol prisms in

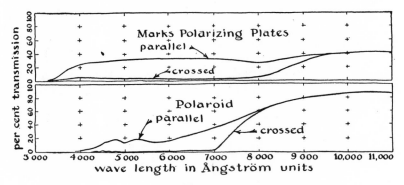

Fig. 39.

series transmit a maximum of about 32 per cent of unpolarized white light. At the other extreme, two Nicol prisms accurately crossed are quite opaque. For example, they will not transmit enough sunlight to make the disk of the sun discernible. However, to obtain this degree of opacity, the Nicol prisms must be crossed very precisely (to an accuracy of the order of 1 second of arc).

The new polarizers have the advantage over Nicol prisms that they can polarize a beam of greater aperture (both areal and angular). Two applications of the new polarizers are illustrated in Figs. 40 and 41.

One of these, illustrated in Fig. 40, applies to the measurement of strain in glass. Objects to be tested for strain, as,

[56] Strong, J., *J. O. S. A.*, *26*, 256 (1936).

for example, glass-to-metal seals, are immersed in a jar fitted
with parallel glass sides and containing a liquid medium
having the same index of refraction as the glass.   This
medium may, for example, be a mixture of the proper proportions of carbon disulphide and benzene or a mixture of
zylene and alcohol.   Polarized light obtained from a lamp by
reflection off black glass at the polarizing angle (or reflection
off the back of an exposed photographic plate which has been
developed, fixed, and dried) is viewed through a full-wave

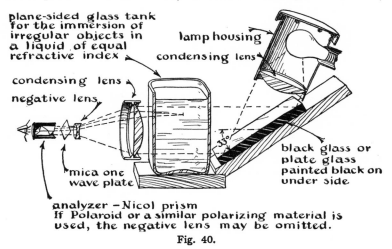

plane-sided glass tank
for the immersion of
irregular objects in
a liquid of equal
refractive index

lamp housing
condensing lens

condensing lens
negative lens

black glass or
plate glass
painted black on
under side

mica one
wave plate

analyzer – Nicol prism
If Polaroid or a similar polarizing material is
used, the negative lens may be omitted.

Fig. 40.

mica plate and analyzer.   (The construction of the full-wave
plate is described below.)   When a full-wave plate is placed
in front of the analyzer, slight variations of the polarization
over the field of view are manifest as variations of color from
the purple of the unstressed condition.

Engineering applications of polarized light.   The property
of isotropic transparent materials that a strain makes them
double refracting is used by engineers for studying the magnitude and distribution of stress produced by loading various
two-dimensional structures, such as, for example, the shapes
represented by the cross section of a dam.[57]   An arrange-

[57] Brahtz, J. H. A., *Rev. Sci. Instruments*, *5*, 80 (1934).
Goetz, A., *Rev. Sci. Instruments*, *5*, 84 (1934).

ment for such studies using spherical mirrors and the new polarizers is shown in Fig. 41. The astigmatism (due to using the mirrors off axis) can be balanced out, at least in part, by tipping the camera lens about a horizontal axis by a suitable amount. The model of the shape to be tested is usually made from a clear sheet of Bakelite or Marblette. Table XII gives the coefficient of forced double refraction for various materials suitable for constructing models.

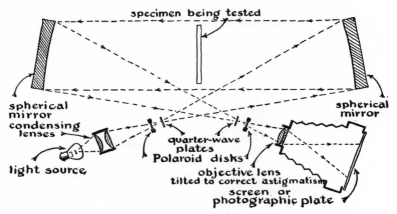

Fig. 41.

The quarter-wave plates are used in the illustrated arrangement to allow the elimination of the pattern of isoclinics (the lines along which the principal stress in the specimen has a constant inclination) from the pattern of isochromatics (the lines along which the quantity $(p - q)$ has a constant value). Here p and q are the principal stresses produced in the model by the applied loading. Methods of determining the magnitude of the quantities p and q from the measured isoclinics and isochromatics cannot be described here, since they are quite complicated.[58]

---

[58] Coker, E. G., and Filon, L. N. G., *A Treatise on Photo-Elasticity*. London: Cambridge University Press, 1931; New York: The Macmillan Company, 1932.

Horger, O. J., *Jour. of Applied Physics*, 9, 457 (1938). This article contains a good bibliography on the subject.

However, in spite of this, the experimental method of studying the stresses in many structures is easier than the theoretical method, and the experimental method has the advantage over the theoretical method that it carries with it the conviction of a more direct appeal to nature for the information desired.

Quarter-, half-, and full-wave plates. Quarter-, half-, and full-wave plates are made of quartz, selenite, or mica cut or split parallel to the optical axis. The thickness of the plate is made such that the relative retardation of the ordinary and extraordinary ray is $\frac{1}{4}$, $\frac{1}{2}$, or 1 full wave length. The thickness τ required for a quarter-wave plate is

$$\tau = \frac{\lambda}{4(n_e - n_o)}, \tag{2}$$

where n_e is the index of the crystal for the extraordinary ray and n_o for the ordinary, and λ is the wave length in question. For mica the thickness of a quarter-wave plate for the D

TABLE XII

Material	Elastic Limit (lbs./square inch)	Coefficient of Forced Double Refraction (Brewster's)
Glass...................	....	2.7
Celluloid...............	4000	11.1
Bakelite................	5500	44.5
Phenolite...............	7000	56.7
Marblette..............	2750	132.5

Carleton, R. B., *Rev. Sci. Instruments*, 5, 30 (1934).
Solakian, Arshag G., *Mech. Eng.*, December, page 767 (1935).

lines is about 0.036 mm. Although for mica the quantity $(n_e - n_o)$ varies from specimen to specimen,[59] it can be taken as essentially constant for all wave lengths. Therefore, the thickness of a quarter-wave plate is roughly proportional to the wave length for which it is intended.

[59] Einsporn, E., *Phys. Zeits.*, *37*, 83 (1936).

A quarter-wave plate, when it is set perpendicular to a beam of polarized light with its principal directions at 45° to the azimuth of polarization, retards one half of the polarized light until its phase is 90° behind the phase of the other half, thus producing circular polarized light. Conversely, a quarter-wave plate will change circular to plane-polarized light. A half-wave plate, similarly oriented, transforms plane-polarized light to plane-polarized light rotated in azimuth by 90°.

The principal directions of mica are determined by interposing it between crossed Nicols. The principal directions are parallel and at right angles to the azimuth of polarization of the incident light when the mica (of any thickness) is so oriented that it does not affect the cutoff of the second Nicol.

Tutton's test[60] for distinguishing between the two principal directions in a quarter-wave plate is to place the plate between crossed Nicols (with its plane perpendicular to the axis of the beam of incident white polarized light) oriented in an azimuth such that the restored light is a maximum. The principal directions in the plate now make angles of 45° with the azimuth of vibration of the incident polarized light. The mica plate is rotated first about one principal direction and then about the other, so that, in each case, light traverses a thicker layer of mica. In one case the color passes from bluish gray through iron gray to black, and in the other case the color passes from white to yellow and then through colors of a higher order. The latter color sequence corresponds to rotation about the principal direction of slower vibration in the mica and the first case corresponds to the principal direction of faster vibration in the mica.

Splitting of mica. Quarter-wave plates are most easily made from mica, since it is easily split to the thickness required.

The stock sheets are split from clear mica plates.[61] The

[60] Kaplan, Joseph, *J. O. S. A.*, *14*, 186 (1927).
[61] Mica is obtainable from Eugene Munsell, 200 Varick Street, New York City.

starting sheet is trimmed to about 3 inches square with sharp tin snips so as to have clean edges. (The exact size of the starting sheet is immaterial.) One corner of the starting sheet is then frayed out by rubbing it, and a clean dissecting needle is introduced to divide the sheet approximately in half. A drop of water is introduced in the cavity so produced.[62] The mica is then split all around the edges by working the needle along, point first, at an angle of about 30°, so that the first cleavage starts inside the boundary of the sheet. This avoids a terraced cleavage. After the needle has gone around the circumference, a second drop of water is introduced, and the plates are drawn apart. The water so facilitates cleavage that the sheets may be separated almost as easily as the pages of a book. This process is repeated until the thickness is approximately 0.036 mm or as thin as desired. Each time, the sheet is divided so as to give two sheets of approximately the same thickness.

Mica gauges.[63] A gauge may be made up as shown in Fig. 42. To make such a gauge the principal directions are

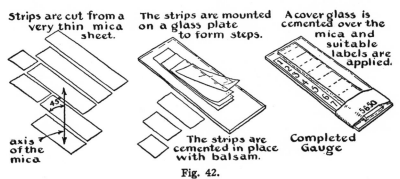

Strips are cut from a very thin mica sheet.

The strips are mounted on a glass plate to form steps.

A cover glass is cemented over the mica and suitable labels are applied.

axis of the mica

The strips are cemented in place with balsam.

Completed Gauge

Fig. 42.

first marked on a starting plate. The thinnest possible sheet is then split from the starting plate and cut up into strips about $\frac{1}{4}$ inch wide. The strips are cut at an angle of 45° with the principal directions. These strips are then cut to

[62] Strong, J., *Rev. Sci. Instruments*, *6*, 243 (1935).
[63] Wright, Lewis, *Light*, page 289. New York: The Macmillan Company, 1892.

give rectangles with lengths of 2 inches, $1\frac{7}{8}$ inches, $1\frac{3}{4}$ inches, $1\frac{5}{8}$ inches, and so forth. (See Fig. 42.) The strips are next cemented (with balsam) between glass plates as illustrated, care being exercised to see that none of the strips are mounted upside down or rotated end for end. The steps so formed are then indexed.

The retardation per step of the gauge is determined as follows: After the analyzer is set for maximum transmission

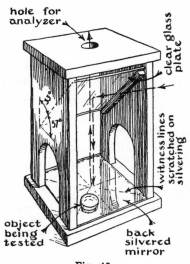

hole for analyzer

clear glass plate

45°

57°

witness lines scratched on silvering

object being tested

back silvered mirror

Fig. 43.

of the light, the gauge is placed on the mirror of the Norremberg doubler (see Fig. 43) either parallel or perpendicular to the azimuth of polarization. A sodium light should be used for illumination. The index number of the step which gives opacity is noted. The step giving opacity is a quarter-wave plate for the D lines. Other steps are proportionately greater and less.

Using the gauge. The gauge is used as follows: First, the analyzing Nicol of the Norremberg doubler is set for extinction. The mica of unknown thickness is placed on the bottom mirror of the doubler, with its principal direction making an angle of 45° with the azimuth of polarization to give maximum transmission. Then the gauge strip is laid on top of the mica so that it is either parallel or perpendicular to the azimuth of polarization. At one of these orientations, the steps show "interference" colors, and at the other, and proper one, opacity is obtained for one or two of the steps. The calibration value of the step which gives opacity corresponds to the retardation of the mica sample. Interpolation may be required to make a delicate measurement.

Magnification of lenses. The transverse magnification of a lens is the ratio of image diameter to object diameter, or, expressed another way, it is the ratio of transverse image displacement to transverse object displacement. For a simple lens the magnification is given by the ratio of image distance to object distance. For a system such as a spectrometer, which has a collimating element (lens or mirror) with the object at or near its focal plane and a telescope element also with the image at or near its focal plane, the magnification produced is the ratio of the focal length of the telescope element to that of the collimating element.

Another case, encountered in a telescope, is that in which parallel light is received by the objective and observed by an eyepiece adjusted so that its focal plane is very near the focus of the objective. Here, the angular magnifying power is the ratio of the focal length of the objective to that of the eyepiece.

The longitudinal magnification of an image-forming system gives the ratio of the displacement of the image along the optical axis to the displacement of the object. In the case of a system composed of two lenses (or mirrors) with the object and image at or near the respective focal planes of these elements, the longitudinal magnification is given by the square of the ratio of the focal lengths.

Other properties of lenses. When a beam of parallel light is focused with a thin lens on the optical axis, its focal length f is given by the expression

$$\frac{1}{f} = \left(\frac{1}{r_1} + \frac{1}{r_2}\right)(n - 1), \tag{3}$$

where r_1 and r_2 are the respective radii of curvature of the two surfaces of the lens, and n is the index of refraction of the material from which the lens is constructed. The r's are taken positive if the curvature acts to converge the light.

If the light is inclined to the optical axis of the lens, it exhibits astigmatism as shown in Fig. 44. For example, the best focus of a distant star, which would be a small hard spot of light on the optical axis, is a soft image when the lens is inclined. The diameter of the smallest image is known as the "circle of least confusion." Within the focal distance giving the smallest off-axis image, the lens gives at one particular distance a rather sharp line focus, which is perpendicular to the plane passing through the image and the optical axis. Also, outside this image another rather sharp line focus is obtained. This line focus is perpendicular to the first line and parallel to the plane referred to above.

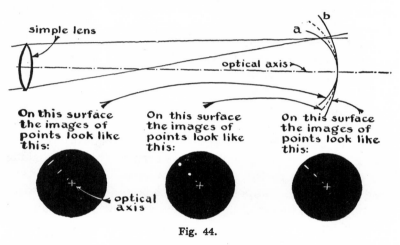

Fig. 44.

The astigmatism of a simple lens is illustrated in Fig. 44. The locus of the inner astigmatic images is a circle, a, having a diameter

$$d = \frac{f}{3 + n^{-1}}, \tag{4}$$

or $0.275\,f$ for $n = 1.5$, and the locus of the outer astigmatic images is a circle, b, of diameter

$$d = \frac{f}{1 + n^{-1}}, \tag{5}$$

or $0.6\,f$ for $n = 1.5$.

Properties of mirrors. The mirrors generally used in optics are conic sections of revolution and the flat. They are paraboloidal for focusing parallel light, ellipsoidal for two conjugate real focii, and hyperboloidal for two conjugate focii, one of which is virtual. The spherical mirror is, of course, suited for focusing light from a source at its center of curvature exactly back on the center.

When a spherical mirror of radius R is used to focus parallel light striking it at an angle, the image exhibits astigmatism, and the lines corresponding to the two circles shown in Fig. 44, determined by the positions of the astigmatic images, are a circle of diameter R and a straight line, respectively. (See Fig. 21, Chapter XI.)

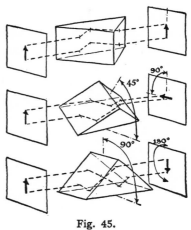

Fig. 45.

Properties of prisms. Some interesting properties of a right-angle prism are illustrated in Fig. 45.

This prism, viewed through the long face and perpendicular to the vertex of the 90° dihedral angle in one azimuth, has the interesting and often useful property of returning a beam of light back on its path, regardless of the angle of incidence on the long face in the other azimuth. Fig. 46 illustrates the corresponding property for the corner of a cube.

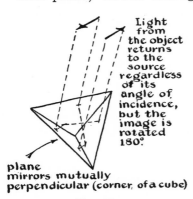

Light from the object returns to the source regardless of its angle of incidence, but the image is rotated 180°.

plane mirrors mutually perpendicular (corner of a cube)

Fig. 46.

Optical recording systems. Professor Hardy has written an excellent article on recording systems as applied to oscillographs.[64] We can refer only to his results. He concludes

[64] Hardy, A. C., *J. O. S. A.*, *14*, 505 (1927).

that a simple optical system with a single lens in front of the galvanometer mirror will give as much illumination on the recording film, on a basis of equal resolving power, as any other possible stigmatic system. Furthermore, he points out that the focal length of the simple systems should be chosen so that the limit to the resolving power is set by the photographic material rather than by interference effects. Although 25 lines/mm or more can be resolved by photography, Hardy sets an arbitrary practical limit of 0.1 mm as the resolving power of the photographic material. To obtain maximum illumination and at the same time to conserve on the use of photographic materials, the simple lens should be chosen to give a spot at least 0.1 mm wide.

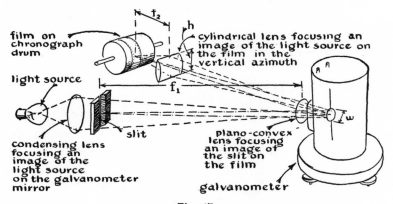

Fig. 47.

However, by using an astigmatic optical system such as the one shown in Fig. 47, it is easily possible to obtain nine times as much illumination as with the simple lens. Furthermore, the astigmatic system has the additional advantage that rotation of the galvanometer mirror about a horizontal axis does not produce a vertical deflection of the image on the recording film.

The calculation of the maximum velocity at which the recording spot can traverse the photographic emulsion and still yield a perceptible trace is treated in Chapter XI.

This treatment includes the astigmatic case illustrated in Fig. 47. Owing to the recent developments in fast photographic emulsions, the data given in Table VI, Chapter XI, for the various materials may be regarded as being distinctly conservative.

A bibliography of some of the best works on the subjects treated in this chapter is given in a footnote.[65]

[65] Baly, E. C. C., *Spectroscopy.* New York: Longmans, Green and Company, 1927.

Forsythe, W. E., *Measurement of Radiant Energy.* New York: McGraw-Hill Book Company, 1937.

Hardy, A. C., and Perrin, F. H., *The Principles of Optics.* New York: McGraw-Hill Book Company, 1932.

Lecomte, J., *La Spectre Infrarouge.* Les Presses Universitaires de France, 1928.

Meyer, Charles F., *The Diffraction of Light, X-rays and Material Particles.* Chicago: University of Chicago Press, 1934.

Schaefer, C. L., and Matossi, F., *Das Ultrarote Spektrum.* Berlin: Julius Springer, 1930.

Wood, R. W., *Physical Optics,* Third Edition. New York: The Macmillan Company, 1934.

CHAPTER X

Photoelectric Cells and Amplifiers

BY

A. E. WHITFORD

Introduction

THE photoelectric cell has found an important place in the physical laboratory as a device for the measurement of the intensity of radiation, and as such may be classed with the thermocouple and the photographic plate. In common with the photographic plate its response varies with wave length, so that it does not measure energy directly, as does the thermocouple. The photographic plate, because of its ability to integrate extremely long exposures, can be used to measure smaller quantities of radiation than can the photoelectric cell. But the photographic plate has the definite disadvantage that its blackening is a complicated function of intensity and exposure time, necessitating a series of calibration exposures whose intensity ratios are known. Furthermore, plate grain, local variations in emulsion sensitivity, and nonuniform development place limitations on the precision obtainable in photographic photometry. Both the photocell and the thermocouple, when used with suitable precautions, give a response linear with respect to the intensity, and both are capable of giving more precise results than the photographic plate. In the infrared beyond about 10,000 Å, the thermocouple (or other heat-sensitive devices such as the bolometer) must be used. At shorter wave lengths, however, it is possible to measure much smaller amounts of radiation with the photoelectric cell than with the thermocouple.

Limit of detection compared. An attempt to set an ultimate limit for any of the above-mentioned detectors of radiation must of necessity be approximate, because the working limit depends on various factors such as the angular size and shape of the source, the spectral distribution of the radiation it gives out, and the presence or absence of background radiation. Because the stars offer a common basis for comparing the response of light-sensitive devices to weak sources, they are chosen as reference standards in this discussion. The magnitudes of the stars form a logarithmic scale such that an intensity ratio of 100 times corresponds to 5 magnitudes. Thus 1 magnitude represents an intensity ratio of $\sqrt[5]{100}$, or 2.512. . . . In general, the difference in magnitude between two stars whose intensities are I_1 and I_2 is given by $m_1 - m_2 = 2.5 \log_{10} I_2/I_1$. A candle at a kilometer has been found[1] equivalent to a star of visual magnitude + 0.8, approximately the brightness of Altair. From these relations one may easily derive an equation giving the amount of light received by a telescope from a given star. If m is the visual magnitude of the star, d the diameter of the telescope in inches, and Q the amount of light expressed in lumens,[2] then it may be shown that

$$2.5 \log_{10} Q = 7.57 - 30 + 5 \log_{10} d - m.$$

As an example, we may compute the amount of light received by a 1-inch telescope from the polestar,[3] which has a visual magnitude of 2.1. Substitution in the formula gives 1.5×10^{-10} lumen. Of course, the stars differ among themselves as to the spectral distribution of the light they give out. In this comparison, stars of spectral class G_0 having

---

[1] Russell, H. N., *Astrophys. J.*, *43*, 129 (1916).

[2] The lumen is the unit of luminous flux. It is equal to the flux emitted in a unit solid angle by a uniform point source of 1 international candle.

[3] Polaris, in combination with a small laboratory telescope, provides a convenient order-of-magnitude standard source for testing the responses of photoelectric cells to weak radiation. It is a variable, with a period of about 4 days, and an amplitude between maximum and minimum of 0.08 magnitude to 0.16 magnitude, depending on the spectral sensitivity of the measuring device. Its year-round availability and negligible diurnal motion are reasons for its choice over more constant stars.

the same temperature as the sun are selected. As is well known, the radiation curve of the sun is roughly that of a black body at 6000°K. The results for four detectors of radiation are given in Table I. These represent the limit reached in actual practice and not the theoretical limit. In the case of the photoelectric cell and thermocouple, for which the response is a "pointer reading," the criterion for limit of detection is taken as the average deviation of successive deflections from the mean when measuring a star near the useful limit of the instrument.

TABLE I

Limit of Detection for Stars of Solar Type

Detector	Exposure Time (minutes)	Telescope Diameter (inches)	Limiting Magnitude (visual)	Lumens ($\times 10^{-14}$)	Ergs/sec. ($\times 10^{-9}$)
Photographic plate[a]	240	5	16.3	0.8	0.5
Unaided human eye[b]	...	0.32	8.5	4	2.5
Photoelectric cell[c]	1	60	19.5	6	4
Thermocouple[d]	0.3	100	9.5	160,000	100,000

[a] Ross, F. E., and Calvert, Mary, *Atlas of the Milky Way.* Chicago: University of Chicago Press, 1934.
[b] Russell, H. N., *Astrophys. J., 45,* 60 (1917).
[c] Smith, S., *Astrophys. J., 76,* 486 (1932); *Mt. Wilson Contr. No. 457.*
[d] Pettit, E., and Nicholson, S. B., *Astrophys. J., 68,* 279 (1938); *Mt. Wilson Contr. No. 369.*

The data given in Table I are for response to a point source emitting "white" light, that is, light having the spectral quality of sunlight. For cases in which the image of the source cannot be made very small, the thermocouple must have larger receivers, and the limit is not as small as that given in the table by a factor of 5 to 10. The photographic plate also suffers when the source is an extended luminous area, because the light is spread over a greater area on the emulsion. According to Biltz,[4] at 4360 Å it requires an energy of the order of 10^{-2} erg/cm^2 at the emulsion surface to give a perceptible blackening. The response of the photoelectric cell is independent of image size and shape as long as the image is not larger than the cathode. This gives it considerable advantage over the photographic plate in rapid measurement of low surface brightness.

The thermocouple, of course, measures energy independent of the spectral distribution of the light. The response curve of the human eye is given in Fig. 4, page 410. At the wave length of maximum visibility, 1 lumen = 1.61×10^{-3} watt. The variation of the sensitivity of various photographic plates with wave length is given by Mees.[5] The spectral response curves of various types of photoelectric cells are given on page 401. Assuming that the limit of detection is set by the smallest current that can be measured, these curves may be considered to give the limit of detection as a function of wave length. The case cited in Table I in which 4×10^{-9} erg/sec. was the limit probably represents a favorable instance. By choice of a suitable cell for each spectral region, the range from 2500 Å to 9500 Å can be covered with a limit of detection not greater than 10^{-7} erg/sec.

Types of cells. Two general types of cells have been found useful in the physical laboratory. One is the photoemissive cell, historically the oldest. In this type electrons are ejected from a metallic surface by the action of light and

---

[4] Biltz, M., *Phys. Zeits.*, *34*, 200 (1933). If the star image cited in Table I is assumed to be a round, uniformly illuminated spot 0.06 mm in diameter, the energy received at the plate is easily computed to be 0.25 erg/cm^2, or 25 times the figure given by Biltz. The difference may be ascribed to three factors: (1) Part of the radiation came in wave lengths to which the plate was insensitive. (2) The limit in stellar photography is set by lack of contrast between the star image and sky background. The sky brightness is so low that it does not affect other less sensitive detectors of radiation very seriously. (3) When the blackened area is very small, a higher density is required to make the image perceptible. Hubble, E., *Astrophys. J.*, *76*, 107 (1932); *Mt. Wilson Contr. No. 453.*

[5] Mees, C. E. K., *J. O. S. A.*, *21*, 753 (1931), *22*, 204 (1932), *23*, 229 (1933), *25*, 80 (1935).

are collected on an electrode maintained at a positive potential by an external battery.   The other type is the photovoltaic cell, a comparatively recent development.   In these cells light causes a transfer of electrons across the rectifying boundary between two dissimilar materials, such as copper and copper oxide, or selenium and another metal.   The current is sent through the external circuit entirely by the voltage generated within the cell, and no battery is required.

A third type of light-sensitive device, the photoconductive cell, depends for its action on the change in resistance of certain materials, such as selenium, when exposed to light. Though greatly improved in recent years, these cells have not found much application in the physical laboratory.   A serious drawback is the nonlinear response to light.[6]

Characteristics of emissive-type cells.   The spectral sensitivity of various types of photoemissive cells is shown in Fig. 1.   The relative height of the various curves is only approximately correct, since there is considerable individual variation in cells of the same type.   The vertical scale is intended to represent the average emission of good-quality vacuum cells obtained from commercial manufacturers.

The cesium oxide cells are sensitive to the greatest range of wave lengths and are therefore probably the type most generally useful in the laboratory.   This type of sensitization was developed to meet the need for a cell that would have a high response to light from incandescent tungsten bulbs, in which most of the energy comes in the red and infrared.   Cesium oxide cells are very widely used in commercial applications of the photoelectric cell, such as for the reproduction of sound in motion pictures.   Indeed, since their introduction in about 1930, the production of emission cells of other types has become almost negligible.

The cesium oxide cell has one drawback when it is used for measuring the light from very faint sources.   It has relatively large dark current, due at least in part to thermionic

---

[6] For further information see Henney, K., *Electron Tubes in Industry.* Second Edition.   New York: McGraw-Hill Book Company, 1937.

emission from the sensitive surface at room temperature. Currents as large as 10^{-9} ampere have been reported.[7] Present-day cells, when of a design which minimizes insulation leakage over the bulb and base, usually have a dark current of the order of 10^{-11} to 10^{-12} ampere. If the photocurrent is very much (say 1000 times) smaller than this, it

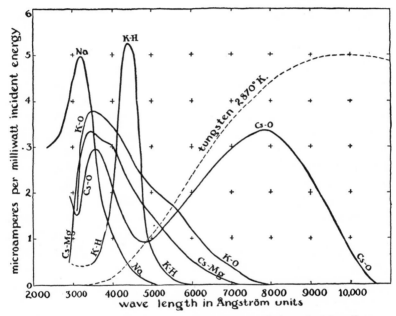

Fig. 1. Spectral sensitivity of various types of photoelectric cells.

will be masked by unavoidable irregularities in the dark current. The dark current can be reduced to 10^{-15} ampere or less by refrigerating the cell with solid carbon dioxide. This has been done by Hall[8] and Bennett[9] in their application of cesium oxide cells to the photometry of stars. Details of the design of such an arrangement are given on page 424.

In certain applications, the high infrared sensitivity of the

[7] Kingsbury, E. F., and Stillwell, G. R., *Phys. Rev.*, *37*, 1549 (1931).

[8] Hall, J. S., *Astrophys. J.*, *79*, 145 (1934).

[9] Bennett, A. L., *Pub. Am. Astr. Soc.*, *8*, 209 (1935).

cesium oxide cell is inconvenient. For example, in comparing the color of certain objects, it may be desired to measure
the intensity through a blue filter. Almost all blue filters
made of glass or gelatin are more or less transparent to the
infrared, so that with a cesium oxide cell large error will be
made unless an additional filter to remove the infrared is
used. The standard filter for removing the infrared is a
solution of copper salt.[10] Two special glass filters are also
satisfactory. These are the Corning Glass Company's Aklo
and the Jena BG-18.[11]

The potassium oxide cell is valuable in applications to
colorimetry and photometry when infrared sensitivity is
undesirable. Ordinary filters may be used with it, without
particular attention to infrared leaks. It has a fair degree
of red sensitivity, with a threshold at about 8000 Å, and a
higher green and blue sensitivity than the cesium oxide cell.
The thermionic emission is negligible. Cesium-magnesium
cells are also useful for applications of this type. The threshold for this type of surface is at about 7000 Å.

Potassium hydride cells are sensitive to a fairly narrow
range of wave lengths, mainly in the blue, with a maximum
at about 4400 Å. Their sensitivity to white light and particularly to light from incandescent tungsten is considerably
lower than for cesium oxide cells. However, in the photometry of stars, which are in general much hotter than incandescent lights and give out correspondingly greater
amounts of blue light, potassium hydride cells have been
found extremely valuable. For this work, an important
advantage is their extremely low dark current, limited, it
seems, only by the insulation of the bulb. Smith[12] has
reported a dark current of only 5×10^{-18} ampere for a
potassium hydride cell in a fused-quartz bulb.

---

[10] Gibson, K. S., *J.O.S.A.*, *13*, 267 (1926), recommends 57 g of $CuSO_4 \cdot 5H_2O$
to 1 liter of water; about 2 cm is required. A transmission curve is given in
Fig. 24, Chapter IX.

[11] Jena glass filters are obtainable from the Fish-Schurman Corporation,
250 East 43rd Street, New York City.

[12] Smith, S., *Astrophys. J.*, *76*, 486 (1932); *Mt. Wilson Contr. No. 457.*

For the ultraviolet the cesium oxide cell can be used.   For applications in which the cell must be sensitive only to the ultraviolet, several types of cells are available, with different thresholds.   Sodium cells are sensitive mainly to wave lengths in the range 2000 Å to 4000 Å, with a slight response to visible light.   For the shorter wave-length portion of the ultraviolet a thorium, titanium, or tungsten cathode may be used.   Thorium is sensitive from 2500 Å to 3600 Å, titanium from 2500 Å to 3200 Å, and tungsten from 1700 Å to 2700 Å. Insufficient data are available for plotting spectral response curves of these tubes along with those given in Fig. 1, but the response is believed to be comparable to that of a sodium cell at wave lengths below 3000 Å.   These cells are especially useful in investigations of the biological effects of radiation.

In Table II is collected a representative list of photo-electric cells of the emission type obtainable from American manufacturers.   When several cells which differ only as regards size of cathode or type of base are available, only one is listed.   The sensitivity rating (except as otherwise noted) is based on the response to light from incandescent tungsten at a color temperature of 2870°K., which has been tentatively adopted as a standard source for comparing photocells.   This is roughly the operating temperature of a 300-watt gas-filled tungsten bulb designed for general illumination purposes.   When tested with a bulb at a lower temperature, cesium oxide cells will give a slightly higher apparent rating, but the rating of the blue-sensitive cells will be affected unfavorably.   For rough tests gas-filled Mazda bulbs of from 50 watts to 100 watts may be used. At normal voltage these lamps have an efficiency of approximately 1.0 candle power/watt (within 10 to 20 per cent) and operate at about 2700°K.[13]

The insulation between cathode and anode is an important factor when a cell is to be used to measure a very faint source. If the insulation is not good enough, the dark current due to

---

[13] For further information see Moon, P. H., *Scientific Basis of Illuminating Engineering*.   New York: McGraw-Hill Book Company, 1936.

TABLE II

PHOTOELECTRIC TUBES

Manufacturer's Type Number	Manufacturer	Description	Type of Cathode	Typical Sensitivity (Microamperes/lumen)	Base	Terminal on Bulb (if any)
PJ–14[a]	GE	vac	Cs-O	28	std	cathode
PJ–22	GE	vac	Cs-O	14	std	...
PJ–23	GE	gas	Cs-O	75	std	...
FJ–114	GE	vac	Cs-O	35	bayonet	...
71–AV	GM	vac	Cs-O	25	std	...
71–A	GM	gas	Cs-O	120	std	...
71–TA[b]	GM	gas	Cs-O	120	std	anode
1038–A[c]	GM	gas	Cs-O	120	none	...
5A	WE	vac	Cs-O	20	std	...
8A	WE	gas	Cs-O	100	std	...
D–97087	WE	gas	Cs-O	...	none	2 seals
917	RCA	vac	Cs-O	20	std	anode
918	RCA	gas	Cs-O	110	std	...
919	RCA	vac	Cs-O	20	std	cathode
920[d]	RCA	gas	Cs-O	110	std	...
CE–1	CE	gas	Cs-O	150	std	...
CE–15[b]	CE	gas	Cs-O	150	std	anode
WL–734	WH	vac	Cs-O	15	std	...
WL–735	WH	gas	Cs-O	60	std	...
SR–53	WH	vac	Cs-O	25	special	...
SR–63	WH	gas	Cs-O	125	special	...
WL–770	WH	vac	Cs-Mg	0.75	std	anode
WL–773	WH	vac	Th	0.10[e]	std	cathode
WL–767	WH	vac	Ti	0.02[e]	std	cathode
WL–774	WH	vac	W	0.001[e]	std	cathode
FJ–76[f]	GE	vac	Na	...	...	...
71–D	GM	gas	K-O	8[g]	std	...
... [h]	...	gas	K-H	3	...	...

Typical sensitivity is rating when exposed to tungsten light at 2870°K., except as otherwise noted. Std base means regular four-pin radio base. When no terminal on bulb is mentioned, both terminals come out through pins in the base. Manufacturers: GE, General Electric Company, Schenectady, New York; GM, G-M Laboratories, 1731 Belmont Avenue, Chicago, Illinois; RCA, RCA Manufacturing Company, Harrison, New Jersey; WH, Westinghouse Lamp Company, Bloomfield, New Jersey; CE, Continental Electric Company, Geneva, Illinois.

[a] Listed as "special high sensitivity cell similar to PJ-14."

[b] High insulation cell with internal guard ring.

[c] Quartz bulb; terminals through common seal, but special sheath provided.

[d] Twin cell. Two cathodes and two anodes in single bulb.

[e] Response to total radiation from S-1 lamp in Corex bulb, with standard reflector, at a distance of 1 foot.

[f] Quartz bulb; also available in gas-filled type.

[g] Not manufacturer's figure; estimated from other data.

[h] As far as is known, this type of cell is not now regularly produced by any American commercial manufacturer, although it might be obtained on a special order. Those used in astronomical photometry have been made by Professor J. Kunz, Department of Physics, University of Illinois. The General Electric Company, Ltd., Magnet House, Kingsway, London, W. C. 2, manufactures a gas-filled potassium cell known as the Osram KG-7.

---

leakage may be many times larger than the photocurrent. For example, in certain cells designed for use in the sound head of motion-picture projectors, in which the photocurrent may be on the order of 1 microampere, the two terminals come out to pins on a standard four-prong radio-tube base. In general, cells of this type are not satisfactory for currents smaller than about 10^{-10} ampere. In some cells the connection to either the cathode or the anode is made via a separate cap on the bulb, and thus a considerable length of clear glass bulb is interposed between the terminals to serve as insulation. Cells without a base in which the terminals come out through a common pressed seal are better than those with a base, but not as good as those in which there are two seals at opposite ends of the bulb.

In many cases the leakage current over the surface of the bulb can be practically eliminated by a guard ring at a proper place on the cell. This can be made by wrapping a few turns of fine wire around the cell and painting with aquadag[14] or a mixture of lampblack and mucilage. The guard ring should be connected to a point in the circuit such that the potential difference across the insulation on the cell will be as near zero as possible. In some processes of manufacture, particularly of cesium oxide cells, a thin deposit is left on the

---

[14] Aquadag is obtainable from the Acheson Colloids Corporation, Port Huron, Michigan.

inside walls of the bulb, which greatly reduces the insulation resistance. The obvious remedy is an internal guard ring, and some manufacturers regularly provide this feature on certain of their cells.

In general, insulation leakage currents are greatly reduced by cooling, because of the quasi-electrolytic nature of such conduction. For instance, the dark current of an RCA 917 cell fell from about 10^{-10} ampere to about 10^{-13} ampere when cooled with dry ice. The latter current is not a serious detriment except when the highest sensitivity is required. It thus becomes possible to use an inexpensive commercial cell to measure rather faint sources. A suitable arrangement for refrigerating cells with dry ice is described on page 424.

The manufacture of cells. The prospective user of photoelectric cells will find it by far the most economical procedure as regards both time and money to purchase the cells from an established manufacturer. The production of highly sensitive cathodes is still very much an art which has never been fully described in the literature and requires some experience to master. Most manufacturers will accept orders for special cells with internal guard rings or other modifications required in particular applications.[15]

Vacuum and gas-filled cells. In vacuum cells the anode merely collects all of the electrons ejected from the light-sensitive cathode. The current for a given light increases rapidly with voltage up to about 25 volts and then gradually becomes saturated and does not increase further. The introduction of an inert gas at a pressure of a few tenths of a

---

[15] For workers who wish to experiment with the making of cells, the following references will give fairly complete instructions:

Hughes, A. L., and DuBridge, L. A., *Photoelectric Phenomena.* McGraw-Hill Book Company, 1932. Chapter 12 gives a summary of methods for all types of cells.

Nottingham, W. B., *Frank. Inst., J., 206,* 637 (1928). Details for alkali-hydride cells.

Prescott, C. H., Jr., and Kelley, M. J., *Bell System Techn. J., 11,* 334 (1932). Detailed analysis of the process for cesium oxide cells.

Rentschler, H. C., Henry, D. E., and Smith, K. O., *Rev. Sci. Instruments, 3,* 794 (1932). Deposition of thorium, tungsten, and many other metals on the cathode by a sputtering process.

millimeter permits an amplification of the original photo-current due to ionization by collision. Fig. 2 shows the relation between the voltage and the current for the same sensitive surface in a vacuum and with gas.   With increasing voltage the gaseous amplification factor increases until at a certain voltage a self-maintaining glow discharge sets in, which, if continued for more than a few seconds, may seriously damage the sensitive surface.   The glow voltage is lower the greater the illumination.   Thus a cell which is

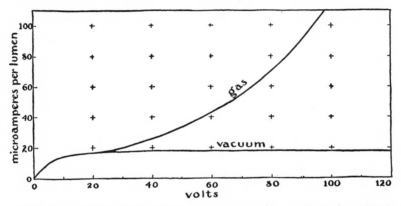

Fig. 2.   Volt-ampere characteristics of vacuum and gas-filled photoelectric cells.

safely below the glow voltage in the dark or for low illumination levels will glow when exposed to strong light.   A gaseous amplification factor of 10 is about the maximum usually recommended.   The gas pressure in commercial cells is usually adjusted so that 90 volts is the maximum safe voltage on the cell for illumination of the order of 0.1 lumen. However, when used with faint sources, this may be exceeded somewhat and an amplification factor of 20 to 40 realized. When a voltage increase of 10 volts doubles the response, the safe limit has been reached.   Amplification factors as high as 600 have been reported,[16] but a gas cell becomes very unstable when too near the glow voltage.

[16] Steinke, E., *Zeits. f. Physik*, *38*, 378 (1926).

A protective resistance of at least 100,000 ohms should always be in the circuit of a gas-filled cell to limit the current to nondestructive values in case of a glow discharge.

The speed of response of a vacuum cell is limited only by the transit time of the photoelectrons, though usually the amplifier sets the limit. Gas-filled cells, however, have a definite time lag. When used with a modulated light signal, the response falls off gradually at the higher audio frequencies, the reduction becoming serious at 10,000 cycles. Data on the frequency response characteristic are supplied by cell manufacturers, particularly for cells to be used in sound reproduction.

When operated on the steep part of the current-voltage curve, gas cells may give a nonlinear response to light. The voltage across the cell is reduced when exposed to light by the amount of the potential drop in the external resistance, and with reduced voltage, the cell is less sensitive. On the other hand, the gaseous amplification factor is greater for more intense illumination, causing an error in the opposite sense. No general rule can be laid down; each situation must be analyzed separately. In most laboratory applications, however, in which the intensity is usually low, difficulties with nonlinear response are less likely to be encountered. In fact, most of the drawbacks of gas-filled cells become less serious when used with faint sources. Recently Stebbins and Whitford[17] calibrated a gas-filled potassium hydride cell over a thousandfold range in intensity at a constant cell voltage. The largest current was about 3×10^{-12} ampere. They found no departures from linearity significantly greater than the probable error, which was about 1 per cent.

Photoelectric currents are feeble enough at best, and the gain provided by gaseous amplification is often just the margin of safety between satisfactory and unsatisfactory

[17] Stebbins, J., and Whitford, A. E., *Astrophys. J.*, *87*, 237, 1937; *Mt. Wilson Contr. No. 586.*

operation. However, when the light intensity is great enough, vacuum cells are to be preferred because of their greater stability.

Photovoltaic cells. In its usual form the photovoltaic cell consists of a thin metallic disk, coated with a film of sensitive material, sealed in a moisture-proof case with a glass window, and provided with suitable terminals. On some cells the terminals are two pins spaced to fit two of the holes of a standard four-prong radio socket. Cells of the photovoltaic type are manufactured by the General Electric Company, G-M Laboratories, Inc., Westinghouse Electric and Manufacturing Company (Photox), and Weston Electrical Instrument Corporation (Photronic cell).

Fig. 3 shows the relation between current output and illumination for the Weston Photronic cell with various

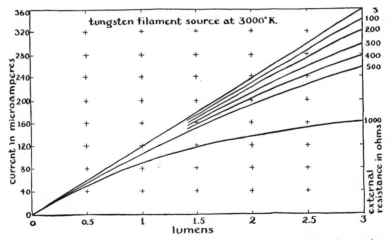

Fig. 3. Response of Photronic cell as a function of illumination for various values of the external resistance.

external resistances. The total current generated by the light is believed to be proportional to the light intensity. However, this current divides between the internal and external resistance. The internal resistance of the cell is about 7000 ohms in the dark, decreasing rapidly with

increasing illumination.[18]   As the figure shows, the result is
a nonlinear current output unless the external resistance is
quite small.   With a low-resistance meter, however, the output is practically linear and amounts to 120 microamperes/
lumen for a tungsten lamp at 3000°K.

The spectral sensitivity curve of the Photronic cell is
shown in Fig. 4, along with the sensitivity curve of the

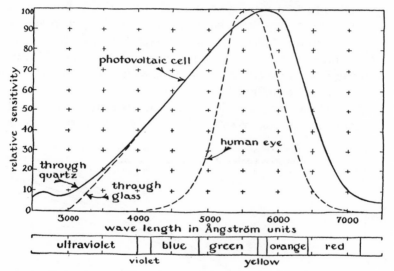

Fig. 4. Spectral sensitivity of Photronic cell, compared with that of the
human eye.

human eye.   By use of a suitable filter, the response curve
of the cell may be modified to match that of the eye very
closely.   Such a filter is supplied by the makers of the cell.

The photovoltaic cell, when used with a sensitive d'Arson-
val galvanometer, gives very stable and reproducible deflections.   If the Photronic cell mentioned above were used
with a galvanometer having a current sensitivity of 2×10^{-10}
ampere/mm, 1 mm would correspond to 1.7×10^{-6} lumen.
The sensitive area of the cell is about 0.012 square foot.
From this it may be computed that 1 mm deflection would

[18] Romain, B. P., *Rev. Sci. Instruments*, *4*, 83 (1933).

correspond to the amount of light received by the cell from a standard candle at 85 feet. A slight gain might be realized by using a more sensitive galvanometer, but it is not worth while to push the sensitivity to the extreme limit, because of the comparative ease with which much smaller amounts of light may be measured with an emission-type cell and amplifier.

Amplification of the output of photovoltaic cells is not feasible, because of their low voltage sensitivity.[19] Because of the high capacity (0.5 microfarad) between the terminals, the response to modulated light intensities falls rapidly with increasing frequency, and the cell is not well adapted to sound reproduction. The power sensitivity is high and a sensitive relay can be operated directly on the output if there is a change in illumination of 0.2 lumen or more.[20] In many applications of the photoelectric cell to automatic control mechanisms, in which only an on-and-off signal is required, this is a simple and convenient arrangement.

For laboratory measurements, the photovoltaic cell is recommended in applications in which there is sufficient intensity available, because of its simplicity and compactness, and because it does not require an external battery.

Amplification of photoelectric currents. Photoelectric cells of the emission type may be used with galvanometers down to about the same limit of light intensity as that given above for photovoltaic cells. For fainter sources some more sensitive current-measuring device must be used. Electrometers of various types can be used, and in certain applications may be the most desirable instrument. In particular, the Lindemann electrometer, or the Cenco-Dershem modification of it, is useful when light weight and compactness are important considerations. In the last few years, however, it has increasingly been the practice to amplify small photo-

---

[19] Wilson, E. D., *Rev. Sci. Instruments*, *2*, 797 (1931).

[20] Suitable relays are manufactured by the Weston Electrical Instrument Corporation and the G-M Laboratories, Inc.

electric currents up to the level at which they can be read on a galvanometer.   The advantages of amplification are that (1) currents which must be measured by the rate-of-drift method with an electrometer can be measured by the more convenient steady-deflection method, and (2) the amplifier is more rugged and portable than the electrometer.   But for attaining the ultimate limit in measuring photoelectric currents, the Hoffmann electrometer is probably still the best instrument.

In case the photoelectric current is varying rapidly with time, the variations can easily be amplified many thousand-fold by means of a multistage a.c. amplifier, the technique for which has been highly developed because of numerous applications in the radio, telephone, and motion-picture industries.   In the laboratory, however, it is usually desired to measure the photoelectric current due to a steady source. Hence d.c. amplification must be used.

Direct-current amplifiers. The fundamental circuit of a single-tube d.c. amplifier is shown in Fig. 5.   The photo-current passes through a resistance R_0, and the resulting

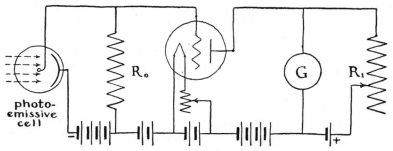

Fig. 5.   Direct-current amplifier for photocurrents.

voltage drop alters the grid potential of the tube.   The consequent change in plate current is read on the galvanometer.   The normal plate current of the tube is balanced out by adjustment of R_1 so that the galvanometer reads zero when there is no light on the cell.   Since R_1 is usually at least fifty times the galvanometer resistance, the galvanometer will indicate very nearly the entire change in plate current. If i_0 is the photocurrent, the galvanometer current i_1 is then $i_1 = i_0 R_0 g_m$, where g_m is the mutual conductance of the tube. The mutual conductance, more correctly called the grid-plate transconductance, is defined by the relation $g_m = di_p/de_g$, where i_p is the plate current and e_g is the grid voltage. To obtain high current amplification it is necessary to make R_0 as great as possible. It is useless, however, to increase R_0 indefinitely, because it is shunted by the grid-to-filament resistance of the tube itself. With most tubes designed for use in radio receivers this resistance is not over 10^8 ohms. The instability of the plate current is such that it is not worth while to use a galvanometer with a sensitivity better than 10^{-8} ampere/mm. Such a circuit is therefore limited to measuring currents greater than 10^{-12} ampere.

The comparatively low value of the grid-to-filament resistance in ordinary tubes is due not so much to poor

TABLE III

RECOMMENDED OPERATING CONDITIONS AND OTHER ESSENTIAL DATA FOR TWO MAKES OF ELECTROMETER TUBES

	FP-54	D-96475
Filament voltage..........	2.5 volts	1 volt
Filament current..........	0.09 ampere	0.27 ampere
Space-charge grid voltage...	4 volts	4 volts
Plate voltage.............	6 volts	4 volts
Control grid voltage.......	4 volts	3 volts
Input resistance...........	10^{16} ohms	10^{16} ohms
Control grid current.......	10^{-15} ampere	10^{-15} ampere
Plate current.............	60 microamperes	85 microamperes
Plate resistance...........	45,000 ohms	25,000 ohms
Mutual conductance.......	20 microamperes/volt	40 microamperes/volt

insulation as to charges reaching the grid inside the tube. Any variation of the grid current with voltage constitutes a conductance. Metcalf and Thompson[21] made a systematic study of the sources of current to the grid and methods of

---

[21] Metcalf, G. F., and Thompson, B. J., *Phys. Rev.*, *30*, 1489 (1930).

eliminating or reducing them. As a result, a new tube known as the FP-54 was developed especially for the amplification of small direct currents. It is made by the General Electric Company. The Western Electric Company makes a similar tube, known as the D-96475. These tubes have an inner space-charge grid to shield the control grid from positive ions emitted by the filament. They are operated at a very low plate voltage to avoid ionization of the residual gas.

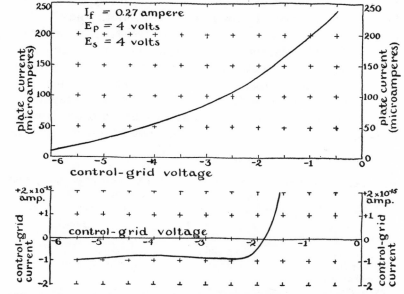

Fig. 6. Plate- and grid-current characteristics of Western Electric D-96475 tube.

Because they replace an electrometer, they are often called electrometer tubes. Their grid resistance is approximately 10^{16} ohms.

The recommended operating conditions and other essential data for the two makes of electrometer tubes are shown in Table III.

Characteristic curves showing the plate current and control grid current of a typical D-96475 tube are set forth in Fig. 6. The slope of the grid-current curves gives the grid

conductance, and the reciprocal of the slope is the grid resistance.   The control grid is operated at -3 volts, because
the curve is nearly flat at that point.   The slope of the plate-
current curve gives the mutual conductance.   The curvature
of the plate-current curve is quite noticeable, and is sufficient
to cause appreciable nonlinearity if the grid voltage changes
by 0.1 volt, a rather large change in most applications.

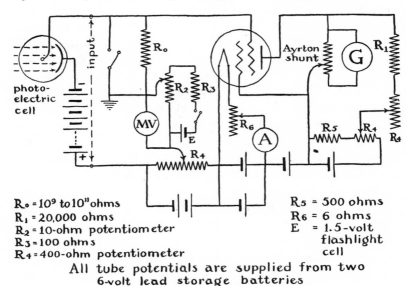

$R_0 = 10^9$ to10^{11}ohms
$R_1 = 20,000$ ohms
$R_2 = 10$-ohm potentiometer
$R_3 = 100$ ohms
$R_4 = 400$-ohm potentiometer

$R_5 = 500$ ohms
$R_6 = 6$ ohms
E $= 1.5$-volt
     flashlight
     cell

All tube potentials are supplied from two
6-volt lead storage batteries

Fig. 7.   Circuit for amplification of photocurrents using the D-96475 tube.

Fig. 7 gives in detail the constants of a simple circuit
employing the D-96475 for the measurement of the photoelectric currents.   By choosing a resistance R_0 of the proper
value, and varying the galvanometer shunt, a very wide
range of currents may be covered.   The calibration circuit
in the control-grid lead provides a means of testing the
sensitivity, which should be of the order of 100,000 mm/
volt for a galvanometer sensitivity of 4×10^{-10} ampere/mm.

The stability of the plate current in such a circuit of course
determines the smallest current that may be measured.   A
slow drift in the galvanometer zero will not cause a serious

loss in accuracy if the rate is constant during the time of one observation, since it may easily be averaged out by taking alternate zeros according to a definite schedule.   In certain applications of electrometer tubes, such as measurement of α particles, when continuous registration over long periods is required, a very low drift rate is necessary.   In any case it is desirable to reduce drift as much as possible.

Random fluctuations of the zero, on the other hand, place a definite limitation on the useful sensitivity of the amplifier. These may be due to external conditions, such as mechanical vibration, poor insulation, poor contacts, stray electric and magnetic fields, or residual atmospheric ions settling on the grid lead.   By suitable precautions, disturbances due to such causes can be practically eliminated.   There remain inherent and unavoidable fluctuations caused by variations in filament emission and by shot effect and Johnson effect (thermal noise) in the grid circuit.   In actual practice, uneven filament emission is found to be unimportant compared to the two latter sources of fluctuations.   A quantitative discussion of these factors is reserved for a later paragraph.

Contrary to statements which have appeared in the literature, battery potential fluctuations are not a limiting factor in using a simple circuit of the type shown in Fig. 7.   The stability is determined in the grid circuit, as is shown by the fact that the zero is much steadier with the high resistance R_0 shorted out.   The effects of variable filament emission remain.   To gauge the effect of the battery fluctuations only, the tube may be removed and replaced by fixed resistances equivalent to the filament resistance and to the static filament-to-plate resistance.   The galvanometer will then be perfectly steady, except possibly for a slow uniform drift, showing that there are no sudden changes in battery voltage large enough to affect the stability.

One cause of drifts is temperature variation, which changes battery voltages and the resistance of various parts of the circuit.   If the temperature is constant, the galvanometer in the circuit shown in Fig. 7 drifts slowly in the direction of decreasing plate current. This is caused mainly by a decrease in the filament current as the battery discharges. The larger the filament battery the slower the drift—hence the paralleling of cells in Fig. 7. As soon as equilibrium is reached, the rate of drift is less than 1 mm/minute at a sensitivity of 100,000 mm/volt. For most laboratory measurements such a rate is not a serious drawback.

The simplest method of controlling drift is to introduce a counterdrift whose rate can be adjusted. Hafstad[22] placed

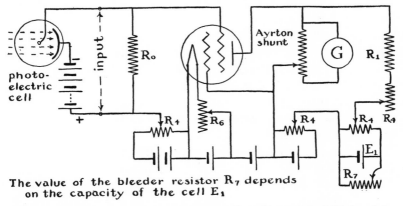

The value of the bleeder resistor R_7 depends on the capacity of the cell E_1

Fig. 8. Control of drift by introducing adjustable counterdrift in plate circuit. Resistances have the same values as in Fig. 7.

a countercell in the filament circuit and bled it with a variable resistance. A smaller cell is required if the counterdrift is introduced in the plate circuit. An arrangement of this type, similar to one described by Bearden,[23] is shown in Fig. 8. Part of the voltage which balances out the plate current of the tube comes from the cell E_1, which is being discharged through R_7. The discharge rate is set so that if all the voltage for balancing out were taken from E_1, the drift would be in the direction of increasing plate current. Then by varying the amount of voltage taken from the loaded and unloaded cell, the normal drift due to decreasing

[22] Hafstad, L. R., *Phys. Rev.*, *44*, 201 (1933).
[23] Bearden, J. A., *Rev. Sci. Instruments*, *4*, 271 (1936).

plate current may be compensated. The advantage of this
method is that the drift rate may be changed immediately
without altering anything in the circuit that requires some
time to reach a new equilibrium. The cell E_1 may be a
flashlight cell, or if a rechargeable cell is desired, an Edison
storage cell.   In cases where the tube is to be operated continuously over long periods, the cell E_1 may be eliminated
and the battery discharging resistor attached directly to the
last cell of a storage battery. The drift rate is then regulated by varying the discharge current. This requires some
patience to adjust.

Numerous circuits have been devised with a view to
making the plate current of a vacuum tube independent of
small changes in supply voltage. The former two-tube
circuits[24] required tubes with matched characteristics, which
are often difficult to obtain. Recently practically all balanced circuits have consisted of a single tube in a suitable
resistance network.

The single-tube circuit originated by DuBridge and
Brown[25] has been successfully used in many laboratories.

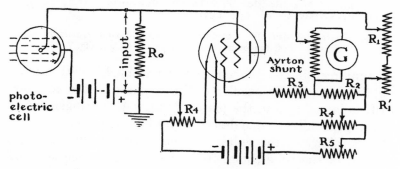

Fig. 9.   DuBridge and Brown's balanced circuit for the FP-54 tube.

It is shown in Fig. 9.   It can be regarded as a Wheatstone
bridge in which R_1 and R_2 form two of the resistance arms,

[24] DuBridge, L. A., *Phys. Rev.*, *37*, 392 (1931).
  Wynn-Williams, C. E., *Phil. Mag.*, *6*, 324 (1928).
  [25] DuBridge, L. A., and Brown, H., *Rev. Sci. Instruments*, *4*, 532, 1933.   See
Turner, L. A., *Rev. Sci. Instruments*, *4*, 665 (1933), for other circuits.

and the filament-to-plate resistance and filament-to-space-charge-grid resistance form two other arms. The resistance R_3 may be considered a part of the tube resistance. A condition that the galvanometer current be zero is obviously

$$R_1 I_p = R_2 I_s.$$

In order for this condition to remain satisfied when the battery voltage changes, or the filament emission changes for any reason, it is further necessary that

$$\frac{dI_p}{dI_f} = \frac{R_1}{R_2} \cdot \frac{dI_s}{dI_f}.$$

For these conditions to be satisfied in general, it would be necessary for the I_p versus I_f and I_s versus I_f curves to be straight lines intersecting at a common point on the I_f axis. Of course, the tubes do not have this characteristic, but over short ranges the tangents to the I_p and I_s curves do satisfy this condition, and it is possible to adjust the resistances in the circuit so that this can be made to occur at approximately the rated filament current.

The resistance R_3 is necessary to provide a voltage drop of 2 volts, since the space-charge-grid voltage of the FP-54 is 4 volts and the plate voltage is 6 volts. For the D-96475 tube, in which both the space-charge-grid and the plate operate at 4 volts, it would be omitted. In a typical setup with the FP-54 tube, R_6 was 45 ohms, R_3 was 4000 ohms, R_2 was 2000 ohms, and R_1 was a 10,000-ohm rheostat, with R_1' a 50-ohm rheostat for fine adjustment. R_4 was a 50-ohm potentiometer. The procedure in balancing the circuit is as follows: With the galvanometer shunted to one tenth or one hundredth of its full sensitivity and R_1 adjusted so that the galvanometer reads zero when I_f is near its rated value, I_f is slowly varied by means of the rheostat R_5. With the galvanometer connected so that a positive deflection is caused by a decrease in the plate current, the deflection should pass through a maximum value for some value of I_f. If the galvanometer deflection goes off scale before the maximum is reached, it may be brought back by an adjustment of R_1.

If the value I_f for maximum is not within a few per cent of the rated value for the tube, the adjustment of R_4 and R_1 will bring the balance point to a different value I_f. The adjustment is finally made with the galvanometer at full sensitivity. Each adjustment will require a few minutes' waiting for a new thermal equilibrium to be established.

The advantage of this ingenious circuit is that any change in the filament emission due to variation in battery voltage or deactivation of the filament is compensated. Also short-period fluctuations in the filament emission are balanced out, and the stability with R_0 shorted out is somewhat improved over that obtained with the circuit of Fig. 7.

Some workers have experienced difficulty in obtaining the balanced condition for tubes of different characteristics. Penick[26] has given a thorough analysis of balanced circuits, with special application to the D-96475 electrometer tube. He suggests a modification of the DuBridge and Brown circuit which in effect amounts to attaching the leads from the plate and space-charge-grid leads of the bridge to separate taps on the resistance R_4. In practice this is best done by using two potentiometers in parallel. This introduces an additional element of flexibility in the circuit and enables a balance point to be reached for tubes of widely different characteristics. However, there are considerable individual variations in electrometer tubes, and sometimes with a particular tube it may not be possible to reach a balance point with reasonable values for the other circuit constants.

The best type of circuit for a particular application must be decided upon the basis of the conditions of use. The limiting sensitivity obtainable is about the same for all types of circuits. A balanced circuit is probably preferable when the use is to be irregular or intermittent because of much shorter warm-up time. A simple uncompensated circuit

---

[26] Penick, D. B., *Rev. Sci. Instruments, 6,* 115 (1935). Full references to the literature are given.

requires several hours to reach equilibrium. However, if it is to be used daily, there is no objection to letting the filament run continuously.

In applications in which the circuit is to be used for both steady deflections and rate-of-drift measurements, the balanced circuit becomes rather complicated, because whenever the control-grid bias is changed, in order to find equilibrium potential the entire circuit must be rebalanced.

In order to reach high sensitivity by the steady-deflection method the resistance R_0 must be made very large. If it is much larger than 10^{11} ohms, the time constant of the input circuit becomes unduly long, and considerable time is wasted in waiting for deflections to reach their final value. The highest sensitivity is best obtained by the rate-of-drift method. To do this the anode of the photoelectric cell (or other sources of the current to be measured) is connected directly to the control grid of the tube with no other resistance. A high-insulation switch free from contact potentials is necessary for grounding the grid. When the tube is operated at the rated control-grid voltage, the grid current is approximately 10^{-15} ampere. If the grid is "floated" by opening the grounding switch, it will draw this current and drift in the direction of less negative grid potential. In order to eliminate this drift, the grid bias must be changed to such a value that the positive and negative components of the grid current are equal and the grid current is zero. When operating at this so-called "equilibrium potential," the grid resistance, as shown by the slope of the lower curve in Fig. 6, is considerably reduced but is still usually as high as 10^{14} ohms and is quite satisfactory for use in the rate-of-drift method. The equilibrium potential is found by observing the drift when the grounding switch is opened for various values of the control-grid potential until a value sufficiently near zero drift is reached. The galvanometer must be brought back to zero after each change in the grid bias, by adjustment of the resistance in the plate circuit. The procedure for measuring a small photoelectric current is then to observe the drift rate with the light alternately on and off. This may be done by timing the drift over a particular interval of the galvanometer scale, but better results will be obtained if the galvanometer deflections are continuously recorded photographically. The value for the slope of the drift curve does not then depend on observations at two particular points. In fact, in all measurements in which the inherent fluctuations set the observing limit, improved accuracy will be obtained with photographic registration.[26a]

Measurements made by the rate-of-drift method may be connected with steady-deflection measurements by measuring the same current by both methods. In effect this constitutes a measurement of the capacity of the grid circuit.

Experimental details. The photoelectric cell and electrometer tube must be enclosed in a light-tight metal box. If high sensitivity is required, the container should be evacuated in order to eliminate the effect of residual ions in the air caused by cosmic rays. A suitable form for the container consists of a brass cylinder with a light window on the side. The amplifying tube and photoelectric cell are best supported entirely from one end plate in order to facilitate removal for adjustment. The vacuum seal may be made with a rubber gasket. A vacuum of the order of 1 mm of mercury is sufficient. The necessary switching arrangements can be operated by means of cams on a shaft which turns through a conical ground joint in the end plate. A separate metal shield over the tube inside of the container is advisable, and this may be made to serve also as a light shield to screen the photoelectric cell from the light of the filament. In case the container is not evacuated, it should be kept dry by the use of calcium chloride or phosphorus pentoxide.

A satisfactory design for mounting the cell and tube in an evacuated brass tank is shown in Fig. 10. The diagram is largely self-explanatory. The construction of vacuum tanks, valves, and gaskets is treated in Chapter III.

[26a] A suitable optical arrangement for photographic recording of galvanometer deflections is shown in Fig. 47, Chapter IX.

When a cesium oxide cell must be refrigerated to reduce the thermionic emission, the design shown in Fig. 11 meets the requirements.   Here the problem is to have the cell as cold as possible, but to keep the light window from fogging

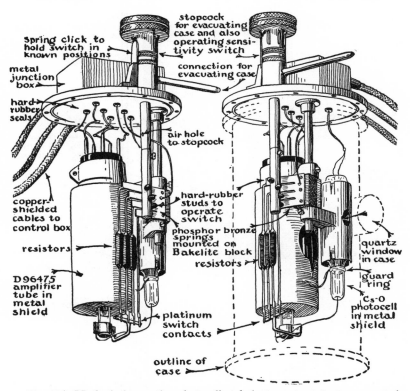

Fig. 10.   Method of mounting photocell and electrometer tube in evacuated brass tank.   (If circuit is grounded at the usual point, as in Fig. 7, the Bakelite insulation of the phosphor-bronze springs is unnecessary.   They may be attached directly to the brass post as shown in Fig. 11.)

and the wax seals from becoming too cold and brittle.   This necessitates some rather steep thermal gradients, which are successfully withstood by the Pyrex tube around the cell. To maintain isothermal conditions, the dry-ice compartment is made of sheet copper, and the Pyrex tube is sheathed with copper.

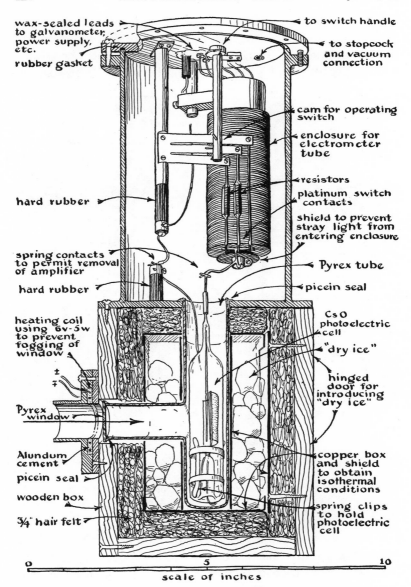

wax-sealed leads
to galvanometer,
power supply,
etc.

rubber gasket

to switch handle

to stopcock
and vacuum
connection

cam for operating
switch

enclosure for
electrometer
tube

resistors

platinum switch
contacts

shield to prevent
stray light from
entering enclosure

hard rubber

spring contacts
to permit removal
of amplifier

hard rubber

Pyrex tube

picein seal

heating coil
using 6v-5w
to prevent
fogging of
window

CsO
photoelectric
cell

"dry ice"

hinged
door for
introducing
"dry ice"

Pyrex
window

Alundum
cement

picein seal

wooden box

¾" hair felt

copper box
and shield
to obtain
isothermal
conditions

spring clips
to hold
photoelectric
cell

0   5   10

scale of inches

Fig. 11. Evacuated container for photocell and electrometer tube, with
provision for refrigerating the cell to reduce thermionic emission.

In both Fig. 10 and Fig. 11 is shown a convenient switching arrangement which provides the possibility of using any one of three grid resistors, or of floating the grid for rate-of-drift measurements. This design requires no other support for the sensitive grid lead than that furnished by the tube itself. Should other support be necessary, only the best insulating materials should be used. Amber or fused quartz is recommended. All insulating surfaces, including the photoelectric cell and the exterior of the amplifying tube, must be kept free from grease or dirt and should be handled as little as possible. They may be cleaned by swabbing with cotton moistened with 95 per cent ethyl alcohol.

All parts of the circuit should be enclosed in metallic shielding. The various control resistances, the galvanometer shunt, and necessary meters may be mounted in a metal or metal-lined box such as that shown in Fig. 12.

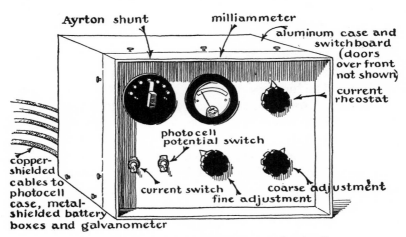

Fig. 12.   Control box for electrometer tube circuit.

Placing the battery in a shielded box is also advisable. Temperature insulation on this box to cut down drifts will be helpful. The shielded multiconductor cables available from radio supply houses will be suitable for connections between these various units, or the necessary wires may be pulled through a flexible metal hose.[27]

Whenever possible, all connections should be soldered, using only rosin flux. A flux made by dissolving rosin in alcohol will be found convenient; it may be applied with a brush. It is usually not necessary to solder the wires to the pins of the tube base, but a socket which grips the pins tightly must be used. The soldering of connections to the battery terminals is particularly important.

The batteries should be kept in first-class condition; the tops should be kept clean and dry. They should be charged at a moderate rate. It will be found advantageous to operate them only on the middle portion of the discharge curve.

The resistances, rheostats, and potentiometers should be of good quality. Wire-wound resistors may be obtained from any radio supply house. General Radio Type 371 potentiometers have been found satisfactory. Ohmite model H and model J units are also to be recommended. The inexpensive small wire-wound potentiometers of the type used in radios are not above suspicion, but Clarostat controls have been found entirely satisfactory by some workers. The high resistances to be used in the control-grid circuit are supplied commercially with values up to 10^{12} ohms.[28] These resistors have proved so satisfactory that it is not worth while for the worker to attempt to make his own.

In certain applications, in which portability is required or vibration makes it difficult to use a sensitive galvanometer, an additional stage of amplification may be necessary. DuBridge[29] used a 112A triode for the second stage and obtained an over-all current amplification of 4×10^7. The indicator was a microammeter. The design of the second stage is not critical, and almost any tube with a high mutual conductance is satisfactory. However, for most laboratory

[27] Such hose is obtainable from the American Metal Hose Company, Waterbury, Connecticut.
[28] These resistors may be purchased from the S. S. White Dental Manufacturing Company, Industrial Division, 10 East 40th Street, New York City.
[29] DuBridge, L. A., *Phys. Rev.*, *37*, 392 (1931).

applications a single electrometer tube and galvanometer is
preferable.   A galvanometer with a sensitivity of 5×10^{-10}
ampere/mm at 1 m is simple and foolproof, and amply
sensitive to show the inherent unavoidable fluctuations of
the amplifier.

Other low-grid-current tubes. Several workers have
pointed out that many commercial radio tubes, when operated at low potentials, have greatly reduced grid currents, and

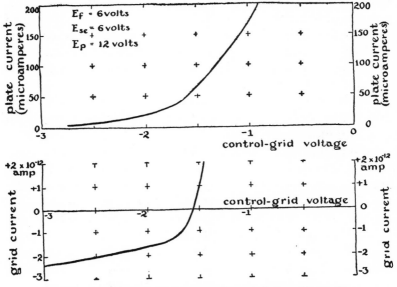

Fig. 13.   Plate- and grid-current characteristics of RCA 38.

frequently by selection a tube may be found which has a grid
current as low as 10^{-12} ampere.   After a careful investigation Johnson found[30] that the RCA 38 pentode had good
characteristics in this respect.   Dunning[31] has recommended
the Western Electric 259-B screen grid tube.   MacDonald[32]
has found the RCA 22 very satisfactory at low voltages and
has given complete data on its characteristics.

[30] Johnson, E. A. and A. G., *Phys. Rev.*, *50*, 170 (1936).
  Johnson, E. A., and Neitzert, C., *Rev. Sci. Instruments*, *5*, 196 (1934).
[31] Dunning, J. R., *Rev. Sci. Instruments*, *5*, 387 (1934).
[32] MacDonald, P. A., *Physics*, *7*, 265 (1936).

The grid current of a tube is often the most important characteristic in choosing a tube to amplify small currents or small voltage. The following procedure is convenient in obtaining data for plotting the grid-current curve: The plate current is plotted as a function of the grid voltage in the usual way, first with no resistance in the grid circuit and then with a high resistance in series. The horizontal difference between the two curves represents the potential drop in the resistance due to the grid current, and by dividing this voltage difference by the value of the resistor, the grid current in amperes is found. A shielded box is necessary.

Characteristic curves for the RCA 38 pentode from Johnson's data are shown in Fig. 13. This probably represents the results for a selected tube. From the slope of the lower curve it is found that the grid resistance at -2 volts is 10^{12} ohms. At equilibrium potential this is reduced to 5×10^{10} ohms.

Gabus and Pool[33] found that the RCA 954 acorn pentode can be operated in such a way as to have a very low grid current and correspondingly high input resistance. The No. 3 grid, normally used as the suppressor, is used as the control grid. Owing to the peculiar construction of the tube, this grid is very well insulated. The No. 1 grid, normally the control grid, is connected to the cathode. The No. 2 grid, normally the screen grid, is operated at a positive potential and acts as in the electrometer tube to protect the control grid from positive ions emitted by the cathode.

A particular 954 tube tested under conditions similar to those recommended by Gabus and Pool had the following characteristics: Heater voltage, 4 volts; grid No. 1 connected to cathode; grid No. 2 at $+ 13.5$ volts; grid No. 3 at $- 4$ volts; plate at $+ 6$ volts; plate current, 60 microamperes; mutual conductance, 100 microamperes/volt; plate resistance, 35,000 ohms; amplification factor, 3.5; grid current, 4×10^{-13} ampere.

---

[33] Gabus, G. H., and Pool, M. L., *Rev. Sci. Instruments*, *8*, 196 (1937).

For many applications in measuring currents down to 10^{-13} ampere, any of the above-mentioned tubes will be found quite satisfactory and much less expensive than electrometer tubes.

High-gain direct-current amplifiers.   Direct-coupled multistage d.c. amplifiers similar to the familiar a.c. amplifiers have been used very little because of the necessity of a separate power supply for each stage and because of difficulties with cumulative drift and instability.

Horton[34] has described an ingenious circuit in which extremely high gain is realized by utilizing one high-mu

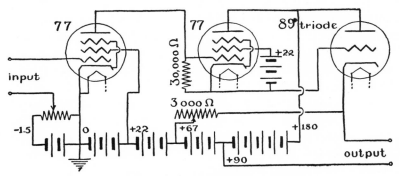

Fig. 14.   Horton's high-gain d.c. amplifier.

pentode as the load resistance for another.   In this way high amplification can be obtained without the very high plate supply voltage that would be necessary if a pure ohmic resistance were used for the load.   The circuit is shown in Fig. 14.

All plate potentials are supplied by a 180-volt battery, and the insulation between the heater and cathode of these tubes is sufficiently good that a common heater battery may be used.   The over-all mutual conductance of this three-tube amplifier is about 4.5 mhos.   If the amplifier is to work into a high-impedance load, such as a cathode-ray oscillograph, the type 89 output tube may be omitted and the load con-

34 Horton, J. W., *Frank. Inst., J.*, *216*, 749 (1933).

nected directly between the cathode of the second pentode and the 90-volt tap of the plate battery. In this case the voltage amplification is about 2500. Because of the capacity shunt through the heaters, the circuit has a poor response for high audio frequencies. In a similar circuit described by Schmitt,[35] in which separate heater batteries are used, this limitation is largely removed. Circuits of this type have found special application in the measurement of physiological potentials in which the resistance in the input circuit is low. Since the 77 tube (and similar high-gain pentodes) have a rather low grid-to-filament resistance, it is advisable to add a preliminary stage when measuring photoelectric currents. This would consist of an electrometer tube or other low-grid-current tube, operated from separate batteries. With such a combination a stable current amplification of 10^{10} is possible, and the indicating instrument may be a milliammeter.

Alternating-current amplifiers. One great advantage of an a.c. amplifier is that all the tubes of a multistage amplifier may be operated from a common power supply. The signal is transmitted from one stage to the next by means of a condenser or transformer, which, while providing insulation against steady potentials, offers a low impedance path for a.c. signals. Since only rapid variations are passed along, such an amplifier is insensitive to drifts in the plate current of any tube, and to gradual changes in the supply voltage. The characteristics of a.c. amplifiers have been treated so extensively elsewhere [36] that they will be considered only briefly here. The discussion will be limited to resistance-capacity coupling.

[35] Schmitt, O. H. A., *Rev. Sci. Instruments*, *4*, 661 (1933).

[36] Chaffee, E. L., *Theory of Thermionic Vacuum Tubes.* New York: McGraw-Hill Book Company, 1933.

Glasgow, R. S., *Principles of Radio Engineering.* New York: McGraw-Hill Book Company, 1936.

Henney, K., *Radio Engineering Handbook*, Second Edition. New York: McGraw-Hill Book Company, 1935.

The Radio Tube Manual, issued by the RCA Manufacturing Company, Harrison, New Jersey, contains much practical information.

Fig. 15 shows a photoelectric cell and three-stage amplifier for use with modulated light intensities in the audio-frequency range.   The power is supplied from the 110-volt a.c.

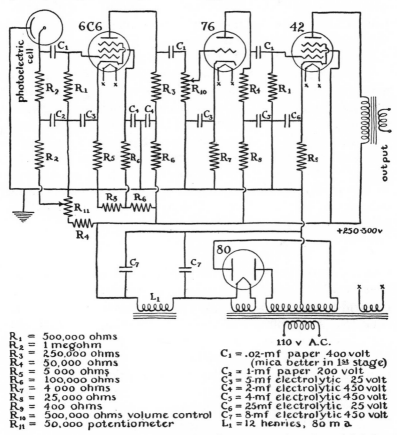

R₁ = 500,000 ohms
R₂ = 1 megohm
R₃ = 250,000 ohms
R₄ = 50,000 ohms
R₅ = 5 000 ohms
R₆ = 100,000 ohms
R₇ = 4 000 ohms
R₈ = 25,000 ohms
R₉ = 400 ohms
R₁₀ = 500,000 ohms volume control
R₁₁ = 50,000 potentiometer

110 v A.C.

C₁ = .02-mf paper 400 volt
       (mica better in 1st stage)
C₂ = 1-mf paper 200 volt
C₃ = 5-mf electrolytic 25 volt
C₄ = 2-mf electrolytic 450 volt
C₅ = 4-mf electrolytic 450 volt
C₆ = 25mf electrolytic 25 volt
C₇ = 8-mf electrolytic 450 volt
L₁ = 12 henries, 80 m a.

Fig. 15.   Three-stage a.c. amplifier for photocurrents from a modulated or interrupted light source.

line, rectified and filtered in the usual manner to provide the necessary d.c. voltages.

In order for the coupling condensers C_1 to perform their function of transmitting the voltage variation of the plate of one tube to the grid of the next, their impedance must be small compared with the associated grid resistor R_1.   The reactance of a condenser in ohms is given by the well-known formula $X = 1/(2\pi f C)$, where f is the frequency in cycles per second and C is the capacity in farads. A simple computation shows that when $C_1 = 0.02$ microfarad, the reactance becomes equal to 500,000 ohms, the value of the grid resistor R_1, at a frequency of 16 cycles. This, then, is roughly the low-frequency cutoff of the above amplifier.

The high-frequency cutoff is determined by the tube capacities shunting the plate-load resistors and grid resistors. At high frequencies, the coupling condenser has negligible impedance, so that the coupling resistors may be considered to be in parallel. Considering first the photocell circuit, the resistors R_2 and R_1 have a resistance in parallel of 333,000 ohms. The capacity shunting this is the sum of the capacity of the photocell, the connections, and the dynamic input capacity of the first tube. The dynamic input capacity is given by the expression

$$C = C_0 + C_{gf} + [1 + \mu R_l/(R_p + R_l)]C_{gp},$$

where C_0 is the capacity of the photoelectric cell and connections, C_{gf} is the grid-to-cathode capacity of the tube, C_{gp} is the grid-to-plate capacity, μ is the amplification factor of the tube, R_p is the plate resistance of the tube, and R_l is the plate-load resistance. In a screen-grid tube, such as the 6C6, the grid-to-plate capacity is very small, and the last term is therefore unimportant. The grid-to-cathode capacity is about 6 micro-microfarads. The total capacity may be roughly 15 micro-microfarads, which has a reactance equal to 333,000 ohms at a frequency of 34,000 cycles. This is the high-frequency cutoff for the input circuit. If a gasfilled cell is used, its lower response at high frequencies must of course be taken into account.

The situation in the coupling between two stages follows the same general reasoning. In place of the capacity of the photocell there is the plate-to-cathode capacity of the tube delivering the signal to the coupling network. Also, the dynamic plate resistance of the tube is in parallel with the resistors of the coupling network. The high-frequency cutoff may be regulated by attaching a shunting condenser to either the plate-load resistor or the grid resistor. This has been analyzed by Johnson,[37] who showed that by proper choice of coupling and shunting condensers, an amplifier may be fairly sharply tuned to a single frequency.

The necessary negative voltage for the grid of each tube is obtained by a self-bias resistor in the cathode lead. If the a.c. variations in plate current are allowed to pass through this resistor, the grid bias will be altered in such a direction as to produce a serious degenerative effect, and the amplification is much reduced. Consequently the bias resistor is shunted by a by-pass condenser, which must provide a low-impedance path for the a.c. component of the plate current. To keep the impedance less than that of the bias resistor at the lowest frequencies amplified, a rather large capacitance is sometimes required, but inexpensive low-voltage electrolytic condensers are available for the purpose.

Some care is necessary to prevent regenerative coupling of the first and last stages through the common power supply, the result of which is to produce a type of oscillation known as motorboating. The remedy is a decoupling filter of the resistance-capacity type in voltage lead to the photocell, and to the screen grid and plate of each tube except the power tubes. The principle to be followed is that the condenser in each filter unit should offer an impedance to the signal about 10 times less than its associated resistor at the lowest frequency passed by the amplifier. This is equivalent to the requirement that the time constant RC of each filter unit be 10 times longer than the time constant of the grid coupling condenser and resistor. For the amplifier shown in Fig. 15 the time constant of the coupling circuits is 0.01 second throughout. The time constant of the plate and screen-grid decoupling filters of the 6C6 tube (R_6C_4) is 0.2 second, thus more than meeting the requirement. It is worth while to have a good margin of safety in the filters for

---

[37] Johnson, E. A., *Physics*, 7, 130 (1936).

the photocell and first tube, which are, of course, most sensitive to feedbacks. All such filters also act to eliminate any ripple in the rectified d.c. voltage from the power pack. Shielding of the photocell and first tube is necessary to eliminate undesirable pickup.

The above-described amplifier is illustrative of the general design of a.c. amplifiers. For detecting very small light intensities, additional precautions must be taken, with special attention given to the first stage. A grid resistor of high value is used and the cell connected directly to the grid without a coupling condenser. A tube with low grid current is desirable, but an electrometer tube is ruled out because of its very low amplification factor and its sensitivity to microphonic disturbances. The RCA 38 or the Western Electric 259B operated at reduced voltages is probably the most satisfactory tube for the first stage. Careful shielding is of course necessary. Each tube with its coupling resistors and condenser should be in a separate metal compartment, with an adjacent enclosure for the associated bias resistor and decoupling filters. The tube for the output stage must be selected with special reference to its load. The next to the last tube is usually of a type intermediate between a voltage amplifier and a power amplifier. Johnson and Neitzert[38] have described an amplifier for small a.c. voltages which used RCA 38 pentodes at reduced voltages for all stages except the output. Separate plate batteries are used for each stage, but the plate current is low enough so that small units can be used. They may therefore be placed in the same compartment with the tube. Difficulties with regenerative coupling through the plate power supply are thus eliminated. Dunning,[39] in a paper on amplifiers for detecting single ionizing particles, gives many practical suggestions.

Fluctuation noises in vacuum-tube circuits. The background fluctuations of the currents in vacuum tubes which

[38] Johnson, E. A., and Neitzert, C., *Rev. Sci. Instruments*, *5*, 196 (1934).
[39] Dunning, J. R., *Rev. Sci. Instruments*, *5*, 387 (1934).

determine the smallest signal that may be detected have long gone by the name of "noise," a term which is convenient even when there is no conversion of the currents into sound. When extraneous disturbances due to vibration, poor shielding, poor insulation, poor connections, and the like are eliminated by suitable precautions, there remain three inherent sources of noise, originating in the first tube and its input circuit:

1. Thermal noise in the grid resistor.
2. Shot effect of currents in the grid circuit.
3. Tube noise.

It is important to the laboratory worker to be able to calculate the expected noise voltage in a particular circuit, or he may erroneously attribute the noise to an extraneous disturbance and waste much time in attempting to improve something that cannot be improved, except possibly by redesigning the circuit. Pearson[40] has published a discussion of the subject and has given data on low-noise tubes made by the Western Electric Company.

The mean square voltage appearing across the grid resistance R as a result of thermal agitation of charge within it is given by

$$\overline{E_T^2} = 4kTR \int_{f_1}^{f_2} \frac{df}{1 + 4\pi^2 R^2 C^2 f^2},$$

where k is Boltzmann's constant, T is the absolute temperature, f_2 and f_1 are the upper and lower limits of the band of frequencies passed by the amplifier, and C is the dynamic input capacity of the first tube.

In case the second term in the denominator of the above integrand is small compared with unity for all frequencies between f_2 and f_1, as is required in order to avoid frequency

[40] Pearson, G. L., *Physics*, *5*, 233 (1934).
See also Johnson, E. A. and A. G., *Phys. Rev.*, *50*, 171 (1936).
For data on RCA 38 see Johnson, E. A., and Neitzert, C., *Rev. Sci. Instruments*, *5*, 196 (1934).

distortion, the expression for thermal noise becomes, for a temperature of 300°K.,[41]

$$\overline{E_T^2} = 1.64 \times 10^{-20} R(f_2 - f_1).$$

As an example, we may compute that the thermal-noise voltage across a resistance of 1 megohm connected to an amplifier which has a band width of 10,000 cycles (that is, the audio-frequency range) would be 13 microvolts.

The mean square voltage due to shot fluctuations of the grid current is

$$\overline{E_S^2} = 2eI_oR^2 \int_{f_1}^{f_2} \frac{df}{1 + 4\pi^2 R^2 C^2 f^2},$$

where e is the electronic charge and I_o is the sum of the absolute values of the positive and negative components of the grid current.

The same equation applies for the shot effect of the photo-current from vacuum cells. In gas-filled cells each photo-electron releases an average charge $\mu_o e$, where μ_o is the gaseous amplification factor. For rough computation $\mu_o e$ may be used as the unit of charge in the formula, but Kingsbury[42] found that actually the noise is somewhat greater than that computed on this assumption.

Tube noise cannot be less than the thermal noise in the internal plate resistance. A variety of factors serve to make it several times this theoretical minimum. The usual way of rating tubes is to give the resistance which, if placed in the grid circuit, would give the same noise voltage in the output as that produced by the tube itself. Low-noise tubes have an equivalent resistance of from 4000 ohms to 40,000 ohms. Tube noise is unimportant in amplifiers designed for amplification of photocurrents, since the resistance in the grid circuit is practically always much higher than these values.

---

[41] Boltzmann's constant $k = 1.37 \times 10^{-16}$ erg/degree. At 300°K., or room temperature, $kT = 0.41 \times 10^{-13}$ erg $= 0.41 \times 10^{-20}$ joule. The latter unit is, of course, the proper one to use in connection with coulombs, volts, amperes, and farads. The electronic charge $e = 1.6 \times 10^{-19}$ coulomb.

[42] Kingsbury, B. A., *Phys. Rev.*, *38*, 1458 (1931).

When measuring very small currents with an electrometer tube, the grid resistor is made very large, or the floating-grid method is used. Under these conditions, where the circuit itself, rather than the galvanometer, determines the speed of response, the equations for thermal noise and shot noise take on a simple form. As shown by Hafstad,[43] the following relations then hold:

$$\overline{E_T^2} = \frac{kT}{C},$$

and

$$\overline{E_S^2} = \frac{eI_gR}{2C}.$$

It is to be noted that the thermal noise is independent of resistance and is therefore a very general limitation on all electrometers. If $C = 10^{-11}$ farad, a practical minimum for the grid circuit, including photocell and connections, the thermal noise for 300°K. may be calculated to be 20 microvolts. If $R = 2 \times 10^{11}$ ohms and $I_g = 10^{-15}$ ampere, the computed shot noise is 1.3 microvolt, negligible in comparison with thermal noise. The resultant uncertainty in a current measurement is 10^{-16} ampere.

However, if a resistance of 5×10^{10} ohms or less is used with a 6-second galvanometer, the galvanometer limits the speed of response, an effect equivalent to increasing the capacity. The observed noise voltage is then reduced to about 8 to 10 microvolts. A large capacity in the grid circuit would also reduce the noise voltage, but the deflection time would be increased by just enough to make the precision remain the same.

When the tube is operated with the grid at the equilibrium potential, R is the input resistance of the tube itself, about 10^{14} ohms, and I_g has two components, each of 10^{-15} ampere. The computed shot noise is then 40 microvolts. The thermal noise is of course unchanged from the previous case. With a total noise voltage of $\sqrt{40^2 + 20^2} = 45$ microvolts, the uncertainty in any measurement of charge then amounts to

[43] Hafstad, L. R., *Phys. Rev.*, *44*, 201 (1933).

4×10^{-16} coulomb, or, for a collection time of 1 minute, an uncertainty in the current of 7×10^{-18} ampere. In this case it is advantageous to have a low capacity. These are theoretical limits, but with reasonable care they may be realized in practice.

Applications of Photoelectric Cells

General remarks on photoelectric photometry. The most important laboratory use of the photoelectric cell is in photometry. Used properly, it is capable of giving results of high precision. It should be remembered, however, that very few cells have a constant sensitivity. Both the absolute sensitivity and the color response may change with time. For this reason, in careful measurements the photoelectric cell should be called upon only to make comparisons between a standard and an unknown source. Some cells are subject to fatigue when exposed to a bright light. If the linear relation between current and light intensity is to be depended on over a range of more than two- or threefold, it must be tested. The inverse-square law offers a convenient method.

If the light is to be projected on the sensitive surface by an optical system, the illuminated area should not be too small. An out-of-focus image about 1 cm in diameter is satisfactory. The light from different successive sources should cover the same area as nearly as possible. This reduces errors from local variations in sensitivity on the surface.

There are three general methods in photoelectric photometry:

1. Substitution method. The cell is exposed alternately to the standard source and to the unknown, and the relative deflections noted. This is the simplest and most direct method and is capable of giving excellent results. Of course it depends on the linearity of the cell and the current-measuring instrument.

2. Balanced-cell method. Two cells are connected in opposition, and the intensity of either the standard or the

unknown is reduced by suitable means until there is a balance. Although the method can be made very sensitive to unbalance, there is a fundamental objection to depending on the constancy of the two cells over any extended period.

3. Flicker method. The two sources shine alternately in rapid succession on the cell. The intensity of the brighter is cut down by a suitable intensity reducer until the flicker is zero. The amplifier may be of the a.c. type. A 6E5 tuning indicator ("magic eye") makes a very satisfactory detector of the minimum.[44] This is an excellent method, because the linearity of the cell and amplifier is not an issue.

When used in heterochromatic photometry, the photoelectric cell may give a judgment of relative brightness entirely different from that given by the eye, owing to the difference in spectral response. A cell with a spectral-response curve like that of the eye must be used if the visual standards of brightness are to be carried over without modification. The Westinghouse Photox cell meets this requirement very closely without the addition of any filters. The Weston Electrical Instrument Company supplies a suitable filter for use with the Photronic cell when a response curve like that of the eye is required.

For certain kinds of colorimetric measurement, the relative intensity through filters of various colors can give much useful information. Examples are the whiteness of paper[45] and the color temperature of a lamp[46] or a star.[47] However, such results are so dependent on the particular cell and particular filters used that they can be relied on only if continually checked against some kind of standard. The

---

[44] Garman, R. L., Rev. Sci. Instruments, 8, 327 (1937).

Waller, L. C., RCA Review, 1, 111 (1937).

[45] Davis, M. N., Paper Trade Journal, July 4, 1935, page 36. The commercial instrument, known as a reflectance meter, is available from the General Electric Company.

[46] Campbell, N. R., and Ritchie, Dorothy, Photoelectric Cells, page 214. New York: Isaac Pitman and Sons, 1934.

[47] Stebbins, J., and Whitford, A. E., Astrophys. J., 84, 253 (1936); Mt. Wilson Contr. No. 547.

infrared transparency of practically all glass and gelatin filters mentioned on page 402 must be borne in mind.

Spectrophotometry. The first requisite in photoelectric spectrophotometry is a good monochromator. A double monochromator is to be preferred because of the greatly reduced stray light of other wave lengths than the one being used.[48]

The principal spectrophotometric measurements made in the laboratory involve spectral-radiation curves of luminous sources, spectral-transmission curves, and spectral-reflectance curves. For spectral-radiation curves, the thermocouple is preferable to the photoelectric cell because it measures energy directly. If, however, the intensity is too low for the thermocouple, a photoelectric cell may be used, provided its spectral-sensitivity curve is accurately known, so that corrections to get the energy may be applied for each wave length. The spectral-sensitivity curve for the cell can be determined by comparison with a thermocouple, using a bright light as the source for the monochromator. This is the general method for obtaining the curves shown in Fig. 1.

Spectral-transmission curves of filters, for example, may be very easily determined with a monochromator and a photoelectric cell. The intensity with the filter in and out of the beam gives the percentage transmission for each wave length. If the cell cannot be placed close enough to the slit to receive all of the exit beam, an additional lens is necessary. A minor adaptation enables absorption cells to be introduced into the beam for investigating the spectral-absorption curves of solutions.[49] Measurements of specular reflecting

---

[48] Preston, J. S., *Journ. Sci. Instruments*, *13*, 368 (1936), has described a simple method of eliminating errors due to stray light in a monochromator. Shutters which may occult half of the slit length are fitted to the entrance and exit slit. A reading is taken with the shutters set to let the light go through. Then one shutter is reversed, and any light coming through is stray light, for which appropriate corrections may be made.

[49] Hogness, T. R., Zscheile, F. P., and Sidwell, A. E., *J. Phys. Chem.*, *41*, 379 (1937).

Zscheile, F. P., Hogness, T. R., and Young, J. F., *J. Phys. Chem.*, *38*, 1 (1934).

power may be carried out in the same way, except that it will, of course, be necessary to move the photocell when shifting from the direct to the reflected beam.

For determinations of diffuse reflectance it is customary to illuminate the object at 45° incidence and observe along a line normal to the surface. The reflectance is measured relative to that of some standard material, such as magnesium carbonate. The fluorescence of certain materials causes difficulty, which can be eliminated only by having the reflection occur before the light beam passes through the monochromator.

All of the above-mentioned methods of spectrophotometry involve the linear response of the photocell and the current-measuring instrument. In practical cases this is not likely to cause appreciable error, but in precision work the linearity must be investigated. Mention should be made of the Hardy automatic recording spectrophotometer,[50] which works on the flicker principle and is thus independent of the cell and amplifier characteristics and variations in light intensity. This instrument is adaptable to many kinds of measurements and gives very accurate results. It is manufactured commercially by the General Electric Company.

Densitometers. In photographic photometry it is necessary to have some means of measuring the density of the photographic deposit. The photoelectric cell has found wide use as the light-sensitive unit of objective densitometers. Since photographic photometry consists of interpolation between standards whose intensity ratio is known, spectral sensitivity and exact linear response are not crucial matters.

For sensitometry of photographic materials, when an area several millimeters square is of uniform density, good results can be obtained by a very simple arrangement without any optical system at all. An automobile headlight is mounted

---

[50] Hardy, A. C., *J. O. S. A.*, *18*, 96 (1928), *25*, 305 (1935). An instrument working on a similar principle is described by Sharp, C. H., and Eckweiler, H. J., *J. O. S. A.*, *23*, 246 (1933).

12 to 18 inches above a flat opaque screen with a rectangular aperture of the desired size cut in it.   A photovoltaic cell is mounted directly behind the aperture and connected to a galvanometer.   The plate is best laid on the aperture emulsion side down to reduce scattering effects.   Miss Mohler and Miss Taylor[51] have described a reflection densitometer almost equally simple and easy to construct.   Difficulties with stray light, and the effect of scattering in the emulsion will, however, be reduced if a simple projection system is introduced.

For many problems it is desired to know the density on a very small area of the plate—hence the term *micropho-tometer* for densitometers which are designed for such

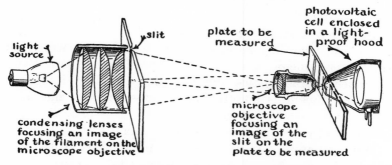

Fig. 16.   Optical system of Lange's microphotometer.

applications.   Lange[52] and Milligan[53] have described micro-photometers using photovoltaic cells.   The optical system of the Lange instrument is shown in Fig. 16.   The condensing lens forms an image of the lamp filament in the principal plane of the microscope objective, which is adjusted to give a sharp image of the slit in the plane of the emulsion.   The projected image of the slit may be made as narrow as 0.01 mm.   The instrument is capable of giving rather high resolution.

[51] Mohler, Nora M., and Taylor, Delia Ann, *J. O. S. A.*, *26*, 386 (1936).

[52] Lange, B., *Zeits. f. techn. Physik*, *13*, 600 (1932).

[53] Milligan, W. O., *Rev. Sci. Instruments*, *4*, 496 (1933).

The optical design and other features of microphotometers have been reviewed by Harrison.[54] To eliminate errors caused by scattered light, it is customary to use at least two slits in high-resolution instruments. In order to obtain sufficient sensitivity with reasonable speed of response, it is necessary to use an emission-type cell and amplifier. For the amplifier an RCA 38 pentode, connected as in Fig. 5, is satisfactory.[55] Suitable operating conditions and circuit constants are as follows: Heater, 6 volts from storage battery. Control grid, − 1.5 volts; screen grid, + 6 volts; plate, + 12 volts; all from small radio batteries. Plate current, 60 microamperes. Mutual conductance, 150 microamperes/volt. Grid resistor, 10^8 to 10^9 ohms. Galvanometer, 5×10^{-8} ampere/mm. A cesium oxide vacuum photocell is recommended.

Measurements of the transmission of solutions as a function of depth and concentration can also be made advantageously by photoelectric methods. Many procedures for chemical analysis which formerly used visual methods are now carried out with increased precision by employing a photoelectric cell.[56]

The light absorption of a solution is a logarithmic function of the concentration. Over a certain range the density of a photographic plate is a logarithmic function of the intensity. It would therefore be convenient to have an amplifier with a logarithmic response in order to make a direct-reading densitometer. Hunt[57] found that a remote cutoff tube such as the type 78 can be made to have an accurately logarithmic response over a voltage range of about tenfold. By using three tubes in cascade, he was able to extend this range to over a thousandfold. This arrangement is for alternating-

[54] Harrison, G. R., *J. O. S. A.* and *Rev. Sci. Instruments*, 19, 267 (1929); *J. O. S. A.*, *24*, 59 (1934).

[55] Kron, G. E., private communication.

[56] Withrow, R. B., Shrewsbury, C. L., and Krayhill, H. L., *Indust. & Engin. Chem. (Analytical Edition)*, 8, 214 (1936).

Strafford, N., *Analyst*, *61*, 170 (1936).

[57] Hunt, F. W., *Rev. Sci. Instruments*, *4*, 672 (1933). See also Ballantine, S., *Electronics*, *1*, 472 (1931).

current voltages only. Müller and Kinney[58] have applied this principle to measuring the concentration of solutions. They report that the open circuit e.m.f. of a Weston Photronic cell is also a logarithmic function of intensity.

Amplification of small galvanometer deflections. The ultimate sensitivity of a moving-coil galvanometer is set by the Brownian movement. Because of the limitations of the optical system it is difficult to realize this limit in a galvanometer with a reasonably short period. Moll and Burger[59] described a thermo-relay in which a rotation of the coil of

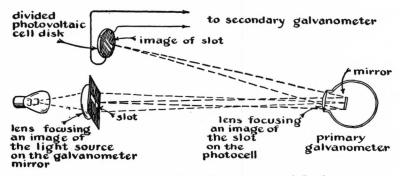

Fig. 17. Amplification of small galvanometer deflections.

only a few seconds of arc was amplified and read on a second galvanometer. More recently, amplification schemes using photoelectric cells[60] have come into use, with some improvement in the speed of response.

The simplest method of amplification involves a balanced photovoltaic-cell arrangement. The sensitive disk of a Weston Photronic cell is removed from the case. This may be done by unscrewing the back, warming gently, if necessary, to soften the pitch seal. The conducting layer on the

[58] Müller, R. H., and Kinney, G. F., *J. O. S. A.*, *25*, 342 (1935).

[59] Moll, W. J. H., and Burger, H. C., *Phil. Mag.*, *50*, 6211 (1925).

[60] Jones, R. V., *Journ. Sci. Instruments*, *11*, 302 (1934).

Moss, E. B., *Journ. Sci. Instruments*, *12*, 141 (1935). This is a general review of the subject.

See also Taylor, A. H., *Rev. Sci. Instruments*, *8*, 124 (1937).

top surface is divided into two parts by scratching a line along a diameter of the disk with a sharp instrument. Any loose particles must be brushed away. If this process is carried out properly, the two halves of the top conducting layer will be insulated from each other. Fig. 17 shows the optical arrangements. An automobile headlight bulb is focused on the mirror of the primary galvanometer by a simple lens, in the plane of which is a rectangular slot. The galvanometer lens forms an image of the illuminated slot on the divided disk of the photovoltaic cell. The two halves of the top conducting layer are connected to the secondary galvanometer, which indicates the difference in the illumination on the two sides of the center line. A distance of 1 or 2 feet between the photocell and the primary galvanometer is sufficient. The secondary galvanometer may be placed wherever it is convenient.

A current amplification of 200 is easily obtained with such an arrangement, which is sufficient to make the Brownian motion quite noticeable. Another application would be to couple two short-period, low-sensitivity galvanometers by such a device to form a high-sensitivity combination with rapid response. The over-all linearity is, of course, open to suspicion and must be tested.

Thyratrons. The introduction of a gas into a hot-cathode tube greatly increases the power it can handle, owing to the neutralization of space charge by the positive ions formed. However, the grid-control characteristic is quite different from that of a high-vacuum tube. With the grid sufficiently negative, the tube is nonconducting. At a certain critical grid potential, whose value depends on the plate voltage, the discharge starts, and the tube is said to "fire." The grid then loses control of the plate current because of a sheath of positive ions around it. The discharge can be stopped only by removing the plate voltage. The voltage drop in the tube is practically independent of current and amounts to about 15 volts. The current must be limited by resistance in the external circuit to a safe value.

The name *thyratron*[61] was first applied to these tubes only by the General Electric Company, but is coming into general use. Other terms sometimes used are *gaseous triode* and *grid-controlled rectifier*. The Westinghouse Lamp Company and the RCA Manufacturing Company also make tubes of this type. The gases used are argon and mercury vapor. Mercury-vapor tubes have the disadvantage, which is, however, usually not serious, that the characteristics are a function of the ambient temperature. Argon tubes are not subject to this variation, but are limited in their power-handling ability. The General Electric FG-81, the largest argon-filled tube, is rated at 0.5 ampere maximum average plate current and 180 volts maximum plate voltage.

In most applications gaseous triodes are used with an alternating plate voltage. During the negative half of the cycle the grid regains control. The output is then a pulsating direct current. Tubes may be used in pairs if full-wave operation is desired.

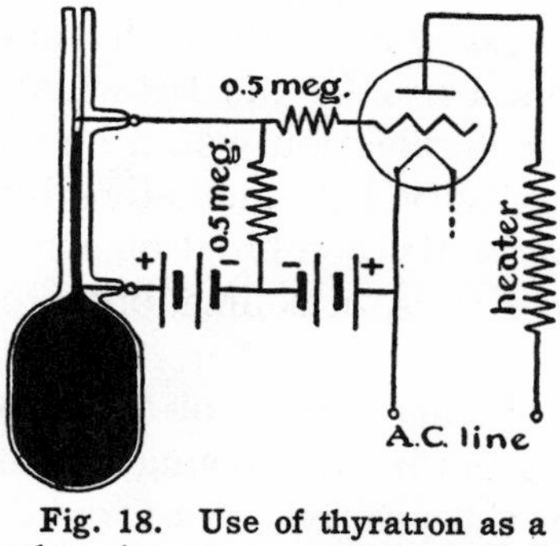

Fig. 18. Use of thyratron as a relay in a mercury-controlled thermostat.

The simplest application is as a relay. As compared to a mechanical relay, the gaseous triode requires much less power to operate, is faster and quieter, and has no contacts to pit, wear, or stick. Fig. 18 shows a gaseous triode used as the relay in a thermostat controlled by a mercury thermometer. A load of 2 kilowatts may be switched on and off with a current at the mercury contact of a few microamperes. The mercury is thus protected from contamination due to sparking.

This particular application is merely illustrative. The control may be exercised by a photoelectric cell, and the load

---

[61] For many details about characteristics and uses, see Hull, A. W., *Gen. El. Rev.*, *32*, 213, 390 (1929); *Physics*, *4*, 66 (1933).

may be a light, a motor, or a magnet.   If response to even smaller grid power is required, a four-electrode tube known as a shield-grid thyratron is available.[62]

Continuous variation of the average plate current between zero and full value may be obtained by a phase-shift circuit, shown in Fig. 19.   The phase of the alternating grid voltage is varied by the relative values of C and R.   If R is very large, the grid voltage is 180° out of phase with the plate voltage, and the tube is always nonconducting.   If R is zero

or very small, the grid voltage is in phase with the plate voltage, and the tube fires at the beginning of each positive half-cycle and carries the maximum current.   At an intermediate value, the grid voltage will reach the critical potential at some time during the positive half-cycle, and the tube conducts for the remainder of the half-cycle.   A

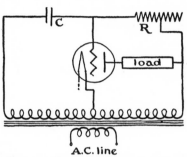

Fig. 19.   Phase-shift circuit for control of thyratron.

smooth and fairly linear variation of the average current is thus possible.   The resistance R may be a vacuum tube or a photoelectric cell.

In Fig. 20 is shown a phase-shift circuit for maintaining a constant temperature in a furnace.[63]   In a test, the temperature of a furnace at approximately 880°C. was held constant within 0.06°C.   The temperature is measured by a thermocouple.   (A resistance thermometer would do as well.)   The potentiometer is set to balance at the desired constant temperature.   An automobile headlight bulb is imaged on the galvanometer mirror by the lens L_1.   The galvanometer lens L_2 forms an image of L_1 on a V-shaped slot in front of the photocell.   The amount of light reaching the cell (which should be of the gas-filled type) determines the current

[62] Livingston, O. W., and Maser, H. T., *Electronics*, April, 1934.
[63] Zabel, R. M., and Hancox, R. R., *Rev. Sci. Instruments*, 5, 28 (1934).

through the thyratron and thus regulates the furnace temperature. R_1 is in parallel with the regulator circuit and
carries most of the heater current, thus making it possible to
use a smaller tube. R_2 limits the current through the tube to
its rated maximum value. C may be a 200 micro-microfarad
variable condenser.

This arrangement is an example of a type of control mechanism that will be found generally useful in the laboratory.

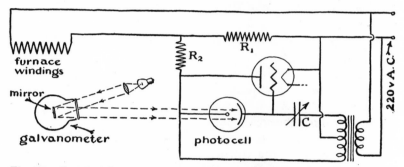

Fig. 20.   Constant temperature regulator using a photocell in a phase-shift
circuit.

It differs from the simple on-and-off control provided by
relays in that the correcting influence approaches zero gradually as the error diminishes, and "hunting" is thereby
eliminated.   The same principle is applicable to devices for
maintaining constant speed, constant current, or constant
voltage.   With two lights and two photocells, it may be used
to control a motor which will balance a bridge or a scale, or
perform any other "centering" operation.[64]

---

[64] For further applications see Henney, K., *Electron Tubes in Industry*,
Second Edition.   New York: McGraw-Hill Book Company, 1937.

CHAPTER XI

Photography in the Laboratory[1]

IN this chapter we will treat of photography and the photographic procedures used in making and recording observations in experimental science and especially in recording spectra.

Comparison of the sensitivities of the eye with the photographic emulsion. The relative visibilities of the various

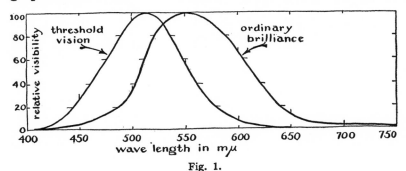

Fig. 1.

colors of the spectrum are shown in Fig. 1. To illustrate the differences of response to various wave lengths between the eye and the photographic plate, these visibility curves are to be compared with the sensitivity curves for ordinary, orthochromatic, and panchromatic emulsions that are shown in the top section of Fig. 2.

[1] I wish to acknowledge the use of material from the following sources for the preparation of this chapter:

Elementary Photographic Chemistry. Rochester: Eastman Kodak Company, 1931.

Fowle, F. E., *Smithsonian Physical Tables.* Washington: The Smithsonian Institution, 1934.

Hardy, A. C., and Perrin, F. H., *The Principles of Optics* (chapter on photography). New York: McGraw-Hill Book Company, 1932.

Neblette, C. B., *Photography.* New York: D. Van Nostrand Company, 1930.

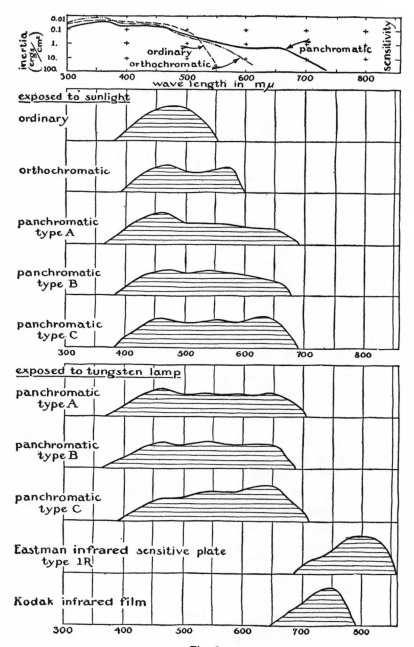

Fig. 2.

450

Wedge spectrograms are illustrated in the lower sections of Fig. 2. These spectrograms were taken using sunlight and the light of a tungsten lamp as the light source. The height of the shaded areas indicates the sensitivity of the emulsion.

Owing to the emission characteristics of these light sources and the opacity of the lenses used for violet and ultraviolet light, the wedge spectrograms exhibit maxima at about 4700 Å, whereas, actually, the sensitivities of the emulsions, as indicated by the curves at the top of Fig. 2, show the maxima to be in the ultraviolet. However, the wedge spectrograms do give an indication of the performance of different emulsions in the camera.

Table I illustrates the relative sensitivities of the eye and the photographic plate to a line-shaped light source on a dark field. This table, together with the appearance of a spec-

TABLE I

Color of Linear Image of Light on Dark Background Just Visible at a Glance	Time Required to Register the Line Photographically on a Panchromatic Plate
Violet............................	1 minute
Blue (4500 Å).....................	5 minutes
Green (5200Å).....................	30 hours
Red hydrogen.....................	17 minutes
Extreme red......................	1 minute

The material for this table appeared in the *Scientific American* a few years ago.

trum line, may be used to determine the approximate exposure time for a spectrum plate.

Hurter and Driffield curves. The characteristics of photographic films and plates are simply represented by Hurter and Driffield curves[2] (designated hereafter as H and

[2] Hurter, F., and Driffield, V. C., *Jour. Soc. Chem. Ind.*, *9*, 455 (1890).

Ferguson, W. B., *The Photographic Researches of Ferdinand Hurter and Vero C. Driffield.* Royal Photographic Society, 1920.

D curves). An H and D curve is shown in Fig. 3. This curve represents the relationship between photographic response and the exposure to white light which is required to produce this response. The response, measured by the

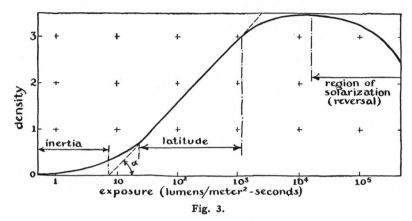

Fig. 3.

photographic density, Δ, is plotted as ordinate against the logarithm of the exposure, Σ, as abscissa. Δ is defined by the equation

$$\Delta = \log_{10} \frac{1}{T}, \tag{1}$$

in which T is the transmission of the film or plate in question.

The shape of the H and D curve depends upon the character of the emulsion, and also, if colored light is used, upon the wave length or color characteristics of the light used for exposure. Actual photographic materials may exhibit a curve differing considerably from the one shown in Fig. 3. For example, the curve does not always exhibit a definite straight segment in which Δ is proportional to the logarithm of exposure. The curve of Fig. 3 is somewhat idealized, but it represents the general character of the relationship between Δ and $\log \Sigma$.

The exposure range represented by the straight segment is, by definition, the latitude of the emulsion. Table II gives the latitude of typical emulsions, from which we see that fast emulsions have the greatest latitude and lantern slides and process emulsions the least, the variation of latitude in these emulsions being eightfold. In Table II the latitude is expressed as the ratio of the exposure at the upper end of the straight segment to the exposure at the lower end.

TABLE II

LATITUDE OF PHOTOGRAPHIC EMULSIONS

Photographic Material	Latitude (ratio of exposure at limits of the straight segment of the Δ-log Σ curve for development to γ_∞)
Motion-picture film:	
Extra fast and normal............	200
Panchromatic...................	300
Positive.......................	50
Commercial:	
Ordinary.......................	75
Orthochromatic.................	75
Panchromatic...................	75
Process plates....................	25
Lantern-slide plates...............	25

Smithsonian Tables, page 342 (1936).

The contrast of an emulsion, γ, is, by definition, the slope of the straight segment of the H and D curve. If this segment makes an angle α with the log Σ axis,

$$\gamma = \tan \alpha. \tag{2}$$

The contrast varies with development time but tends to approach a limit as the development time is increased. This limiting value, γ_∞, allows comparisons to be made between the contrast characteristics of various types of emulsions. Values of γ_∞ for different emulsions are given in Table III. It will be noted that positive films, lantern slides, and process emulsions exhibit the most contrast, while fast emulsions exhibit less contrast.

The curve shown in Fig. 4, the so-called Weber-Feckner curve, illustrates the variation of the subjective response of the eye to field brightness. In several respects it is like an H and D curve.

TABLE III

RELATIVE CONTRAST OF PHOTOGRAPHIC EMULSIONS

Material	γ_∞
Super-speed motion-picture film...............	1.4
Par-speed motion-picture film....:............	1.6
Motion-picture positive film..................	2.7
Commercial orthochromatic...................	2.2
Commercial panchromatic....................	2.2
Ordinary commercial........................	2.2
Process plates.............................	3.0
Lantern-slide plates........................	3.2

Smithsonian Tables, page 342 (1934).

The Weber-Feckner curve employs the logarithm of field brightness as abscissa, and this curve exhibits an inflection point near which it is closely approximated by a straight line. The proportionality of Δ for an H and D curve, as well as the subjective response of the eye for a Weber-Feckner curve, to the logarithm of the "amount of light"

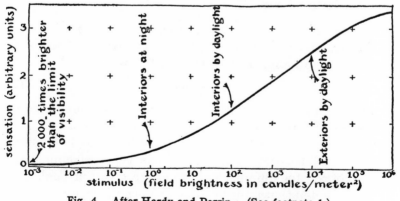

Fig. 4. After Hardy and Perrin. (See footnote 1.)

indicates why photographs look natural. It also indicates why the ordinary fading type of exposure meter works as well as it does.

The contrast sensitivity of the eye is related to the slope of the Weber-Feckner curve, and it is such that one can just distinguish a difference in brightness of about 2 per cent between contiguous uniformly illuminated fields. It is of interest to point out that the contrast of a field can be enhanced by photography by about ninefold—threefold by the photographic process of taking the primary photograph and threefold by the printing process. Accordingly, it is possible to see detail in a photograph which is invisible to the unaided eye.

The H and D speed of a photographic material S is defined as 34 divided by the inertia expressed in lumen seconds per square meter.

$$S = \frac{34}{i}. \tag{3}$$

The inertia, illustrated in Fig. 3, is the exposure represented by the intersection of the extrapolated straight segment of the H and D curve with the line $\Delta = 0$.

Reciprocity law. The photophysical and photochemical effects produced in a plate by the exposure Σ are measured by the density Δ. Equal effective exposures Σ' produce equal densities under the condition of controlled development. To a degree of approximation sufficient for most applications (precise photometric photography excepted) the effective exposure is equal to the product of the illumination on the plate, I, multiplied by the time of exposure t. Thus,

$$\Sigma' = \Sigma = I \cdot t. \tag{4}$$

This is the so-called Bunsen and Roscoe reciprocity law.

For greater accuracy it is necessary to replace Eq. 4 by more complicated expressions. One of them, Schwarzschild's,[3] takes into account the difference in effectiveness when the emulsion is exposed a short time to a bright light and when it is exposed a long time to a dim light. Schwarzschild's relation is given below:

$$\Sigma' = I \cdot t^p. \tag{5}$$

---

[3] Schwarzschild, K., *Astrophys. J.*, *11*, 89 (1900).

We may take the behavior of motion-picture positive film as an example to show to what extent the Bunsen and Roscoe law fails. For the range of illumination intensities from 1 to 33,000 it is found that p varies from 0.68 to 1.00, the maximum intensity being 131 lumens/m^2 and the exposure time varying between 18.2 hours and 2.5 × 10^{-4} second.

Another factor to be considered in predicting the photographic response to a given exposure is whether the illumination is intermittent or continuous. The photographic emulsion is incapable of responding as completely to an exposure impressed as short flashes of light as to an equal uniform exposure. Also, everything else being equal, the photographic response is diminished if the time interval between flashes increases.[4]

The resolving power. The resolving power of a photographic plate may be measured by the number of lines per millimeter which can be distinctly photographed. The

TABLE IV

RESOLVING POWER OF PHOTOGRAPHIC EMULSIONS

Material	Optimal Resolving Power (lines/mm)
Motion-picture film:	
Extra fast	50
Normal	55
Panchromatic	50
Positive	80
Ordinary commercial	65
Commercial orthochromatic	65
Commercial panchromatic	60
Process ordinary	90
Process panchromatic	75
Lantern slide	100

Smithsonian Tables, page 343 (1934).

[4] For a more complete treatment of the failure of the reciprocity law, see Jones, L. A., "Measurements of Radiant Energy with Photographic Materials," *Measurement of Radiant Energy*. New York: McGraw-Hill Book Company, 1937.

resolving power varies by a factor of about 2 for the ordinary photographic materials. For lantern-slide plates the resolving power is about 100/mm, but for fast motion-picture film it is only half as great, or about 50/mm. (See Table IV.)

Light sources. Photographs are frequently taken with achromatic lenses. The flint components of these lenses will not transmit light at wave lengths shorter than about 3300 Å. The transmission curve for a moving-picture projection lens containing a flint component is shown in Fig. 5. In practice a

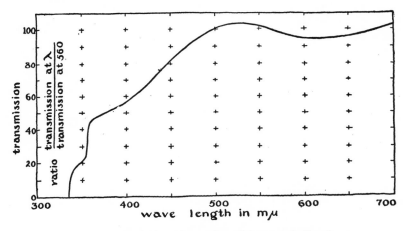

Fig. 5. Transmission of a motion-picture projection lens.

wave-length limit of 3800 Å is often low enough to define the behavior of a photographic material when account is taken of this opacity of the lenses used and also when the ultraviolet emission of ordinary light sources is considered.

The spectral energy distributions in the light of various tungsten lamps used for photography are given in Fig. 6. It will be noted that the emission is weak at short wave lengths. The spectral distribution of sunlight is also given there. As a matter of convenience for comparing the curves, the intensities are all set equal to 1 at 5600 Å.

The color temperatures of various sources are given in Table V. Of these, the photoflash lamp is of special interest.

It is of value for inside photography, since it eliminates the danger and smoke of flashlight powder and the expense of other suitable sources such as the electric arc. This lamp is an ordinary pear-shaped bulb filled with aluminum foil and oxygen. The foil is ignited by a "fuse," or small chemical

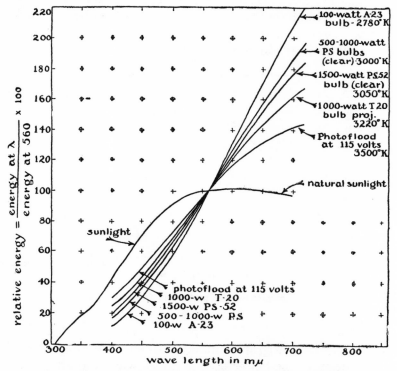

Fig. 6. Data for tungsten lamps supplied by the General Electric Company, Nela Park, Cleveland, Ohio.

flash, set off by applying 3 volts or more to the screw socket of the base. When two or more of the lamps are close together, it is necessary to apply voltage to the base of only one of them and the others will go off "sympathetically." The light generated is 22 to 180 thousand lumen seconds, depending upon the size of the lamp. This light is emitted in an interval of time varying from $\frac{1}{50}$ to $\frac{1}{25}$ second. Half the total radiation is emitted in an interval of $\frac{1}{100}$ to $\frac{1}{200}$ second. When the voltage is applied to the base, the lag between the time when the fuse is operated and the instant of maximum illumination is about $\frac{1}{55}$ second, or, if the lamps are "sympathetically" flashed, the lag between the first and second flash is about $\frac{1}{77}$ second. The maximum light intensity from a bulb of the size of an ordinary 75-watt tungsten lamp is 4 to 5 $\times$ 10^6 lumens.

TABLE V

COLOR TEMPERATURES OF VARIOUS SOURCES (TEMPERATURE
OF A BLACK BODY GIVING THE SAME COLOR OF LIGHT)

Source	Color Temperature (°K.)
Sun	5400
Sky	25,000
Nernst filament	2400
Ordinary tungsten lamp	2780 to 3000
Photoflood lamp	3500
Flash powder	3800
Ordinary cored carbon arc	4000
Photoflash lamp	>5000

Filters. For photographing with the microscope, in order to prevent excessive heating, it is necessary to use a water filter to absorb out heat radiation from the light emitted from the carbon arc. Frequently, copper chloride or sulphate is added to the water in the cell to increase its infrared absorption. These additions do not materially attenuate the transmission of the cell for yellow, green, and blue light.

On the other hand, when it is required to transmit the infrared and absorb the visible rays, one can use a cell containing a solution of iodine in carbon disulphide.

Color filters for use in photography can be made up from solutions, or they may be purchased in the form of colored gelatin films, either unmounted or mounted between glass plates. The unmounted films are the cheapest, and they generally serve as well as those that are mounted. Transmissions for some of the Wratten gelatin filters[5] used in photography are given in Fig. 7.

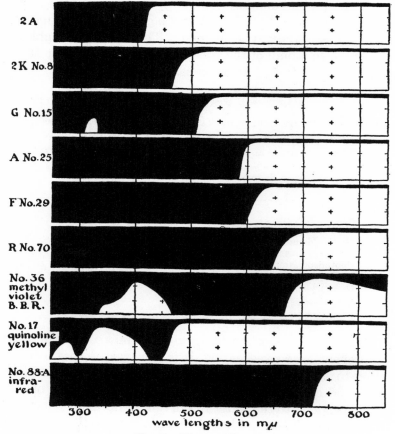

Fig. 7. Wratten filters.

There are several preliminary procedures to be carried out before the photographic emulsion is ready for exposure. These include focusing, sensitizing, annealing, and judging the correct exposure time to be given.

[5] Wratten filters are handled commercially by the Eastman Kodak Company, Rochester, New York. See the book *Wratten Light Filters*, published by that company, price 50 cents.

Focusing. Focusing may be accomplished by taking several pictures at different positions of the plate holder or lens. Sometimes, however, this procedure is not the most convenient one. For example, in focusing the plate in an astronomical telescope, a "knife-edge" test may be used for determining the focus. This is accomplished by means of an attachment which is substituted for the plate holder and which is constructed so that the knife edge comes to the same plane as that occupied by the emulsion when the plate holder is in position. The camera as a whole is then adjusted until the cutting of the knife into the star image results in a uniform decrease in the intensity of the rays that come from different parts of the mirror. After this, when the plate holder is replaced, the emulsion will be in focus.

In a spectrograph a strip of paper across the center of the telescope or collimating lens and parallel to the slit facilitates the determination of the focus. When the photographic plate or viewing glass is not in exact focus, a double image of the spectrum lines is obtained.

A uranium glass plate may be used for focusing ultraviolet light. The fluorescence of this glass is easily visible for the stronger ultraviolet lines in the mercury spectrum.

Sensitizing. Ordinary photographic plates respond to wave lengths from 2400 Å to 5500 Å, with the maximum sensitivity at about 3600 Å. Sensitization is required beyond these limits. Although the photographically active grains themselves are sensitive for all wave lengths shorter than those of the visible spectrum, the emulsion becomes less sensitive at wave lengths below 2800 Å, because of opacity of the gelatin in the emulsion. Although absorption by the gelatin is weak at 2800 Å, it increases at shorter wave lengths, especially below 2400 Å, until the gelatin is completely opaque at 2000 Å. Schumann made the first photographic plates which were sensitive at wave lengths below 2000 Å by using a very thin emulsion almost free from the opaque gelatin. Not only are the Schumann plates useful for photographing in the ultraviolet spectrum, but they also serve in those applications in which the lateral motion in the emulsion is to be rigorously avoided or in which lateral scattering of light must be minimized.

The sensitivity of ordinary photographic plates may be increased at wave lengths below 2400 Å by coating them with a fluorescent substance such as oil.   The sensitivity can be

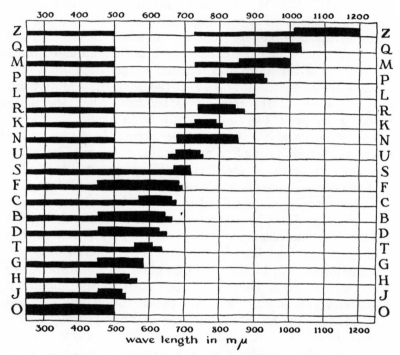

Fig. 8.   Diagrammatic representation of the sensitivity of spectrum plates available from the Eastman Kodak Company.

increased as much as four hundredfold.   A few drops of Nujol or some other oil are spread over the surface with a cotton pad.   After exposure and before development the oil is washed away with acetone.   Harrison has studied the sensitometry of oiled plates, and he states that they may be used for photographic photometry.[6]

[6] Harrison, G. R., *J. O. S. A.*, *11*, 113 (1925).

Plates are sensitized for the red and infrared with dyes. The diagram shown in Fig. 8 represents the characteristics of spectrum plates which are available commercially.[7]

Plates may be hypersensitized by bathing them in either an ammonia or a borax bath. The formulas for these baths are given below.

AMMONIA FORMULA

Bath Temperature: 10° to 12°C.

Ammonia (0.91 sp. gr.)................................. 2 cc
Alcohol...275 cc
Distilled water.......................................725 cc

Immerse 2 minutes. Do not rinse. Dry as quickly as possible after removing surface liquid.

BORAX FORMULA

Bath Temperature: 12°C.

Sodium chloride......................................0.5 g
Borax...2 to 3 g
Distilled water.....................................1 liter

Immerse 2 to 6 minutes. Do not rinse. Soak in methyl alcohol 1 minute. Dry as quickly as possible after removing surface fluid.

The hypersensitizing action of the baths is relatively greater for the slower emulsions. Treatment with the ammonia bath can be expected to produce 100 to 400 per cent increase of speed for the visible spectrum, while infrared plates exhibit an even greater increase in speed of 500 to 2500 per cent. Hypersensitized plates fog rapidly at room temperature, so that they should be used as soon as possible after they are dry. However, they can be kept for a few days in an icebox. After they are removed from the icebox, they should be warmed to room temperature to avoid the condensation of moisture when they are loaded in the camera. The borax treatment is said to be best for Agfa plates, and the ammonia bath for Eastman plates.

Photographic plates may also be hypersensitized by a 36-hour exposure to mercury vapor at ordinary temperatures.[8]

---

[7] Mees, C. E. K., *J. O. S. A.*, *25*, 80 (1935).

[8] See Dersch, F., and Duerr, H., *J. Soc. of Motion Picture Engineers*, *28*, 178 (1937). The effect of exposure to the mercury vapor is said to be more marked after exposure than before.

We see from the H and D curve given in Fig. 3 that a certain exposure is required before the linear part of the curve is reached. R. W. Wood introduced the procedure of pre-exposing the plate to a uniform illumination.[9] Although this allows the attainment of increased density with a given exposure, it does so with attendant loss of contrast. To avoid the Herschel effect, one should use, for the pre-exposure, a wave length that is redder than the light that is being photographed. Other investigators who have experimented with pre-exposure, notably Whipple in connection with stellar spectroscopy and Norman with photographic photometry, may be consulted for further details.[10]

Gelatin shifts. Annealing of the unexposed emulsion may be required for photographic plates such as spectrum plates and astrographic plates on which it is necessary to make measurements of the highest precision. Gelatin shifts may occur on account of strains, in the supporting gelatin layer, which are relieved by the developing process. Accordingly, the position of silver in the developed image may not coincide exactly with the position of the same silver in the latent image. Cooksey and Cooksey observed shifts of the latent image as great as 9μ.[11] These authors found, however, that such shifts are reduced about fourfold by the following annealing procedure: The plate is wet in a neutral solution, washed, and then dried by absorbing the water from the gelatin with alcohol.

More frequently gelatin shifts arise on account of improper drying. Large shifts occur around spots where the gelatin does not dry uniformly. To avoid these shifts it is recommended that, after fixing, the plate be dried in an alcohol bath, in which the removal of water from the gelatin is much more uniform than it is when the drying is effected by evaporation. It is advisable not to use a spectrum plate nearer the edge than 1 cm, since the gelatin shifts are greatest near the edge.

[9] Wood, R. W., *Astrophys. J.*, *27*, 379 (1908).
[10] Norman, D., *J. O. S. A.*, *26*, 407 (1936).
Whipple, F. L., *Lick Observat.*, *Bull.*, No. 442.
[11] Cooksey, D., and Cooksey, C. D., *Phys. Rev.*, *36*, 80 (1930).

Because of their shrinking and expanding, photographic films are unsuitable for precise photography. The effect of changes in the film can, in a large part, be allowed for if coördinate lines (with a reseau) or, in the case of a spectrum, comparison spectral lines, are impressed on the plate at the time of exposure.

Exposure. Photographic films and plates are ordinarily exposed to get proper contrast. As long as the range of

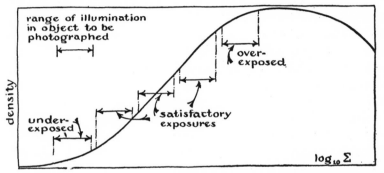

Fig. 9.

illumination in the object to be photographed is small compared to the latitude of the emulsion, the exposure can vary between wide limits. As a result, the density may vary, but as long as the exposure falls within these limits, the contrast obtained will be the same. This is illustrated in Fig. 9.

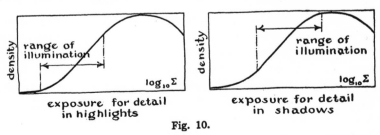

Fig. 10.

If the range of illumination is greater than the latitude as shown in Fig. 10, the exposure should be adjusted to get proper contrast where it is desired. For example, if the highlights are important, the emulsion should be under-exposed for the shadows, and if the shadows are important, it should be overexposed for the highlights.

In photography, particularly artistic photography, one may wish to render detail in both highlights and shadows even where the range of illumination may involve a ratio as great as 3000 to 6000 between the maximum and minimum exposure. Although no film exhibits such a latitude (see Table II), this range of exposure can often be managed by overexposure and underdevelopment. That this procedure yields less contrast and greater latitude is indicated by Fig. 11, in which it will be noted that the projection of the straight segment of the Δ-log Σ curve representing 32 minutes development embraces an exposure range only half as broad as that embraced by the curve for 2 minutes development. Furthermore, the regions of exposure beyond the straight segment do not deviate so much from a straight line for the case of 2 minutes development as for the case of 32 minutes development.

On the other hand, when a subject is "flat," such as a sand dune, the professional photographer takes his largest camera and gives the plate a short exposure and then a long development to get maximum contrast. The photographer uses the large camera inasmuch as a long development time produces graininess, which becomes conspicuous on enlargement.

The correct exposure may be determined by means of an exposure meter and the tables and scales supplied with it. The photronic*-cell type of exposure meter is especially useful, but it has the undesirable feature that its response represents an average of the illumination received over a large solid angle. When the exposure is to be adjusted to the illumination of some small object which is much brighter or darker than its surroundings, it is necessary to put the photronic meter close enough to the object so that it substantially fills the field of view of the meter.

---

* Registered trademark designating photoelectric cells and photoelectric devices manufactured by the Weston Electrical Instrument Corporation.

Tables and calculators like the Wellcome calculator are useful for roughly estimating the exposure.[12]   To increase the chance of getting correct exposure, one should take auxiliary pictures at one half and twice the exposure predicted by the calculator.   Such a practice is especially feasible with miniature cameras, for which the cost of film is small.

The speed of a given photographic material varies with the color characteristics of the illumination, depending upon whether it is sunlight, arc light, or light from a tungsten lamp.   The exposure can be accurately estimated only after taking account of a color factor as well as the intensity of illumination.   The success of an estimate depends largely upon the experience of the photographer.

When unfamiliar conditions of illumination are encountered, the correct exposure is usually determined by trial.   A

TABLE VI

EXPOSURE CHARACTERISTICS OF DIFFERENT PHOTOGRAPHIC EMULSIONS FOR VARIOUS LIGHT SOURCES

Material	Sun	Crater of High-Intensity Arc	Ordinary Arc 4000°K.	Tungsten		
				3200° K.	3000° K.	2800° K.
Super-speed motion-picture film.......	72,000	50,000	16,200	1570	800	400
Par-speed motion-picture film.......	36,000	25,000	8100	780	400	200
Motion-picture positive film..........	3600	2500	820	76	39	20
Bromide paper......	180	125	41	3.8	2	1

Hardy, Arthur C., *J. O. S. A.*, *14*, 515 (1927).

Exposure required to give a perceptible image on various photographic materials.   The values given in the table are $B/\sigma \times 10^{-6}$, where B is the intrinsic illumination in candles per square centimeter and σ is the exposure to give a perceptible deposit in lumen seconds per square centimeter.

[12] This calculator may be obtained from Burroughs Wellcome and Company, 9 East 41st Street, New York City.

succession of trial plates is taken, the exposure of each varying by a factor of 2, 3, or 5.

Table VI is useful for estimating exposure. This table gives the ratio of the intrinsic illumination B to the exposure σ required for the various light sources to yield a perceptible deposit on the photographic material indicated in the left-hand column of the table.[13] B is in candles per square centimeter and σ in lumen seconds per square centimeter, so that the ratio B/σ has the dimensions $1/($solid angle $\times$ seconds$)$. If the product of the quantity B/σ multiplied by the solid angle of the illumination cone on the film and as well by the exposure time is equal to or greater than unity, a perceptible image will result.

The values of B/σ are useful for designing recording instruments to determine the maximum velocity v at which the recording spot can traverse the film and yet produce a readable trace. Let us consider a recording system, say one to record galvanometer deflections. First, we must determine the exposure time and solid angle of illumination. If the width of the spot is d, then d/v gives the exposure time for those areas of the photographic material which have been traversed by the spot. The solid angle of the illumination is determined as follows:

Case I. For the case in which a galvanometer mirror of area A acts as field stop and the light is focused on the film by a spherical lens immediately in front of the galvanometer, the solid angle is A/f_1^2, when f_1 is the distance of the film from the spherical lens.

Case II. For the case in which an astigmatic optical system is used, wherein the width of the galvanometer mirror, w, determines the lateral field stop, and the stop on the cylindrical mirror is h, the solid angle is

$$\frac{w}{f_1} \times \frac{h}{f_2}.$$

Here, f_1 is the distance of the film from a spherical (or

[13] Hardy, A. C., *J. O. S. A.*, *14*, 505 (1927).

cylindrical) lens in front of the galvanometer mirror, and f_2 is the distance of the film from the cylindrical lens near the film. (See Fig. 47, Chapter IX.)

Accordingly, for Case I the condition for obtaining a record is

$$\frac{B}{\sigma} \cdot \frac{A}{f_1^2} \cdot \frac{d}{v} \geq 1$$

and for Case II, the condition is

$$\frac{B}{\sigma} \cdot \frac{w}{f_1} \cdot \frac{h}{f_2} \cdot \frac{d}{v} \geq 1.$$

Development. The aim of development is to render in photographic blackening the variations in illumination registered as the latent image in the photographic emulsion. Sometimes, as in a snapshot, one may wish the rendition to be "normal," so that the positive print will seem to represent faithfully the original scene. On the other hand, one may wish to repress or enhance contrast by changes in the development procedure.

The development process is not completely understood. Grains of silver bromide which have been exposed to light are reduced to metallic silver by the developer, while those not so exposed are not easily reduced. The developer will, however, finally reduce unexposed grains. The reduction of unexposed grains produces a general fogging of the plate, called chemical fog.

The progress of development with time is illustrated in Fig. 11. The various H and D curves shown here represent a series of exposures, on five different plates. Each of the plates was developed for a different length of time, namely, 2, 4, 8, 16, and 32 minutes. It is characteristic of development that the contrast increases with the time of development. At first the increase is rapid; for example, in 2 minutes the contrast of the material represented in Fig. 11 increased from 0.32 at $t = 2$ minutes to 0.58 at $t = 4$ minutes, an increase of 0.26. Later, the rate of increase falls off; for example, in 16 minutes the contrast increased by only 0.3 from 1.4 at $t = 16$ minutes to 1.7 at $t = 32$ minutes. The contrast approaches a limit γ_∞ for very long development. We have referred to this quantity before and tabulated it for representative photographic materials. (See Table III.) An interesting geometrical feature of the H and

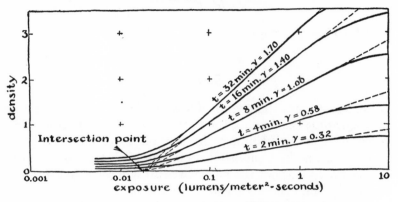

Fig. 11. After Hardy and Perrin. (See footnote 1.)

D curves shown in Fig. 11 is that their extrapolated straight segments have a common intersection point with the line $\Delta = 0$.

Developers are composed usually of four constituents: (1) The reducing agent—metol (elon), pyrogallol, glycin, amidol, or hydroquinone; (2) the alkali accelerator—caustic soda, sodium carbonate, or borax; (3) the preservative—usually sodium sulphite or bisulphite; (4) the restraining agent—potassium bromide.

Most developing solutions will not develop at all unless they are alkaline, and all of them act more rapidly in proportion to the concentration of the alkaline accelerator.

Oxygen dissolved by alkaline solutions may oxidize the reducing agent. In the case of pyrogallol this oxidation is particularly objectionable, for it yields a yellow-colored product which stains the emulsion. Oxidation can be avoided if the preservative sodium sulphite is added to the developer. This substance rather than the pyrogallol reacts with the dissolved oxygen, forming sodium sulphate.

The characteristic effect of the restraining agent, potassium bromide, is to depress the intersection point, referred to above, below the line $\Delta = 0$ and at the same time bromide suppresses development in the low exposure range. A small amount of bromide which is not enough to depress the intersection point much will, however, exert a selective enough restraining effect on the development to inhibit the formation of undesired chemical fog, without having any sensible effect on the development of the desired image.

There are two general procedures for development: time and temperature, or tank development; and factorial, or tray development. By the first method, the film is immersed in a tank of developer for a prescribed length of time. This time is determined by the nature of the film, by the degree of contrast desired, and also by the type, concentration, age, and temperature of the developer.

By the second method, the progress of the development may be watched. Panchromatic emulsions are desensitized to make this possible. The time at which the development is to be terminated is either determined by inspection or calculated from the time required for the image first to appear.

Time and temperature development. The rate of development, as in any chemical reaction, increases rapidly with temperature. It is a practical rule in chemistry (although not a very rigid one) that a reaction rate increases by a factor of 2 for each 10° rise in temperature. This rule applies to development; for example, with pyro-soda developer this factor is 1.5. Time-temperature tables are available for the various developers. However, to get proper contrast and to prevent excessive graininess and fogging, it is advisable to carry on development at the temperature specified by the formula. For developers containing both metol and hydroquinone it is particularly important to develop at the temperature specified in the formula in order to obtain the

proper proportionate effect of each reducer. Metol has a
low temperature coefficient, while hydroquinone has a high
one. As a matter of fact, some operators take advantage of
this difference and use hydroquinone-metol developers warm
to obtain one grade of contrast and cold to obtain another.
This procedure is not recommended, but it does illustrate
the point in question.

The common developers may be made up from the stable
stock solutions listed in Table VII. These solutions are
combined in the proportions given in Table VIII at the time
they are needed, a procedure which is at the same time both
economical and convenient.[14]

TABLE VII

STOCK SOLUTIONS FOR MAKING VARIOUS DEVELOPING BATHS

A	B
Metol or elon..............2.5 g Anhydrous Na_2SO_3..........18 g Water to make.............200 cc	Hydroquinone...............6.7 g Anhydrous Na_2SO_3..........12 g Water to make.............200 cc

C	D
Anhydrous Na_2CO_3........400 g Water to make.............2 liters	KBr......................10 g Water to make.............100 cc

E	F
Anhydrous Na_2SO_3.........400 g Water to make.............2 liters	Borax....................10 g Water to make...........250 cc

Solutions C, D, E, and F are very stable and may be prepared and kept in
large stock bottles. Solutions A and B are less stable, and therefore should be
stocked in small bottles to avoid an excessive amount of air over the solutions.
Use distilled water for making the solutions. Dissolve chemicals for Solutions
A and B in the order listed.

[14] I am indebted to Dr. John McMorris for suggesting these tables.

TABLE VIII

PROPORTIONS FOR COMPOUNDING DEVELOPING BATHS FROM THE STOCK
SOLUTIONS OF TABLE VII

Developer	Solutions					
	A	B	C	D	E	F
Contrast Plate: D-28	34	25	24.5	3.5	0	0
Process tank or tray: D-11	8	27	12.5	5	26	0
Fine grain: D-76	16	15	0	0	38.5	5
D-72 (Chloride paper)	25	37.5	34	2	0	0
D-72 (Bromide paper)	10	15	13.5	0.8	0	0

The quantities are parts, by volume. The developer is compounded in the order A to E in the expressed proportions and then diluted to 100 parts, by volume. For the first three formulas, develop at 65°F. (18°C.). For papers, develop at 70°F. (21°C.). See *Elementary Photographic Chemistry* for further details.

Developers such as Sease 3 give fine grain, but they require extra exposure. So-called compromise developers, such as Edwal 12, yield fine grain, and at the same time they do not require excessive exposure. Compromise developers were first made for use with miniature cameras. Recently, however, they have had some application in astronomy.[15] Formulas for both the Sease 3 and Edwal 12 developers are given below.[16]

SEASE 3

(for twice normal exposure)

Sodium sulphite (anhydrous) .... 90 g
Paraphenylene diamine .... 10 g
Glycin .... 6 g·
Distilled water .... 1 liter

Developing time: 30 minutes at 65°F. (18°C.).

With careful regulation of exposure and developing temperature, negatives are produced which can be enlarged to 50 diameters and beyond.

---

[15] Morgan, W. W., *Astrophys. J.*, *83*, 254 (1936).
[16] The Edwal Laboratories, 732 Federal Street, Chicago, Illinois.

EDWAL 12

(for normal exposures)

Sodium sulphite (anhydrous)...........................90 g
Paraphenylene diamine...............................10 g
Glycin... 5 g
Metol.. 6 g
Water.. 1 liter

Developing time: 12 to 18 minutes at 65° F. (18° C.).

This developer keeps well and will give a finer grain when it is a month or two old than when it is fresh. The fineness of the grain produced also increases after it has been used the first time.

For obtaining fine grain and absence of reticulation, it has been recommended that the temperatures of the developer, rinse water, fixer, and final wash water all be equal to within ± 2°F.

Over-all density is not important for films or plates that are to be printed. The recommended procedure is to disregard density in development. One develops for the desired contrast rather than for a specified average density.

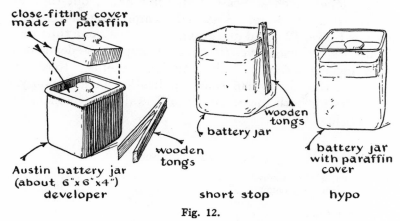

close-fitting cover
made of paraffin

Austin battery jar
(about 6″x6″x4″)
developer

wooden tongs

battery jar

wooden tongs

short stop

battery jar
with paraffin
cover

hypo

Fig. 12.

Fig. 12 shows equipment for developing. The paraffin covers shown protect the solutions from oxidation and evaporation when they are not in use.

Tray development. When the emulsion is immersed in the developer, the time for the first appearance of the image is proportional to the time for its full development. Accordingly, the time for first appearance of the image may be used to determine the proper time of development. This is helpful when the concentrations of the chemicals in the developing bath are different from those specified in the formula. In such a case one would not otherwise know how long to develop. The ratio of the time required for proper development to the time required for the image to appear is a characteristic of the developer and is called the Watkins factor. This factor varies with temperature for two-reducer developers like metol-hydroquinone; but for others it can be used to correct for high or low temperature as well as for deviations in chemical composition of the developer. Watkins factors for several developers are given in Table IX.

TABLE IX

WATKINS FACTORS

Developer	Watkins Factor		
	Soft Contrast	Normal Contrast	Strong Contrast
Pyro-soda.....................	4	6	7
Glycin........................	8	10	12
Hydroquinone.................	6	9	10
Metol........................	10	12	15
Metol-hydroquinone...........	10	12	15

The Wellcome Handbook.

When one is working for high contrast under conditions which allow observation of the progress of development, the rule is to develop in D-28 or D-11 until the image appears on the back of the emulsion. This rule applies particularly to the production of good lantern-slide and spectrum plates.

Aerial fog is often encountered in tray development. It is caused when the plates, wet with developer, are exposed to the air. "Seeding" the developing solution with 5 per cent of old developer, which is rich in bromide, has a negative catalytic action on this fogging. The metals tin, copper, zinc, and their alloys often produce fog and stain on the emulsions when they come in contact with the developers in which the emulsions are treated. For this reason, development in brass and soldered metal trays is to be avoided.

Plates for photometric work should be developed in a tray in a deep solution and brushed continuously with a camel's-hair brush. This accelerates convection near the emulsion and results in more even development. Regions in which the film has a strong exposure give off bromide during development, and unless this is removed by brushing, it restrains further development both at the place it is generated and at adjacent regions in the emulsion.

Plates and films should be held by their edges, ends, and corners, and the fingers should not be allowed to come in contact with the important areas of the emulsion. In some cases the use of rubber gloves is indicated. Important plates should be rinsed in water before development.

Desensitizing. Panchromatic emulsions must ordinarily be developed in the dark. However, the Luppo-Cramer discovery of the desensitizing action of phenosafranine on the unexposed silver grains allows illumination of panchromatic emulsions with a green safelight during the latter stages of development. The selective desensitizing action of this dye on unexposed silver bromide grains is quite mysterious; the development proceeds after the light is turned on as it would in darkness. The plate is separately immersed in the desensitizing solution for 2 minutes in darkness before development (1 part of a stock solution, of $\frac{1}{2}$ g phenosafranine in 1 liter distilled water, to 10 parts water). Pinakryptol green added to the developer may be employed as desensitizing agent. The stock solution is a 1:500 solution of the dye in distilled water—2 to 3 cc of this solution is added to each 100 cc of developer.[17]

---

[17] Neblette, C. B., *Photography*, page 298. New York: D. Van Nostrand Company, 1930.

Fixing. After proper development and washing, it is often adequate to fix the plate or film by immersion in a 20 per cent solution of sodium thiosulphate (hypo) crystals. The hypo dissolves out undeveloped silver bromide grains.

The plate usually carries some developer into the fixing solution and if the fixing solution contains no preservative, the transposed developer will be gradually oxidized and form products which may stain the film. Accordingly, to avoid this effect, fixing solutions are usually compounded with the preservative sodium sulphite added to the hypo. A weak acid is also added to neutralize alkali brought in on the plates. The acid has the further function of stopping development. Fixing solutions may also contain hardeners, such as potassium or chrome alum. These hardeners "tan" the gelatin, prevent excessive swelling and softening of the gelatin, and make it less "soluble" in water.

A short stop is used to stop development and to conserve the acid in the hypo. Plates are immersed in the short stop solution after the development and before fixing.

SHORT STOP

Water...1000 cc
Acetic acid, 28 per cent.................................. 48 cc

This solution is to be made up fresh each time it is used. It does its work in about 5 minutes.

The Eastman bath F-5, made up according to the formula given below, is a good one, and it is recommended for fixing.

EASTMAN ACID HARDENING FIXING BATH F-5

Water at 52°C...600 cc
Hypo crystals...240 g
Sodium sulphite (anhydrous)........................... 15 g
Acetic, 28 per cent................................... 47 cc
Boric acid crystals................................... 7.5 g
Potassium alum.. 15 g
Water to make... 1 liter

The chemicals listed in the formula are to be dissolved in the order given. For best results one should use only fresh fixing solution. It is best to fix plates for twice the time required to clear the gelatin of unreduced silver salts. With acid in the fixing bath the room lights may be turned on a few seconds after the plates are immersed.

Ordinary gelatin melts in water at about 40°C. Normal hardening increases the melting temperature to between 55° and 77°C. However, for extreme hardening, Formalin is used. In less than a minute a 5 per cent solution of this chemical renders the gelatin film insoluble, even in boiling water. Formalin does not work in acid solutions. The following formula is recommended by the Eastman Company:

FORMALIN HARDENER

40 per cent formaldehyde solution............................	10 cc
Sodium carbonate (anhydrous)............................	5 g
Water to make..	1000 cc

Washing and drying. It is necessary to remove the fixing solution from the emulsion by thorough washing. Table X gives the minimum time required for washing various emulsions when the surface of the emulsion is held under a tap so that it is continually in contact with fresh water. But when these materials are washed in a tray without agitation, the diffusion of the fixing chemicals through the emulsion proceeds more slowly. As a working rule, the washing time should not be less than the time required to wash the emulsion under the tap plus the time required to wash the tray. The latter time is determined by measuring the time required

TABLE X

WASHING TIME FOR VARIOUS EMULSIONS

Emulsion	Time (minutes)
Lantern-slide plates......................	3
High-speed negative emulsions.............	7
Chloride papers..........................	15 to 20
Bromide papers..........................	20 to 60

From *Elementary Photographic Chemistry.*

to clear the tray of a strongly colored ink solution. The rate of washing is roughly independent of temperature, and it is also unaffected by hardening if the hardened emulsion has not been dried. A final rinsing with distilled water is recommended. Fig. 13 illustrates methods for washing plates, films, and papers.

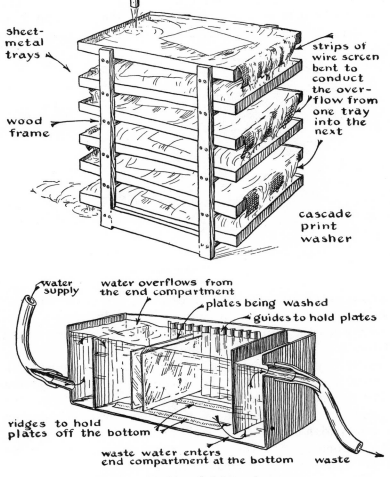

Fig. 13. Washing of plates and papers.

Plates and films are usually dried in a current of dust-free air. The air can be slightly warmed, since the heat of evaporation will keep the emulsion cool. Apparatus suitable for this is illustrated in Fig. 14. Fig. 15 shows a drying cabinet for films.

The dry emulsion on negatives is about 0.0005 of an inch thick and normally contains 8 to 16 per cent moisture. It is five to seven times as thick as this when it is wet. The swelling of gelatin is characterized by the fact that it is anisotropic, being perpendicular to the glass. Even when

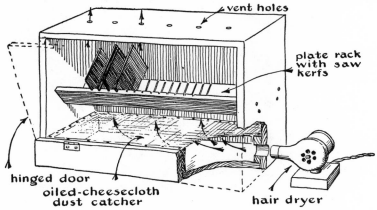

Fig. 14.   Drying cabinet.

gelatin is free from the lateral restraint, offered by the glass support, the swelling is principally in one direction. However, when the film dries unevenly, silver grains are shifted laterally. The edge of a plate dries first, and the shifts produced are appreciable as far back from the edge as 1 cm. Drops of water (tears) or the excessive water held around a dust particle will produce lateral shifts of the emulsion. To avoid these shifts, the emulsion may be wiped with a damp cotton pad, a chamois skin, or better yet, a cellulose sponge. An automobile windshield wiper can be used to remove tears from plates and films.

The plate can be dried in 80 per cent alcohol when maximum accuracy to the edge of the plate is desired and also when distortions such as those caused by dust specks and tears are to be avoided. The alcohol is then evaporated from the emulsion by a current of moist air. If the alcohol or the air is too dry, the water in the gelatin will be reduced below the normal amount, and this subnormal water content

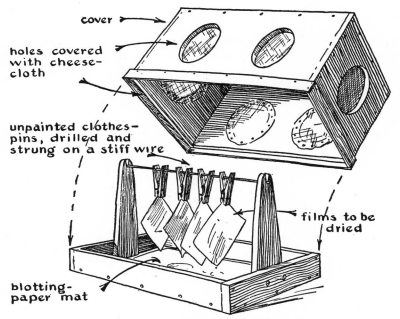

Fig. 15. Drying cabinet for films.

turns the gelatin white. The water content of the gelatin can be raised to remove the milky appearance by breathing on the emulsion once or twice.

Printing and enlarging papers. Negatives are printed on so-called printing-out papers, gaslight papers, or bromide papers. Printing-out papers are exposed to light through the negative until the image develops. The chloride (gaslight) papers are exposed and then developed with chemical developers. They are relatively insensitive and can be manipulated in a lighted room. Bromide papers must be managed in darkness or under a safelight, in the same manner as ordinary unsensitized photographic plates are managed. The chloride and bromide papers are the most important, and we will discuss them here.

The reflectivity-density Δ for papers is defined as follows:

$$\Delta = \log_{10} \frac{1}{R}.$$ (6)

R is the diffuse reflectivity of the paper. H and D curves for chloride contact and bromide enlarging papers, plotting Δ as ordinates against the logarithm of exposure as abscissa,

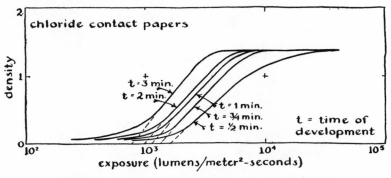

Fig. 16.   After Hardy and Perrin.   (See footnote 1.)

are illustrated in Figs. 16 and 17. It is to be noted that the contrast of these papers, or slope of the straight segment of the Δ-log Σ curve, does not change much with increasing development time. The contrast is more of an intrinsic property of the emulsion than it is with plates and films. Papers are obtainable commercially in various grades, so that if one paper does not give the desired contrast, another grade is used.

The procedure for exposing and developing papers is different from that recommended for plates and films. Proper contrast is important with plates and films, while density is not so important. On the other hand, correct density is important for papers. The procedure for exposing bromide paper, for example, is to adjust exposure so that development for 3 minutes yields proper density.

Development for 3 minutes rather than the 2 minutes usually prescribed yields more contrast in the highlights, as a perusal of the curves of Fig. 17 will show. For the exposure range below 10 lumen seconds/m², it will be noted that the inclination of the H and D curve to the abscissa is greater for the 3-minute development than it is for the 2-minute development.

The proper exposure is determined with narrow test strips of paper. When the density is correct, the image shows a

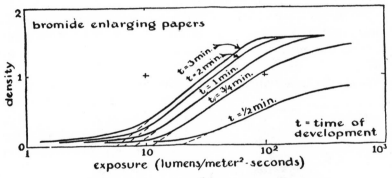

Fig. 17. After Hardy and Perrin. (See footnote 1.)

thin veil of blackening in the highlights, compared with the clear unexposed margins. A common fault in improperly printed negatives arises from overexposure and under-development. *Never develop papers for less than 2 minutes.*

Table XI gives the relative speeds of different papers, so that once the exposure is determined for one 'grade, that for another may be calculated approximately. These values are not and cannot be precise because of unavoidable varia-tions in manufacture. Nevertheless, the table is of value for practical work.

If, in development, a portion of the print fails to come up at a satisfactory rate, owing to an extra high local density of the negative, development may be accelerated locally by applying a piece of cotton wet with warm water or simply by warming the film with heat from the fingers, rubbed on the selected spot.

Some of the organic developers, particularly amidol, are poisonous. The toxicity of developers varies for different people, but contact may be avoided if wooden tongs are used for manipulating prints in the developer. (See Fig. 12.) The print is moved around or the solution is stirred as development progresses. Care must be taken not to allow the wooden tongs to come in contact with the acid of the short stop or hypo of the fixing solution, since these chemicals would ruin the developer solution.

Prints are washed conveniently in a cascade of flat pans as illustrated in Fig. 13. As the fixing of each print is completed, it is put in the bottom pan. But before this is done, the print in the top pan is removed, and the print in the second pan is advanced to the top, and so forth, until the bottom pan is emptied to make ready for the one in the hypo bath. The prints, after washing, are laid emulsion side down on a cheesecloth tray to dry.

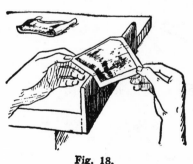

Fig. 18.

As soon as the prints are dry, they are bent along their diagonals in the manner illustrated in Fig. 18 to remove wrinkles. They are then ready for mounting. It may be desirable to flatten them out further by pressing them between the leaves of a book or magazine.

Glossy prints are squeegeed on enameled plates, using a solution of paraffin or Ozokite in benzene to prevent the print from sticking. The solution should be rubbed dry and polished with cheesecloth before the print is squeegeed. Also, for drying glossy prints, chromium-plated brass sheets are now available which do not require paraffin or Ozokite, but only need to be washed and wet with water.

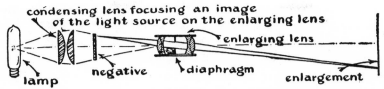

This arrangement gives the greatest contrast.

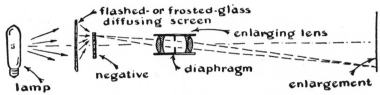

This arrangement gives less contrast.

Fig. 19.

Fig. 19 illustrates two arrangements for enlarging. The so-called specular density is involved in the one shown above and the diffuse density in the lower one. The one above is generally used. The lower arrangement is used in portraiture, or whenever contrast is to be avoided.

TABLE XI

RELATIVE EXPOSURES REQUIRED FOR VARIOUS PAPERS

Paper	Soft	Medium	Contrast
Bromide papers................	$1\frac{1}{2}$	2	5
Chloride papers................	200	300	400

Photographs for publication which require strong contrast should be printed on glossy paper, which exhibits higher contrast than matte paper.

Intensifying and reducing. The function of intensifying is to increase contrast, whereas the function of reducing is primarily to decrease the density. Reducing may, however, increase or decrease contrast or leave it unaltered, depending on the solutions used. The processes of intensifying and reducing will correct errors in the original development, but they will not satisfactorily correct errors of exposure.

The chromium process of intensification will be treated here. It gives a permanent intensified image, in contrast to the mercury process, which is not permanent. To apply the chromium process, the gelatin should be first bathed in a hardening solution. After this, the emulsion is bleached clear in a mixture of 1 part of the following stock bleaching solution with 10 parts water.

BLEACHING SOLUTION FOR CHROMIUM INTENSIFIER

Potassium bichromate.................................. 90 g
Concentrated hydrochloric acid........................ 64 cc
Water to make..1000 cc

The bleached emulsion is then washed for 5 minutes and redeveloped, after which treatment it will exhibit greater contrast. It is then thoroughly fixed and washed. The process may be repeated to obtain even greater contrast. The intensification process does not need to be carried out in the dark.

To obtain extreme contrast the intensified negative is printed on a transparent film, which is then intensified and printed again, and so on, until the desired result is obtained.

Intensification occurs with each photographic process, so that often in the second photographic process (printing) special care is necessary to prevent the development of excessive contrast. It may be necessary to employ a reduction procedure. The various formulas and directions for reducing, with or without change of contrast, are given in *Elementary Photographic Chemistry*.[18]

Some applications of photography. Photographs may be taken in the infrared with a suitably sensitized emulsion, an ordinary lens, and a suitable filter, such as the 88A filter shown in Fig. 7. Heated objects, even a hot electric iron, giving off entirely invisible radiation, can be used for

---

[18] This book is available from firms dealing in photographic supplies or directly from the Eastman Kodak Company, Rochester, New York.

illumination. Hypersensitizing is particularly effective in infrared photography.

R. W. Wood of Johns Hopkins University and W. H. Wright of Lick Observatory were the first to show some of the striking effects that could be obtained in infrared photography. The penetrating power of infrared photographs, giving clear pictures of objects many miles distant, even through light haze, accounts for the present wide application of infrared photography, especially for aerial mapping.

Photographs taken with ultraviolet light have yielded equally striking results. They may be taken through any of the filters that are opaque for the visible spectrum, such as bromine vapor, nickel sulphate solutions, thin silver films, or alkali-metal films. The image in ultraviolet light may be formed by a thin quartz meniscus lens or a quartz fluorite achromat. Ultraviolet photographs taken out of doors are free of shadows.

From photographs of the moon taken through a silver film, as well as photographs taken with a bromine-vapor filter, R. W. Wood ascertained that a spot close to the crater Aristarchus was apparently covered with a layer of sulphur. Sulphur exhibits a high reflectivity in the visible spectrum and a very low reflectivity in the ultraviolet. The crater appeared black in Wood's ultraviolet pictures, in strong contrast with its surroundings. No other substance on the moon has been identified by means of such convincing evidence.

The camera can be used for making drawings. The object to be copied is photographed, and an enlargement is made of it on matte paper. This is traced as desired with India ink. The paper is then treated with a bleaching solution and the photographic image is removed. India ink is waterproof and unaffected by the bleaching solution.

The following hints may aid in obtaining good results in the photography of apparatus for publication. In general, the object should be photographed against a light background, such as a white wall or sheet. Polished surfaces on

the apparatus will produce halation. The places giving
halation (they may be determined by taking a preliminary
picture) must be covered with vaseline and whiting. Best
results are obtained by side-lighting from an open window or
other light source of extended area. A good artificial source
is obtained with a battery of photoflood lamps placed in a
box covered with either tracing cloth or some other translucent diffusing material. To obtain depth of focus in
photographing apparatus, a small aperture and long exposure
should be used. The exposure and development should be
managed to give contrast and to show detail in the shadows.

Miniature cameras are suited to making quantities of pictures under similar conditions (35 may be taken at each
loading). They can be used for copying reference journal
articles and even books. The negatives themselves may be
used as the record, in which case they may be read with the
film turned upside down in an improvised viewing box
equipped with a strong reading lens, or they may be projected on a screen. Also, the negative can be printed on
motion-picture positive film. This does not require an
excessive amount of time, since all the pictures have the
same density, and they are processed in lots of 35 at a time.
The miniature camera and projector is also useful for lectures. Graphs and illustrations can be printed on a single
film in the order required by the lecture.

The photographing of line drawings in pencil is difficult.
A process emulsion should be used, and the illumination
should strike the paper at oblique incidence to avoid specular
reflection from the graphite pencil marks into the camera
lens. The exposure and development are managed in such a
way as to give maximum contrast.

The details of the application of photography to spectroscopy and astronomy can only be touched upon here. In
general, process plates are recommended for photographing
spectra. They are best developed with D-28 or D-11
developer until the developed image shows up through the
glass on the back of the emulsion.

The region in the Δ-log Σ curve lying well within the latitude range of the emulsion is most suitable for photographing spectrum lines. The most desirable density is about 0.5. The optimum light intensity for observation of the lines on a spectrum plate has a brightness value of about 100 candles/m². For much brighter or weaker lights the contrast sensitivity of the eye decreases. "Mixing up the grains" along the length of a weak spectrum line will materially increase its conspicuousness.

Photographic photometry. A spectrogram or stellar photograph usually serves its purpose if the intensity of the light is indicated approximately, provided the angular distribution of the light is recorded with precision. The peculiar suitability of photography for observations of this kind is illustrated by the reference given in a footnote below.[19] Photography may, however, be used to measure the intensity of light quantitatively.

In photographic photometry, the plate is ordinarily used as an indicator to show, by equal densities, when the exposures of two areas are equal, one of the areas being produced by a source of known intensity, and the other by the radiation to be measured. It is important that the two exposures be made under equivalent conditions, that is, equal illumination and time of exposure or equal intervals of illumination if the light is intermittent. Also, it is important to take precautions against errors arising from variations in sensitivity over the surface of the plate.

---

[19] This property, which everyone now takes for granted, was explained by Fox Talbot in the early days of photography as follows:

"Groups of figures take no longer to obtain than single figures. . . . the camera depicts them all at once, however numerous they be. . . .

"It is so natural to associate the idea of labour with great complexity and elaborate detail of execution that one is more struck at seeing the thousand florets of an Agrostic depicted with all its capillary branchlets (and so accurately that none of all this multitude shall want its little bivalve calyx, requiring to be examined through a lens) than one is by the picture of the large and simple leaf of an oak or chestnut. But in truth the difficulty is in both cases the same. The one takes no more time to execute than the other for the object which would take the most skillful artist days or weeks to trace or to copy is effected by the boundless powers of natural chemistry in the space of a few seconds."

We will describe two methods of spectral photometry here. There are many possible sources of error in photometric work, and the treatment given here should be supplemented by reference to articles on this subject listed below.[20]

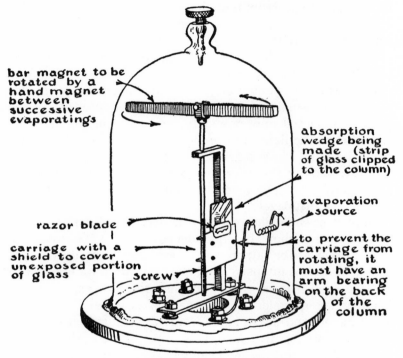

bar magnet to be rotated by a hand magnet between successive evaporatings

absorption wedge being made (strip of glass clipped to the column)

evaporation source

razor blade

carriage with a shield to cover unexposed portion of glass

screw

to prevent the carriage from rotating, it must have an arm bearing on the back of the column

Fig. 20. Making of a step-weakener.

By the first procedure which we will discuss, a so-called step-weakener is mounted directly in front of the entrance slit of the spectrograph. For the first exposure, the slit is

[20] Abney, W. de W., "On the Variation in Gradation of a Developed Photographic Image When Impressed by Monochromatic Light of Different Wavelengths," *Roy. Soc., Proc.*, 68, 300 (1901).

Harrison, G. R., "Instruments and Methods Used for Measuring Spectral Light Intensities by Photography," *J. O. S. A.*, 19, 267 (1929).

Jones, L. A., "Photographic Spectrophotometry in the Ultraviolet Region," *National Research Council, Bull*, No. 61, 109 (1927).

Jones, L. A., and Sandvik, O., "Spectral Distribution of Sensitivity of Photographic Materials," *J. O. S. A.*, 12, 401 (1926).

illuminated through the step-weakener with the light to be measured. For the comparison exposure the slit is then illuminated an equal time by the light of known intensity and known spectral distribution, this exposure being made adjacent to the first exposure.

The step-weakener may be a glass or quartz plate coated with strips of platinum (or some other metal) of increasing opacity, or it may be a series of neutral filters of gelatin. The illumination along the slit, which would otherwise be uniform, is attenuated by the step-weakener in varying amounts, usually in geometrical proportion.

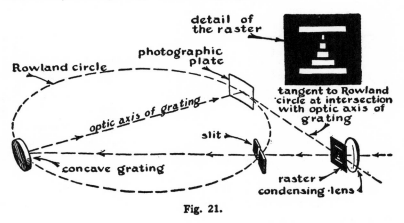

Fig. 21.

The step-weakener is difficult to make and calibrate. Fig. 20 illustrates a procedure for making one by evaporation.

From the calibration of the step-weakener at the wave length in question one can determine the relative light intensities of the different steps. To obtain the calibration, the densities of the various strips of the step-weakener are measured on a microphotometer.

A photograph of the raster shown in Fig. 21 or a raster cut out of thin sheet metal can be used instead of a step-weakener. The use of a raster avoids the necessity for calibration. In a uniform beam of parallel light the quantity of light transmitted by each element of the raster is determined by its area. The use of a raster requires an astigmatic optical system. The raster is ordinarily mounted so that, in a vertical azimuth its image is focused on the slit, whereas in a horizontal azimuth the parallel light transmitted by it is focused on the slit.

Fig. 21 shows the ingenious way in which Frerichs has used a raster, taking advantage of the natural astigmatism of a Rowland grating setup.[21]   In this setup, adjacent areas of the spectral image vary in intensity in the ratio 16:1:2:4:-8:16.   Fig. 22 illustrates the method of determining the relative intensities of two or more lines.   The lines must be near each other in the spectrum, so that the differences in

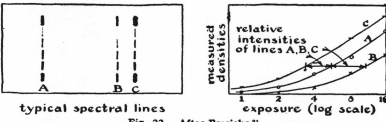

typical spectral lines   exposure (log scale)
Fig. 22.   After Frerichs.[21]

sensitivity of the plate for the wave lengths involved are negligible and so that the H and D curves for each wave length are the same.   Three lines photographed through the raster by this setup are illustrated.   The densities of the segments of the photographed lines are measured with a microphotometer, and plotted as shown.   It is to be noted that the scale of abscissa is logarithmic, the interval in abscissa being equal for each step of the raster.   Each spectral line determines an H and D curve, and the lateral displacements necessary to bring the three H and D curves into coincidence determine the relative intensities of the lines.   By this procedure an accuracy of about 3 per cent can be expected.

[21] Frerichs, R., "Photographische Spektralphotometrie," *Handbuch der Physik*, Vol. 19, Chapter 23.   Berlin: Julius Springer, 1928.

CHAPTER XII

Heat and High Temperature

IN this chapter we will first consider some of the elementary aspects of the theory of heat transfer. Following this we will deal with various techniques of obtaining high temperatures, of temperature control, and of temperature measurement.

Heat conduction. The steady state. The rate Φ (expressed in calories per second) at which heat flows across an isothermal surface element of area A, in a homogeneous medium, is proportional to A, to the conductivity of the material, K, and to the temperature gradient dT/dx perpendicular to the surface, thus:

$$\Phi = - KA\frac{dT}{dx} \text{ calories/sec.} \tag{1}$$

In the case of a rectangular parallelopiped with opposite ends maintained at the temperatures T_1 and T_2, Eq. 1, when integrated, becomes

$$\Phi = - \frac{KA}{x}(T_2 - T_1) \text{ calories/sec.,} \tag{2}$$

in which A is the cross-section area of the parallelopiped perpendicular to the temperature gradient and x is the separation between the isothermal surfaces T_1 and T_2. Here K is assumed to be constant in the temperature range between T_1 and T_2. Values of the heat conductivity for various materials are given in Table I.

TABLE I

THERMAL CONDUCTIVITY, K, DIFFUSIVITY, h, AND RELAXATION TIME, τ, FOR AN INFINITE SLAB OF 2 CM THICKNESS ($x_0 = 1$ CM)

Material (at room temperature, unless otherwise specified)	K (cal./cm/sec./°C.)	h^2 (cm²/sec.)	τ (sec.)
Aluminum[a]	0.480	0.826	0.49
Bismuth[a]	0.0194	0.0678	6.0
Brass (yellow)[a]	0.204	0.339	1.19
Constantan (60 Cu 40 Ni)[b]	0.054	0.062	6.5
Copper[a]	0.918	1.133	.357
Gold[a]	0.700	1.182	.34
Invar[c]	0.026	0.02	20
Wrought iron and mild steel[a]	0.144	0.173	2.3
Cast iron and carbon steel[a]	0.11	0.12	3.3
Lead[b]	0.083	0.209	1.9
Mercury[a]	0.148	0.0327	12.4
Monel metal[d]	0.06	0.056	7.2
Nichrome or Chromel[d]	0.032	0.034	11.9
Nickel[d]	0.215	0.23	1.8
Platinum[d]	0.167	0.239	1.69
Silver[a]	1.006	1.737	0.233
Tungsten: Room temperature[d]	0.38	0.59	0.69
1400°C.[d]	0.258	0.315	1.28
2100°C.[d]	0.296	0.325	1.24
Bonded silicon carbide, 25° to 1000°C.[e]	0.024	0.055	7.3
Graphite, 0° to 100° C.[d]	0.315	1.2	0.34
Quartz glass: 0°C.[d]	0.0033	0.0083	49
1000°C.[d]	0.0064	0.0105	38
Hard porcelain, 20° to 1000°C.[d]	0.003 to 0.004	0.0028 to 0.0056	144 to 72
Fired natural soapstone[d]	0.003 to 0.0067	———	
MgO[d]	0.0015 to 0.0036	0.00167 to 0.00333	240 to 120
Al₂O₃[d]	0.0016 to 0.0084	0.0023 to 0.0116	176 to 35
Sintered Al₂O₃, 900°C.[d]	0.013	0.0119	34
Mica[d]	0.0008 to 0.0014	0.00132 to 0.00232	306 to 174
Glass[a]	0.0024	0.0057	71
Air, 0°C.[a]	0.000055	0.179	2.3
Asbestos (loose)[a]	0.0004	0.0035	116
Average firebrick, 0° to 800°C.[a]	0.004	0.0074	55
Concrete (stone), 20° to 1000°C.[a]	0.0027	0.0056	72
Cork (ground)[a]	0.00012	0.0017	238
Paraffin[a]	0.00061	0.001	404
Water[a]	0.00143	0.00143	283
Pine wood: Across grain	0.0002	0.0012	340
With grain	0.0006	0.0036	122

[a] Ingersoll, L. R., and Zobel, O. J., *An Introduction to the Mathematical Theory of Heat Conduction.* Boston: Ginn and Company, 1913.

[b] Fowle, F. E., *Smithsonian Physical Tables.* Washington: The Smithsonian Institution, 1934.

[c] King, W. J., *Mechanical Engineering, 54,* 275 (1932).

[d] Espe, W., and Knoll, M., *Werkstoffkunde der Hochvakuumtechnik.* Julius Springer, 1932.

[e] Hering, C., *Am. I. E. E., J., 29,* 485 (1910).

Shape factors. For many of the actual cases encountered, the geometry is not so simple as it is with the parallelopiped, and the integration of Eq. 1 may be quite difficult. Generally, however, the integral may be expressed by an equation of the form

$$\Phi = - KS(T_2 - T_1) \text{ calories/sec.,} \tag{3}$$

in which S, the so-called shape factor, depends upon the size and shape of the space between two isothermal surfaces maintained at temperatures T_1 and T_2.

For a rectangular parallelopiped the shape factor, from Eq. 2, is

$$S = \frac{A}{x}. \tag{4}$$

For two concentric cylindrical isothermal surfaces (long in comparison with their radii) of length l, maintained at temperatures T_1 and T_2, respectively, the value of S in terms of l and their radii r_1 and r_2 is

$$S = \frac{2.73l}{\log_{10}r_2/r_1}. \tag{5}$$

For two concentric spherical isothermal surfaces, one of radius r_1 at temperaturé T_1 and the other of radius r_2 at temperature T_2, the shape factor is

$$S = \frac{4\pi}{\left(\dfrac{1}{r_1} - \dfrac{1}{r_2}\right)}. \tag{6}$$

A heat problem which often arises in the laboratory requires the estimation of the heat loss of an electric furnace. The inner furnace wall, which is approximately at uniform temperature, is taken as one isothermal surface, and the outer surface of the furnace, at somewhat above room temperature, is taken as the other isothermal surface. Langmuir, Adams, and Meikle have given shape factors for several special cases which may be applied to problems of this type.[1] However, to make an estimate of heat loss of a

---

[1] Langmuir, I., Adams, E. Q., and Meikle, G. S., *Amer. Electrochem. Soc., Trans.*, *24*, 53 (1913).

cylindrical furnace, if the inner furnace tube is long and surrounded by a layer of insulating material as shown in Fig. 1, we may apply Eq. 5. Or, for the case shown in

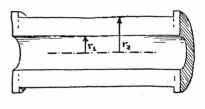

see Fig. 17

Fig. 1.

Fig. 2, we may apply Eq. 6, taking r_1 and r_2 as the dimensions of the approximating spherical surfaces, indicated in the figure by dotted lines. These estimates are not expected to be precise, but they are usually accurate enough to settle the questions which arise when one designs a furnace.

The shape factor can also be determined experimentally, using the similarity between the law for the flow of heat, Eq. 1, and Ohm's law. The experimental determination of S is accomplished by measuring the electrical shape factor, S', for wooden models that simulate the inner and outer isothermal temperature surfaces of the heat problem in question. These model surfaces are coated with copper foil and serve as electrodes. The region between these surfaces is filled with a saturated solution of copper sulphate with $\frac{1}{2}$ per cent (by volume) sulphuric acid added. The conductance of this solution is determined by applying alternating voltage to the copper electrodes. Alternating current is used to prevent polarization at the electrodes. The equation giving the electrical shape factor is

$$i = -K'S'V, \qquad (7)$$

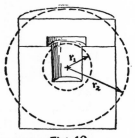

see Fig. 19

Fig. 2.

V and i being the measured voltage drop and current. K', the electrical conductivity of the solution, may be determined by a separate experiment, using a box of cross section A' and length x' with copper end plates. For this box the shape factor is A'/x' (as in Eq. 4). To transform

S' to S, divide S' by the scale factor to which the model was constructed. For example, if the model was made to half scale, $S = 2S'$.

Heat conduction. The nonsteady state. The thermal behavior of a homogeneous body is described in a Cartesian system of coördinates by the following fundamental differential equation:

$$\frac{\delta T}{\delta t} = \frac{K}{\rho c}\left(\frac{\delta^2 T}{\delta x^2} + \frac{\delta^2 T}{\delta y^2} + \frac{\delta^2 T}{\delta z^2}\right). \tag{8}$$

Here t is the time, T is the temperature of a point in the body represented by the coördinates x, y, and z, dT/dt is the rate at which this temperature changes, and K, ρ, and c represent physical quantities for the material of which the body is composed, namely, the heat conductivity, density, and specific heat. The combination of these constants in the form $h^2 = K\rho c$ is convenient. h is called the thermal diffusivity of the material.

In one dimension, Eq. 8 takes the form

$$\frac{dT}{dt} = \frac{K}{\rho c}\frac{d^2 T}{dx^2}. \tag{9}$$

If dT/dt equals zero, and if we integrate d^2T/dx^2 once, we get the equation which represents the steady-state problem:

$$\frac{dT}{dx} = M. \tag{10}$$

From physical considerations, the integration constant M is seen to have the meaning

$$M = -\frac{\Phi}{KA}, \text{ and } \Phi = -KA\frac{dT}{dx}, \tag{11}$$

which is the same as Eq. 1.

A more general form of Eq. 8 includes an added term to take account of energy transformations associated with a change of state, and so forth, which will not be considered here.

There are infinitely many solutions to the fundamental differential equation, Eq. 8. Those which are appropriate for a given problem usually comprise an infinite series, the sum of which conforms to the requirements of the geometry of the body, and to the so-called boundary conditions set forth in the problem. The mathematical procedures involved in getting the series required for a particular problem were originally developed by Fourier over a hundred years ago; and these procedures have been extended by other mathematicians to include a great variety of more or less complicated cases.[2] Here, without taking up the mathematical procedures involved, we will discuss the results of their application to some typical heat problems.[3]

The infinite slab.   First, let us determine the temperature at various points in a plane-parallel slab which, to start with, is at a uniform temperature T_0. We will find the temperature at various places in the slab as a function of the time which elapses after the slab has been immersed into an environment maintained at a fixed temperature T_1. We will assume that T_1 is lower than T_0. (The changes required to apply the results so obtained for the opposite case, in which T_1 is higher than T_0, are obvious.) Practically, if the extension of the slab is great compared to its thickness, this becomes a one-dimensional problem, and to describe it we will take a Cartesian coördinate system which is oriented so that the faces of the slab coincide with the planes $x = + x_0$ and $- x_0$.

The solution of Eq. 8, which we want, is a series, the terms of which depend on both x and t. The sum of the series yields a uniform temperature throughout the slab at $t = 0$; and also at all times it gives a temperature gradient at the surfaces which conforms to the requirements of Newton's law of cooling.

Newton's law of cooling states that the heat lost per unit

[2] Carslaw, H. S., *Introduction to the Mathematical Theory of the Conduction of Heat in Solids*, Second Edition. London: The Macmillan Company, 1921.

Ingersoll, L. R., and Zobel, O. J., *The Mathematical Theory of Heat Conduction, With Engineering and Geological Applications*. Boston: Ginn and Company, 1913.

[3] I am indebted to Dr. R. M. Langer for the treatment of nonsteady heat flow presented in this chapter.

area of surface, W, by the slab to its environment, is proportional to the difference between the surface temperature T_{x_0} and the temperature of the bulk of the medium in which it is immersed, T_1:

$$W = N(T_{x_0} - T_1) \text{ calories/sec./cm}^2. \tag{12}$$

W may be resolved into heat lost by radiation, $W_{\text{rad.}}$, and heat lost by convection, $W_{\text{conv.}}$. The temperature gradient at the surface is determined by the value of W and the thermal conductivity of the material of which the slab is composed.

Stated algebraically, the boundary conditions which our solution of Eq. 8 must satisfy are

$$\text{at } t = 0; \ T = T_0 \text{ throughout the slab} \tag{13}$$

and, for all values of t;

$$\text{at } x = x_0 \qquad \frac{dT}{dx} = -\frac{N}{K}(T_{x_0} - T_1) \tag{14a}$$

and also at

$$x = -x_0 \qquad \frac{dT}{dx} = \frac{N}{K}(T_{x_0} - T_1). \tag{14b}$$

The solution of Eq. 8 which satisfies these conditions is

$$T = T_1 + \frac{4}{\pi}(T_0 - T_1) \sum_0^\infty \frac{\sin \frac{a_n \pi}{2}}{a_n\left(1 + \frac{\sin a_n\pi}{a_n\pi}\right)} e^{-\frac{a_n^2\pi^2h^2t}{4x_0^2}} \cos \frac{a_n\pi}{2}\frac{x}{x_0}, \tag{15}$$

where the a_n's are roots of the transcendental equation

$$\frac{2x_0N}{\pi a_n K} = \tan \frac{a_n\pi}{2}. \tag{16}$$

The values of a_n may be determined graphically from the intersection points of the two functions of a_n,

$$y = \frac{\pi a_n K}{2x_0N}, \text{ and } y = \cot \frac{a_n\pi}{2}. \tag{17}$$

Before discussing various aspects of this solution, let us make the substitution,

$$\tau = \frac{4x_0^2}{\pi^2h^2}, \tag{18}$$

in the exponential terms. τ is called the relaxation time. The reason for this will appear presently.

At the beginning, that is, when t has small values compared with τ, the accurate expression for T requires several terms of the series given by Eq. 15, in spite of the fact that the series is a rapidly converging one. However, soon after $t = \tau$, all the exponential terms become insignificant except the first one ($n = 1$). This is because a_1 is smaller than the other values of a_n. Soon after $t = \tau$, Eq. 15 reduces to

$$T = T_1 + \frac{4}{\pi}(T_0 - T_1)\left[\frac{\sin\frac{a_1\pi}{2}}{a_1\left(1 + \frac{\sin a_1\pi}{a_1\pi}\right)}e^{-a_1{}^2\frac{t}{\tau}}\cos a_1\frac{\pi}{2}\frac{x}{x_0}\right]. \quad (19)$$

The first factor in the brackets is a constant, the second determines the decay of the temperature difference ($T - T_1$), and the third factor is the space distribution function for the temperature. The relaxation time is evidently the interval required for the temperature, initially uniform, to assume approximately the distribution given by the last factor in Eq. 19.

The value of a_1 for a body (with vertical sides) in air at room temperature is obtained from Eqs. 35, 48, 12, and 16:

$$W_{conv.} = 1.3 \times 10^{-4}(T_0 - T_{x_0}) \text{ calorie/sec./cm}^2. \quad (35a)$$

$$W_{rad.} = 1.5 \times 10^{-4}(T_0 - T_{x_0}) \text{ calorie/sec./cm}^2. \quad (48a)$$

Thus

$$N = 2.8 \times 10^{-4} \text{ calorie/sec./cm}^2/°C.$$

To illustrate how Eq. 19 may be applied, let us consider the case of a telescope mirror of 2 cm thickness which is to be tested by the Foucault knife-edge test. For a reliable test, if this mirror is brought from a room in which it is either warmer or cooler than the air of the testing room, it will be necessary to wait until the mirror has adjusted itself to the new temperature. If the glass is 15 cm or more in diameter and is exposed to the room air on both sides, we may regard it as an infinite slab and apply Eq. 19 to determine its thermal behavior. For the glass we may take $K = .0024$ and $h^2 = .0057$. This gives $\tau = 71$ seconds, and by means of Eq. 16, we get $a_1 = 0.219$.

Substituting this value of a_1, Eq. 19 can be written in the form

$$\log_{10}\left(\frac{T_1 - T_x}{T_1 - T_0}\right) = -3 \times 10^{-4}t + 0.15 + \log_{10}(\cos 0.34x). \quad (20)$$

This solution is valid after more than 71 seconds have elapsed. To get the thermal behavior at the start, the logarithm of $(T_1 - T_x)/(T_1 - T_0)$ can be plotted as ordinate against t as abscissa. The series of parallel straight lines obtained for $t > 71$ seconds are then extrapolated to the common point where the abscissa and the ordinate are equal to zero, bearing in mind that $T_{x=\pm x_0}$ changes rapidly with time when $t = 0$ and $T_{x=0}$ changes very slowly. This method is not very precise, and a more exact solution is to be obtained from Eq. 15. This formula is rather difficult to manage, except in special cases. Two of these are treated below.

Eq. 15 can be simplified for the extreme cases of relatively fast cooling, where $Nx_0/K > > 1$, and relatively slow cooling, where $Nx_0/K < < 1$. In the first case a_n is approximately $(2n + 1)$, $\sin(a_n\pi/2)$ is $(-1)^n$, and the expression for temperature simplifies to

$$T = T_1 + \frac{4}{\pi}(T_0 - T_1)\sum_0^\infty \frac{(-1)^n}{2n+1}e^{-\frac{(2n+1)^2 t}{\tau}}\cos(2n+1)\frac{\pi x}{2x_0}. \quad (21)$$

For slow cooling, where $Nx_0/K < < 1$, the slab is practically isothermal, and the temperature is given by

$$T = T_1 + (T_0 - T_1)e^{\frac{Nh^2}{Kx_0}t}. \quad (22)$$

The solution of problems of this character will be useful to the experimenter when he encounters questions of design involving the accommodation of objects to changes of temperature.

The application to optical testing has already been discussed. In optical testing with the Foucault knife-edge test, lack of thermal equilibrium distorts the figure of an optical surface and gives rise to troublesome convection currents.

The relaxation time. The relaxation time for a cylinder is approximately half that for a slab, when $2x_0$, the thickness of the slab, and $2r_0$, the diameter of the cylinder, are equal. The relaxation time for a sphere or cube is approximately one quarter of that for a corresponding slab. In most of the nonsteady-state problems encountered, it is sufficient to know the relaxation time. The relaxation time can be interpreted as the time for a heat pulse to travel into the center of the slab, a distance x_0. The relaxation times are given in Table I for a slab thickness of 2 cm ($x_0 = 1$ cm) for different materials. It must be remembered that for different values of x_0 the time required for the heat to penetrate to the center of the slab is proportional to x_0^2.

The relaxation time for graphite, which is approximately the same as that for copper, is especially noteworthy. The extreme values for τ given in Table I are about $\frac{1}{4}$ second and 404 seconds for silver and paraffin respectively.

Periodic temperatures. Let us consider a slab of thickness x_0 having a harmonic surface temperature $T_1 = A \cos \omega t$. If τ is the relaxation time for the slab, the interior temperature is given by the expression

$$T = A \cos \omega t - \frac{4A\omega^2\tau^2}{\pi} \sum_0^\infty \frac{\dfrac{(-1)^n}{(2n+1)^5}}{1 + \dfrac{\omega^2\tau^2}{(2n+1)^4}} \left\{ \frac{(2n+1)^4}{\omega^2\tau^2} e^{-(2n+1)^2\frac{t}{\tau}} \right.$$

$$\left. - \cos \omega t + \frac{(2n+1)^2}{\omega\tau} \sin \omega t \right\} \cos (2n+1)\frac{\pi x}{2x_0}. \quad \textbf{(23)}$$

The exponential term can be neglected after the relaxation time, and the temperature is then given by the summation. Unless $\omega\tau > > 1$, the convergence of the series is rapid enough to make the first term a good approximation for it:

$$T = A \left\{ \left(1 - \frac{4}{\pi} \frac{\omega^2\tau^2}{1 + \omega^2\tau^2} \cos \frac{\pi x}{2x_0}\right)\cos \omega t \right.$$
$$\left. + \left(\frac{4\omega\tau}{\pi(1 + \omega^2\tau^2)}\right)\sin \omega t \, \cos\frac{\pi x}{2x_0}\right\} \cdot \quad (24)$$

The product $\omega\tau$ is the ratio of the relaxation time to the period of the impressed harmonic temperature multiplied by 2π. If $\omega\tau$ is small, the plate follows the impressed temperature closely with an out-of-phase component, $\sin \omega t$, proportional to $\omega\tau$, and the amplitude of the temperature fluctuation is proportional to $\cos (\pi x/2x_0)$.

When $\omega\tau > > 1$, the temperature near the surface is approximately the same as if the slab were infinitely thick, while the temperature in the center is practically constant.

The temperature at a distance x from the surface of an infinitely thick slab is given, after a long time, by the expression

$$T = Ae^{-\sqrt{\frac{\omega}{2}}\frac{x}{h}}\cos \left(\omega t - \sqrt{\frac{\omega}{2}}\frac{x}{h}\right), \quad (25)$$

where $A \cos \omega t$ represents the surface temperature. Thus, the amplitude decreases exponentially with depth according to the law $e^{-\sqrt{\frac{\omega}{2}}\frac{x}{h}}$. There is a time lag of $\sqrt{x^2/2\omega h^2}$ in its harmonic variation, relative to the phase of the surface temperature.

The sphere. When a sphere or cylinder that is initially at a uniform temperature T_0 is introduced into a medium at a lower temperature T_1, the equations similar to those for the slab are:

For a sphere of radius r_0,

$$T = T_1 + \frac{4Nr_0^2}{\pi K}(T_0 - T_1)\sum_1^\infty \frac{\sin\frac{a_n\pi}{2}}{a_n\left(\frac{a_n\pi}{2} - \sin a_n\pi\right)}e^{-\frac{an^2\pi^2h^2t}{4r_0^2}}\frac{\sin\frac{a_n\pi r}{2r_0}}{r}, \quad (26)$$

where a_n are the roots of

$$\tan \frac{a_n\pi}{2} = \frac{\frac{a_n\pi}{2}}{1 - \frac{Nr_0}{K}}, \quad (27)$$

and after the relaxation time the term representing the temperature distribution (corresponding to $\cos(a_1\pi x/2x_0)$ in Eq. 15) is

$$\left\{ \frac{\sin \frac{a_n\pi r}{2r_0}}{r} \right\}$$

When $Nr_0/K \approx 1$, the temperature is given approximately by the expression

$$T' = T_1 + \frac{8}{\pi^2}(T_0 - T_1)\frac{Nr_0^2}{K}\sum_0^\infty \frac{(-1)^n}{(2n+1)^2}e^{-\frac{(2n+1)^2\pi^2h^2t}{4r_0^2}}\frac{\sin\frac{(2n+1)\pi r}{2r_0}}{r}. \quad (28)$$

When $Nr_0/K \gg 1$, that is, for relatively fast cooling, the temperature is given approximately by

$$T = T_1 + \frac{2r_0}{\pi}(T_0 - T_1)\sum_1^\infty \frac{(-1)^{n-1}}{n\left(1-\frac{K}{Nr_0}\right)^2}e^{-\frac{n^2\pi^2h^2t}{r_0^2}\left(1-\frac{K}{Nr_0}\right)^2}$$

$$\times \frac{\sin\left(1-\frac{K}{Nr_0}\right)\frac{n\pi r}{r_0}}{r}. \quad (29)$$

In the case of slow cooling, in which $Nr_c/K \ll 1$, the temperature is sensibly the same throughout the sphere, and its change with time is given by the expression

$$T = T_1 + (T_0 - T_1)e^{-\frac{3Nh^2t}{Kr_0}} \quad (30)$$

The cylinder. For a cylinder of radius r_0, the temperature in terms of the well-tabulated Bessel functions J_0 and J_1 is

$$T = T_1 + 2(T_0 - T_1)\sum_1^\infty \frac{1}{\mu_n\left(1+\frac{K^2\mu_n^2}{N^2r_0^2}\right)J_1(\mu_n)}e^{\frac{-\mu_n^2h^2t}{r_0^2}}J_0\left(\mu_n\frac{r}{r_0}\right), \quad (31)$$

where the μ_n's are roots of the equation

$$\frac{\mu_n}{r_0}J_1(\mu_n) = \frac{N}{K}J_0(\mu_n).$$

In limiting cases the μ_n disappear. For example, when $Nr_0/K \gg 1$, that is, when we have fast cooling, the μ_n's are close to the roots of $J_0(\mu_n) = 0$, and the temperature is given approximately by the equation.

$$T = T_1 + 2(T_0 - T_1)\left\{\frac{1}{1.25}e^{-\left[2.4\frac{h}{r_0}\left(1+\frac{K}{Nr_0}\right)\right]^2 t} \cdot J_0\left(2.4\left[1+\frac{K}{Nr_0}\right]\frac{r}{r_0}\right)\right.$$

$$-\frac{1}{1.87}e^{-\left[5.52\frac{h}{r_0}\left(1+\frac{K}{Nr_0}\right)\right]^2 t} J_0\left(5.5\left[1+\frac{K}{Nr_0}\right]\frac{r}{r_0}\right)$$

$$\left. + \text{etc.}\right\}. \tag{32}$$

Temperatures at the center are obtained without the help of tables of Bessel functions because $J(0) = 1$.

When $Nr_0/K << 1$, with practically uniform temperature throughout the cylinder,

$$T = T_1 + (T_0 - T_1)\, e^{-\frac{2Nh^2 t}{Kr_0}}. \tag{33}$$

If $Nr_0/K \approx 1$, the first term of Eq. 31 dominates after the relaxation time. The Bessel function can be expanded, and then the temperature is given by

$$T = T_1 + (T_0 - T_1)\left(1 + \frac{2K}{Nr_0}\right)\left\{\frac{\left(1 + \frac{2K}{Nr_0}\right) - \left(\frac{r}{r_0}\right)^2}{1 + \frac{2K}{Nr_0} + \frac{4K^2}{N^2 r_0^2}} e^{\frac{-4h^2 t}{r_0^2\left(1+\frac{2K}{Nr_0}\right)}}\right\}. \tag{34}$$

Heat transfer by free convection. Except for a few special cases, the estimation of heat loss by free convection is quite complicated or even impossible. The special cases which have been solved include plane surfaces and wires cooled by convection. The work on this subject up to 1933 has been summarized by W. J. King.[4] Among the various methods for calculating convection losses, that of Langmuir is the simplest.[5] His method applies when the surfaces are small, such as those encountered in the laboratory. As it

---

[4] King, W. J., *Mechanical Engineering, 54,* 190, 275, 347, 410, 492, 560 (1932).

[5] Langmuir, I., *Amer. Electrochem. Soc., Trans., 23,* 299 (1913); *Phys. Rev., 34,* 401 (1912).

Rice, C. W., *International Critical Tables, 5,* 234. New York: McGraw-Hill Book Company, 1929.

applies to a vertical surface, his method consists of calculating the heat conduction through a postulated stagnant air film of 0.45 cm thickness, thus:

$$W = \frac{-K}{0.45}(T_2 - T_1) \text{ calories/sec./cm}^2. \tag{35}$$

Here K is the thermal conductivity for air, T_1 is the absolute temperature of the vertical surface, and T_2 is the ambient temperature. A more complete theory shows that W is proportional to $(T_2 - T_1)^{5/4}$ and to the fourth root of the height of the vertical surface. K, in Eq. 35, is not independent of temperature, and, except for small temperature drops, the heat transfer is given by the expression

$$W = \frac{-1}{0.45}\int_{T_2}^{T_1} K dT = -\frac{(\phi_2 - \phi_1)}{0.45} \text{ calories/sec./cm}^2. \tag{36}$$

Values of ϕ for air are given in Table II to facilitate calculation. These values are defined by the expression

$$\phi = \int_0^T K dT. \tag{37}$$

TABLE II

VALUES OF ϕ FOR AIR

Temperature (°A.)	Calories/sec./cm
0	0
100	0.00098
200	0.00401
300	0.00924
400	0.0160
500	0.0243
700	0.0451
900	0.0709
1100	0.1017
1300	0.1376
1500	0.1776
1700	0.222
1900	0.271
2100	0.325
2300	0.384
2500	0.447

Langmuir found that heat losses by free convection from a horizontal surface facing upward are 10 per cent greater than they are from a vertical surface, and they are 50 per cent less from a surface facing downward than they are from a vertical surface.

The procedure for calculating the convection losses from wires is also treated by Langmuir.

Heat transfer by radiation. The energy emitted by a surface of area A radiating the heat spectrum between the wave lengths λ and $\lambda + d\lambda$ is

$$\Phi_{d\lambda} = \pi \epsilon_\lambda J_\lambda d\lambda \text{ calories/sec.} \tag{38}$$

This represents the summation of energy in respect to the solid angle over the hemisphere (angle 2π steradians). Here $\epsilon\lambda$ is the emissivity of the surface. This is the ratio of the emission of the surface to that which would obtain for a "black body" at the same temperature. $J\lambda$ is the energy radiated per unit solid angle by a black body of the same area at wave length λ for a unit wave-length range, $d\lambda = 1$ cm.

So-called black-body radiation is defined as the thermal radiation coming from the surface of a body which is in temperature equilibrium with all of its surroundings. For example, the inner surface of a cavity in an opaque material at a uniform temperature emits black-body radiation. In fact, black-body radiation is obtained experimentally from just such a cavity. The wall of the cavity is pierced to form a small aperture to serve as an outlet for the radiation, the hole being small enough not to disturb the equilibrium perceptibly. The name *black-body radiation* comes indirectly from Kirchoff's law, which states that the emission and absorption coefficients of any body are equal. A black body with an absorption coefficient of unity, $\alpha\lambda = 1$, therefore, by Kirchoff's law, has an emission coefficient of unity, $\epsilon\lambda = 1$.

The Planck expression for $J\lambda$ is a function of the wave length, λ, and the absolute temperature, T.

$$J_\lambda = \frac{A c_1}{\lambda^5}\left(\frac{1}{e^{\frac{c_2}{\lambda T}} - 1}\right) \text{ calories/sec./cm/steradian.} \tag{39}$$

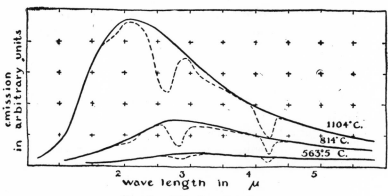

Fig. 3. After Jean Lecomte.

This formula describes the distribution of energy in the heat spectrum, and its plot against λ at different temperatures is illustrated in Fig. 3.

For $\lambda T = 0.3$ this expression is approximated to within 1 per cent by the so-called Wiens formula,

$$J_\lambda' = \frac{Ac_1}{\lambda^5} e^{-\frac{c_2}{\lambda T}} \quad \text{calories/sec./cm/steradian.} \quad (40)$$

As λT becomes $<< 0.3$, J_λ becomes asymptotic to J_λ.

For $\lambda T = 80$ the expression is approximated to within 1 per cent by the so-called Rayleigh-Jeans formula,

$$J_\lambda^{\bullet} = \frac{Ac_1}{c_2\lambda^4} T \quad \text{calories/sec./cm/steradian.} \quad (41)$$

As λT becomes $>> 80$, $J_\lambda^{\bullet}$ becomes asymptotic to J_λ. The values of the constants c_1 and c_2, where λ is expressed in centimeters, are $c_1 = 2.81 \times 10^{-13}$ calorie/sec./cm²/unit solid angle; and $c_2 = 1.432$ cm degrees.

The total heat lost by a unit area of the surface of a "black body" is the quantity expressed by Eq. 38 integrated over all wave lengths. This gives Stefan's formula:

$$\Phi = \pi \int J_\lambda d\lambda = A\sigma T^4 \quad \text{calories/sec.} \quad (42)$$

Most surfaces have a total emission which may be expressed as

$$\Phi = A\epsilon_T\sigma T^4 \quad \text{calories/sec.} \quad (43)$$

Here σ has the value of 1.38×10^{-12} calorie/sec./cm^2/ degree[4].

The heat emitted by a flat surface of area A into a cone which is defined by a solid angle $d\Omega$ is

$$d\Phi = A \cos \theta \frac{d\Omega}{\pi} \epsilon_T \sigma T^4 \text{ calories/sec.} \qquad (44)$$

Here $A \cos \theta$ is the projected area of the source and $d\Omega/\pi$ is the fraction of the total heat emitted in the direction θ defined by the element $d\Omega$.

ϵ_T is an emissivity averaged over all wave lengths, and it is ordinarily "constant" only for a small temperature range. For porous nonmetallic substances it is very nearly unity, regardless of the color of the material.   Naturally, the visible color of a body does not determine its infrared "color." Some bodies, such as white lead, are almost completely black throughout the heat spectrum, while the reverse is true for other substances, notably soot and black paper, both of which are transparent for the long wave-length end of the heat spectrum. ϵ_T for aluminum paints, around room temperature, varies between 0.3 and 0.5.   For nonmetallic pigment paints $\epsilon_T = 1$.

For clean metals, ϵ_T varies with the temperature in such a way that the total emissivity is conveniently represented by an expression of the form

$$\Phi = A M T^m \text{ calories/sec.} \qquad (45)$$

Here M and m are constants.   Values of M and m for some common metals are given in Table III.

TABLE III

RADIATION CONSTANTS OF METALS

Metal	Temperature Range (°K.)	M	m
Silver.................	610 to 980	7.16×10^{-14}	4.1
Platinum..............	640 to 1150	5.50×10^{-16}	5.0
Nickel.................	463 to 1280	2.39×10^{-15}	4.65
Iron..................	700 to 1300	7.65×10^{-18}	5.55
Nichrome..............	325 to 1310	4.30×10^{-13}	4.1

The heat transfer by radiation between two parallel black isothermal surfaces of area A at absolute temperatures T_1 and T_2, which are separated by a small distance, is

$$W = \sigma(T_2{}^4 - T_1{}^4) \text{ calories/sec./cm}^2. \tag{46}$$

$$W = 1.38\left\{\left(\frac{T_2}{1000}\right)^4 - \left(\frac{T_1}{1000}\right)^4\right\} \text{ calories/sec./cm}^2. \tag{47}$$

If the temperature difference, $(T_2 - T_1)$, is small, this heat transfer may be expressed so:

$$W = 5.5 \times 10^{-12}T^3\Delta T \text{ calories/sec./cm}^2. \tag{48}$$

Thus, owing to the fact that the absolute temperature enters the expression to the third power, we see that the importance of radiation as an agency for heat transfer becomes greater at higher temperatures, until finally, in comparison, ordinary conduction becomes negligible.

At extremely high temperatures, the action of an insulator is the same as the action of a radiation baffle or series of baffles. The effect of baffles can be illustrated by the example of two infinite plane-parallel black surfaces at temperature T_1 and T_2. If a thin black baffle is interposed between these two surfaces, the transfer by radiation is reduced to one-half its original value. Two baffles reduce it to one-third, three baffles to one-fourth, and so forth, and if, instead of black baffles, polished metal reflectors are used, the insulation effect is even greater. In high-temperature furnaces the furnace tube with its winding is frequently surrounded by a thin sheet of some metal like molybdenum to serve as a baffle to reflect back most of the radiant energy emitted by the tube and so to decrease the power required. Sometimes, too, a second refractory furnace tube may surround the first to act as an insulator.

Low temperatures. Moderately low temperatures are obtained in the laboratory by immersion in baths of ice, salt and ice, dry ice, liquid air, and so forth. The various temperatures so attained are listed in Table IV. For obtaining extremely low temperatures, the methods required are very elaborate.[6]

TABLE IV

Freezing Mixtures and Constant-Temperature Cooling Baths

Bath	T (°C.)
N_aCl, 33 parts, plus snow, 100 parts..........................	−21.3
$CaCl_2 + 6H_2O$, 100 parts, plus snow, 70 parts.................	−54.9
Liquid nitrogen......Boiling point.........................	−195.8
Liquid oxygen.......Boiling point.........................	−183
Solid CO_2..........Sublimation point.....................	−78.5
Mercury...........Melting temperature....................	−38.9

Methods of obtaining high temperatures. *Flames.* The use of flames affords the most simple and convenient means of obtaining high temperatures.

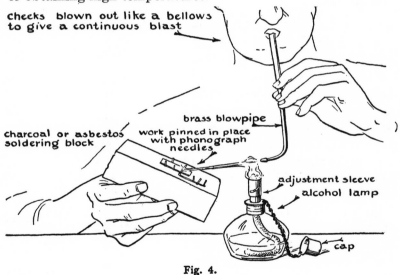

cheeks blown out like a bellows to give a continuous blast

charcoal or asbestos soldering block

work pinned in place with phonograph needles

brass blowpipe

adjustment sleeve

alcohol lamp

cap

Fig. 4.

Fig. 4 illustrates the use of a blowpipe with the alcohol lamp, showing how the cheeks are used as bellows to give continuous air pressure.

---

[6] Meissner, W., *Handbuch der Physik*, Vol. 11, Chapter 7. Berlin: Julius Springer, 1926.

Fig. 5 illustrates the ordinary Bunsen burner. The Bunsen burner is simply a tube arranged with a fuel gas jet in the bottom and air ports in the sides near the bottom. It draws air in through these ports by injector action of the gas jet. The air drawn into the tube at the bottom is mixed with the fuel gas as it passes up through the tube; and above the top of the tube this air reacts chemically with the gas fuel to produce the flame.

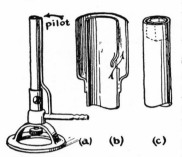

Fig. 5. Pilot attachment (b) is obtainable from the Forster Manufacturing Company, 2916 Otis Street, Berkeley, California, and attachment (c) is obtainable from the Central Scientific Company, Chicago, Illinois.

The Bunsen burner draws only about half as much oxygen through its ports as is required for burning the fuel. If more air were mixed with the gas, the velocity of propagation of the flame would be greater than the upward velocity of the gas in the tube, and the flame would "backfire." However, additional air required for combustion of the gas is supplied to the flame above the burner tube; owing to the more abundant supply of air, at the edges of the flame the propagation velocity is greater than the upward velocity of the gas, so that the fire does not blow itself out.

Natural gas, which contains less hydrogen than coal gas, has a much smaller flame velocity. (The heat of combustion and the chemical composition of some commercial fuel gases

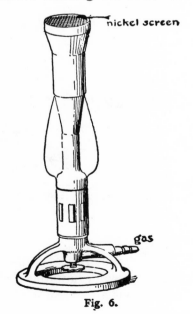

Fig. 6.

TABLE V

Commercial Fuel Gases

Gas	B.t.u. per Cubic Foot	Per Cent H_2	Per Cent CO	Per Cent Methane and Ethane	Per Cent Propane and Butane
Coal gas.....	527	58	6	27	0
Natural gas..	1100	0	0.1	89	2
Bottled gas...	3037	0	0	0	100

Central Scientific Company Catalogue.

are shown in Table V.) Accordingly, with natural gas there is a greater tendency of the burner to blow out than with coal gas. This has resulted in the invention of fixtures like those shown in Fig. 5(b) and (c), which serve to retard the upward velocity of a portion of the gas mixture. The flame formed by this slowed-up portion does not blow out, and it prevents the main flame from doing so. A small tube may be soldered to the burner as shown in Fig. 5 at (a) to act as a pilot as well as to prevent the flame from blowing out.

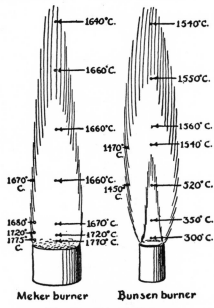

Meker burner   Bunsen burner

Fig. 7.   After F. Haber.

The Meker burner is a Bunsen-type burner with the top of the burner tube flared out and fitted with a nickel grill. This is illustrated in Fig. 6. The Meker burner can burn coal gas with a higher air admixture than the Bunsen burner, because the grill, acting as a Davy lamp screen, prevents

the flame from backfiring.   The hot inner blue cone of the
Bunsen flame is replaced here by an array of small cones,

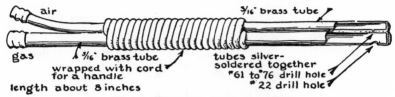

Fig. 8.   After Ernst von Angerer.

one over each element of the grill.   This array produces a
flame which is both hotter and more uniform over an extended area than the Bunsen flame. . The temperature distributions in the Bunsen and Meker flames, with coal gas
fuel, are shown in Fig. 7.

To obtain a higher temperature than either the Bunsen or
Meker will yield, the fuel is burned with air or oxygen under

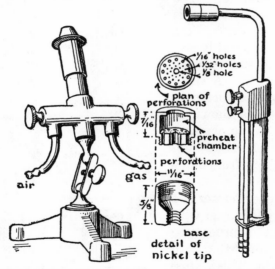

Fig. 9.   The burner shown at the right, for natural-gas fuel, is obtainable from
the Forster Manufacturing Company, 2916 Otis Street, Berkeley, California.

pressure at the end of an orifice with burners such as the
ones shown in Figs. 8 and 9.   When natural gas is burned

with air, a special tube end is required.   (See Fig. 9.)   Another method of burning gas to get a high temperature is to

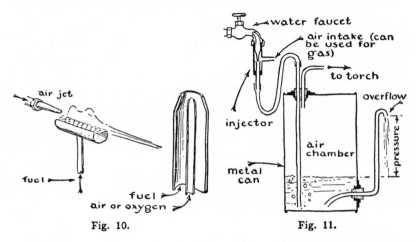

Fig. 10.   Fig. 11.

project a jet of air or oxygen through a gas flame as shown in Fig. 10.   A simple method using a water aspirator for obtaining compressed air at moderate pressures is shown in Fig. 11.

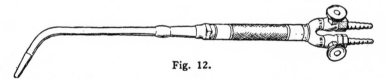

Fig. 12.

Extremely high temperatures are attained with oxyhydrogen or oxyacetylene torches.   Commercial torches like the one illustrated in Fig. 12 are recommended for these fuels.[7]   These torches are equipped with a mixer, usually in the handle, to produce a homogeneous solution of the fuel and oxygen gases. It is very important to have such a homogeneous mixture of oxygen and fuel;

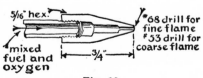

Fig. 13.

[7] These torches are obtainable from the Linde Air Products Company, 30 East 42nd Street, New York City.

otherwise the torches would blow themselves out. The type of orifice used is illustrated in Fig. 13. Fig. 14 shows the distribution of temperature in the oxyacetylene flame and also in the carbon arc.[8]

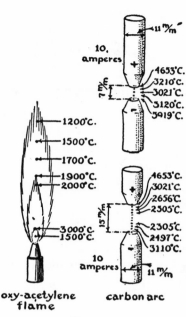

oxy-acetylene flame   carbon arc

Fig. 14.

A furnace is required to heat objects to higher temperatures than those that are obtainable with torches. Gas furnaces for use in the laboratory are shown in Figs. 15 and 16.

Oxygen-gas furnaces can be made to yield very high temperatures; for example, Podszus and von Wartenburg, Linde, and Jung have described furnaces with a zirconium dioxide tube using illuminating gas or oil vapor as fuel.[9] These furnaces attain temperatures of about 2600°C.[10]

Electric furnaces. Electric furnaces for temperatures to 500°C., useful for such applications as the baking out of charcoal traps, can be made by winding a coil of Nichrome or Chromel wire on an iron tube as shown in Fig. 17. The

---

[8] Flame and carbon-arc temperature:

Kautny, Th., *Leitfaden für Azetylenschweisser*, page 86. Halle: Marhold, 1925.

Mathiesen, W., *Untersuchungen über den elektrischen Lichtbogen.* Leipzig: Haberlandt, 1921.

[9] Podszus, E., *Zeit. für angew. Chem., 30,* 17 (1917), *32,* 146 (1919).

von Wartenburg, H., Linde, H., and Jung, R., *Zeit. für anorg. u. allgem. Chemie, 176,* 349 (1928).

[10] For treatment of high-temperature refractories see Swanger, W. H., and Caldwell, F. R., *Bureau of Standards J. of Research, 6,* 1131 (1931).

Many of the high-temperature refractories are obtainable from the Foote Mineral Company, Philadelphia, Pennsylvania.

See Langmuir, I., "Flames of Atomic Hydrogen," *Indust. and Engin. Chem., 19,* 667 (1927).

tube is first covered with a piece of mica or asbestos sheet to avoid shorting out the winding. A simple way of fastening the ends of the winding is illustrated in Fig. 18. Various

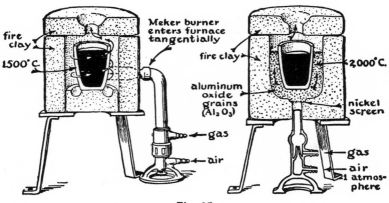

Fig. 15.

types of insulation may be used. For example, the inner tube and its resistance wire winding may be covered with several layers of asbestos. The furnace is assembled with transite[11] ends, using Insa-lute cement. It is necessary to avoid contact between the Insa-lute cement and the furnace wire at elevated temperatures.

Nickel wire is suitable for a furnace winding. However, its resistance changes approximately twofold when it is heated from room temperature to 500°C. This behavior is in contrast to the behavior of the nickel-chromium alloys,

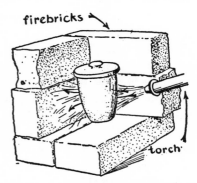

Fig. 16. An improvised furnace.

---

[11] Transite is an asbestos fiber and Portland cement mixture formed under high pressure into dense, monolithic sheets of high strength, rigidity, and durability. It may be purchased from the Johns-Manville Corporation, 22 East 40th Street, New York City.

whose change of resistance is negligible. The change of resistance of nickel may or may not be desirable; it may be desirable to have a large coefficient if the resistance is to be used for regulating the temperature of the furnace.

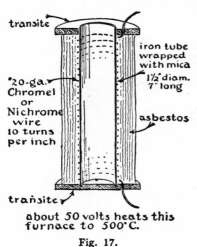

transite

iron tube wrapped with mica
1½ diam.
7" long

°20-ga. Chromel or Nichrome wire 10 turns per inch

asbestos

transite

about 50 volts heats this furnace to 500°C.

Fig. 17.

Electric furnaces which operate in air to 1100°C. may be made with the nickel-chrome alloys as resistors, a porcelain, Alundum, quartz, or magnesia tube being used to support the winding. Diatomaceous earth makes an excellent insulator.[12] A useful furnace construction for the laboratory is illustrated in Fig. 19.

Platinum may be used as resistor for temperatures greater than 1100°C., when it is desired to have the furnace operate in air. This resistor will operate up to a temperature limit of 1600°C. In order to obtain a furnace temperature as near this limit as possible, Orton and Krehbiel used a Chromel "booster" winding on a tube mounted outside of and concentric with the platinum winding.[13] The platinum wire may be wound on quartz glass, which has a temperature limit in air of 1300°C., on unglazed porcelain, for which the limit is 1400°C., or on clay, with a limit of 1700°C. However,

method of securing ends of winding

Fig. 18.

[12] This may be obtained from Johns-Manville under the trade name Sil-O-Cel. The calcined diatomaceous silica comes as a coarse granular material and as molded insulating bricks.

[13] Orton, E., Jr., and Krehbiel, J. F., *Amer. Ceramic Soc., J.,* 10, 375 (1927).

best of all is an Alundum tube (alumina with clay binder). Its limit, 1900°C., is above that of the platinum.

Silicon is formed from quartz or porcelain in a reducing atmosphere, and silicon attacks platinum. Accordingly, it is best to use a platinum-wound furnace in an oxidizing atmosphere. If, however, the wire is wound on an Alundum tube, it may be operated in a reducing atmosphere.

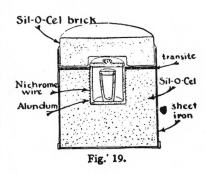

Fig. 19.

Molybdenum or tungsten can be used as a resistor in an atmosphere of hydrogen; the limiting temperatures attainable are 2200°C. and 3000°C. respectively. As a support for the resistor winding, Alundum can be used to 1900°C., magnesia to 2200°C., zirconia to 2500°C., and thoria to

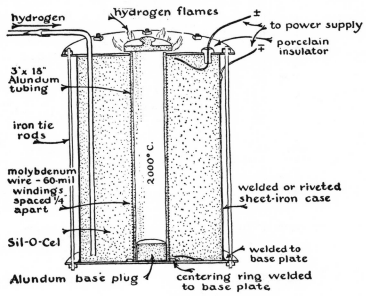

Fig. 20.   Hydrogen furnace.

3000°C.   Porcelain is unsuitable, for the reason given above; namely, hydrogen blackens it at high temperatures.[14]   A tungsten (or molybdenum) furnace is shown in Fig. 20. Most refractories cannot be subjected to high temperatures

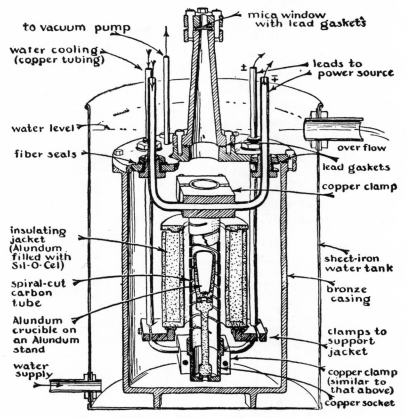

Fig. 21.   The Arsem furnace.

in vacuum because they either evaporate or are reduced by the vacuum (oxygen formed by dissociation is pumped away).

Carbon and graphite tube furnaces can be operated to a

[14] For tables of physical and chemical properties of refractories see Hougen, O. A., *Chem. and Met. Eng.*, *30*, 737 (1924).

temperature of 2000°C. in vacuum.   Above this temperature the carbon begins to vaporize, and at 2500° C. the rate of evaporation is rapid.   In hydrogen or nitrogen the temperature limit is 2000°C.   At this limit chemical action between the carbon and the gas sets in.   However, in an atmosphere of carbon monoxide, carbon resistors may be used at temperatures over 3000°C. A furnace designed by Arsem,[15] which may be operated either in an atmosphere of carbon monoxide or in vacuum, is shown in Fig. 21.   This furnace has its resistor tube cut into a

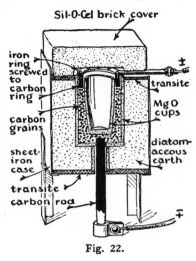

Fig. 22.

spiral to increase its resistance and flexibility.   Connections are made to the ends of the resistor tube with water-cooled copper jaws.

Carbon grain resistors such as the one shown in Fig. 22 have a higher electrical resistance than solid carbon and are often useful in the laboratory.

A carbon-arc furnace is shown in Fig. 23.

Fig. 24 shows apparatus used for melting metals in vacuum by heating with high-frequency current. It is peculiar to this method that the metal charge is at a higher temperature

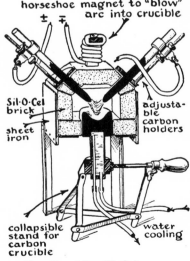

Fig. 23.   After W. Schuen.

[15] Arsem, W. C., *Am. Electrochem. Soc., Trans.*, *9*, 153 (1906).

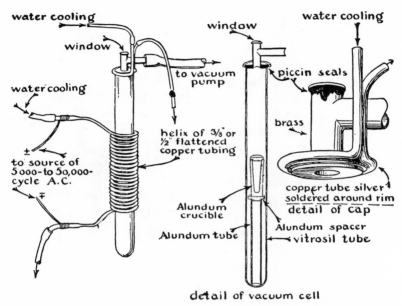

Fig. 24. Apparatus for melting metals in vacuum with high-frequency currents.

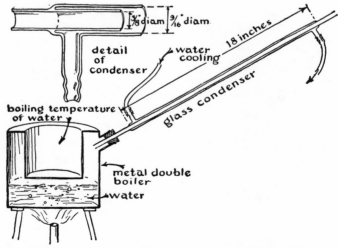

Fig. 25. Air bath. A Liebig condenser with a narrow cooling chamber is most efficient.

than the crucible, a fact of practical value when working with extremely refractory metals.[16]

Fixed temperatures. Constant temperature may be maintained at 0°C. with melting ice, and at the boiling temperature of water by means of a device such as the one illustrated in Fig. 25. Other liquids and solids may be used for maintaining other constant temperatures; for example, a temperature of 444.6°C. is obtained by boiling sulphur. Some of the fixed temperatures useful for the calibration of thermometers and thermocouples are given in Table VI.

TABLE VI

STANDARD TEMPERATURES

Bath	$T(°C.)$
Carbon dioxide (sublimation temperature)	−78.51
Mercury (melting temperature)	−38.87
Ice (melting temperature)	0
$Na_2SO_4 \cdot 10H_2O$ (transition temperature)	32.38
$MnCl_2 \cdot 2H_2O$ (transition temperature)	50.09
Steam condensation (at 760 mm pressure)	100
Naphthalene (boiling temperature)	217.96
Tin (melting temperature)	231.84
Benzophenone (boiling temperature)	305.9
Sulphur (boiling temperature)	444.6

Thermostatic devices. Here we cannot treat all of the many devices described in the literature for controlling the temperatures of furnaces and thermostatic baths.[17] How-

[16] Northrup, E. F., *Frank Inst., J.*, *195*, 665 (1923).

Equipment for high-frequency heating is obtainable from the Ajax Electrothermic Corporation, Trenton, New Jersey.

[17] Haagn, E., *E. T. Z.*, *40*, 670 (1919).

Haughton, J. L., and Hanson, D., *Engineering*, *104*, 412 (1917).

Haughton, J. L., *Journ. Sci. Instruments*, *9*, 310 (1932).

Roberts, H. S., *J. O. S. A. 6*, 965 (1922).

White, W. P., and Adams, L. H., *Phys. Rev.*, *14*, 44 (1919).

The Fish-Schurman Corporation is United States agent for German thermostats covering the temperature range − 35°C. to 300°C.

See also the following:

Beattie, J. A., *Rev. Sci. Instruments*, *2*, 458 (1931).

Roebuck, J. R., *Rev. Sci. Instruments*, *3*, 93 (1932).

Concerning the use of the thyratron for temperature control see the following:

Hull, A. W., *Gen. El. Rev.*, *32*, 213, 390 (1931).

Zabel, R. M., and Hancox, R. R., *Rev. Sci. Instruments*, *5*, 28 (1934).

Zabel and Hancox were able to get a constant temperature of 880°C. ± .06°.

ever, the principle on which they operate is the same, namely, the balancing of the heat input to the furnace against its heat losses.   The heat input is controlled by a pilot indicator which is continually kept oscillating about a mean position corresponding to the desired temperature.   When it is on either one or the other side of the mean position, it modulates the heat input: When the pilot indicates the temperature low, the heat input is automatically increased, and when it indicates high, the heat input is diminished.   In this sense one does not maintain a constant temperature but a periodic one which varies between more or less fixed limits about a mean temperature.

As an example of a temperature-regulating device, let us consider a furnace with its winding made one arm of a self-balancing Wheatstone bridge, the bridge current in this arm serving at the same time as furnace heating current.   The furnace winding must be made of nickel, molybdenum, tungsten, or platinum for this type of regulator, since the nickel-chromium alloys do not have a suitable temperature coefficient of resistance.   The other resistances in the Wheatstone bridge may be rheostats made from a low-temperature-coefficient alloy such as constantan.   The bridge galvanometer serves as the pilot to control the heating current.

Let us compare this method with one which employs a thermocouple inside the furnace as a pilot.   We see that there will be more lag between the time the heat input is altered and the time it affects the thermopile.   As a result, with the thermocouple pilot the limits of the fluctuation of the furnace temperature are separated more than they are when the resistance of the heater wire serves as the pilot.

Even when the furnace heater wire serves as the pilot, there are fluctuations due to the period of auxiliary instruments.   These temperature fluctuations may be diminished simply by interposing alternate shells of thermal "ballast" and insulator between the furnace winding and the region that is to be kept at a constant temperature.   The temperature diffusion through such alternate shells is slow. The furnace tube itself, which separates the heater wires from the constant temperature region within, is usually adequate for this, because of its relatively low diffusivity, h; for example, one may obtain temperatures constant to about

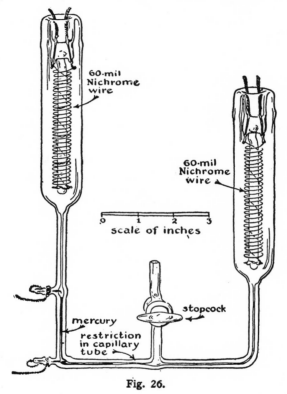

60-mil Nichrome wire

60-mil Nichrome wire

scale of inches

stopcock

mercury

restriction in capillary tube

Fig. 26.

0.01°C. inside the furnace tube even when the period of temperature oscillation of the furnace wiring outside is of the order of 30 seconds.

The device shown in Fig. 26 is convenient for temperature regulation.[18] The two bulbs of this device have equal volumes, and they are equipped with identical nickel-

[18] Proctor, R. F., and Douglas, R. W., *Journ. Sci. Instruments, 9*, 192 (1932).

chromium alloy heaters and connected electrically as shown in the diagram, Fig. 27. The bulbs are filled with air and the pressures on either side of the mercury column are such as to hold the top surface of the mercury at the level of the tungsten contact when the voltage drop over the left resistance (see Fig. 26) is the same as the voltage drop over the right resistance. These voltage drops are equal when the temperature-sensitive feeler resistance is the same as the fixed constantan resistance. (See Fig. 27.) These resistances are adjusted to be equal at the desired temperature. If the temperature of the feeler resistance is too high or too low, the heating in the two bulbs is unequal, and the resulting change in pressure in the bulbs opens or closes the mercury contact, and this in turn operates a relay actuating the heating and bridge current.[19]

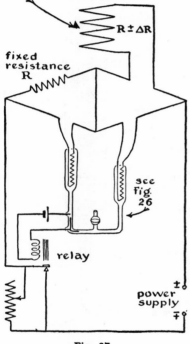

heater to be kept at a constant temperature or "feeler" resistor whose resistance varies with the ambient temperature

R ± ΔR

fixed resistance R

see fig. 26

relay

power supply ±

Fig. 27.

The resistance used to operate the regulating device may be either the heater resistance or it may be separate from the heater. In the latter case this arrangement is suitable for maintaining a constant temperature in a room. The feeler resistance is strung back and forth near the ceiling of the

---

[19] Mercury thermoregulators, relays, and electric bath heaters are handled by American Instrument Company, 774 Girard Street, N. W., Washington, D. C.

room (at about 8 feet above the floor). For such an application the heaters, which the regulating device controls, are situated in front of the ventilator air inlet to the room.

Thermostat baths use water for ordinary temperatures, oil or eutectic salt mixtures for elevated temperatures, and alcohol for low temperatures. Beattie gives the composition of two eutectic baths. (See Table VII.) These baths are useful in the temperature range above 120°C. The lower limits of their temperature ranges overlap the upper temperature limits of mineral-oil baths (150° to 200°C.) and heavy cylinder oil baths (150° to 300°C.).

The temperature of a water bath is controlled by regulating the heat onput. A mercury-in-glass bulb with contacts coupled to a relay as shown in Fig. 18, Chapter X, is suitable for a bath heated electrically. The device shown in Fig. 28 is effective for controlling the temperature of a gas-heated

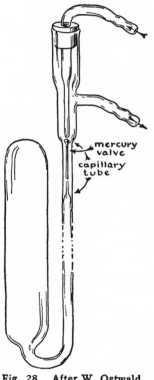

mercury valve
capillary tube

Fig. 28. After W. Ostwald.

TABLE VII

HIGH-TEMPERATURE BATH FLUIDS

Bath	$T(°C.)$
Mineral seal oil..	200
Heavy cylinder oil.....................................	150 to 300
30% $LiNO_3$ by weight ⎫ 14% $NaNO_3$ by weight ⎬ .... 56% KNO_3 by weight ⎭	120 to 500

Beattie, *Rev. Sci. Instruments,* 2, 458 (1931).

bath. The aperture through which the gas for the flame
passes is regulated by the thermal expansion and contraction
of the mercury. With these devices the fluctuations of the
bath are about 0.1°C.

Temperature measurement. Temperature is always
measured practically by a measurement of some temperature-
sensitive property, such as light emission, electrical resistance, length, volume, thermal e.m.f., and so forth. All
physical properties which vary with temperature are possibilities for such a measurement, although some properties,
like electron emission, are so strongly influenced by chemical
impurities or by the past physical history of the thermo-
metric substance that they are useless.

Liquid-in-a-bulb thermometers depend upon change of
volume with temperature for their readings. Among them,
two are of unusual interest. One, which was manufactured
in Germany at one time, used gallium as liquid and fused
quartz for the bulb and capillary. This thermometer was
useful up to a temperature of about 1000°C., in contrast to
the mercury thermometer, which is ordinarily useful only to
200°C. However, with a high pressure of nitrogen (up to
40 atmospheres) mercury-in-glass thermometers may be
heated considerably above 200°C. A graphite thermometer
with molten tin as the liquid has been made by Northrup.[20]
This thermometer may be used to 1680° without chemical
reaction between the tin and the graphite. As tin does not
boil at 1680°C., Northrup thinks that the limit in temperature of this thermometer is probably several hundred degrees
higher. The position of the tin in the graphite capillary is
determined by a tungsten feeler. For gallium the temperature range from the melting point to the boiling point is from
29.7° to 1600°C., and for tin it is from 231.8° to 2260°C.
The operation of the two thermometers described above
depends upon these unusually long temperature intervals
between the melting points and boiling points.

---

[20] Northrup, E. F., *Pyrometry*, page 464. New York: published by the Am.
Inst. of Mining and Metallurgical Engineers at the office of the secretary, 1920.

Thermocouples operate by virtue of the temperature dependence of the thermal e.m.f. generated by two substances in contact. The thermocouple may be employed in the laboratory for temperature measurement from liquid air temperatures to the melting temperature of molybdenum.

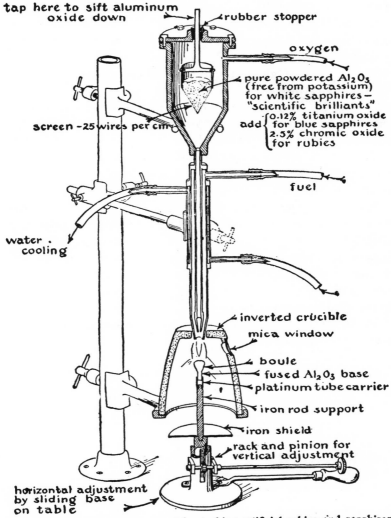

tap here to sift aluminum oxide down

rubber stopper

oxygen

pure powdered Al₂O₃ (free from potassium) for white sapphires — "scientific brilliants"

screen -25 wires per cm

add { **0.12% titanium oxide for blue sapphires** **2.5% chromic oxide for rubies** }

fuel

water cooling

inverted crucible

mica window

boule

fused Al₂O₃ base

platinum tube carrier

iron rod support

iron shield

rack and pinion for vertical adjustment

horizontal adjustment by sliding base on table

Fig. 29.   Verneuil's arrangement for making artificial rubies and sapphires.
Verneuil, A., *Ann. de Chemie et Physique*, *3*, 20 (1904).

The base metals commercially available are commonly used as thermoelectric wires.   Chromel-Alumel wires have a high coefficient of thermal e.m.f.   They are obtainable from the factory matched to give the temperature to ± 5°C. Copper and constantan wires also have a high thermal e.m.f. These wires have the advantage over Chromel-Alumel that they are easily soldered. ، The LeChatelier combination (platinum and 10 per cent platinum-rhodium) is used for precision measurements.   Special thermocouple metals, such as tungsten, molybdenum, and their alloys, are useful at very high temperatures.

It may be desired to calibrate a particular thermocouple with fixed standard-temperature baths such as those listed above in Table VI.   The best procedure is to use the calibration curve supplied by the factory, which gives the e.m.f. at frequent temperature intervals, and to plot an empirical correction curve for it from the calibration data.

Radiation pyrometers determine temperature by the measurement of light emission.   There are several types, and descriptions of them and their operating characteristics appear in many books.   The type in most common use measures, with a special photometer, the intensity of monochromatic light (6600 A) emitted by the incandescent body whose temperature is being measured.

Table VIII is useful for estimating the temperature of a body from its color.

TABLE VIII

Color Temperatures

Color	Approximate Temperature (°C.)
Incipient red heat............	500 to 550
Dark red heat...............	700
Bright red heat..............	900
Yellowish-red heat...........	1100
Incipient white heat..........	1300
White heat..................	1500

CHAPTER XIII

Notes on the Materials of Research

Alkali metals. One of the alkali metals may be required for the sensitive surface of a photocell or as a thin-film filter for ultraviolet light; or in the vapor phase the metal may be used for the demonstration of the phenomenon of resonance radiation. For these and other applications we will outline, briefly, some of the ways of manipulating these very reactive metals.

The alkali metal may be prepared from the alkali chloride, reduced with calcium metal in an evacuated glass tube:

$$2M\mathrm{Cl} + \mathrm{Ca} \rightarrow \overline{2M} + \mathrm{CaCl_2}. \tag{1}$$

The reaction progresses in the indicated direction at elevated temperatures on account of the removal of the free alkali metal, M, by evaporation. This reaction may be varied: A chromate of the alkali metal may be used instead of the chloride, and zirconium metal may be used instead of calcium. The reaction applies to the preparation of all the alkali metals, with the exception of lithium, which reacts with the glass or quartz; lithium is best reduced from its chromate with zirconium metal in an iron apparatus.

We will consider, in detail, how potassium may be prepared by the reaction indicated in Eq. 1. Pulverized potassium chloride and calcium metal filings are mixed together in a closed-end iron tube in stoichiometrical proportions (3.7 g KCl to 1 g Ca). This iron tube is introduced into the thickened end of a hard-glass tube as shown in Fig. 1. The glass is thickened in order to allow the attainment of the maximum temperature; at lower temperatures where a thinner glass wall would collapse the reaction pro-

ceeds very slowly. After the iron tube is introduced, the
hard-glass tube is closed by fusing the glass with the hand
torch. After a good vacuum is attained, the chemicals are
heated, slowly at first and finally strongly until the reaction
is complete. The chemicals may be heated until the glass
starts to soften, but too much heat should be avoided, since
it will distill calcium metal. The reduced and once-distilled
metal condenses in the bend of the tube as shown in Fig. 1.
From there, it is worked down with the flame into the
receiving ampoule, where it is sealed off as illustrated.

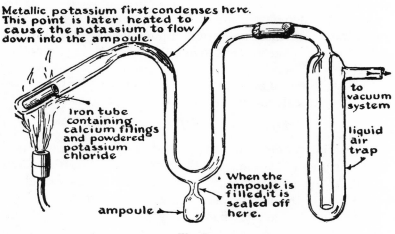

Fig. 1.

The alkali metals react vigorously with air, and the
ampoule should be opened without exposing the metal to
air. This is done by the following procedures: The ampoule
is constructed of Pyrex glass with an annular tungsten ring
to spring the glass. After the ampoule is mounted in the
vacuum system, the tungsten ring is heated with a high-
frequency induction coil until the glass breaks. (See Fig. 2.)

A scheme which does not involve the use of high-frequency
heating but which breaks the glass by impact is illustrated by
Fig. 3. The illustrated depression in the tube wall acts as
a safety to confine the armature and prevent accidental

fracture of the ampoule until the apparatus is sealed onto the high-vacuum system.   During this sealing operation the depression is blown out of the way of the armature.   The armature is operated in the vacuum, by means of an external electromagnet, to break the tip of the ampoule, thus exposing the alkali metal. The tip may be scratched with a file to facilitate breaking.

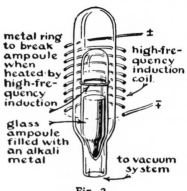

The ampoule may be cooled in a beaker with dry ice in the bottom and carbon dioxide vapor above.   The tip is opened under the surface of the carbon dioxide vapor.   The ampoule is then quickly transmitted to the vacuum system, sealed in, and evacuated. The expansion of carbon dioxide in the ampoule through the tip prevents access of air to the alkali metal.

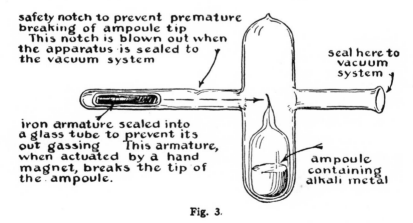

Fig. 3.

The alkali metals, as obtained commercially in small cubes or irregularly shaped pieces, are packed submerged under kerosene.   The metal may be cleaned and manipulated as follows:[1] First the metal is washed in dried petroleum ether or benzene to free it from kerosene. The petroleum ether or benzene is dried by shaking it in contact with calcium chloride. (Carbon tetrachloride or chloroform should not be used to wash the metal, since an explosive compound is formed.) The metal is then fused in the bottom of an 8-mm glass tube and sucked up into a 1-mm capillary glass tube with a rubber hose. This 1-mm tube is sealed off with a flame just above the metal. At the other end the alkali is protected from the air by soft wax. A suitable length of this composite

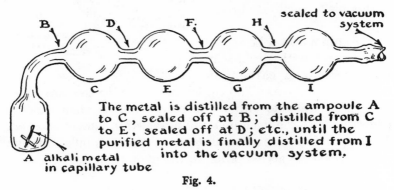

The metal is distilled from the ampoule A to C, sealed off at B; distilled from C to E, sealed off at D; etc., until the purified metal is finally distilled from I into the vacuum system.

A alkali metal in capillary tube

Fig. 4.

glass-metal rod may be cut off with wire cutters and introduced into a distilling bulb fastened to the vacuum system where the metal is desired. (See Fig. 4.)

A distillation procedure[2] for sodium metal is illustrated in Fig. 5 whereby the metal is refluxed under vacuum to free it of hydrogen and carbohydrates (the hydrogen contained in potassium or sodium, measured as a gas at atmospheric pressure, may amount to one or two hundred times the volume of the metal). The metal cubes are washed to free them of kerosene, as described above, and then they are introduced into Chamber I. After the whole system is evacuated, the metal is fused in this chamber. Chamber I acts as a separating funnel. The fusion is accomplished by the

---

[1] Wood, R. W., *Phys. Rev.*, *44*, 353 (1933).
[2] I am indebted to Dr. Carl F. J. Overhage for this procedure.

application of a soft flame, so that the metal runs into Chamber II, leaving the dross behind. Chamber I is then removed at the seal-off. The metal is heated in Chamber II with a small electric furnace. Here it is refluxed for several

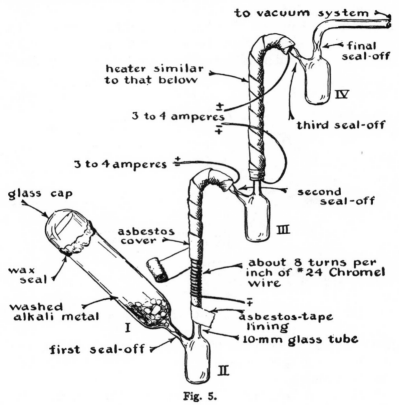

to vacuum system

final seal-off

heater similar to that below

3 to 4 amperes

third seal-off

IV

3 to 4 amperes

second seal-off

glass cap

asbestos cover

III

wax seal

about 8 turns per inch of #24 Chromel wire

washed alkali metal

I

asbestos-tape lining

10-mm glass tube

first seal-off

II

Fig. 5.

hours. The distilled metal condenses in the asbestos-insulated tube above Chamber II. This refluxing allows hydrogen and hydrocarbon vapors to be pumped away. After this treatment the metal is distilled into Chamber III by a heater wire around the condenser tube. Chamber II is then removed at the seal-off. Chamber III may be the receiver for the metal, or it may be further refluxed and distilled into a final receiving ampoule. Electric heat is recommended for distilling the alkali metal, since there is some danger of breaking the glass if it is heated with a torch.

In manipulating the alkali metals the following precautions should be observed: The amount of metal manipulated should never be greater than necessary. A box of sand should be at hand for the control of accidental fires. The alkali metals should never be allowed to come in contact with water. Used metal and apparatus containing the alkali

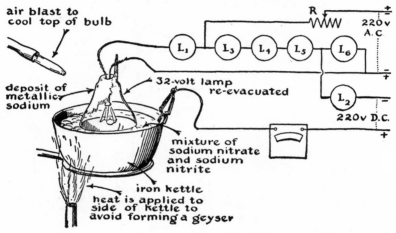

Fig. 6.

metals should be disposed of by burying only. It is advisable to wear goggles to protect the eyes while manipulating the alkali metals.

Sodium may be prepared by electrolysis through the soda-glass walls of an electric lamp. A 32-volt lamp, which has a larger tungsten filament wire than the 110-volt lamp, is best for this purpose. The lamp bulb is first evacuated by means of a side tube sealed on for this purpose. It is then dipped in a bath of fused sodium nitrate and nitrite and connected to a source of electrical energy as shown in Fig. 6. Current is carried from the tungsten filament to the glass walls of the lamp bulb by electrons or by means of a sodium discharge, or in special cases by means of an argon discharge. The practical details of this procedure are due to Dr. R. C. Burt, who graphically described the procedure as one which allows the vacuum to be electroplated with sodium.[3] The free metal is formed from the reduced sodium ions (which migrate through the solid glass electrolyte when a current flows). These ions are reduced by electrons, or negative sodium (or argon) ions. Faraday's law applies to the electrolysis. The spectrum of the sodium vapor discharge has been photographed and the spectrum indicates high purity of the electrolyzed metal. Impurities were estimated by Dr. Burt as being present, at most, in the proportion of 2 parts per

Fig. 7. Fluoresence of sodium vapor.

million. Sodium prepared by electrolysis is characterized by the fact that it is completely free of hydrogen and carbohydrates.

The electrolysis current varies from a few milliamperes when the current is carried entirely by electrons to a few hundred milliamperes when it is carried by sodium ions. The sodium discharge is obtained by simply removing the air blast on the lamp bulb which normally serves to keep the metal condensed.

Burt states that the spectrum from the sodium discharge is not reversed; a warmed lamp containing sodium will

[3] Burt, R. C., *J. O. S. A.*, *11*, 87 (1925).

fluoresce if the light of the sodium discharge from another lamp is focused on it.   (See Fig. 7.)

Sodium may be introduced into quartz photocells by means of a graded seal as shown in Fig. 8.

Potassium can be electrolyzed through a potassium glass which is free of sodium and lead.   A bath of fused potassium nitrite and nitrate is used.

The alkali metals potassium and sodium may be dissolved in the volatile solvent, liquid ammonia, and deposited where

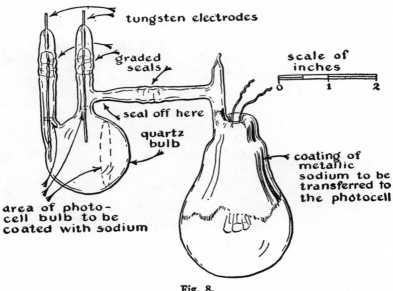

Fig. 8.

they are desired by boiling away this solvent.   Lithium is managed in a similar manner with aethylamine as solvent.

All the alkali metals react with glass at elevated temperatures and especially with lead glass, with which they should not be allowed by come in contact.

The resistance of Pyrex-glass tubes toward sodium can be improved if they are lined with a film of borax or boracic acid.   The tube to be lined is filled with a hot saturated solution of borax.   The borax precipitates from this solution as crystals on the inner glass walls of the tube as the solution cools. When the glass has become lined with a thin coating of crystals, the solution is drawn off and the tube carefully dried. It is then evacuated, and the water is driven off by heating. At first the heating is gentle, but finally the tube is fired at the maximum temperature the glass will stand. This gives the tube a smooth sodium resistant inner surface.

The potassium-sodium alloys, lying within the composition range 45 to 90 per cent potassium, are liquid at room temperature.

Alkali-earth metals. The chief uses of the alkali-earth metals, as getters, depend on their reactions with oxygen to form oxides, with carbon dioxide to form carbides and oxides, with water to form hydrides and oxides, and with nitrogen to form nitrides.

When fresh calcium filings are heated in a quartz tube or heavy-walled Pyrex side tube, connected to an apparatus such as a thermopile, the calcium reacts with all the residual gases (except the noble gases). A fairly good vacuum can be obtained with such a side tube even when starting at atmospheric pressure. For example, the argon spectrum may be obtained in a discharge tube evacuated from half of an atmosphere pressure with such a calcium side tube. Each time the tube is evacuated from atmospheric pressure with calcium, the residual pressure of argon (calculated from its abundance in the atmosphere) is increased by 7 mm.

Barium is a more reactive metal than calcium.[4] It is used as a getter for commercial radio tubes. For this application, the metal is sometimes cast in a seamless tube of nickel or copper which is drawn down to wire. These composite wires are known as Niba and Cuba wires. The wires are cut into short lengths, which are introduced into radio tubes and other places where the getter action is desired. The volatile

---

[4] Barium and strontium metal of a guaranteed purity of 99.5 per cent may be purchased from the Varlacoid Chemical Company, 15 Moore Street, New York City.

core metal is subsequently boiled out of the nickel or copper
covering tube by means of heat generated with a high-
frequency induction coil.

Mercury.   Although mercury approaches the noble metals
in chemical inertness, it is easily contaminated, especially by
other metals.   This is because, as a liquid, it is a fairly good
solvent.   A simple test for the purity of a sample of mercury

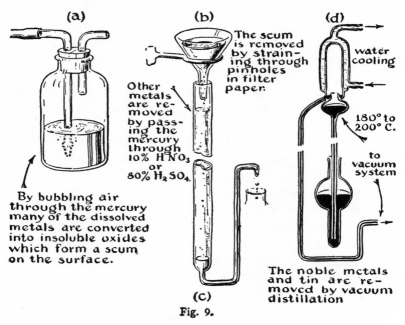

(a)

(b)

(d)

The scum
is removed
by strain-
ing through
pinholes
in filter
paper.

water
cooling

Other
metals
are re-
moved
by pass-
ing the
mercury
through
10% HNO_3
or
80% H_2SO_4.

180° to
200° C.

to
vacuum
system

By bubbling air
through the mercury
many of the dissolved
metals are converted
into insoluble oxides
which form a scum
on the surface.

The noble metals
and tin are re-
moved by vacuum
distillation

(c)

Fig. 9.

is to raise a clean glass rod slowly up through the metal
surface.   If the mercury is clean, the glass will come up
without any adhering mercury droplets.

The contaminations commonly found in mercury may be
classified according to the manner in which they can be easily
removed.   First come surface contaminations by materials
which do not dissolve in the liquid metal and may, accordingly, be removed by filtering the metal through pinholes in
filter paper or through a chamois skin.   Second, there are the
dissolved metals.   Those which are oxidizable are first con-

verted to insoluble oxides by the blowing of air through the mercury as shown in Fig. 9(a). The oxides form a scum on the mercury surface and may later be filtered off. Mercury is practically free of impurities of this type if, after air has been blown through the liquid metal $\frac{1}{2}$ hour, no scum has formed on the surface. The alkali metals fall into this class of impurities; here also belong zinc, with a high vapor pressure, and copper and lead, with low vapor pressures. These metals, which are more reactive than mercury, can also be removed by exposing the mercury to a solution of 10 per cent HNO_3 or 80 per cent H_2SO_4. This is shown in Fig. 9(b). Thirdly, there are the dissolved metals, such as the noble metals and tin, which cannot be removed by oxidation or acid. Copper and lead may also be considered as belonging to this class of contaminations. These metals are removed by vacuum distillation of the mercury at a temperature of about 180° to 200°C. (at which temperature the mercury distills at the rate of approximately $\frac{1}{2}$ g/cm²/sec.) as indicated by Fig. 9(c).

The vapor pressure of mercury is given in Table I. It is to be noted thoughtfully that at room temperature the

TABLE I

VAPOR PRESSURE OF MERCURY

Temperature (°C.)	Vapor Pressure (mm)
0	.0002
20	.0013
100	.27
200	17

vapor density of mercury is many times greater than the accepted nonpoisonous concentration limit, which is 1 milligram of mercury per cubic meter. According to Stock, continual breathing of air containing only 15 micrograms per cubic meter of mercury for a few weeks will make most persons ill.[5] The vapor pressure of mercury is hazardously high in many laboratories. In a Berlin physical laboratory the typical concentration of mercury vapor in the air was found to be about 20 to 60 micrograms per cubic meter; in one room it was 500 micrograms per cubic meter. Heat produced by turning on mercury pumps doubled the concentration of mercury vapor in the air.[6]

Platinum metals. Platinum is chemically resistant to alkalies and hydrofluoric acid. However, it is attacked by chlorine vapor and aqua regia. Metallic salts should not be heated in platinum under conditions which may result in the reduction of the metal and the consequent debasement and embrittlement of the platinum. This applies particularly to lead salts. The elements phosphorus and silicon also attack platinum and make it brittle, and they may change its other properties. For example, even the small amount of silicon introduced into the platinum when it is heated in contact with porcelain in a reducing atmosphere makes an appreciable change in the thermoelectric power and electrical resistance.

Platinum is so ductile that wires may be drawn directly as fine as 20μ diameter. By Wollaston's procedure a platinum rod is covered with a close-fitting silver tube, and this composite rod is drawn through wire dies. After the silver has been etched off the final wire with nitric acid, the platinum wire obtained may be as small as $\frac{1}{2}\mu$ in diameter. Wollaston wire is often used for fuses to protect delicate instruments.[7]

A physical property of platinum which is of interest to the physicist is its "transparency" to hydrogen gas at temperatures above 700°C. (See Fig. 10.) This property is employed to obtain very pure hydrogen.

[5] Stock, A., and Cucuel, F., *Ber. deutsch. chem. Ges.*, *67*, 122 (1934).

[6] Müller, K., and Pringsheim, P., *Naturwiss.*, *18*, 364 (1930). See also Turner, J. A., *Pub. Health Bull.*, *39*, No. 8 (1924). Goodman, Clark, "Mercury Poisoning, A Review of Present Knowledge," *Rev. Sci. Instruments*, *9*, 233 (1938).

[7] Wollaston and Taylor process wires are handled by Baker and Company, 54 Austen Street, Newark, New Jersey.

Littelfuses are obtainable from radio supply houses.

Platinum is a refractory metal. For this reason it may be used for furnace windings and as a base for oxide cathodes.

Iridium is harder and more resistant to chemical attack than platinum; it is not attacked by aqua regia. Accordingly, it is often alloyed with platinum in proportions up to 30 per cent to yield a metal which is superior to platinum in respect to chemical resistance and hardness.

Rhodium is alloyed with platinum (90 Pt to 10 Rh) to yield the LeChatelier thermocouple alloy. Rhodium is a bright inert metal and for this reason it is used for electroplating other metals.

Osmium is the most refractory metal of the platinum family, with a melting temperature of 2700°C. It was once

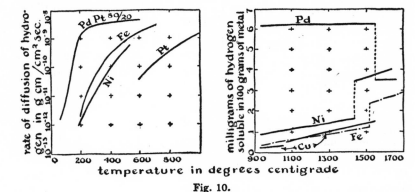

Fig. 10.

Borelius, G., and Lindblom, S., *Ann. d. Physik*, *82*, 201 (1927). Smithells, C. J., and Ransley, C. E., *Roy. Soc.*, *Proc.*, *150*, 172 (1935). Sieverts, A., *Zeits. f. Metallkunde*, *21*, 37 (1929).

used in incandescent lamps but has now been replaced by tungsten for this use. Incidentally, it is the heaviest known substance, having a density of 22.5 g/cm³.

Palladium is the least noble of the platinum metals. It oxidizes when heated in air and is dissolved in nitric acid. Hydrogen diffuses through palladium more rapidly than through platinum. At atmospheric pressure palladium will dissolve about 6 mg H_2 per 100 g of metal to form the "alloy" Pd_2H. The hydrogen is given off again if the metal is heated, in vacuum, to temperatures above 300°C. (See Fig. 10.) This property affords a convenient source of extremely pure hydrogen in small quantities.

The refractory metals: Tungsten, molybdenum, tantalum, and so forth. Tungsten is the most refractory metal and also the strongest. Wires of .0014 inch in diameter exhibit a tensile strength of 590,000 lbs./square inch. Tungsten is quite "unorthodox" in its behavior with respect to cold working and heat. Passing it through dies makes it more ductile, while heating it to a temperature greater than 1000°C. causes recrystalliza-tion and makes it brittle, a situation just opposite to the behavior of most metals. The ductility of tungsten at ordinary temperatures is due to its long fibrous crystal grains. Fig. 11 shows the ductility of tungsten at vari-ous temperatures. It will be noted that recrystallized brittle tungsten is ductile if heated to temperatures greater than 200°C.

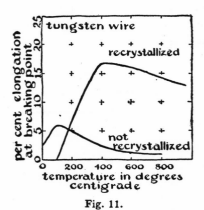

Fig. 11.

Espe, W., and Knoll, M., *Werkstoff-kunde der Hochvakuumtechnik*, page 18. Berlin: Julius Springer, 1936.

Traces of water vapor are corrosive on the tungsten fila-ments in vacuum electric lamps. The water molecule reacts with hot tungsten to form tungsten oxide and atomic hydro-gen, both of which evaporate to the glass wall of the bulb, where, owing to catalytic effect of the glass, they react to give metallic tungsten and water vapor again. The water molecule is now free again to repeat its action on the tungsten filament.

Tungsten reacts with oxygen and carbon monoxide, in vacuum, to form oxides and carbides. Tungsten is not attacked or affected by mercury vapor or hydrogen gas. In air, at a yellow heat, tungsten reacts with oxygen to form volatile oxides, which distill off as white smoke.

Molybdenum is more ductile than tungsten. Otherwise, it is very similar to tungsten, and the two metals form alloys in all proportions. Some of these alloys are used commercially. Their properties are, in general, a compromise between the higher melting temperature of tungsten, on the one hand, and the greater workability and machinability of molybdenum, on the other.

Molybdenum and tungsten do not soft-solder or amalgamate with mercury, but both metals may be welded to nickel or Advance alloy. Nickel is frequently welded to tungsten to facilitate connecting it by spot-welding, soldering, or brazing to other less refractory metals.

Tungsten or molybdenum may be cleaned by heating the metal to a red heat and rubbing its surface with a piece of potassium or sodium nitrite.

In many respects tantalum is like molybdenum and tungsten.[8] Tantalum, when it is very pure, is one of the most ductile metals. However, when heated in hydrogen or air, tantalum becomes brittle. To anneal tantalum, it must be heated to about 800°C. in a vacuum better than 5×10^{-2} mm of mercury. Because tantalum readily gives off occluded gas if heated above 800°C., it is used as a construction material in vacuum tubes.

To spot-weld this metal successfully, it must be submerged under carbon tetrachloride or water. It may be machined using carbon tetrachloride as a cutting fluid, and spun using hard laundry soap as lubricant.

Columbium occurs with tantalum and has many properties in common with it. It is less refractory and more ductile than tantalum. It is used as a substitute for tantalum.

Rhenium is the heaviest member of the manganese subgroup in the periodic table, and it is very refractory, its melting temperature being only about 200° below that of tungsten.

---

[8] Tungsten, molybdenum, and tantalum may be obtained from the Fansteel Products Company, Inc., North Chicago, Illinois, and Callite Products Company, 595 Forty-Ninth Street, Union City, New Jersey.

Alloys. *Invar.* The iron-nickel alloy, 63.5 Fe, 36 Ni, 0.5 Mn, is known as Invar. Its coefficient of expansion is only low for temperatures below 120°C., being 4×10^{-7} per degree centigrade. The heat conduction of Invar is also very low, being only $\frac{1}{40}$ that of copper. Invar does not corrode. It is used for the construction of surveyor's tapes and instruments in which the dimensions are required to remain constant in spite of temperature changes. The alloy melts at 1425°C.

Electrical-resistance alloys.[9] Nickel-chromium alloys are characterized by a high electrical resistance (about 58 times that of copper), a low temperature coefficient of resistance, and a high resistance to oxidation. Examples are Chromel

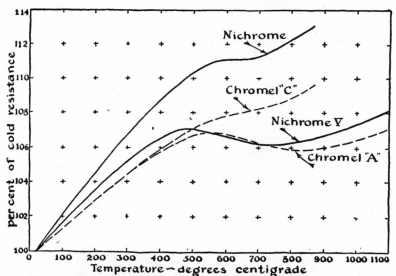

These curves represent average values. Actual samples of the materials may depart from these values from negligible amounts at 20°C to as much as ±4½% at 1100°. For precise work samples of the material to be used should be tested.

Fig. 12.

---

[9] Chromel is manufactured by the Hoskins Manufacturing Company, Detroit, Michigan. Nichrome is manufactured by the Driver Harris Company, Harrison, New Jersey.

A and Nichrome V, of which the typical composition is 80 Ni and 20 Cr, with the melting point at 1420°C.

When some iron is added to the nickel-chromium alloys, it makes them more ductile. Nichrome and Chromel C are examples of these iron-containing alloys. The typical composition of Nichrome is 60 Ni, 12 Cr, 26 Fe, 2 Mn, and of Chromel C, 64 Ni, 11 Cr, 25 Fe. The melting temperatures of these alloys are 1350° and 1390°C. respectively. The change of resistance with temperature for these alloys is illustrated in Fig. 12.

Thermocouple alloys. Chromel P gives a useful basemetal thermocouple in combination with the alloy Alumel (94 Ni, $2\frac{1}{2}$ Mn, $\frac{1}{2}$ Fe). The thermocouple wires are welded together under a borax flux to make the junction. None of the Chromels braze, but they all may be welded to nickel.

Constantan (45 Ni, 55 Cu) has practically zero temperature coefficient of resistance up to a temperature of 400°C. Also, it gives a high thermal e.m.f. against copper, making an excellent thermocouple. Constantan exhibits high resistance to oxidation and corrosion. It solders easily.

Solders. Solders are required to flow onto the surface of the metals to be joined and to alloy with the surface layers of the metals. Also, they should be ductile, have high strength, and be noncorrosive.

Silver solder best meets all these requirements. It is used for joining brass, steel, stainless steels, and many other metals. Silver solders are, in effect, brazing alloys of the composition (4. Cu to 3 Zn) with silver added. A solder melting at 693°C. contains 65 per cent silver, while one melting at 760°C. contains but 20 per cent silver.

High-quality soft solder is half tin and half lead. Solders are often made with a higher content of lead, since the tin component is more expensive than lead. Such solders are inferior, since it is the tin component that makes the solder run well and adhere well. "Half-and-half" solder melts at 188°C. The properties of various solders are given in Table II.

TABLE II

Properties of Solders

Solder	Composition	Melting Point (°C.)	Flux
Soft solder:			
Wood's metal........	Bi 50, Cd 12.5, Pb 25, Sn 12.5	61	A
soft solder eutectic....	Pb 36, Sn 64	181	A
half-and-half.........	Pb 50, Sn 50	188	A
Hard solder:			
silver solder..........	Ag 45, Cu 30, Zn 25	720	B C
brazing compound....	Cu 54, Zn 46	875	B
Intermediate solder.....	Ag 20, Cu 3, Zn 2, Sn 75	400	A

Composition of fluxes:

A—(a) Flux: 40 $ZnCl_2$, 20 NH_4Cl, 40 H_2O.
　　(b) Paste: 90 Petrolatum, 10 NH_4Cl.
　　(c) Solution of rosin in alcohol.
B—(a) Thin paste composed of water and 10 parts powdered borax and 1 part boracic acid.
　　(b) Borax applied dry.
C—Handy flux. Manufactured by the Handy and Harman Company, Bridgeport, Connecticut. This is an excellent flux. It has a lower melting point than borax.

Brass and bronze. Brass is the most widely used construction material in the physical laboratory. It is fundamentally a copper-zinc alloy. Red brass (10 to 20 per cent zinc), or so-called Tombak alloy, is used for making flexible corrugated tubes (such as Silphon tubes) when maximum ductility is required; yellow or common brass, which contains copper and zinc in the proportions 65 to 35, with small lead additions to increase its machinability, is used where springiness is desired.

Brasses are less expensive than the copper-tin alloys or bronzes. They are also softer and more ductile. Brasses are used for drawing and rolling, whereas bronzes are primarily casting materials. Bronze castings are much more likely to be vacuum tight than brass castings. Also, because bronzes have small crystals of the hard brittle compound Cu_4Sn, they make good bearing metals (the 68.2 copper bronze, Cu_4Sn, is the true speculum metal used for optical gratings and for mirrors).[10]

Duraluminum. The aluminum alloy with composition 95 Al, 4 Cu, $\frac{1}{2}$ Mg, $\frac{1}{2}$ Mn, is known as Duraluminum. Duraluminum is employed extensively in many cases where brass was formerly used. For about 45 minutes after it has been heat treated at 530°C. and quenched in water, Duraluminum is ductile and can be rolled, bent, or cold-worked. After this interval a copper aluminum compound is precipitated out of solid solution, and this precipitate "keys" the crystals of the alloy at their slip planes, giving the alloy increased hardness and strength. The tensile strength, originally 30,000 lbs./square inch after quenching, becomes as great as 75,000 lbs./square inch after cold-working ánd aging. Duraluminum rivets are frequently stored in buckets cooled with dry ice. They may be used as desired, for this low temperature arrests the aging process, and the metal does not harden until after it has warmed up to room temperature.

Wood.[11] Two kinds of wood are obtained from a tree: heartwood and sapwood. The heartwood is formed early in the life of the tree and, as the name implies, is found near the center of the trunk. Protoplasms present when the tree is young are gradually replaced by deposits of gum, minerals, tannin, and pigments to form this heartwood as the tree becomes older. These substances make it heavier, stronger, and in most cases darker than the sapwood. The heartwood of the redwood tree, which is particularly free from gums and oils, is an exception. In other heartwoods there are abun-

---

[10] Lord Ross' famous 60-inch mirror contains 70 Cu 30 Sn; an old Roman mirror contains 64 Cu, 19 Sn, 17 Pb; an Egyptian mirror contains 85 Cu, 14 Sn, 1 Fe. Brady, G. S., *Materials Handbook.* New York: McGraw-Hill Book Company, 1931.

[11] Fowle, F. E., *Smithsonian Physical Tables.* Washington: The Smithsonian Institution, 1934.

Koehler, Arthur, *Properties and Uses of Woods.* New York: McGraw-Hill Book Company, 1924.

Marks, L. S., *Mechanical Engineers' Handbook.* New York: McGraw-Hill Book Company, 1930.

"Mechanical Properties of Woods Grown in the United States," Department of Agriculture, Bull. 556.

dant deposits. For example, in lignum vitae, these compounds produce an oiliness (especially when the wood is wet) which makes it suitable as a bearing material.

Sapwood, or the outer part of the tree, is more pliable than heartwood. Therefore, in using such woods as hickory and ash, which are noted for their adequate strength, the outer part of the trunk may be preferred to the heartwood because of its pliability.

Effects of temperature. Some of the effects of temperature on wood are due to the gum deposits. High temperature softens these gums, making the wood weaker and more liable to split. On the other hand, low temperatures produce increased brittleness.

The thermal expansion of wood in directions parallel and perpendicular to the grain is given in Table III. It will be noted that the expansion parallel to the grain is less for wood than for most of the metals. This property is a useful one, and it should be kept in mind and used in the construction of instruments where invariance of length is desired, as, for example, in a telescope tube, in which the relative distance between the optical components should not change with changes in temperature.

TABLE III

LINEAR EXPANSION OF WOOD AND VARIOUS OTHER SOLIDS PER UNIT LENGTH PER DEGREE CENTIGRADE $\times 10^{-6}$

Material	Expansion	
Aluminum	23.0	
Cast brass	18.7	
Cast iron	12.0	
Steel	11.4	
Glass, plate and crown	9.0	
	Parallel	Perpendicular
Maple	6.3	48
Oak	4.9	55
Pine	5.4	34
Walnut	6.5	48
Sugar maple	2.1	..

The heat conductivity of several common types of wood is given in Table IV. The conduction of heat is from two to four times as great along the grain as it is across it. The conductivity depends, in a large measure, on the moisture content. To obtain maximum heat insulation, the wood must be dry. To keep it dry, particularly if the wood is to be exposed to low temperatures, it should be coated with paraffin.

TABLE IV

HEAT CONDUCTION OF WOOD AND SOME OTHER MATERIALS IN C. G. S. UNITS

Material	Specific Gravity	Heat Conductivity
Wood:		
Balsa................................	0.12	.00012
Hard maple.........................	0.61	.00038
White pine:		
along the fiber.................	0.50	.00027
across the fiber................	0.50	.00010
Cotton—firmly packed.............	....	.00010
Hair, felt..........................	....	.000085

Effects of moisture. One drawback to the use of wood as a material for construction, especially for scientific apparatus, lies in the fact that its dimensions may change considerably with its change in moisture content. We may take the shrinkage from the green to the dry condition as an index of the changes one may expect with changes in humidity and residual curing. This shrinkage (radial and tangential) for several woods is given in Table V.

TABLE V

SHRINKAGE OF WOOD FROM THE GREEN TO THE DRY CONDITION

Wood	Tangential (%)	Radial (%)	Ratio
Magnolia, evergreen......................	6.6	5.4	1.2
Redwood...............................	4.4	2.6	1.7
Sugar maple...........................	9.5	4.9	1.9
Sugar pine............................	5.6	2.9	1.9
Pine, northern white...................	6	2.3	2.5
Range of all commercial woods..........	4.2 to 14	2 to 8.5	..

Wood Handbook, United States Department of Agriculture, September, 1935

Among the hardwoods, evergreen magnolia is prized as one which does not warp. This may be understood by referring to Table V, where we see that of all the woods it is the one whose radial and tangential shrinkages are most nearly equal.

Most of the shrinkage in wood is at right angles to the grain; the longitudinal shrinkage, taken from the green to the cured condition, is seldom greater than $\frac{1}{10}$ to $\frac{1}{3}$ per cent. (It is greater than this for some woods, particuarly woods grown under strong compression. Yellow pine compression wood, for example, may shrink longitudinally as much as $2\frac{1}{2}$ per cent when it is cured. Redwoods also exhibit considerable longitudinal shrinkage. However, longitudinal shrinkage is negligible for most of the other woods.) This property of wood, in addition to the low thermal expansion parallel to the grain, explains why wood has been used so successfully for rulers; it may suggest other applications for wood in the laboratory.

When a piece of wood is carved or cut to precise dimensions that are to be maintained, it should be painted at once with several coats of shellac, in order to maintain the moisture equilibrium already established. Linseed oil is less effective, while paraffin is more effective than shellac for this purpose. Molten paraffin is applied by pouring it over the surface with a spoon. The boiling of wood in paraffin causes it to become brittle.

Strength of wood. Strength and rigidity do not vary from wood to wood as much as is commonly supposed. For example, the bending strength of shagbark hickory is only 2.6 times as great as that of sugar pine, and pine is inferior to hickory in rigidity by a factor of only 1.9. Pine differs from hickory not so much in stiffness as in brittleness— pine breaks where hickory bends. Spruce, of all the common woods, has the highest strength for its weight.

The tensile strength of wood varies in different directions. Along the grain its strength is ordinarily from ten to twenty times as great as it is across the grain. Also, the modulus of

TABLE VI

Properties of Wood

Property	Sugar Pine	Per-simmon	Sugar Maple	Evergreen Magnolia	Shagbark Hickory
Specific gravity..............	.37	.81	.62	.51	.74
Static bending: fiber stress at elastic limit (1000 lbs. per sq. inch).....................	6.4	15.4	10.4	7.8	11.9
Static bending: modulus of rupture (1000 lbs. per sq. inch)...	8.6	23.7	15.8	12.5	22.6
Static bending: modulus of elasticity (1,000,000 lbs. per sq. inch).....................	1.21	2.48	1.82	1.48	2.29
Static bending: work in bending to maximum load (lbs. per cu. inch).....................	5.0	16.9	13.6	12.3	26.3
Impact bending: energy of dropped hammer to cause complete failure (relative)....	26	54	51	38	100
Compressional fiber stress at the elastic limit parallel to the grain (1000 lbs. per sq. inch)..	4.74	9.21	6.06	3.94	
Maximum crushing strength (1000 lbs. per sq. inch).......	5.2	14.1	8.6	6.6	10.7
Compressional fiber stress at the elastic limit (perpendicular to the grain) (1000 lbs. per sq. inch).....................	.64	3.91	1.62	1.25	2.47
Tensional strength perpendicular to the grain (1000 lbs. per sq. inch).....................	.35	1.52	.77	.78	...
Shearing strength parallel to the grain (1000 lbs. per sq. inch)..	1.1	2.7	2.5	1.7	2.3
Hardness on the side (relative)..	4	100	45	35	...

elasticity is correspondingly greater along the grain. This anisotropy is avoided in plywoods, formed by gluing together three, five, seven, or nine layers of wood, the consecutive layers being arranged with their grain axes lying mutually perpendicular. Plywoods with the greatest number of layers are most resistant to splitting and are most nearly isotropic. The thick plywoods use cores of wormy chestnut. The ease with which woods are cut and carved is proportional to their homogeneity or the degree of similarity between the physical properties of the spring and the summer growth. Also, it is desirable to have a fine grain, a quality possessed by many hardwoods, especially mahogany. Of the common softwoods, poplar and sugar pine are the most homogeneous and easiest to work.

Some wood substitutes are now available which are nearly isotropic. These are formed of bonded cellulose fibers. Although they are quite homogeneous, they are not so easily worked as wood with the plane and chisel, and nailing splits them. They can be sawed with the ordinary wood saw. Masonite is an example of such a wood substitute.[12] It comes, chiefly, in three grades, a light material which is a good heat insulator, a harder material which is suitable for making boxes for instruments, and an oil-tempered waterproof material.

Waxes and cements. The physicist uses waxes and cements to seal windows into apparatus, tubes in plates, tubes together, and so forth. He uses them also to support and fasten down lenses, prisms, and mirrors. Of all waxes available, the most useful for making improvised supports and seals is the so-called universal wax.

Universal wax. Universal wax is made from 1 part Venetian turpentine and 5 parts beeswax. It is usually, although not necessarily, colored with vermilion. It should be made up in small quantities, for it oxidizes, with the result that it becomes hard and loses its desirable properties. Old pieces may be useful if the outside oxidized layers are removed and discarded. The usefulness of this wax depends upon its adhesive and plastic properties. It is quite plastic at the slightly elevated temperature attained when the wax is worked between the fingers. When it cools, it becomes fairly rigid.

Beeswax and rosin. Beeswax and rosin compound is prepared by melting together equal parts of beeswax and rosin. Its softening point is at the temperature which just begins to

---

[12] Masonite Corporation, 111 West Washington Street, Chicago, Illinois.

feel hot (47°C.) and it is liquid at 10° above this temperature. Its outstanding property is its adhesiveness to cold metal. It is not very strong, but its strength is adequate for sealing vacuum systems and for fixing apparatus, as, for example, fastening a prism to the prism table of a spectrometer. It can be applied with a brush, an eye-dropper, or the blade of a knife. To secure the best bond to cold metal, the wax should be applied smoking hot with an eye-dropper or a knife. When it has been used for sealing down a bell jar, it can be removed with a putty knife, remelted, and used over and over. The smoking temperature distills off some of the beeswax, causing the compound to become harder. It may be retempered by adding more beeswax. There are many applications for which this wax is not suitable because it shrinks a great deal on solidifying. It is best "dissolved" by a mixture of equal parts of carbon tetrachloride and ethyl alcohol.

Shellac. In its pure state, shellac in stick form is known as lapidarist's cement. It has a high tensile strength and shear strength. (Both are about 3800 lbs./square inch.) Only the natural orange shellac possesses this high strength. The main ingredient of the better grades of sealing wax and especially banker's wax is shellac.

Shellac is used in commerce chiefly for the manufacture of phonograph records, varnishes, and as an insulator in the electrical industry. It has a higher resilience than almost any other wax, and it is this property which gives long life to phonograph records.

The best solvent for shellac is alcohol. This solution yields a varnish which has many uses in the laboratory. When it is very thick, it is useful for hunting leaks in vacuum systems.

Shellac is polymerized by heat, giving a product which is harder, has a higher softening temperature, and is less soluble in alcohol than the uncured material. This polymerization is accompanied by a chemical loss of water and a two- to threefold increase in molecular weight. Half of the uncured shellac is transformed into this harder variety by heating for 30 hours at 90°C.; at 150°C. it is completely transformed in 3 hours. When the pure shellac is to be used as a cement, it is desirable to have it in the unpolymerized state.

Commercial shellac may legally be designated as pure although it may contain as much as 3 per cent rosin. This materially weakens it. It is possible, however, to obtain shellac which is free from this adulterant.[13]

Tempered shellac. When shellac is tempered with 20 to 40 per cent wood tar, we have a wax similar to the familiar DeKhotinsky cement. This wax is not affected by water, carbon disulphide, benzol, petroleum benzine, or turpentine. It is affected only slightly by ether, chloroform, and sulphuric, nitric, or hydrochloric acids.

When DeKhotinsky cement is heated in a flame, it emits an odor and is somewhat inflammable. A new variety of tempered shellac, which has no odor and is not so inflammable, is now sold by the Central Scientific Company under the trade name of Sealstix. Sealstix has a greater working range of temperature than pure shellac and a very high strength.

Shellac can be tempered with butyl phthalate. The resulting compound has a very low vapor pressure and is particuarly suitable for high-vacuum work. It is odorless and relatively noninflammable.

Shellac can also be tempered to varying degrees with oil of cassia. About 10 per cent oil is quickly added to the molten shellac. The oil gives a compound with an agreeable odor. It is useful for many purposes when its vapor pressure is not important.

Shellac can also be tempered with amyl acetate for use when the vapor pressure of this constituent is unobjectionable. Most of this solvent evaporates when the cemented elements are maintained at an elevated temperature (80°C.) for an hour or so. A mixture of 2 ounces of amyl acetate to

---

[13] Pure orange shellac is obtainable from William Zinsser and Company, 516 West 49th Street, New York City.

100 g of shellac gives a cement with a strength in excess of 2500 lbs./square inch.[14]

Picein. This sealing compound is characterized by low vapor pressure, plasticity at room temperature, and chemical inertness. Its low working temperature (it becomes quite plastic at 50°C. and is liquid at 80°C.), together with its adhesiveness, recommends it for many applications. Besides its use for sealing tubes together and repairing leaks in vacuum systems, it is also used in the optical industry. It is practically unaffected by alcohol. Picein is immune even to a short immersion in cold dichromate cleaning solution. It is dissolved by benzol and turpentine. Its insulating qualities are said to be as good as amber if it is not overheated. It comes in two grades, the second being characterized by a liquefying temperature of 105°C.[15]

Apiezon compounds.[16] Apiezon compounds are especially refined residues of paraffin oils freed from high vapor pressure constituents.

The sealing compound "Q" contains graphite. It is plastic at ordinary temperatures and has a vapor pressure of 10^{-4} mm at room temperature, and, applied to ordinary twine, it is recommended as a packing for vacuum valves.

Apiezon wax "W" has the lowest vapor pressure of any of the waxes now available. It is necessary to heat this wax to 180°C. in order to raise its vapor pressure to 10^{-3} mm of mercury. It melts at 70°C., but it can best be applied at 100°C. or higher. Molten, it wets metals and glass and is quite fluid. It is fairly strong at ordinary temperatures. It is soluble in zylene.

Silver chloride. Silver chloride is recommended for seals that must hold at elevated temperatures. It melts at 455°C. It is insoluble in water, alcohol, benzol, and acid. It is,

---

[14] This cement was developed by Marcus H. Brown.

[15] Picein and a rubber packing material, *Dichtungsgummie*, are obtainable from the distributing agents of the New York Hamburg Rubber Company, Schrader and Ehlers, 239 Fourth Avenue, New York City.

[16] Apiezon compounds are obtainable from the James G. Biddle Company Philadelphia, Pennsylvania.

however, soluble in a solution of sodium thiosulphate. Most metals and glasses are wet by fused silver chloride. It is useful for sealing optically worked windows on a discharge tube. The window, after being sealed, is cooled slowly to prevent it from cracking.

Espe and Knoll describe an enamel which they recommend for cementing optical plane parallels on a discharge tube.[17] This is a mixture of clay and boracic acid, the melting point of which is 450° to 600°C. It is applied, as is silver chloride, by heating both the window and discharge tube in an electric oven.

The bonding materials which we have considered above are thermoplastics. With the exception of shellac, the changes in their properties are reversible with temperature. We will now treat those substances which set, which can be vulcanized, and which polymerize by the application of heat. They include the synthetic resins, rubber cements, and inorganic cements.

Synthetic resins treated of here fall into three broad divisions. These are, first, the polymerized phenol aldehydes, of which Bakelite is an example; second, the condensation products formed by polyhydric alcohols with polybasic acids (these are termed alkyd resins, of which Glyptal is an example); and third, the polymerized derivatives of methacrylic acid, of which Lucite and Plexiglas are examples.

Bakelite.[18] Bakelite comes in several forms that are useful to the physicist. The properties of these vary from liquid or soluble solids in the uncured condition to stable insoluble solids in the cured condition. Bakelite in the latter condition is obtainable in the form of clear, transparent sheets, blocks, tubes, and so forth. This material is light (density, 1.27) and strong (7000 lbs./square inch), is a good electrical insulator, and is insensitive to moderate heat. In this completely polymerized form it does not melt, and it chars only

---

[17] Espe, W., and Knoll, M., *Werkstoffkunde der Hochvakuumtechnik*, page 157. Berlin: Julius Springer, 1936.

[18] Bakelite is manufactured by the Bakelite Corporation of America, 247 Park Avenue, New York City.

at a temperature of 285°C.   Chemically, it is relatively inert. The completely polymerized Bakelite is unaffected by hot water, oils, greases, alcohol, acetone, benzene, dilute mineral acids, including hydrofluoric, and soap.   It is practically nonhygroscopic.   These properties recommend it as a material for making transparent chemical apparatus, such as burettes, pipettes, beakers, and so forth.   Transparent forms of Bakelite are suitable for making models for photoelastic studies with polarized light.

Several molded and laminated products bonded with Bakelite are available commercially.   These have canvas, wood fiber, asbestos, or graphite as a base.   The asbestos-base material is especially heat resistant, and the graphite-base material is useful for dry bearings.

Bakelite varnishes usually consist of solutions of the unpolymerized form.   After application and drying, the varnish films are transformed to the insoluble form by baking.

Bakelite cements come in the form of solids and viscous liquids.   The solid form melts at about 80°C. (in hot water) and is transformed by heat to a form which does not melt. The liquid forms contain a volatile solvent.   It is first necessary to evaporate this by preliminary heating of 1 to 4 hours at 80°C., after which the residue is polymerized by heating for 2 hours at 120°C.   A self-hardening cement is available which will set at room temperature.   Vacuum seals made with these cements have a low vapor pressure and can be used to temperatures slightly above 100°C.

A general-utility cement can be made by mixing Bakelite varnish with red lead.   This hardens rapidly and will withstand high pressure, steam, oil, and moderate heating.

Alkyd resins.[19]   Alkyd resins are formed by the condensation of phthalic anhydride on glycol, glycerol, or other polyhydric alcohols.   Glycol phthalate is useful as a vacuum-sealing cement because of its low vapor pressure, fluidity, and wetting power when melted.   In addition, it

[19] Alkyd resins may be obtained from the General Electric Company.

may be cured to give it increased strength and inertness. It is also noted for its adhesiveness to aluminum. It is inert toward mineral oils. Dehydrating catalysts, such as zinc oxide, hasten the cure of these compounds and serve as a filler to economize on the resin, as, for example, in lamp-basing cements.

Lucite and Plexiglas. Lucite and Plexiglas are trade names for methyl (and ethyl) methacrylate, polymerized derivatives of methacrylic acid.[20] These materials are sold as a cast resin in the form of sheets, rods, and tubes, as a thermoplastic powder, and as the unpolymerized liquid.

The methyl methacrylate monomer is a mobile liquid which can be polymerized in almost any desired form. The monomer boils at 100°C. and has a heat of polymerization of about 80 calories/g. As it is obtained from the factory, it contains an inhibitor, such as hydroquinone or pyrogallol, to prevent it from polymerizing at room temperature. To use the liquid, this inhibitor is removed by washing with caustic, the liquid is dried, and an accelerator, usually benzoyl peroxide, is added to catalyze the polymerization. The volume of the monomer is 20 per cent greater than the volume of the polymer finally obtained, so that considerable art must be invoked to prevent the formation of voids when the monomer condenses.

The polymerized methyl methacrylate, Lucite, has the optical properties given in Table VII. (See also Table VI, Chapter IX.) The polymers are inert toward water and insoluble in the straight chain hydrocarbons, alcohols, and ethers and in most fats, oils, and waxes. They are, however, dissolved by lower ketone and ester solvents, and by mixtures of the aromatic hydrocarbons when small amounts of alcohol are added.

These polymers are vastly different from Bakelite and the plastic, Catalin, in respect to cutting. Whereas Catalin and

---

[20] Lucite is manufactured by E. I. duPont de Nemours and Company, Wilmington, Delaware. Plexiglas is manufactured by Röhm and Haas Company, 222 West Washington Square, Philadelphia, Pennsylvania.

TABLE VII

PERCENTAGE OF ULTRAVIOLET TRANSMISSION OF LUCITE AT DIFFERENT WAVE LENGTHS

Wave Length (Å)		Transmission (%)
Sheet Thickness 1 inch	Sheet Thickness 0.1 inch	
3020	....	1
3120	2860	5
3140	2920	12
3170	2980	25
3280	3020	50
3500	3340	75

Bakelite quickly remove the edge from high-speed steel (in fact, cold-rolled steel is just about as good for cutting them as high-speed steel), Lucite and Plexiglas can be cut by the hour without the edge of the tool becoming dulled.

Fish-glue cement. A cement which is inert toward most organic solvents is made from a thick solution of 3 ounces of fish glue, $\frac{1}{4}$ ounce of potassium bichromate, and a little am-- monia. The cement so formed is allowed to dry and is then heated in an air oven until it assumes a chocolate-brown color. This cement is often used on Pulfrich refractometers.

Rubber cements. Rubber cements are conveniently classi- fied as follows: nonvulcanizing cements, which attain their strength simply by the evaporation of a solvent; vulcanizing cements, in which a chemical change occurs after the evapo- ration of the solvent; and thermoplastic cements. Some of the vulcanizing cements contain sulphur, while others are vulcanized simply by painting a vulcanizing liquid, sulphur chloride, on the rubber after it has been applied.

The synthetic thermoplastic rubber-like products Neo- prene (manufactured by DuPont Company) and Koroseal (manufactured by the Goodrich Rubber Company) have many useful properties. These materials are remarkably stable chemically; they are inert toward acids and alkalies, as well as many fats and oils.

Plaster of Paris. This is frequently used to support large glass bulbs containing mercury. The plaster suspended in water to the consistency of a paste is cast between the bulb and a loose-fitting wooden support. Salt shortens the time required for plaster of Paris to set, while a trace of glue acts in the opposite way. The glass may first be wiped with oil so that the plaster will not adhere to it. This facilitates subsequent dismantling.

Litharge and glycerin. This combination gives a cement useful for the same type of applications for which plaster of Paris is useful. It is inert toward water, most acids, and all alkalies, and holds up to temperatures of 260°C. It is prepared by mixing pulverized Litharge (which has been first thoroughly heated at 400°C.) with pure glycerin to the consistency of a paste.[21]

Other irreversible cements. Water glass forms cements when mixed with the carbonates or oxides of calcium, magnesium, zinc, lead, or iron. In a few hours these mixtures set to rock hardness. Combined with talc, water glass makes a cement which holds even at a red heat. This cement will not chip off from glass at liquid air temperatures.

Zinc oxychloride cement is used extensively in dentistry. It is formed from a 60 per cent zinc chloride solution and zinc oxide powder mixed to the consistency of a thick paste. These constituents react to give zinc oxychloride. To insure that the oxide is free from carbonate, it should first be heated until it turns yellow to calcine the carbonates.

Nine parts kaolin mixed with one part borax give a cement useful to 1600°C. The constituent powders are mixed, and water is added to facilitate application. After the water evaporates, the cement is slowly heated to a yellow heat in order to set it.

Insa-lute cement, a commercial product, is a thick white

[21] von Angerer, Ernst, *Technische Kunstgriffe bei physikalischen Untersuchungen.* Friedr. Vieweg und Sohn, 1936.

suspension of refractory substance in water glass. It sets on drying to form a white material having the texture of porcelain. It is an electrical insulator and stands firing to about 1100°F. It adheres to metal, glass, and porcelain. It attacks chromium-alloy wire at elevated temperatures and should not be used in contact with it. One should use a refractory cement such as Alundum cement in contact with chromium-alloy wires.

Glue. Unquestionably, the best bonding material for wood is glue. Glues are more effective for the lighter woods, which contain less oils and resins, than for the dense woods. There are three kinds of glue: casein, blood albumin, and animal glues. The first two are useful for general construction work. The animal glues exhibit greater strength, but they are softened by moisture. Casein glue is made from milk protein and lime. Blood glues contain caustic soda and water glass. Both the latter glues require heat and pressure for their application. They are water resistant and are used for making plywood.

Animal glue is best applied hot. Cabinet and pattern makers usually keep a hot glue pot. For occasional use, however, air-drying glues are quite satisfactory for joining wood as well as leather. Air-drying glue is applied to the surfaces which are to be fastened together. The glue films on these surfaces are allowed to dry until the glue is definitely stringy. At this stage the surfaces are clamped together, and the glue is allowed to become completely dry.

Lubrication. There are two kinds of lubrication with liquids. In the first and most common kind, called complete lubrication, the bearing surfaces are separated by a layer of oil about .005 inch in thickness. The friction, and consequently the amount of heat produced in the lubricant, depend on the thickness and viscosity of the liquid.

In the second kind of lubrication the surfaces are in contact. Friction and galling are diminished and prevented by an absorbed surface film. The tenacity with which this film adheres and the effectiveness with which it reduces friction are determined by a quality called the oiliness of the liquid. The lubrication of surfaces in contact is called boundary lubrication. In general, mineral oils are more suitable for the first type of lubrication, and vegetable and animal fats, as well as soaps, are more suitable for the boundary lubrication. The friction in the case of boundary lubrication is usually less when the surfaces are covered with a surface film of high molecular weight. High viscosity (which is associated with high molecular weight) gives more friction in the case of complete lubrication.

Sir Wm. B. Hardy and Miss Ida Doubleday[22] have studied the coefficient of boundary friction for various materials, and the results of their study are illustrated by Fig. 13.

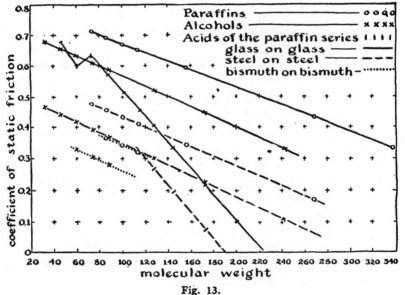

Fig. 13.

The boundary friction is represented in this figure for glass rubbing on glass, steel on steel, and bismuth on bismuth. The coefficient of friction is plotted as ordinate

---

[22] Hardy, W. B., and Doubleday, Ida, *Roy. Soc., Proc.*, *100A*, 550 (1921–1922).

against the molecular weight of the lubricant as abscissa. The paraffins and the alcohols and acids of the paraffin series are the liquids used as lubricants.

We see that for very high molecular weights, particularly in the case of the fatty acids, the coefficient of friction is expected to be zero, and, indeed, for some compounds Hardy found the static friction to be less than the minimum amount that he could measure.

Of these results, Hardy and Doubleday say:

It will be seen that for each chemical series, and for each solid, the curve is a straight line.   The equation is therefore

$$\mu = b - aM$$

where M is molecular weight and a and b are parameters.   The effect of the nature of the solid face is unexpectedly simple.   In changing from glass to steel the curve for a series is merely moved parallel to itself, and in changing from steel to bismuth there is a further shifting.   Therefore, in the equation the parameter a is independent of the nature of the solid face and dependent only on chemical type, varying from one chemical series to another.   The parameter b, on the other hand, is dependent upon the nature of the solid face as well as upon the chemical series.

From the above expression one might expect the coefficient of friction for two dissimilar surfaces to be a mean of the coefficient for the two separate surfaces, and Table VIII, from the paper of Hardy and Doubleday, shows how well this expectation is realized.

The addition of a small amount of fatty acid to a mineral oil materially improves lubrication, especially where the bearing surfaces come in contact and the character of lubrication changes from the complete type to the boundary type. The higher efficiency of boundary lubrication obtained in this way is due to the adsorption of a fatty acid film of high molecular weight on the bearing surfaces.

The suitability of a lubricant for use in a scientific instrument often depends primarily upon the ability of the lubricant to form stable films which cover the surface of the

TABLE VIII

Coefficients of Friction

Slider	Plate	Lubricant		
		Butyl Alcohol	Amyl Alcohol	Octyl Alcohol
Glass	Glass	0.606 }mean	0.585 }mean	0.5176 }mean
Steel	Steel	0.3924} 0.4992	0.375} 0.48	0.2981} 0.4078
Glass	Steel	0.493	0.48	0.41
Glass	Glass	0.606 }mean	..	0.5176 }mean
Bismuth	Bismuth	0.30 } 0.453	..	0.25 } 0.3838
Bismuth	Glass	0.451	..	0.38
Steel	Steel	0.3924 }mean	..	0.2981 }mean
Bismuth	Bismuth	0.30 } 0.3464	..	0.25 } 0.274
Bismuth	Steel	0.348	..	0.27

Hardy, W. B., and Doubleday, Ida, *Roy. Soc., Proc., 100A*, 564 (1921–1922).

metal and produce a diminution of static friction between sliding metal parts. Oils which are rich in vegetable or animal fats are superior to petroleum oils in this regard. Hydrated lanolin is an excellent lubricant for sliding friction heads in which a low starting (or static) friction is important. Unfortunately, it is somewhat corrosive.

Colloidal graphite added to oil is similarly adsorbed on bearing surfaces. It is useful for the lubrication of spectrometer cones and, in machinery, it is especially useful for the running-in operations to form a hard polished Beilby layer on the bearing surfaces.[23]

For extremely heavy-duty lubrication, mutton fat or Dutch grease is recommended. Dutch grease is simply a combination of mutton fat with heavy petroleum oils.

It is desirable for clocks and other delicate mechanisms to have an oil that is chemically stable, does not corrode the metal parts, does not escape by spreading or evaporating, and does not freeze easily.

[23] Finch. G. I., "The Beilby Layer," *Science Progress, 31*, 609 (1937).

The oils from the head and jaw of the porpoise (Nye watch oil) and blackfish satisfy these qualifications most completely. These oils, however, are quite expensive ($125.00 a gallon). Sperm oil is next in quality.

Soap is a good lubricant for wood. Water is used between rubber and metal surfaces. Talc is often used as a dry lubricant for nailing and so forth. Also, graphite, especially colloidal graphite, forms a good dry lubricant at ordinary and elevated temperatures. It is used for lubricating lock barrels. Colloidal graphite dispersed in water or glycerin has film-forming properties which recommend it for some applications. The glycerin dispersion is useful at low temperatures.

Soapstone.[24] When soapstone, or massive talc, is heated to 500°C., it gives off absorbed water. Heating it to 850°C. drives off the remaining water, and finally heating to 1300°C. gives a complete transformation of the mineral constituents. When the material is transformed, the corresponding overall change of hardness is from 1 to 6 on Moh's scale. Owing to these properties, soapstone is very useful in the laboratory, since it can be easily machined before it is fired, and after it is fired it gives a hard material having many desirable properties. The shrinkage from firing is less than 1 per cent. Firing from 24 to 48 hours at 1100°C. is the usual practice. It is said that a material with iron content is not suitable for use in a vacuum, since it gives off gas. Imported Italian soapstone is exceptionally free from iron impurities and is obtainable in large blocks.[25]

Finely divided talc can be pressed and fired at 1400°C., giving a sintered body like that obtained from the massive mineral. The shrinkage of the powder on firing is about 8 per cent. After firing, it has the property that it is not attacked by acids or alkalies. It can be welded to glass.

---

[24] Hughes, H. H., *Bureau of Mines, Inf. Circ.*, No. 6553 (1931).
Ladoo, Raymond B., Bureau of Mines, Bull. 213, pages 80–81.
[25] Soapstone is obtainable from M. Kirchberger and Company, 1425 Thirty-Seventh Street, Brooklyn, New York.

Talc, both fired and unfired, is chemically inert; it is not attacked by acids (except slowly by hydrochloric acid) or by alkalies.   Fig. 14 shows the electrical resistance of talc and some other refractory materials as a function of temperature.

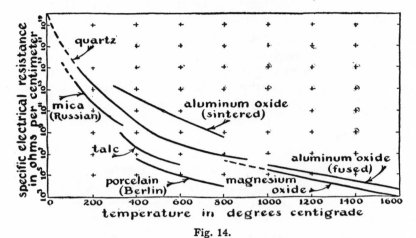

Fig. 14.

Espe, W., and Knoll, M., *Werkstoffkunde der Hochvakuumtechnik*, page 199. Berlin: Julius Springer, 1936.

CHAPTER XIV

Notes on the Construction and Design of Instruments and Apparatus

The cutting of metals. In essence, the cutting of metal in the lathe, the milling machine, and so forth, amounts to the continuous driving of a hard-metal wedge, the tool, under the surface layer of the work. Fig. 1 illustrates a typical tool. In the lathe the work moves and the tool is stationary, while in the milling machine the opposite is the case. This difference, however, is immaterial. The important factors are the cutting angle, the rake, the clearance, and the speed and feed with which the cutting operation is carried out.

The cutting angle is illustrated in Fig. 1. For hard and brittle metals it is best to have this angle large; for soft

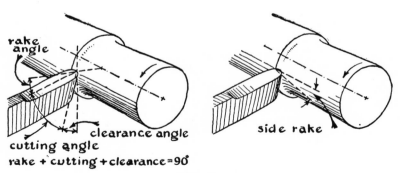

Fig. 1.

tenacious metals it is best to have the cutting angle small. For example, the cutting angle usually varies from 75° for brass and cast iron to 40° for steel and even less for copper and aluminum. Thin, keen tools with a small cutting angle will not stand up under severe cutting conditions as well as the blunt ones, because the blunt tools conduct heat away from the tip more effectively.

The rake angle is illustrated in Figs. 1 and 2. The dimension of the rake angle determines the amount of deformation or cold working of the metal chip removed. This cold working is diminished, and the heat generation is also diminished when the rake angle is increased. With large rake angles the forces acting between the chip, or turning, and the tool are more tangential than normal. It is desirable to diminish normal forces when cutting soft tenacious metals which tend

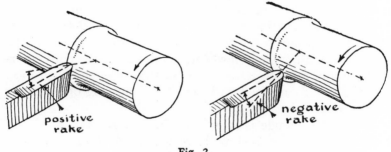

positive rake   negative rake

Fig. 2.

to stick to the tool. For brass, the rake angle should be nearly zero—it may be even a little less than zero. (See Fig. 2.)

In the lathe the clearance angle is the angle included between the inner surface of the tool and the direction of relative motion at the tip of the tool. (See Fig. 1.) It is important, especially for boring, to have this angle great enough to prevent the heel of the tool from riding on the work. Clearance angles vary from 35° for soft tenacious metals to 10° for cast iron and brass.

The higher speeds of the lathe should be used for cutting brass except when turning castings or using the cutting-off tool. Unless the proper speed is used with the cutting-off tool, it will chatter. The proper speed and feed for this tool depends upon the size of the work, but in general these factors are to be determined by trial. A wooden plug inserted in a tube lessens chattering when the cutting-off tool is used. Fig. 3 shows a method of shaping a cutting-off tool which minimizes chattering. In this tool, side rake is balanced against asymmetry of the end so that the tool cuts squarely into the material. The point of the tool is ground on the side of the tool adjacent to the piece on which a finished edge is desired. The other piece may exhibit a slight burr.

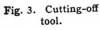

Fig. 3. Cutting-off tool.

For cutting steel, the speed should be as fast as the tool will stand without burning. For final cuts, however, a moderate speed gives a better finish.

Tools with a round nose give smooth finish cuts. Fig. 4 shows such a tool having about 10° clearance for cutting either brass or cast iron. The tool shown here has a slight double side rake, and it will cut in the direction of either the headstock or the tailstock.

The function of a lubricant in cutting metals is in most cases primarily to cool the chip and tool to prevent sticking. Brass, bronze, and cast iron may be machined dry, (except in the operations of tapping, knurling, and polishing, for which machine oil is used). Soluble oil or lard oil is used for tenacious metals such as steel. Kerosene or turpentine is often used for aluminum. Milk may be used for copper. Lead and babbitt are turned dry, but they are oiled for filing, drilling, and threading.

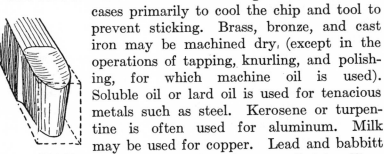

Fig. 4. Finishing tool.

The lathe.[1]   The lathe is by far the most versatile machine in the shop. It can accomplish nearly all the operations that are done on other machines, such as the miller, the shaper, the grinder, the drill press, and so forth, besides the

---

[1] By Roger Hayward.

many operations which it alone can do.   For this reason it
seems right that we should devote some space to a discussion
of its properties.

The essential parts of the lathe are the spindle, tailstock,
saddle (or carriage), ways, slide rest, and compound rest.
The spindle is supplied with power and rotates in close-
fitting bearings, which constrain it to turn on a single fixed
axis.   The tailstock is a socket, the axis of which is supposed
to coincide with the axis of rotation of the spindle.   It is
mounted on guides in the ways so that its distance from the
end of the spindle may be fixed to suit the work at hand.
The saddle, or carriage, is used primarily to support a cutting
tool and to allow it motion parallel to the axis of rotation of
the work.   The ways are metal guides on which the carriage
and tailstock move.   They are formed on the bed, or framework of the lathe, and are supposed to be parallel to the axis
of the spindle.   The slide rest consists of ways with a slide.
Its ways are supposed to be perpendicular to the axis of
rotation.   It is mounted on the saddle, and serves to adjust
the distance of the tool from the axis of the spindle.   The
compound rest also consists of a set of ways with a slide.   It
is mounted on the slide rest and can be adjusted to move the
tool that it carries in any horizontal direction with respect
to the axis of the spindle.

Lathes are usually equipped with two chucks, one with
three jaws and the other with four.   In the three-jawed
chuck the jaws are moved by the rotation of a spiral or scroll
within the body of the chuck.   This system is mechanically
very poor.   The jaws never approach the center at the same
rate.   As a consequence, round objects mounted in it are
seldom accurately centered.   If the chuck will center work
within 0.003 of an inch, it is about all that can be expected.
The three-jawed chuck is good only for work in which all
the surfaces are to be turned at one setting, the work then
being cut off.   Once the work is removed from the chuck,
it is practically impossible to replace it concentric with
the surfaces already done.

In the four-jawed chuck the jaws are capable of independent adjustment. Therefore the accuracy of the centering of the work in a four-jawed chuck will depend upon the skill of the mechanic. With a dial indicator, and a little practice, work can be centered within 0.0002 of an inch in 5 or 10 minutes. The four-jawed chuck can also be used for holding eccentric or irregular work.

A dial indicator is a measuring device which can be mounted on the tool post in such a way that a projecting lever or plunger will bear against the work as it turns. The dial then indicates the eccentricity of the work directly in thousandths of an inch. It can be supplied with attachments for reaching into holes. It is sometimes desirable, however, to center a piece of work on a prick-punch mark. In this case a pencil with a rubber eraser in its end may be used. The tip is inserted in the prick-punch mark, and the eraser is placed in the tailstock. The indicator is then placed to bear against the pencil, and as the work is rotated, it shows the eccentricity of the punch mark.

The primary operation which a lathe can perform is to execute a truly circular cut on a piece of material. This operation is accomplished by mounting the work directly on the spindle, or by mounting it between the spindle and the fixed bearing in the tailstock, so that it can be rotated against the tool. The perfection of roundness of the work depends in either case upon the perfection of the spindle bearings. If the spindle wabbles, the tool cut is, of course, not true.

The tool is mounted so that it can be moved in a horizontal plane passing nearly through the rotation axis. As the work rotates, the moving tool makes a continuum of circular cuts. These generate, in general, a conical surface. Of the possible cones two are of special interest in machine work: one, that of zero taper, is the cylinder, and the other, that of infinite taper, is the flat surface produced by a facing cut. All others come under the head of taper cutting.

Generation of a cylindrical surface is possible if the tool

moves truly parallel to the axis of rotation of the work. In practice this is never the case, although in good lathes the error is usually negligible. When the work is mounted on the spindle, this parallel motion of the tool in respect to the axis is possible only if the ways of the carriage are parallel to the spindle, and if the ways themselves are straight. They are usually quite straight in the horizontal sense, but in the vertical sense the wearing of the ways tends to make them concave, with the result that the carriage moves up and down as it travels. For this reason it is always desirable to have the tip of the tool at the same height from the ways as the axis of rotation, for the error introduced by its up and down motion is then minimized.

If the work is mounted on dead centers, that is, if it is supported on conical points between the spindle and the tailstock and is turned by a dog bearing on the face plate, then truth of the work depends upon parallelism of the ways to a line between the two points, or centers. The tailstock is usually in error. It may be out of line laterally, a fault that one can usually correct by taking a trial cut, measuring the two ends, and setting the tailstock over again, using the adjusting screws which are usually provided. If the tailstock center is too high or too low, there is little to be done except to keep the tool at the average height of the two centers, thus minimizing the errors. Sometimes the ram, or plunger, in the tailstock which carries the center does not move parallel to the axis of the spindle. Thus, it may be well centered when the ram is retracted but not when the ram is extended. Sometimes the tip of the dead center, that is, the center in the tailstock, is bent or worn, in which case the remedy is obvious. If the live center, the one in the spindle, is untrue, it makes no difference unless the work is to be reversed and further machined. The live center is usually of soft steel, and for nice work it is common practice to true it by turning down its tip before mounting the work.

One way to turn a cylinder of uniform diameter is to lash the work to the face plate with thongs and to support it with a follower rest mounted on the carriage directly opposite the tool. This practice will insure uniformity of diameter but will not insure the straightness of the work. Sometimes in machining slender objects, one end of the work is held in a chuck while the other end is supported by the tailstock. This is bad practice, for the removal of the material from the work may relieve internal stresses, especially in cold-rolled steel and in rolled or drawn brass. As a result, when the work is removed from the lathe, it is found to be bent, the tailstock having supported the work in a flexed condition. The better practice is to support the work between centers, using a follower rest to prevent flexure. Occasionally, a second tool is mounted on the opposite side of the work and in an inverted position. This serves to preserve the uniform diameter of the work. In thread cutting it can also serve to reduce the drunkenness of a long screw thread, but it obviously requires very accurate setting of the two tools.

In boring cylindrical holes, if the work is mounted on the spindle, the truth of the work is solely dependent upon the truth of the ways. If the work is mounted on the carriage, however, a boring bar can be threaded through the rough bored hole and mounted between dead centers. A tool mounted on this bar describes a very nearly perfect circle, and as the work is fed over it, a hole of uniform diameter is automatically generated. The straightness of the ways determines the straightness of the hole, but parallelism (or the lack of it) of the ways to the axis of the spindle or to the axis of the boring is of no moment. For short holes a fly cutter may be mounted on the spindle, and the result will be the same as with a boring bar. In most work which can be mounted on the spindle the hole is bored to almost the required size, and then a reamer is passed through it to bring it to size and uniform diameter.

In turning long tapers, a taper attachment should be used, if one is available. If not, the work is mounted on dead centers, and the tailstock is set over the proper amount. The angle of taper is a function of both the amount of the setover and the length of the work. Since the length of the work, that is, the distance between the points where the axis of the work intersects the axes of the headstock and the tailstock, cannot be accurately measured, it is impossible to predetermine the exact angle of the taper which will be cut. Consequently, the amount of setover of the tailstock must be determined by trial.

The compound-slide rest is used to cut short tapers. It is usually the least accurate feature of the lathe, so that high

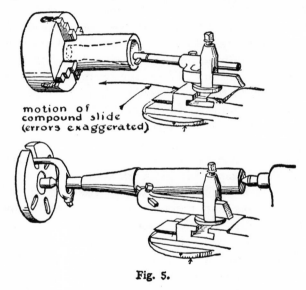

motion of
compound slide
(errors exaggerated)

Fig. 5.

precision with it is not to be expected. The graduations which are used to determine the angle of motion are generally very inaccurate and should be regarded only as something on which to base an estimate. The slide, because of its shortness, is usually not straight. It can nevertheless be used successfully for turning and boring short tapers to match, such as for lug valves and stopcocks, since the errors of curvature can be made to match. The female part is first mounted on the spindle, and the tapered hole is bored with the boring tool cutting on the far side of the hole, the lathe running backwards. When this is done, the face plate or chuck holding the piece should be removed bodily from the lathe, leaving the work undisturbed. This will permit the replacing of it for further operations, if necessary, without having to recenter the work. The male taper is then mounted, preferably between dead centers, and turned, the compound rest being used as it was set for boring, thereby insuring that the tapers will match. If the slide is not straight, the tool should be set so that its tip overhangs the slide as much as did the boring tool for the female part. If the same part of the slide is used, the errors in one taper will match those of the other. The male part, being on dead centers, may be removed from the lathe and tried in the female part and replaced for further machining, until the desired fit is obtained. For the final fit they should be lapped together with Bon Ami or some other suitable abrasive. (See Fig. 5.)

We cannot go into the arts of filing and scraping. They are treated in many of the standard works on machine practice and tool making. Filing and scraping afford the machinist opportunity for the fullest display of his manual skill. Both are, like the figuring of an optical surface, a process of delicate testing alternated with the careful manual removal of metal in order to obtain the desired surface. In filing, the testing is usually executed with the ordinary measuring instruments—the straightedge, the square, and the calipers. In scraping, the testing is done with Prussian blue, and always the two parts are scraped until an intimate and complete contact between them is obtained. Testing flats are made three at a time. The three plates are each scraped until any one of them will make satisfactory contact with either of the other two.

From the above discussion it will be noted that the limits of accuracy characteristic of the different operations can be roughly classified. There are, on the one hand, operations such as the generation of a circular cut, or the fitting of a taper to a cone by lapping, which are automatically accurate to a high degree. There are other operations which depend upon the truth built into the machine, for example, the cutting of a straight cylinder in a lathe or the milling of ways. Finally, there are those operations which depend upon the skill of the machinist. Examples are the mounting of work in the machine in order to have new cuts consistent with former ones, and the execution of filing operations to a line. There are many opportunities for the machinist to use his ingenuity to advantage in the attainment of precision. We have already mentioned examples in which the cuts on work in the three-jawed chuck are all done at one mounting, and in which the same part of the compound-slide ways are used for cutting male and female tapers, and so forth.

Soft soldering. Good soldered joints require thorough cleaning and, in addition, the use of a so-called "flux." The function of the flux is to etch the surface free of contamination and protect it, as well as the solder, from oxidation.

The most useful flux for soft soldering is made from a mixture of 2 parts zinc chloride to 1 part ammonium chloride dissolved in a minimum amount of water. This flux is often spattered about when the soldering copper is applied, and unless it is thoroughly removed, it promotes corrosion, especially on iron. If the work is washed with soda solution, the corrosive action of zinc chloride and acid flux is, in large measure, neutralized. In addition to corrosion, the spattered flux may also give rise to electrically conducting surface layers on parts of the apparatus where high insulation is required. For such work, a solution of rosin in alcohol is an excellent nonconducting flux (for soldering copper wires). Also, so-called noncorrosive pastes are available at most hardware stores. These are made from vaseline (90 per cent) and ammonium chloride (10 per cent).

Three things are needed for successful soldering. In addition to cleanliness and flux, sufficient heat is required. Some soldering is done entirely with a flame, while some is done entirely with a soldering copper. However, the nicest jobs are done with a combination of these, especially when the work is on complicated apparatus and when several relatively large parts are to be joined together. A soft flame played over the surface of the whole work supplies basic heat, keeping the work at a temperature of 125° to 150°C. The higher temperature that is required for soldering is then obtained locally by the application of the hot soldering copper. This soldering procedure minimizes the danger of melting off parts previously joined, a possibility to contend with when a flame alone is used. Also, the amount of solder added and the extent to which the solder flows is more easily controlled with the soldering copper than with a flame alone. On the other hand, the use of a flame to supply basic heat facilitates heating with the soldering copper and increases the effectiveness with which the molten solder can be made to wet the work and flow as desired.

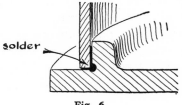

Fig. 6.

A seam to be soldered is first "tinned" at a high heat, and then at a lower temperature a fillet is made with the help of the soldering copper. The purpose of the fillet is to insure that the solder does not draw away and allow an opening to form in the seam as it cools. Fig. 6 shows how a recess cut in an inconspicuous place will serve the same purpose as a fillet.

Many of the alloy steels, as well as cast iron, magnesium, aluminum, tungsten, and molybdenum, cannot be easily soft-soldered.

Hard soldering. Although there are some intermediate solders which melt at temperatures between the melting temperatures of soft solder and silver solder, they have never had wide use. These solders may be useful in special cases, but for general work they do not have the reputation of silver solder, which, for strength, ductility, wetting power, penetration, and resistance to corrosion, is unsurpassed.[2]

[2] Especially good for hard soldering is Easy-flo solder (M.P. 620°C.), manufactured by the Handy and Harman Company, Bridgeport, Connecticut.

The heat for silver soldering is obtained with the oxy-acetylene torch for large work and with an air-gas or oxygen-gas torch for small work. The metal to be soldered is pre-heated, with the application of the flame favoring those parts which are most massive and which have the highest heat conduction. A general preheating of the whole work prevents warping and also facilitates the intense final heating of the joints that are to be brazed.

The regions to be wet and joined by the silver alloy are painted with a thin paste mixture of 5 to 10 parts of pow-dered borax, 1 part powdered boracic acid, and water. Dry borax can also be used. The use of paste has the advantage of neatly defining the areas which will be wet with the alloy. The alloy will spread over the surface only to the extent that it has been brushed with the paste. The flux for stainless steel is made from 1 part borax and 1 part boracic acid, and these powders are wet with a saturated zinc chloride solution.

For large work the silver solder is applied in the form of wire or rod after the work is well fluxed and has attained the proper temperature. The solder wire should also be coated with flux. For small work small pieces of silver solder, either short lengths of wire or bits of sheet solder, may be applied, together with flux, before the work is heated. When the parts to be joined fit together neatly, only a film of the silver solder is needed to give a good joint. The use of more solder is wasteful. Charcoal (medi-cated so that it does not burn) and asbestos blocks can be used for holding the work and for proper positioning of the parts to be joined. (See Fig. 7.)

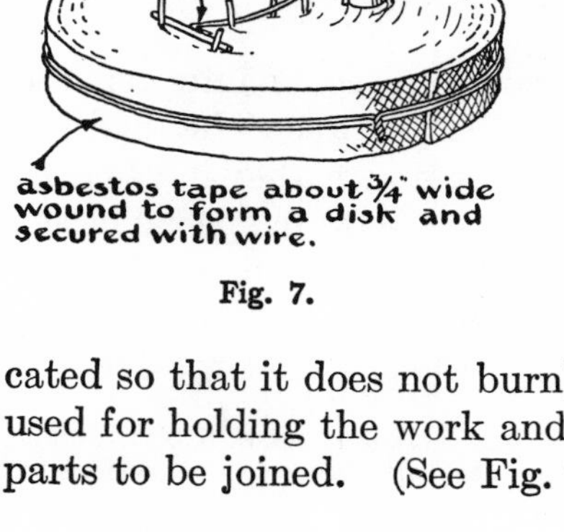

Heat may be applied with a hand torch or with a Bunsen burner and blowpipe.

old phonograph needles used to hold work in place

bits of silver solder

(flux not shown)

asbestos tape about ¾" wide wound to form a disk and secured with wire.

Fig. 7.

After the joint is made, the flux is best removed by quenching the work in cold water. This procedure is not recommended for large parts or for those requiring high accuracy, since some warping is always produced by quenching. Borax flux will dissolve slowly in hot dilute sulphuric acid in cases in which such treatment can be applied.

Spot welding. Another much-used method of joining metals in the laboratory is spot welding with an electric current. Ordinarily, the spot-welding apparatus obtains its electric energy from a transformer with a capacity of 1 or 2 kilowatts. The primary winding is connected to the alternating-current supply and it is equipped with taps or is connected in series with a rheostat to control the welding current. The secondary winding is usually a few turns of heavy copper wire on rod (about $\frac{5}{32}$ inch in diameter), with the winding ratio such that the secondary delivers about 6 volts. The heavy copper winding terminates at two copper electrodes, which serve to apply the potential to the joint to be welded. The welding is effected by the Joule heat generated between the metal surfaces to be welded when the current is passed in the primary of the transformer for a fraction of a second. The heating produced is regulated by the rheostat and by the length of the time that the switch is closed. The electrodes are brought in contact

TABLE I

ADAPTABILITY OF METALS TO SPOT WELDING

Best	Good	With Difficulty
Nickel to iron	Nickel to $\begin{cases} \text{tungsten} \\ \text{molybdenum} \\ \text{tantalum} \end{cases}$ Iron to $\begin{cases} \text{copper} \\ \text{constantan} \end{cases}$	Nickel to $\begin{cases} \text{copper} \\ \text{aluminum} \end{cases}$ Iron to $\begin{cases} \text{tungsten} \\ \text{molybdenum} \\ \text{tantalum} \end{cases}$ Aluminum to aluminum

All other metals are spot-welded with difficulty (except with a protecting atmosphere and thyratron-controlled current pulse).

with the work, and a definite pressure is applied, usually by means of a foot pedal.   The pressure and duration of the current are important.   Inadequate pressure results in burning and "spitting" at the joint, while too much pressure decreases the joint resistance and consequently the heating action.

Metals which weld together best are those of similar melting temperature T_m °C. and heat conduction K.   Table I shows the relative spot-welding characteristics of the different laboratory metals as determined by Espe and Knoll.[3]

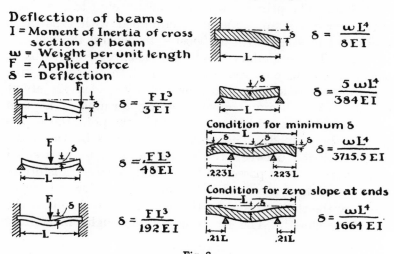

Deflection of beams
I = Moment of Inertia of cross section of beam
w = Weight per unit length
F = Applied force
δ = Deflection

$$\delta = \frac{w L^4}{8 E I}$$

$$\delta = \frac{F L^3}{3 E I}$$

$$\delta = \frac{5 w L^4}{384 E I}$$

$$\delta = \frac{F L^3}{48 E I}$$

Condition for minimum δ

$$\delta = \frac{w L^4}{3715.5 E I}$$

.223L   .223L

$$\delta = \frac{F L^3}{192 E I}$$

Condition for zero slope at ends

$$\delta = \frac{w L^4}{1664 E I}$$

.21L   .21L

Fig. 8.

See Wright, W. H., *Pub. Lick Obs.*, 9, 50 (1907).

Wires with different melting temperatures and heat conductivities weld together best when their diameters d are related as follows:

$$\frac{d_1}{d_2} = \frac{K_2}{K_1} \sqrt[3]{\frac{T_{m_1}^2}{T_{m_2}^2}}. \tag{1}$$

Instrument design. *Deflections.*   The subject of instrument design is one to which a great many authors have

[3] Espe, W., and Knoll, M., *Werkstoffkunde der Hochvakuumtechnik.*   Berlin: Julius Springer, 1936.

given their attention. We will treat of the general aspects
of the subject, such as the application of the principle of
kinematical design and the
calculation of deflections and
flexures as they pertain to
instruments.

When an element of an in-
strument is subjected to varying forces that are due to uneven friction between the
moving parts, the designer
must be able to determine
the effect of these variations.

Such' problems are often
difficult to solve precisely,
owing to the complex geometry involved. However, it is
often sufficient for the designer to know the answer to
within 50 or 100 per cent.
Estimations to this accuracy
are often possible if one makes
an ingenious choice of a simple
geometric shape whose deflection may be taken as a first
approximation to the deflection of the part in question.
The formulas for determining
the deflections of the simple
geometrical shapes, variously
loaded and supported, are
given in Fig. 8. The moments
of inertia of the cross section
of beams about the axis

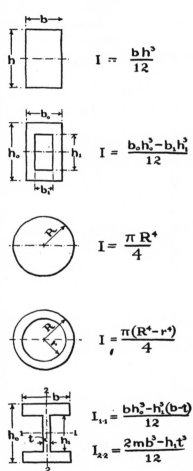

Fig. 9. Moments of inertia of
other sections can be found in me-
chanical-engineering handbooks.

passing through their center of gravity are required for
these calculations. The moments of inertia for rectangular
bars, rods, tubes, and I-beams are given in Fig. 9.

Fig. 10 gives the formulas for calculating the collapsing pressures for spherical and cylindrical shells and plane circular plates loaded with an external pressure. These formulas are useful for designing vacuum tanks.

In making apparatus, the physicist seldom needs, for reasons of economy, to limit the mass of the instrument.

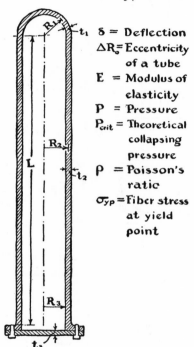

δ = Deflection

ΔR_o = Eccentricity of a tube

E = Modulus of elasticity

P = Pressure

P_{crit} = Theoretical collapsing pressure

ρ = Poisson's ratio

σ_{yp} = Fiber stress at yield point

Collapsing pressure for a hemispherical end

$$P_{crit} = \frac{2 E t_1^2}{R_1^2 \sqrt{3(1-\rho^2)}}$$

Collapsing pressure for a cylindrical tube where $L \geqq 20 R_2$

$$m = \frac{R_2}{t_2} \qquad n = \frac{\Delta R_o}{R_2}$$

$$P_{crit}^2 - \left[\frac{\sigma_{yp}}{m} + \frac{(1+6mn) E\, t_2^3}{4\,(1-\rho^2) R_2^3} \right] P_{crit} + \frac{\sigma_{yp}\, E\, t_2^3}{4 m (1-\rho^2) R_2^3} = 0$$

Theoretical limiting pressure for a circular end plate clamped at its edges.

$$P_{crit} = \frac{4 \sigma_{yp}\, t_3^2}{3 R_3^2}$$

Deflection at center for a circular end plate clamped at its edges

$$\delta = \frac{3 P R_3^4 (1-\rho^2)}{16 E\, t_3^3}$$

Theoretical limiting pressure for a circular end plate unclamped

$$P_{crit} = \frac{8 \sigma_{yp} t_3^2}{3 R_3^2 (3+\rho)}$$

Deflection at center for a circular end plate unclamped

$$\delta = \frac{3 P R_3^4 (1-\rho)(5+\rho)}{16 E\, t_3^3}$$

Fig. 10.

Timoshenko, S., *Theory of Elastic Stability*. New York: McGraw-Hill Book Company, 1936. See also "Proposed Rules for the Construction of Unfired Pressure Vessels Subjected to External Pressure," *Mechanical Engineering*, April, 1934. Graphical solutions are given in this reference for short as well as long tubes.

Accordingly, for the construction of spectrometers and other instruments, which require very accurate relative positioning of the various elements, the physicist often uses an I-beam of generous proportions and excessive strength. If the instrument is a spectrometer, one or more of the faces of the I-beam are planed to afford a base for the mounting of lenses, slits, and a prism or grating table.

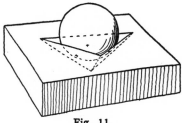

Fig. 11.

Kinematical design.[4] The different ways in which the principle of kinematical design may be used for positioning the various elements of an instrument are illustrated by Figs. 11 to 23.

According to the principle of kinematical design, a body must have at least (6 − n) points in contact with a second reference body if it is to have only n degrees of freedom, relative to the reference body. Fig. 11 shows a spherical ball held in a trihedral cavity in a plate by the force of gravity. Relative to the plate, the center of the ball is uniquely defined by the three contacts with the plate. There remain

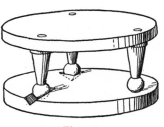

Fig. 12.

three degrees of freedom of rotation for the ball about three mutually perpendicular axes.

The principle of kinematical design is further illustrated by Fig. 12, which shows a tripod with a ball at the extremity of each of its legs. The plate on which the tripod rests has a V-groove and a trihedral cavity in its surface. One ball rests in the cavity, the second in the groove, and the third

[4] See the following:

Pollard, A. C. F., *The Kinematical Design of Couplings in Instrument Mechanisms*. London: Adam Hilger, Ltd., 1929.

Whitehead, Thomas North, *The Design and Use of Instruments and Accurate Mechanism*. New York: The Macmillan Company, 1934.

on the plane surface of the plate. When one of the balls is in the trihedral cavity, then, as far as translations are concerned, the tripod may be regarded as fixed by the three points of bearing between the ball and the sides of the trihedral cavity. If, however, a second foot rests in the

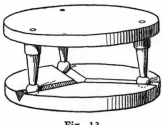

Fig. 13.

V-groove, there are two more point contacts between the ball and the sides of the groove. The tripod is now restrained by five point contacts and has, accordingly, one degree of freedom, which is a rotation about an axis passing through the centers of the constrained balls. The tripod's position is finally completely determined when the third leg comes to rest on the plane, giving the sixth point of contact.

Fig. 13 shows another way in which the tripod may have its position uniquely defined relative to a base plate. Here the terminal balls of the tripod legs rest in radial grooves machined in the plate. Each ball makes two contacts with the base plate, making a total of six contacts.

These applications of kinematical design are often useful, as, for example, when the base plate is attached to an instrument and the tripod carries some element which must be repeatedly removed and replaced in exactly the same position. The application shown in Fig. 13 has the advantage over the one shown in Fig. 12 that the

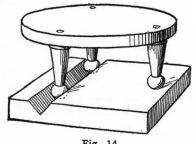

Fig. 14.

centers of the table and the base plate have the same relation to each other laterally, independent of difference in their temperature expansion.

Fig. 14 shows a case in which one degree of freedom, that is, of translation, is achieved by placing two balls in V-

grooves, with the third on a flat surface.   Five contacts
between the plate and the tri-
pod are involved.

Other examples of the
achievement of one degree of
freedom by five appropriate contacts are shown in Figs. 15 to 19.
The method shown in Fig. 15,
and especially Fig. 16, is often
used for typewriter carriages.

Figs. 17 and 18 are more or
less self-explanatory.   In

Fig. 15.

Fig. 17 gravity acts as the so-called locator.   The locator, as
its name implies, insures that the bearing points remain in
contact.   The arrangement
shown in Fig. 18 is used by
the Leitz Company for the
vertical motion of their microscope tube.

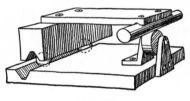

Fig. 16.

Fig. 19 shows a simple and
easily constructed device used
to move a Foucault testing
knife edge.   Its design is kinematical.

In most of the examples given here the contacting areas
are small.   Accordingly, the
wear on them may be great.
Often, in practice, point contacts are extended to line contacts as shown in Figs. 20, 21,
and 22.   Or, point contacts
may be extended to surface
contacts, as shown in Fig. 24.
Even so, one still retains substantially all of the virtues of
the more rigorous type of design, where contact areas are
small.   And, in addition, wear is materially reduced.

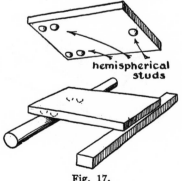

hemispherical
studs

Fig. 17.

Fig. 20 shows how one degree of freedom is achieved for focusing the reading microscope of the Cambridge Instrument Company's comparator.

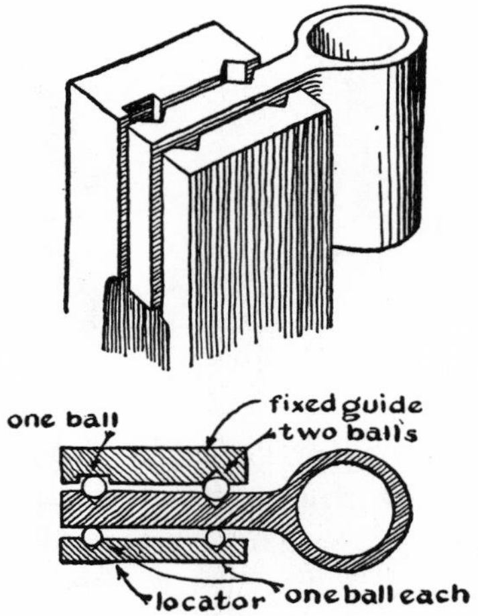

Fig. 21 shows a type of support which might be used for an optical bench. For example, with it a lens holder may be moved back and forth along two horizontal rods and clamped at any desired position.

Fig. 22 illustrates how one degree of rotation may be obtained. The rod involved here may also translate along its axis unless a constraint is applied, as, for example, a fixed ball in contact with the end of the rod.

one ball   fixed guide
            two balls

locator   one ball each

Fig. 18.

Fig. 23 shows how geometrical design may be applied to a tangent screw.

Generally, the construction of an instrument is easier if the design follows the kinematical principle than it is when

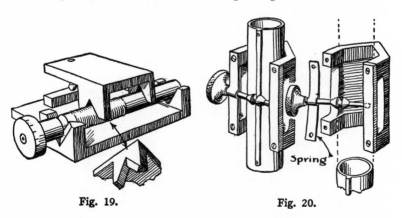

Fig. 19.   Fig. 20.

constructed in accordance with the practices of conventional machine design. Conventional designs, in which one uses cones, ways, and lapped journals to achieve one degree of freedom, either lead to overconstraint in the position of the parts or they are not uniquely defined.   Only five contacts are required to constrain the parts as desired; any more are redundant, like the fourth leg of a stool.

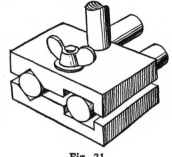

Although one degree of translation is achieved easily by following the kinematical principle, as we have seen in Figs. 14 to 21, the conventional cone, when properly lapped, affords a better construction for the achievement of one degree of freedom of rotation.

Fig. 21.

One feature of the kinematical design which distinguishes it is exemplified by the figures illustrating one degree of translation, such as Fig. 17; although the motion may not be

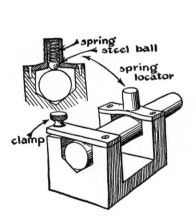

spring
steel ball

spring
locator

clamp

Fig. 22.

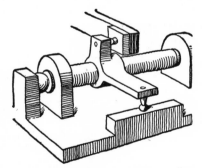

Fig. 23. Here a locator (not shown) will be required to maintain the contacts. A better construction would have the plane, which controls the orientation of the nut, on the opposite side of the screw.

straight, owing to imperfect construction, still it is possible to predict the deviation from straightness from the measured errors of construction.

Steel balls are often used in kinematical design.   They

are obtainable matched in size to 0.00005 inch, and in addition they are truly spherical to this accuracy. Precision balls can be obtained which are spherical to within a tenth of the limit mentioned above.

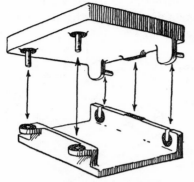

Fig. 24. Semi-kinematical design of the support for the base plate of an instrument. See *The Design and Use of Instruments and Accurate Mechanism*, footnote 4.

Fig. 25 shows a good design of an adjustable mirror cell. It will be noted that this cell has four adjusting screws. Because it facilitates the making of the adjustments, this number is recommended instead of three, in spite of the fact that one of the screws is not needed, and its use leads to strain in the cell.

Vibrationless supports. Many delicate instruments, and particularly high-sensitivity galvanometers, must be protected from the vibrations produced by automobiles in the street, elevators, machinery in the basement, and vibrations from other sources which are always present in a building. In most cases, the vertical components of these vibrations

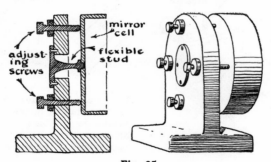

Fig. 25.

are harmless and can be ignored. Although the effect of the horizontal components on an instrument such as a galvanometer may be small, especially if the moving system is dynamically balanced on its suspension fiber, it is, however, necessary for the most delicate work to eliminate these horizontal components as far as possible by mounting the instrument on a vibrationless support.

The problems involved in obtaining a suitable support are similar to some of the problems encountered in designing a seismograph, and anyone planning to develop a special vibrationless support of his own design will find the literature on seismographs helpful. Briefly, all vibrationless supports can be considered as an oscillating system loosely coupled mechanically to the walls, ceiling, or floor of the room. The shielding effect of the support is determined by the resonance between it and the wall. For example, if the natural period of oscillation of the support is long compared to that of the vibrations of the wall, it will be so far out of resonance that its response will be feeble. It is, of course, necessary that the support be damped so that its own natural oscillations will be suppressed. Also, it must be protected from air currents. Naturally, one selects the most stable place for mounting the vibrationless support. A pier which has a separate foundation from the rest of the building is ideal.

A modification of the Julius suspension has been designed by R. Müller.[5] This suppresses only the horizontal vibrations. A simplified construction of his design, which has been used successfully by the author, is shown in Fig. 19, Chapter VIII. The support is loaded so that it has a period of about 2 seconds. This support uses the internal friction of oil in pie pans to dampen it. Light oil is used, and the pans are filled to the height which is observed to produce maximum damping of the natural oscillations of the system. The advantages of this support over a Julius suspension are that it can be mounted on a shelf in the corner of the room and easily boxed in to protect it from air currents, whereas a Julius suspension must be hung from the ceiling. It is more difficult to make adjustments of the galvanometer with the Julius suspension than with this support, because the Julius

---

[5] Müller, R., *Ann. d. Physik*, *1*, 613 (1929).

suspension is not easily clamped. The Müller support can easily be clamped for making adjustments of the galvanometer by dropping two tapered pins in the holes indicated in the figure.

One type of vibrationless support is made by placing a large mass, say a slab of stone, on a pile of newspapers. Here the shearing friction in the papers damps horizontal oscillations. Another method involves supporting the machine by steel springs wound with friction tape for damping.

Other methods of eliminating vibrations involve supporting apparatus on tennis balls or sponge rubber. These are particularly useful for stopping vibrations near their source, as, for example, preventing vibrations from vacuum pumps from being transmitted into the walls and floor of the building. The damping in this case is due to the internal friction of the rubber.

CHAPTER XV

Molding and Casting

BY

ROGER HAYWARD

PROCEDURE in molding and casting metals has changed very little since the beginning of history. There have been changes in the attendant mechanism, but the essential methods are the same as those used by prehistoric man. Because the casting of metals seemed a wonderful thing to those who did not practice the art, those who did guarded jealously the details of their craft, lest others find out how easy it was.

The object of this chapter is to acquaint the reader with a general working knowledge of the subject. Few laboratories are equipped with facilities for handling molten metals, so that the experimenter will often be obliged to have casts made by commercial foundries; but they are usually equipped for him to make his own patterns from which the casts are made. He will find it economical to do so, for the cost of having the patterns made may be many times the cost of the casts. In order to construct his patterns with intelligence, he should have an understanding of current foundry practice.

The lost-wax method. The methods of casting metals fall into two classes: one, the "cire perdue," or "lost wax," and the other, "sand casting." The lost-wax method consists in burying a wax model, or pattern, in sand and fire clay, and then burning the wax out, leaving the mold ready to receive the metal. This method is employed in sculpture, and in dentistry for the casting of gold teeth, inlays, and so forth, when only one cast is wanted, for obviously there can be only one cast made from a single pattern. Hence the name "lost wax." The method is useful for making small irregular objects. It is particularly good for casting small parts in gold, silver, or platinum, for ordinarily the experimenter is loath to work such objects from solid metal. He finds it a nuisance to save the chips and filings that are too valuable to lose.

The advantage of the lost-wax method is that the pattern may be of any imaginable complexity. Undercutting or the lack of it is of no importance. The only problem is in the arrangement of gates and risers for admitting the metal and for allowing the air to escape. In the case of hollow sculpture the core is usually supported in the mold by rods of the same metal as that of which the statue is to be cast.

The wax used is a mixture of beeswax and paraffin. This mixture can be procured already prepared at a dental-supply house, or it can be made up readily, for the proportions are not critical. The wax is first softened by being heated until it is pliable; it is then roughly formed with the hands; and after that it is carved into the desired shape (Fig. 1). The carving may be done with any sharp instrument. If the operator cuts away too much, he may replace it by picking up a piece of wax with a pair of tweezers, softening the wax in the flame, and then touching the tweezers to the spot that is to be filled in. The tweezers act much as a ruling pen. Fig. 1 shows the making of a mandrel for winding the spiral tungsten coils used in evaporating metals. This object is taken as an example because the double spiral thread that is required is very difficult to cut on a lathe. As will be seen from the illustration, it can easily be modeled in wax.

Small models are held on the tip of a small rod. To remove the model from the rod, a piece of hot metal is held against the rod until it becomes warm enough for the wax at the tip to melt and allow the model to drop off. A hot-wire tool, such as is described in the chapter on quartz-fiber technique, would be a useful one for this purpose. When the model is finished, it is stuck on the end of a tapered metal pin, which serves to support the model while the mold is being made, and which, when removed, leaves a channel, or sprue, through which the metal can flow. The object illustrated in Fig. 1 is shown as being modeled directly on

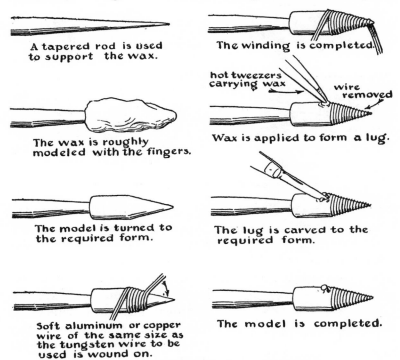

A tapered rod is used to support the wax.

The wax is roughly modeled with the fingers.

The model is turned to the required form.

Soft aluminum or copper wire of the same size as the tungsten wire to be used is wound on.

The winding is completed.

hot tweezers carrying wax   wire removed

Wax is applied to form a lug.

The lug is carved to the required form.

The model is completed.

Fig. 1. Lost-wax casting. Making the model.

the tapered rod that also serves to form the sprue. Since the wax alone would hardly be strong enough to stand the winding of the wires that form the threads, the pin is shown as extending to the tip of the model—a procedure peculiar, of course, to the example illustrated.

If the object is to be cast in lead, type metal, babbitt, tin, pewter, solder, or other such metals, the mold may be made of plaster of Paris. If it is to be of gold, silver, copper, brass, or other metals having a higher melting point, the regular dental investment material procurable at a dental-supply house should be used.   This material is mixed with

The required amount of water is placed in a bowl.

The mixture must stand until this little pile is thoroughly wet.

The plaster or investment material is sprinkled in with the fingers.

The mixture is stirred gently from the bottom to free the bubbles.

The mix is ready to use.

Fig. 2.   Proper method for mixing plaster of Paris.

water and sets in about a minute.   It should be mixed in the same way as plaster of Paris (Fig. 2): A bowl is partly filled with water, and the investment is sprinkled into the water with the fingers until the level of the investment, which spreads out under the water, reaches the level of the water.

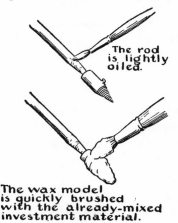

The rod is lightly oiled.

The wax model is quickly brushed with the already-mixed investment material.

Fig. 3.   Lost-wax casting.   Preparing the model for the mold.

Do not stir until all the investment has been added.   If there is a little pile standing above the water in the center of the bowl, wait until it is wet, and then stir gently to free any trapped bubbles.   (Before starting the mold, oil the pin lightly to prevent the investment from sticking to it.)   With a soft brush, paint the outside of the model with the investment and water mixture (Fig. 3).   Immediately hold the object in the mold container, and pour in the rest of the investment. Continue to hold the object until the investment is set (Fig. 4). The mold container should be an iron sleeve. A section of pipe faced off on the bottom in the lathe will do. Dentists use a ring which tapers 5° to 10°, the small end being the bottom. The taper serves to prevent the entire mold from being forced out of the ring and destroyed while the metal is being forced in. This point will appear obvious in a later paragraph, which describes the process of pouring the metal.

The model is suspended in an iron sleeve and the rest of the mix is poured in.

Fig. 4. Lost-wax casting. Making the mold.

As soon as the investment has set, pull out the supporting rod, and around the hole, or sprue, carve a small funnel to receive the metal (Fig. 5). Be careful to remove any bits of material that fall down the sprue. Place the whole thing in a ring stand and heat with a Bunsen burner. Heat until the whole mold is red hot, to make sure that the last traces of wax and moisture are driven off (Fig. 6).

The rod is warmed and withdrawn.

A funnel is cut around the hole.

Fig. 5. Lost-wax casting. Making the sprue.

The mold is heated to redness to drive off the moisture and burn out the wax.

The mold is then ready to be filled

Fig. 6. Lost-wax casting. Burning out the wax.

The mold is now completed and ready to receive the metal. There remains the problem of getting the metal to flow into the mold. When the sprues are tiny and the masses of metal small, the surface tension may prevent the metal from flowing. Also, the trapped air in the mold will be a real obstacle. Dentists use a vacuum method for getting the air out of the mold. ˙ A metal disk with a hole in the center communicates with a small tank by means of a pipe. The pipe has a stopcock, which is kept closed until the metal is melted. A

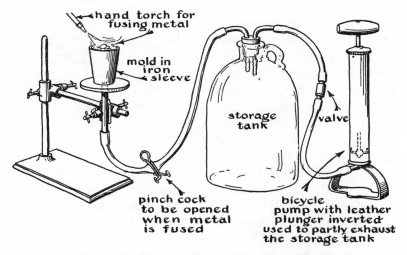

Fig. 7.   Lost-wax casting.   Vacuum method for filling the mold.

small hand pump is attached to the tank for reducing the air pressure to about one-half to one-fourth atmospheric pressure. The mold is placed on the disk, and the metal is melted in the funnel on the top of the mold with a blast lamp. When the metal is completely molten, the cock is opened, and the air in the mold is drawn out through its porosity, allowing the metal to flow in. Of course, air leaks around the cast, but that does not matter, since the object is to reduce the air pressure in the mold for only a few seconds. This method will make the finest of casts.

Fig. 7 shows a setup of the type described above, which

can easily be assembled with the aid of a bicycle pump and a few accessories.

Another method is to force the metal into the mold with steam. The metal is melted in the top of the mold as before. When it has melted, a large piece of moist clay is quickly pressed down onto the mold. The steam generated will force the metal into the mold. When this method is used, the mold should be placed on a perforated plate to allow the air to escape at the bottom (Fig. 8).

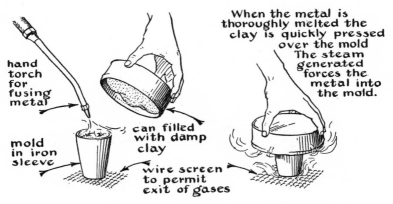

Fig. 8.   Lost-wax casting.   Steam method for filling the mold.

Still another method introduces the metal into the mold by means of a centrifuge, which need be only a simple device consisting of a bar pivoted to rotate in a horizontal plane. A spring is arranged to rotate the arm, and a movable trigger acts as a stop to prevent the rotation until the metal is molten. The mold is placed in a holder at the end of the arm with its sprue facing the pivot. The crucible, a small trough of firebrick or any other suitable material, is mounted on the arm with the end of the trough adjacent to the sprue. The procedure is to cock the spring, place the mold in the holder, place the metal in the trough, and heat it with a hand torch. When the metal is ready, the trigger is pulled, and the whole arm spins on the pivot, the centrifugal force carrying the metal into the mold. For this method the bottom of the mold should be made especially strong; otherwise it may give way and the molten metal be thrown about the room. This method is used by commercial jewelers as well as by some dentists. Fig. 9 shows a centrifuge of the type described. For casting the object illustrated in Fig. 1, this method should probably be used, since the top of the mold would hardly be large enough to contain the required amount of metal.

In any of the foregoing methods metals such as gold, silver, copper, brass, and so forth, should be liberally sprinkled with borax as they are fused. This treatment prevents

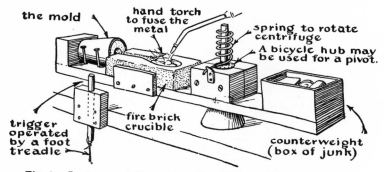

Fig. 9.   Lost-wax casting.   Centrifuge method for filling the mold.

oxides from forming. Metals such as lead, babbitt, solder, and so forth, may be kept covered with powdered charcoal for the same purpose.

Patterns for sand casting. Sand casting from permanent patterns of metal or wood is the method commonly employed for all manner of mechanical parts, irrespective of size or of metal. Die casting is the only other method of importance, but it is restricted to commercial work in which the otherwise prohibitive cost of the metal dies is absorbed in the tremendous quantity of casts to be produced. In making the patterns for sand casting, the first step is to make a careful drawing of the object (Fig. 10). Over this drawing a second one should be made (Fig. 11), which is the pattern drawing. It can be made on thin paper. For future

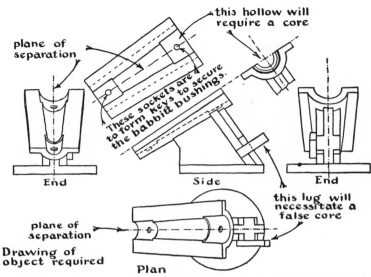

this hollow will require a core

plane of separation

These sockets are to form keys to secure the babbitt bushings.

End

Side

End

plane of separation

Drawing of object required

Plan

this lug will necessitate a false core

Fig. 10. Sand casting. Mechanical drawing for the polar-axis mounting for a small telescope.

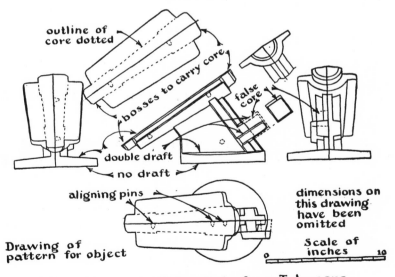

outline of core dotted

bosses to carry core

false core

double draft

no draft

aligning pins

dimensions on this drawing have been omitted

Drawing of pattern for object

Scale of inches

0   10

A Design for the Polar Axis for a Telescope

Fig. 11. Sand casting. Mechanical drawing of the pattern.

convenience it is well to dimension the pattern drawing copiously.

As an object for the illustrations that demonstrate sand casting, a polar axis for a telescope has been chosen. The axis is designed to have babbitt bearings. Such a design eliminates the necessity for chucking the whole axis in a lathe and boring it—a job to be accomplished only in a very large lathe. Figs. 10 and 12 show drawings of the parts required, and Fig. 24 shows the completed mounting.

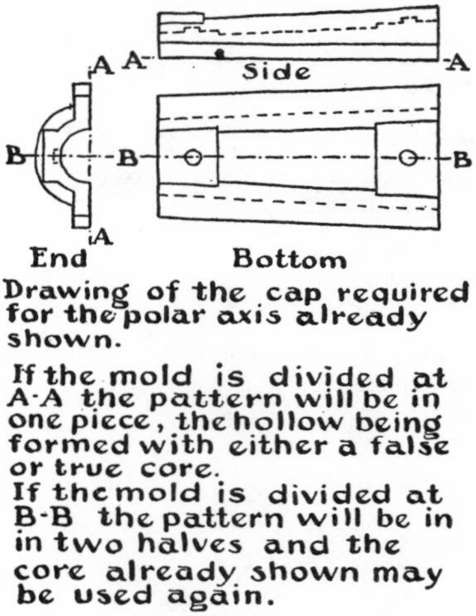

End   Bottom

Drawing of the cap required for the polar axis already shown.

If the mold is divided at A-A the pattern will be in one piece, the hollow being formed with either a false or true core.
If the mold is divided at B-B the pattern will be in in two halves and the core already shown may be used again.

Fig. 12. Sand casting. Drawing of the cap for the polar axis.

In planning the pattern, the first thing that must be determined is the plane of division of the mold. This plane should pass through the object in such a way that both parts of the pattern can be drawn from the sand mold. The plane must intersect the object in such a way that all points on the object, when they are projected normally to the plane, will fall on or within the intersection. It is to this plane that all questions of "draft" are referred. If there is no single plane that will fulfill the requirements, one must be chosen which will come the nearest possible, and the parts that do not conform will have to be accomplished with cores.

The pattern will be divided along the plane of division unless the plane happens to coincide with one surface of the object, in which case the pattern will be in one piece (Fig. 12). Since the usual cases are those in which the pattern must be divided into two halves, we will describe the procedure for a two-piece pattern. The designer need not be limited to the two-piece pattern, but the multi-piece pattern is so seldom employed that it is not within the scope of this chapter to treat of it.　The reader is referred to books on commercial founding.

Since parallel-sided objects can not be withdrawn from sand without the friction of the sides destroying the walls, it is necessary to taper the sides slightly.　This taper is called "draft," and it may be as little as $\frac{1}{2}°$ for fine commercial work.　In most work, however, 3° is regarded as the proper draft angle.　Round objects need no draft when the plane of separation passes through the axis.　When the requirements of the object are such that there can be no draft on one of the faces, that is, when that face must be at a right angle with the plane of separation, then the draft on all opposite faces should be doubled (Fig. 11).

If there is a projection on one of the pieces of the pattern that does not touch the dividing plane, then between it and the dividing plane must be provided a separate block which can be removed after that half of the mold is made.　This block is called the "false core," and the volume which it occupies in that half of the mold will be replaced by an equal volume of sand in the other half of the mold.　The false core must also have draft.　It will be seen later in the description of the process for making a mold that false cores must be used on only one piece of the mold, and that this must be the piece which has the holes to receive the pegs that hold the parts of the pattern in alignment.　Since this is the part that is molded first, it must be capable of lying flat, with the plane of separation in contact with a table.　If false cores are required on the other piece of the mold, they must be regarded as true cores.　The blocks must be fixed in place and a core box made for them as will be described later in this chapter.

If there is to be a hole through the object, bosses must be put on the pattern wherever the hole comes through the surface of the object.　These bosses are to form sockets in the mold for carrying the ends of the core, thereby preventing its floating in the molten metal.　The bosses must have draft angles to conform to the rest of the pattern. Separate drawings should be made of the cores, the drawings to include the bosses just mentioned (Fig. 18).

A core is any piece of sand or mold material that is molded separately and inserted in a mold, thereby forming a hole or cavity in the finished cast. If the core comes to the surface of the pattern at only one place, the boss to receive it must be long enough to support the core as a cantilever. Should this prove impractical, projections may be made on the core which will bear against the inside of the mold and carry the core. These projections will leave holes in the finished cast which will have to be plugged. Still another way is to use metal supports to carry the core. The supports are in the form of pins with broad heads and crooked shanks, and they are pressed into the sand by the molder. They weld with the metal of the cast. It is well to remember that not only must the core be supported against gravity in the empty mold, but it must also be restrained from floating in the molten metal when the mold is filled.

Since nearly all metals shrink in solidifying, patterns have to be made enough larger to compensate. The amount of shrinkage varies with the metal. A list of shrinkage scales is given in Table I.

TABLE I

Shrinkage Scales

Metal	Shrinkage (inches)	Metal	Shrinkage (inches)
Aluminum............	$3/16$	Dow metal alloy......	$5/32$ to $3/16$
Aluminum alloys.......	$5/32$	Gunmetal bronze......	$1/8$ to $3/16$
Aluminum bronze......	$1/4$	Lead................	$5/16$
Brass................	$3/16$	Mal. iron............	$1/8$
Britannia.............	$1/32$	Manganese bronze.....	$1/4$
Bronze...............	$3/16$	Nickel-steel alloy......	$1/4$
Carbon steel..........	$3/16$ to $1/4$	Phosphor bronze......	$1/8$ to $3/16$
Cast iron (gray)........	$1/10$ to $5/32$	Steel................	$1/4$
Cast iron (white).......	$1/4$	Tin.................	$1/12$
Copper..............	$3/16$	Vanadium-steel alloy..	$1/4$

This shrinkage is the amount that must be added per foot to a pattern. For convenience, shrink rules may be purchased that are the correct amount oversize but are calibrated as ordinary rules.

For patterns that are to be cast many times, it is usual to reproduce the original wooden pattern in aluminum or some other metal, and to use this metal pattern for making the molds. In such case the original wooden pattern must be made large enough to allow for shrinkage of both metals. The allowance should be the sum of the shrinkages of both metals. Metal patterns are better for repeated use, since commercial foundries are quite rough on the wooden ones. Furthermore, several metal patterns may be reproduced from the first wooden one, and from these many molds may be made at a time. Thereby the cost of production is reduced.

The rate of solidification of metal in the mold is a function of the thickness of the metal. Since the greater part of the shrinkage occurs at the instant of solidification, it is apparent that unequal thicknesses of metal in the same pattern will cause a certain amount of distortion and warping. For this reason patterns are usually designed to have as uniform a thickness throughout as possible. Of course, the warping may be unimportant,- since small projecting lugs on large casts will be carried by large masses of metal. Nevertheless, care should be exercised in designing the patterns to preserve the equality of thickness. Metals cooling from the molten state do not necessarily shrink evenly as the temperature falls. White cast iron, for instance, shrinks a while, then expands a little, and then continues shrinking. Gray iron expands twice and phosphorous iron three times. Thus, in casts of uneven thickness one part may be shrinking while another is expanding, with the result that the casts will be under stresses. In fact, the casts may be broken by the stresses. The hand wheels that are used to tighten the brakes on freight cars are made with spiral spokes, because the uneven cooling of the thick hub and the thin rim sets up stresses in the spokes which might break them if they were straight.

Pure metal, such as aluminum, copper, tin, or zinc, may be cast in almost any thickness. The case is different with the alloys, especially with those alloys in which there is a great difference between the melting points of the constituent metals. The alloys cooled slowly have time to grow large crystals. In fact, some of the constituent metals may crystallize out, so that thick alloy castings may be weak and full of crystal pockets. The best thickness for alloy castings

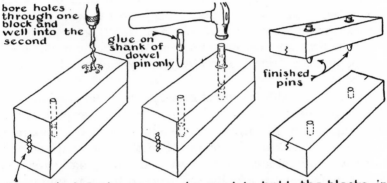

Fig. 13. Sand casting. Method of using wooden dowels to hold the two halves of the pattern in alignment.

seems to be between $\frac{3}{16}$ and $\frac{5}{16}$ inch. Even $\frac{1}{8}$ inch is not too thin. All metals, pure or alloyed, must be cast in a thickness sufficient for the metal to reach all parts of the mold before it sets. However, this matter is not too important, for a good molder can arrange his gates to insure that the molten metal reaches all parts of the mold before it solidifies.

Patterns are usually made of wood—white pine, sugar pine, or mahogany. The wood should be clear and well seasoned. If the pattern is in two pieces (not including false cores), they must be pinned together in such a way that they can be separated and reassembled by the molder. In making the pattern, it is well first to make the division part with its pins. Wooden dowels may be used, or special pins and sockets, which can be purchased from a hardware dealer (Figs. 13 and 14).

In general, the construction of patterns follows the usual practice in carpentry and cabinetmaking. The parts may

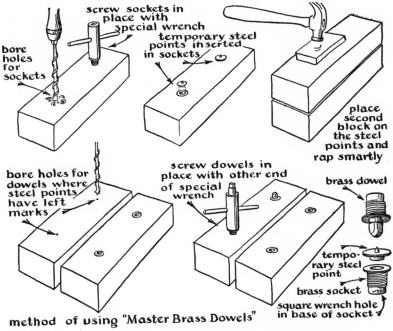

method of using "Master Brass Dowels"

Fig. 14. Sand casting. Method of using patented dowels.

be glued together at will, and all the tricks of joinery may be employed, provided the finished result is the desired shape. The exterior surfaces of the pattern should be carefully smoothed. Any roughnesses or irregularities in the surfaces, particularly in the draft surfaces, will mean that the molder will have to rap the pattern vigorously to free it from the mold, with the result that the mold, and consequently the cast, will be larger than designed.

Each piece of pattern, including the false cores, should be provided with a rapping plate, which is set in flush with the parting face (Fig. 15). These plates can be purchased from a hardware dealer. They provide a hole for rapping and a hole for a lifting screw, or handle, which the molder will use in withdrawing the pattern from the sand.

In making casts it has been found that sharp, internal corners and dihedral angles are a source of trouble. The sharp edges of the mold may crumble, or strains in the metal may cause the cast to break at these corners. To avoid such trouble, it is the practice to round the corners,

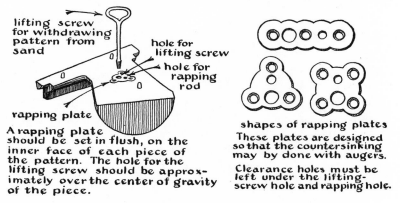

lifting screw for withdrawing pattern from sand

hole for lifting screw

hole for rapping rod

rapping plate

A rapping plate should be set in flush, on the inner face of each piece of the pattern. The hole for the lifting screw should be approximately over the center of gravity of the piece.

shapes of rapping plates

These plates are designed so that the countersinking may by done with augers.

Clearance holes must be left under the lifting-screw hole and rapping hole.

Fig. 15.   Sand casting.   Rapping plates.

and the corners so rounded are called "fillets." They may be carved in the pattern, but it is easier to make them of wax. The wax can be purchased at hardware stores. It comes on spools or in strips in the form of an extruded ribbon of the proper profile. Before the ribbon is used, the pattern must be shellacked. The ribbon, cut into convenient lengths, is rubbed into place with a hot tool that has a ball-shaped end (Fig. 16). The fillets are sold in sizes according to the radius desired, and the tools can be made or purchased to correspond. After the fillets are finished, the whole pattern is again shellacked. In patterns that are to be used only once the fillets may be made of plastiline or plasticine, which can be purchased at an artists' supply house. Only the hardest grade should be used. It will stick quite well to the shellacked pattern, and may be modeled with the fingers or with wooden modeling tools. It should be shellacked when it is finished. For larger work, leather fillets can be purchased in many sizes. They are glued directly to the wooden pattern, finished with sandpaper, and shellacked.

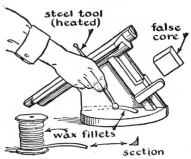

Fig. 16. Sand casting. Method of applying wax fillets.

If there are no cores, clear shellac is used over the whole pattern; but if there are cores, the projections which correspond to the ends of the cores are left in the clear shellac finish or are painted red, while the rest of the pattern is finished with shellac and lampblack. The shellac and lampblack are usually mixed to give a dead black finish. The mixture is liberally thinned with alcohol. The reason for this color distinction is that it tells the molder where the cores belong (Fig. 17).

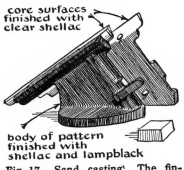

Fig. 17. Sand casting. The finished pattern.

If the pattern has cores, the next problem is to make the core boxes. These are essentially wooden molds, in which the cores are cast. The requirements for draft and shrinkage are the same as for the patterns. If the core requires a two-piece mold, as for cylindrical shapes and the like, the plane of division need have no relation to the plane of division of the original pattern. There is no need to pin the two sides of the core box together, for the two halves of the core are made separately and are stuck together after they are baked. When the two halves are alike, it is necessary to make a box for only one side. If simple cylindrical cores are required, it is unnecessary to make the boxes at all, for most foundries have stock boxes, or even stock cores. In general, core boxes are carved from solid wood, and they are frequently more complex than the pattern itself (Fig. 19).

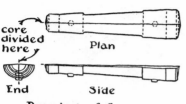

Drawing of Core

Fig. 18. Sand casting. Mechanical drawing of the core.

The core in the illustration is shown to be made in two pieces, because the surface in the mold which it has to fit has draft. If the pattern had no draft on this top face, the core could easily be in one piece.

Core boxes are made of sugar pine or any other clear and workable wood, and they are finished with shellac like the patterns. One point is important: Since the pattern shows only the ends of the core, and since the core may be unsymmetrical longitudinally, it is well to make the ends different, so that the molder will get the core in the proper orientation.

The process of making cylindrical core boxes, as it has been practiced for years, is very interesting. A core-box plane is used, the face of which is two surfaces at 90° to each other. The plane iron comes through the edge of these surfaces and is sharpened to conform to them. Two parallel lines are drawn on the surface of the stock that is to be used.

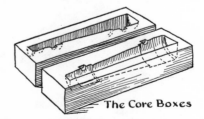

Fig. 19. Sand casting. The core boxes.

The plane is made to cut away all the wood possible without removing the two lines. The 90° angle automatically generates a semicircular groove (Fig. 20). The plane can be used to generate conical shapes as well.

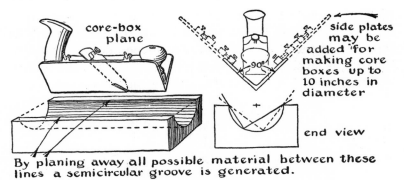

core-box plane

side plates may be added for making core boxes up to 10 inches in diameter

90°

end view

By planing away all possible material between these lines a semicircular groove is generated.

Fig. 20.   Core-box plane.

Sand casting. The procedure for making the mold is as follows: The molder first separates the pattern and sets the part that has no pegs with its separation plane face down on the table, putting the false cores in place. Around this piece he puts a wooden or metal frame called a "drag." The "drag" and the "cope" together constitute the "flask," which is a framework to contain the sand forming the mold. The cope and the drag are open rectangular boxes without lid or bottom. They are fitted with crossbars to help hold the sand. There are three sockets in the rim of the drag and three corresponding pins in the rim of the cope which permit them to be separated and reassembled in the same relation as shown in Fig. 21(a).

The molder next sprinkles molding sand through a riddle, or sieve, until the drag is half full. Molding sand is a mixture of fine clear sand and a small amount of clay, and sometimes a little powdered charcoal or graphite. It has been moistened until a handful compressed will retain the print of the hand and will form a fairly firm piece, but moistened not so much but that it can be shaken through a riddle of about ¼-inch mesh, the riddle being shaken vigorously. Molding sand is used over and over again with only the addition necessary to replace the inevitable losses.

When the drag has been half filled, the sand is carefully tamped around the pattern. A wooden implement is used which is about the shape and size of a dumbbell except that one end is flat and the other is a blunt, truncated wedge as shown in Fig. 21(b).   More sand is added and tamped until the drag is level, full, and firmly tamped.   The sand is then perforated with a thin metal wire to assist the escape of

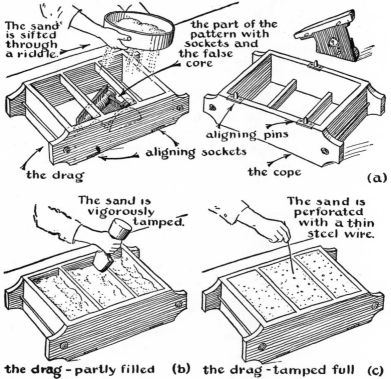

The sand is sifted through a riddle.

the part of the pattern with sockets and the false core

aligning pins

aligning sockets

the drag

the cope   (a)

The sand is vigorously tamped.

The sand is perforated with a thin steel wire.

the drag - partly filled   (b)   the drag -tamped full (c)

Fig. 21.   Sand casting.   Filling the drag.

steam and gases that are given off when the metal is poured in.   This is illustrated in Fig. 21(c).   The drag is now picked up bodily and inverted on the table, exposing the separation face of the pattern. The false cores are removed as shown in Figs. 21(d) and 21(e).

The other half of the pattern is next placed on the part already molded, the pegs insuring alignment of the parts.

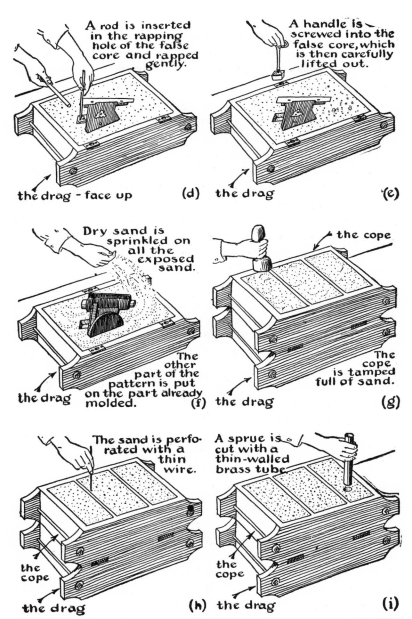

A rod is inserted in the rapping hole of the false core and rapped gently.

the drag - face up (d)

A handle is screwed into the false core, which is then carefully lifted out.

the drag (e)

Dry sand is sprinkled on all the exposed sand.

The other part of the pattern is put on the part already molded.

the drag (f)

the cope

The cope is tamped full of sand.

the drag (g)

The sand is perforated with a thin wire.

the cope

the drag (h)

A sprue is cut with a thin-walled brass tube.

the cope

the drag (i)

Fig. 21 (continued). Sand casting. Removing the false core and filling the cope.

613

Dry sand is sprinkled over all the exposed sand of the mold as illustrated in Fig. 21(f) to prevent the two halves of the mold from sticking together. The cope is placed on the drag. It is filled with sand and is tamped, as was the drag, as shown in Fig. 21(g). The sand is pierced many times with a thin wire, as in the case of the drag, in the manner illustrated in Fig. 21(h).

At a point in the sand well clear of the pattern, a sprue is cut deep enough to reach a little below the separation plane. It is cut with a piece of thin-walled brass tubing which is pressed gently into the sand and removed, bringing with it a plug of sand as shown in Fig. 21(i). The hole left is about an inch in diameter, large enough for casts of 10 to 100 pounds. It is well to cut the hole an inch at a time. It is not cut to communicate directly with the pattern, for the force of the descending metal might injure the mold. A trough is cut around the top of the hole as illustrated in Figs. 21(j) and 21(k), and into this the metal will be poured.

The cope is now carefully lifted off the drag and laid beside it, face up. A rod is inserted in the rapping plate and rapped smartly in all directions to break the adhesion of the sand as shown in Fig. 21(l). A handle is screwed into the rapping plate, and the pattern is carefully withdrawn from the sand as illustrated in Fig. 21(m).

A channel, or "gate," is next cut along the parting plane from the mold to the sprue. The reason for not cutting the sprue to communicate directly with the mold is that the sudden rush of heavy metal directly into the mold might injure it. The horizontal gate breaks the fall of the metal as shown in Figs. 21(m) and 21(n).

The mold should be closely inspected for broken corners and edges that must be carefully mended and modeled with steel molder's tools. Bits of sand that have fallen in are brushed away with a soft brush or are blown out with a bellows. A cloth bag half full of powdered graphite is shaken over the mold, and frequently powdered graphite is painted on the surface of the mold with a soft camel's-hair

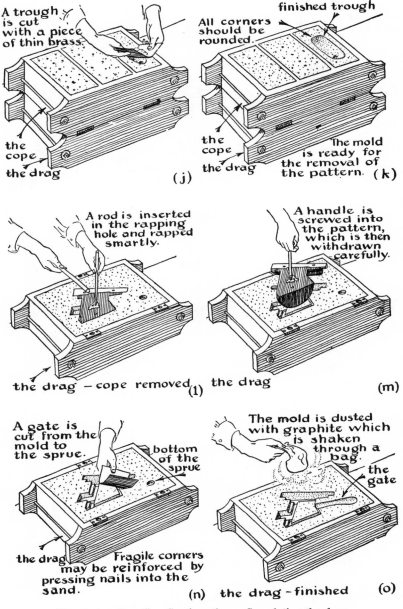

A trough is cut with a piece of thin brass.

the cope

the drag (j)

finished trough

All corners should be rounded.

the cope

the drag

The mold is ready for the removal of the pattern. (k)

A rod is inserted in the rapping hole and rapped smartly.

the drag — cope removed (l)

A handle is screwed into the pattern, which is then withdrawn carefully.

the drag (m)

A gate is cut from the mold to the sprue.

bottom of the sprue

the drag

Fragile corners may be reinforced by pressing nails into the sand. (n)

The mold is dusted with graphite which is shaken through a bag.

the gate

the drag – finished (o)

Fig. 21 (continued). Sand casting. Completing the drag.

615

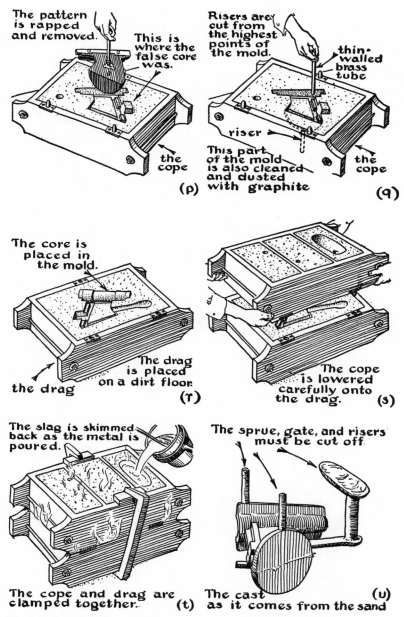

The pattern is rapped and removed. This is where the false core was. the cope (p)

Risers are cut from the highest points of the mold. thin-walled brass tube. riser. This part of the mold is also cleaned and dusted with graphite. the cope (q)

The core is placed in the mold. the drag. The drag is placed on a dirt floor. (r)

The cope is lowered carefully onto the drag. (s)

The slag is skimmed back as the metal is poured. The cope and drag are clamped together. (t)

The sprue, gate, and risers must be cut off. The cast as it comes from the sand (u)

Fig. 21 (concluded). Sand casting. Finishing the cope and filling the mold.

616

brush as shown in Fig. 21(o). In iron and steel castings this coating of graphite is responsible for the very hard surface layer. Its function is to harden the surface of the mold, and also partly to fill the grainy surface of the sand.

The pattern is removed from the cope as illustrated in Fig. 21(p) in the same manner as from the drag. If the cast is complicated or very large, a riser or several risers are cut in the cope. They are like the sprue, except that they are cut from the highest parts of the mold. In complicated molds they assist in carrying off the entrapped air; in large molds they serve to collect the slag that rises to the surface, and to provide reservoirs for extra metal that will flow back into the mold as the metal within cools and shrinks. This is shown in Fig. 21(q).

The mold is now ready to receive the cores and to be put together. For thin casts in alloy the halves of the mold may be heated with a blowtorch to drive off the water nearest the surface, which otherwise would cool the metal before it had time to flow.

Cores are made by filling the core boxes with a mixture of coarse sand and a binder. The core boxes are tamped full and leveled off with a straightedge. They are then inverted

TABLE II

BINDERS

Binder	Amount
Linseed oil..............	2 per cent by volume
Molasses................	2 per cent by volume
Pitch...................	5 per cent by weight
Resin...................	4 per cent by weight

on sheets of metal, rapped, and removed, leaving the halves of the core, which are baked for a few hours in an oven. The baked halves are stuck together with the mixture of which they are made, or with mucilage or paste, and are baked again (Fig. 22).   Pure silica sand which has passed through a 50-mesh screen and has been retained on a 70-mesh screen should be used.   Many substances may be used as binders, a complete list of which the reader will find in books on founding.   The ones most easily available are given in Table II, together with the amounts to be used.

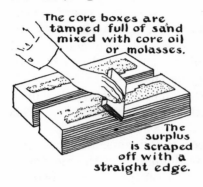

The core boxes are tamped full of sand mixed with core oil or molasses.

The surplus is scraped off with a straight edge.

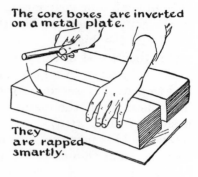

The core boxes are inverted on a metal plate.

They are rapped smartly.

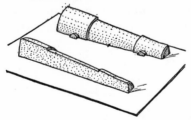

The boxes are removed and the cores are baked in an oven for two hours at about 350° F.

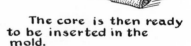

The halves of the core are stuck together with sand and core oil, or mucilage, and are again baked for an hour.

The core is then ready to be inserted in the mold.

Fig. 22.   Sand casting.   Making the cores.

If linseed oil is used, the cores must be baked at 425°F. for $1\frac{1}{2}$ hours.   For the others 350°F. for $1\frac{1}{2}$ hours will do.   Linseed oil makes the strongest cores, and pitch and resin the weakest.

When the cores are thin and fragile, they are frequently reinforced with iron wires. If the cores are very bulky, provision should be made for conducting away the gases that will be formed in them and that will blow the cast apart if allowed to remain unvented. Such provision is made by laying strips of wax in the sand as the cores are being made. When the cores are baked, the wax is driven off, leaving holes for the gases to escape through.

The completed cores are placed in the molds, and the flask is reassembled. The halves—the cope and drag—should be securely clamped together, for otherwise the metal may actually float the cope off and let out the metal as shown in Fig. 21(t). The mold is now ready to be filled as illustrated in Figs. 21(r) and 21(s).

For production work, when numbers of identical casts are required, match boards are used. These are boards having pins and sockets that correspond to those in the cope and drag, one to fit the cope and one to fit the drag. The two halves of the pattern are permanently fixed to the boards, properly placed to insure correct matching of the two. The halves of the mold are then made separately. They may even be made by separate workmen, and are not assembled until the time for the pouring. In the case of metal patterns several are placed on each board so that a number may be cast at a time.

The molten metal should be poured gently into the mold. It is well to skim back the slag and scum that form on the top of the metal in the crucible or ladle. For the soft metals, which can be handled in iron containers, a kettle having a spout that communicates with the bottom may be used. The floating slag and oxides will be left in the kettle. In molds involving large masses of metal it is common for the workmen to stir the metal in the mold. They churn it up and down in the riser with an iron rod. This action prevents the metal in the riser from solidifying until the outer shell of the cast has set. As the center of the cast sets, the metal in the riser descends and prevents shrinkage pockets from being left in the top of the cast. The escaping gases usually burn briskly, but if they burn too much at the division of the mold, the flames should be doused with water to save the flask from being badly charred.

Large casts are usually left overnight to cool. Smaller ones may be immediately dug out of the mold. In fact, it is the practice in a certain instrument company to remove the small casts immediately from the sand and throw them red hot into the water. The steam generated blows away the sand and even blows out the cores, leaving the casts virtually clean.

When the sprues and gates and risers have been cut off, the cast is ready to be machined or otherwise finished as shown in Fig. 21(u).

In having the casts made it is often desirable to estimate the weight of the finished casts before they are ordered. Such an estimation is easily made: Weigh the pattern, allow for the cores, and multiply the result by a coefficient which is the ratio of the weight of the pattern material to the weight of the metal of the cast. A short list of these coefficients is given in Table III.

TABLE III

RATIO OF WEIGHTS OF FINISHED CASTS TO WOOD PATTERNS

Metal	White pine 26 lbs. per cu. ft.	Mahogany or yellow pine 34 lbs. per cu. ft.
Cast iron (gray) 449 lbs. per cu. ft.	17.3	13.2
Mal. iron 474 lbs. per cu. ft.	18.2	13.9
Steel 480 lbs. per cu. ft	18.4	14.1
Copper alloy 535 lbs. per cu. ft.	20.6	15.7
Aluminum alloy 180 lbs. per cu. ft.	6.9	5.3

If one is making one's own casts, enough metal must be figured to include the sprues and risers. Foundries do not

charge for this metal, since they cut it off and use it over
again.

Babbitt metal is essentially a mixture of lead and tin with
the addition of enough antimony to cause the metal to expand slightly when it freezes.   Many variations of this alloy

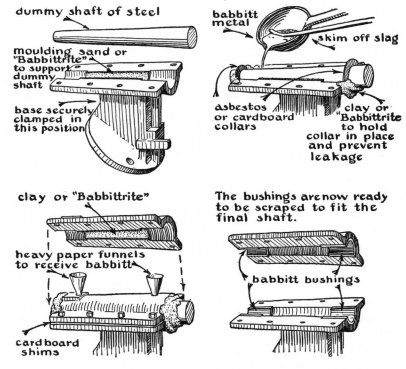

A dummy shaft must be used because the uneven
heating by the babbitt metal might warp the finished
shaft and ruin it.

Fig. 23.   Method of making a babbitt bearing.

are commercially available having different properties, some
being suitable for high-speed bearings and others for bearings
which must work under heavy loads.   Bearings of babbitt
are usually cast in some sort of carrier, so that the babbitt
forms a bushing.   These bearings are sometimes cast as

solid plugs, which are then bored and reamed to size. More frequently they are cast in two halves with a dummy shaft in place. For many purposes such bearings are good enough just as they are, but for precision bearings they should be scraped to fit the spindle. A dummy shaft should always be used, because the hot babbitt metal is apt to warp the shaft. Fig. 23 shows the method of casting a split bearing.

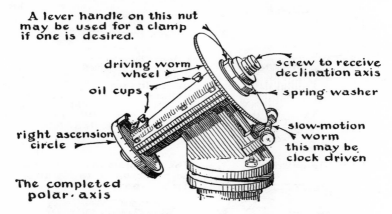

A lever handle on this nut may be used for a clamp if one is desired.

driving worm wheel

screw to receive declination axis

oil cups

spring washer

right ascension circle

slow-motion worm this may be clock driven

The completed polar axis

Fig. 24. The completed polar axis for a small telescope.

Cuttlebone casting. There remains one other method of casting which might be found useful in the laboratory. This is cuttlebone casting. The desirable properties of the method are the ease and rapidity with which a cast can be produced: A mold can easily be made and filled in half an hour. The objects to be cast should not exceed the dimensions of $\frac{1}{4}$ inch in thickness, $1\frac{1}{2}$ inches in width, and 3 inches in length. The patterns should be of metal, since they must be subjected to pressure. Draft angles can be very slight, or they may be ignored altogether. There can be no cores. Fig. 25 shows the method quite clearly. Cuttlebones can be procured from a pet shop or drug store for a few cents. The soft, calcareous face is easily crushed and takes a very firm imprint of any object that is pressed into it. Difficulty of pressing thick patterns into the cuttlebone can be overcome

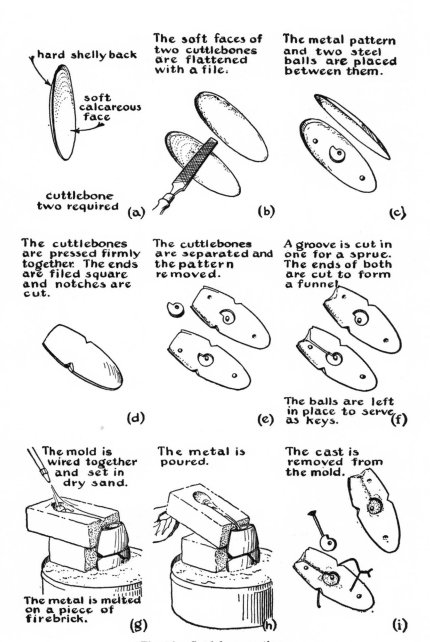

hard shelly back

soft calcareous face

cuttlebone two required (a)

The soft faces of two cuttlebones are flattened with a file. (b)

The metal pattern and two steel balls are placed between them. (c)

The cuttlebones are pressed firmly together. The ends are filed square and notches are cut. (d)

The cuttlebones are separated and the pattern removed. (e)

A groove is cut in one for a sprue. The ends of both are cut to form a funnel.

The balls are left in place to serve as keys. (f)

The mold is wired together and set in dry sand.

The metal is melted on a piece of firebrick. (g)

The metal is poured. (h)

The cast is removed from the mold. (i)

Fig. 25. Cuttlebone casting.

by repeatedly pressing the pattern into the bone, the crushed material being brushed out of the imprint after each operation. The cuttlebone will stand quite high temperatures and is sufficiently porous to allow the air in the mold to escape.

Subject Index

A

Accidental counts in coincident measurements with Geiger-Müller counters, 301
Accuracy of the estimation of a scale reading, 325
Acetylene, a fuel for blowing Pyrex, 2
Adiabatic heating of a thermopile by sound waves, 329
Aerial fog, 475
Aerosol, 153, 313
Alcohol, drying of photographic plates in, 464
Alcohol lamp, 511
Alkali-earth metals, 539
Alkali halide crystals, 365
Alkali metals:
    alloys, liquid at room temperature, 539
    ampoule for, 532
    as research material, 531
    manipulation of, 533, 536
    solvents for, 538
    windows for vapors of, 357
Alkyd resins, 559
Alnico magnet, 148
Alpha particles in ion chambers, 246
Alphasol (see Aerosol)
Alumel, 547
Alumina, levigated, 33
Aluminum:
    films:
        adhesion of, 166
        proper thickness of, 180
        reflection of, 375
    paint, total emissivity of, 509
    sheet for vacuum joints, 127
    -surfaced mirror, 343
    technique for evaporation of, 171
Amateurs, mirrors made by, 56
Amber, cleaning to improve electrical insulation, 257
Ammonia formula for hypersensitizing, 463
Amplification:
    of alternating current, 430–434
    of galvanometer deflections, 326, 444
    of photocurrents, 412–430
Amplifier tubes:
    grid current of, 414, 428
    low-grid-current types of, 427
Ampoule for alkali metals, 532
Annealing:
    of glass, 12
    of photographic emulsions, 464
    temperatures of glass and quartz, 5

Antimony, films for thermojunctions, 329
Apiezon compounds:
    compound "Q" for packing vacuum valves, 132, 134
    oils, 113
    properties of; 557
    wax "W," use of in vacuum technique, 126
Arc:
    carbon, 348
    high-pressure mercury, 353
    iron, 351
    low-pressure mercury, 351
    sodium, 356
    super-high-pressure mercury, 353
Arsem furnace, 521
Artistic photography, 466
Aspheric surfaces of revolution, working of, 57
Aspirator, water, construction of, 20
Astigmatism:
    avoidance of, 41, 51, 56
    correction of, 63
    of lenses, 391
    test for, 67
Atmosphere, transmission of the, 384

B

Babbitt metal, 621
Background, effect of, in Geiger counter work, 300
Baffles:
    for oil diffusion pumps, 116
    thermal insulation properties of, 510
Bakelite:
    for models, 386
    properties of, 558
Balance, torsion, made with quartz fibers, 214
    calibration of, 215
Ballast, lamp, 347
Balls, steel, 590
Barium, as a getter, 106, 539
Baths, constant-temperature cooling, 511
Beeswax and rosin mixture, 129, 554
Beeswax-coated tools, 50
Beilby layer, 566
Bell jar, sealing of a, 129, 555
Bending:
    of glass tubes, 10
    of quartz fibers, 209
Bentonite, 37
Beryllium:
    evaporation of, 170
    sputtering of, 165

625

Biscuit cutter, 36
Bismuth films for thermojunctions, 329
Black-body radiation, 507
Black coats of bismuth, antimony, or zinc, 331
Blackening of thermocouple receivers, 316
Blocking:
    procedure for, 84
    wax, 80
Boiler temperatures of diffusion pumps, 111, 118
Bol lamp, 353, 356
Bolometer, 307, 338
Borax formula for hypersensitizing, 463
Bottles, cutting of, 7
Boundary conditions, 498, 499
Bourdon gauge made from flat quartz tubing, 213
Brass, 548
Breaking strength of quartz fibers, 191 (table)
Breath figures, 165
Bromide of potassium in photographic developers, 471
Bromine vapor filter for the ultraviolet, 362
Bronze, 548
Brownian motion:
    in electroscopes and electrometers, 251–253
    in radiometry, 326, 327, 336
Bulbs, blowing of glass, 21
Bunsen and Roscoe reciprocity law, 455
Bunsen burner, 512
Burning-on method of metalizing glass, 151
Burnishing of silver, 157, 158
Butyl phthalate:
    for oil diffusion pumps, 113
    tempering of shellac with, 556

C

Calcite:
    generation of optical surfaces on, 84
    optical working of, 87
    principal axis and orientation of, 87
Calcium:
    as a getter, 106, 539
    for evacuating a thermocouple, 322
Calculators for estimating the exposure in photography, 466, 467
Calibration:
    of photometric instruments, 305
    of quartz-fiber torsion balance, 215
Calrod heater, 117
Camphor for cutting glass, 36
Capacity, electrical:
    of electrometers, 222, 224
    of electroscopes, 219
Carbon:
    arc, 348
    arc furnace, 521
    dioxide, vapor pressure of, 122
    for polishing, 89
    -grain furnace, 521
    monoxide, vapor pressure of, 122
    tube furnace, 520

Carborundum grits, 30
Casting:
    babbitt metal, 621
    cuttlebone method (see Cuttlebone casting)
    lost-wax method (see Lost-wax casting)
    sand method (see Sand casting)
Cast-iron tools for optical work, 41
Castor oil, use of, on rubber tubing, 127
Catalin, 560
Cathode sputtering, 159
Cell, adjustable, for a mirror, 590
Cellophane, transmission of, 360
Cements, 554
Cements, irreversible, 562
Centering of lenses, 82
Ceresin, insulation for electrometers and electroscopes, 194, 258
Characteristic sensitivity of a thermopile, 332
Charcoal:
    as a getter, 105
    for evacuation of a thermopile, 310
    trap, total obstruction, 114
Charge sensitivity:
    of electrometers, 221, 223, 254 (table)
    of electroscopes, 219, 254 (table)
China paints, coating of quartz fibers with, 202
Christiansen filter, 372
Chromel, 546
Chromel P, 547
Chromium:
    evaporation of, 170, 176
    oxide for polishing, 33, 89
    process for intensifying photographs, 486
Circle of least confusion, 392
Circuit:
    for counting coincidences, 289–291
    for doubling rectified voltage from transformer, 293
    for extinguishing Geiger-Müller counters, 278–282, 286
    for extinguishing thyratrons, 282, 283
Clean dry surfaces, 165
Cleaning:
    for silvering, 152
    of glass tubes, 8
    of mercury, 540
    of mirrors for aluminizing, 167
    of tungsten and molybdenum, 545
    with ions, 165
Cleaning solution, 154
Clock, use of, in optical figuring, 53
Cloth polishing, 33
Coelostat, 342
Coiling of glass tubes, 11
Coincident circuit for Geiger-Müller counters, 289–291
Colors, wave lengths of various, 342
Color temperatures, 459
Columbium, 545
Coma of an optical system, 78
Compensated thermopiles, 322, 323
Compton electrometer, 236–238
Condenser, Liebig, 522

Conductance of vacuum pumping lines, 98
Conductivity, thermal:
   of gases, 95
   of various materials, 494
Constantan, 547
Constriction:
   of glass tubes, 22
   seal-off, 102
Contrast:
   obtainment of, 486
   of photographic emulsions, 453
Contrast sensitivity of the eye, 455
Convection, heat transfer by free, 505
Cooper-Hewitt mercury light, 352
Copper, evaporation of, 175
Copper films chemically deposited, 159
Copper-to-glass seals, 25
Core boxes, 609, 610, 611, 618
Cored carbons, 348
Cores:
   binders for, 617
   for molding, 602–619 (see also Pattern making, cores)
   sand for, 618
   venting of, 619
Corex A, red-purple glass, transmission of, 352, 372
Corundum, 31
Counter:
   circuits for recording counts of, 282–286
   consistency of data from, 302–304
   errors in using Geiger counters, 299–304
   Geiger-Müller, 262–275
      accidental counts in coincident circuits, 301, 302
      behavior of, 263–267
      circuits for extinguishing, 278–282, 286
      circuit used with fast counter to operate recorder, 276, 277
      coincident circuit for, 289–291
      construction of, 267–269
      conventional circuit for operating recorder, 276–278
      copper-in-glass, 268
      cosmic-ray, 262, 271, 289
      efficiency of, 269, 272
      fast and slow counters, 265, 266
      fast counters, 269–271
      gamma-ray, 273
      gases used in, 269, 270
      Geiger's circuit, 259, 275
      large, 280–282
      photoelectric, 273–275
      plateau, 263
      sensitivity of, 271, 272
      special uses of, 272–275
      study of action of, with oscilloscope, 265
      threshold potential of, 263
      X-ray, 273
   high-voltage sources for, 292–294
   multivibrator circuit for operating recorder, 283–286

Counter (cont.):
   point, 259
      use of in measuring β-rays, 272
   probabilities in Geiger counter work, 298
   proportional, 260
   recording counts, 275–291
   scaling counts due to, 287–289
Cross hairs, quartz-fiber, 214
Crystals, optical working of, 87
Cuba wires, 539
Cutting:
   of glass plate, 34
   of metals, 369
   of tubes and bottles, 7
   zones of polishing tools, 51
Cuttlebone casting, 622–624

D

Damping of vibrationless support with oil, 591
Deflections of beams, etc., 582
DeKhotinsky cement, 556
Densitometers, photoelectric, 441
Density, photographic, 452
Desensitizing of photographic emulsions, 476
Desiccating chemicals, 107
Detectable energy, minimum, for a thermopile and galvanometer, 337
Development, photographic:
   equipment for, 474
   general discussion of, 469
   general discussion of solutions for, 470
   stock solutions for, 472
   time for, of papers, 483
Diamond glass cutter, 35
Diamond saw, 37
Diffusion pumps:
   general discussion of, 111
   glass and metal, 119
   multiple-jet, 116
   oil, 115
      construction of, 115
      up-jet, 119
   throat clearances of, 116
Diffusivity:
   thermal, 494 (table)
   definition of, 497
Discharge tube:
   as vacuum gauge, 137
   capillary, 357
   construction of a, 25
Dispersion, optical, of synthetic materials, 361
Dolezalek electrometer:
   adjustment of, 233, 235
   charge sensitivity of, 234, 235
   voltage sensitivity of, 234, 235
Double refraction, coefficient of forced, 387
Draper machine:
   description of, 39
   grinding with, 42
   polishing with, 49

Drawings made with a camera, 487
Dreft, 313
Drifts:
first- and second-order, of a galvanometer, 322
of electrometers, 250–251
Drying:
of benzene and petroleum ether, 534
of photographic emulsions, equipment for, 478, 480, 481
of photographic papers, 484
Drying agents, 107
Duraluminum, 549
Dutch grease, 566

E

Edge grinding of lenses, 82
Edwal 12 developer, 473
Efficiency of Geiger-Müller counters, 269, 272
Effusion equation, 97
Elastic limit of polarizing sheets, 387
Electrical properties of fused silica, 194
Electrodes:
discharge tube, 25
high-current, 130
high-potential, 131
platinum, 23
Electrolysis of sodium through glass, 536
Electrometers:
charge sensitivity of, 221, 223, 254 (table)
comparison of sensitivities of various instruments, 253, 254 (table)
Compton, 236–238 (see also Compton electrometer)
definition of, 217
design of high sensitivity, 240
Dolezalek, 231–236 (see also Dolezalek electrometer)
effective capacity of, 221, 224
general theory of, 219–225
Hoffmann, 238–241, 253, 412
insulators for, 257, 258
limitations on sensitivity:
due to Brownian motion, 251–253
due to drift, 250–251
due to magnification, 251, 411
Lindemann, 242
maximum value of charge sensitivity of, general theory, 221, 224
optimum value of applied voltage, 221, 224
period of, 223
Perucca, 242
relationships between charge sensitivity, voltage sensitivity, period, and total or effective capacity, 221
steady deflection measurements with, 248–250
string, 241, 242
useful sensitivity in X-ray work, 245–247
voltage sensitivity of, 220, 223, 254 (table)
Wülf string, 242

Electrometer suspensions:
quartz-fiber, 213
Wollaston wire, 256
Electrometer tubes:
characteristics of, 413
circuits for, 415–422
practical details in use of, 422–427
Electroscopes:
advantages and disadvantages over electrometers, 254
charge sensitivity of, 219, 254 (table)
definition of, 217
effective capacity of, 219
general theory of, 217–219
gold-leaf, 225
insulators for, 257, 258
Lauritsen, 228
limitations on sensitivity due to Brownian motion, 251–253
Regener, 228
torsion type, 229–231
voltage sensitivity of, 218
Wilson tilted, 225
Wülf bifilar, 226–228
Emery grits, 30
Emissivity, thermal:
of metals, 509
of paint, 509
Enamel for cementing windows, 558
Engraved silver circles, polishing of, 89
Enlarging:
equipment for, 485
papers, 481
Errors, effect of background on, 300
Errors in Geiger counter work, 299–304
Ethane, vapor pressure of, 122
Ethylene, vapor pressure of, 122
Evacuation, 99
Evaporation:
apparatus for, 109
of thermojunctions, 329
process of, 168
temperature for, 169
Exposure:
for photographic recording instruments, 468
of a photographic material, 455, 465
of photographic papers, 482, 483
Exposure meters, 466
Extinguishing circuits for Geiger-Müller counters, 278, 282, 286
Eye:
limit of detection of, 398
sensitivity of, 449
Eyepiece tests, 67

F

False cores, 603–616
Fernico, 27
Fibers, quartz (see Quartz fibers)
Figuring:
fingers as tools for, 61
general discussion of, 51
on the hand-lever machine, 82
tools, interpretation of the action of, 52

Filters:
 for isolating mercury lines, 374
 for photography, 459
 for the ultraviolet, 363
 glass and Wratten, 371, 372
 heat-sensitive, 375
 infrared transparency of, 402
 metal, for the ultraviolet, 361
 Schott glass, 353
Fine grain, obtainment of, 474
Fine grinding, 44
Fish-glue cement, 561
Fixing, 477
Flame spectra, 358
Flats:
 figuring of, 58
 testing of, 64
Fluctuations in vacuum tube circuits, 416, 434–438
Fluorescence:
 of minerals, 353
 of sodium vapor, 537
Fluorite optics, 359
Focal isolation, 380
Focusing in photography, 461
Forks for holding quartz fibers, 197
Formulas for strength of externally loaded vessels, 584
Foucault knife-edge test, 63, 69, 500
Fraunhofer lines, 341
Freezing mixtures, 511
Friction:
 coefficients of boundary, 566
 on clean glass, 166
Frilling of lacquer films, 158
Fuel gases, 513
Furnace heat losses, estimation of, 495, 496
Furnaces, electric and gas, 516
Fused silica:
 electrical properties, 194
 hardness, 194
 surface tension of molten silica, 194
Fusing of quartz fibers together, 211

G

Gaede rotary vacuum pump, 100, 102
Galvanometer:
 deflections, photographic recording of, 468
 elimination of drift of the, 327
 for a thermopile, 324
 telescope and scale for the, 324
Gases:
 fuel, 513
 laws of ideal, 93
Gasket:
 lead fuse wire, 128
 rubber, 127
Gauges:
 Bourdon, 213
 mica, for quarter-wave plates, 389
 use of, 390
 vacuum, 137
Geiger counters, 259–304 (see also Counters, Geiger)

Geiger-Müller counters, 262 (see also Counters)
Gelatin shifts on photographic plates, 464
Getters, 104, 539
Gland, packing, 134
Glass:
 blowing, 1–28
 cutting of plate, 34
 filters, 371
 for protecting the eyes from ultra-violet light, 202
 outgassing of, 102
 thin ribbons of, 329
 transmission in the ultraviolet of various types of, 360
Globar, 348
Glow discharge for cleaning glass, 168
Glue, 563
Glyptal, 126, 131, 558
Gold:
 evaporation of, 175
 films, deposited chemically, 159
 foil, for thermocouple receivers, 315
Gold leaf:
 electroscope, 225
 mounting of, in an electroscope, 255
 prepared by evaporation, 316
Graphite:
 as a lubricant, 566, 567
 as stopcock lubricant, 133
Grinding:
 tests of the surface after, 43
 theory of, 30

H

Haidinger's fringes, 66
Halation, 488
Half-silvered mirrors:
 burnishing of, 158
 preparation of, 157, 162, 185
Half-wave plates, 387
Hand-lever machine, 79
Hardening of photographic emulsions, 478
Hardness, extended scale of, 31
Hardness of fused silica, 194
Hard soldering, 579
Hartmann's test, 77
Heat-absorbing filters, 370
Heat conduction:
 cylinder, 504
 in a telescope mirror, 500
 infinite slab, 498
 nonsteady state, 497
 of wood, 551
 periodic temperatures, 502
 sphere, 503
 steady state, 493
Heat spectrum, 364
Heliostat, 342
Herschel effect, 464 ?
High-frequency:
 coil for hunting leaks in glass, 135
 discharge for cleaning glass, 167
 heating of metals, 522

High-voltage sources for Geiger counters, 292–294
Hilger-Müller double monochromator, 377
Hoffmann electrometer, 238–241, 253
Hoffman packless valve, 133
Hot-wire holder for melting waxes, 198
Housekeeper glass-to-metal seals, 26
Humidity, measurement of, 382
Hurter and Driffield curves, 451, 452
Hydrofluoric acid, use of, 313
Hydrogen:
  "alloy" with palladium, 543
  atomic, 544
  diffusion apparatus, 23
  furnace, 519
  sources of the, continuum, 357
  "transparency" of platinum to, 542
Hyperbolizing:
  by rouge polishing, 63
  with an aluminum film, 184
Hypersensitizing of photographic emulsions, 463
Hysteresis, thermal, of fused silica, 190

I

Image, imperfect, formed by a galvanometer, 324
Index of refraction of synthetic materials, 361
Inertia, moments of, 583
Inertia of a photographic emulsion, 455
Infrared:
  characteristic frequencies in the, 364
  photography, 487
  radiations, laboratory source of, 346
  transmission of various materials in the, 365
Ink eraser for cleaning glass, 153
Insa-lute cement, 562
Instrument design, 582
Instruments, useful in working with quartz fibers, 199–205
Insulators for electrometers and electroscopes, 257, 258
Insulite, 28
Intensifying, photographic, 485
Invar, 546
Ionization gauge, 143
Ions, cleaning of glass with, 165, 167
Iridium, 543
Iron arc, 351
Iron oxide, surface stains, removal of, 87
Isochromatics, 386
Isoclinics, 386

J

Joining quartz fibers by fusion, 211
Joints:
  making of glass, 17
  tongue and groove, 127
  vacuum, 126

K

Kaolin cement, 562
Kinematical design, 585

Kinetic theory of gases, 96
Kinetic vacuum systems:
  construction of, 125
  definition of, 107
Knife-edge test (see also Foucault knife-edge test):
  employment in Schlieren-methode, 63
  for focusing a camera, 461
  interpretation of shadows of the, 72
Knudsen gauge, 138, 148
Koroseal, 561
Kovar, 27

L

Lacquer films:
  deposition of metal on, 330
  formation of, 330
  for protecting silver mirrors, 158
Langmuir vacuum gauge, 138, 146
Lanolin, as a lubricant, 566
Lantern-slide plates, procedure for obtaining good, 475
Lathe, 371
Latitude of photographic emulsions, 452, 453
Lead fuse-wire gasket, 128
Leaks:
  hunting for, 134
  virtual, 123
  with tungsten-glass seals, 24
Lemon-peel surface on glass, 33
Lens, achromatic, transmission of, 457
Lenses, properties of, 391
Liebig condenser, 522
Light sources for photography, 457
Limit of detection for receivers of radiation, 397
Lindemann electrometer, 243
Lining up of a system of mirrors, 78
Liquid air:
  temperature of, and other refrigerants, 511
  thermopiles at the temperature of, 340
  trap to estimate fraction of residual pressure in a vacuum due to condensable vapors, 150
Litharge and glycerin cement, 562
Lithium:
  preparation of, 531
  solvent for, 538
  spectrum, 358
Littelfuses, 144
Littrow arrangement for a spectrometer, 379
Lost-wax casting:
  centrifuge method, 600
  description of, 593–600
  fluxes, 600
  molding materials, 595, 596
  steam method, 599
  vacuum method, 598
Lubrication, 563
Lucite:
  description of, 560
  ultraviolet transmission of, 561 (table)
Lumen, defined, 397

M

Magnesia:
  filter, 375
  windows, 357
Magnesium:
  as a getter, 106
  perchlorate drying agent, 107
  spark, 357
Magnification:
  of lenses, 391
  useful, with microscopes for reading instruments, 251
  useful, with telescope and scale, 251
Magnitude, stellar, defined, 397
Magnolia, evergreen, 552
Manometer, mercury, construction of, 22
Marblette, for construction of photoelastic models, 386
Masonite, 554
McLeod gauge, 137, 138
Mean free path, 94
Measuring of a spectrum plate, technique for, 350
Mechanical motion in vacuum, 133
Meker burner, 513
Melting quartz fibers together, 211
Mercury:
  arc:
    cold low-pressure, 355
    high-pressure, 353
    low-pressure, 351
    super-high-pressure, 353
  as a research material, 540
  cleaning of, 540
  diffusion pumps, 112
  filters for isolating the spectrum lines of, 374
  hypersensitizing of photographic emulsions with, 463
  poisoning, 541
  seal for a stopcock, 133
  traps, 120
  vapor pressure of, 122, 541
Metals:
  outgassing of, 102
  polishing of, 88
  total thermal emissivity of, 509
Methane, vapor pressure of, 122
Methyl methacrylate, 560
Mica:
  for quarter-wave plates, 387
  gauges:
    description of, 389
    using of, 390
  principal directions of, 388
  splitting of, 388
  thin films of, 329
  ultraviolet transmission of, 364
Micromanipulators for working quartz fibers, 202, 203
Microphotometer:
  photoelectric, 442
  use of a radiometer in the, 308
Microradiometer, 306, 338
Microscopes, use of, in working with quartz fibers, 196, 200, 204, 208

Minerals, lamp for fluorescing, 355
Miniature cameras, 488
Mirror:
  cell for, 590
  improvement of figure by evaporation of aluminum, 184
  pellicle, 77
  perforated, construction of, 46
  properties of various types of, 392
Modulus of rigidity of quartz fibers, change of, with temperature, 191 (table), 192, 194
Moh's hardness scale, 31
Molding (see Sand casting)
Molecular weight, measurement of, 148
Molybdenum:
  as a getter, 106
  properties of, 544
  wire-wound furnace, 519
Moments of inertia of structural members, 583
Monochromators:
  for obtaining high spectral purity, 376
  transmission of, 377
  uses of mirrors in, 378
  water, 379
Mud saw for glass, 37
Multiple-jet diffusion pumps, 116
Multiple-junction thermopile receiver, 320
Multivibrator circuit, 283–286

N

Naphthene oils, 113
Needles used in work with quartz fibers, 199
Neodymium filter, 358
Neon spectrum, 356
Neoprene, 561
Nernst filaments:
  construction of, 347
  properties of, 346
Newtonian diagonal mirror, construction of, 37
Newton's:
  fringes, 63
  law of cooling, 498, 499
Niba wires, 539
Nichrome, 547
Nickel as a furnace winding, 517
Nicol prisms, transmission of, 384
Nitrocellulose films, transmission of, in the infrared, 366
Nitrosodimethylanalin filter for the ultraviolet, 363
Norremberg doubler, 390

O

Octoil, 113, 124
Oil diffusion pumps, 115
Oil, sensitizing of photographic emulsions with, 462
Optical testing, 63
Oscillographs, optical recording for, 393
Osmium, 543

Outgassing:
  of an ionization gauge, 144
  of glass and metals, 102
Oxygen-gas torches, 195

P

Packing gland, 134
Packless valve, 133
Paint, thermal emissivity of, 509
Palladium, 543
Paper, polishing glass with, 33
Papers, photographic:
  drying of, 484
  response to light of, 484
  washing of, 481
Parabolizing:
  by rouge polishing, 61
  with an aluminum film, 180
Paraboloidal off-axis mirror, 378
Paraffin, high-melting-point:
  transmission of, 366
  windows, 319
Parallax in knife-edge testing, 75
Partially reflecting films:
  preparation by evaporation, 185
  preparation with a silvering solution, 157
  silver, burnishing of, 158
Pattern making:
  amount of metal required for casts, 620
  cores, 603-619
  dowel pins, 606, 607
  draft, 602, 603
  false cores, 603-616
  fillets, 608, 609
  finishing, 609
  match boards, 619
  metal patterns, 605, 619
  rapping plates, 608, 614, 615
  shrinkage, 605
  wood for, 606
Pedestal, for optical working of a 6-inch mirror, 41
Pellicle mirror, 77
Peltier effect, 339
Peltier heat, 333
Pencil, photography of drawings in, 488
Period:
  of electrometers, 223
  of various electrometers and electroscopes, 254 (table)
Perucca electrometer, 242
Pfund's iron arc, 351
Phenosafranine, as a photographic desensitizer, 476
Photocell (see also Photoelectric cells):
  barrier layer, use of, as a relay, 326, 411
  introduction of sodium into a, 538
Photoelectric cell (see also Photocell):
  applications of, 438, 448
  dark current of, 401, 402, 406
  emission type, characteristics of, 400, manufacturers of, 404
  gas-filled, 407

Photoelectric cell (cont.):
  insulation of, 405, 425
  limit of detection of, 398
  linear response of, 396, 408, 410
  photovoltaic type, 409-411
  with relay, 411
  refrigeration of, 401, 406, 424
  spectral sensitivity of, 401, 410
  vacuum, 407
Photoelectric counters, 273-275
Photoflash lamp, 458
Photographic emulsions:
  sensitivity of, 449
  swelling of, 480
Photographic papers, relative speed of, 485
Photographic plate, limit of detection of, 398
Photographs, preparation of, for publication, 485, 487, 488
Photography:
  applications, 486
  in the infrared, 487
  in the ultraviolet, 487
Photometry, photographic, 489
Photronic-cell exposure meter, 466
Picein wax:
  joints made with, 130
  properties of, 557
  seals made with, 129
Pinakryptol green as a photographic desensitizer, 476
Pin holes, construction of, 69
Pirani gauge, 138, 145, 146
Pitch:
  for polishing tools, 46
  testing of polishing, 46
Planck formula, 507
Plane parallels:
  and Haidinger's fringes, 67
  construction of, 84
Plaster of Paris, 562, 596
Plateau of Geiger counters, 260, 263
Platinum:
  as a furnace winding, 518
  black, 321
  -glass seals, 23
  metals, 542
  evaporation of the, 170, 175
Plexiglas, 560
Plywood, 553
Point counter, Geiger, 259, 260
Point, pulling a, 12
Poisoning, mercury, 541
Poisson's law, 299
Polarization, 364, 384
Polarized light, engineering applications of, 385
Polaroid, transmission of, 384
Polish:
  test for, 51
  theory of the generation of, 30
Polishing:
  methods of, 32
  of optical surfaces, 49
  on the hand-lever machine, 81
Porcelain-Pyrex seal, 28
Porcelain-to-metal seal, 152

Potassium:
  filters, 361
  preparation of, 531
  spectrum, 358
Precipitated chalk for cleaning glass, 153
Pre-exposure of photographic emulsions, 464
Preheating of glass, 8
Preservation of quartz fibers, 209
Pressing of polishing tools, 49
Printing papers, 481
Prism:
  properties of the, 393
  right-angle, construction of a, 82
Probabilities in Geiger counter work, 298
Probe for testing conductivity of metal-coated quartz fibers, 198
Pumping lines:
  conductance of, 98
  resistance of, 99
Pumping speed, 97
  measurement of, 98
Pumps:
  diffusion, 111
  roughing, 101
  Sprengel, 102
  Toepler, 102
Putty powder as a polishing agent, 33
Pyrex glass:
  in glass blowing, 1
  sodium resistant inner surface for, 538
  transmission of, 372
Pyrometer, radiation, 382, 530

Q

Quarter-wave plates, 387
Quartz:
  changes in the transmission limit of, 352
  fibers:
    bending of, 209
    bow-and-arrow method of producing, 208
    care in handling, 207, 209
    coating with metals, 200–202
    complete assembly for working, 204
    cross hairs for microscope and telescope eyepieces, 214
    drawing and shrinking, 210
    electrometer suspensions, 213
    finding a small quartz fiber under a microscope, 208
    handling, 207, 209
    joining a small fiber to a larger piece of quartz, 211
    joining one fiber to another, 211
    making of, 205–208
    manipulators for working, 200, 202, 203
    microscopes useful in working with, 196, 204, 208
    oval fibers, 148, 212
    preservation of, 209

Quartz (cont.):
  fibers (cont.):
    size, means of estimating without use of microscope, 197, 208
    straightening of, 209
    testing for impurities on, 207
    use in radiation thermocouples, 315, 317
    viscosity of, 193
  for quarter-wave plates, 387
  fused, 188–216 (see also Silica, fused)
  optical properties of, in the infrared, 367
  optical surfaces in, 84
  optical working of, 87
  test for optical rotation of crystal, 84

R

Radiation, heat transfer by, 507
Radiometer, 307, 338
Radiometric instruments, 305
Raster for photographic photometry, 491
Rayleigh-Jeans formula, 508
Raytheon voltage regulator, 344
Reciprocity law in photography, 455
Recording systems, optical, 393
Rectifiers for high-voltage sources, 292–294
Reducing of photographs, 485
Reflecting and transmitting coats:
  of aluminum, 187
  of silver, 186
Reflection of metals:
  apparatus for measuring, 376
  in the infrared spectrum, 367
  in the visible and ultraviolet spectrum, 375
Refractories, specific electrical resistance of various, 568
Refractory metals, 544
Refrigerant liquids, 121
Refrigerator, electric, to trap oil vapors, 124
Regener's electroscope, 228
Regulators, high-voltage, 294–298
Relaxation time, 494, 499, 500, 502
Relays for thermopile currents, 326
Residual ionization in ion chambers, 245
Residual-ray:
  isolation of infrared radiations, 367, 382
  wave lengths, 368
Resistance:
  of vacuum pumping lines, 99
  specific electrical, of various refractories, 568
Resolving power of photographic emulsions, 456
Resonance radiometer, 327
Reticulation, avoidance of, in photographs, 474
Rhenium, 545
Rhodium, 543
Ring seals, 19
Ring tool for making a Schmidt lens, 92
Rochelle salt method for silvering, 152

Rock salt:
  optical working of, 87
  optics, 359
Ronchi test, 77
Rotation of work in glass blowing, 9
Rouge:
  for burnishing silver, 157
  for polishing, 32
  washing of, 49
Roughing pumps, 101
Rubber cements, 561
Rubies, apparatus for making, 529

S

Sand casting:
  gates, 606, 614, 615
  molding for, 611–616
  risers, 616, 617
  sand for, 611
  sprues, 613–616
  venting, 612–614
Sapphires, apparatus for making, 529
Saws for glass, 37
Scale-of-two circuits, 287–289
Schlieren-methode:
  and optical testing, 63
  light source for, 358
Schmidt camera:
  contour of lens for, 90
  description of, 89
  grinding and polishing of lens for, 92
  lens, rough grinding of, 43
Schumann plates, 461
Schwarzschild's law, 455
Scissors used in working with quartz
    fibers, 199
Seal-off constrictions:
  construction of, 22
  outgassing of, 102
  vacuum, 128
Seals:
  copper-to-glass, 25
  metal and porcelain vacuum, 152
  Porcelain-Pyrex, 28
  ring, 19
  tungsten-glass, 23
Sease 3 developer, 473
Seeding of a photographic developer,
    475
Selenite for quarter-wave plates, 387
"Self-photograph" of an aluminizing
    source, 174
Sensitivity:
  maximum possible, of thermopiles,
      338
  of electrometers and electroscopes:
    comparison of, 253, 254 (table)
    for cosmic-ray work, 247, 248
    for X-ray work, 245–247
  of galvanometer-thermopile combina-
      tion, 335
  of Geiger counters, 271, 272
  of radiometric instruments, 327
  of various instruments, criterion for
      maximum useful, 251
Sensitizing of photographic emulsions,
    461
Shadows cast by mercury vapor, 355

Shape factors:
  determination by experiment, 496
  formulas for, 495
Shellac:
  properties of, 555
  tempered, 556
Short stop, photographic, formula for, 47
Shrinkage scales, 604
Shrinking of glass, 11
Shutter for thermopiles, 322
Silica, fused:
  chemical properties of, 189
    reaction with the noble metals, 189
  elastic properties of, 190
    modulus of rigidity, change of with
        temperature, 194
    modulus of rigidity of quartz fibers,
        191 (table), 192
    Young's modulus of quartz fibers,
        191 (table)
    Young's modulus of quartz fibers,
        change of with temperature, 194
  flat tubing, making of, 213
  physical properties, 189
  thermal expansion, coefficient of, 189,
      190 (table)
  thermal hysteresis, 190
  ultraviolet light from hot quartz and
      protection of the eyes, 202
  viscosity of quartz fibers, 193 (table)
Silica gel as a getter, 105
Silver:
  chloride, 557
  evaporation of, 175
  polishing of, 89
  reflection of, 375
  solder, 547
Silvering process, chemical, 152
Six-inch mirror, 41
Sleeks, 50
Soap as a lubricant, 567
Soapstone, 567
Sodium:
  action of, on Pyrex, 356
  arc, 356
  flame spectrum, 358
  purification of, by distillation, 534
  quartz photocell, construction of, 538
  resistant surface for Pyrex, 538
Soft solder, 547
Soft soldering, 578
Soldering of thermocouple wires, 314
Solders, 547
Solvents for the alkali metals, 538
Sparks, for exciting spectra, 357
Spectra, photography of, 488
Spectral sensitivity:
  of human eye, 410, 449
  of photoelectric cells, 401, 410
Spectrophotometry:
  photoelectric, 440
  photographic, 492
Spectroscope, pocket, 341
Spectrum:
  of cored carbon arc, 349
  of super-high-pressure mercury lamp,
      349
  plate, technique for measuring, 350

Specular reflection from a fine-ground surface, 45
Speculum metal:
  composition and properties of, 549
  optical working of, 88
  polishing of, 50
  reflectivity of, 375
Speed of photographic emulsion, 455
Speed factor of diffusion pumps, 97
Spherical tools, turning of, 81
Spherometer, 43
Spindle machine, high-speed, for optical working, 79
Splitting of mica, 388
Spot welding, 581
Sprengel pump, 102
Sputtering:
  of thermojunctions, 329
  process, 159
  rates for various metals, 163–164
Squeegee process for drying photographic papers, 484
Star tool for optical working, 61
Static vacuum system, 107
Stefan's formula, 508
Stellite:
  optical working of, 89
  reflection of, 375
Step-weakener, 490
Stopcock, 133
Straightening quartz fibers, 209
Strain point for glass and quartz, 5
Strain tester, 385
Strength:
  breaking, of quartz fibers, 191 (table)
  of wood, 552
Striae, test for, in quartz, 87
String electrometers, 241, 242
Sulphur:
  chloride, vulcanizing with, 561
  on the moon, 487
  solvent for, 127
Sun, as a light source, 341
Sunlight, spectral distribution of, 458
Support:
  of optical work, 39
  vibrationless, 328, 590
Surface tension:
  lowering of, 313
  of molten silica, 194
Suspensions for electrometers made from quartz fibers, 213
Sylphon bellows for "packing" valves, 132

T

Talc:
  as lubricant for optical working, 45
  properties of, 567
Tantalum:
  as a getter, 105
  cutting, spinning, and spot welding of, 545
  properties of, 544
Tarnish, prevention of, 159, 187
Taylor process wires, 312
Telescope and scale for galvanometer, 324

Temperature:
  color, 459
  control, use of a thyratron in, 447
  equalization of, in optical testing, 56, 500
  estimation from color, 530
  fixed, 523
  high, methods of obtaining, 511
  low, 510
  measurement of, 528
  of evaporation for various metals, 169 (table)
  standard, 523
Templates, 43, 44
Testing:
  of vacuum in a thermopile, 311
  optical, 63
Thallium spectrum, 358
Therapeutic lamp, 352
Thermal expansion:
  of fused silica, 189, 190 (table)
  of glass and metals, 5
  of wood, 550
Thermal hysteresis of fused silica, 190
Thermocouple:
  alloys, 547
  base metals for a, 530
  LeChatelier, alloy, 530
  limit of detection with the radiation, 398
  stellar-radiation, 320
  wires for the radiation, 311
  by Pfund's process, 319
Thermoelectric power of Bi against the alloy 95 Bi:5 Sn, 333
Thermoelectromotive force of bismuth crystals, 331
Thermojunctions, construction of, 313
Thermopile, radiation:
  at liquid air temperatures, 340
  characteristic sensitivity of, 332
  compensated, 322
  design of, 331, 332
  general summary of work on, 337
  distinguishing features of, 306
  evacuation of, with calcium, 322
  galvanometer for, 324
  receiver, common, for the junctions of, 320
Thermo-relay, 326, 331
Thermostat baths, 527
Thermostatic devices, 523
Thin films of mica, splitting of, 329
Threshold potential of Geiger counters, 260, 263
Thyratrons, 445–448
  use of, in recording circuits, 282, 283
Time and temperature photographic development, 471
Time intervals between random events, 298
Timing of optical figuring, 53
Tin, oxide of, for polishing, 32
Toepler pump, 102
Tombak alloy, 548
Torches, 514, 515
  for working quartz fibers, 195

Torsion balance made with quartz fibers, 214
Torsion type of electroscope, 229, 231
Toxicity of photographic developers, 484
Trade-mark on tungsten lamp, removal of, 345
Transition zones in optical figuring, 51
Traps:
  charcoal, 124
  for oil vapor, 123
  mercury, 120
Tray development, 474
Tungsten:
  as a getter, 106, 544
  -glass seals, 23
  lamp, 343
    with quartz bulb, 345
  properties of, 544
  wire-wound furnace, 519
Turned-down edge on a mirror, 57
Turpentine for cutting glass, 36
Tutton's test for the principal axes of mica, 388
Tweezers used in working with quartz fibers, 199
Twyman phenomenon, 37

U

Ultraviolet:
  light, 359
  photography, 487
  thermocouple receiver for the, 321
  transmission of glasses in the, 360
Uniform evaporated films, 177
Universal wax, 554
Up-jet diffusion pumps, 116
Uranium glass for determining the focus in the ultraviolet, 461
Uviol glass for a Schmidt lens, 91

V

Vacuum:
  equipment for evaporation, 176
  gauges, 137
  pump oils, vapor pressure of, 122
  system:
    kinetic, 107
    static, 107
  thermopile, construction of a, 308
Valve:
  needle, 196
  packing for a vacuum, 132
  packless, 133
  vacuum, 131
Vapor pressure:
  of carbon dioxide, 122
  of mercury, 122, 541
  of vacuum pump oils, 122
  of water, 122
  of waxes, 103
Vessels, externally loaded, formulas for, 584
Vibrationless support, 328, 590
Virtual leaks, 123
Viscosity:
  of gases, 95
  of glass, 6

Viscosity (cont.):
  of quartz fibers, 193 (table)
  of various solids, 193 (table)
Visibility of small quartz fibers, 200
Voltage:
  doubler, 293
  optimum for electrometers, 221, 224
  regulators, 294, 298
  Raytheon, 344
  sensitivity:
    of electrometers, 220, 223, 254 (table)
    of electroscopes, 218, 254 (table)
  sources for Geiger counters, 292–294

W

Wadsworth arrangement for a spectrometer, 379
Washing:
  of emery, talc, or rouge, 45
  of photographic emulsions, 478
    equipment for, 479
  of photographic papers, 484
Watch oil, 567
Water:
  absorption of the vapor of, 107
  bath, regulator for, 527
  filter, 369
  optical properties of, in the ultraviolet, 379
  vapor pressure of, 122
Watkins factors for tray development, 475
Wax, lost-wax casting, 594
Waxes:
  used for holding quartz fibers, 199
  useful to physicists, 554
  vapor pressure of, 103
Weber-Feckner curve of the response of eye, 454
Wedge spectrograms, 451
Welding:
  of thermocouple elements by Pfund's procedure, 321
  of thermocouple wires with condenser discharge, 320
  of vacuum apparatus, 126
Welsbach mantle, 345
Wheel cutter for glass plates, 34
Wiedemann-Franz:
  coefficients, 311, 312, 333
  formula for, 335
    of Bi and the alloy 95 Bi:5 Sn, 333
  law, 339
Wiens formula, 508
Wilson tilted electroscope, 225
Windows:
  for alkali-metal vapors, 357
  for thermopiles, 317
  sealing of, 129
Wires for thermojunctions, 311
Wollaston:
  prism, 364
  wire, 542
    annealing of, 257
    preparation of and mounting of, 256, 257

Wood:
   heat conductivity of, 551
   polishing glass with a base of, 41
   properties of, 549
   shrinkage of, 551
   strength of, 553
   thermal expansion of, 551
Wood's metal:
   composition of, 548
   use of, 314
Working temperature of glass and quartz, 5
Wratten filters, 371
Wülf:
   bifilar electroscope, 226–228
   string electrometer, 242

Y

Yield point of glasses, 6
Young's modulus for quartz fibers, 191
   (table)
   change of, with temperature, 194

Z

Zählrohr (see also Counters, Geiger-Müller), 262
Zinc oxychloride cement, 562
Zonal:
   defects, figuring of, 57
   knife-edge testing, 72
Zones:
   cutting and transition, 51
   false, 61

Name Index

A

Abbott, C. G., 307
Abney, W. de W., 490
Adams, E. Q., 495
Adams, L. H., 523
Aitken, J., 165
Alterthum, H., 356
Anderson, J. A., 77
Andrews, M. R., 104
Angerer, Ernst von, 159, 514, 562
Arsem, W. C., 521

B

Babcock, Harold D., 351
Bäckström, H. L. G., 363
Bacon, J. S., 104
Badger, R. M., 323
Bailey, B. L., 31
Baker, T. J., 165, 166
Ballard, A. H., 31
Baly, E. C. C., 352, 395
Barnes, B. T., 353
Barnes, R. B., 326, 346, 366, 375
Bateman, H., 299
Baur, E., 169
Bearden, J. A., 120, 124, 417
Beattie, J. A., 523, 527
Becker, J. A., 124
Beckman, Arnold O., 146
Benford, F., 349
Bennett, A. L., 401
Bierens de Haan, David, 178
Biltz, M., 399
Bol, C., 353
Bonét-Maury, P., 177
Bonner, L. G., 366, 375
Borelius, G., 543
Bose, E., 346
Boys, C. V., 189, 194, 208, 306
Brackett, F. S., 306
Brady, G. S., 549
Brahtz, J. H. A., 385
Brandenstein, Maruscha von, 113
Brashear, John A., 87, 152, 154
Brice, R. T., 357
Bridgman, P. W., 339, 365
Brode, W. R., 363
Brose, H. L., 134
Brown, H., 418
Brown, Marcus H., 557
Brubaker, G., 262
Brunner, R., 169
Buckley, O. E., 143
Burch, C. R., 113
Burger, E. E., 27

Burger, H. C., 306, 326, 444
Burt, R. C., 537
Busch, H., 347
Buttolph, L. J., 356, 374
Byck, H. T., 117

C

Caldwell, F. R., 516
Calvert, Mary, 398
Campbell, N. R., 439
Carslaw, H. S., 498
Cartwright, C. H., 171, 308, 311, 320, 326, 332, 335, 337, 340, 348
Case, F. A., 152
Chaffee, E. L., 430
Christiansen, C., 373
Christoph, W., 264, 275
Cittert, P. H. van, 306, 329, 331
Coblentz, W. W., 306, 307, 370
Coker, E. G., 386
Compton, A. H., 236
Compton, K. T., 159, 223
Cooksey, C. D., 464
Cooksey, D., 464
Copley, M. J., 117
Crawford, W. W., 112
Crookes, Sir W., 163, 307
Cucuel, F., 542
Curtiss, L. F., 258, 268
Czerny, M., 326, 330, 337, 379

D

Davis, M. N., 439
Dersch, F., 463
Dewar, Sir James, 105
Doubleday, Ida, 564, 565, 566
Douglas, R. W., 525
Driffield, V. C., 451
DuBridge, L. A., 406, 418, 426
Duerr, H., 463
Duffendack, O. S., 357
DuMond, J. W. M., 132, 145, 148
Duncan, R. A., 153
Dunning, J. R., 273, 427, 434
Dunnington, F., 144
Dunoyer, L., 93
Dushman, S., 93, 100, 106, 143, 353

E

Eckart, Carl, 302
Eckweiler, H. J., 441
Edlefsen, N. E., 357
Einsporn, E., 387
Ellison, Rev. Wm. F. A., 31, 34

Elvgard, E., 375
Espe, W., 169, 494, 544, 558, 568, 582
Esterman, I., 117
Evans, R. D., 273, 300

F

Faessler, A., 273
Ferguson, W. B., 451
Filon, L. N. G., 386
Finch, G. I., 31, 566
Firestone, F. A., 306, 308, 320, 327
Forbes, George S., 382
Forsythe, W. E., 321, 346, 353, 395
Found, C. G., 143
Fourier, J. B. J., 498
Fowle, F. E., 370, 449, 494, 549
Fowler, R. D., 357
French, E. A. H., 159
French, J. W., 31
Frerichs, R., 492
Freundlich, H., 364
Fruth, H. F., 159

G

Gabus, G. H., 428
Gaede, W., 111, 112, 138
Gardner, I. C., 152
Garman, R. L., 439
Gaviola, E., 72, 73, 172, 185
Geiger, H., 259, 260, 262
Getting, I. A., 286
Gibson, K. S., 402
Glasgow, R. S., 430
Glimm, K. O., 113
Goetz, A., 93, 385
Goodman, Clark, 542
Griffith, H. D., 347
Grove, W. R., 159
Güntherschulze, A., 163

H

Haagn, E., 523
Haber, F., 146, 513
Hafstad, L. R., 417, 437
Hale, C. F., 145
Hall, J. S., 401
Hancox, R. R., 447, 523
Hanle, W., 264
Hansen, W. W., 221
Hanson, D., 523
Hardy, A. C., 393, 395, 441, 449, 467, 468
Hardy, J. D., 326, 378
Hardy, Wm. B., 165, 564, 565, 566
Harries, W., 353
Harris, L., 329, 330
Harrison, G. R., 379, 443, 462, 490
Haughton, J. L., 523
Hayward, Roger, 571
Heidt, Lawrence J., 382
Heins, H., 326
Heller, G., 356
Hemmendinger, A., 272
Henderson, Joseph E., 119, 124
Hendrix, D. O., 33, 34

Henney, K., 400, 430, 448
Henry, D. E., 406
Hering, C., 494
Herzberg, G., 357
Hettner, G., 307
Hickman, K. C. D., 113, 119, 120, 124, 138
Hippel, A. v., 353
Ho, T. L., 112, 117
Hoffmann, G., 217, 238
Hoger, O. J., 386
Hogness, T. R., 440
Holladay, L. L., 359
Honda, K., 193
Horton, J. W., 429
Hougen, O. A., 520
Housekeeper, W. G., 25
Hubble, E., 399
Hughes, A. L., 406
Hughes, H. H., 567
Hulburt, E. O., 164
Hull, A. W., 27, 446, 523
Hunt, F. V., 289, 443
Hurter, F., 451

I

Iida, K., 193
Ingalls, Albert G., 31, 34, 152
Ingersoll, L. R., 494, 498
Ising, G., 336
Ives, H. E., 345

J

Jacobi, G., 357
Jaycox, E. K., 124, 143
Jeans, Sir James, 508
Jenkins, F. A., 117
Johansen, E. S., 306
Johnson, A. G., 427, 435
Johnson, E. A., 329, 330, 427, 433, 434, 435
Jones, L. A., 456, 490
Jones, R. V., 444
Jung, R., 516

K

Kaplan, Joseph, 388
Karrer, E., 345
Kautny, Th., 516
Kaye, G. W. C., 93, 96, 189, 225
Kayser, H., 350
Kennedy, R. G., Jr., 104
Kelley, M. J., 406
Kellner, L., geb. Sperling, 365
Kerschbaum, F., 146
Keyston, J. E., 134
King, W. J., 494, 505
Kingsbury, E. F., 345, 401, 436
Kinney, G. F., 444
Kirchoff, G. R., 507
Klemperer, O., 260
Klose, W., 99
Klumb, H., 112, 113, 308
Knoll, M., 169, 494, 544, 558, 568, 582
Knudsen, M., 99, 148

Koehler, Arthur, 549
Kohlschütter, V., 163
Kolin, A., 275
Korth, K., 365
Krayhill, H. L., 443
Krehbiel, J. F., 518
Kreuchen, K. H., 274
Kron, G. E., 443
Kyropoulos, S., 365

L

Laby, T. H., 96
Ladoo, Raymond B., 567
Land, E. H., 364
Lange, B., 442
Langer, R. M., 498
Langley, S. P., 307
Langmuir, I., 103, 106, 111, 146, 159, 495, 505, 507, 516
Lau, E., 357
Lauritsen, C. C., 228
Lawrence, E. O., 357
Lebedew, P., 306
Lecomte, J., 395, 508
Leighton, P. A., 355
Leighton, W. G., 355
Leimbach, G., 307
Leitgebel, M., 169
Lindblom, S., 543
Linde, H., 516
Lindemann, A. F., 243
Lindemann, F. A., 243
Litton, Charles V., 116
Littrow, O., 379
Livingston, O. W., 447
Locher, G. L., 264, 274
Luckiesch, M., 359

M

MacDonald, P. A., 427
Manley, J. H., 357
Marks, L. S., 549
Marshall, A. L., 103
Maser, H. T., 447
Mathiesen, W., 516
Matossi, F., 326, 395
Maxwell, James Clerk, 96
McAlister, E. D., 306, 373
McKelvy, E. C., 152
McMillan, Edwin, 119
McMorris, John, 472
Mees, C. E. K., 399, 463
Meikle, G. S., 495
Meissner, W., 511
Melvin, E. H., 365
Metcalf, G. F., 413
Meyer, Chas. F., 395
Meyer, O., 96
Mierdel, G., 159
Miller, Dayton C., 157
Milligan, W. O., 442
Mohler, Nora M., 442
Moll, W. J. H., 306, 326, 331, 444
Mollet, P., 330
Molthan, W., 112
Moon, P. H., 403

Morgan, W. W., 473
Moss, E. B., 444
Mugele, R. A., 300
Müller, K., 542
Müller, R., 591
Müller, R. H., 444
Müller, W., 262
Munch, R. H., 357

N

Neblette, C. B., 449, 476
Neitzert, C., 427, 434, 435
Nernst, W., 346
Newman, F. H., 93
Nichols, E. F., 307, 367
Nicholson, Seth B., 306, 370, 398
Norman, D., 464
Northrup, E. F., 523, 528
Norton, F. J., 103
Nottingham, W. B., 406

O

O'Bryan, H. M., 361
Ollendorff, F., 169
Orton, E., 518
Ostwald, W., 527
Overhage, Carl F. J., 534

P

Paschen, F., 306
Pearson, G. L., 435
Penick, D. B., 420
Perrin, F. H., 395, 449
Perucca, E., 242
Pettit, Edison, 306, 322, 370, 398
Pfund, A. H., 138, 158, 306, 319, 321, 326, 327, 346, 351, 367, 378
Phipps, T. E., 117
Pickels, W. M., Jr., 145, 148
Pickering, W. H., 282
Pirani, M. von, 145
Planck, M., 507
Plettig, V., 379
Podszus, E., 516
Pohl, R., 168, 171, 273
Pollard, A. C. F., 166, 585
Pollard, E., 262
Pool, M. L., 428
Porter, R. W., 34, 77
Prescott, C. H., Jr., 406
Preston, J. S., 440
Pringsheim, P., 168, 171, 542
Proctor, R. F., 525

R

Ramsperger, Herman C., 133, 365
Randall, H. M., 378
Ransley, C. E., 543
Rayleigh, Lord, 31, 165, 508
Regener, V. H., 228
Reger, M., 356
Reichenheim, O., 357
Reinkober, O., 191
Rentschler, H. C., 406

Rice, C. W., 505
Ridgway, R. R., 31
Ritchie, Dorothy, 439
Ritschl, R., 168, 171
Roberts, H. S., 523
Roebuck, J. R., 523
Romain, B. P., 410
Rompe, E., 169
Rose, John E., 132
Ross, F. E., 398
Ross, Lord, 549
Rossi, B., 289
Rubens, H., 306, 346, 367, 380
Russell, H. N., 397, 398
Rutherford, E., 275

S

Sager, T. P., 104
Sandvik, O., 307, 490
Sanford, C. R., 113, 119
Schaefer, C. L., 395
Schmidt, W., 370
Schmitt, O. H. A., 430
Schuen, W., 521
Schumann, V., 461
Schwarzschild, K., 455
Scott, Howard, 27
Sharp, C. H., 441
Sherwood, R. G., 102
Shidei, J., 375
Shonka, F. R., 302
Shrewsbury, C. L., 443
Sidwell, A. E., 440
Sieverts, A., 543
Simon, H., 143
Simpson, O. C., 117
Skellett, A. M., 145
Sloan, D. H., 117
Smiley, C. H., 89
Smith, A. E., 357
Smith, K. O., 406
Smith, S., 307, 398, 402
Smithells, C. J., 543
Smythe, W. R., 272
Spooner, Lawrence W., 382
Stanley, L. F., 145
Stebbins, J., 408, 439
Stefan, J., 96, 508
Steinke, E., 407
Stillwell, G. R., 401
Stintzing, H., 112
St. John, Chas. E., 351
Stober, F., 365
Stock, A., 541
Strafford, N., 443
Straude, H., 375
Street, J. C., 271
Strömgren, B., 89
Strong, J., 166, 176, 185, 321, 357, 365,
    366, 382, 384, 389
Swanger, W. H., 516
Sweetser, S. P., 103

T

Talbot, Fox, 489
Taylor, A. H., 359, 444
Taylor, C. S., 152
Taylor, Delia Ann, 442
Tear, J. D., 307
Tenney, H. M., 117
Thompson, B. J., 413
Thomson, K. B., 357
Thorndike, Edward M., 178
Thornton, R. L., 117
Timoshenko, S., 584
Töpler, A., 63
Turner, A. F., 379
Turner, J. A., 542
Turner, L. A., 418

V

Van de Graaf, R. J., 134
Van Lear, G. A., Jr., 327
Verneuil, A., 529

W

Wadsworth, F. L. O., 154, 379
Waller, L. C., 439
Wartenburg, H. von, 516
Webster, D. L., 136
Weigert, F., 375
Weinhart, H. W., 143
Weyrich, Paul, 308
Whipple, F. L., 464
White, W. P., 523
Whitehead, Thomas North, 585
Whitford, A. E., 408, 439
Wiens, W., 508
Williams, Robley C., 170
Wilson, C. T. R., 225
Wilson, E. D., 411
Withrow, R. B., 443
Wollaston, W. H., 542
Woltersdorff, W., 321, 326
Wood, R. W., 63, 158, 358, 361, 365
    374, 380, 395, 464, 487, 534
Woodward, R. H., 271
Wright, Lewis, 389
Wright, W. H., 487, 582
Wülf, Th., 226, 242
Wynn-Williams, C. E., 273, 287, 418

Y

Young, J. F., 440

Z

Zabel, R. M., 104, 120, 417, 523
Zaikowsky, W. M., 133
Zobel, O. J., 494, 498
Zscheile, F. P., 440

Please
56 Highfield Avenue
London NW11 9UD
0181 201 8878

CW00673223

ArtScroll Halachah Series®

Rabbi Nosson Scherman / Rabbi Meir Zlotowitz

General Editors

The Laws of

Published by

Mesorah Publications, ltd

פתחי הלכה

NIDDAH

A comprehensive exposition of their underlying concepts and applications

by **Rabbi Binyomin Forst**

FIRST EDITION
First Impression . . . December, 1997

Published and Distributed by
MESORAH PUBLICATIONS, Ltd.
4401 Second Avenue
Brooklyn, New York 11232

Distributed in Europe by
J. LEHMANN HEBREW BOOKSELLERS
20 Cambridge Terrace
Gateshead, Tyne and Wear
England NE8 1RP

Distributed in Israel by
SIFRIATI / A. GITLER — BOOKS
10 Hashomer Street
Bnei Brak 51361

Distributed in Australia & New Zealand by
GOLDS BOOK & GIFT CO.
36 William Street
Balaclava 3183, Vic., Australia

Distributed in South Africa by
KOLLEL BOOKSHOP
22 Muller Street
Yeoville 2198, Johannesburg, South Africa

Please address any questions
or comments regarding the
contents of this volume to the author:

Rabbi Binyomin Forst
566 Oak Drive
Far Rockaway N.Y. 11691

Typography by Compuscribe at ArtScroll Studios, Ltd.

Printed in the United States of America by Noble Book Press
Bound by Sefercraft, Quality Bookbinders, Ltd. Brooklyn, N.Y.

תפארת בנים אבותם

This book is dedicated in honor of

R' Mayer Neuhoff

ר׳ מאיר בן חיים צבי נייהאף נ״י

by his son

Dr. Shlomo Neuhoff נ״י

בס"ד עש"ק פ' עקב תשנ"ו

הנה ידידי הרה"ג מוהר"ר בנימין פארסט שליט"א הראה לי חלק
מחבורו על הלכות נדה שמכין לדפוס, וכבר איתמחי גברא בספריו
הקודמים בהלכה, שגדולי תורה ומורי הוראה מפורסמים עיטרו
אותם בהסכמותיהם, ונתקבלו בין לומדי תורה ומבקשי דבר ה' זו
הלכה בתשואות חן, וחזקה על חבר שכמותו שאינו מוציא מתחת
ידו שאינו מתוקן. ובודאי שגם ספרו זה, הכתוב בשפה ברורה שפת
המדינה השווה לכל נפש, ומסודר יפה דבר דבר על אפניו. יהי'
לתועלת רבה להוסיף טהרה וקדושה בבית ישרא'.
והנני מברכו שיזכה להמשיך לשבת באהלה של תורה וללון
בעומקה של הלכה לאוי"ט מתוך בריאות הגוף ומנוחת הנפש
ושמחת לבב!

אברהם יעקב הכהן פאם

אברהם יעקב הכהן פאם

RABBI J. ROTH
1556-53rd Street
Brooklyn, N.Y. 11219
Tel. (718) 435-1502

יחזקאל ראטה

אבדק"ק קארלסבורג

באראפארק ברוקלין נ.י. יע"א

בעזה"י

לסדר ופרצת ימה וקדמה וגו' תשנ"ח

הן בא לפני מע"כ הרב הגאון המו"מ חובר חיבורים מחוכמים מאד
נעלה מו"ה בנימין פארסט שליט"א הלו בעומקה של הלכה. זה יותר
מעשרים שנה מוכר לי לעוסק במשא ומתן של הלכה בשים שכל
וסברא ישרה להדמות מילתא למילתא עפ"י יסודי גדולי הפוסקים
ראשונים ואחרונים וכבר איתמחי האי גברא יקירא בחיבוריו
הקודמים שהי' בהן תועלת לרבים. ועכשיו בא בלוחות שניות
בחיבור מסודר על הלכות נדה לזכות בהן בנות ישראל וכבר נודע
גודל מעלת טהרתן של ישראל אשר אין ערך אליו ויש בזה זיכוי
עצום למען ידעו לילך בדרך טהורה. ובזכות טהרה נזכה במהרה
להבטחת וזרקתי עליכם מים טהורים וטהרתי אתכם.

הכוה"ח למען טהרתן של ישראל

יחזקאל ראטה

❧ Table of Contents

PREFACE   17
OVERVIEW   23

BOOK ONE — GENERAL PRINCIPLES

CHAPTER ONE — Choose a Rav for yourself   33
    A. The importance of choosing a Rav   34
    B. Being inappropriately lenient or strict   34
    C. Asking *sheilos* anonymously   35
    D. Guidelines regarding asking *sheilos*   37

CHAPTER TWO — What makes a woman a *niddah*   39
Halachic overview   40
Introduction: What is *dam niddah*?   45
I — The ramifications of the *niddah* status   46
II — Torah law and Rabbinic law   48
    A. The requirement of *hargashah*   49
    B. Days of *niddah* and *zivah*   51
    C. The color shade   57
III — The blood flow   58
IV — Stains — *kesamim*   60
V — Opening of the uterus — *pesichas hakever*   60
    A. A substance discharged from the body   61
    B. Gynecological examinations   61
    C. Contractions before childbirth   62
VI — Childbirth   63
    A. Torah law   63
    B. Rabbinic law   65
    C. A miscarriage   66
VII — Exceptions   66
    A. *Teliyah bemakeh:* blood attributable to a wound   66
    B. *Dam besulim:* hymeneal bleeding   67
VIII — Self-declared status   67
IX — A blood flow while cohabiting   67

CHAPTER THREE — *Hargashah*: the sensation of a flow   69
Halachic overview   70
I — Introduction   72
    A. The parameters of *hargashah*   72
    B. The definition of *hargashah*   74
II — A woman who experiences a *hargashah*   77

A. A real *hargashah*   78
B. A woman who feels a discharge   85
C. A feeling of external dampness   91

CHAPTER FOUR — Credibility   93
Halachic overview   94
Introduction   95
I — The trust the Torah accords a woman   97
    A. Issues pertaining to the expected period   98
    B. A woman who becomes a *niddah*   99
II — Retracting a claim   101
    A. A simple retraction   102
    B. A retraction based upon an *amasla* (justification)   103
    C. Encouraging a retraction   106
    D. Using a *niddah* status in jest or quarrel   107
III — Reliability with regard to colors   107
    A. Judgment of colors by an amateur   107
    B. A questionable *bedikah* cloth   108
    C. A *bedikah* cloth that was lost   109
    D. Relating a *halachic* decision   110
V — Deciding *halachic* matters regarding one's wife   110

BOOK TWO — *BEDIKOS*: INTERNAL EXAMINATIONS

CHAPTER FIVE — *Bedikos*: why, when and how   115
Halachic overview   116
I — Blood found upon a *bedikah* cloth and
    blood found upon a garment   123
II — *Eid bedikah:* the examination cloth   124
    A. The categories of cloths used for *bedikah*   124
    B. The proper cloth to be used for a *bedikah*   127
III — The manner in which a *bedikah* is performed   130
IV — *Bedikos:* when and whether   135
    A. When are *bedikos* required?   135
    B. When are *bedikos* not required?   137
V — A lost *bedikah* cloth   139

CHAPTER SIX — *Bedikos*: inspecting the *bedikah* cloth   141
I — The immediate inspection   142
    A. The method of inspection   142
    B. Inspection by day versus night   144
II — Questionable *bedikos*   146
    A. The impropriety of being needlessly strict   146
    B. The danger of being improperly lenient   147

III Storing the cloth	147
D. Keeping the cloth for an extended period	148
E. Conduct in the interim	148
III — Asking a *sheilah*	149
A. Asking a *sheilah* personally	149
B. Providing the Rav with all relevant information	149
C. Asking a second opinion	152
IV — Colors and shades	153
A. General considerations	153
B. Colors	155
C. Additional factors	159
D. Changes of color	160
V — Repeating a *bedikah*	164
A. After a *hefseik taharah*	165
B. A *bedikah* of the seven "clean" days	166
VI — *Teliah:* attributing the stain to another source	166

BOOK THREE — *KESAMIM*: STAINS

CHAPTER SEVEN — Kesamim: general principles	169
Halachic overview	170
I — The unique *halachic* status of a *kesem*	175
A. Introduction	175
B. A *kesem* according to Torah law	175
C. A *kesem* according to Rabbinic law	177
D. The practical difference between a *kesem* and a *reiyah*	178
E. Checking for a *kesem*	179
II — Evaluating the *kesem*	180
A. Showing a *kesem* to a Rav	180
B. Keeping a *kesem* for an extended period	180
C. A *kesem* that was lost	180
III — To whom the laws of *kesamim* apply	181
IV — Avoiding *kesamim* problems	182
V — Performing a *bedikah* after finding a *kesem*	183
VI — *Kesamim* that precede a menstrual period	183
VII — A *kesem* associated with a *hargashah*	184
A. A stain found after a definite *hargashah*	185
B. A stain found after a possible *hargashah*	185
CHAPTER EIGHT — Kesamim: the size, shape and color	187
I — The size of the stain	188
A. The rationale of the *gris* size	188
B. The applicability of the *gris* size today	190

C. Measuring a *gris*   191

D. Situations where the *gris* measurement may not apply   194

E. Preventing *kesamim* from reaching a *gris*   199

II — The color of the stain   199

III — The shape of the stain   200

CHAPTER NINE — *Kesamim*: the garment   201

I — A colored garment   202

A. Why colored garments are excluded   203

B. Defining a colored garment   204

C. Issues pertaining to colored garments   206

D. Wearing colored garments to avoid *kesamim* problems   207

E. Problems that may be encountered

even when wearing colored garments   209

II — An object not susceptible to *tumah*   210

III — A pre-checked garment   215

CHAPTER TEN — *Kesamim*: the location   219

A. Stains on a garment or object   220

B. Stains on the body   224

C. Indirect contact   227

D. A stain found on her husband   227

CHAPTER ELEVEN — Attributing a *kesem* to another source   229

A. The required conditions for *teliyah*   230

B. Examples of *teliyos*   238

C. Attributing a stain to her husband or child   240

D. Attributing a *kesem* to another woman   242

E. Attributing a stain to her *niddus* period   242

F. Attributing a *kesem* to an unknown source   243

G. A stain found during the first three

of the seven "clean" days   244

BOOK FOUR — *VESTOS*: ESTABLISHING A PATTERN

CHAPTER TWELVE — *Vestos* made simple   253

CHAPTER THIRTEEN — *Vestos*: general principles   257

I — Introduction   258

A. The concept of *vestos*   258

B. A tentative *vest (she'aino kavuah)* and an established *vest*

(kavuah)   263

C. The duration of a *vest* — 263

D. The types of *vestos* — 263

E. Uprooting a *vest: akiras vest* — 266

II — The beginning of the cycle — 266

A. From what does one calculate the *vest:* a flow, a *bedikah* or a stain? — 266

B. From when does one calculate the *vest?* — 269

III — When the *vest* day passes — 274

CHAPTER FOURTEEN — *Vest kavuah* and *she'aino kavuah* — 275

I — The difference between a *vest kavuah* and a *vest she'aino kavuah* — 276

A. *Akiras vest:* eliminating a *vest* — 277

B. *Onah beinonis* — 277

C. The requirement of a *bedikah* on the *vest* day — 277

D. *Bedikos* at the time of cohabitation — 280

E. A woman who finds blood after cohabitation — 285

F. Ruling out other *vestos* — 286

G. Bleeding which can be attributed to a wound — *teliyah* — 286

H. Unusual *vestos* — 286

I. When the *onas havest* passes — 287

II — A *vest hashaos* — a *vest* dependent upon hours — 288

III — A woman who has both a *vest kavuah* and a *vest she'aino kavuah* — 290

CHAPTER FIFTEEN — The three basic *vestos* — 291

I — *Vest haflagah:* a *vest* based upon the interval between periods — 292

A. What is a *vest haflagah?* — 292

B. Computation of a *vest haflagah* — 293

II — *Vest hachodesh:* a *vest* based upon the day of the month — 297

A. What is a *vest hachodesh?* — 297

B. Unusual cases — 298

III — Differences between a *vest haflagah* and a *vest hachodesh* — 302

IV — *Onah beinonis:* the median *vest* — 302

A. The underlying logic — 302

B. The thirtieth or thirty-first day — 304

C. The duration of the *onah beinonis* — 305

D. Situations in which the *onah beinonis* is subject to controversy — 308

CHAPTER SIXTEEN — Unusual patterns in *vestos* — 311

A. *Vest hadilug:* an incremental *vest* — 312

B. *Vest haseirug:* an alternating *vest* — 318

C. *Vest hashavuah:* a *vest* based upon days of the week — 319

CHAPTER SEVENTEEN — Akiras Vest: uprooting a *vest*   323

I — Uprooting a *vest kavuah* and a *vest she'aino kavuah*   324

    A. A *vest kavuah*   324

    B. A *vest she'aino kavuah*   325

    C. A dormant *vest*   325

II — Uprooting a *vest she'aino kavuah*
       through establishing a *vest kavuah*   328

III — Uprooting different types of *vestos*   329

    A. Elimination of *a vest haflagah*   329

    B. Elimination of *vest hachodesh*   335

CHAPTER EIGHTEEN — *Vest haguf*: a physical manifestation   337

I — The basic *halachos* of a *vest haguf*   338

    A. What constitutes a *vest haguf*   338

    B. A *vest haguf* as compared to other *vestos*   340

II — A "simple" *vest haguf* and a *vest hamurkav*   341

    A. A simple *vest haguf*   341

    B. A *vest haguf murkav* — a complex *vest*   342

III — The duration of the *onas havest*   346

    A. A *vest hamurkav*   346

    B. A simple *vest haguf*   347

IV — A *vest hamurkav she'aino kavuah*   351

V — A *vest hamurkav* that concludes as a simple *vest*   352

VI — *Onah beinonis* with regard to a *vest haguf*   352

VII — Uprooting a *vest haguf*   353

    A. A simple *vest haguf*   353

    B. A *vest haguf hamurkav*   354

CHAPTER NINETEEN — Induced *vestos*   357

    A. *Vest HaOnes*: a *vest* induced by external physical factors   358

    B. *Vest HaAchilos*: a *vest* caused by eating certain foods   362

    C. A menstruation regulated medically   363

CHAPTER TWENTY — Women who are exempt from *Vestos*   369

    A. *Besulah* — a minor   370

    B. *Meuberes* — a pregnant woman   371

    C. *Meinekes* — a nursing woman   375

    D. *Zekeinah* — an elderly woman   378

CHAPTER TWENTY ONE — Starting a *vestos* calendar   383

CHAPTER TWENTY-TWO — The day of the *vest*   391

Introduction   392

I — *Halachos* pertaining to the *onas havest*   393

     A. The prohibitions and requirements   393

     B. The duration of the prohibition   401

     C. *Onas havest* under special circumstances   405

II — The problematic days   408

III — When the *onas havest* passes   413

IV — One who loses their calendar   413

BOOK FIVE — GYNECOLOGICAL ISSUES

CHAPTER TWENTY-THREE — Gynecological examinations:

     the issues involved   421

Halachic overview   422

I — Anatomical terms   423

II — The *halachic* issues involved   427

     A. *Teliah b'makah* — attributing bleeding to an injury   428

     B. *Ne'emanus - halachic* acceptability of a doctor's claim   434

     C. *Pesichas hakever* — the opening of the uterus   437

     D. A summary of the *halachic* issues   440

III — General guidelines   442

IV — Scheduling gynecological procedures   445

CHAPTER TWENTY-FOUR — Gynecological procedures   449

     A. General considerations   450

     B. Common gynecological procedures   451

     C. External gynecological procedures   461

     D. Gynecological procedures performed during pregnancy   462

     E. Hysterectomies   465

     F. Fertility procedures   467

     G. Contraception   470

     H. Gynecological Conditions   471

     I. Common gynecological terms   472

APPENDICES   475

BIBLIOGRAPHY   491

SUBJECT INDEX   503

INDEX OF PRIMARY SOURCES   525

✒ Preface

מָה אָשִׁיב לַה׳ כָּל תַּגְמוּלוֹהִי עָלָי

It is with both a sense of gratitude to the *Ribono Shel Olam* and trepidation that I present this *sefer* to the English-reading public. Gratitude,
because *Hashem* has granted me the ability to complete the third volume
in this series. Gratitude, for giving me the undeserved privilege to have
my previous *sefarim* on *Hilchos B'rachos* and *Hilchos Kashrus* reprinted
many times and accepted by the public. Trepidation, because an error in
Hilchos Niddah is more serious than one in most other matters of *halachah*.
One who authors a work on *Hilchos Niddah* bears an enormous responsibility since any flaw in his work may cause others to transgress a serious
prohibition. It is in this vein that I pray fervently to the *Ribono Shel Olam*
the prayer of R' Nechunya ben Hakanah: יְהִי רָצוֹן מִלְפָנֶיךָ ה׳ אֱלֹקַי שֶׁלֹּא
יֶאֱרַע דְּבַר תַּקָּלָה עַל יָדִי וְלֹא אֶכָּשֵׁל בִּדְבַר הֲלָכָה . . . וְלֹא אוֹמַר עַל טָמֵא טָהוֹר
וְלֹא עַל טָהוֹר טָמֵא — May it be Your will, Hashem, that a mishap not come
about through me and I may not stumble in a matter of law and... may I
not say regarding something which is *tamei* that it is *tahor* and not regarding something which is *tahor* that it is *tamei*."

✒ About this work

Authors of works on *halachic* subjects usually caution their readers not
to rely on the book for *halachic* decisions or to use it as a substitute for consulting a Rav when necessary. Perhaps a book on *Hilchos Niddah* requires
no such warning. It is obvious that a layman cannot decide these crucial
matters on his own. *Hilchos Niddah* pertains to one of the severest prohibitions in the Torah, one that is punishable by *kareis* and is among the cardinal prohibitions that Torah law demands that יֵהָרֵג וְאַל יַעֲבוֹר — one must
forfeit his life rather than transgress the prohibition. *Hilchos Niddah* is also
at the core of the sanctity of the Jewish family and people. At the same

time, *Hilchos Niddah* is one of the more difficult and intricate subjects in *halachah*. No one could expect to master the subject without rigorous study of the primary sources beginning with the Talmudic sources, the *Tur, Beis Yosef, Shulchan Aruch* and its commentaries through contemporary responsa. It should be apparent to anyone that one must choose a Rav as a guide in these difficult *halachos*. This work is not able, nor is it intended, to replace the guidance of a competent and experienced Rav. On the contrary, the subject of the very first chapter in this work is the absolute necessity of developing a regular and open relationship with a Rav and how indispensable he is regarding these *halachos. Perhaps* the most frequently used phrase in this book is "a Rav must be consulted." Therefore, it seems unnecessary to caution the reader not to use this work as a *halachic* do-it-yourself manual. What, then, is the purpose of this book? This book is designed to be used on several levels. It is intended as a study guide for those seeking an introduction to the basic concepts of *Hilchos Niddah*. We will attempt to describe the underlying framework of these *halachos* from their primary sources and slowly guide the reader through the more intricate sections of these *halachos*. Our discussions will culminate in clear, practical advice in relating and adapting these principles to real-life situations. The reader will be informed as to what may be considered clear, decisive and accepted *halachic* practice and which *halachic* questions remain subject to varying opinions and situations. There are numerous situations where there is no *halachic* consensus. In these cases, we cannot present clear practical guidance other than explaining the nature of the controversies among *halachic* authorities. One may ask why we have not consulted with one of the recognized Torah sages of our generation and followed his opinion throughout. The obvious answer is that there are several *gedolim* of such stature, each with his own unique tradition and opinion. To present the opinions of each would only confuse the reader further. Therefore, we chose to leave these questions to be answered by one's individual Rav. At the same time, we used the footnotes to note the various opinions of past and contemporary published *Poskim*.

In addition, this work may be used by some who have studied the primary sources and wish to crystallize their understanding of *Hilchos Niddah* in an organized and practical manner. The opinions of the *Poskim* are set forth in a logical sequence. Their opinions are clearly examined and compared in the footnotes so that even the advanced student will find additional source material for continued research. We have provided a comprehensive index so that the reader may easily find any *halachah* covered in this volume. Furthermore, we added an index following the order of *Meseches Niddah* and *Shulchan Aruch, Yoreh Deah, Hilchos Niddah, Taz* and *Shach,* so that one studying these primary sources will be able to find their practical applications.

There will be those who will find fault in our presenting these *halachos* to the English-reading public in a detailed manner. Their justifiable concern is that one may abuse this work as a substitute for consulting a Rav. Although we have tried to prevent this from happening, we share their concern. However, it is our firm belief that whatever danger there may be is far, far outweighed by the positive effect of a book of this type. There are important *halachos* that many may be unaware of. There are common mistakes that are made by the most sincere couples. Every Rav has his horror stories of couples who were married for several years but were ignorant of basic principles. It is our hope that this work will help dispel many of these errors.

In previous works, we briefly summarized each section or chapter. In this work, we substituted a *halachic* overview to most chapters. In this way, a beginner may acquaint himself with the basic principles of the subject before attempting the detailed *halachos.* A more experienced reader may choose to skip the overview and go directly to the chapter itself. One may wish to use the overview as a review instead.

We found it impossible to do justice to *Hilchos Niddah* in one volume. Therefore, this volume covers those *halachos* found in *Yoreh Deah* chapters 183 through 190. The *halachos* regarding the preparations of a *kallah,* the *halachos* regarding a *chasan* and *kallah* after consummating their marriage, the *halachos* of *harchakos* — the separations that a husband and wife must keep while she is a *niddah* — the *halachos* of the preparations for and of the seven "clean" days, those of the preparations for and the actual laws of *tevilah* will all be explored in Volume Two which we hope, *b'ezer Hashem,* to present to the public in the future.

✍ How to use this book

It is suggested that a beginner use this book in the following manner: One should read Chapters One and Two in their entirety or read only Chapter One and the *halachic* overview of Chapter Two. Then one should read only the overview of Chapters Three, Four, Five and Seven. The reader should then proceed to Chapter Twelve and follow the instructions at the end of Chapter Twelve. Once one understands the basic principles, he may continue on to Chapter Two (if not done the first time),

Chapters Five through Ten and Chapter Twenty-Three. The remaining chapters are more complex and should be studied last.

✎ Acknowledgments

The author wishes to express his gratitude to the following individuals who assisted him in producing this volume.

DR. SHLOMO NEUHOFF has dedicated this *sefer* in honor of his father R' MEIR NEUHOFF נ״י . May *Hashem* reward him for his exceptional act of *kibud av* and for his assistance in publishing this volume. In addition, Dr. Neuhoff has been of utmost help in producing the medical section of this work. He has selflessly spent many hours advising the author in regard to gynecological matters and gave generously of his time to review and correct the material.

The author was privileged to benefit from the comments and corrections of the following three *talmidei chachamim* who reviewed most of the manuscript for *halachic* accuracy and offered many insightful and useful suggestions: RABBI DOVID DILMAN of *Yerushalayim*, RABBI DOVID COHEN and RABBI MOSHE GORDON both of Far Rockaway, New York.

DR. SIDNEY JAKUBOVICS reviewed and edited most of this work. The book has benefited greatly from his organizational skills. He read and reread the manuscript many times and contributed significantly to the clarity and readability of the more difficult sections. In addition, Dr. Jakubovics was an enormous help with the medical sections of the book. Those sections would not have been possible without his help and encouragement. Dr. Jakubovics did this work לז״נ בלומא בת חיים שמחה and גיטל בת יוסף אלעזר.

The author was privileged to have the medical sections of this work reviewed in their final form by DR. ROBERT C. WALLACH, professor of clinical obstetrics and gynecology at the New York University School of Medicine. Dr. Wallach is the director of gynecological oncology at the New York University Medical Center and professorial lecturer at Mt. Sinai School of Medicine and director emeritus of obstetrics and gynecology, Beth Israel Hospital. Dr. Wallach offered much advice and enhanced the medical accuracy of those sections.

MRS. YOCHEVED NISSAN was, as before, an invaluable help in producing this book. Her grammatical and literary skills significantly enhanced the quality and style of the book. In addition, Mrs. Nissan, in her capacity as a *kallah* teacher par excellence, was especially helpful with the sensitive issues found in this volume.

The author is indebted to the following individuals who reviewed sections of the book for *halachic* accuracy: RABBI HERSHEL AUSCH, RABBI FEIVEL COHEN, RABBI ZEV COHEN, RABBI YAIR HOFFMAN and RABBI YAAKOV REISMAN.

MR. JONATHAN RIKOON, MR. DON HAIRONSON and my son-in-law LIORE ZEV ALROY were most helpful with many useful comments and corrections.

I am grateful to the Torah Academy for Girls, Bais Yaakov of Long Island and to its stimulating and inspiring students. I value my close personal friendship with its Dean, RABBI MOSHE WEITMAN. My years of association with the school as its *halachah* instructor was the major stimulus to author *sefarim* in practical *halachah*.

I extend my sincerest thanks to RABBI MEIR ZLOTOWITZ and RABBI NOSSON SCHERMAN for undertaking to publish this work and for their many helpful suggestions; to RABBI SHEAH BRANDER who enhanced the beauty of this book with his graphic skills; to RABBI AVROHOM BIDERMAN who was an invaluable partner in this endeavor; to REB ELI KROEN whose special touch added so much to the cover and the charts; to TOBY HEILBRUN and MINDY WEIL who typeset the book; MRS. FAIGIE WEINBAUM who dilligently proofread; and to entire the ArtScroll staff each in his or her own area of expertise.

Above all, I extend my deepest feelings of gratitude to my dear parents MR. And MRS. SIEGMUND FORST and my mother-in-law REBETZIN Y. SCHWAB. Their years of self-sacrifice, devotion, inspiration and encouragement have guided me in all my endeavors. May *Hashem* grant them many healthy years to derive true *nachas* from their children, grandchildren and great-grandchildren. עוֹד יְנוּבוּן בְּשֵׂיבָה דְּשֵׁנִים וְרַעֲנַנִּים יִהְיוּ.

I take this opportunity to note the memory of my father-in-law RABBI MORDECHAI SCHWAB זֵכֶר צַדִּיק לִבְרָכָה, who left an indelible mark on my life, that of my children and that of anyone who had contact with him. He was a living *mussar sefer* and an inspiration to all. The *chizuk shemiras hamitzvos* generated by this *sefer* should be a merit for his *neshamah* in *Gan Eden*.

I cannot adequately express my gratitude to my wife MILKA. This and my other works would have been impossible without her sacrifice and encouragement. May *Hashem* grant us many years of true *nachas* from our children and grandchildren. May He grant our sincerest desire that they follow in the path of their forebears — one of dedication to Torah and *yiras shamayim*.

Binyomin Forst

Marcheshvan 5758 / November 1997
Far Rockaway, New York

❧ Overview

The laws of *niddah* are a vast and complex body of *halachos*. However, these *halachos* go far beyond the technical aspects of "what to do." The entire arena of *Taharas Hamishpachah* resonates with significance and meaning and impacts on the family on many levels. It impacts on the physical and emotional relationship between husband and wife. Most profoundly, observance of the laws of *niddah* effects the fundamental relationship between the couple and the Torah. Let us examine some of the deeper meanings in *Hilchos Niddah* and how these *halachos* affect the marriage relationship.

❧ Sarah's Tent

וַיְבִאֶהָ יִצְחָק הָאֹהֱלָה שָׂרָה אִמּוֹ
כְּלוֹמַר, וְנַעֲשִׂית דּוּגְמַת שָׂרָה אִמּוֹ. שֶׁכָּל זְמַן שֶׁשָּׂרָה קַיֶּימֶת הָיָה נֵר דָּלוּק
מֵעֶרֶב שַׁבָּת לְעֶרֶב שַׁבָּת וּבְרָכָה מְצוּיָה בָּעִיסָה וְעָנָן קָשׁוּר עַל הָאֹהֶל.
וּמִשֶּׁמֵּתָה פָּסְקוּ, וּכְשֶׁבָּאת רִבְקָה חָזְרוּ (בראשית כד סז, ופרש"י שם.)

> "And Yitzchak brought [Rivkah] into the tent and behold, she was Sarah, his mother. That is to say, she became the image of Sarah, his mother. For all the time that Sarah was alive, a lamp would be lit continuously from Sabbath eve to Sabbath eve, and a *b'rachah* would be found in the dough, and a cloud would be stationed over the tent. But once she died, they stopped. And when Rivkah came they returned."   *Rashi, Bereishis 24:67*

Maharal (*Gur Aryeh* ad loc.) explains that these three aspects, the lit lamp, the *b'rachah* in the dough and the cloud over the tent, refer to the three *mitzvos* specifically assigned to women: *niddah*, *challah* and kindling the *Shabbos* light. Each of these three *mitzvos* represents a different dimension in the intensely close relationship between a woman and *Hashem*. The comparison of the *Shabbos* light to the lamp and *challah* to the dough are obvious. The relationship between *niddah* and the cloud is less clear. *Maharal* explains that the cloud over Sarah's tent — the *annan kashur* — is analagous to the *annanei hakavod,* clouds of glory that were stationed over the *Mishkan.* Indeed, *Maharal* (*Netzach Yisrael* Ch. 54) notes, that wherever the *Shechinah* came to dwell, it was manifested by an *annan,* a heavenly cloud. The cloud signifies the connection between *Hashem* and the palce where he dwells. Thus, the cloud over Sarah and Rivkah's tent symbolized the presence of the *Shechinah.* By scrupulously keeping the laws of *niddah,* both Sarah and Rivkah brought the presence of the *Shechinah* into their tents. *Taharas Hamishpachah* — the laws of *niddah* — are so called because they bring *taharah* (purity) and *kedushah* (holiness) to the entire *mishpachah,* the entire family, thereby permitting the *Shechinah* to dwell among them.

Taharas Hamishpachah involves both husband and wife. A woman cannot keep these *halachos* without the full support, participation and partnership of her husband. However, the bottom line depends upon the unqualified commitment of the woman. Thus, she, in effect, determines whether the *shechinah* dwells in their home and in their marriage.

Unlike other cultures and religions, Judaism teaches that the physical act of intimacy is permeated with sublime *kedushah.* The cleaving of *Hashem* to *Bnei Yisrael* is compared, in many *Midrashic* and Kabbalistic sources, to the physical bond between man and wife. Indeed, this metaphor forms the allegoric framework of *Shir HaShirim.*[1] The *cherubim* in the holy of holies were symbolic of the cleaving of man to wife and of *Hashem* to His people.

It is no coincidence that the word used to connote marriage is "*kiddushin.*" *Kabbalists* note that when marital relations are performed in holiness, the *Shechinah* is present. The Talmudic texts that note the inclusion of the *yud* and *hei* of *Hashem's* name in the words "*ish*" and "*ishah,*" as well as those that note the three partners (*Hashem,* father and mother) in the creation of a child, allude to the Divine Presence at the very moment of intimacy (see *Ramban, Igeres HaKodesh* Ch. 2). The holiness of this act is manifest in its ability to do something that is beyond the power of any other human function: It draws a G-dly soul into this world and produces a living human being. In this, man and wife mirror the G-dly act of creation. Viewed in this way, the *mitzvah* of onah[2] thus

---

1. And many verses in *Tanach,* see, for example, *Yeshayah* 54:5, 62:5.

2. The term "*onah*" (which literally is translated as "a time") is used in chapters relating to the laws of *vestos* in reference to the time period during which one must *abstain* from one's wife. It is also used by *Chazal* in the term "*mitzvas onah*" in reference to the time of marital relationship between man and wife. This is an example of the *kedushah* of *lashon hakodesh,* for the holy tongue avoids expressions that can be interpreted in a vulgar manner.

becomes one of the holiest of all human functions, provided that it is kept within Torah guidelines and not distorted.

A man and a woman alone are incomplete; together, they achieve their original completeness — *shleimus,* as they were in their original form in *Gan Eden.* Wholeness is, in itself, a form of G-dliness as is indicated by the word *Shalom,* which signifies both wholeness and is one of the names of *Hashem.*[3]

Mitzvas onah, in its proper form, is an act of <u>giving;</u> in its distorted form, it is an act of <u>taking.</u> Each partner gives of <u>themselves</u> to the other. This, too, is an aspect of holiness since giving is a G-dly act. *Hashem* is the ultimate Giver. The line between the higher form of marital relations and its lower form parallel the line between giving and taking. Giving can be G-dly; taking is selfish and base.

It is difficult to maintain the purity of *mitzvas onah* in its higher form since, by nature, one is attracted to it by desires of self-gratification. It is extremely difficult, if not impossible, to raise it completely to a level of *kedushah.* Nevertheless, we aspire to rise above these selfish feelings and become givers, not takers. Taking is body oriented: One is attracted to another's body. Giving is person oriented: One is attracted to another human being as a person and wishes to share oneself with them. Giving is the ultimate goal of our *avodas Hashem* and of our desire for a healthy marriage. To help us focus on the person, not the body, *mitzvas onah* is done in a darkened room.

Mitzvas onah can be a holy act that brings closeness to the *Shechinah.* Through proper observance of *mitzvas onah* a Jewish home becomes a dwelling for the *Shechinah* and is graced by an *annan* — a heavenly cloud. *Mitzvas onah,* when performed properly, suffuses a home with Divine Presence. The physical act can in this way be compared to the *Beis HaMikdash* in which the *Shechinah* dwelled. Accordingly, Divine wisdom prohibited this act from being done while a woman is in the state of *tumas niddah.* Just as a woman is forbidden to enter the *Beis HaMikdash* while in a state of *tumah,* so, too, the couple may not engage in marital relations while the woman is in a *niddah* state.[4] Holiness is incompatible with *tumah.* The physical act of intimacy stripped of its potential for holiness is forbidden by the Torah.

---

3. It is therefore understandable why, when a *sotah* is brought to the *Mishkan, Hashem* says that "My Name that was written with *kedushah* should be erased to bring *shalom* between man and wife." This is because *shalom* between man and wife is, in itself, *Hashem's* Name. Thus, ultimately, the Name is not being erased.

4. In this light, the end of *Parshas Metzora* takes on a unique meaning. Immediately after the *parshah* of *niddah* and *zavah,* the verse says "You shall separate the Children of Israel from their contamination; and they shall not die as a result of their contamination <u>if they contaminate My Tabernacle that is among them.</u>"

In this sense, a woman's monthly preparation to purify herself from the *niddah* status is preparation to uplift the physical act of intimacy to holiness. The man's counterpart to this is the *bris milah*, in which his body is refined by means of removing the impurity attached to it from birth. In light of this, it is interesting that the penalty, *kareis*, is the same for one who enters the *Beis HaMikdash* while *tamei*, a couple who cohabit while the woman is a *niddah* and one who does not enter into the covenant of circumcision.

⌇ *Richuk vekiruv* — attraction and repulsion

Everything in creation is flawed and incomplete (*Maharal, Gur Aryeh, Bereishis* 1:11[33]). This is inherent in creation itself. *Maharal* explains (in *Ner Mitzvah* p.8 and in *Netzach Yisrael* Ch. 3) that creation, by its very nature, must be lacking. The object created needs the Creator and is lacking without Him. A system of *mashpiah* (benefactor) and *mushpah* (bebeficiary) necessitates the *mushpa* being lacking and needing the *mashpia*.

Because the world is flawed, it cannot maintain a state of abiding exaltedness; failure is inherent in creation. *Maharal* explains that for this reason אָדָם אֵין צַדִּיק בָּאָרֶץ אֲשֶׁר יַעֲשֶׂה טּוֹב וְלֹא יֶחֱטָא, "no man is so righteous in the world that he does [only] good without sinning" (*Koheles* 7:20). Adam and Chava could not maintain themselves in *Gan Eden*. As a result of the sin of the *Eitz Hadaas*, this inherent flaw became even more profound. *Bnei Yisrael* could not maintain themselves after *Har Sinai* and they succumbed to the golden calf. Even before *Bnei Yisrael* entered *Eretz Yisrael*, the seeds were sown for the exile which is foretold in the Torah.

While it may seem incompatible with the perfect nature of *Hashem* to create a flawed world, it is consistent with the basic nature and purpose of the world. The world, and man, were not *created* perfect — they were created to *reach* perfection. This is the ultimate goal of man and the world. In light of this, man's failing has a deeper aspect. Every fall is a potential vehicle for attaining even greater heights. שֶׁבַע יִפּוֹל צַדִּיק וָקָם, "the *tzaddik* falls seven times and rises" (*Mishlei* 24:16). *Sifrei Chassidus* explain that this does not simply mean that he is able to rise even though he falls; rather, he falls in order to rise even higher; he rises as a result of the fall, יְרִידָה לְצוֹרֶךְ עֲלִיָה. Therefore, the world necessarily functions in a system of יְרִידָה וְעֲלִיָה — falling and rising, טוּמְאָה וְטַהֲרָה — spiritual defilement and cleansing, רִיחוּק וְקִירוּב— repulsion and attraction. Through *cheit*, one can arrive at *teshuvah* and the achievement of an even greater cleaving to *Hashem*. Through *tumah*, one can achieve even greater *taharah* (see *Rambam, Pirush*

HaMishnah, Parah 3:3). And through distance, one can achieve even greater closeness.

This is also the nature of the relationship between *Hashem* and *Yisrael*. Because of the deficient nature of this world, man cannot remain in continuous closeness to *Hashem*, regardless of man's exalted nature. Even the *Kohein Gadol* is warned וְאַל יָבֹא בְכָל עֵת אֶל הַקֹּדֶשׁ. See *Sichos Mussar* (R' *Chaim Shmulevitz*) 1:16, citing the *Chassid Yaavetz*, who explains that this was the cause of the Sin of the Golden Calf. *Bnei Yisrael* became too accustomed to the *Ohel Moeid* in their midst and it lost value in their eyes. They eventually despised it and looked for another god. *Moshe* realized this and therefore removed the *Ohel Moeid* from the camp.

This may be the reason why one who is *tamei* must leave the camp of the *Shechinah*. Often, one becomes *tamei* because he was careless, and thus shows a disrespect to the *Shechinah* resulting from overfamiliarity. The cure is to move away from that closeness until he appreciates the presence of the *Shechinah* anew. Thus, the *richuk* is for the purpose of *kiruv*.

This is the idea behind *Bnei Yisrael's* continuous struggles. We fail, *Hashem* punishes us; we return to Him only to fail again. He drives us out of His land when we lose an appreciation of His closeness. We must long and pray that He renew that closeness.[5]

The relationship between *Yisrael* and *Hashem* is compared to that of a woman to her husband. The relationship between them is also based on the same closeness / separateness cycle. The separateness (*tumah*) is manifest in the *galus* and the closeness (*taharah*) in the *geulah*. Thus, we find that *Chazal* compared the *galus* period to that of a *niddah*.

לְפִיכָךְ הקב"ה מְדַמֶּה טוּמְאַת יִשְׂרָאֵל לְטוּמְאַת הַנִּדָּה שֶׁנִּטְמְאָה כָּךְ עָתִיד הקב"ה לְטַהֵר
אֶת יִשְׂרָאֵל (תנחומא מצורע יב)

Therefore *Hakadosh Baruch Hu* compares the *tumah* of *Yisrael* to the *tumah* of a *niddah* who became *tamei* and cleansed herself of her *tumah*. So, too, in the future *Hakadosh Baruch Hu* will cleanse *Yisrael*.

Tanchuma, Parshas Metzora 12

Bnei Yisrael are compared to the moon which waxes and wanes in relation to its closeness to the sun. The sun represents *Hashem* and the moon, *Bnei Yisrael*. The sun, which is always complete, represents the masculine. It is כְּחָתָן יֹצֵא מֵחֻפָּתוֹ *"like a groom emerging from his bridal chamber"* (*Psalms* 19:6). The moon, which is subject to a monthly cycle of waxing and waning, represents the female (*Recanti, Parshas Metzora*). During its waning

---

5. This concept is also expressed in every *b'rachah* that we recite. The *b'rachah* begins in second person (נוכח) בָּרוּךְ אַתָּה and ends in the third person (נסתר) אֲשֶׁר קִדְּשָׁנוּ.

period, the moon seems to move away from its partner, only to return and come toward him again. This return, however, is not simply returning back to the old: It is an elevation from the old into something new. The new moon is called the "*chidush halevanah*" or the "*molad*," the rebirth. That is why a month is called "*chodesh*" — new.

A woman at the end of her days of *tumah* has also been renewed. The relationship between man and wife is invigorated and refreshed (see *Machsheves Charutz, R' Tzadok HaCohen of Lublin*, 10). The wife reappears to her husband and her desirability to him has been enhanced by waiting (see *Niddah* 31b). By abstaining from him for seven (or, today, twelve) days, she becomes as dear and new to him as on their wedding day. Thus, the laws of *niddah* protect the couple from the coldness of overfamiliarity and satisfy a very basic psychological need of both man and woman.

✍ He dwells amongst them in the midst of their *tumah*

In the relationship between *Hashem* and *Yisrael*, there is a closeness even while they are apart,

חֲבִיבִין הֵן יִשְׂרָאֵל שֶׁאַף עַל פִּי שֶׁהֵן טְמֵאִין שְׁכִינָה בֵּינֵיהֶם שֶׁנֶּאֱמַר הַשּׁוֹכֵן אִתָּם בְּתוֹךְ טוּמְאוֹתָם (במדבר רבה פרשה ז)

Yisrael is beloved to *Hashem*, for even though they may be *tamei*, the *Shechinah* dwells among them, as it is written: He who dwells amongst them in the midst of their *tumah*. *Bamidbar Rabbah* 7.

In the relationship between G-d and *Bnei Yisrael*, there are two levels: one of *kedushah* and closeness and one of הַשּׁוֹכֵן אִתָּם בְּתוֹךְ טוּמְאוֹתָם, of the *Shechinah* remaining among them even when they are impure. These two levels are also reflected in the relationship between man and wife. Indeed, we cited the words of *Chazal* who compare the times of separateness between *Hashem* and *Bnei Yisrael* to the separateness between man and wife during her *niddus*. It is most interesting that unlike all other *arayos* prohibitions, a man may be alone (*yichud*) with his wife. Thus, while he may not be <u>close</u> to her, he is <u>with</u> her. Similarly, *Hashem*, in times of *galus*, while not close to us, is with us, הַשּׁוֹכֵן אִתָּם בְּתוֹךְ טוּמְאוֹתָם. See *Resisei Lailah* 33.

A couple experiences two phases throughout much of their married life: one of physical closeness and one of physical separateness. However, even during the time of separateness there is a bond between them.

Love in marriage is love in a deeper sense; it is not merely sensual "love." True, a couple needs to express their love in a physical manner. This is the *mitzvah* of *onah*. It is the glue which holds the marriage together and has the potential for infusing it with holiness. However, lest we lose sight of the larger view and focus only on the limited aspect, the Torah gives us the monthly separation caused by *niddus*. This forces a couple to express their love and fondness in ways other than by physical contact. It is also a challenge. Do we become irritable and dissatisfied with one another? Then we have lost sight of what marriage really is. During such times, a man and wife are charged to maintain a closeness despite their physical separation. This is regulated by distinct rules to prevent them from crossing the line from closeness to physical contact. While they may not have physical contact, they remain deeply devoted to one another and their affection is not diminished, הַשֹּׁכֵן אִתָּם בְּתוֹךְ טוּמְאֹתָם. The *niddus* phase, during which the physical is eliminated from their relationship, serves as a vehicle to uplift their relationship from one based on sensual pleasure to one based on true respect, affection, trust and the deep joy of sharing a common goal.

BOOK ONE

כללי הלכות נדה
General Principles

Chapter One — Choose a Rav for Yourself
Chapter Two — What Makes a Woman a Niddah
Chapter Three — Hargashah
Chapter Four — Credibility

CHAPTER ONE

עשה לך רב

Choose a Rav for Yourself

☐ The importance of choosing a Rav.

☐ The uniqueness of *hilchos niddah*.

☐ Being inappropriately lenient or strict.

☐ Asking *sheilos* anonymously.

☐ Guidelines regarding asking *sheilos*.

A. The importance of choosing a Rav

One of the most essential points which must be conveyed in this work is not a *halachah* in *hilchos niddah*; rather, it is a *Mishnah* in *Pirkei Avos* (1:6): רב עשה לך — one must have a Rav. As important as a Rav is for guidance in matters of Kashrus or Shabbos, he is indispensable regarding *hilchos niddah*. The *halachos* of Kashrus and Shabbos have been ingrained in us since our youth, and while there are individual *halachos* that we are unaware of, we know the major concepts and their most basic applications. This is not so with *hilchos niddah*. When a couple gets married, the young husband and wife are faced with an entire gamut of new and difficult *halachos*. A *chassan* and *kallah* study the pertinent *halachos* before marriage, but this is not enough.[1] One must find time after marriage to study and review these *halachos* thoroughly and carefully. And even this is not enough; one needs a Rav.

Speaking to a Rav about private and personal matters may be uncomfortable for a young couple. However, they must realize that, at best, they know only the very basic structure of *hilchos niddah*, i.e., what to do if everything goes exactly like clockwork. Once we realize that the human body is far from predictable, the necessity of choosing a Rav becomes clear. There may be rare women who are fortunate and never have problematic *bedikos* or questions about *vestos, harchakos, chatzitzos* or *tevilah*. But many women do not suddenly stop staining on the fifth day. It is very common to find a stain on the *hefseik taharah* cloth. Some may think that any shade other than red is acceptable. This is not so. Many colors are hard to judge. Some browns are permitted; some are not. An innocent looking stain may have a slightly reddish hue or a thin reddish edge. The layman is not trained to distinguish between one hue and another. One must show the cloth to a Rav. Often it is difficult to decide which day begins the *vest* interval or which day to set as the *onas havest* during which one must abstain. A Rav will clarify these issues. Women are often examined by a gynecologist. This may cause bleeding which may or may not render a woman a *niddah*. A Rav must be consulted. We mention but a few of the instances in which one must consult a trained Rav.

B. Being inappropriately lenient or strict

One who does not find the need to consult a Rav may unknowingly be violating one or more of the *halachos* of *niddah*. A woman may be relying

---

1. First of all, the time allotted can never be adequate to cover <u>all</u> of *hilchos niddah*. Secondly, the weeks of preparation before a wedding are weeks filled with activity, distractions and stress. It is not the best time to learn anything new, much less something as complex and serious as *hilchos niddah*.

upon unacceptable *bedikos* or omitting necessary *bedikos*. She may have a *chatzitzah* on her body during *tevilah* or she may not know to abstain on a day that she is required to do so.

Conversely, some may take the strict approach and discard every questionable *bedikah* or abstain on any day that they think may perhaps be a *vest* day. This is also improper. One should not needlessly abstain on days that may not actually be *vest* days or assume that a *bedikah* cloth is unacceptable unless one is certain. At times, even a red stain on a *bedikah* cloth may be recognized by a Rav as originating from a source which will not make the woman a *niddah*. Not every stain on a garment necessarily renders a woman a *niddah*. Each questionable stain must be evaluated by a trained Rav. A woman doing unnecessary and excessive *bedikos* may cause irritation. A Rav can advise her when to do less than the normally required *bedikos*.

One should not resolve every question by accepting the stricter approach. Just as it is unacceptable to be lenient where one should be strict, so, too, it is inappropriate to be strict where one may be lenient.[2] This is both *halachically* inappropriate and unwise. The *niddah* status of a woman is a strain both on the relationship between husband and wife and on their individual emotions. This has always been so and is certainly true today when life is altogether more stressful.

For all of these reasons, one needs a Rav in whom one has confidence and with whom one feels comfortable discussing personal questions regarding *hilchos niddah*.

C. Asking *sheilos* anonymously

There are those who do not identify themselves when asking a *sheilah*. Some call on the phone without leaving their name; some drop off a *bedikah* cloth anonymously. This is acceptable in certain sensitive situations. It is understandable that a woman is hesitant to show a soiled garment to a Rav. However, one must bear in mind that a Rav is no less a professional than a physician and treats these matters sensitively and discretely. Some women may feel uncomfortable divulging personal information to a community member. However, a Rav has many other matters on his mind. He often does not, nor wishes to, remember other people's personal matters. In addition, a Rav is one's trusted Torah authority. Even if one's *sheilah* requires revealing very intimate information, the Rav will protect one's dignity and privacy zealously.

---

2. See *Vidui* of *Rabbeinu Nissim*: "את אשר התרת אסרתי ואשר אסרתי התרתי" — what You permitted, I forbade; and what You forbade, I permitted."

One may ask, "But why must I identify myself to the Rav?" It is important to understand that a Rav does not answer all questions in the same manner. Not every *sheilah* is black and white; there is a certain amount of latitude. A Rav knows to deal with each *sheilah* individually according to the woman's or her husband's particular circumstances. One woman may be unusually tense about her *bedikos*; perhaps she will be told to minimize the frequency or scope of her *bedikos*. Another woman may constantly feel real or imagined *hargashos*; a Rav may reassure her and tell her to ignore these sensations if he perceives that they are insignificant. Another woman may forget vital *bedikos* often or frequently neglect to record her *vest* day on the calendar; perhaps she will be reminded of the severity of these *halachos*. One couple has fertility problems, another has *shalom bayis* problems. The Rav must answer their questions with appropriate sensitivity and leniency. *Halachah* has a degree of flexibility which is useful in these situations. The Rav will speak to the couple with concern and understanding. He may perceive that, in a particular case, he must find any possible leniency.[3] At times, a physician may advise a couple to undergo fertility treatment or hormonal therapy; they should discuss the options with their Rav. An experienced Rav can advise them whether to pursue these options. He may advise them to get a second opinion; he may recommend a physician in whom he has confidence. At times a Rav, through experience, may realize that the woman has a medical problem which she may be unaware of. In short, the Rav is a *halachic* decisor, a friend, a confidant and, yes, even a therapist.

One who speaks to a Rav on the phone anonymously does not avail herself of this guidance. In addition, when one speaks to a Rav personally, the Rav is able to elicit additional information which may help him understand the problem. When one asks a question over the phone, the communication is less flexible. Also, it is possible that after the Rav answers the question, he realizes that he should have inquired about a particular point which is vital to the *sheilah* or added an additional word of advice. Once the anonymous caller hangs up, this cannot be done.

However, there are situations where one may feel too embarrassed to identify himself or herself and there are individuals who are always uncomfortable bringing *bedikos* to a Rav. In such cases, one should feel free to call anonymously and ask any *sheilah*. Many *Rabbonim* have drop-off boxes where one can drop off *bedikos* with identifying numbers. A Rav will respect and cooperate with anyone's feeling of privacy. Usually, once

---

3. See *Teshuvos VeHanhagos* 1:508[45].

a woman develops confidence in a particular Rav, she will no longer mind divulging her identity.

A woman should never feel hesitant or reluctant to ask a question for fear of disturbing the Rav or of sounding stupid or ignorant. A Rav who deals with *niddah* questions expects to be called and consulted. The laws of *niddah* are complex and it is understandable that one may ask the Rav a seemingly simple question or that one may ask the same question more than once. Far, far better to ask than to err.

D. Guidelines regarding asking *sheilos*

It is useful at this point to note several guidelines concerning asking *sheilos*.

> 1. Whenever one has a questionable *bedikah* cloth, it should be stored properly. It should not be placed on an unclean surface or on a surface where dirt particles may settle on it. It should not be placed, when damp, on a tissue or in an envelope since it may adhere to the surface. It should not be placed in a closed plastic bag for an extended period since this may cause the color to change unnaturally. Preferably, It should be placed on a clean surface to dry and then placed in an open plastic bag or envelope, identifying the *bedikah*.
>
> 2. *Bedikos* should not be stored for many days. They should be shown to a Rav the same day or the next day, if possible. One should not save the *bedikos* of several days to show all at once since *bedikos* may change colors over the course of several days.
>
> 3. *Bedikos* should be clearly marked, identifying them as a *hefseik taharah, moch dachuk* or a simple *bedikah*. Each *bedikah* should be marked according to the day and time of day it was performed. The marking may be done on the corner of the cloth itself or on the envelope.
>
> 4. When a garment soiled with a *kesem* must be shown to a Rav, one can minimize the discomfort by folding the garment in a manner so that the stained section is immediately visible. The garment can then be placed in an unsealed, small plastic (sandwich) bag to be shown to the Rav.
>
> 5. If the questionable stain is not readily apparent, it should be brought to the attention of the Rav. If the spot is very small and

difficult to locate, one should either mark it with an arrow, draw a circle around it or stick in a stick-pin near the questionable spot.

6. A Rav should be informed if the *sheilah* is from a bride before her wedding, a bride recently married or from a pregnant or nursing woman. One should inform the Rav if the woman recently underwent a gynecological procedure.

7. A woman who is about to undergo a gynecological procedure should consult a Rav beforehand regarding the scheduling of the procedure and how to avoid becoming a *niddah*.

8. A woman who has had unusual difficulty producing a clean *hefseik taharah*, or who often finds stains during her seven "clean" days, should inform the Rav of this fact. In addition, a woman who has a vaginal irritation should notify the Rav when she shows him a *bedikah* cloth.

9. All questionable *bedikos* and *kesamim* should preferably be shown to the Rav by day.

10. Once a Rav rules that a *bedikah* cloth is unacceptable, one may not show it to another Rav unless the second Rav is informed of the decision of the first Rav.

11. Keeping a *vestos* calendar is difficult; for newlyweds it can be an exasperating experience. A couple should bring their *vestos* calendar to their Rav for guidance during the first few months of marriage. He will help them calculate the days during which one must abstain.

CHAPTER TWO

What makes a woman a *niddah*

☐ What is *dam niddah?*

☐ Torah law and Rabbinic law.

☐ *Reiyas dam:* a menstrual flow.

☐ *Pesichas hakever:* opening of the uterus.

☐ *Hargashah:* a sensation.

☐ Childbirth.

Halachic Overview

The following chapter is a general introduction to the laws of *niddah*. Many *halachos* mentioned in this chapter are discussed in detail in subsequent chapters.

1. A woman becomes a *niddah* with the onset of a uterine discharge of blood. This prohibits her to cohabit with her husband. She remains a *niddah*, even after cessation of the flow, until she undergoes a specific purification process.

2. The prohibition of cohabitation with a *niddah* is among the thirty-six cardinal prohibitions punishable by *kares* when committed willingly. In addition, the prohibition of *niddah* extends to any personal physical contact between a *niddah* and any man (whether her husband or a stranger). Any pleasurable contact, e.g. hugging or kissing, is Biblically prohibited and punishable by *malkos* (flogging). Moreover, any personal bodily contact between a *niddah* and any man, even if not for pleasure, is prohibited.

3. Any woman (married or single) above the age of twelve is assumed to be a *niddah* and is subject to all the prohibitions of *niddah*. Since single women do not (and should not) use the *mikveh*, any pleasurable contact between any man and a woman above the age of twelve is prohibited by Torah law and is punishable by *malkos*. This should expose the fallacy of those who claim that one need not be *"shomer negiah."* One who is confronted with such claims should discuss the matter with his or her Rav.

4. A woman becomes a *niddah* even if the blood never left her body. *Niddus* begins the moment even a minute amount of blood flows from the uterus into the vagina, even if it subsequently does not leave her body.

5. According to Torah law, a woman does not acquire the status of *niddah* through the flow of menstrual blood alone; the flow must be accompanied by a physical sensation — a *hargashah* — which signals the onset of menstruation. *Halachah* generally assumes that any menstruation is accompanied by this physical sensation and thereby brings about a Biblical status of *niddah*.

6. *Poskim* offer three descriptions of a *hargashah:* a) a bodily trembling associated with the onset of the menstrual flow, b) the actual feeling of the opening of the uterus and c) in the opinion of some *poskim*, the sensation of an internal flow. These opinions and their *halachic* ramifications are discussed further in Chapter Three.

7. Under Rabbinic law a woman becomes a *niddah* even without any of the physical sensations described above. Thus, if a woman experiences an external flow, even without any of the physical sensations listed above, or even if she merely finds a blood stain (a *kesem*) of a certain size on her garment, she is a *niddah* according to Rabbinic law.

8. A woman who did an internal examination with a *bedikah* cloth and found *dam* on the cloth must suspect that there was a *hargashah* as well, and she may be a *niddah,* even according to Torah law. Similarly, if blood is found on a cloth used to clean herself immediately after cohabitation, she may be a *niddah* according to Torah law. In each of these cases we suspect that the *hargashah* was masked by the sensation of the *bedikah* or the cohabitation. The practical application of these *halachos* will be discussed in detail in Chapter Three.

9. A woman who saw no *dam* but experienced a *hargashah* must suspect that some blood flowed from her body. Even if she subsequently does an internal examination and finds nothing, she is considered a *niddah.* We suspect that perhaps a very minute amount of blood was expelled and was dissolved in her vaginal fluids. These *halachos* will be discussed in Chapter Three.

10. A woman who becomes a *niddah,* even if only through a mere speck of *dam* (either as a flow or on a *bedikah* cloth) or through a *kesem* (which is judged to be *tamei*), must wait a minimum of five days and count seven "clean" days after the flow has ended. These seven days are called the "*shivah nekiyim* — the seven clean days." They are required in the process of *taharah* which culminates in *tevilah* (immersion in a *mikveh*).

11. Uterine blood causes *niddus* regardless of whether it is liquid or dry. A woman who finds a substance of questionable color in her vaginal area, on a *bedikah* cloth or on a garment, must be concerned that it may be dried blood which renders her a *niddah.* The specimen should be shown to a Rav to determine whether it is actually dried blood, mucous or a piece of dried skin.

12. Any shade of red or black found on an examination cloth or a garment (stains on a garment require a specific size) renders a woman a *niddah.* Pure yellow, blue or green shades do not. Certain shades of brown may be considered *dam niddah,* whether found on an examination cloth or on a garment, and should be shown to a Rav. Newlyweds should show any color (including yellow) to a Rav until they learn to properly identify different shades with certainty. See Chapter Six for the details of these *halachos.*

13. Any appearance of menstrual blood, at any time, renders a woman a *niddah,* whether the blood is part of her normal menstrual cycle, mid-cycle bleeding or any unusual and unexpected blood flow. Even a woman who has a set pattern (*vest kavuah*) for her period, and sees blood at another, unusual time, is a *niddah.* A woman in mid-pregnancy or during nursing, or even a woman in post menopause who experiences a uterine blood flow, finds blood on a *bedikah* cloth or a *kesem* becomes a *niddah.*

14. Any uterine blood flow, whether caused by natural means or external influences, is considered *dam niddah.* This includes uterine bleeding caused by medical (i.e., hormonal) treatment, a medical examination or a bad fall.

15. A woman who bleeds from a vaginal or cervical wound or abrasion caused by a medical examination or from any other cause is not necessarily a *niddah.* Often a doctor will reassure his patient that the blood found after a gynecological examination is not uterine blood and therefore is not a problem. This may be, but it is not necessarily so. One should never rely on the doctor alone for *halachic* matters; a Rav <u>must</u> be consulted. Often, the Rav will speak with the doctor to clarify the medical situation before reaching a *halachic* decision. See Chapter Twenty-Three.

16. If a woman finds a stain upon her garment, or on an object upon which she had been sitting, without experiencing a *hargashah,* the stain is called a *kesem* and renders her a *niddah* by Rabbinic law. A *kesem* differs from an actual *re'iyah* because it came without *hargashah* and could conceivably be attributed to a source other than *dam niddah.*

17. A *kesem* renders a woman a *niddah* under the following conditions: a) the stain must be larger than the size of a bean called a *gris* (the size of a U.S. penny), b) the stain must be on a white, not a colored, object, c) the object upon which the stain is found must be susceptible to *tumah,* d) the stain cannot reasonably be attributed to another source and e) the stain is found on a location where menstrual blood may have stained. These and related *halachos* are discussed in detail in Book Three.

18. A woman who feels a *hargashah* and then finds a *kesem* becomes a *niddah,* regardless of the size of the stain and regardless of the object upon which the blood is found. Therefore, when a woman shows a stain to a Rav, she should inform him if she felt any sensation at the time she was wearing the garment.

19. If a woman's uterus opened a specific width (regardless of the cause), we must be concerned that perhaps a minute amount of blood left the

uterus even if no blood is visible. This is called *"pesichas hakever"* and renders her a *niddah*. This is discussed in Chapter Twenty-Three.

20. If a woman finds a substance that was discharged from her body, she must be concerned about several *halachic* (as well as medical) issues: a) The secreted substance may be dried blood, which certainly renders her a *niddah* (unless a Rav, upon consulting a physician, determines that its source is a wound in the cervical or vaginal area). b) Even if the substance is not red, brown or black (and is therefore not considered blood), perhaps it is large enough to cause *pesichas hakever* when it left the uterus thereby rendering her a *niddah*. A Rav must be consulted.

21. Whenever a doctor performs a gynecological examination, we must ascertain whether the examining instrument penetrated the uterus. If the doctor did not use an instrument in his examination, we assume that the uterus was not opened. A Rav must be consulted.

22. If any blood appears following a gynecological examination or the doctor claims that there was indeed bleeding, she may be a *niddah*. The woman should ask the doctor whether the uterus was penetrated, where the blood came from and in particular whether the instrument may have caused any trauma which may cause bleeding. If the doctor claims that the blood is from trauma, she should inquire whether or not he sees the actual bleeding site. At a minimum the woman should ascertain the name of the procedure and the type of instrument used. This information should be forwarded to a Rav who will decide whether or not she is *tehorah*. See Chapter Twenty-Three where this subject is discussed in detail.

23. A woman must <u>never</u> rely upon the doctor alone to decide whether or not she is a *niddah*. All information provided by the doctor must be referred to a Rav.

24. It is possible that a woman may find blood on a *bedikah* cloth, a garment or may even notice blood leaving her body and yet not become a *niddah*. If the blood is attributable to a source other than the uterus, *halachah* may, at times, assume that it is not *dam niddah*. This is dependent upon many factors and its rules differ depending upon whether she finds the blood on a *bedikah* cloth or on a garment. A Rav must always be consulted. These rules will be discussed in Chapter Six regarding *bedikos*, Chapter Eleven regarding garments and Chapter Twenty-Three regarding gynecological examinations.

25. Hymenal blood is not *dam niddah*. It is caused by a wound and is not associated in any way with menstrual bleeding. Nevertheless, *Chazal*

decreed that hymenal bleeding renders a woman a *niddah*. The reasons for this, and its *halachos,* will be discussed in Volume Two .

26. When a woman is in the process of childbirth, the uterus opens sufficiently to render her a *niddah* (as a result of *pesichas hakever*). *Poskim* rule that when a woman has difficulty walking due to her contractions, the uterus opened sufficiently to render her a *niddah*. Contemporary authorities rule that neither widely spaced contractions nor early dilation of the uterus fall into this category. This topic is discussed in Chapter Twenty-Four.

27. The Torah ordains that a woman who gives birth (a *yoledes*), regardless of whether the child is alive or stillborn, becomes *tamei* as a *niddah*. The Torah law of a *yoledes* is unique and different from the *halachah* as practiced today. This will be discussed later in this chapter.

28. A woman who gives birth to a male is *tamei* as a *niddah* regardless of whether or not blood flowed as a result of the childbirth. She must count seven "clean" days and then immerse herself in a *mikveh*.

29. A woman who gives birth to a female is governed by the same *halachah* except that, even after counting seven "clean" days, she cannot be *tovel* until fourteen days have passed since the birth.

30. A woman who gives birth through a Caesarean section is not included in the *halachos* which pertain to a *yoledes*. However, she will become a *niddah* due to vaginal bleeding.

31. If a woman has a miscarriage and the fetus was under forty days old, the birth is not halachically considered a birth, but she is a *niddah* because of the blood that appeared. If, however, she carried the fetus for forty days or more, the miscarriage is considered a birth regarding the *halachos* of *niddah*. If the fetus is unrecognizable as either male or female, she may not immerse herself until fourteen days have passed.

32. A woman may acquire the status of a *niddah* by merely stating that she is a *niddah*. Thus, a woman who tells her husband that she is a *niddah* becomes a *niddah* by virtue of her statement, whether it is true or not. Any subsequent claim that her statement was not serious, but was actually said in jest, has no validity. She requires the five-day waiting period, a *hefseik taharah*, seven "clean" days and *tevilah*. There are, however, times when her retraction is accepted. These *halachos* will be discussed in Chapter Four.

33. If a woman experiences a blood flow during marital relations, she must consider several factors. First, since she becomes a *niddah* immedi-

ately, she and her husband are immediately transgressing the prohibition against cohabitation with a *niddah*. They must immediately disengage. It is of utmost importance that this be done carefully and properly. The *halachos* regarding this predicament will be discussed in Volume Two. Even if she does not experience a blood flow while cohabiting, but immediately afterwards, a Rav must immediately be consulted. A Rav should be consulted, even after one such occurrence, for guidance as to what steps should be taken in the future.

Introduction: What is *dam niddah?*

Proper understanding of the *halachos* of *niddah* requires some knowledge of the internal organs associated with the menstrual process. *Poskim* mention three organs in reference to the menstrual flow: 1) the *beis hachitzon* (the external chamber) or *prozdor*[1] (the vestibule) — the vagina. 2) the *tzavar harechem* (the "neck" of the uterus) — the cervix. 3) the *makor* (or *rechem, eim* or *kever*)[2] — the uterus.

The uterus is the organ at the center of the procreative process: Its function is to provide the embryo with the proper environment to develop into a fetus until it is sufficiently developed to be born. In this sense, the uterus is the source of human life; hence, it is called "*makor*" (source) or "*eim*" (mother).

The uterus is also at the core of the *niddah* process, the menstrual flow. The interior of the uterus is covered with a lining called the endometrium. After an ovum (egg) is fertilized, it is implanted into the endometrium where it further develops as an embryo. If no fertilization takes place or no implantation occurs, the ovum is expelled and the uterus sheds its lining. The menstrual flow is the result of this shedding of the uterine lining and accumulated blood. This blood is discharged through the cervix and leaves the body by way of the vagina. In this sense, the uterine flow is associated with death since the anticipated life was not actualized; hence, it is called "*kever*" (grave). Thus, the menstrual cycle is a cycle of life and death, hope and disappointment.

Divine wisdom has ordained that a woman becomes *tamei* (ritually

---

1. As a result of the ambiguity of the definition of *beis hachitzon* and *prozdor*, it is extremely difficult to reconcile medical and anatomical understanding with the descriptions offered by *Chazal* and *Rambam*. Much has been written in *halachic* literature on this subject. See *Tosfos Yom Tov* (*Niddah* 2:5), responsa *Bach* (*Hachadashos* 34), *Sidrei Taharah* 194:26, responsa *Chasam Sofer Y.D.* 167, *Graz* (*Kuntres Acharon* 183:2) and *Chazon Ish Y.D.* 92:27,28. See Chapter Twenty-Three where these issues are discussed in greater detail.

2. Or *cheder*, a term occasionally used by *Chazal*.

impure) with the onset of the menstrual flow and this prohibits her from cohabitation with her husband. She remains *tamei*, even after cessation of the flow, until she undergoes a purification process. The culmination of this process coincides with the time when the woman is close to ovulation and is thus most fertile. This is also when the uterine lining has again thickened to accommodate a fertilized egg.

> Note: In this work, we will use the Hebrew terms *"tamei"* or *"tumah"* instead of their English counterpart — "ritually impure." Similarly we will often use the word *"dam"* in the place of "blood." We will also use the term "Torah law" rather than "Biblical law" when we distinguish between laws that are of Biblical origin and those that are of Rabbinic origin.[3] We will often use the term "menstruation" or "menstrual flow" in the place of "uterine flow." However, one should note that *niddus* is caused by any flow from the uterine lining even though it is not part of her menstrual cycle.

I. The ramifications of the *niddah* status

The laws of *niddah* are two-fold. They relate to the general realm of *tumah* and *taharah*, ritual uncleanliness and purification. They also pertain to the realm of *issur v'heter* — prohibited and permitted acts.

In terms of *tumah*, *niddah* is no different from all other laws of *tumah*. In earlier times, these laws were of vital concern. One who was *tamei* was forbidden to eat *terumah*, any part of a *korban* (sacrifice) or enter the *Beis Hamikdash* complex. Today, to our sorrow, we have not merited the rebuilding of the *Beis Hamikdash* and we are unable to purify ourselves completely from many types of *tumah*. Consequently, the additional *tumah* of *niddah* has no practical relevance to us.

The second application of the laws of *niddah* pertains to *issur* (prohibition).[4] A woman in the status of *niddah* may not have relations with her husband, even after the menstrual flow has ended, until she properly purifies herself. This Biblical prohibition is among the thirty-six cardinal prohibitions punishable by *kares* when committed knowingly. Thus, if a

---

3. We used the term "Torah law" even though the term "Biblical law" is more exact in contradistinction to Rabbinic law which is not Biblical.

4. *Poskim* discuss the question of whether the *issur* of *niddah* is, essentially, an issue of *tumah* or *issur*. Do we apply the rules of *tumah* or the rules of *issur* to the prohibition of *niddah*? For example, in a case of *safek* (doubt) do we apply the rules of *safek tumah* or *safek issur*, each of which follow a criterion of its own? See *Shev Shemaitisa* 1:12, responsa *Noda B'Yehudah* Y.D. 2:12, *Avnei Neizer* C.M. 139, *Asvan DeOraisa* 21 and responsa *Achiezer* E.H. 1:7.

man knowingly cohabits with a *niddah* (whether his wife or any other married or unmarried woman)[5] or any *ervah*,[6] both he and she are punished by *kares*. If they do so unknowingly (i.e., the husband and wife are unaware that she was a *niddah*), each is liable for a *korban chatas* (an atonement sacrifice).[7] The prohibition of *niddah* extends to any personal, physical contact between a *niddah* and any man (whether her husband or a stranger). In the opinion of most *Rishonim*, pleasurable contact, e.g., hugging or kissing, with any *ervah* is Biblically prohibited,[8] albeit punishable only by *malkos* (flogging), not *kares*. Indeed, any personal bodily contact , even if not for pleasure, is prohibited. It is with great hesitation that *poskim* permit a woman even to be examined by a male physician.[9] Some authorities suggest (although this is not the common custom) that a woman choose a female physician, if one is available. Indeed, in spite of the lenient custom in some communities, *poskim* have not sanctioned the practice of women and men exchanging handshakes.[10]

---

5. *Beis Yosef* end of 183, *Rema* 183:1, see also *Pleisi* 183:3.

6. There are three basic types of *ervah*: a) those relatives (whether blood relatives, e.g., a sister or aunt, or relatives through marriage, e.g., a sister-in-law) enumerated in *Vayikra* 18:6-20 and 20:10-21, b) any married woman, c) a *niddah* (even one's own wife).

7. The severity of *kares* is evident, since it entails either one's soul's being severed from its heavenly source (see *Rambam, Pirush HaMishnah, Sanhedrin,* Chapter 10, see also *Ramban, Toras HaAdam* [p.292 Shavel ed.], *Likutei Amarim [Tanya]* 3:5, *Nefesh HaChaim* 1:18, *Pri Migadim, O.C., Pesichah Koleles* 3:18), one's own premature death (see *Tosfos, Shabbos* 25a and *Moed Katan* 28a regarding whether *kares* involves one's death before the age of fifty or sixty), or the death of one's children. (*Rashi, Shabbos* 25a maintains that *kares* involves both one's premature death and the death of one's children. See an opposing opinion in *Tosfos, Yevamos* 2a. *Shaarei Teshuvah* (3:119-125) maintains that different types of *kares* apply to different prohibitions.) However, it may be appropriate to note that one who incurs a liability for a *korban chatas* must, in addition to the actual sacrifice, do a proper penance. *Rema* (*Y.D.* 185:4) rules that since today one cannot offer a *korban*, one must, in addition to the penance, fast for forty days (or fast forty-eight or seventy-two consecutive hours, see *O.C.* 568:4) in place of the *korban*. One who willfully transgressed a transgression of *kares* should seek sagacious advice as to the proper form of *teshuvah*.

8. *Rambam* 21:1, *Sefer HaMitzvos* 2:353, *Sefer HaChinuch* 188, *Rabbeinu Yonah* (*Iggeres HaTeshuvah*), *Rashba* (attributed responsa 127), *Ritva* (*Shabbos* 13b), *Meiri* (*Sanhedrin* 66b) and responsa *Rivash* 425. *Ramban* (*Hasagos, Sefer HaMitzvos* ibid.) and *Tashbatz* 3:58 contend that the prohibition is Rabbinic (*Ramban* speculates that perhaps it is a Biblical prohibition not punishable by *malkos*; however, his tone, throughout, indicates that he considers it a Rabbinic prohibition). *Shulchan Aruch* (*Even HaEzer*) 20:1 and *Shach Y.D.* 157:10 follow the opinion of *Rambam* and most *Rishonim*. In truth, the issue of whether the prohibition is Biblical or Rabbinic should be insignificant, since it is prohibited, in any case (see *Igros Moshe E.H.* 4:60).

9. See *Shach* 195:20.

10. See *Mishnah Berurah* 217:16, see also *Igros Moshe O.C.* 1:113, *E.H.* 1:56, 4:32[9]. One who anticipates being in a difficult situation should discuss the question with a Rav.

It may be appropriate at this juncture to lay to rest the myth of "I am not *shomer negiah.*" Any woman who has reached puberty is assumed to have experienced a menstrual flow.[11] Once the status of *niddah* has been achieved, the woman remains a *niddah* until she completes the purification process which will be described in Volume Two. Thus, since single women do not (and should not) use the *mikveh*,[12] any woman above the age of twelve is assumed to be a *niddah*. We noted the opinion of most *Rishonim* that any pleasurable contact between a man and a *niddah* is prohibited by Torah law and punishable by *malkos*. This prohibition is at least equal to one who eats non-kosher food. In addition, the prohibition of *niddah* is included in the general category of *gilui arayos* (illicit relationships) which is one of the three cardinal sins for which one must forfeit his life rather than to submit to the transgression. This requirement applies not only to actual cohabitation, but to any pleasurable physical contact as well.[13] The claim that one is not "*shomer negiah*" is analogous to stating that one is not "*shomer Shabbos,*" which, in effect, means that one is not "*shomer Torah.*" There may be young pseudoscholars who wrap themselves in a cloak of superior knowledge, and allege that their extensive research on the subject has led them to the conclusion that there is no prohibition of *negiah* or that it is subject to a difference of opinion.[14] Some individuals mislead less educated young women with claims of a non-existent *psak* (halachic decision) that *negiah* is permitted. A young woman faced with such claims should discuss the matter with her Rav.

II. Torah law and Rabbinic law

The Torah law of *niddah* differs in many ways from the *halachos* of *niddah* that we observe today. One difference pertains to the type of flow that renders a woman a *niddah*. A woman will not become a *niddah*

---

11. See *Igros Moshe O.C.* 1:26, who rules that once a girl reaches the age of eleven, one should refrain from even listening to her singing. Physical contact is a far more serious offense.

12. See responsa *Rivash* 425 and *Beis Yosef Y.D.* end of 183. See also responsa *Rav Paalim* 4:16, *Sidei Chemed* (*Yom HaKippurim* 1:6), *Elef LaMateh* on *Mateh Efraim* 606:8 and responsa *Yabia Omer O.C.* 1:30, regarding the custom of *tevilah* on *Erev Yom Kippur* for unmarried women.

13. See *Sidei Chemed* (*Chassan V'kallah* 12) vol. 7 p. 28,29. See gloss of Rav E. Waldenberg to *Nishmas Avraham Y.D.* p.295.

14. Anyone sincerely believing so will do himself well by reading the words of R' Yonasan Eibschitz (see *Pleisi* end of 195) cited in *Sidei Chemed,* ibid.

according to Torah law unless the flow is accompanied with a physical sensation called *hargashah*. A second difference relates to the time during her cycle that the flow appears, whether during the time called "*niddah* days" or the time called "*zivah* days." A third difference between Torah and Rabbinic requirements relates to the color of the blood.

A. The requirement of *hargashah*

1. Torah law:

According to Torah law, a woman does not acquire the status of *niddah* through the discharge of menstrual blood alone. The flow must be accompanied by a physical sensation — a *hargashah*. A blood flow alone without any physical sensation will not, according to Torah law, render a woman a *niddah*.[15] It is commonly assumed that any menstrual flow is accompanied by a physical sensation and causes a Biblical status of *niddah*.[16]

What exactly is a *hargashah*? There is no Talmudic description for the feeling other than the stipulation that it be felt "*bivsarah* — in her flesh" — an internal awareness. *Poskim*[17] offer three descriptions of this sensation:[18]

> a. a bodily trembling associated with the onset of the menstrual flow. Some *Poskim* describe it as a stinging sensation similar to the sensation of one who begins to urinate.

> b. the actual feeling of the opening of the uterus.

> c. in the opinion of some *poskim*, the sensation of an internal flow, either the sensation of a flow from the uterus itself into the vagina, or, perhaps, any feeling of a fluid movement in the vaginal area.

---

15. In the opinion of some *Poskim*, if the blood certainly came from her body, a woman is a *niddah* by Torah law even without a *hargashah*. See *Sidrei Taharah* 190:93, s.v. "וכבר" citing Maharam Lublin. This will be explored in detail in Appendix B.

16. See *Rambam Issurei Biah* 9:1. Many women today claim that they do not feel any inner sensation at the onset of their period. See Responsa *Teshuras Shai* 457, cited in *Darchei Teshuvah* 183:6. Nevertheless, it is commonly assumed by *Poskim* that there must have been some sensation, even if the woman was unaware of it.

17. See *Chavos Daas* 183:2(c), 190:1(c) and *Pischei Teshuvah* 183:1.

18. See responsa *Maharam Shick* (Y.D. 184:1) who implies that any sensation that a woman usually feels at the onset of the flow is considered a *hargashah,* not only the three types mentioned by *Poskim*.

These opinions and their *halachic* ramifications are discussed further in Chapter Three.

2. Rabbinic law:
Rabbinic law has ordained that a woman becomes a *niddah* even without any physical sensation. Thus, if a woman experiences a discharge (even without any of the physical sensations listed above), she is a *niddah* according to Rabbinic law.

3. Exceptions to the *hargashah* requirement:
Although the appearance of *dam* without a *hargashah* cannot bring about *niddus* according to Torah law, there are exceptional cases in which we suspect that there may have been a *hargashah* and we must consider the woman a *niddah* even according to Torah law.

> a. A woman who did an internal examination with her *bedikah* cloth and found *dam* on the cloth must suspect that there was a *hargashah* as well.[19] Usually, *dam* appears with a *hargashah* and perhaps, in this case, she mistook the *hargashah* for the sensation of the *bedikah*.[20]

> b. If *dam* is found on a cloth that she used to clean herself with immediately after cohabitation we must also suspect that the *hargashah* was masked by the sensation of the cohabitation.[21]

> c. If a woman finds *dam* immediately[22] after urination we suspect that she confused the *hargashah* with the sensation of urination.[23]

The *halachos* relating to these cases will be discussed in further detail in Chapter Three.

4. The practical relevance of *hargashah:*
The previous discussion as to what constitutes a *hargashah* may seem irrelevant since, according to Rabbinic law, any blood flow renders a woman a *niddah*. Nevertheless, the presence or absence of a *hargashah* is vital in several situations:

___

19. *Pleisi* 183:1, *Chavos Daas* 183:2[c], *Sidrei Taharah* 183:2 and 190:93.

20. See *Rambam* 9:1.

21. *Chavos Daas* 183:2[c].

22. See *Igros Moshe Y.D.* 4:17[13].

23. *Chavos Daas* ibid.

a. An appearance of *dam* in the form of a *kesem* without a *hargashah* will not render a Rabbinic status of *niddah* in all circumstances. Factors to be considered include: the size of the blood stain, the color of the garment, the location of the stain and whether the object upon which it is found is *mekabel tumah* (susceptible to *tumah*.) An appearance of *dam* with a *hargashah*, however, renders the woman a *niddah*, regardless of size and regardless of the object upon which the *dam* is found. Thus, it is imperative that the Rav who is ruling on the status of a stain be informed if the woman felt any sensation. If there was a sensation, it must be accurately described to the Rav.

b. Since a *hargashah* is directly associated with the onset of a menstrual flow, a woman who senses a *hargashah* must suspect that some blood did, indeed flow from her body. The fact that no blood was found does not prove that no blood left the uterus. Even if she does an internal examination and finds nothing, we may nevertheless speculate that perhaps she was rendered a *niddah* by a very minute flow which was lost.[24] These *halachos* will be discussed in Chapter Three.

B. Days of *niddah* and *zivah*

1. Torah law:

According to Torah law, a woman's cycle is divided into two parts: the *niddah* days and *zivah* days. *Niddah* days are those days during which it is normal for a woman to begin her menstrual flow. *Dam* seen during those days renders a woman a *niddah*. *Zivah* days are those days in which it is unusual for her to experience a blood flow. *Dam* seen during those days renders her a *zavah*.

Although the "normal" days to experience a flow may be variable, Torah law dictates that all women be governed by one standard. Sinaitic tradition divides a woman's cycle into seven *niddah* days, during which her flow is "normal," and eleven *zivah* days, during which she is not expected to experience a blood flow. The first blood flow a woman experiences renders her a *niddah* for a

---

24. See Y.D. 190:1.

span of seven days called *"yemei niddah"* — days of *niddah*. Upon conclusion of these seven days, the eleven *yemei zivah* begin. The term *"yemei zivah* — days of *zivah"* should not be understood to mean that we actually expect a woman to experience a *zivah* discharge during the course of those days. On the contrary, we expect no discharge. *Zivah* is unusual and rarely occurs. If, however, bleeding does occur during the course of the eleven days, it is considered *zivah,* not *niddah,* and is governed by different laws.

Once the eleven days of *zivah* pass, the days of *niddah* return.[25] Thus, the *zivah* days are also referred to by *Chazal* as the eleven days "between *niddah* and *niddah."* This does not suggest that we actually expect the *niddus* to recur after eleven days, since a total of only eighteen days have passed since the beginning of her cycle. Indeed, *Chazal* note that the next menstrual cycle usually begins only after thirty days.[26] However, if the menstrual flow does commence after the eleven *yemei zivah* (i.e., after day eighteen), it is considered a normal (*niddah*), rather than abnormal (*zivah*) occurrence. Whenever menstruation begins (whether immediately after the eleven *yemei zivah* or at a later date), the woman again becomes a *niddah* for seven days. At the end of these seven days, the eleven days of *zivah* begin again.[27]

□← seven *niddus* days →□← eleven potential *zivah* days →□← seven potential *niddus* days→□

The Torah laws of *niddah* and *zivah* are fundamentally different:

a. The Torah laws of *niddah*:

At the onset of the menstruation during *niddah* days, a woman becomes a *niddah* for seven days, regardless of whether the flow continues for seven days, for one day or even for one moment. In all cases, she remains a *niddah* until the completion of the seven days. Towards the

---

25. If a woman becomes a *zavah,* i.e., she saw a flow for three days during the eleven *zivah* days, she cannot return to her *niddah* days until she counts seven "clean" days.

26. See *Niddah* 9b. This is known as the *onah beinonis* — the average interval. See Chapter Fifteen.

27. This is the opinion of all authorities with the exception of the *Rambam*. He seems to maintain that once the second seven (potential *niddah*) days have passed without any blood flow, the woman returns to the potential *zivah* days. For example, if her flow begins on the twenty-sixth day from the onset of the earlier period, she will become a *zavah,* not a *niddah*. *Poskim* find many difficulties with *Rambam's* opinion. Among the obvious problems is that the Talmud states that the normal length of a period is thirty days. According to *Rambam,* the normal cycle of every woman would render her a *zavah*. See *Aruch HaShulchan* 183:12-27 for an explanation of *Rambam's* view.

end of the seventh day (i.e., before sundown), she checks herself (*hefseik taharah*) to ascertain that the flow has stopped. If there is no sign of blood, she may then purify herself with immersion in the *mikveh* any time after nightfall. Even if the flow continued until just before sundown of the seventh day and then abruptly stopped, she may check herself immediately to ascertain that the bleeding has stopped,[28] immerse herself after nightfall[29] and become *tehorah*.

b. The Torah laws of *zivah*:

While the *tumah* of *zivah* and the prohibition against cohabitation with her parallel those of a *niddah*, the means by which a woman becomes a *zavah* are more complex. A woman who experiences a discharge during one of the eleven potential *zivah* days (whether one discharge at any time during the day or several discharges in the course of the same *zivah* day) becomes a "minor" *zavah*. In Talmudic terminology, she is known as a "*zavah ketanah*." A *zavah ketanah* must check herself (*hefseik taharah*) before nightfall of the first day to ensure that the blood flow has completely stopped, and count the following day as one "clean day." In this sense, she is known by the term "*shomeres yom k'neged yom*" — one who observes a day (free of discharge) for a day (in

---

28. See *Tur Y.D.* 183. She must check herself before sunset of the seventh day; otherwise, we assume that the flow continues.

29. In the original Torah law in which a woman was *tovel* after only seven days, a woman was required to wait until nightfall before *tevilah*. If she was *tovel* earlier, the *tevilah* was invalid. The reason for this is as follows: There are two levels of *tumah*: "active" and "residual" *tumah*. For example, one who holds a *sheretz* (a dead rodent) is actively *tamei* as long as he continues to grasp the *sheretz*. Once he drops the *sheretz*, his contact with the source of *tumah* is broken and his *tumah* is only residual. Residual *tumah* can be removed through the proper purification process, i.e., immersion in a *mikveh*. Active *tumah* cannot be removed through *tevilah*. Any attempted purification while still in contact with the *tumah* is called "*tovel v'sheretz b'yado*" — immersion (in a *mikveh*) while still grasping a *sheretz*. For this reason, the immersion of a *niddah* must not take place before nightfall after the seventh day. Since the *tumah* of *niddus* continues actively for seven days, even if the actual blood flow stopped on the first day, any *tevilah* done before nightfall constitutes *tovel v'sheretz b'yado* and is ineffective. After nightfall, however, her *tumah* is merely residual and may be removed through *tevilah*. Today, women must wait a minimum of five days before counting seven "clean" days and being *tovel*. Even today a woman is required to be *tovel* after nightfall. This is not Torah law. There are, therefore, cases in which a woman, with permission from a Rav, may be *tovel* by day.

which she experienced discharge). If, upon inspection, she finds herself free from any further bleeding, her *zivah* is over and she may cleanse herself of her *tumah* through immersion in a *mikveh* at the end of the second day.[30] If, upon inspection, she again finds a discharge or her flow continues into the second day, she is still considered a *zavah ketanah* or *shomeres yom k'neged yom*. She must check herself before nightfall at the end of the second day and count the third day as a "clean" day. If no *dam* appears on the third day, she may immerse herself at the end of the third day. If she finds a flow on the third day or even if she finds three small discharges, one in each of three consecutive days, her status changes significantly: She is now a *zavah gedolah* (a "major" *zavah*).[31] A *zavah gedolah* requires not one, but seven "clean" days. Thus, after the flow stops completely she must check herself before nightfall and begin counting seven "clean" days, starting the following day. Upon completion of these seven days, she may immerse herself in a *mikveh* to purify herself. After this *tevilah*, she has removed the *tumah* and may cohabit with her husband. However, she may neither enter the *Beis Hamikdash* nor eat from sacrificial

30. Actually, she could immerse herself immediately after sunrise according to the rule of *miktzas hayom k'kulo* (passage of part of the day is the equivalent of passage of all that day). This same principle, applied to the laws of mourning, permits mourners to end their *shivah* (seven days of mourning) on the morning, rather than at the end, of the seventh day. While this *tevilah* is permitted by Torah law, *Chazal* prohibited a woman from immersing herself until the end of the day (whether the one "clean" day of a *zavah ketanah* or the seventh "clean" day of a *zavah gedolah*, or even the seventh "clean" day of any *niddah* today). *Chazal* were concerned that she may immediately cohabit with her husband following the early immersion and perhaps subsequently, in the course of the day, she may see *dam* again, thus invalidating the "clean" day. This prohibition is subject to a difference of opinion among *Rishonim*. Most (*Rashi*, *Niddah* 67b, *Tosfos* ibid., *Smag* and *Mordechai* cited in *Beis Yosef* 183) contend that *Chazal* forbade even the *tevilah* itself out of fear that she may cohabit. *Rambam* (*Hilchos Issurei Biah* 6:14) seems to maintain that *Chazal* prohibited only the cohabitation, while the *tevilah* itself is permitted. See *Beis Yosef* 183 and *Aruch LaNer* (*Niddah* 67b) for a discussion of this point.

31. A woman may become a *zavah gedolah* even if the flow started on the ninth day of her *yemei zivah* and continued through the tenth and eleventh days. If, however, the flow did not start before the tenth day, she cannot become a *zavah gedolah* since only two days remain of her *zivah* days. The twelfth day is actually the first day of the *niddah* days and any blood seen on that day renders her a *niddah*, not a *zavah*. A woman who saw *dam* on the eleventh day becomes *temei'ah* but needs no "clean" day, and may immerse herself in the morning of the twelfth day providing that the bleeding stopped before the end of the eleventh day.

offering until she brings a sacrifice (*korban*) on the eighth day or at any time thereafter.

In summary: There are four basic differences between *niddus* and *zivus*: a) Onset: *Niddus* is possible at any time except during the eleven *zivah* days. *Zivus* is possible only during the eleven days following *niddus*. b) Duration of the *tumah: Dam niddah* always causes *tumah* for seven days, regardless of the duration of the flow, i.e., whether there was a brief flow or a flow for seven days. In contrast, the *tumah* of *zivah* depends upon the length of the flow, i.e., whether she bled for three days or less. c) Days to be counted: *Niddus* does not require a counting of "clean" days. *Zivus* requires the counting of one or seven "clean" days. d) *Taharah* process: A *niddah* needs only *tevilah* for her purification, while a *zavah gedolah* requires a *korban* as well.

		A) Onset	B) Duration of the *tumah*	C) Days to be counted	D) *Tahara* process
NIDDUS		a) days 1-7 b) anytime after day 18	minimum of 7 days	seven days, either with bleeding or without, providing that the bleeding stops before nightfall	*tevilah* only
ZIVUS	a) *zavah ketanah*	days 8 through 18 following *niddus*	one or two days of bleeding followed by one "clean" day	one "clean" day	*tevilah* only
	b) *zavah gedolah*	days 8 through 18 following *niddus*	three or more days of bleeding, followed by seven "clean" days	seven "clean" days	*tevilah* and *korban*

The *niddah* and *zivah* days: This chart is to simplify and clarify the Torah laws as explained in the text. Nowadays, a woman who has even a minute uterine discharge must wait five days, count seven "clean" days after the flow has stopped and be *tovel. Poskim* treat this with all the severity of a Torah law.

2. Rabbinic law and custom:

Based upon the above, a woman whose cycle is eighteen or more days (as is normal for most women) will only become a *niddah,* never a *zavah.* Thus, according to Torah law, she would be *tamei* only seven days of each menstrual cycle. However, *Chazal* were concerned that, as a result of the many hardships and wanderings that Jews have endured throughout the ages, people might well be confused by these complicated calculations. Specifically,[32] they were concerned that a woman may have a non-uterine discharge on the first of her *niddah* days and, thinking that it is menstrual blood, will start counting seven *niddah* days.[33] In actuality, the menstrual blood may begin on the seventh day from the non-uterine discharge, which, in reality, is the first of her actual *niddah* days. The woman would thus require six additional *niddah* days, even if there is no longer a flow. To avoid this problem, *Chazal* ruled that a woman who sees a flow for one or two days should wait six "clean" days (thereby insuring that whenever the actual flow began, she will not immerse herself before the completion of seven *niddah* days). In addition, they ruled that a woman who has a discharge on three consecutive days must count seven "clean" days regardless of when in her cycle the discharge occurs (since, perhaps, she confused her *niddah* days with her *zivah* days and her assumed *niddah* days are actually *zivah* days).[34] Eventually, in Talmudic times, the custom emerged that even a woman who saw only a speck of *dam* should count seven "clean" days so as not to differentiate between a *niddah* and a *zavah.*[35] This custom is known as the custom of Jewish women cited by *R' Zeira.*

This custom was commended by *Chazal* and instituted as a

---

32. See *Niddah* 66a.

33. This error may be due to several factors: She may mistake the color shade of the flow, confusing red with another color. The color may be red but not of uterine origin. The error may also be caused by a flow that started on the tenth and eleventh days of her *zivah* days. This woman may erroneously assume that she is a *zavah* and miscalculate her *niddah and zivah* days. In actuality, the twelfth day (the supposed third *zivah* day) is really the first of her *niddah days.* Thus, she is a *niddah,* not a *zivah* (see *Ran, Niddah* 66a).

34. These rules were instituted by *R' Yehudah HaNassi* (*Niddah* 66a).

35. The rationale behind this is that, at times, even a drop of *dam* may require the woman to count seven "clean" days. For example, if a woman sees a drop of blood during her seven "clean" days, her previous days are invalidated and she must begin a new counting of seven "clean" days. Some women may misunderstand the distinction between a drop of blood during the seven "clean" days and blood found at other times. See *Ramban, Hilchos Niddah* 1:18. See *Beis Yosef* 183 for a detailed discussion of these and related issues.

binding requirement for all women.[36] Accordingly, the *halachah*, as universally practiced for well over a thousand years, requires that a woman who sees even a minute amount of blood must count seven clean days after the flow has ended. *Poskim* treat this rule with all the severity of a Biblical requirement.[37]

C. The color shade

According to Biblical law, only four shades of red qualify as *dam niddah*.[38] Any other shade of red fluid does not render a woman a *niddah*. In addition, a flow of black fluid renders a woman a *niddah* since black blood may have originally been red.[39] In Biblical times, a woman who experienced a blood flow and was uncertain whether it was one of these shades would bring the specimen to a Rav who was trained to differentiate among shades of red.[40]

During later Talmudic times, many *chachamim* were not confident of their ability to distinguish properly among various shades of red.[41] *Chachamim* of later generations assumed that they, too, lacked the skills to properly distinguish among shades of red. Thus, the custom eventually developed not to differentiate between variations of red.

The *halachah* as practiced today considers any shade of red (whether light or dark in addition to black, as *dam niddah*.[42] In addition, many shades of brown are considered reddish and are *tamei*. See Chapter Six for a further discussion as to which colors and shades are *tamei*.

In summary: Rabbinic law or custom has expanded the rules of *niddah* in the following three ways:

> 1. Even a flow without sensation and even a stain on a garment renders a woman a *niddah*.
>
> 2. A woman who experiences even a minute amount of blood must count seven "clean" days.

---

36. *Ramban*, ibid. 1:19. See a discussion of this requirement in *Shiurei Sheivet HaLeivi* 183:1[6]. See *Badei HaShulchan* 183:1 s.v. ואפילו, regarding a case where this rule causes a woman to miss her ovulation time and makes it impossible for her to conceive.

37. See *Beis Yosef* 196, regarding the question of whether one *bedikah* during the seven days suffices. He comments: "One may not be lenient regarding that which is a question of *kares*."

38. *Niddah* 19a.

39. Ibid.

40. See *Devarim* 17:8, see *Rashi* and *Ramban*.

41. See *Niddah* 20b, *R' Yochanan* and *R' Zeira* would not rule on shades of red.

42. *Tur* 188.

3. Any shade of red or black is considered *tamei* and renders a woman a *niddah*.

> *Having established the basis for the laws of niddah as proscribed by Chazal, we will now examine in further detail some of the issues which have been alluded to above. Our discussion will cover the following topics: the blood flow; kesamim (stains); the opening of the uterus; hargashah (the sensation of the beginning of the period) and childbirth.*

III. The blood flow

A woman who experiences a discharge of blood becomes a *niddah*, regardless of whether or not she has reached adulthood[43] and regardless of whether or not she is married.[44] A blood flow need not leave her body: She becomes a *niddah* the moment the blood flows from the uterus into the vagina, even if it subsequently never leaves the body[45] The following factors do <u>not</u> in any way affect whether or not she becomes a *niddah*:

1. The amount:

Although most subjects of *tumah* require a minimum size to transmit the *tumah*,[46] *niddah* is one of the exceptions. Even a discharge of a minute amount of blood[47] requires a woman to count seven "clean" days. This applies to *dam* seen as a flow or even to a stain found on a *bedikah* cloth. A stain found on a garment, however, is governed by the laws of *kesamim* (see IV below) and requires a minimum size.

---

43. The rules of stains (*kesamim*), however, apply only to a woman who reached adulthood, as will be explained in Chapter Seven.

44. As noted above, since any young woman, upon reaching maturity, begins her menstrual cycle, and since today unmarried women do not immerse themselves in a *mikveh*, one must assume that any female twelve years or older is a *niddah* and is governed by all rules relevant to a *niddah*. Accordingly, since a *niddah* is one of the *arayos*, any physical contact between a male and female above the age of twelve is forbidden.

45. Y.D. 183. The blood must leave the cervix entirely, i.e. pass the external os of the cervix fully and enter the vagina, see *Rambam* 5:2, *Sidrei Taharah* ibid. no. 3. Thus, if blood is found in the vagina itself, the woman is a *niddah* even though the blood has not left the body (see *Rambam* 5:2,5).

46. For example, a piece of *neveilah* (an animal carcass) must be the minimum size of an olive; a *sheretz* (a dead rodent) — the size of a lentil seed; a bone of a dead human — the size of a barley kernel.

47. *Niddah* 40a, Y.D. 183:1, *Shach* §3.

2. The color:

As noted above, accepted practice today considers any shade of red or black as *dam niddah*. Pure yellow, blue or green colors are not *dam niddah*. Certain shades of brown may be considered *dam niddah*, whether found on an examination cloth or on a garment, and should be shown to a Rav. Newlyweds should show <u>any</u> color (including yellow) to a Rav until they learn to properly identify different shades. See Chapter Six for the details of these *halachos*.

3. The timing:

Any discharge of uterine blood, at any time, renders a woman a *niddah*, whether the blood is part of her normal menstrual cycle, mid-cycle bleeding or any unusual and unexpected blood flow. Even a woman who has a set pattern (*vest kavuah*) for her period, and discharges blood at another unusual time, is a *niddah*. A woman who is in mid-pregnancy, is nursing or who is post menopausal becomes a *niddah* if she sees menstrual blood.

4. The form:

Dam niddah causes *tumah* regardless of whether it is liquid or dry.[48] A woman who finds a substance of questionable color in her vaginal area, on a *bedikah* cloth or on a garment, must be concerned that it may be dried blood which renders her a *niddah*. The specimen should be shown to a Rav to determine whether it is actually dried blood, mucous or a piece of dried skin. A competent Rav may be able to distinguish between them.[49] If the substance is of sufficient size, it may prove problematic even if its color has no similarity to blood. A large substance may cause *pesichas hakever* (an opening of the uterus) which renders a woman a *niddah*, even if no *dam* appears (see V below).[50]

5. The cause:

Any uterine blood flow, whether caused by natural means such as menstruation, by external influences, such as hormonal treatment, or by physical interference such as a bad fall or a gynecological examination renders a woman a *niddah*. If, however, a woman bleeds from a wound or from an abrasion to the vagina or to the cervix caused by a medical examination or any other cause, the

---

48. Y.D. 188:4.

49. See 188:4-6.

50. See 188:3.

bleeding will not necessarily cause her to become a *niddah*. Often a physician will reassure the patient that the blood found after an examination is not menstrual blood and is not a problem. This may be, but is not necessarily so. One should never rely upon the physician alone for *halachic* matters. A Rav must always be consulted. Medical evaluations may not satisfy *halachic* requirements. Often, the Rav will consult with the physician before reaching a decision. See Chapter Twenty-Three where this issue is discussed in detail.

IV. Stains — *kesamim*

According to Torah law, a woman becomes a *niddah* only if the flow is accompanied by a *hargashah* (an internal sensation). Rabbinic law, however, considers her a *niddah* even if she only finds a *kesem*. The term *kesem* refers to a stain found upon a woman's garment or upon an object upon which she has been sitting. A *kesem* differs from a *re'iyah* (an actual blood flow) because it is not associated with a *hargashah* and, secondly, it could conceivably have come from a source other than the uterus. A woman who finds a *kesem* becomes a *niddah* by Rabbinic law. There are, however, several limitations to this rule.

1. The stain must be larger than the size of a bean called a *gris*.
2. The stain must be on a white, not a colored, object.
3. The object upon which the stain is found must be susceptible to *tumah*.
4. The stain cannot, reasonably, be attributed to another source.

These and related *halachos* are discussed in detail in Book Three.

V. Opening of the uterus — *pesichas hakever*

At times, a woman may acquire *niddah* status even without any visible appearance of *dam*. For example, the Talmud[51] rules that whenever the uterus opens, one must assume that some *dam* has been discharged, thus rendering the woman a *niddah*. Accordingly, if any substance leaves the uterus, we assume that some *dam* was discharged with it, even if no *dam* is visible.[52] However, this is dependent upon the size of the substance. There

---

51. *Niddah* 21b.

52. *Y.D.* 188:3.

is disagreement among *Poskim* about the size of the opening that constitutes *pesichas hakever*. *Poskim* also disagree whether this rule is limited to an internally induced opening of the uterus or if it includes even an externally induced opening. For example, if an object (e.g., an examining instrument) is inserted into the uterus, should we assume that some *dam* was discharged due to the opening of the uterus, or should we assume that the Talmud was referring only to an internally induced opening (i.e., a piece of bodily tissue that was discharged by the body by way of the uterus)? Some opinions do not differentiate between the two;[53] others rule that only an internally induced opening is assumed to cause a discharge of *dam*.[54] This subject is discussed in detail in Chapter Twenty-Three. Some of the issues relating to *pesichas hakever* are:

A. A substance discharged from the body

If a woman finds a substance that was discharged from her body, she must be concerned about several *halachic* (as well as medical) issues. a) The substance may be dried blood, which certainly renders her a *niddah* (unless a Rav determines that its source is a wound in the vaginal area). b) Even if the substance is not red, brown or black and is not considered blood, one must be concerned that perhaps it is large enough to cause *pesichas hakever*. A Rav must be consulted.

B. Gynecological examinations

It is general practice to follow the opinion of those *Poskim* who rule that even an externally induced uterine opening causes *pesichas hakever*. Therefore, whenever a physician performs a gynecological examination utilizing an instrument that penetrates the uterus, we must be concerned that perhaps the uterus was opened sufficiently to cause *pesichas hakever*. Even if the uterus was not opened sufficiently to qualify as *pesichas hakever*, there is concern that the instrument may dislodge some uterine blood. A Rav must be consulted. The following is the general guideline regarding gynecological examinations. The subject is discussed thoroughly in Chapter Twenty-Three.

> 1. If the physician used no instrument in his examination, we assume that the uterus was not opened. Often a physician uses a speculum merely to enable him to examine the vaginal area. This

---

53. *Noda B'Yehudah* II:120, cited in *Pischei Teshuvah* 194:4.

54. *Tiferes LeMoshe* 188, see *Binas Adam* 12:13[23] and *Chazon Ish Y.D.* 83:1.

presents no problem. However, if another instrument were used, one must ascertain the type of procedure and the type of instrument and consult a Rav.

2. If no blood appeared, one may rely upon a physician who claims that he did not insert any instrument into the uterus. If, however, any blood appears, the blood itself may render her a *niddah*. Even if she herself sees no blood, but the physician informs her that there was bleeding, she may be a *niddah*. The woman should ask the physician where the blood came from and inquire, in particular, whether the instrument may have scraped her. If the physician claims that the blood is from an abrasion, she should inquire whether or not he sees the actual bruise. If he cannot locate the bruise, she should ask whether the bleeding is from the uterus. Finally, she should ask the name of the procedure. This information should be forwarded to a Rav who will decide whether or not the woman is *tehorah*.

3. A woman should not rely upon the physician to decide whether or not she is a *niddah*. Often a gynecologist may claim that he is experienced with other observant patients, has spoken to Rabbis and knows the *halachah*. One may not rely upon such claims. A physician is respected for his expertise in medical matters; indeed, a Rav does not, and should not, make assumptions on medical matters without consulting a gynecologist. Similarly, the gynecologist, even if he is learned in *halachah*, should leave *halachic* matters to a Rav, who is an expert in his field. All information provided by the physician should be presented to a Rav. As noted earlier, the Rav may wish to discuss the case with the gynecologist. Any responsible gynecologist is cooperative in such matters.

C. Contractions before childbirth

When a woman has begun the process of childbirth, her uterus opens to a degree that renders her a *niddah*. *Poskim* rule that when a woman is placed upon the travailing chair, we must be concerned that the uterus has opened to this degree and caused a discharge of *dam*.[55] Therefore, a woman who has difficulty walking due to her contractions must consider herself a *niddah*.[56] Contemporary authorities rule that neither widely spaced contrac-

---

55. The source of this ruling is Responsa *Nachlas Shivah* 9, quoted in *Pischei Teshuvah* 194:8.

56. See *Sidrei Taharah* ibid. citing *Mishnah* (*Ohalos* 7:4).

tions nor initial dilation of the uterus fall into this category.[57] Some *Poskim* rule that even if her water breaks she is not rendered a *niddah* if she can produce a clean *bedikah*, while others disagree. Some *Rabbonim* rule that if the mucous plug come out the woman becomes a *niddah* since the plug is usually accompanied with blood. Others disagree. These issues are discussed in greater detail in Chapter Twenty-Four.

VI. Childbirth

The Torah[58] ordains that a woman who gives birth (regardless of whether the child is alive or stillborn) becomes *tamei* similar to a *niddah*. The Torah law of a *yoledes* (one who gave birth) is different from the *halachah* as it is practiced today.

A. Torah law

When a woman gives birth, she is subject to two contradictory laws: a) The birth itself brings days of *tumah* (*yemei tumah*) upon her, even if the birth was unaccompanied by blood. *Tumas yoledes* (the *tumah* caused by childbirth) has nothing to do with *dam niddah*. The blood that accompanies childbirth is not necessarily *dam niddah*. Indeed, even one who gives birth without any blood becomes *tamei*. The childbirth itself, not the blood, is the cause of the *tumah*.[59] b) When the *yemei tumah* pass, she enters a stage in which she is unaffected by any *dam*, i.e. she may actually experience a blood flow and nevertheless be *tehorah*.[60] The bleeding is called *"dam tohar"* and the days are called *"yemei taharah."* The number of days that are considered *yemei tumah* and *yemei taharah* depends upon whether the woman gave birth to a male or a female. There is also a special *halachah* regarding a woman who gave birth during *zivah*.

1. Birth of a male:
After giving birth to a male, a woman is *tamei* for seven days, regardless of whether or not blood flowed as a result of the childbirth. She may be *tovel* the night following the seventh day and

---

57. See *Igros Moshe Y.D.* 2:76 and *Shiurei Sheivet HaLeivi* 194:2[4]. He notes that dilation can begin as early as the sixth month and is common by the beginning of the ninth month. This dilation is caused by the pressure of the fetus against the uterine opening, but is not a sign of imminent birth.58. *Vayikra* 12:2.

58. *Vayikra* 12:2.

59. *Y.D.* 194:1.

60. She is therefore permitted to her husband even while the *dam* is flowing.

remove the *tumah*. Seven "clean" days are not required (in this respect *tumas yoledes* is similar to that of the Torah law of *niddus*). Following this *tevilah*, she is *tehorah* for thirty-three days, even if she has a blood flow. The blood flow may be uterine blood, but the Torah decrees that she is *tehorah* nonetheless. After the passage of a total of forty days from the day of birth, the woman reverts to the status of any other woman.

2. Birth of a female:

A woman who gives birth to a female is governed by a similar rule, except that all the days are doubled. She is *tamei* for fourteen days and *tehorah* for sixty-six. After the completion of eighty days, she is governed by the same rules as any woman.

3. A Caesarean section:

A child born through a Caesarean section causes no *tumas yoledes*,[61] even if she bleeds uterine blood thorough the incision.[62] The woman will, however, become a *niddah* because of vaginal bleeding.

4. Childbirth during days of *zivah*:

In Torah law (today we are not practically affected by the laws of *zivah*) a woman who gave birth during her *yemei zivah*[63] and had a blood flow during childbirth[64] and the following two days becomes concurrently a *yoledes* and a *zavah*. Accordingly, she requires two sets of days: a) seven or fourteen days of *tumah* (depending upon whether she gave birth to a male or female) followed by b) seven "clean" days. Interestingly, the second set of days (i.e., the seven "clean" days) must be "clean" from any blood flow, even blood that is halachically *dam tohar*. For example:

---

61. *Niddah* 40a. *Y.D.* 194:14.

62. *Niddah* 41b.

63. This is certainly an unusual occurrence, since a woman has no menstrual cycle during pregnancy. Nevertheless, it is possible that a woman had a minor blood flow a week before childbirth. That blood flow rendered her a *niddah*. Her blood flow during childbirth on the following eighth day and the additional flows on the ninth and tenth day render her a *zavah*.

64. If, however, no blood was present at childbirth, she does not become a *zavah*. An interesting dispute in the Talmud (*Niddah* 37a) concerns a woman who had a flow for three consecutive *zivah* days and gave birth during her seven "clean" days without bleeding. Should the birth itself be the equivalent of a blood flow and thereby void all the seven "clean" days, should it void only the day of the birth itself or is it not considered a blood flow and irrelevant to the seven "clean" days? Most *Rishonim* rule that a birth without bleeding has no effect on the seven "clean" days, see *Tur Y.D.* 194.

a. If she bears a male, she must wait seven days and begin counting seven "clean" days. Any blood flow during the second set of seven "clean" days voids the count even though the blood is essentially *dam tohar*. Conversely, the first seven days, i.e., the seven days of *tumah* (or part thereof), may be used for her second seven days — the seven "clean" days if no *dam* appears.

b. A woman who bears a female and experiences a blood flow during delivery and the two following days may check herself before the end of the third day and begin her seven "clean" days on the following day. At the end of ten days, she has completed her seven "clean" days; however, she may not be *tovel* until the end of the fourteen days of *tumah*.[65] Thus, the seven "clean" days are counted <u>both</u> as seven "clean" days for a *zavah gedolah* and as part of the fourteen *tumah days* of a female.

> In summary: The days of *tumah* of a *yoledes* (seven or fourteen) are considered *tamei*, regardless of whether or not *dam* appeared. Similarly, days of *taharah* (thirty-three or sixty-six) are *tahor*, regardless of whether or not *dam* appears. However, the seven "clean" days of *zivah* require seven days without any blood flow, regardless of whether those days are considered days of *tumah* or days of *taharah*.

B. Rabbinic law

Rabbinic law differs from Torah law regarding childbirth in two respects. *Chazal* assumed that any opening of the uterus causes some blood flow from the uterus. This concept was discussed above. Thus, any birth must be considered a birth with uterine *dam*. Since Jewish women accepted upon themselves the custom of counting seven "clean" days after any appearance of uterine *dam*, as noted above, every birth is considered a birth with *zivah* and requires seven "clean" days.

In addition, the custom developed[66] to disregard the rule of *dam tohar*

---

65. See *Tur* and *Shulchan Aruch*, Y.D. 194:1.

66. *Ramban* (*Hilchos Niddah* 7:20, cited in *Taz* 194:1) seems to imply that this is part and parcel of the Talmudic custom quoted by *R' Zeira*. However, *Rambam* (11:5,6) cites this as a *Gaonic* innovation. He contends that the custom of *R' Zeira* applies only to *dam tamei*, not *dam tohar*.

entirely. Although originally this was subject to local custom,[67] it has been accepted by later *Rishonim* as definitive *halachah* from which one may not deviate.[68] Therefore, a woman who experiences a blood flow or merely finds a blood stain during the thirty-three days of *taharah* following a male birth or the sixty-six days of *taharah* following a female birth must treat it as any other flow and count seven "clean" days.

C. A miscarriage

The status of a woman who has a miscarriage depends upon whether or not the miscarriage took place forty days after conception. If the fetus was less than forty days old, the rules of *tumah* and *taharah* of *yoledes* do not apply; she is merely a *niddah* and may count seven "clean" days and be *tovel*. If, however, she carried the fetus for forty days or more, *tumas leidah* applies. If the fetus is unrecognizable as male or female, she must follow the more stringent *tumah* days of a female. Therefore, after the blood flow stops, she must do a *hefseik taharah* and count seven "clean" days since according to Rabbinic law every birth is considered a birth with *zivah*. However, she may not immerse herself before completion of a total of fourteen days, including the day of the miscarriage itself, since the fetus may have been female and would require fourteen days of *tumah*.

VII. Exceptions

We have discussed the various means by which a woman becomes a *niddah*. We have learned that any uterine blood discharged from the body, regardless of size or form, renders the woman a *niddah*. There are, however, exceptions. A woman may experience a blood flow without becoming a *niddah*.

A. *Teliyah bemakeh:* blood attributable to a wound

At times, a woman may find blood on a *bedikah* cloth or on a garment or even notice blood leaving her body and *halachically* be unaffected by it. If the blood is attributable to a source other than the uterus, we may, at times, assume that it is not *dam niddah*. This is dependent upon many factors and the rules differ depending upon whether she finds the blood on

---

67. See *Rambam* (11:5-7) who notes that in his time this custom was accepted in Mideastern countries and Spain, but not in France.

68. *Rema* 194:1, see *Beis Yosef* ibid. and *Darchei Moshe* no. 2 who notes that the lenient custom had already disappeared by his time.

a *bedikah* cloth or on a garment. A Rav must be consulted. These rules will be discussed in Chapter Six regarding *bedikos* and Chapter Eleven regarding garments.

B. *Dam besulim:* hymeneal bleeding

An exception in the opposite vein is *dam besulim,* hymeneal bleeding. Hymeneal blood is not *dam niddah;* it is caused by a wound and has no connection to menstrual bleeding. Thus, according to Torah law it will not render a woman a *niddah.* Nevertheless, *Chazal* decreed that hymeneal bleeding renders a woman a *niddah.* The reasons for this, and its *halachos,* will be discussed in Volume Two.

VIII. Self-declared status

A woman may acquire the status of a *niddah* by merely stating that she is a *niddah.* Her subsequent retraction may be unacceptable and she remains a *niddah* based upon the original statement.

A woman who tells her husband that she is a *niddah* is treated as a *niddah* by virtue of her statement, whether her statement was truthful or not.[69] Any subsequent claim that her statement was not serious has no validity.[70] She must be treated, and indeed she must treat herself, as if she is a *niddah.* She requires the five-day waiting period, a *hefseik taharah* and seven "clean" days. However, there are times when her retraction is accepted. These will be discussed in Chapter Four.

IX. A blood flow while cohabiting

If a woman experiences a blood flow while cohabiting, several factors must be considered. First, since she is a *niddah* immediately, she and her husband are transgressing the prohibition against relations with a *niddah.* They must immediately disengage. However, it is of utmost importance that this be done carefully and properly. The *halachos* governing this situation are found in *Shulchan Aruch.*[71] Secondly, even if the flow did not occur during cohabitation, but afterwards, there is reason to suspect that

---

69. 185:3.

70. *Shach* 185:2.

71. 185:4. One may not immediately completely disengage since withdrawal from a *niddah* during erection is punishable by *kares.* Rather, he should lift the rest of his body as much as possible by leaning on his hands and feet and wait for erection to end before totally disengaging.

marital relations may be a stimulant for her menstrual cycle. If this is proven true by occurring three times, she is forbidden to have marital relations with her husband and they should divorce. In actuality, this rarely, if ever, results in a divorce, since the bleeding can usually be attributed to another source. Nevertheless, she must take steps to determine whether or not the appearance of blood is connected to marital relations. A Rav must immediately be consulted after even one occurrence for advice as to what steps should be taken before a problem develops. These *halachos* are discussed in Chapter Fourteen, Section I,E.

CHAPTER THREE

הרגשה

Hargashah: the Sensation of a Flow

☐ The Biblical requirement of a *hargashah.*

☐ The difference between a *hargashah* and *vest haguf.*

☐ The definition of *hargashah.*

☐ Exceptions to the *hargashah* rule.

☐ A woman who feels a *hargashah.*

☐ A woman who is accustomed to feeling *hargashos.*

☐ A woman who feels an external dampness.

HALACHIC OVERVIEW

1. There are two types of sensations that will be discussed in this work. One is *vest haguf* — the physical manifestation of the approaching flow, as described in Chapter Eighteen. *Vest haguf* is the symptom; the feeling or achiness a woman may experience at the approach of her cycle but usually before menstruation. It may appear hours, or even days, before the actual onset of the flow. Another is *hargashah,* the sensation of the actual start of the flow; it is the signal that she is a *niddah* immediately. This *hargashah* is the subject of our chapter.

2. *Poskim* offer three descriptions of a *hargashah:* a) a bodily tremble associated with the onset of the menstrual flow, b) the actual feeling of the opening of the uterus, c) the sensation of an internal flow.

3. According to Torah law, a woman is not a *niddah* through the flow of menstrual blood unless it is accompanied by a *hargashah*. Rabbinic law, however, ordained that a woman may become a *niddah* even without the accompaniment of a physical sensation.

4. A woman who did a *bedikah* and found *dam* on the cloth or a woman who cleaned herself, even externally, immediately after cohabitation, and found *dam*, is *temei'ah* according to Torah law. We suspect that she actually felt a *hargashah* but mistook it for the sensation of the *bedikah* or the cohabitation.

5. There are two other sensations similar to *hargashah*. One is the sensation of a vaginal flow. Another is a feeling of dampness outside the body. While most *Poskim* rule that the sensation of a vaginal flow is not a real *hargashah,* it cannot be ignored. All authorities agree that the feeling of a dampness outside the body, without any other sensation, is not considered a *hargashah*.

6. It is very unusual for a woman to experience a sensation of the opening of the uterus, a bodily tremble associated with a blood flow or an internal flow. These *hargashos* will be discussed at length in the text of this chapter. This overview will be limited to the more common question regarding a woman who feels an external discharge or who feels a dampness outside the body.

7. A woman who feels an external discharge should do a *bedikah.*

> ◀ Any *dam*, regardless of size, found on the cloth renders her a *niddah* (even if she experienced none of the other sensations listed above).

- If she finds a color that is certainly not problematic, she is *tehorah*.
- If nothing is found on the cloth, a Rav should be consulted.
- If she finds a stain on her garment, the stain should be inspected. If it is an acceptable color, she is *tehorah*. If the stain is an unacceptable color (any size and even on a colored garment), one must ask a *sheilah*. Even a small stain on her garment cannot be disregarded if it is found after the sensation of a discharge. She must ask a *sheilah*.
- If she finds both an acceptable stain and a tiny red spot on her garment, she should ask a *sheilah*.

8. A woman who is accustomed to finding clear discharges should discuss with a Rav whether or not she should do a *bedikah* after each sensation of discharge.

- If she does a *bedikah* and finds nothing on the cloth, or if she did not do a *bedikah*, she is *tehorah*.
- In the following cases, she certainly cannot rely upon the fact that her discharges are usually clear and she must do a *bedikah*: a) the sensation of a discharge occurred on the day of her expected period, b) the sensation occurred on the thirtieth day from her last period, c) she has no established *vest* and the sensation occurred after the time that her period usually starts.
- A pregnant or nursing woman who has established that her discharges are usually clear, perhaps, may disregard any sensation of a discharge. One should ask a Rav.

9. Some authorities rule that a woman who wears a tightly fitting undergarment need not do a *bedikah* when she feels a discharge but should merely check her undergarment. If she finds an unacceptable color on the garment, even if it is less than a *gris*, she must ask a Rav.

10. A feeling of external dampness without the sensation of a discharge is not considered a *hargashah*. However, it cannot be dismissed entirely, since it indicates that some fluid may have been discharged.

11. A woman who is accustomed to feeling a sensation of dampness and has established that these feelings are usually a clear fluid, and it is not the time that she normally expects her period, should nevertheless consult a Rav as to whether she is required to do a *bedikah* each time she experiences the sensation.

12. A woman who has not established a tendency for clear discharges, and feels a dampness, should check her undergarment when convenient.

🍁 If she finds a stain on her garment, it can be treated as any *kesem*; thus, if it is less than a *gris*, she is *tehorah*.

🍁 If the garment is clean from any stain, she is *tehorah*; no further action is necessary.

I. Introduction

A. The parameters of *hargashah*

According to Torah law, a woman does not acquire the status of *niddah* through the flow of menstrual blood alone. The flow must be accompanied by a physical sensation — *hargashah*.[1] *Chazal*[2] derive this from the verse in the Torah[3] דָּם יִהְיֶה זֹבָה בִּבְשָׂרָה — *her discharge from her flesh being blood.* The word *"bivsarah"* implies that the discharge must be felt within her flesh. Thus, a mere blood flow without a physical sensation will not, according to Torah law, render a woman a *niddah*.[4]

However, Rabbinic law ordained that a woman becomes a *niddah* even without a physical sensation. Thus, if a woman experiences a flow, even without a physical sensation, she is a *niddah* according to Rabbinic law. This can occur in two ways: a) a *kesem* — a stain found on her garment, or b) a blood flow without a *hargashah*, i.e., she is certain that she felt no *hargashah*. The laws of *kesamim* are discussed in Book Three. See Appendix A and B for an analysis of the issues involved in a blood flow without a *hargashah*.[5]

There are cases when an appearance of blood gives us reason to suspect that there may have been a *hargashah*.

---

1. See *Chavos Daas* 196:3[b], that this applies to the initial flow only. However, once a woman becomes a *niddah* and requires seven "clean" days, those days must be free of any blood flow. Thus, even a blood flow without *hargashah* will invalidate the counting of the seven days according to Torah law. She must, thus, begin her seven "clean" days again.

2. *Niddah* 57b.

3. *Vayikra* 15:19.

4. *Poskim* raise a fundamental question regarding the Biblical requirement of *hargashah*. Is *hargashah* a) an absolute requisite for Biblical *tumas niddah,* or b) is it merely a means by which we verify that the blood was actually discharged from her body? In other words, if there were proof that the blood is from her body, would she be a *niddah* by Torah law, even without *hargashah*? This question is discussed in detail in Appendix A.

5. If a woman knows for certain that the blood came from her body, but she felt no sensation, she is a *niddah*, in the view of most *Poskim*, according to Rabbinic law only. However, there is a disagreement among *Poskim* as to whether or not a blood flow without a *hargashah* is completely analogous to and governed by the same rules as a *kesem*. This issue is discussed in Appendix B.

1. A woman who did an internal examination with a *bedikah* cloth and found *dam* on the cloth[6] must suspect that there was a *hargashah* as well.[7] The reason for this is that *dam* usually does appear with a *hargashah* and perhaps, in this case, she mistook[8] the *hargashah* for the sensation of the *bedikah*.[9]

2. If *dam* is found on a cloth with which she cleaned herself, even externally, immediately[10] after cohabitation, we must also sus-

---

6. See *Chavos Daas* 190 end of 1[b], who notes that this is true even if she did not find *dam* on the first *bedikah* cloth, but found blood on a second cloth with which she wiped herself externally (*kinuach*) immediately after the first *bedikah*, she must also suspect that there may have been a *hargashah*. If she does not wipe herself, but finds a *kesem* afterwards, it is considered a regular *kesem*; see Appendix A.

7. See *Sidrei Taharah* 190:93 (s.v. "ועוד כתבתי" at end), in explanation of *Rambam* 9:1, *Pleisi* 183:1, *Chavos Daas* 183:2[c], *Sidrei Taharah* 183:2 and 190:93, *Chochmas Adam* 113:30, *Pischei Teshuvah* 183:1 and *Aruch HaShulchan* 183:55. *Sidrei Taharah* ibid. and 190:1, *Chavos Daas* 187:8[b], responsa R' Akiva Eiger 1:62, and *Aruch HaShulchan* 183:55 conclude that, according to *Rambam*, when a woman finds blood on a *bedikah* cloth, we assume that she <u>certainly</u> felt a *hargashah* and is certainly *temei'ah* according to Torah law. Accordingly, in a case involving a *safek bedikah*, one cannot combine the *safek hargashah* to create a *s'fek s'feika*, see responsa *Har Tzvi, Y.D.* 152. See also *Graz* 183:3 and *Kuntres Acharon* 2 and *Tzemach Tzedek, Piskei Dinim* 183. A slightly different approach is found in responsa *R' Chaim Or Zarua* 112, who rules that if blood is found in the vagina, it is considered "*bivsarah*" — "in her flesh," even if there was no sensation. Thus, *R' Chaim Or Zarua* agrees with *Rambam*, albeit for a different reason.

8. If the woman was conscious of the possibility of *hargashah* at the time of *bedikah* but insists that she felt no *hargashah*, some *Poskim* maintain that she is not a *niddah* according to Torah law. See responsa *Neta Shashuim* 21 and *Tiferes Tzvi* 30, cited in *Lechem VeSimlah* 183:2[s], 190:2[l] and *Pische Zuta* 190:102. Others disagree (*Lechem VeSimlah* cites this view in the name of "*acharonim*"), and contend that a woman cannot differentiate between the sensation of the *bedikah* cloth and a real *hargashah*. *Pische Zuta* ibid. seems to follow this view as does *Binas Adam* 8. See also last note to *Graz* 183:3, that this can be inferred from *Tosfos*. *Chavos Daas* 190:1[b] notes that a woman certainly cannot differentiate between the sensation of cohabitation and that of a real *hargashah*. See also *Shiurei Sheivet HaLeivi* 190:54[7]. See Appendix A.

9. See *Rambam* 9:1. There are, however, two exceptions to this rule: a) *Poskim* assume that it applies only to a *bedikah*. If, however, the cloth was not inserted into the vagina, but was used merely to wipe the area externally (*kinuach*), we cannot assume that there was a *hargashah* (*Pleisi* 183:1, cited in *Lechem VeSimlah* 190:2[l]). The sensation of an external *kinuach* cannot be confused with that of a real *hargashah*. Nevertheless, even blood found on an external *kinuach* is *tamei* according to Rabbinic law. b) Similarly, there is a difference of opinion regarding a *bedikah* done internally but not deeply. Some *Poskim* imply that since it did not come near the cervix, one need not be concerned with *hargashah*; see *Sidrei Taharah* 183:2 and *Pischei Teshuvah* 183:1. See further discussion in responsa *Eimek HaTeshuvah* 1:137 and *Shaarei Taharah* 37.

10. See 187:1 and *Shach* 1 who notes that in regard to this *halachah* "immediately" refers to the time period referred to in the *Mishnah* (*Niddah* 14a) as "אחר כך." If the blood is found later than that (אחר אחר), it is not considered related to the *hargashah*. *Rema* 187:1 notes that we do not know the exact time frame of אחר כך. *Pri Deah* 190:7[sl] speculates that it is the amount of time to walk twenty-two cubits (about twelve seconds). Different *Poskim* cite different times: *Aruch HaShulchan*

pect that she mistook the *hargashah* for the sensation of the cohabitation.[11]

3. A woman who finds *dam* immediately[12] after urination must suspect that she confused the *hargashah* with the sensation of urination.[13] The practical application of this *halachah* will be discussed in Chapter Nine II,4.

In addition, any normal menstrual flow is presumed[14] to be accompanied by a physical sensation, even though it may not be consciously felt, and causes a Biblical status of *niddah*.[15]

B. The definition of *hargashah*

It should be noted at this point that *hargashah* as described in this section differs entirely from the concept of *vest haguf*

187:14 contends that it is "a very short time, only a few minutes"; *Chezkas Taharah* 187:20, closer to a half a minute and *Shiurei Sheivet HaLeivi* 187:1[11], ten minutes.

11. *Chavos Daas* 183:2[c]. However, if the blood was found on a garment after cohabitation, she is *tehorah* according to Torah law since the blood may be from another source. See *Sidrei Taharah* 190:93 s.v. "ומעתה" and s.v. "נחזור". See also Appendix A.

12. See *Igros Moshe Y.D.* 4:17[13].

13. *Chavos Daas* ibid. If the blood is found upon a garment, *Sidrei Taharah* ibid. is lenient in this case as well.

14. *Chazal* assumed that a woman experiences a *hargashah* when she menstruates. See *Niddah* 3a. *Rambam* (*Issurei Biah* 9:1), notes that if a woman finds blood in her vagina we presume that it was accompanied by a *hargashah*. Although *Rambam* is referring to a case in which the woman did a *bedikah* and we thus assume that she confused the *hargashah* with the sensation of the *bedikah* , nevertheless, if *dam* would not normally appear with *hargashah* we would have no right to assume that she confused the two sensations.

15. Many women today claim that they do not feel any inner sensation at the onset of their period. This has already been noted by responsa *Shev Yaakov* 40 and *Teshuras Shai* 457, cited in *Darchei Teshuvah* 183:6. Nevertheless, *Poskim* presume that most women who menstruate do experience a *hargashah* and are *temei'ah* according to Torah law (see *Aruch HaShulchan* 183:61,62 and *Igros Moshe, Y.D.* 4:17[12]). We assume that there must have been some sensation which, due to distraction, the woman was unaware of. Apparently, this too is considered *hargashah* (see *Rashi, Niddah* 58a and *Tosfos* 57b s.v. הרואה). Thus, even according to those opinions (see Appendix A) who maintain that *hargashah* is a necessity for *tumas niddah*, she is a *niddah* according to the Torah. Certainly, according to *Sidrei Taharah's* understanding of *Rashi, Tosfos* and *Raavad* and certainly according to *Tosfos Rid*, who maintain (see Appendix A) that whenever *dam* certainly came from the woman, she becomes a *niddah* even without a *hargashah*, the absence of *hargashah* today is irrelevant. The mere fact that the blood came from her body is sufficient to render her a *niddah* according to Torah law. Contemporary *Poskim* were certainly aware that women claim that they feel no *hargashah*. Nevertheless, not one of the *Poskim* suggests that women today are not *niddos* according to Torah law.

— the physical manifestation of the approaching flow described in Chapter Eighteen. *Vest haguf* is a sensation or symptom that an individual woman may experience at the approach of her cycle (e.g. a head, back or stomach ache). It may appear hours, a day or even several days before the actual onset of the cycle. Thus, if a woman feels a *vest haguf* ache and subsequently finds a *kesem* less than a *gris*, it may be ignored.[16] This *vest* is important as a signal that the menstrual flow is imminent: The woman will shortly become a *niddah* and precautionary measures must be observed (see Chapters Thirteen and Twenty-Two). *Hargashah*, however, is the sensation of the actual onset of the flow, the signal that she is a *niddah* immediately.[17]

Although there is no Talmudic description of *hargashah, Poskim*[18] offer three descriptions of this sensation.[19]

1. In the opinion of some *Rishonim*,[20] the feeling consists of a bodily tremble associated with the onset of the menstrual flow. Some authorities describe this as a sensation similar to the sensation when one begins to urinate.[21]

2. Other *Rishonim* define *hargashah* as the actual feeling of the opening of the uterus.[22]

3. Some authorities contend that, in addition to the above, the

---

16. See *Poseiach Shaar, Miluim* 3.

17. This distinction is clear from the manner in which *Tur* and *Shulchan Aruch* 190:1 describe *hargashah*, i.e., a sensation of the blood itself; see also *Chinuch* 207. However, responsa *Maharam Shick* (*Y.D.* 184:1) seems to interchange the conditions of *vest haguf* with those of *hargashah*. See also *Imrei Baruch* on *Chavos Daas* 189. *Pardes Rimonim* (p. 24) interprets the *Rambam* in a similar manner. However, *Aruch HaShulchan* 183:59 dismisses this interpretation of *Rambam*. He argues, quite convincingly, that since the Talmud notes that a woman may mistake a *hargashah* for the sensation of cohabitation, urination or a *bedikah*, they were referring to a *hargashah* in the cervical or vaginal area. For this reason, he even doubts whether *Rambam* really meant that a feeling of a bodily tremble is considered a *hargashah*.

18. See *Chavos Daas* 183:2[c], 190:1[c], *Sidrei Taharah* 190:1 and *Pischei Teshuvah* 183:1.

19. In footnote 17, we noted the opinion of responsa *Maharam Shick* (*Y.D.* 184:1) that any physical sensation a woman usually feels at the onset of the flow is considered a *hargashah*, not only the three types mentioned by *Poskim*.

20. *Rambam: Issurei Biah* 5:17.

21. See responsa *Chasam Sofer* (*Y.D.* 167).

22. *Terumas HaDeshen* 246, see also *Y.D.* 188:1, 190:1.

sensation of any internal flow is also considered a *hargashah*.[23] Others oppose this view entirely and maintain that the sensation of an internal flow is not a *hargashah*.[24] Some *Poskim* differentiate between different types of flows. They accept, in theory, that a sensation of an internal flow is considered a *hargashah*, but they contend that this applies only to a sensation of a flow through the uterine opening.[25] In their opinion a mere feeling of a flow within the vagina is not a *hargashah*. Most contemporary authorities follow this view that the sensation of a vaginal flow is not a *hargashah*.[26] Some authorities contend that even when a woman feels only an external flow (i.e., a flow from the vagina to the outside) we must suspect that perhaps she actually felt an internal flow.[27] All authorities agree that if she only felt a dampness outside the body, but no flow, it is not considered a *har-*

---

23. Responsa *Noda B'Yehudah* (*Y.D.* 1:55, as understood by *Chavos Daas* ibid). Although this seems to be the opinion of *Graz* as well (see *Kuntres Acharon* 193:2), *Tzemach Tzedek, Y.D.* 97[12] notes that *Graz* retracted this view and agrees with *Chavos Daas* cited below (note 25) that the sensation of an internal flow is considered a *hargashah* only if felt from the uterus. See also *Chochmas Adam* 113:1 who maintains that the sensation of a flow is a *hargashah*, but he is ambiguous as to whether he is referring to a sensation of a uterine flow or even the sensation of a vaginal flow.

24. Responsa *Chasam Sofer* (*Y.D.* 145, 153, 167 and 171). *Chasam Sofer* bases his opinion on that of his revered mentor R' Nosson Adler. In responsa 167 *Chasam Sofer* notes that this question was the subject of a dispute between responsa *Shev Yaakov* and *Maharsheishach*. *Shev Yaakov* contends that *hargashah* is the opening of the uterus while *Maharsheishach* maintains that it is the sensation of a flow. See also *Sidrei Taharah* 190:1 and *Aruch LaNer* (*Niddah* 57b).

25. *Chavos Daas* 190:1[b], responsa *Avnei Neizer, Y.D.* 223, *Tzemach Tzedek, Y.D.* 97[12] quoting *Graz*, *Yeshuos Yaakov* 183:1 and *Mahari Assad Y.D.* 194. See also *Tur* beginning of 183.

26. See responsa *Sheivet HaLeivi* 2:88, *Shiurei Sheivet HaLeivi* 190:1[2] and *Shaarei Taharah* p. 8, quoting Rav Y. S. Eliashiv.

27. *Igros Moshe, Y.D.* 4:17[7]. He maintains that a sensation of a flow from the uterus is a *hargashah*. In addition, he maintains that one should suspect any sensation of an internal (vaginal) flow as being a sensation of a uterine flow since women are unable to differentiate between the two. Indeed, for this reason, he contends that even if a woman merely felt fluid leaving the vagina (external flow), we must suspect that there may have been a *hargashah*. However, if she merely feels an external dampness, there is no problem of *hargashah*. A similar position is taken by *Sheivet HaLeivi* (5:113) who, although in principle, agrees with *Chasam Sofer*, nevertheless notes that it is difficult to be lenient today with regard to an external flow since many women are confused as to what type of flow they actually felt. It is interesting to note that R' Baruch Frenkel (*Baruch Taam*), in his notes on *Noda B'Yehudah* (ibid. printed as appendix to *Yoreh Deah* section of *Noda B'Yehudah*), questions the entire premise and possibility of a sensation of a uterine flow. He contends that it is physically impossible to feel a flow inside the body (for example, one cannot sense the movement of urine from the bladder). Sensation of a flow is only possible when the fluid is warmer than the area into which it is flowing or when a fluid leaves the body. It would therefore be impossible for a woman to feel blood flowing from the

gashah.[28] In the course of this chapter, we will use the term "uterine flow" when referring to a flow from the uterus to the vagina, the term "vaginal flow" when referring to a flow in the vagina itself and the term "external flow" or "external discharge" when referring to a flow from the vagina through the vaginal opening.

II. A woman who experiences a *hargashah*

We noted above that a woman who has a blood flow but feels no internal physical sensation is not a *niddah* according to Torah law. The discharge of blood without any *hargashah* renders her a *niddah* only according to Rabbinic law. In this section, we will discuss the opposite case: the status of a woman who feels a *hargashah* but finds no *dam.*

A woman who feels a *hargashah* but finds no blood must be concerned that perhaps even a minute amount of uterine blood accompanied that sensation.[29] Certainly, a *hargashah* alone will not render her a *niddah,* but it should give us cause for concern that perhaps some blood accompanied the sensation. If so, what steps must be taken? We will discuss the three *hargashos* listed above.

It is very unusual nowadays for a woman to experience a sensation of the opening of the uterus, a bodily tremble associated with a blood flow or even a sensation of a uterine flow. The only *hargashos* that are quite common is perhaps the feeling of a vaginal flow or, more commonly, an external discharge which, in the opinion of most *Poskim,* is not considered a *hargashah.* We will, nevertheless, discuss the *halachos* pertaining to a woman who feels a real *hargashah,* since they are the basis of the rules that apply to a sensation of any discharge. The *halachos* of the sensation of a vaginal flow and an external discharge are discussed in section B.

---

uterus to the vagina. Apparently R' B. Frenkel was not concerned about a vaginal flow from the body since he maintained that the sensation of fluid leaving the body is certainly not *hargashah.* The view of R' B. Frenkel stands in total contrast to that of *Igros Moshe.*

28. *Igros Moshe* ibid. *Sheivet HaLeivi* ibid.

29. An exception to this is a woman who feels a *hargashah* during cohabitation. See *Chavos Daas* 190 end of 1[b] who notes that during cohabitation it is impossible to differentiate between a *hargashah* of *dam* and a *hargashah* of the cohabitation itself. Thus, a woman who feels a *hargashah* during cohabitation need not separate from her husband. However, *Chavos Daas* must concede that if she feels a distinct *hargashah* of her menstruation she must tell her husband since *Shulchan Aruch* (Y.D. 185:4) instructs the husband of the necessary course of action in this case.

A. A real *hargashah*

A woman who feels the sensation of an opening of the uterus, a bodily tremble[30] or even a uterine flow should immediately[31] do a *bedikah*[32] to ascertain whether or not she discharged *dam*.[33]

1. If *dam* is found on the cloth, she is a *niddah*, even according to Torah law. As in all *bedikos*, even the smallest stain found on the cloth renders a woman a *niddah*. This particular *bedikah* is stricter yet. A common *bedikah* renders her a *niddah* because there <u>may</u> have been a *hargashah*. The *dam* on this *bedikah* cloth <u>certainly</u> was accompanied by a *hargashah*; therefore, it unquestionably renders her *temei'ah*, even according to Torah law.[34]

2. If, upon inspecting the cloth, she finds[35] an acceptable color, she

---

30. *Poskim* equate these two *hargashos*. Note, however, that *Chochmas Adam* 113:1 (cited in *Pischei Teshuvah* 190:4) believes that a bodily tremble is not considered a *hargashah* for certain. In his opinion, if she experiences a bodily tremble, checks herself and finds nothing, she is *tehorah*. *Aruch HaShulchan* 183:59 seems less than sure that a bodily tremble is considered a *hargashah*. While *Taharas Yisrael* 190:9 follows this opinion, *Chasam Sofer, Y.D.* 150, and *Maharam Shick* 186 disagree and maintain that a bodily tremble is a *hargashah*. Since other *Poskim* do not mention the view of *Chochmas Adam*, one may assume that they, too, disagree. In short, in the opinion of *Chochmas Adam*, the descending order of *hargashos*, in significance, is: 1) internal discharge, 2) opening of the uterus and 3) bodily tremble. In the opinion of other authorities the order is: 1) opening of the uterus, 2) bodily tremble and 3) internal discharge.

31. *Y.D.* 188:1 refers to an immediate *bedikah*, "ובדקה מיד." The advantage of an immediate *bedikah* is twofold: a) If the *bedikah* is immediate and clean, some *Poskim* rule that she is *tehorah*; see note 47[b]. b) If the *bedikah* is not immediate, some *Poskim* rule that even if she finds a clear discharge, she is *temei'ah*, since a minute speck of blood may have been lost in the interim or the clear discharge may not be associated with the *hargashah*. See note 35 for a definition of "immediate."

32. See *Pische Zuta* 190:5, who notes that if she checks herself externally (i.e., she wipes the outside of the vaginal opening) and finds either blood or a clear discharge, she need not do any further *bedikah*. See note 39 below.

33. *Poskim* raise a fundamental question: Is the purpose of this *bedikah* merely to discover a cause for the *hargashah*, or is it also to ascertain that the *hargashah* was not caused by *dam*? In other words, is it sufficient for the *bedikah* to show that the *hargashah* may have been caused by a clear discharge, or must the *bedikah* prove that no blood appeared? This question is discussed in Appendix C.

34. See footnote 7, that even when a woman finds blood on a regular *bedikah* cloth, according to some *Poskim* we are <u>certain</u> that she experienced a *hargashah*.

35. *Chavos Daas* 188:2[b], 190:3[b] maintains that if she did not do the *bedikah* immediately, she is *temei'ah*, even if she subsequently finds an acceptable color (see *Darchei Teshuvah* 188:17, for a difference of opinion as to what constitutes "immediate"). See *Badei HaShulchan* 188:1 s.v. "ובדקה" who explains (indeed *Chavos Daas* 190:37[b] alludes to this himself) that *Chavos Daas* is consistent with his view (see Appendix C), that the purpose of the *bedikah* is not only to find a clear discharge as an alternate cause of the *hargashah*, but to prove definitely that there was no *dam*. Therefore, if the *bedikah* was not immediate, we must be concerned that perhaps a minute amount of *dam* was

may attribute the sensation to that discharge and she is *tehorah*.[36]

3. If she finds a stain[37] on her garment[38] before she does a *bedikah*:

---

lost and the clear discharge appeared later. While other *Poskim* disagree in principle with *Chavos Daas*, they give no clear limit as to how late the *bedikah* may be done. See *Sidrei Taharah* 190:4, who assumes that a clear mucous found on a *bedikah* done later cannot be attributed to the *hargashah*. Nevertheless, he is uncertain how immediate the *bedikah* must be. *Igros Moshe Y.D.* 4:17[10] seems to follow the stricter view of *Chavos Daas* that a *bedikah* done later is useless. See also *Shiurei Sheivet HaLeivi* 190:1[12],who rules that if she did the *bedikah* more than thirty minutes after the *hargashah*, it is ineffective. Responsa *Tiferes Tzvi* (R' Tzadok HaCohen) 1[8] rules that even if she did the *bedikah* much later, it is acceptable, but he sets no time limit. *Aruch HaShulchan* 190:8 takes an extremely lenient view. He rules that if an acceptable color was found within twenty-four hours of the *hargashah*, she is *tehorah*. *Taharas Yisroel* 190:6 follows his view. In contrast, responsa *Tzemach Tzedek Y.D.* 133[3,5] takes an extremely stringent view. He is doubtful whether or not a *bedikah* done even two or three minutes later is effective. In summary: We have no consensus among *Poskim* regarding how closely the *bedikah* must follow the *hargashah*. *Tzemach Tzedek* (*Piskei Dinim* 190:1) leaves the decision to the discretion of the Rav. However, If the woman finds a clear mucous on an undergarment that she was wearing at the time, she is *tehorah*.

36. *Y.D.* 188:1. See *Chasam Sofer* 168, who contends that if only a light fluid, commonly found in the vagina, is found on the cloth, it cannot be attributed to the *hargashah*. *Maharsham* (cited in *Pische Zuta* 190:5) rules that if the cloth is merely damp, the dampness cannot be attributed to the *hargashah* but if the mucous has some substance it may be considered the source of the *hargashah*. Responsa *Tiferes Tzvi, Hil. Niddah* 1[8], seems to disagree completely with *Chasam Sofer*. Indeed, it seems from *Terumas HaDeshen* (the original source of this *halachah*) that he is more lenient regarding a thinner mucous than a thicker one. If one would accept *Maharsham's* modification of *Chasam Sofer's* view, the *halachah* would be as follows: If the fluid is merely a dampness without any substance, it cannot be attributed to the *hargashah* since such dampness is always found in the vagina. If the fluid is a mucous of some substance it can be attributed to the *hargashah*. If the mucous is thick and similar in consistency to blood, *Terumas HaDeshen* essentially attributes the *hargashah* to the mucous, but is hesitant to rule leniently since the mucous may be confused with actual blood. See also *Shiurei Sheivet HaLeivi* 190:1[11] and *Pische Zuta* cited in note 39. One can contemplate on the purpose of the "clean" *bedikah*. Is it merely to show that the clear discharge <u>may</u> be the result of the *hargashah*, or must it show that <u>in all probability</u> the clear discharge came from the *hargashah*? The above-mentioned ruling of *Chasam Sofer* flows from his understanding of the purpose of this *bedikah*. As noted in Appendix C, *Chasam Sofer* seems to disagree with *Chavos Daas* regarding whether or not the *bedikah* must prove that no *dam* is present. However, *Chasam Sofer* requires that the *bedikah* prove that there is a possible explanation for the *hargashah* other than *dam*. Accordingly, *Chasam Sofer* contends that a light fluid which is normally found in the vagina does not prove that the fluid is attributable to the *hargashah*. Similarly, in responsa 180 regarding a woman who checked herself with a cloth that may have been previously soiled and found only a clear discharge, *Chasam Sofer* rules that she is *temei'ah*. Had the purpose of the *bedikah* been to show that the *hargashah* may have produced a clear discharge, the *bedikah* would have been valid. However, since, in the opinion of *Chasam Sofer*, the purpose is to show that the discharge most probably is from the *hargashah*, this *bedikah* is not acceptable. See note 45 below.

37. It would seem that if the stain was found shortly after her *hargashah* but is dry, it cannot be attributed to the *hargashah*.

38. In an area where blood may have fallen from her vagina; see Chapter Ten.

a. If the color of the stain is acceptable, she is *tehorah* and need not do a *bedikah*.[39]

b. If she finds a red (or any unacceptable color) stain (even less than a *gris*) on her garment (even a colored garment) subsequent to this *hargashah*, she is a *niddah*.[40] Any further *bedikah* is inconsequential.

c. If she finds a stain larger than a *gris*, but she thinks it can be attributed to a source outside her body, she is *temei'ah*

---

39. *Pische Zuta* 190:5, responsa *Sheivet HaLeivi* 2:88 and *Shiurei Sheivet HaLeivi* 190:1[12]. *Pische Zuta* seems to be referring to any garment, while *Sheivet HaLeivi* is referring to a tightly fitting garment. (In his responsa, *Sheivet HaLeivi* was referring to a case of a *hargashah* of a flow or a discharge, which essentially are not considered *hargashos*. However, in *Shiurei Sheivet HaLeivi*, he was referring to a real *hargashah*.) The clear stain found on her garment is even more effective than a *bedikah* in two respects:

a) *Pische Zuta* cites an opinion that an external *bedikah* is even more acceptable than an internal one. An internal *bedikah* will usually produce a light fluid which is not necessarily attributable to the *hargashah*, as noted above, while a discharge found upon an external *bedikah* is usually a thicker mucous, more attributable to the *hargashah*. Similarly, a clear stain found upon her garment is a better indication than a *bedikah* that the *hargashah* was caused by mucous, not blood. (However, we noted in Appendix C, that in the opinion of *Chavos Daas* the purpose of the *bedikah* is not just to show an alternate cause of the *hargashah* but to prove that there was no *dam*. Accordingly, they could not accept the view of *Pische Zuta*, since an external *bedikah* and certainly a discharge on the garment does not prove that there was no blood in the vagina. Furthermore, according to *Chasam Sofer Y.D.* 180, cited in Appendix C, the garment would have to be one that was checked for cleanliness before the *hargashah*; otherwise, the clear stain is not necessarily attributable to the *hargashah*.)

b) If the garment upon which the stain was found is a tightly fitting garment, i.e., an undergarment, there is an additional reason why the stain found on it is more effective than a *bedikah*. We noted in footnote 31 that if the *bedikah* is not done immediately after the *hargashah*, it may be ineffective since there is the possibility that a drop of blood may have appeared and subsequently dissolved. However, a garment that was worn throughout the time of the *hargashah* certainly caught any blood that may have left the body; thus, the garment could be considered a *bedikah* done immediately. See *Tiferes Tzvi* cited in note 47[c].

40. The reason that a *kesem* needs a minimum size and is *tamei* only on a white garment is because a *kesem* is not associated with *hargashah* and thus is not *tamei* according to Torah law. In this case, she experienced a *hargashah*; therefore, these limitations do not apply. If there is reason to suspect that the stain came from another source, a Rav should be consulted. See *Binas Adam* 16, and *Tiferes Tzvi* cited in *Pischei Teshuvah* 190:3. It seems from *Chasam Sofer, Y.D.* 167 that he disagrees with this. *Chasam Sofer* argues that if a woman felt a *hargashah* and checked herself with a cloth that was not previously checked for cleanliness, she is *temei'ah*. Had he held the same regarding a *kesem*, he would have noted so. See *Shaarei Tohar* 10:11, who contends that if the *kesem* was noticed twenty-four hours after the *hargashah*, the *hargashah* is inconsequential to the *kesem* (even though she wore the garment throughout the twenty-four period). However, she obviously must still contend with the *hargashah* itself.

(unless she is accustomed to finding clear discharges). Since she felt a discharge we are led to believe that the stain is from her body rather than a foreign source.[41]

4. If a woman does a *bedikah* with a cloth that was not checked for cleanliness beforehand,[42] and finds both an acceptable color and a tiny red spot on the cloth, she must consult a Rav.[43] *Poskim* disagree as to whether she can attribute the larger acceptable stain to the *hargashah* and ignore the red spot that is less than a *gris*.[44]

5. If she finds both an acceptable color and a tiny red spot on her garment, she should ask a *sheilah*.[45]

6. If nothing is found on the *bedikah* cloth or on her garment, we must assume that a minute amount of *dam* left the uterus and renders her a *niddah*.[46] A Rav should be consulted.[47]

---

41. Responsa *Pri Hasadeh* 3:61, cited in *Darchei Teshuvah* 190:16.

42. See Chapter Five, where we noted that one must use a cloth that was checked beforehand.

43. Had she not felt a *hargashah*, she would be *tehorah*, since the red spot is less than a *gris* and the cloth was not checked beforehand; *Y.D.* 190:36. A small spot on a cloth that was not pre-checked may be attributable to blood from lice. Since, in previous times, lice were very prevalent, *Chazal*, in certain cases, permitted a *bedikah* cloth upon which a stain less than a *gris* was found. The parameters of this *halachah* are set forth in *Shulchan Aruch* ibid. Note that this case of a cloth that was not pre-checked is unique and applies only to a cloth that was never checked or washed. One should not assume that a regular *bedikah* with a small stain can be permitted.

44. See responsa *Givas Shaul* 67 (cited in *Pischei Teshuvah* 188:5) who is lenient in this case. However, *Chavos Daas* (190:69[c] cited in *Pischei Teshuvah* 190:6) rules that she is *temei'ah* since most *hargashos* are caused by *dam*. This opinion is shared by responsa *Beis Shlomo* (*Y.D.* 2:36) and *Chasam Sofer* (*Y.D.* 150). *Maharam Shick* (*Y.D.* 186) rules that if the red spot is less than the size of commonly found lice, she is *tehorah*. If the spot is larger than lice (or if lice are not common), she is *temei'ah* even though the spot is less than a *gris* (see note 59). See also *Sheivet HaLeivi* 4:104. In Appendix C, we discussed the view of *Chavos Daas* that the purpose of the *bedikah* is to prove that there was no *dam*. Accordingly, in this case, she is certainly *temei'ah*, since there was a speck of *dam* which cannot be proven not to be associated with her *hargashah*.

45. In the opinion of *Chavos Daas* 190:37[b], she is *temei'ah*. Perhaps, in the opinion of *Givas Shaul* cited above, she is *tehorah*. On one hand, this case is more lenient than the case cited above, since we are dealing with a *kesem* rather than a *bedikah* cloth. Conversely, it can be argued, the previous case is more lenient since the red spot on the *bedikah* cloth that was not checked beforehand can be more easily attributed to another source. The stain on a pre-checked garment is more difficult to attribute to a foreign source. See *Chasam Sofer* (*Y.D.* end of 180), who seems to be lenient in this case (although he adds that one who is strict is praiseworthy). However, following the view of *Chasam Sofer* cited in Appendix C, she should be required to do a *bedikah* to ascertain that no blood left her body.

46. Most fluids leaving the uterus are blood; thus, since she felt fluid leave the uterus, it must be assumed to be blood (see *Chochmas Adam* 113:1).

47. See *Y.D.* 190:1 based upon *Terumas HaDeshen*. A Rav must bear in mind the following considerations:

a) Although *Shulchan Aruch* and practically all *Poskim* follow the ruling of *Terumas HaDeshen* that she is considered a *niddah*, it is noteworthy that *Rema* (*Darchei Moshe* 188:2),responsa *Radvaz* 1:149 and responsa *Sheilas Yaavetz* 2:5 are very skeptical of the *Terumas HaDeshen's* conclusion. See *Sidrei Taharah* 190:3, that even *Beis Yosef* is hesitant with regard to this *halachah*. See responsa *Divrei Chaim* (*Y.D.* 1:34) who establishes that *Ramban* (*Niddah* 12a) disagrees with *Terumas HaDeshen*. Thus, although most *Poskim* and *Shulchan Aruch* follow the opinion of *Terumas HaDeshen,* the opinions of *Radvaz* and *Sheilas Yaavetz* are applied in cases when other lenient considerations are appropriate. See also *Darchei Teshuvah* 190:24, citing *Teshuvah MeAhavah*.

b) If she checked herself immediately upon feeling the *hargashah* and found nothing, *Pleisi* 190:3, rules that she is *tehorah*. *Chavos Daas* §2[c] disagrees. *Pischei Teshuvah* §5,6 infers that *Sidrei Taharah* follows the opinion of *Pleisi* (as does responsa *Tzemach Tzedek* 132). However, *Noda B'Yehudah* (*Y.D.* 2:119) follows the stringent opinion of *Chavos Daas*, as does *Aruch HaShulchan* 190:6,13. Responsa *Chasam Sofer* (*Y.D.* 168) is undecided on the issue. Responsa *Tzemach Tzedek, Y.D.* 133[5] relies upon the lenient position of *Radvaz* cited above if she did the *bedikah* up to two minutes after the *hargashah* and nothing was found. Those *Poskim* who follow the stricter view feel that the speck of blood may have been diluted and dissipated during those seconds before the *bedikah*. See *Noda B'Yehudah* (*Y.D.* 2:119) who concedes that if she did an immediate *bedikah* but checked it only much later and found nothing, one may assume that there may have been a clear discharge which has since dried. She is therefore *tehorah*. *Tiferes Tzvi* 190 end of 1, and *Mekor Chaim* 6, cited in *Darchei Teshuvah* 190:17, take an opposite view. They argue that, on the contrary, a *bedikah* that was done later is better, in this case. They contend that our assumption that the *hargashah* must be associated with blood is true only if she did the *bedikah* soon after the *hargashah* and no blood was found. In this case, we have no choice but to assume that a bit of blood must have been lost, since the *hargashah* must be attributed to something. If, however, she did the *bedikah* much later, the *hargashah* is attributable to a clear discharge that may have since dried.

In summary: If the woman checked herself immediately after the *hargashah* and found nothing, *Pleisi, Sidrei Taharah* and *Tzemach Tzedek* rule that she is *tehorah*. *Chavos Daas, Noda B'Yehudah* and *Aruch HaShulchan* consider her a *niddah*. If she did the *bedikah* a significant while after the *hargashah, Tiferes Tzvi* and *Mekor Chaim* rule that she is *tehorah*.

c) See *Tiferes Tzvi* (R' Tzadok HaCohen) 2:1[14], who maintains that a garment worn tightly against the body is considered a *bedikah* for these purposes. Thus, since women wear undergarments, it should be considered as if she did a *bedikah* immediately (or, better yet, at the time of the *hargashah* itself). Thus, according to *Pleisi, Sidrei Taharah* and *Tzemach Tzedek*, she is *tehorah*. Perhaps, in this case, even *Chavos Daas* would concede (since there is less chance of a speck of blood being lost). Furthermore, we noted that according to *Noda B'Yehudah*, if she did not inspect the *bedikah* cloth until much later, we can assume that there may have been a clear discharge that has since dried. Accordingly, if she did not check her undergarment until later, perhaps she may similarly assume that a clear discharge has already dried. Thus, in this case, all *Poskim* would agree that she is *tehorah*. However, *Igros Moshe Y.D.* 4:17[10] rules that even if she was wearing tightly fitting undergarments, she is *temei'ah*, since a minute amount of blood may have been discharged and lost. He holds this view even if the woman only felt an external discharge, not an opening of the uterus. One may find a basis for his opinion in the words of *Terumas HaDeshen* cited in *Beis Yosef* beginning of 190, who notes that the reason a woman is *temei'ah* after experiencing a *hargashah* and finding nothing is because a minute amount of blood may have dissolved (presumably, in the vaginal fluid). Therefore, the fact that she wears a tightly fitting garment is immaterial.

d) *Toras HaShelamim* 190:2, *Pischei Teshuvah* 190:7 and *Chochmas Adam* 113:2 rule that a pregnant or nursing woman who felt an opening of the uterus and found nothing on her *bedikah* cloth is

7. If she is not completely certain that she felt a sensation, she

tehorah. These women usually do not have menstrual bleeding and commonly find other discharges. *Sidrei Taharah* 190:3 seems to accept this view. See, however, R' Akiva Eiger 190:1, who cites dissenting opinions. *Chasam Sofer, Y.D.* 168, also disagrees with *Toras HaShelamim,* while *Graz* 190:2, *Taharas Yisrael* 190:13 and *Aruch HaShulchan* 190:13 follow the lenient opinion of *Toras HaShelamim. Aruch HaShulchan* adds that a woman after menopause shares this status. Responsa *Beis Shlomo, Y.D.* 36, contends that *Toras HaShelamim* was lenient only if she checked herself and found nothing. If, however, she never checked herself, *Toras HaShelamim* concedes that she is *temei'ah. Chazon Ish* 89:1 is lenient only if the woman has actually established that she sees clear discharges during pregnancy. With this differentiation, he reconciles the apparent dispute among the *Poskim* cited above, as follows: *Toras HaShelamim* was referring to a pregnant woman who usually finds clear discharges, while those that oppose his view were referring to a woman who does not. See *Shiurei Sheivet HaLeivi* 190:1[14], who rules that only a woman who is actually nursing can be included in this *halachah,* not a woman within twenty-four months of childbirth, even though she has the status of a nursing woman regarding other *halachos.*

In summary: *Toras HaShelamim, Pischei Teshuvah, Chochmas Adam, Sidrei Taharah, Graz, Taharas Yisrael* and *Aruch HaShulchan* rule that a pregnant or nursing woman who felt a *hargashah* and found nothing on her *bedikah* is *tehorah. Chasam Sofer* and others cited in R' Akiva Eiger consider her a *niddah. Chazon Ish* is lenient only if the woman usually finds clear discharges during her pregnancy.

e) See *Daas Torah* 190:1, citing *Mei Niddah* that if a woman who has a *vest kavuah* feels a *hargashah* at a time other than her expected period and finds nothing on the *bedikah* cloth, she is *tehorah.* This is also the opinion of *Chazon Ish Y.D.* 89:1, cited above. *Daas Torah* notes that *Chasam Sofer, Y.D.* 168, disagrees. Actually, all *Poskim* cited in d) who do not differentiate between a pregnant woman and one who is not pregnant would certainly disagree with *Mei Niddah.*

f) Some *Poskim* are lenient (in certain cases) regarding a woman who checked herself three times after *hargashos* and found nothing. She has established that her *hargashos* do not imply that there was *dam.* Apparently, these *Poskim* felt that it was farfetched to assume that each time a *hargashah* was felt, a minute amount of blood was lost. Thus, in the future, if she finds nothing after a *hargashah,* she is *tehorah.* See *Darchei Teshuvah* 188:18 citing responsa *Shaarei Deah,* and 190:15, citing *Tuv Taam Vodaas.* See also *Darchei Teshuvah* 190:22 and *Daas Torah* 190:1 citing *Mei Niddah.* Note that these *Poskim* were referring to specific cases, not establishing a regular guideline. The *halachos* regarding this woman will be discussed in 8 below.

g) *Shiurei Sheivet HaLeivi* 190:1[11] contends that the rule of the *Terumas HaDeshen* is merely a *chumra* (stringency) based upon *safek* (doubt). Therefore, whenever there are additional doubts, one may be lenient.

h) Occasionally, a Rav realizes that a woman may only be imagining that her uterus opened. See *Shiurei Sheivet HaLeivi* 190:1[11], who notes that most women cannot even describe the sensation of the opening of the uterus. Therefore, if the Rav feels that the woman is unduly nervous and obsessive about *hargashos,* he should convince her to ignore the imagined sensations. However, if she is insistent and positive that she felt an opening of the uterus, he has no choice but to declare her *temei'ah.* Therefore, if the Rav feels that she is only imagining the *hargashos,* he should consider ruling that she is *tehorah* without giving a reason. A woman who is compulsive about *hargashos* will not accept his suggestion that the *hargashos* are a product of her imagination.

i) If neither of these lenient factors apply (i.e., she did not check herself immediately, she is not pregnant or nursing and the Rav is unwilling to rely upon any of the other leniencies) and the should nevertheless do a *bedikah*.[48] If nothing is found, she may consider herself *tehorah*.[49]

8. A woman who is accustomed to feeling her uterus open and finding only clear[50] (or any non-problematic) discharges[51] may nevertheless be required to check herself each time that this sensation occurs.[52] If she checks herself and finds no discharge at all, some *Poskim* rule that she is *tehorah*.[53] One should consult a

woman is told that she is a *niddah*, she should not recite a *b'rachah* upon her *tevilah* (*Shiurei Sheivet HaLeivi* 190:1[11]) since we are not absolutely certain that she had a blood flow. *Aruch HaShulchan* 200:1 rules that one recite a *b'rachah* on any *tevilah* required by *halachah*. It seems that this would apply in our case as well.

48. *Aruch HaShulchan* 190:13.

49. This ruling is based upon the fact that even if she certainly felt a sensation, but found no blood, her *tumah* is only that of a doubtful status (*safek*) because we are not sure that there actually was *dam*. Thus if, in addition, she is unsure as to whether or not she had a *hargashah*, it is merely a *s'fek s'feika* (a double doubt), see responsa *Noda B'Yehudah* 2:118,119, *Teshuvah MeAhavah* 3:363 and *Aruch HaShulchan* (ibid.).

50. See note 36. It would seem that similarly, in this case, this applies only a woman who actually finds discharges of substance. If she merely finds a dampness on the cloth, it cannot be attributed to the *hargashah*.

51. See responsa *Divrei Chaim*, Y.D. 1:34, 2:66. He was referring to a woman who had checked herself thoroughly many times in the past and often even had a cloth (*moch*) or a tampon inside her vagina at the time she experienced the *hargashah*, yet always found a clear discharge. It would seem, from *Divrei Chaim* presenting the situation in this manner, that three mere *bedikos* do not suffice to establish that her discharges are usually clear. However, *Maharsham* (*Daas Torah* 190:1) cites responsa *Shaarei Tzedek* 138, who accepts the validity of simply checking three times. (*Divrei Chaim* is referring to the *hargashah* of internal discharge, not the opening of the uterus. We are merely using his definition of the term "accustomed" regarding her seeing clear discharges.) See also *Igros Moshe*, Y.D., 4:17[9], who stipulates that she must establish this fact for each of her varied activities, i.e., during work, resting, day or night. If she established that she finds clear discharges during one type of activity, it has no bearing upon a *hargashah* during a different type of activity.

52. *Aruch HaShulchan* 190:9. However, *Badei HaShulchan* 188:22 relies upon *Tiferes Tzvi*, cited above, that a tight-fitting undergarment is considered a *bedikah* regarding this *halachah*. Thus, she is only required to check her garment at a later time.

53. See *Chochmas Adam* 113:3, who rules that she is *tehorah*. Even though *Chochmas Adam* is referring to the *hargashah* of internal discharge, we may infer that it would apply to the sensation of the opening of the uterus as well, since *Chochmas Adam* 113:1 equates the two, as does *Aruch HaShulchan* 190:9. Most other *Poskim* (the oft-quoted *Divrei Chaim* and *Maharsham*) who mention the concept of a woman accustomed to feeling *hargashos* are referring to the sensation of an internal flow, not the sensation of opening of the uterus. We have no reason, however, to assume that they differentiate between the two. *Badei HaShulchan* 188:22 is uncertain whether one may rely upon these opinions during the days that she normally menstruates. For example, if she normally menstruates between the the twenty-fifth and twenty-ninth days, can she ignore *hargashos* that she feels during those days? During this time, it is equally probable that the *hargashah* is from her

Rav.[54] If she finds a small red spot on her garment, she should consult a Rav.[55]

B. A woman who feels a discharge

Most questions of *hargashah* today do not pertain to a sensation of an opening of the uterus or even of a flow directly from the uterus, since both of these sensations are rare. Rather, most questions about *hargashos* deal with a sensation of a vaginal flow or an external discharge. Although we noted earlier that most *Poskim* maintain that these sensations are not considered a *hargashah*, *Poskim* advise a woman to do a *bedikah* after experiencing such a sensation.[56]

1. Results of the *bedikah*:

a. If any *dam* is found on the cloth, she is certainly a *niddah*. A stain of any size on a *bedikah* cloth renders her a *niddah*, even without a sensation.

b. If she finds a color that is certainly not blood, she is *tehorah*. We may attribute the sensation to the discharge of the color she found.[57]

---

period as from clear discharges. *Chazon Ish*, *Y.D.* 89:1, is lenient regarding a pregnant or nursing woman or a woman with a *vest kavuah* who usually finds clear stains. It would seem that he would also be lenient regarding a woman without a *vest kavuah* but who never menstruates before certain days (the *Terumas HaDeshen's vest*; see Chapter Fourteen I,D,2,d).

54. *Poskim* note that responsa *Beis Shlomo* 2:36 and responsa *Beis Yitzchok* 2:15 disagree with *Chochmas Adam*. *Taharas Yisroel* 190:4 does not rely upon *Chochmas Adam* regarding a sensation of the opening of the uterus. Similarly, responsa *Tzemach Tzedek, Y.D.* 133[7], relies upon *Chochmas Adam's* opinion only regarding a sensation of a discharge. One would assume that even those *Poskim* cited by R' Akiva Eiger 190:1, who hold that a pregnant woman is no different than any other regarding *hargashos*, would concede that a woman accustomed to clear discharges is *tehorah*; see *Chazon Ish* 89:1, cited above (note 47[d]). *Divrei Chaim, Y.D.* 1:34, raises a novel point: We know that a woman who has a bleeding wound in the uterine area may attribute any blood that she may find to that wound. Thus, he argues, even if we accept *Terumas HaDeshen's* premise that a *hargashah* is analogous to a blood flow, why can't we attribute all the *hargashos* of a woman who usually finds only clear discharges to clear discharges?

55. See *Binas Adam* 113 end of [16].

56. Most contemporary *Poskim* do not exempt her from a *bedikah*. See, however, *Aruch HaShulchan* 190:9.

57. We have seen above A,2, that even a real *hargashah* may be disregarded if one finds a clear color on the *bedikah* cloth. A sensation of a discharge, which is not really a *hargashah*, may certainly be disregarded. Indeed, even those who require the *bedikah* to immediately follow a real *hargashah* (see note 31) would concede that, in this case, it is not necessary. See *Tzemach Tzedek, Y.D.* 133[6],

c. If nothing is found, perhaps we should assume that a minute amount of *dam* left the uterus and was subsequently lost. A Rav should be consulted.[58]

d. If she finds both an acceptable color and a tiny red spot on a *bedikah* cloth that was not checked beforehand, she should consult a Rav.[59]

e. If she is not completely certain that she felt a sensation,

---

who is lenient in this case. However, if the woman feels a discharge during her seven "clean" days, *Tzemach Tzedek* (ibid. 7) requires that she do the *bedikah* within two minutes of the *hargashah*. We noted above that most other *Poskim* oppose this view and accept a *bedikah* done later, even if she felt a real *hargashah* and even during the seven "clean" days.

58. See note 47 above. In this case, we have more reason to be lenient since *Chasam Sofer* dismisses the entire concept of a feeling of a discharge being considered a *hargashah*. *Chasam Sofer* (Y.D. 150) contends that even if we concede to the *Noda B'Yehudah* (which he does not) that a sensation of discharge is a *hargashah*, it is only relevant if she actually finds *dam*. The *dam* is then considered a flow with a *hargashah*. However, if she finds nothing, we certainly cannot consider her a *niddah*. *Divrei Chaim*, Y.D. 2:66, follows *Chasam Sofer's* ruling in this case. *Chasam Sofer*, however, is not lenient regarding a sensation of discharge on the day of her expected *vest*; see also *Pische Zuta* 184:11. See also *Shiurei Sheivet HaLeivi* 190:1[11], who is lenient based upon the above considerations. However, *Chochmas Adam* 113:1 rules that even in the case of a sensation of a discharge (which he considers an absolute *hargashah*), if nothing is found, she is *temei'ah*. A similar position is taken by *Igros Moshe* Y.D. 4:17[8], who rules that she is *temei'ah*. *Darchei Teshuvah* 190:14 cites conflicting views on the matter. If, as is common, she merely felt an external discharge, not a uterine flow into the vagina, one probably can rely upon *Chavos Daas* who rules that, even according to *Noda B'Yehudah*, only a feeling of uterine flow is considered a *hargashah*. In addition, as noted, R' Baruch Frenkel claims that one cannot feel any internal flow; thus, the feeling must have been an external flow. However, *Igros Moshe* (ibid.) seems to be strict even in this case. If, as is usually the case, she was wearing an undergarment which was checked much later and found to be clean, perhaps we may assume that the sensation was caused by a clear discharge which has since dried. See note 47[c] above. At times, a Rav may feel that a woman is overly concerned about imagined *hargashos*. Based upon the above, he might reassure her not to be concerned with *hargashos* (see *Shiurei Sheivet HaLeivi* 190:1[11] and ruling of R' Moshe Feinstein, cited in *Hilchos Niddah* (R' S. Eider) vol. 1 p. 14 (64). See note 47[h] above.

   In summary: According to *Chasam Sofer*, *Divrei Chaim* and *Sheivet HaLeivi*, she is *tehorah*. According to *Chochmas Adam* and *Igros Moshe*, she is *temei'ah*. One should determine whether it was the day of her expected *vest* (in which case there is reason to be more stringent), whether she was wearing a tightly fitting undergarment, whether the sensation was of an internal or external flow and whether the woman is perhaps overly anxious about *hargashos*.

59. In this case, one probably can be lenient, since the status of the *hargashah* is not firmly established. Those *Poskim* cited above who are strict in this case were referring to a real *hargashah* (see *Taharas Yisrael* 190:14, who is lenient providing that it is not one of the first three of the seven "clean" days). See *Chasam Sofer*, Y.D. 150, who clearly differentiates between the two *hargashos*. He rules that if she merely felt a discharge, she is *tehorah*. However, *Chasam Sofer* is only lenient with regard to a red spot the size of lice which were common in his day. Thus, since lice are not common today, his lenient opinion does not apply. (This conforms with *Chasam Sofer's* position regarding

and she found nothing on her *bedikah,* she may consider herself *tehorah.*[60]

2. If she finds a stain on her garment, she need not do a *bedikah.* The stain should be inspected.

    a. If the stain is an acceptable color, she is *tehorah.*[61]

    b. If the stain (any size, even on a colored garment) is an unacceptable color, she must ask a *sheilah.* It is important to note that a woman who feels a discharge and subsequently finds a small stain on her garment cannot disregard that stain because of its size. She must ask a *sheilah.*[62]

---

other cases in which he links the limitation of a *gris* to the actual prevalence of lice. Other *Poskim* do not accept his position.) See *Maharam Shick, Y.D.* 186, who differentiates between the two types of discharges, unlike *Chasam Sofer* who treats them equally. In *Maharam Shick's* opinion, if she felt an <u>uterine</u> discharge, he agrees with *Chasam Sofer* that one can only be lenient regarding a spot the size of commonly found lice (see note 44 above). If, however, she felt only a <u>vaginal flow,</u> he is lenient regarding any stain less than a *gris,* even if it is larger than common lice *(Maharam Shick* is unclear in his terminology. However, since he refers to *Chavos Daas,* it seems that one should interpret his words in this manner). *Divrei Chaim* 2:66 seems to follow this latter view.

60. See *Aruch HaShulchan* 190:13, and other *Poskim,* cited above (note 49), who were referring to a real *hargashah.* In the case of a sensation of a vaginal or external flow, we have additional reasons to be lenient. Perhaps she need not even bother to check herself, particularly if she is accustomed to such sensations.

61. *Pische Zuta* 190:5. See also *Sheivet HaLeivi* 2:88 and *Shiurei Sheivet HaLeivi* 190:1[12].

62. See *Binas Adam,* end of [9]. Although *Binas Adam* (in *Chochmas Adam* 113:1) happens to consider the sensation of discharge a *hargashah,* it seems that the *halachah* being discussed is not dependent upon the rule of *hargashah* per se. Rather, he holds that whenever the blood certainly came from the body, even if the amount is less than a *gris,* she is *temei'ah* according to Rabbinic law. *Taharas Yisrael* seems to follow this view. However, if the stain is found on a colored garment, it seems from *Binas Adam* that she is *tehorah.* See a similar position taken in responsa *Tuv Taam Vodaas* 2:66, and *Mahari Assad* cited in *Darchei Teshuvah* 188:20. It seems from *Chasam Sofer Y.D.* 167 that he disagrees. Note that *Chasam Sofer* maintains that a sensation of a flow is not a *hargashah.* Thus, he rules that if she felt a flow and checked herself with a cloth that is not pre-checked for cleanliness, she is *tehorah.* Certainly, if the stain is found on a garment, not on a *bedikah* cloth, *Chasam Sofer* would be lenient. Obviously, he disagrees with these arguments. See also responsa *Sheivet HaLeivi* 5:102,113. However, *Igros Moshe, Y.D.* 4:17[10], disagrees. In his opinion, even if she checks her garment and finds nothing, she is *temei'ah* unless a *bedikah* was done immediately. In this, *Igros Moshe* is asserting three important points: a) A sensation of even external flow may indicate a *hargashah* (we noted this opinion earlier, see note 27). b) The *bedikah* must be done immediately; if it is done at a later time it is useless. c) An undergarment is completely ineffectual in determining that no blood left the uterus. He contends that a minute amount of blood may have been discharged but did not stain the garment. On all three points, *Igros Moshe* stands in variance with the opinions of most other authorities. All of the above refers to a stain that was found soon after the *hargashah.*

    If the stain was found some time after the *hargashah,* many Rabbonim rule that we can assume that they are not related; rather, the *hargashah* may be due to some urine or other fluid which has

c. If she finds an acceptable stain and a tiny red spot on her garment, she should ask a *sheilah*.[63]

d. If she finds a stain larger than a *gris*, but she thinks it can be attributed to a source outside her body, i.e., she treated a child with a cut,[64] she is *temei'ah* (unless she is accustomed to finding clear discharges). Since she felt a discharge we are led to believe that the stain is from her body rather than a foreign source.[65]

3. A woman accustomed to feeling discharges:
A woman who is accustomed to finding clear[66] discharges (i.e., she did a *bedikah* or checked her garment three times and found them stained with an acceptable color)[67] should ask a *sheilah* whether or not she is required to do a *bedikah* after each sensation.[68]

---

since dried, while the stain, because it is less than a *gris*, is inconsequential. See *Posei'ach Shaar* 3:14.

63. Perhaps we can assume that the sensation was caused by the clear discharge, while the red stain, which is less than a *gris*, may be disregarded. See responsa *Avnei Neizer, Y.D.* 222[7], who is lenient in a similar case. He is referring, however, to a case where the woman usually finds clear discharges. On the other hand, in his case, the woman felt a real *hargashah* of the opening of the uterus, while, in our case, she merely felt an external discharge. Thus, in balance, the cases may be comparable. The *halachah* in this case is not completely clear.

If the red stain is definitely part of the general stain, i.e., the clear stain is surrounded by a red edge, she is *temei'ah* even though the total area of the entire stain is less than a *gris* (*Chavos Daas* 190:37[b]) . The only reason we can ignore the *hargashah* is because we assume that it was caused by the clear stain. Accordingly, the clear stain certainly came from the uterus. Thus, since the red is part and parcel of that clear stain, it, too, is from the uterus. Had she not felt the sensation, she would be *tehorah*, since the total area of the stain is less than a *gris*. In that case if the total area of the stain is larger than a *gris* and the red edging itself is less than a *gris*, *Poskim* disagree whether or not the clear stain combines with the red area to equal a *gris*. See *Taz* 190:41, *Chavos Daas* 190:9[b] and *Sidrei Taharah* 190:93 cited in Chapter Eight note 19.

64. Usually, a *kesem* that can be attributed to another source is *tehorah*, see 190:18.

65. Responsa *Pri Hasadeh* 3:61, cited in *Darchei Teshuvah* 190:16.

66. See note 36 above.

67. See note 51 above. We noted that some *Poskim* stipulate that she must prove this on many occasions. It does not seem that three simple *bedikos* are sufficient. However, other *Poskim* rely upon a woman checking herself three times; see *Daas Torah* 190:1, *Taharas Yisrael* 190:4 and *Shiurei Sheivet HaLeivi* 190:1[11].

68. *Aruch HaShulchan* 190:9 rules that she should check herself. Most *Poskim* cited below, e.g., *Maharsham* and *Divrei Chaim*, were referring to a woman who did not check herself or a woman for whom it would be very difficult to check after each *hargashah*. They did not imply that she need not do so, if she can. See, however, *Darchei Teshuvah* 188:18, who quotes these authorities as ruling that no *bedikah* is necessary. See also *Avnei Neizer, Y.D.* 222[4], 223[5], who finds a basis to spare the woman a *bedikah* after only a sensation of external flow (he was referring to a woman for whom these *bedikos* caused difficulties, but his arguments apply in any case). See also *Tzemach Tzedek, Y.D.*

a. If she finds nothing on the *bedikah* cloth, or if she did not do a *bedikah,* she is nevertheless *tehorah.*[69] Similarly, if she finds a red spot and a clear discharge on a cloth which was not pre-checked, she is *tehorah.*[70]

b. In the following cases, a woman who senses a real *hargashah* or even a discharge cannot rely upon the fact that her discharges are usually clear. She must do a *bedikah.*

> i. if the sensation occurred on the day of her *vest kavuah.*[71]

> ii. if the sensation occurred on the thirtieth day from her last period.[72]

> iii. if she has no set *vest,* and the sensation occurred after the time that her period usually starts (i.e., if she usually gets her period between the twenty-eighth and thirty-second day, and she felt the discharge after the twenty-eighth day).[73]

133[6] who follows a similar reasoning to conclude that if no *bedikah* was done, she is *tehorah. Darchei Teshuvah* (ibid.) also cites responsa *Neta Soreik, Y.D.* 51, who rules that a woman who feels a discharge and is accustomed to seeing clear discharges need not check herself. He is lenient even regarding the seven "clean" days and even if the woman is unable to differentiate between an internal and an external discharge. We noted in 47[h] and 58 above that a woman who is overly anxious about imagined *hargashos* should possibly be advised not to do *bedikos.* We also noted in 47[c] above, that a tightly fitting undergarment may be considered a *bedikah* even regarding a woman who actually felt the opening of the uterus which is certainly a *hargashah.* It should be even more acceptable regarding a woman who merely felt a discharge, since a discharge is not essentially a *hargashah.* In addition, in this case, we have an additional factor: She is accustomed to finding clear discharges. A Rav must weigh these, together with other factors, before advising a woman whether or not to do *bedikos.*

69. See *Chochmas Adam* 113:3, *Aruch HaShulchan* (ibid.), responsa *Tzemach Tzedek, Y.D.* 133[6], responsa *Maharsham* 1:188, *Divrei Chaim* 1:34, 2:66, *Daas Torah* 190:1, *Pische Zuta* 190:4, responsa *Avnei Neizer, Y.D.* 222. However, responsa *Beis Shlomo* (*Y.D.* 2:36) disagrees. He rules that even a woman who only felt a discharge and is accustomed to clear discharges cannot assume that the discharge was clear.

70. *Taharas Yisrael* 190:14.

71. See *Maharsham* and *Divrei Chaim* ibid. and *Pische Zuta* 190:3.

72. *Imrei Yosher* cited in *Darchei Teshuvah* 190:21, *Pische Zuta* ibid. Presumably, *Maharsham* and *Divrei Chaim* would agree to this.

73. *Divrei Chaim, Y.D.* 2:66, implies that one may be lenient only pertaining to a woman accustomed to feeling discharges who has a specific *vest,* and feels the *hargashah* on a day other than the *vest* day. A similar view is held by *Chazon Ish, Y.D.* 89:1. In the case in iii, where she feels the *hargashah* during those days that she usually menstruates, they would probably not be lenient, since during the days that she usually menstruates, she is not considered a woman who has a *vest.* The advantage of a woman who has a *vest* is that the period is not expected any other day. See *Kitzur*

c. Most *Poskim* do not differentiate between a discharge felt during her seven "clean" days and a discharge felt any other time.[74]

d. A pregnant[75] or nursing[76] woman who has established that her discharges are usually clear, perhaps, may disregard any sensation of a discharge. A *sheilah* should be asked.[77]

e. Some authorities rule that a woman who wears a tightly fitting undergarment need not do a *bedikah* when she feels a discharge but should merely check her undergarment.[78] If she finds an unacceptable color on the garment, even if the stain is less than a *gris*, she must ask a *sheilah*.[79]

Hilchos Niddah (R' A. Pfoiffer) 6:12. See *Badei HaShulchan* 188:22, who notes that, similarly, a woman who is accustomed to feeling certain physical manifestations before her period (e.g., a head or stomach ache) may be lenient regarding a sensation of a discharge if no such physical manifestations are present. Note that this leniency regarding a woman who is accustomed to feeling physical manifestations refers only to a woman who is also accustomed to finding clear discharges.

74. *Maharsham* (ibid.) and *Divrei Chaim* (Y.D. 1:34) are lenient even pertaining to the seven "clean" days (even during the first three days). However, *Igros Moshe*, Y.D. 4:17[9], rules that she must specifically establish that her discharges during the seven "clean" days are *tahor*; otherwise, she must be concerned about any *hargashah* during that time. Once it is established that even the discharges during the seven "clean" days are *tahor*, she may be lenient about future *hargashos* during those days. *Shiurei Sheivet HaLeivi* takes a similar position.

75. There is disagreement among authorities at which point a woman is considered pregnant regarding these *halachos*. *Chazal* assume that a woman is *halachically* considered "pregnant" only after three months of pregnancy. Today, women usually do not experience a period once they become pregnant. Accordingly, there are views that, today, a woman is *halachically* considered pregnant as soon as her pregnancy is medically confirmed. See Chapter Twenty.

76. *Chazal* consider a woman in the status of "nursing" for the twenty-four months following childbirth. This is based upon the fact that, in previous times, women did not experience a blood flow throughout that period. Today, since the situation has changed, some authorities rule that only a woman who is actually nursing has this status. See Chapter Twenty.

77. We noted the opinion of *Toras HaShelamim* 190:2, and R' Akiva Eiger 190:1, above, note 47[d]. In this case, we are dealing with the *hargashah* of a discharge which may not be considered a *hargashah* at all. Since her discharges are usually clear, perhaps all *Poskim* agree that a *bedikah* is not necessary. In addition, one assumes that she wears tightly fitting undergarments; thus one should be able to rely upon *Tiferes Tzvi* that no *bedikah* is required.

78. See responsa *Sheivet HaLeivi* 2:88. See note 47[c] above.

79. See *Binas Adam* 113 end of [16]. If she found the stain much later than the *hargashah* of the discharge, perhaps we may assume that the discharge was a clear mucous or urine which has dried in the interim, while the stain less than a *gris* may be ignored.

A woman who often feels discharges should be encouraged to check herself three times to establish that her discharges are usually clear and to avail herself of the leniencies cited above.[80]

C. A feeling of external dampness

A feeling of external dampness (i.e., she feels a dampness between her legs) without the sensation of a discharge is, in itself, not considered a *hargashah*.[81] However, *Poskim* do not dismiss it entirely since it indicates that some fluid may have been discharged.

> 1. If she is accustomed to feeling a sensation of dampness and has established that these feelings are usually a clear fluid, and it is not during the days that she normally expects her period, she should ask a Rav if she may ignore the feeling and not even bother to do a *bedikah* or even check her garment.
>
> 2. If she has not established such a tendency, some *Poskim* advise that she check her undergarment when convenient.[82]
>
> 3. If she did not do a *bedikah* or check her garment, she is nevertheless *tehorah*.[83]
>
> 4. If she found a stain on her garment, it can be treated as any *kesem*; thus, if it is less than a *gris*, she is *tehorah*.[84]

---

80. *Shiurei Sheivet HaLeivi* 190:1[11].

81. Responsa *Divrei Chaim*, Y.D. 2:66. *Igros Moshe*, Y.D. 4:17[7], explains that even if the dampness would have originated from some other source, her sensation would be the same. Thus, this sensation certainly cannot be considered a *hargashah*. See also *Shiurei Sheivet HaLeivi* 190:1[2].

82. *Shiurei Sheivet HaLeivi* 190:1[2]. If her garment is white, this is reasonable since, if the stain is more than a *gris*, she will become *temei'ah*. However, if her garment is colored, it is difficult to understand why she should check herself, since, in any case, she is *tehorah*. It seems that, in this case, one cannot be lenient with a colored garment. See below note 84. The *halachah* in this case is not completely clear.

83. *Shiurei Sheivet HaLeivi* 190:1[2].

84. *Igros Moshe*, Y.D. 4:17[7]. He adds that if the blood went directly onto the garment or pad without touching her body, i.e. she feels the dampness on a pad and not on her body, it is considered a *kesem* on a garment, not on her body. Thus, even *Rambam*, who holds that a *kesem* on the body is *tamei* even if less than a *gris*, would concede that, in this case, she is not a *niddah*. It seems that, in the opinion of *Igros Moshe*, if the woman feels a dampness on her body, although it is not considered a *hargashah*, it is nevertheless considered a *kesem* on the body and on the garment. This would then depend upon the disagreement between *Chavos Daas* 190:6 and R' Akiva Eiger (ad loc.). This has major consequences regarding the case of a woman who was wearing a colored garment. In *Igros Moshe's* view, if she feels a dampness on her body as well, it is a *kesem* on the body, not the garment; thus, the color of the garment is not significant. The *halachah* in this case is not completely

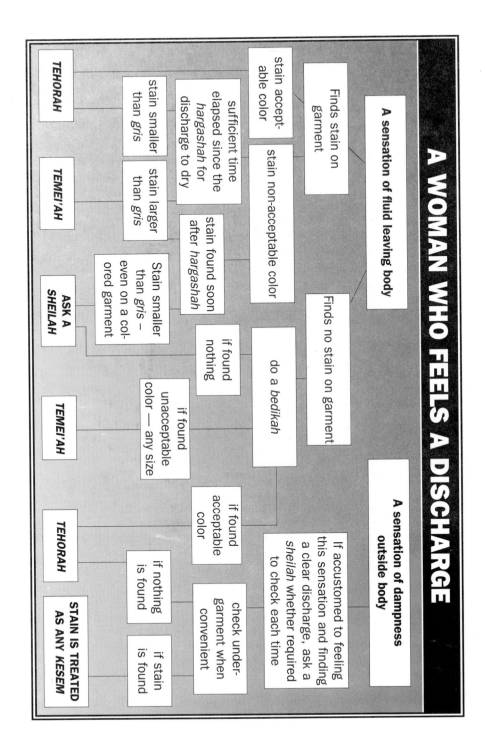

A WOMAN WHO FEELS A DISCHARGE

A sensation of fluid leaving body

Finds stain on garment
- stain accept-able color
- stain non-acceptable color

Finds no stain on garment
- do a *bedikah*

A sensation of dampness outside body

If accustomed to feeling this sensation and finding a clear discharge, ask a *sheilah* whether required to check each time

check under-garment when convenient

stain acceptable color → TEHORAH
- stain smaller than *gris* → TEHORAH
- stain larger than *gris* → TEMEI'AH

sufficient time elapsed since the *hargashah* for discharge to dry
- stain smaller than *gris*
- stain larger than *gris*

stain found soon after *hargashah*
- Stain smaller than *gris* – even on a col-ored garment → ASK A SHEILAH

if found nothing
if found unacceptable color — any size → TEMEI'AH

if found acceptable color → TEHORAH

if nothing is found

if stain is found → STAIN IS TREATED AS ANY KESEM

CHAPTER FOUR

נאמנות
Credibility

☐ The trust the Torah accords a woman.

☐ Contradictory claims.

☐ *Amasla.*

☐ Reliability with regard to colors.

☐ Relating a halachic decision.

☐ A husband deciding *halachic* matters concerning his wife.

HALACHIC OVERVIEW

1. A woman is considered *tehorah* until the day of the expected *vest*. Her husband need not ask her whether or not her period began. He may assume that she is *tehorah* even if she is sleepy and would be incapable of telling him that she is *temei'ah*.

2. When the day of the expected period arrives, husband and wife must abstain from marital relations. Even after the day has passed, relations are forbidden until she specifically states that she did the required *bedikah*.

3. When a woman has a blood flow at any time of the month she becomes a *niddah*. Her husband is prohibited to cohabit with her until she specifically indicates that she was *tovel* (immersed herself) in a *mikveh*.

4. If a woman claims that she was *tovel,* and sufficient time has passed to enable her to count the five preliminary and seven "clean" days, her claim is accepted. This is true even though she usually requires more than five preliminary days to do a *hefseik taharah*.

5. A woman who tells her husband that she is a *niddah* may not retract her statement. She requires the five-day waiting period, a *hefseik taharah* and seven "clean" days. Even if she alleges that she was merely joking she cannot retract her statement unless she does so within a time span of approximately two seconds.

6. If it was obvious to her husband at the time of the original statement that she was joking or that she was provoked by anger, he may accept her retraction.

7. If a woman offers a justification (an *"amasla"*) for her original statement, a Rav may allow the original statement to be retracted; for example, a woman states that she is a *niddah* and later claims that she based this on the mistaken belief that a stain on her garment rendered her a *niddah,* but subsequently realized that the stain was caused by a bruise. The rules of *amasla* are difficult; one must discuss a case of *amasla* with a Rav, and <u>never judge it by oneself.</u>

8. A woman who, upon returning from the *mikveh,* claims that she did not immerse herself, cannot retract her statement even if she offers an excuse. One must consult a Rav.

9. A woman who tells her husband, at the time of her expected period, that the period arrived, cannot retract that statement, even with an excuse.

It should be apparent from these *halachos* that it is improper for a couple to jest about whether or not she is *tehorah* or to use it as a weapon when quarreling.

10. Judging colors on a *bedikah* cloth or on a garment is very difficult. Even a slight variation of shade may determine that a color is *tamei*. A woman who finds a stain similar to one that a Rav previously permitted may consider herself *tehorah* only if she is absolutely positive that the color is not problematic. If she has any doubt whatsoever, she must show it to a Rav.

11. A woman who shows a stain to another woman can rely upon the second woman's claim that she obtained a lenient ruling on the exact same color only if the second woman is absolutely certain that the color of the stain is not even questionable. The second woman can also be relied upon to take the cloth to a Rav and report back his ruling.

12. If a woman loses her *bedikah* cloth before she is able to check it for a stain, she may ignore the *bedikah*. It is as if no *bedikah* was done.

13. If the *bedikah* is a *hefseik taharah* or a *bedikah* of the seven "clean" days, it must be repeated.

14. If she noticed a problem on the cloth but loses it before she is able to ask a *sheilah*, she is *tehorah* only if she can positively identify the color or show the Rav a non-problematic color that is exactly the same as the one that was lost.

15. A woman who tells her husband that a Rav ruled leniently on her *bedikah* cloth is believed, even if she does not divulge the name of the Rav.

16. A woman who claims that a Rav ruled leniently on her *bedikah* cloth, and, upon inquiry, is subsequently contradicted by the Rav himself, is not believed.

Introduction

Relying upon another Jew's testimony pertaining to matters of *halachah* is actually not an issue of credibility or trust at all. It is a unique manner in which *halachah* functions. I may lend a large sum of money to someone whom I trust. I may purchase a used car from a credible dealer. My decision is based upon whether or not I feel comfortable entrusting this person with my money. It is my money and I may risk losing it as I choose. A Torah prohibition, however, is not <u>mine.</u> I cannot entrust an issue regarding a Torah *issur* to one who is not acceptable according to the standards of the Torah itself. My personal confidence and trust in the person are completely irrelevant.

While the Torah's rejection of an individual's testimony may, at times, be due to the person's reputation,[1] in most cases it is simply a matter of the way *halachah* functions. In certain situations *halachah* simply does not accept the testimony of any single individual. In these cases, even one with an impeccable reputation may not be relied upon. See footnote for specific examples.[2]

The *halachos* of *niddah* are predicated upon mutual trust between man and wife. A wife relies upon her husband in matters of *halachah* (e.g., when he informs her of a decision rendered by their Rav, she is not expected to

---

1. See *Y.D.* 2.

2. It is a well-known fact that the testimony of a single witness (עד אחד) is not accepted in most money matters, nor is it accepted regarding marriage or divorce or before a *beis din* determining whether to inflict any punishment. In these cases even the most pious individual with an impeccable reputation for integrity would not be accepted by *halachah*.

A single witness is accepted in matters regarding Torah prohibitions. The Talmudic term for this is עד אחד נאמן באיסורים, "*eid echad ne'eman b'issurim*" — a single witness is believed in matters of most Torah prohibitions. Even in this restricted scope, *halachah* differentiates between a) a witness who testifies that an object is <u>prohibited</u> and b) one who testifies that an object is <u>permissible.</u> a) A single witness may not declare an object <u>prohibited</u> if the object was previously in a permitted status. For example, he is not believed if he states that a non-Jew caused wine to become *yayin nesach* (wine touched by a non-Jew) unless the wine was either his or in his control. These rules are discussed in *Y.D.* 127:1. A single witness may testify that an object is <u>permitted</u> only if the object was in a questionable status. If, however, the object was in a prohibited status, the witness may not be relied upon unless he had the ability to remove the prohibition. For example, if one testifies that the required tithes (*terumah* and *maasros*) were set aside from produce of *Eretz Yisrael,* he would not be believed unless he had the ability to remove the tithes himself or have them removed by others. See *Rema, Y.D.* 127:3.

A clear proof that "trust" in *halachah* is not a matter of actual believability but merely the manner in which *halachah* functions is found in the following case. If Reuven were to testify in *Beis Din* that Shimon ate non-kosher meat, *Beis Din* would dismiss his testimony (as it relates to a matter of punishment). Indeed Reuven himself would be punished with *malkos* for relating *lashon hara* since his testimony served no constructive purpose. However, if Reuven testifies that a piece of questionable meat is non-kosher, he has established the meat as non-kosher. If two witnesses subsequently testify in *Beis Din* that Shimon ate the meat in question, *Beis Din* will (based upon their testimony) punish Shimon with *malkos.* Reuven's testimony regarding the meat is indirectly responsible for *Beis Din's* decision to inflict *malkos* upon Shimon, even though they would never accept Reuven's testimony to directly inflict *malkos.* Obviously we are not dealing with believability. Based on all the above, it should not be surprising that even if one with the most impeccable reputation (e.g., the *Chofetz Chaim*) were to testify in a situation where a single witness is not accepted, his testimony would be unacceptable. We certainly "believe" him, but we are technically unable to accept his testimony.

check its accuracy). Similarly, a husband relies upon his wife to inform him of any change in her *niddah* status. Indeed, the concept of trust, i.e., that one Jew may rely upon another in matters of most[3] prohibitions[4] (e.g., to relate that a questionable piece of meat is indeed *treif*), is, in the opinion of some *Rishonim*,[5] derived from the trust that the Torah accords to a woman. This is learnt from the verse regarding a *zavah* (a woman with a blood flow, see Chapter Two) — "*vesafrah lah*" — she (the *zavah*) should count (the seven "clean" days) for <u>herself</u> (implying that she is relied upon to count).[6] The Torah certainly believes the woman when she states that she counted her days without finding any blood. There are, however, situations where this trust may be strained. It may be because the woman made contradictory statements or because her actions seem to contradict her claims. This problem is not exclusive to a woman: A man in similar circumstances would be equally suspect. We discuss cases pertaining to a woman only because much of *hilchos niddah* is based upon the information which a woman provides her husband about her *niddah* status. We will also discuss cases in which we are concerned that women are not knowledgeable or experienced enough to identify shades and colors. We will further clarify the question of whether a husband may trust himself to decide matters of *hilchos niddah* relevant to himself.

I. The trust the Torah accords a woman

The Torah relies completely upon the wife to inform her husband when her period is expected and when it began, when she accomplished a successful *hefseik taharah*, that she had completed the seven

---

3. With the exception of *davar she'b'ervah* — matters pertaining to *gittin* (divorces) and *kiddushin* (marriage) etc.

4. As opposed to monetary or criminal matters which require two witnesses.

5. *Tosfos, Gittin* 2b, s.v. "עד."

6. Nevertheless, there are instances where a woman is relied upon less than a man; see *Rema* 127:3. Examples of this are cases where the prohibition is not certain (ibid.) or where it is very difficult to remove prohibited matter from a particular food; *Shach* 127:30. This is based upon the Torah's perception of feminine nature. See a discussion of this and related topics in "The River, the Kettle and the Bird" by Rabbi Aharon Feldman (Jerusalem 1987). Many psychological studies have been done on the subject of gender differences in cognitive abilities. See "The Psychology of Sex Difference," E. E. Maccoby and C. N. Jacklin, 1974, Stanford University Press. "Sex Related Differences in Cognitive Functioning," M. Wittig and A. Peterson, 1979, Academic Press. "Tech. Report 1982-83," Johnson O'Connor Research Foundation. "Personality and Individual Differences," 1991 Vol 12. No. 11, Pergamon Press. The author is indebted to Dr. Norman Blumenthal for his help in gathering these sources.

"clean" days and was *tovel* properly. A woman who misleads her husband in any of these matters causes him (and herself) to transgress the cardinal prohibition of *niddah*. The husband may (or should) then divorce her without paying her a *kesubah*.[7] If he chooses to remain married, it is questionable whether and under what circumstances he may continue to trust and rely upon her in matters of *niddah*.[8]

A. Issues pertaining to the expected period

1. Until the arrival of the day of the expected *vest*, a woman is considered *tehorah*. She need not be asked whether or not her period started or whether or not she found a *kesem*. Indeed, even if she is sleepy and cannot answer questions with clarity, her husband may assume that she is *tehorah* since her period is not yet expected and she has not indicated any change in her status.[9]

2. When the day of the expected period (if she has an established *vest*, or the thirtieth day for a woman who has no established *vest*)[10] arrives, the couple may not have marital relations,[11] even if she does a *bedikah*. Even after the day has passed, they may not cohabit until the husband inquires whether or not his wife did the required *bedikah*.[12] He may not rely upon the fact that she is awake and acts as if she is *tehorah*,[13] since she may not realize that a *bedikah* was required.[14] If sufficient time has passed

---

7. *Even HaEzer* 115:1.

8. See *Chavos Daas* 185:1[b], *Aruch HaShulchan* §3 and *Darchei Teshuvah* §5. See *Taharas Yisrael* §1, regarding whether her *teshuvah* is effective with regard to enabling her husband to rely upon her in the future. See *Pische Zuta* §2 and *Taharas Yisrael* §8, regarding a case where both husband and wife willingly transgressed the prohibition of *niddah* and did *teshuvah*. May the husband rely upon his wife in the future?

9. 184:1, *Taz* §1, *Shach* §31.

10. 184:12, *Shach* §34.

11. See Chapter Twenty-Two that, in the opinion of some authorities, any intimate physical contact is prohibited.

12. 184:11, see *Aruch HaShulchan* §46 and *Darchei Teshuvah* §60.

13. *Chavos Daas* 184:14[b], 32[c].

14. Thus, perhaps even *Lechem VeSimlah* (cited in 26 below), who rules that a husband who has not been away from home need not explicitly ask his wife whether she was *tovel*, would concede in this case that he must ask her whether she did a *bedikah*; see *Shiurei Sheivet HaLeivi* 184:11[3] and *Badei HaShulchan* 184:11, s.v. "עד." However, *Shiurei Sheivet HaLeivi* argues that since we follow the opinion of *Lechem VeSimlah* in a case of a woman who was certainly a *niddah* it seems illogical to be more stringent in a case of where there is merely a possibility that she may have become a *niddah*.

for the expected period to end, for her to count five and then seven "clean" days and to immerse herself in a *mikveh*, he may assume that she did so and that she is *tehorah*,[15] even if she is sleepy and not alert.[16] It should be noted that this assumption on the part of the husband pertains only to a case where he does not know for a fact that her period came. If she was certainly a *niddah*, she must specifically state that she was *tovel* (see B1 below).

3. If she passes only a *vest she'aino kavuah*, a non-established *vest*,[17] her husband need not ask her specifically if she menstruated or if she did a *bedikah*. In the opinion of many *Poskim* this applies only if she is awake. However, if she is sleeping he is forbidden to cohabit with her.[18]

B. A woman who becomes a *niddah*.

1. Once it has been established that a woman menstruated (or even if she merely found a *kesem* which was ruled *tamei*[19]), she is considered in a prohibited *status*[20] until she specifically states that

---

15. 184:11. In this case, we have a *s'fek-s'feika* — a double doubt. Perhaps the period never came and even if it did, perhaps she was *tovel*. She also has a prior status of permissibility — *chezkas taharah*. In addition, since she usually immerses herself, we can safely assume that she did so (*Torah HaShelamim* 185:1). Even a very young woman, who is usually ashamed to go to the *mikveh*, may be assumed to have immersed herself (*Taz* 184:16). If, however, the husband was not expected home the night of the assumed *tevilah*, he cannot assume that she was *tovel* (see *Taharas Yisrael* 92), since women are usually not *tovel* if their husbands are not expected (*Aruch HaShulchan* 184:50. It seems from *Aruch HaShulchan* that even if she is awake, he cannot assume that she is *tehorah*, if he has been away, unless she tells him or indicated so in some other manner — see B,1 below).

16. See *Shiurei Sheivet HaLeivi* 184:11[5], who explains that one is not expected to verify her status and ask her whether or not she is *tehorah* since one may assume that if she were not *tehorah*, she would be alert enough to tell him so even if she is sleepy.

17. As opposed to a *vest kavuah* or the thirtieth day which is the equivalent of a *vest kavuah*. A woman who passes a *vest she'aino kavuah* without doing a *bedikah* is no longer required to do that *bedikah*.

18. *Pardes Rimonim* 184:30[sc} and *Aruch HaShulchan* §46. *Chavos Daas* 1[b] disagrees. He rules that even if she is sleeping he may assume that she is *tehorah*. *Taharas Yisrael* §95 follows the stricter position.

19. *Darchei Teshuvah* 185:1. See *Darchei Teshuvah* 184:63, who cites *Mei Niddah* that if she is only a *niddah* due to a *kesem* and sufficient time has elapsed for her to do *tevilah*, perhaps she is permitted to her husband even without his inquiry regarding *tevilah*. *Mei Niddah* reaches no definite conclusion.

20. Thus, it is forbidden for her husband to even touch her (*Darchei Teshuvah* 185:4).

she immersed[21] herself[22] and removed her *niddus*.[23] In the opinion of some *Poskim*, she must state so clearly. Thus, even if she acts in a manner that indicates that she is *tehorah*, her husband must specifically ask whether she immersed herself.[24] Others disagree and maintain that if she acts[25] in a manner that indicates that she is *tehorah*, he may assume that she is *tehorah*.[26] Most later authorities follow this second lenient opinion.[27]

2. If the woman claims that she was *tovel*, but the husband knows that twelve days have not passed since the onset of the period, he certainly may not believe that she is *tehorah*.[28]

---

21. She need not actually say she immersed herself. It is sufficient if she says that she is now *tehorah* (*Darchei Teshuvah* 6).

22. One cannot assume she is *tehorah* without her saying so, even if sufficient time has passed for her to immerse herself (see *Rema* 185:1).

23. 185:1.

24. *Chavos Daas* 185:1[c] rules that even if she lays near him, he must specifically ask her whether she was *tovel* or whether she is *tehorah*.

25. One should note that this applies only if she approaches him on her own initiative; however, he may not approach her and assume that her acquiescence implies that she was *tovel*. See *Pardes Rimonim*, M.Z. 185:1 and *Taharas Yisrael* 4.

26. *Lechem VeSimlah* 185:1 argues that the opinion of *Chavos Daas* (cited above) is only applicable if the husband was away and returns unexpectedly. If, however, he was home and knows that it was her time for *tevilah* and that there was no hindrance to her *tevilah*, and certainly if he knows that she was preparing herself for *tevilah*, it is not necessary for him to explicitly ask her whether or not she was *tovel*. The fact that she comes to him is sufficient proof.

27. *Aruch HaShulchan* §4 rules that even if she merely handed something to him (which is forbidden while she is a *niddah*), he may assume that she is *tehorah*. However, her accepting what he hands her is not sufficient proof (*Taharas Yisrael* 185:4, see note 25). See also *Shiurei Sheivet HaLeivi* §1[2] who follows the lenient opinion, but notes that there is a basis for one who wishes to follow the stricter opinion. *Darchei Teshuvah* §7 seems to lean toward the stricter opinion. It would seem that the husband should follow the lenient opinions if he understands that his wife may be annoyed if, after all her effort in making herself *tehorah*, he seems less than trusting, but he must wait until she somehow indicates that she was *tovel*. *Be'er Moshe* 4:58 suggests that if the husbands suspects that she may be annoyed if asked whether she was *tovel*, he should preface his question by telling her, "according to *Shulchan Aruch* I am required to ask you whether you were *tovel*." In 4:59 he rules that if the husband drove her to the *mikveh* and waited for her there, he is not required to ask her whether she was *tovel*, since she remained in the *mikveh* sufficient time to be *tovel*.

28. 185, *Taz* and *Shach* §1. However, he should not jump to hasty conclusions since this is a matter of great import. Perhaps she found a *kesem* before her *niddah* flow and started her preliminary five days earlier. Perhaps she mistakenly waited only four days instead of five. If this is the case, a Rav should be consulted.

3. If ample time may[29] have passed since the onset of her period to enable her to count the five preliminary and seven "clean" days, her husband may accept her claim[30] that she immersed in a *mikveh,* even if she usually requires more than five preliminary days before achieving a successful *hefseik taharah.*[31]

II. Retracting a claim

If a woman states[32] that she is a *niddah* she is treated as a *niddah* by virtue[33] of her statement,[34] whether she was truthful or not.[35] Any subsequent claim[36] that her statement was not serious, but rather was in

---

29. Even if the husband is not sure when the period started, e.g., he cannot remember whether it started Sunday or Monday and therefore cannot be positive that sufficient days have passed, he may rely upon her claim (*Shach* 185:1, see, however, *Tiferes Tzvi* cited in *Darchei Teshuvah* §8).

30. Even if her husband notices blood on her garments, and she maintains that it came from some other source, she is believed (*Rema* 185:1). He must, however, inquire why her garments are stained (*Darchei Teshuvah* §9). If, for any good reason, the husband suspects that his wife was not *tovel,* he should try to verify the *tevilah,* see *Aruch HaShulchan* 185:3. This is a delicate situation and should be handled with appropriate care and discretion.

31. *Taz* §1.

32. If she makes this claim publicly, it is a matter of more serious concern. See B2 below.

33. This follows a *halachic* principle: שויא אנפשיה חתיכה דאיסורא — one can, by declaration, render something as if it were a forbidden object. Thus, the woman, by declaring herself a *niddah,* has, in effect, forbidden her husband upon herself. *Pri Migadim Y.D.* 1:39[mz], proves that שויא אנפשיה is a Biblical precept even in a case where the statement is refuted by witnesses.

34. There is discussion among *Poskim* as to how שויא אנפשיה functions. Some maintain that it operates according to the *halachah* of a *neder* — a vow, by which one can create a prohibition upon an object. In the same manner, the woman created a prohibition upon herself. Others maintain that it functions according to the principle that a person is always believed in matters pertaining to himself (where no one else is negatively affected) אדם נאמן על עצמו. See *Shaar HaMelech* (*Ishus* 9:15), responsa *Noda B'Yehudah* (E.H. 2:23), *Chavos Daas* 185:5[c], responsa *Chasam Sofer* (E.H. 78). *K'sav Sofer* (Y.D. 87), *Shev Shemaitisa* 6:8,19, *Imrei Binah* (Y.D. §2) and *Pischei Teshuvah* (Y.D. 1:18). *Noda B'Yehudah* (ibid.) brings a novel proof that שויא אנפשיה does not function as a *neder,* for if it does, how was Rabban Gamliel able to command Rabbi Yehoshua (*Rosh HaShanah* 25a) to travel on the day which Rabbi Yehoshua himself claimed was *Yom Kippur?* Another proof is offered by *Maaseh Choshev* in his gloss on *Shaar HaMelech* (ad. loc.). He maintains that if שויא אנפשיה functions as a *neder* the husband should be able to undo the vow since he is empowered to be *mafir* (undo) any *neder* that his wife vows. One should note that שויא אנפשיה can only function in a restrictive manner (*lechumra*), not in a permissive manner (*lekula*). For example, if she claims and then denies that she menstruated, though she is deemed *temei'ah,* she cannot used this alleged menstruation to uproot a *vest.*

35. 185:3.

36. Even if she produces witnesses who testify that she is not a *niddah,* she cannot retract her state-

jest,[37] has no validity. She must be considered, and indeed she must consider herself[38] as a *niddah*. She requires the five-day waiting period, a *hefseik taharah* and seven "clean" days. There are differing opinions among *Poskim* whether a *b'rachah* should be recited over her *tevilah*.[39]

A. A simple retraction

There are, however, the following cases where her retraction is accepted:

1. An immediate retraction:
If upon declaring herself a *niddah*, she retracts immediately, i.e., within the time span of saying the three words "*shalom alecha rabbi*"[40] (approximately two seconds), her original declaration of *niddus* is void.[41]

2. An obvious untruth:
If, at the time of her original statement, it was obvious to her husband from her manner that she was not serious, she may, even at a later time, simply retract her declaration of *niddus*. *Poskim* cite two examples:

a. A declaration made in jest:
If it was obvious to her husband at the time of the origi-

---

ment which remains in effect in spite of the facts. We may be convinced of the fact, but her statement to the contrary has an effect of its own. See *Chavos Daas* 185:3[b], see also *Noda B'Yehudah* (E.H. 1:58) and *Mishneh LeMelech* (*Ishus* 9:15) citing *Rashba*. See, however, R' Akiva Eiger to Y.D. 1:12, citing *Mishneh LeMelech*. Even if enough time has elapsed to enable her to count seven "clean" days and immerse herself, her retraction is invalid. Usually, in a case such as this she has what is called a "*migo*," and her honesty would be beyond question. (A *migo* is a Talmudic concept by which one who makes an improbable claim must be believed if he had the ability to win his case by choosing a more probable claim. We assume that the person must be honest, otherwise he would have chosen the more believable claim.) This woman has a *migo*, for had she been dishonest, she could have claimed that she immersed herself, which is a more probable and acceptable claim than her retraction. Nevertheless, her original claim that she became a *niddah* stands, therefore since, in effect, she conceded that she did not undergo a *tevilah*, she remains *temei'ah* (*Chavos Daas* ibid. see *Darchei Teshuvah* §11,18).

37. *Shach* 185:2.

38. See R' Akiva Eiger to Y.D. 1:12 citing *Bechor Shor*.

39. See responsa *Rav Pe'alim*, Y.D. 1:37, who rules that she recites a *b'rachah* since *halachah* declares her a *niddah*. It seems that a similar view is held by responsa *Pnei Levi* cited in *Darchei Teshuvah* §29. However, responsa *Mahari Steif* 271 contends that a *b'rachah* is not recited.

40. *Mishnah Berurah* 206:12.

41. *Rema* 185:3.

nal *niddus* declaration that she was joking, her subsequent claim that it was only a joke is accepted. Nevertheless, she should be reprimanded not to jest in this manner.[42] The subject of her *tumah* or *taharah* should not be a matter of jest.

b. A declaration provoked by anger:

If it was obvious to her husband at the time of her original *niddus* declaration that the claim was provoked by anger, and subsequently she acts in a manner which shows that she actually is not a *niddah*, i.e., she lies near him, he may assume she is *tehorah* without her specifically stating so.[43] If, however, he was not aware originally that her claim was provoked by anger, he cannot assume so (even if she behaves as if she is *tehorah*) without her specific explanation that she had been provoked by anger, which may be accepted as an *amasla* (see below).[44]

B. A retraction based upon an *amasla* (justification)

There is an additional situation in which a retraction is accepted. This is where she provides a justification (referred to in *halachah* as an "*amasla*")[45] for originally making a misleading statement. Although her statement seemed serious at the time, if she recants and offers an *amasla*, her explanation may be accepted;[46] for example, if she later claims that she had originally assumed she was a *niddah* because she found a stain on her garment, but subsequently retracted her claim when she realized that the stain was caused by a bruise.[47] In another case cited by *Poskim* a woman who declared herself a *niddah* during a quarrel with her husband and later claims that she

---

42. *Aruch HaShulchan* 185:10.

43. *Rema* 185:3, according to *Aruch HaShulchan* §12, *Chasam Sofer* notes to Y.D. 3, *Badei HaShulchan* §29. Apparently, if she does not act in a manner that indicates that she is *tehorah*, he cannot assume so even if at the time of the original statement it was obvious to him that she was provoked in anger.

44. *Aruch HaShulchan* ibid.

45. See *Daas Torah*, Y.D. 1:63, for an analysis of many issues involved in *amasla*.

46. 185:3. Even if this occurred during the day of her expected period, *K'sav Sofer*, Y.D. §87, and *Darchei Teshuvah* §28.

47. *Shach* 3. See *Pischei Teshuvah* §3, regarding an instance when she not only verbally declared her *niddus*, but she actually donned *niddah* clothes after finding a stain, but subsequently realized that the stain was caused by a bruise. See note 51 below.

alleged to be a *niddah* only because of their quarrel is believed. Even if they were not quarreling, but she later explains that she had acted in anger, if this is in accordance with her normal behavior and moods, the husband may accept her retraction.[48] A Rav should be consulted.

The limitations of an *amasla*:

1. Public display of her *niddus:*
In previous times, women wore specific garments during their *niddus* stage. If a woman publicly dons these garments at any time, she establishes herself as a *niddah*.[49] If she subsequently claims that she is not a *niddah* and that she wore these garments for some other reason, she is not believed, even with an *amasla*.[50] There is a disagreement among *Poskim* if this rule applies in the case of a woman who claims that she donned *niddah* clothes because she actually thought she was a *niddah*.[51]

2. Public announcement of her *niddus:*
In the opinion of some *Poskim*, if she told several people that she is a *niddah*, it is the equivalent of donning *niddah* clothes and any subsequent *amasla* is invalid.[52] Others disagree.[53]

3. Retaining the *niddah* status for a longer period:
If she retains her claim to be a *niddah* for thirty days or longer, she can no longer remove it with an *amasla*[54]

---

48. Responsa *Radvaz* 4:264.

49. This more definitively establishes that she is a *niddah* than merely stating so verbally. In *Talmudic* times, she was flogged if she donned *niddah* clothes and subsequently transgressed the prohibition of *niddus;* see *Kiddushin* 80a. However, a woman who verbally states that she is a *niddah* is not flogged if she subsequently transgresses the prohibition. Her verbal claim is not sufficient to definitively place her in the status of a *niddah*. This is the subject of dispute among *Acharonim;* see *Rambam* (*Issurei Biah* 1:13), *Magid Mishnah* (ad. loc.), *Biur HaGra*, E.H. 3:11, *Sidrei Taharah* 185:1 and *Shev Shemaitisa* 6:10.

50. We cannot accept that any rational woman would publicly don *niddah* clothes if she were not actually a *niddah*. *Taz* 185:2, *Shach* §5.

51. *Chavos Daas* §3[b] rules that since, in this case, she had good reason to don *niddah* clothes, an *amasla* is accepted. *Pleisi* §2, however, argues that a woman would normally check to ascertain whether the blood she found was menstrual or bruise blood before she dons *niddah* clothes. Thus, since she donned *niddah* clothes, her claim that the blood was from a bruise is contradicted. *Graz* §7 agrees with *Pleisi* albeit for another reason. *Pischei Teshuvah* §3 assumes that *Maharik* cited in note 57 also agrees with *Pleisi*. See *Pische Zuta* §5 and *Darchei Teshuvah* §11 and §26.

52. Maharal of Prague according to *Taz* §2.

53. *Toras HaShelamim* 185:3. See *Darchei Teshuvah* §15.

54. *Pischei Teshuvah* 185:5 citing *Beis Shmuel*, E.H. 19:22. See also *Darchei Teshuvah* §20.

4. Even cases 1,2 and 3, in which an *amasla* is ineffective, have exceptions:

> a. If the husband knows that the *amasla* is true,[55] and certainly if he was privy to it originally,[56] it is accepted.
>
> b. If the intended effect was possible only through donning *niddah* clothes, announcing her *niddah* status or retaining the *niddah* status for thirty days, the *amasla* is accepted.[57]

5. *Amasla* cannot establish a fact:

Some *Poskim* maintain that an *amasla* works only to undo the original statement, but it cannot establish a fact of its own. Two examples of this concept follow:

> a. A woman who, upon returning from the *mikveh*, claims that she did not immerse herself, and then retracts her statement, is not believed. In the opinion of some *Poskim*, even if she offers an *amasla* it may not be accepted. Since she had been in the forbidden state of *niddus*, even if the *amasla* removes her negative claim, i.e., that she was not *tovel*, we have no positive basis to assume that she was *tovel*.[58] A Rav must be consulted.[59]

---

55. Responsa *Rema* 2. *Rema* cites a fascinating proof. Yitzchok told Avimelech, king of the Philistines, that Rivkah was his sister. Nevertheless, he did not refrain from privately treating her as his wife although even a Noahide is forbidden to marry his sister. Obviously, his *amasla* was that he feared being killed because of her. In this case, since both he and Rivkah knew of the *amasla* beforehand, it was accepted. See a similar reasoning in *Taz* §2.

56. *Taz* §2.

57. Responsa *Rema* 2. The case in question pertains to a woman who had three miscarriages and suspected that she was a victim of *ayin hara* — an "evil eye" (caused perhaps by jealousy of her pregnancy). Thus, in the beginning of her pregnancy, she announced that she was a *niddah* in order to hide her pregnancy as long as possible. See also *Shach* 185:5 and responsa *Chasam Sofer* (Y.D. 9), cited in *Pischei Teshuvah* 185:5. However, *Toras HaShelamim* §6 cites responsa *Maharik* 87, who rules that, even in this case, her retraction is not accepted. See *Darchei Teshuvah* §11 and note 51 above.

58. Although usually her statement that she was *tovel* is accepted, in this case, it merely cancels the previous statement. Thus, the two statements are negated.

59. See *Pische Zuta* §4. See *Pri Deah* (S.L. §5) for an interesting variation of this question. He cites the following case: A woman's time of *tevilah* was a certain night. Throughout the night, she continued to observe the laws of *harchakos* (the separations which a *niddah* and her husband must observe). The husband assumed that she was not *tovel* and acted accordingly. The following evening, she told her husband that she actually was *tovel* the previous night and offers an *amasla* for not telling him so then. *Pri Deah* offers two reasons to be lenient in this case: a) Since the fact of her *tevilah* can easily be verified by asking the *mikveh* attendant, she would certainly not lie. b) She did not actually say that she was not *tovel*; she merely implied so with her behavior.

b. A woman who tells her husband at the time of her expected period that the period arrived may not be able to retract that statement, even with an *amasla*.[60]

6. Cases when suspicion is justified:

At times, we may hesitate to accept an *amasla* because the nature of the events leads us to suspect that the woman is being less than honest.

a. A woman who originally gives one excuse for declaring herself a *niddah*, but, when informed that it is not acceptable, presents another *amasla*, is not believed.[61]

b. A woman tells her husband that her *tevilah* will be Wednesday night. Later, she claims that she was mistaken and actually the *tevilah* should be Tuesday night. *Poskim* rule that if this took place before Tuesday, one may believe her. If, however, she retracts on Tuesday, there is reason to suspect that she is impatient and wishes to immerse immediately. A punctilious individual should ask her to delay her *tevilah* until Wednesday.[62]

7. Caution in resolving questions of *amasla*:

A husband should not judge a situation of *amasla* by himself. He should discuss it with a Rav.[63] Even if an *amasla* is acceptable in *halachah*, some doubt remains. Therefore, considering the fact that the subject regards a prohibition punishable by *kares*, if the husband chooses not to accept the retraction, it is a pious act.[64]

C. Encouraging a retraction

One should never ask one's wife, "Perhaps you were mistaken when

---

60. See *sefer Cheiker Halachah* (*Amasla*, 2), citing responsa *Shoel U'Meishiv* and *Besamim Rosh*. *Cheiker Halachah* also contends that since one assumes that the *vest* comes at its expected time, her statement that the *vest* arrived has an added validity — *raglayim l'davar* — and cannot be retracted, even with an *amasla*. See *Cheiker Halachah* and *Pri Deah* (S.L. 185:5) for an interesting discussion of this topic. However, *Pische Zuta* §4 cites *Mei Niddah* who maintains that an *amasla* is accepted in this case.

61. *Darchei Teshuvah* §19, citing *Pardes Rimonim*.

62. Responsa *Chasam Sofer*, Y.D. 185, cited in *Darchei Teshuvah* 185:7.

63. Responsa *K'sav Sofer*, Y.D. 87.

64. *Rema* 185:3. In this case, she certainly should not recite a *b'rachah* over the *tevilah* (*Darchei Teshuvah* §29).

you thought you became a *niddah*?" This may encourage her to be untruthful.[65]

D. Using a *niddah* status in jest or quarrel

It should be clear from these *halachos* that it is improper to jest about the question of being a *niddah* or to use this issue as a weapon in a quarrel. The *niddah* status should never be brought into marital conflicts and disagreements.

III. Reliability with regard to colors

A. Judgment of colors by an amateur

Judging colors on a *bedikah* cloth or garment is very difficult. A Rav spends countless hours developing his skill and has years of experience in examining innumerable cloths. A Rav may be stricter with certain *bedikos*, i.e., a *hefseik taharah* or a *moch dachuk*, or he may be lenient with other *bedikos* because of a combination of factors. At times, a slight variation of shade may determine that a color is *tamei*. A Rav may permit a *bedikah* cloth with a questionable stain if, according to his experience, he understands that the stain is from a foreign source. We can therefore easily understand the following *halachos*:

> 1. A woman who finds a stain similar to one that was previously permitted by a Rav should not rely upon that fact, but must show the stain to a Rav. Indeed, some *Poskim* maintain that a woman should never evaluate the color of a stain herself and must always show it to a Rav.[66] Nevertheless, a woman eventually develops a sense of which colors are clearly and obviously acceptable under all circumstances. A woman who finds such a stain need not show it to a Rav. However, she should approach this with utmost caution and she must be absolutely certain that the color is permitted.[67]

---

65. *Darchei Teshuvah* 185:3 citing *Chavos Daas* §4[b]. However, if the husband understands that she declared herself a *niddah* solely because of anger, he may ask her if that was the cause (*Chavos Daas* ibid.)

66. *Sidrei Taharah* 188:3, cited in *Pischei Teshuvah* §6, based on *Rashi* (*Niddah* 20b).

67. See *Darchei Teshuvah* 188:25. *Shiurei Sheivet HaLeivi* 188:2[4] cites *Binas Adam* §5, who contends that *Rashi* cited above was referring to Talmudic times when one needed expertise to differentiate between shades of red. However, today that all reds are considered *tamei* a woman may decide on her own that a stain is not similar to red in any way.

One should note that even a brown stain may render a woman a *niddah;* see Chapter Six.

2. While a woman who is absolutely certain regarding the color of the stain may rely upon her own experience, a woman who shows a stain to another woman cannot rely upon the second woman's claim that she obtained a lenient ruling on a similar color.[68] We suspect that the second woman may be mistaken in her comparison. However, if the second woman is so absolutely certain that the color is acceptable that she maintains that it is needless to ask about it, she is relied upon.[69] Similarly, the second woman may take the cloth itself to a Rav, and report back his ruling.[70]

B. A questionable *bedikah* cloth

Poskim discuss the following case: A woman brings a *bedikah* cloth to a Rav and claims that she once showed the exact same color on a different cloth to an authority who permitted it.[71] If the second Rav himself is unsure about the *halachic* status of the color, he cannot approve the color based upon the alleged ruling of the first Rav.[72] This is not necessarily due to mistrust of the woman's testimony, but to the fact that the Rav himself is uncertain about the questionable color. Perhaps the woman, too, is less than certain of her comparison of colors. If she produces the original stain that she claims was permitted by the first Rav and it is indeed similar to the color before us, her comparison is obviously correct. Nevertheless, some *Poskim* contend that we cannot rely upon her claim.[73] Others disagree.[74]

---

68. *Shach* 188:7, *Aruch HaShulchan* §21.

69. See *Binas Adam* 5 and *Divrei Chaim* 2:81.

70. *Shach* ibid.

71. Obviously, we are discussing a case where the authority quoted is an accepted authority whose judgment we would accept.

72. 188:2.

73. *Toras HaShelamim* 188:5. See *Badei HaShulchan* 188:2 *Biurim* s.v. "וֹהיא," who presents two reasons for this: either a) her claim cannot override the doubts that we have about the color. Thus, we suspect that she may be misrepresenting the facts. Or, b) we accept her claim but we suspect that the color of the original stain may have changed since shown to the first Rav. The stain may have been acceptable when shown to the first Rav but changed in the interim to an unacceptable color. Therefore, while the comparison of the two colors may be correct, the original approval may be irrelevant.

74. *Pardes Rimonim* (M.Z. 188 end of 4) and others cited in *Darchei Teshuvah* §26.

C. A *bedikah* cloth that was lost

1. A cloth lost before inspection:

A *bedikah* cloth that is lost before inspection may be ignored. It is, in effect, as if the *bedikah* was not done.[75] Thus, if the *bedikah* was a necessary *bedikah*, it must be repeated. If a *bedikah* was required to confirm that no blood appeared and the cloth is lost without inspection we have no confirmation. For example, if the *bedikah* cloth of a *hefseik taharah* is lost before inspection, it is as if she had not done her *hefseik taharah* and she cannot begin the seven "clean" days. If the *bedikah* was the only one done during the first day or last day of the seven "clean" days, it is as if she had not done those *bedikos* and her seven days may be invalidated. A Rav must be consulted.

2. A cloth lost after inspection:

> a. If she noticed a questionable color on the cloth before it was lost, and she cannot identify the color, there is reason to suspect that the color may have been unacceptable.[76]
>
> b. If she can identify the color as non-problematic, e.g., she describes the color[77] or she shows a color[78] that she claims is exactly the same color as that on the cloth that was lost, her claim is accepted.[79]

---

75. We have no reason to assume that there was a blood stain on the cloth. If this occurred on the day of her *vest kavuah*, *Chavos Daas* 184:11[b] considers the possibility that she is *temei'ah* since she may have had a *hargashah* at the time of the *bedikah*. While *Aruch HaShulchan* §38 agrees with *Chavos Daas*, *Pardes Rimonim* (M.Z. 184:13) and *Chazon Ish, Y.D.* 80:22, disagree and rule that she merely repeats the *bedikah*. *Taharas Yisrael* §71 is lenient with regard to a *bedikah* cloth that is lost by accident and stringent with regard to one purposely discarded. See also *Shiurei Sheivet HaLeivi* 184:9[6].

76. *Chochmas Adam* 111:3 (and in *Binas Adam* 5) rules that she is *temei'ah* since this is a *safek deOraisa* — a doubt regarding Torah law. See, however, responsa *Maharsham* 3:214 who is lenient if the color of the stain was not a real red. He bases his opinion on the fact that since today we consider any red *tamei*, thus if the stain was not actually red but merely slightly reddish, it certainly is not one of the four types of red that are *tamei* according to Torah law. Thus, the doubt regarding the color is merely a *safek deRabbanan*. See *Tzemach Tzedek, Y.D.* 124, who may not agree with this. See also *Shaarei Taharah* p. 147 and *Sheivet HaLeivi* 3:119(9). If a *kesem* is lost under similar circumstances (i.e., she is unsure of the color), *Chochmas Adam* 113:29 is lenient. See, however, *Pische Zuta* 190:47,48 who cites many opposing opinions. See also *Taharas Yisrael* 190:133.

77. *Binas Adam* 5, e.g., she claims it was canary yellow.

78. See *Shiurei Sheivet HaLeivi* 188:2[3].

79. 188:2.

D. Relating a *halachic* decision

1. A husband may accept the claim of his wife that a Rav ruled leniently on her *bedikah* cloth,[80] even if she does not divulge the name of the Rav.[81]

2. If woman claims that a Rav ruled leniently on her *bedikah* cloth,[82] and she is subsequently contradicted[83] by the Rav himself,[84] the Rav's denial is accepted rather than her claim.[85] If, however, the Rav is not accessible, and someone else claims that the Rav never permitted the cloth, the woman's original claim stands intact.[86]

V. Deciding *halachic* matters regarding one's wife

A Rav may rule on the *bedikos* of his own wife,[87] even during the seven "clean" days.[88] Some authorities differentiate between ruling on a

---

80. *Shach* 188:7.

81. *Yad Avraham* 185:3.

82. *Pleisi* §3 rules that this *halachah* pertains only to a *bedikah* cloth, not to a *kesem*. A *kesem* is merely Rabbinic; thus, we may rely upon the woman's word as opposed to the denial of the original Rav. *Toras HaShelamim* §7 does not differentiate between the two. In either case, the Rav is believed; see also *Darchei Teshuvah* §35. *Shiurei Sheivet HaLeivi* notes that later authorities follow the stricter view of *Toras HaShelamim*.

83. *Chavos Daas* §6[b], rules that even if we are convinced that the woman is truthful in her claim that the Rav originally permitted the *bedikah*, nevertheless the Rav is believed since the Rav has the option of retracting his original ruling.

84. Who either claims that he was never shown the *bedikah* or that he was shown the *bedikah*, but ruled it unacceptable (*Darchei Teshuvah* 37).

85. *Rema* 185:3. This is an axiomatic principle in *halachah:* The person quoted is always believed more than the quoter (*Shach* §6). According to *Chavos Daas* cited above, note 83, even if it seems probable that the woman is truthful that the Rav permitted the *bedikah*, we accept the Rav's denial. We assume that he realized later that he was mistaken in his original ruling. However, according to *Pardes Rimonim* (cited in *Darchei Teshuvah* §38) in this case, the woman may be believed. See *Badei HaShulchan* 185:37, who notes that if she is convinced that the Rav permitted the *bedikah*, she should not recite a *b'rachah* on the *tevilah*.

86. *Taz* §3.

87. *Shach* 188:7.

88. See *Binas Adam* 3, *Maharam Shick, Y.D.* 30. Similarly, he may rule on her *hefseik taharah* and *bedikos* of the first three of the "clean" days (see *Darchei Teshuvah* 188:24).

color of a *bedikah* and ruling on the validity of a *tevilah*. They maintain, regarding the first case, that since a woman does not continuously have a flow, his decision that the flow stopped is not contrary to an established fact (*chazakah*). However, in the second case, since a woman who is a *niddah* is continuously *tamei* until she immerses in a *mikveh*, his decision to validate the *tevilah* runs counter to her previous state (also a *chazakah*).[89] Others do not differentiate and maintain that a Rav may even validate his wife's *tevilah*.[90]

---

89. *Chochmas Adam* 109:6 (cited in *Pischei Teshuvah* 188:6), see *Binas Adam* ibid. and *Darchei Teshuvah* 188:24. *Badei HaShulchan* 188:27 (based upon Y.D. 142:9) notes that if his decision is based upon a clearly defined *halachah,* he may decide even in this case.

90. The established fact of *tumah* is not considered a *chazakah* since it can be undone through *tevilah. Aruch HaShulchan* 188:22, *Daas Torah* 18:44, *Chavos Yair* 122, *Maharam Shick,* Y.D. 35. *Shiurei Sheivet HaLeivi* 188, end of 3, contends that most authorities follow this lenient opinion.

BOOK TWO

בדיקות
Bedikos —
Internal Examinations

Chapter Five — Bedikos: Why, When and How
Chapter Six — Bedikos: Inspecting the Bedikah
Cloth

CHAPTER FIVE

בדיקות
Bedikos: Why, When and How

☐ The distinction between a stain on a *bedikah* cloth
  and a *kesem*.

☐ *Eid habaduk*: a pre-checked examination cloth.

☐ The proper cloth to be used for *bedikos*.

☐ The manner in which a *bedikah* is done.

☐ *Bedikos*: when required, when to be avoided.

HALACHIC OVERVIEW

A discharge of uterine blood into the vagina renders a woman a *niddah*, even if the blood does not leave the body. A *bedikah* is an examination of the vaginal canal with a cloth to determine whether any blood is present. A woman is normally required to do *bedikos* at two points in her monthly cycle: a) on the day of her expected period (the *yom havest*). Although she is presently *tehorah* she is required to do *bedikos* to prove that her status has not changed and b) at the time that she is in a *temei'ah* status but wishes to begin her purification process. She is then required to do a series of *bedikos* to ensure that her menstruation has completely ended.

Halachah treats blood seen as a result of *bedikos* and *kesamim* (stains found upon a garment, an object or on her body) differently. Blood from a *bedikah* renders a woman a *niddah* according to Torah law. Therefore, it renders a woman a *niddah*, regardless of the size of the stain or the color of the cloth. A *kesem*, on the other hand, renders her a *niddah* according to Rabbinic law only. Therefore, it renders her a *niddah* only if the stain larger than is the size of a *gris* (the size of a U.S. penny) and only if found upon a white garment or upon an object that is *mekabel tumah* (susceptible to *tumah*).

Preparing to do a *bedikah*:

1. When a woman does a *bedikah*, she must use a cloth pre-checked for cleanliness. The cloth must be inspected by either the woman herself or anyone else, and found to be stain-free. A washed cloth is considered stain-free even if it had not been inspected. In addition, from the time of inspection or washing until it is used, the cloth must be kept in a place that would not compromise its cleanliness.

2. The proper cloth for *bedikah* must be: a) clean, b) white, c) soft, d) of a proper size and e) of a proper material.

> ◄ If the cloth is unclean or even unchecked for stains, we are unable to determine whether a stain found upon it after a *bedikah* was caused by the *bedikah* itself or was on the cloth beforehand.
> ◄ A material of any color other than white may mask a light shade of red and is therefore unfit for use as a *bedikah* cloth.
> ◄ A *bedikah* cloth should be soft. A soft cloth is preferable since it i) is not likely to injure the surface of the vagina, ii) is easier to manipulate into all the crevices of the vagina and iii) is absorbent. The most suitable material for *bedikos* is soft cotton cloth.

• A *bedikah* cloth must be large enough to enable the woman to move it into all crevices of her vagina. *Poskim* generally assume that the proper size of a *bedikah* cloth betwwen three and four inches square.

• One should not use a tampon for a *bedikah* since it cannot be maneuvered into all the crevices in the vagina.

3. A *bedikah* should be done in the following manner:

• The cloth to be used should be checked carefully on both sides to ensure that it is free of any spots. A woman should check the cleanliness of her hands before she handles the *bedikah* cloth.

• A woman performing a *hefseik taharah* should wash the external area beforehand (a *hefseik taharah* is the *bedikah* done before a woman begins counting the seven "clean" days. Its *halachos* will be explained in Volume Two).

• A *bedikah* should be done while standing with one foot lifted on a chair. The woman should place the center of the cloth on her fingertip and fold it over her extended finger. She then should insert the cloth into the vaginal canal as deeply as possible and then gradually remove the cloth while slowly rotating in a manner that ensures, to the best of her ability, that the cloth touches the entire surface of the vaginal canal. She must insert the cloth into all corners and crevices of the vagina.

• A *besulah* (doing *bedikos* in preparation for marriage) usually cannot insert the cloth deeply into the vagina. She should nevertheless insert it as far as she is able and rotate it so that it touches all possible areas while being careful not to injure herself.

• A woman who finds *bedikos* difficult to perform should consult a Rav.

4. Examining the cloth:

• The entire surface of the *bedikah* cloth, including its outer edges, should be examined carefully immediately after use. The cloth may be inspected while it is still damp; one need not wait until it dries.

• **Even the smallest reddish or black speck, visible to the naked eye, found upon a *bedikah* cloth renders the woman a *niddah*.** This should not be confused with a *kesem*, which is insignificant when less than a prescribed size (see Chapter Eight).

◦᷂ A *bedikah* cloth should preferably be inspected during the day in natural light. However, a *bedikah* done at night may be examined at night with an electric light. If the cloth has no trace of any problematic color, it may be discarded; it need not be kept for further inspection by day. If the stain seems even slightly problematic it should be keep for an inspection by daylight.

◦᷂ Any stain found on a *bedikah* cloth must be inspected very carefully. The color is judged not only by its general appearance but by every shade and hue that may be present, regardless of how small. Thus, a seemingly innocent yellow may have, on closer inspection, a slightly reddish hue in one area, a reddish border or a red or black dot which must be shown to a Rav.

5. Asking a *sheilah:*

◦᷂ One should not take *bedikos* lightly. A blood stain on a *bedikah* cloth may render a woman a *niddah* according to Torah law. One who erroneously dismisses a blood stain on a *bedikah* risks transgressing an *issur kares.* This should weigh heavily upon both husband and wife. They should make no assumptions. Stains which seem the least bit problematic must be shown to a Rav.

◦᷂ At the same time one should not disqualify a questionable *bedikah* without consulting a Rav. A woman should make every effort to maintain her status of *taharah* and to return to that status as quickly as possible after her *niddus* period. Therefore, any questionable *bedikah* should be submitted to a Rav.

◦᷂ Newlyweds are not sufficiently acquainted with the color variations and are encouraged to show any shade to a Rav. Eventually, they will learn from experience to differentiate between those colors that are not questionable and those that must always be shown to a Rav.

◦᷂ Even more experienced couples may have trouble differentiating between various shades and colors. Some browns are acceptable, others are not. All questionable *bedikah* cloths must be shown to a Rav. In the interim the couple should assume that the *bedikah* is unacceptable and must act as if the woman is actually a *niddah.*

6. Storing a *bedikah* cloth:

- ❧ A *bedikah* cloth with a questionable stain to be shown to a Rav should be stored properly. It should not be placed on any unclean surface. Preferably, it should be placed, when dry, in an envelope or open plastic bag. A damp cloth may stick to the surface of a paper bag or change colors unnaturally when placed while damp in a plastic bag.
- ❧ Colors often change as they dry. Yet, one need not wait until the stain dries before judging its color. Conversely, it is not necessary to show the *bedikah* cloth to a Rav while still damp. One may wait until it dries. However, one should not keep the cloth for a long period of time since colors fade with the passage of time. If the *bedikah* cloth had a reddish stain which faded and turned brown, the Rav should be notified when shown the *bedikah*.
- ❧ Under normal circumstances, one should not save the *bedikos* of several days to show all at once (as *bedikos* often change colors during the course of several days). Rather each *bedikah* should be shown to the Rav the same or the following day.

7. Marking *bedikah* cloths:

- ❧ If one must save the *bedikos* of several days, they should be clearly marked, identifying them as a *hefseik taharah, moch dachuk,* or a simple *bedikah*. Even simple *bedikos* should be marked to indicate the day and time they were done, e.g., 1A, 1AM or 1M (day one, first i.e., morning, *bedikah*), 3B or 3PM (third day, second, i.e., afternoon, *bedikah*). The marking should be done on the edge of the cloth or on the string.
- ❧ One should call attention to an extremely small and difficult-to-locate spot by marking it with either an identifying arrow or with a circle drawn around it, preferably with a blue or green pen or one may stick a pin close to the spot.

8. Many women are embarrassed and reluctant to show their *sheilos* to a Rav. In this regard, it should be noted that a Rav is a trained professional who knows how to deal with these questions discreetly. Understandably, some women may still hesitate to show their *sheilos* to a community member. Therefore, many *Rabbonim* permit women to drop their *sheilos* in a mailbox along with an identifying phone number or other marking. The Rav can then call the phone number or be available by phone for those

women who wish to call him. While this method is acceptable, it has significant drawbacks. A Rav does not answer all questions in an identical manner. Factors such as those outlined in 9 below may impact on the Rav's decision. A Rav who is not in possession of all the facts and is unfamiliar with the woman's history loses flexibility.

9. A Rav does not merely judge colors. He considers many other factors in reaching his decision. It is therefore imperative that one draw the Rav's attention to any of the following:

- The cloth was not well checked before the *bedikah*.

- The cloth being shown is a *hefseik taharah*, a *moch dachuk* or a regular *bedikah*. In the latter case one should specify which of the seven "clean" days the *bedikah* cloth is from or whether the *bedikah* is from the day of, or the days preceding, her expected period.

- The woman felt a sensation of an internal flow before she did the *bedikah* or found the *kesem*. Similarly, the Rav should be notified if she found the *kesem* after cohabitation or immediately after urination.

- There is reason to suspect that the stain on the *bedikah* cloth or on her garment came from another source, e.g., she has hemorrhoids or a vaginal infection or irritation.

- The *bedikah* cloth or *kesem* is from a pregnant or nursing woman.

- The *sheilah* is from a bride before her wedding or from a recently married bride.

- The woman has had unusual difficulty producing a clean *hefseik taharah*, or has often found stains during her seven "clean" days.

10. Once a Rav rules that a *bedikah* cloth is *tamei*, one may not show it to another Rav, unless one informs the second Rav of the original decision.

11. If a woman loses a *bedikah* cloth before she has a chance to inspect it, a Rav should be consulted.

12. There are times when a *bedikah* is required; otherwise, a woman should avoid doing *bedikos*. Excessive *bedikos* may irritate the vagina which could cause blood to appear on the cloth. A woman is obligated to do the following *bedikos:*

- The *hefseik taharah:* A woman cannot begin her seven "clean" days without doing a *hefseik taharah.* This *bedikah* is done to prove that her menstruation has definitely ended.

- *Moch dachuk:* After the *hefseik taharah* is done, a woman should insert a *moch dachuk.* This is a cloth inserted into the vagina before sundown of the day preceding the seven "clean" days and is removed after dusk of that same day.

- The seven "clean" days: A woman is required to check herself internally twice during each of the seven "clean" days. One *bedikah* is done in the morning and one during the late afternoon.

- The day of the expected *vest:* A woman must do a *bedikah* on the day of her expected period, as is determined by the rules of *vestos.* The method by which one computes the expected day of the *vest* and the amount of *bedikos* required is explained in Book Four.

- A woman who has not established a *vest (vest kavuah)* is required to do a *bedikah* on the thirtieth day from the beginning of her last period. This is explained in Chapter Twenty-Two.

- A woman who felt a uterine or vaginal discharge must immediately do a *bedikah* to ascertain whether or not any uterine bleeding has occurred. This *halachah* is explained in Chapter Three.

- A woman who has no *vest kavuah* is required to do *bedikos* the first three times she cohabits with her husband after the earliest time her period normally comes. This is explained in Chapter Fourteen.

13. One who does a *bedikah* and suspects that the color may be unacceptable cannot merely repeat the *bedikah.* If she is in the middle of her seven "clean" days and finds blood on a *bedikah* cloth, she must repeat the *hefseik taharah* and the seven "clean" days. Similarly, if she finds blood on a *bedikah* done while she is in a *tehorah* state, she is a *niddah,* regardless of the result of a second *bedikah.* A second *bedikah* cannot negate the fact that blood was found on the first cloth. Indeed, contrary to the woman's aspirations, the second *bedikah* may make matters worse and cause her to become a *niddah.* Rather, the first *bedikah* cloth should be shown to a Rav.

14. There is one situation where a repeat *bedikah* should be done. A woman who attempted a *hefseik taharah* and finds blood on the cloth should repeat the *bedikah*. In this case, the first *hefseik taharah* has no practical effect upon her status since she previously was *temei'ah*. Thus, she has much to gain by attempting an additional *hefseik taharah* before sundown. Some *Poskim* require that a woman should wait a few minutes between each *bedikah*.

15. A woman who finds a *kesem* should <u>not</u> do a *bedikah*; rather, the *kesem* should be shown to a Rav. A *kesem* which should render her a *niddah* will do so in spite of a clear *bedikah* done afterwards. On the other hand, an unacceptable *bedikah* following a *kesem* will render the woman a *niddah* regardless of the status of the *kesem*. There is nothing to gain and much to lose by doing a *bedikah* after finding a *kesem*.

16. A woman who finds a stain on a tissue used to clean herself after urination should not check herself, even externally, with another tissue. She should consult a Rav and inquire whether she is considered a *niddah*. A woman should avoid looking at her tissues. It is unnecessary and unwise.

17. A woman who underwent a gynecological examination is not required to do a *bedikah* afterwards. However, if the doctor used an instrument that penetrated the uterus, she may be *temei'ah* even if no blood appears upon the *bedikah* cloth. A Rav should be consulted. These issues are discussed in Chapter Twenty-Three.

Introduction

So much of *Hilchos Niddah* revolves around the intricacies of *bedikos* — when they are required, how they should be done and the acceptability of the various shades of color found upon the *bedikah* cloth — that one may forget the actual purpose of a *bedikah,* namely, to determine whether any uterine blood is found in the vaginal canal. The discharge of even a minute amount of uterine blood into the vagina renders a woman a *niddah* immediately, even if the blood does not leave the body. Therefore, it is critical that a woman be aware of the presence of blood in the vaginal canal. Although we cannot expect a woman to constantly inspect herself for blood, there are times when inspection is mandatory, and logically so. *Bedikos* are normally required at two critical junctures in a woman's monthly cycle: a) at the time her period is expected (although she is still *tehorah*), since at that time we have reason to suspect that a blood flow may have begun although it is not externally apparent; and b) when she wishes to begin her purification process, a series of *bedikos* are required to ensure that the menstrual flow has ended and blood is no longer present in her vagina. See Section IV for a detailed discussion regarding when *bedikos* are required.

I. Blood found upon a *bedikah* cloth and blood found upon a garment

There is a fundamental distinction in *Hilchos Niddah* between blood found upon a *bedikah* cloth and a *kesem* (a stain found upon a woman's garment, an object or her body). This distinction is rooted in the Biblical rule that imposes *niddus* on a woman solely when her uterine flow is accompanied by a *hargashah* — a particular physical sensation associated with the onset of a uterine blood flow. In the opinion of most *Poskim*,[1] blood flow alone, without a *hargashah,* does not render a woman a *niddah* according to Torah law. Accordingly, a *kesem* which is not associated with a *hargashah* renders a woman a *niddah* under Rabbinic law only. By contrast, when she finds blood on a *bedikah* cloth we assume that it was accompanied by a *hargashah,* since a uterine flow is usually accompanied by a *hargashah.*[2] Although the woman may believe that she has not felt a *hargashah,* we are concerned that she may mistakenly have attributed the *hargashah* sensation to the internal manipulations of the *bedikah* cloth.

Kesamim and bedikos differ for another reason in terms of Torah law. A woman becomes a *niddah* according to Torah law only if we have strong reason to assume that the blood came from her uterus. Blood found in the vagina is assumed to originate in the uterus since that is the source of most vaginal blood. However, a blood stain found upon a garment and the like may originate from a source other than the uterus. Indeed it may have originated from a source external to the woman. Therefore, a *kesem* renders a woman a *niddah* under Rabbinic law only. This is true even if we are not aware of any possible source other than the vagina. However, blood on a *bedikah* cloth renders a woman a *niddah* by Torah law since it cannot generally be attributed to any source other than menstrual bleeding.

In summary, blood on a *bedikah* cloth, as opposed to a *kesem,* renders a woman a *niddah* under Torah law for two reasons:

---

1. See Appendix A where the different opinions among Poskim are discussed in detail.

2. *Rambam* (Hil. Issurei Biah) 9:1. *Poskim* disagree whether this is a positive assumption, i.e., we assume, with certainty, that she had a *hargashah* since blood usually appears accompanied by *hargashah,* or a speculative assumption, i.e., we are concerned that there <u>may</u> have been a *hargashah.* See Chapter Three, note 7.

a) A *bedikah*, as opposed to a *kesem*, is associated with a *hargashah* and b) blood on a *bedikah* is strongly assumed to originate in the uterus.

The *halachos* pertaining to a *kesem* are more lenient than those pertaining to *bedikos*. A *kesem* renders a woman a *niddah* only if it is the size of a *gris* and only if it is found on a white garment. These are fundamental leniencies that were incorporated into the original laws of *kesamim* as explained in detail in Book Three. However, a *bedikah* is much stricter. *Halachah* treats a blood stain on a *bedikah* cloth with all the severity of a blood flow.[3] All the lenient *halachos* regarding *kesamim* do not apply to *bedikos*. A blood stain on a *bedikah* cloth renders a woman a *niddah*, regardless of the size of the stain or the color of the cloth. The following additional *halachic* stringencies apply only to a *bedikah*:

> 1. Unlike a *kesem* which may, in some circumstances, be attributed to any reasonable source other than uterine blood (see Chapter Eleven), a stain on a *bedikah* cloth may only be attributed to a more definite source (e.g., a vaginal or cervical bruise that is known to be bleeding). See Chapter Twenty-Three for a detailed discussion of the issues involved.

> 2. A *bedikah* is judged more cautiously than a *kesem*. There are shades or colors which might be dismissed in a *kesem* but which would render a woman a *niddah* when found on a *bedikah* cloth.[4]

II. *Eid bedikah:* the examination cloth

A. The categories of cloths used for *bedikah*

"*Eid habaduk*" is the term used in *halachah* for the *bedikah* cloth. The cloth is called "*eid*," a witness, because it testifies to the woman's *halachic* status,[5] or because we find[6] the Hebrew word "עד" used for a

---

3. Indeed, according to *Shulchan Aruch, Y.D.* 190:54, a blood stain on an examination cloth is the equivalent of a blood flow, even regarding *vestos*. Thus, a woman who finds a stain on a *bedikah* cloth must separate from her husband on the same date of the following month. She must also count an interval from the day of that *bedikah*. We will note in Chapter Thirteen that this *halachah* is not applied in most cases.

4. See Chapter Six, Section IV for a detailed discussion of various colors.

5. See *Tosfos Yom Tov, Niddah* 8:4.

6. *Yeshayahu* 64:5.

piece of cloth.[7] The term *"eid habaduk"* is used to distinguish it from an *"eid she'aino baduk."* The former is a cloth which has been pre-checked for stains; the latter is a cloth which has not been pre-checked. The category of *eid she'aino baduk* can be subdivided into *"eid beinoni"* (lit. a "middle" or "average" *eid*) and *"eid b'chezkas meluchlach"* (lit. a cloth assumed to be soiled).

> ### 1. *Eid habaduk:*
>
> In order not to compromise the color of a *bedikah* stain, a woman must use a pre-checked cloth for all required *bedikos.* A cloth that is not pre-checked may be soiled and may hide a blood stain.[8] In addition, the soiled cloth may affect the color of a blood stain appearing on it. For example, a cloth soiled with a yellow stain may cause a speck of blood to appear brownish. A woman who uses such a cloth may not realize that she has become *temei'ah* and fail to act accordingly. Similarly, an unchecked cloth may have a red stain from an unrelated source. When subsequent to a *bedikah* the stain is noticed on the cloth, we must assume that it came from the vagina and it renders the woman a *niddah.* This could be avoided by using a pre-checked cloth.
>
> A cloth is considered an *eid habaduk* if, prior to use, it was checked, found to be clean and stored in a place that could not compromise its cleanliness.[9] A washed cloth is considered clean even if it was not checked before the *bedikah,* since we assume that the washing removes all stains.[10] In the course of this work, we will assume that every *bedikah* cloth is an *eid habaduk* since this is the type of cloth that is, and should always be, used for *bedikos.* At times, a Rav may dismiss a hardly noticeable stain on a *bedikah* cloth if he assumes that the cloth was not checked thor-

---

7. *Rema* 190:33.1.

8. See *Rashi, Niddah* 17a.

9. 190:38, *Chochmas Adam* 113:36. See *Badei HaShulchan, Biurim* 190:35 s.v. "כל שבדקתו," who cites the opinion of *Sidrei Taharah* §58 and *Beis Meir* 190:36 that a cloth is considered *baduk* even if it was left lying in the open, not stored in a location that preserves its cleanliness (e.g., a drawer). However, *Graz* §71 contends that a cloth is considered *baduk* only if after inspection it was placed in a location that preserves its cleanliness. See *Shiurei Sheivet HaLeivi* 190:38[1] regarding the length of time that may elapse between the original checking and its use for *bedikah.* He maintains that a Rav must decide each case individually based upon the type of location in which it lay in the open.

10. Although, in previous generations, washing did not remove all stains, see 190:46, today, clothes are washed more thoroughly (*Graz* 190:93) and with detergents (*Lechem VeSimlah* 190:54[s]). See also *Shiurei Sheivet HaLeivi* §39 and *Badei HaShulchan* §354.

oughly enough before the *bedikah* to notice a speck of that size. In this case, he considers the cloth *aino baduk* for stains so small.[11]

2. *Eid beinoni:*

An ordinary cloth, i.e., a cloth that was not pre-checked, but one which is assumed to be unsoiled, is called an *"eid beinoni"* — an "intermediate cloth." For example, a garment that was washed, then worn and subsequently used as a *bedikah* cloth is an *eid beinoni*.[12]

3. *Eid b'chezkas meluchlach:*

A cloth taken from a place that could easily soil a clean garment is assumed to be unclean even if the cloth was checked before it was placed there. Thus, a cloth taken from a pile of soiled laundry is an *"eid b'chezkas meluchlach"* (a cloth assumed to be unclean).[13]

A woman who uses an *eid beinoni* or an *eid b'chezkas meluchlach* to check herself internally and finds a questionable stain upon it must ask a *sheilah*. *Halachah* differentiates between different sizes and shapes of stains.[14] These are difficult *halachos* that lie outside the scope of this work and entirely within the domain of a competent Rav.

At times, even a pre-checked cloth may have a status similar (although not completely comparable) to an *eid she'aino baduk*; for example, a woman who does a *bedikah* with a pre-checked cloth, but, before inspecting it, puts it in a place which may compromise its cleanliness. The *halachos* regarding this cloth are complex and are discussed in *Shulchan Aruch*.[15] Any *sheilah* of this type must be discussed with a Rav. A woman should avoid these problems and place any questionable *bedikah* cloth which must be shown to a Rav in a place that will preserve its cleanliness.

Our discussion in this chapter will be limited to the rules regarding an *eid habaduk* since women should use pre-checked or pre-washed *bedikah* cloths and inspect them immediately.

---

11. *Shiurei Sheivet HaLeivi* 183 on *Shach* §3 citing *Chazon Ish*.

12. See *Chasam Sofer, Y.D.* 150, *Sidrei Taharah* 190:55 and *Chochmas Adam* 113:36, who rule that if the stain is less than a *gris* the woman is *tehorah*. These *Poskim* base this on the fact that all garments are stained with specks of lice blood. *Shiurei Sheivet HaLeivi* 190:33[2] notes that this fact is not true today. He is, therefore, uncertain whether this leniency may be applied today.

13. See *Chochmas Adam* 113:37.

14. *Y.D.* 190:36,37.

15. *Y.D.* 190:33-37.

B. The proper cloth to be used for a *bedikah*

A *bedikah* cloth *must* be a) clean, b) white, c) soft, d) of a proper size and e) of a proper material.

1. Cleanliness:

We discussed the cleanliness of the *bedikah* cloth in the preceding section. A clean cloth is an *eid habaduk*, one that was previously checked for cleanliness. If the cloth is unclean or even unchecked for cleanliness, we are unable to determine whether a stain found upon it after a *bedikah* was caused by the *bedikah* itself or was on the cloth beforehand. In addition a stained cloth may hide or distort the color of a blood stain. A woman who uses an unchecked cloth risks needlessly having to conduct herself as a *niddah*. Worse by far is the possibility that she may become *temei'ah* without realizing it (i.e., if the blood stain is masked by the soiled cloth). A small red stain found upon an unchecked *bedikah* cloth may be *tehorah* depending upon its size and shape. However, even if the *bedikah* is *tehorah*, such a *bedikah* may be unacceptable as a required *bedikah* (e.g., a *hefseik taharah*). Even if we assume that the *bedikah* does not prove that she is *temei'ah*, it may be unacceptable as proof that she is no longer menstruating. This is a complex question which must be decided by a Rav.

2. Color:

The purpose of a *bedikah* cloth is to prove that there is no blood in the vaginal canal. Thus, the cloth must be of a color upon which any blood stain, regardless of size or depth of color, will be readily noticeable. A *bedikah* done with a colored cloth is invalid[16] since any material other than white may hide or distort a light shade of red. The *bedikah* must be repeated. Note that even though we invalidate a *bedikah* done with a colored cloth, if a blood stain is noticed on the cloth, it certainly cannot be ignored. (Colored garments are excluded only from the rules of *kesamim*, not *bedikos*, as will be explained in Chapter Nine.) A woman who checked herself with a colored cloth and found an unacceptable color is *temei'ah*.

3. Texture:

A *bedikah* cloth should be soft. A soft cloth is not likely to injure the surface of the vagina,[17] and is easy to manipulate into all the

---

16. *Biur HaGra* 196:20, see also *Tzemach Tzedek, Piskei Dinim* 196:10.

17. The purpose of this is two-fold: a) If the cloth is not soft, she may injure herself and needlessly find

crevices of the vagina. In addition a soft cloth is more absorbent and thus, more likely than a coarse cloth to pick up any blood stain.[18] Nevertheless, if a woman checked herself properly with a coarse cloth, the *bedikah* is valid.[19]

4. Thickness:

While a thinner cloth is softer than a thicker one and is therefore preferable, a very thin cloth (e.g., an old, washed-out shirt) is not preferable since it is less opaque and it may be difficult to notice a small or light stain on its surface. A thin *bedikah* cloth should be inspected by folding it or by placing it over a white sheet of paper. Similarly, a cloth with spaces between the fibers should not be used.

5. Size:

A *bedikah* cloth must be large enough to wrap the index finger from its tip to the second joint. If the cloth is too small, it cannot properly touch the entire surface of the vaginal canal. If the cloth is too large, it will be difficult to insert it into the vagina properly.[20] *Poskim* commonly assume that a *bedikah* cloth should be between three and four inches square.[21]

6. Material:

The Talmud[22] approves of *bedikah* cloths made of the following materials:

   a. Wool:
   Soft, white wool may be used.

---

blood on the cloth (*Sidrei Taharah* 196:21, see *Pische Zuta* §16). b) If the cloth is not soft, she may be concerned about injuring herself and not do a proper *bedikah* (*Rashba* cited in *Lechem VeSimlah* §10[s]).

18. *Lechem VeSimlah* 196:29[l].

19. *Sidrei Taharah* 196:21.

20. See *Pische Zuta* 196:14, who doubts whether a *bedikah* done with a large garment (as opposed to a small cloth) is acceptable even ex-post-facto. See, however, *Chasam Sofer, Y.D.* 150, who objects to using a shirt for a *bedikah* because it may not be clean. He omits a discussion of the size of the garment and seems, therefore, to maintain that size does not invalidate the *bedikah*.

21. See Halachos of Niddah (R' S. Eider) p.64 citing R' Moshe Feinstein zt"l. *Shiurei Sheivet HaLeivi* 196:6[1] writes that the proper size for the average woman is seven by seven or eight by eight centimeters (slightly larger than three inches).

22. *Niddah* 17a.

b. Flax / linen cloth:

Pre-washed linen cloth may be used.[23] Pre-washed linen is whiter,[24] softer[25] and more absorbent than unwashed linen.[26] If the cloth was not pre-washed, the *bedikah* is nevertheless valid.[27]

c. Cotton:

The Talmud advises that cotton is the best material for a *bedikah*.[28] Although it would seem that the Talmud refers to a wad of cotton,[29] *Poskim* advise against using raw cotton for several reasons: a) It is extremely difficult to rotate the cotton and insert it into all the vaginal crevices, b) strands of cotton may remain in the vagina and c) it is difficult to inspect cotton properly. According to commonly accepted practice the preferred material for *bedikos* is cotton cloth.[30]

d. Other materials:

i. Synthetic materials:

Any synthetic material is acceptable for use provided that it is sufficiently absorbent for blood to adhere to it.[31] One who must use a synthetic should test the absorbency of the cloth beforehand. Some cloths may be treated with chemicals which could minutely alter the color of a stain. Such cloths should not be used. As noted, the preferred *bedikah* cloth is cotton.

ii. Tampon:

One should not use a tampon for a *bedikah* since it cannot be maneuvered into all the crevices in the vagina.[32]

---

23. 196:6. *Poskim* mention the condition of pre-washing only regarding linen cloth. It seems that cotton does not require pre-washing. This is implied by the Talmudic source as well.

24. *Rashi, Niddah* 17a.

25. *Sidrei Taharah* 196:21 and *Lechem VeSimlah* §10[s] citing *Rashba. Sidrei Taharah* notes that if this reason is the rationale for using washed linen, she may use unwashed linen if she does not mind the roughness.

26. *Lechem VeSimlah* 196:29[l]. *Pische Zuta* §16 notes that if this is the rationale, even if she does not mind the roughness, she may not use unwashed linen. See also *Lechem* §29. Nevertheless, even according to this rationale the *bedikah* is valid *b'dieved* (since *Sidrei Taharah* §21 proves from the Talmud that the *bedikah* is valid).

27. *Sidrei Taharah* §21.

28. *Niddah* 17a, as interpreted by *Rashi*.

29. See *Sidrei Taharah* 196:22, who notes that perhaps raw cotton is better than cotton cloth.

30. *Shiurei Sheivet HaLeivi* 196:6[4], see *Poseiach Shaar* (*Miluim* 17:19).

31. *Shiurei Sheivet HaLeivi* 196:6[2].

32. Responsa *Be'er Moshe* 2:62. *Badei HaShulchan* 196:97.

iii. Paper:

Paper (e.g., a napkin or paper towel) is coarser than cloth and difficult to insert in all crevices. It should not be used for *bedikos*. Some papers (e.g., tissues) tear easily when one inserts them into the crevices of the vagina. One who, for lack of a proper *bedikah* cloth, did a *bedikah* with paper should consult a Rav.[33]

III. The manner in which a *bedikah* is performed

A *bedikah* should be done in the following manner:

1. Checking the cloth:

A woman doing a *bedikah* should carefully check on both sides of the cloth to ensure that it is free of any spots. If she neglected to do so, and then finds a questionable spot on the *bedikah* cloth, she must inform the Rav that the cloth was not checked beforehand. It is advisable that a woman also check the cleanliness of her hands before she handles the *bedikah* cloth.[34]

2. Washing and douching:

A woman doing a *hefseik taharah* should wash the external area beforehand (the *taharah* process will be explained in detail in Volume Two of this work). A woman doing a *hefseik taharah* may douche beforehand, since any remaining blood in her vagina is residue from her *niddus* and does not concern us. A *hefseik taharah* aims to demonstrate that the old flow has stopped and no new blood has appeared, thus, washing away old blood residue is not a problem. Some authorities maintain that one should wait approximately fifteen minutes between the douching and the *bedikah*.[35] A woman may bathe during

---

33. See *Tzemach Tzedek* (*Piskei Dinim* 196:10) who maintains that a *bedikah* done with any soft material is valid. See *Shiurei Sheivet HaLeivi* 196:6[2] who rules that a *bedikah* with thin paper is valid. However, it is difficult to imagine a *bedikah* done properly with soft tissue paper that tears quite easily. Similarly, it is difficult to do a proper *bedikah* with thicker paper (i.e., paper towel) since it is difficult to maneuver into all the crevices. See *Badei HaShulchan* 196:97.

34. If she does not check her hands, there may be a red stain on her hands which may soil the *bedikah* cloth. In addition, she may notice the stain on her hands after she does the *bedikah*. This stain may be considered a *kesem* and render her a *niddah*. However, if she notices the stain on her hands before she touches the vaginal area she is not necessarily a *niddah*; see Chapter Eight.

35. *Igros Moshe*, Y.D. 2:71. Responsa *Maharil Diskin* 22 requires waiting a few minutes, *Chazon Ish*, Y.D. 81, seems to require waiting a significant amount of time (זמן מרובה). *Chazon Ish* explains

the seven "clean" days in spite of the fact that she must do two *bedikos* daily.[36] A woman should preferably not douche during the seven "clean" days since she may wash away unnoticed a minute amount of uterine blood from the vagina. If she must douche during these days she should do the required *bedikah* beforehand.[37]

3. Position:

Poskim advise that a woman should do the *bedikah* while standing with one foot lifted on a chair.[38] A woman who is unable to do the *bedikah* while standing should ask a *sheilah* whether the *bedikah* can be done while reclining.[39]

4. Insertion of the cloth:

The manner in which a *bedikah* is done should not be learnt from books; it should be taught through demonstration by one's mother or *kallah* teacher. The procedure is basically as follows: The woman places the center of the cloth on her fingertip and folds it over her extended finger. She then inserts the cloth into the vaginal canal as deeply as possible[40] and

---

that a menstrual flow is generally intermittent rather than continuous. In particular, towards the end of the period, the flow occurs only briefly and at relatively larger intervals. Accordingly, since the purpose of a *hefseik taharah* is to prove that the period has ceased, it must prove that any intermittent flow has ceased as well. If a woman douches and then immediately performs a *hefseik taharah*, she has not demonstrated conclusively that the period has ended. The *hefseik taharah* may be clean only because the residual blood was washed away and the intermittent spotting has not yet resumed. *Badei HaShulchan* 196:1, *Biurim* s.v. שתפסוק, notes that since other *Poskim* make no mention of this common occurrence it seems to indicate that they disagree.

36. *Igros Moshe*, Y.D. 2:70. See *Shiurei Sheivet HaLeivi* 184 on *Taz* §13 and *Taharas HaBayis* vol. I p.132, that it is preferable that a woman not bathe on her *yom havest* (see Chapter Twenty-Two) or *onah beinonis*. If she must bathe, she should do a *bedikah* beforehand.

37. *Bach* 196, s.v. "ומ"ש ובספר המצות," explains that the reason that *Smag* requires two *bedikos* daily during the seven "clean" days is to establish that there was no previous bleeding. The morning *bedikah* establishes that there was no bleeding the previous night and the evening *bedikah* prove that there was no bleeding the previous day. According to this reason, if she douches, the *bedikah* proves nothing. However, R' Akiva Eiger (responsa *Tinyana* 60) disputes *Bach's* contention. Practically, responsa *Maharsham* 2:40 permits douching during the seven "clean" days if she made a *bedikah* previously that day. A similar position is taken in *Igros Moshe*, Y.D. 1:94, see also 2:71. See also responsa *Divrei Malkiel* 3:61 and responsa *Chelkas Yaakov* 2:87.

38. See responsa *Chasam Sofer*, Y.D. 148 and *Pische Zuta* §3.

39. See responsa *Tzitz Eliezer* 14:71. Responsa *Kineh Bosem* §97, based upon *Noda B'Yehudah* 1:46, and *Chavos Daas* 186:1[b], note that if the *bedikah* is done while reclining, a woman must insert the cloth very deeply into the vagina since blood may remain there while her body is in a prone position. See *Pischei Migadim* introduction to Chapter 8, who challenges this assertion.

then gradually moves the cloth outward while slowly rotating it in a manner that ensures, to the best of her ability, that the cloth touches the entire surface of the vaginal canal. She must insert the cloth into all corners and crevices of the vagina (*churin u'sedakin*). A woman who finds it difficult to insert the cloth in this manner should consult a Rav.[41] If she merely inserts the cloth into the vagina but not into all crevices, the *bedikah* may be invalid.[42]

A *besulah* (preparing for her wedding) usually cannot insert the cloth deeply into the vagina. She should nevertheless insert

---

40. See *Beis Yosef* 196 p. 80. It would appear from *Shulchan Aruch* 196:6 that both the *hefseik taharah* and the *bedikah* of the first day (or at least the *hefseik taharah* and the *bedikah* of any other day — *Beis Yosef*) must be inserted very deeply into the vagina. This is the opinion cited in the *Tur* (ibid.). See *Bach* who understands this to mean that the cloth should reach the cervix itself. *Beis Yosef* and *Bach* both claim that this is extremely difficult to accomplish. *Bach*, therefore, claims that reaching the cervix is merely a *mitzvah*, not a requirement. *Beis Yosef* similarly comes to the conclusion that the *bedikah* cloth need not be inserted that deeply. He writes, however, that one who is punctilious should do the *hefseik taharah* and one *bedikah* of the seven "clean" days in that manner. In *Shulchan Aruch*, he takes a stricter view stating that every woman (not only one who is punctilious) should insert the cloth that deeply during those two *bedikos* (see *Sidrei Taharah* §24 who is puzzled why R' Yosef Karo changed his position). *Rema*, however, rules that it suffices if the cloth is merely inserted to the best of her ability. See *Shiurei Sheivet HaLeivi* §6[6] who notes that the cloth should **not** touch the opening of the cervix. The area is sensitive and any irritation may cause bleeding. A woman suffering from a dropped uterus (prolapse) should discuss the proper manner in which to do *bedikos* with her doctor and her Rav.

41. See responsa *Noda B'Yehudah* 1, end of 44 and 46, and R' Akiva Eiger, *Tinyana* §34, *Lechem VeSimlah* 196:11[s] who note that if this is painful, one need not press the cloth into the crevices but merely place it on all surfaces.

42. A *hefseik taharah* or *bedikah* of the first day done in this manner is invalid. *Sidrei Taharah* 196:27 deduces this from *Rema* 196:6. *Sidrei Taharah* §23 cites the opinion of *Raavad* (cited in *Beis Yosef* 196 p. 80a), who disagrees and contends that the cloth must be inserted deeply into the vagina, but not necessarily into all crevices. In the opinion of *Raavad*, *churin u'sedakin* was necessary only in earlier times when *tumah* and *taharah* were relevant issues. Indeed, *Noda B'Yehudah* 1:46 contends that, in the opinion of *Raavad*, *Rif* and *Rambam*, the *bedikah* cloth need not be inserted deeply into the vagina. Insertion into the beginning of the vagina is sufficient. See also R' Akiva Eiger, *Tinyana* 34, who follows a similar interpretation of *Raavad*. Accepted *halachah*, however, rejects the opinion of *Raavad* and follows the opinion of *Rashba* and *Rosh* who invalidate a *bedikah* which was not inserted into the crevices. In their opinion, if the cloth is not inserted into the crevices, it is called "*kinuach*" (lit. wiping), not "*bedikah*." *Sidrei Taharah* notes, however, that even *Rashba* and *Rosh* concede that this is only a Rabbinic, not a Torah, requirement. In Torah law, the *bedikah* is valid even without insertion into the crevices. Thus, in a situation where it is impossible to insert the cloth into all crevices, *Sidrei Taharah* contends that *Chazal* did not require that it be done. Accordingly, a *besulah* can do a *hefseik taharah* even though she is unable to insert it into all crevices. *Noda B'Yehudah* 1, end of 46, cited in *Pischei Teshuvah* 196:9, challenges the entire requirement of inserting the *bedikah* cloth into all crevices. While he is reluctant to contradict the *Shulchan Aruch*, he is lenient in the following case:

it as far as she is able[43] and rotate it so that it touches all possible areas while being careful not to injure herself.[44] If she merely wipes herself externally, she has not fulfilled her obligation.[45]

5. A *bedikah* done with the finger:

A woman who had no *bedikah* cloth and merely checked herself with her finger has not fulfilled the obligation of a *bedikah*.[46]

6. Dampening the cloth:

A woman who finds *bedikos* painful due to the coarseness of the cloth may dampen the cloth slightly beforehand.[47] She should not do this on *Shabbos* or *Yom Tov*.[48]

If a woman did the *hefseik taharah* properly and, in addition, inserted a *moch dachuk* properly, then the *bedikos* of all the following days need not be inserted in all crevices. It would seem that *Noda B'Yehudah* is referring to a woman who actually fills her vaginal area with cotton (see *Chavos Daas* 191 end of 8[b]) or who rotates the *moch* beforehand throughout the vaginal canal. A *moch* done in the manner common today, i.e., merely placing a *bedikah* cloth into the vagina, would likely not be a valid substitute for a *bedikah* inserted into the crevices. See a discussion of related issues in *Badei HaShulchan* 196:2 (*Biurim* s.v. "צריכה"). *Chavos Daas* §4, however, completely rejects the opinion of *Noda B'Yehudah*. See also *Lechem VeSimlah* §11[s].

In conclusion, the *hefseik taharah* and the *bedikah* of the first (or at least any one) of the seven "clean" days must be inserted into all crevices. If this is difficult, a Rav must be consulted.

43. See *Sidrei Taharah* 196:23 and *Chochmas Adam* 115:2.

44. If a *kallah* preparing for her wedding finds a speck of blood on her cloth and feels that she injured her *besulim*, she should mention this to the Rav. In the opinion of *Igros Moshe*, Y.D. 1:87, blood from the hymen does not render her a *niddah* unless it appeared through cohabitation. Thus, if it can be established that the hymen is bleeding, she is *tehorah*. If the *bedikah* was a required *bedikah* (e.g., a *hefseik taharah*), the requirement was not met since she has not demonstrated with certainty that the menstrual bleeding has stopped. However, most other *Poskim* disagree with *Igros Moshe*. They maintain that hymenal bleeding renders a woman a *niddah* even if it was not caused by cohabitation. See responsa *Maharsham* 1:210, *Minchas Yitzchak* 4:58 and *Tzitz Eliezer* 10:25[12] and *Mahari Steif* 131. See *Be'er Moshe* 3:142,143, who permits a married woman who finds hymenal blood on a *bedikah* cloth to count seven "clean" days without waiting the preliminary five (or four) days. See *Darchei Teshuvah* 193:21 citing responsa *Chaim Biyad* who seems to follow a position similar to that of *Igros Moshe*, although in §15 *Darchei Teshuvah* cites the contradictory opinion of *Maharsham*.

45. *Chochmas Adam* 115:2.

46. *Sidrei Taharah* 196:22, *Chochmas Adam* 117:9, *Daas Torah* 196:6. *Mei Niddah* (cited in *Daas Torah*) speculates that perhaps a *hefseik taharah* done with the finger is acceptable before the seven "clean"days following a *kesem*, not following a real blood flow. Other *Poskim*, however, do not accept this view. See *Pische Zuta* §15 and *Shiurei Sheivet HaLeivi* §6[1]. *Sheivet HaLeivi* notes a *bedikah* done with one's finger is troublesome because the finger is reddish and a blood speck on it may not be noticeable. This reason alone, however, would not explain why she could not do the *bedikah* with her finger and subsequently wipe it onto a cloth. It would seem that the problem lies in the inability of a finger to absorb blood. See *Badei HaShulchan* 196, *Tziyunim* §192:

47. *Maharsham* cited in *Darchei Teshuvah* 196:57.

48. *Mishnah Berurah* 302:48.

7. A woman who finds *bedikos* generally painful:

If dampening the cloth does not alleviate the problem, she should consult a Rav.[49] A Rav may advise her to pre-treat the vaginal area with cream, KY jelly or vaseline. This should not be done, however, close to the time of the *bedikah* since the cream may prevent blood from adhering to the cloth or from being noticeable.[50] The *bedikah* should be done only after the cream has been completely absorbed by the body or washed away. The *bedikah* cloth itself should not be coated with cream or vaseline.[51]

As noted above, a woman who has difficulty doing a clean *hefseik taharah* should douche beforehand to clear the vagina of any blood residue.[52] In the opinion of some authorities (see 2 above), she should wait approximately fifteen minutes between douching and doing the *bedikah*. We also noted above that a woman may not douche before her *bedikos* of the seven "clean" days.

8. Limiting the number and scope of *bedikos*:

Under special circumstances a Rav may instruct a woman to limit the number of *bedikos* done during the seven "clean" days or to limit the depth of the *bedikos*. A Rav may also instruct her to do some of her *bedikos* by merely wiping the vagina externally.[53] One should, however, note the following:

> a. One may not rely on any of the leniencies mentioned above without direct and explicit instructions of a Rav. One should not rely upon the fact that an acquaintance was given such instructions. Every woman is unique and must be considered individually. Furthermore, instruc-

---

49. See *Noda B'Yehudah* cited above, note 41, that if necessary, the cloth need not be pressed into the crevices but merely placed on the surface of the crevices.

50. See *Be'er Moshe* 2:59 and *Badei HaShulchan* 196:90.

51. Since it may prevent any blood from being visible, see *Badei HaShulchan* 196:90. However, *Shiurei Sheivet HaLeivi* 196:6[8] compares coating the cloth with vaseline to *Maharsham's* permitting it to be dampened, and permits smearing a small amount of vaseline on the cloth. In his supplementary notes, *Sheivet HaLeivi* stipulates that only clear vaseline should be used and that it should be left to dry a bit on the cloth. While there may be a difference between water soluble creams and non-water soluble creams, it would seem that any coating reduces the absorbency of the cloth. One should certainly not use any vaseline or cream without consulting a Rav beforehand.

52. *Maharsham* 3:250.

53. See *Pischei Teshuvah* 196:8 citing *Noda B'Yehudah*.

tions given to a woman for one type of *bedikah* may not be applicable to the same woman for another type of *bedikah*. The *hefseik taharah*, the *moch dachuk*, the *bedikah* of the first of the seven "clean" days and those of the following days may each be subject to different rulings.

b. Any leniencies permitted by a Rav are valid only with respect to the specific circumstances for which they were given. Once circumstances have changed, the Rav must be consulted whether all *bedikos* must be done in the normally required manner. If a problem persists, the Rav will likely refer the woman to a gynecologist.

IV. *Bedikos:* when and whether

There are specific circumstances when a *bedikah* is required; otherwise, *bedikos* are not done. Although *Chazal*[54] commend a woman who does additional *bedikos*, contemporary *Rabbonim* generally discourage unnecessary *bedikos*. The possible reasons for this are: a) Since the woman is not required to do a *bedikah,* there is no reason to go beyond *halachic* requirements and cause unnecessary *niddus*.[55] A woman should rather try to preserve her *taharah* status. b) Excessive *bedikos* commonly cause an irritation in the vagina which, in turn, may cause blood to appear on the cloth. This blood is not uterine blood and should not cause her to become a *niddah*. However, since we cannot be certain that it is not from the uterus, if she does a *bedikah* she will be considered a *niddah*, perhaps unnecessarily.[56]

A. When are *bedikos* required?

A woman is obligated to do *bedikos* under the following circumstances:

    1. The *taharah* process:
      a. The *hefseik taharah:*
      A woman cannot begin her seven "clean" days without doing

---

54. *Niddah 13a* and *Shulchan Aruch* 184:1, 196:9.

55. Even *Chazal,* in their time, were loath to cause unnecessary separation between man and wife. In modern times, when immodesty is rampant and life is full of anxieties and tensions, separation between man and wife causes additional stress and strain in their relationship. Perhaps, in our times *Chazal* would not have recommended additional *bedikos.*

56. *Poseiach Shaar* 8:30 notes that it is common today that excessive *bedikos* cause irritation to the vaginal area. Therefore, a woman should not do *bedikos* unless required to do so.

a *hefseik taharah*.[57] The purpose of this *bedikah* is to determine that the flow has finally stopped. Without this *hefseik taharah*, the seven "clean" days cannot be considered "clean" days. As such, this *bedikah* is the most important of all the *bedikos* of the *taharah* process. The *halachos* of *hefseik taharah* will be discussed in Volume Two.

b. *Moch dachuk:*
After the *hefseik taharah* is done, a woman should insert a *moch dachuk*.[58] This is a cloth inserted into the vagina before sundown of the day preceding the seven "clean" days and is removed after dusk of that same day. The purpose of this *bedikah* is to guarantee that the seven "clean" days started with a status of *taharah*. *Poskim* note that the requirement of a *moch dachuk* is sometimes a *chumra*, not necessarily *halachically* required. Often a Rav will advise a woman to forgo the *moch dachuk*. These *halachos* will be discussed at length in Volume Two.

c. The seven "clean" days:
A woman is required to check herself internally twice during each of the seven "clean" days.[59] One *bedikah* is done in the morning and one during the late afternoon. We noted above that, under special circumstances, a Rav may advise a woman to limit the amount of *bedikos* done during the seven "clean" days. These *halachos* will be discussed in Volume Two.

2. The time of her expected period:

a. The day of the expected *vest*:
A woman must do a *bedikah*[60] on the day of her expected period, as is determined by the rules of *vest*.[61] There is reason to believe that her period may begin on that day, as it has in the past. Thus, she is required to check whether any uterine blood is present in the vagina which would then render her a *niddah*. The method by which one computes the expected day of the *vest* is explained in Book Four.

---

57. 196:5.

58. 196:1.

59. 196:4.

60. Contemporary authorities write that two *bedikos* should be done on the *vest* day. See *Shiurei Sheivet HaLeivi* 188:9[4].

61. 184:9.

b. The thirtieth day:

A woman who has no set *vest* (*vest kavuah*) must consider the thirtieth day from the beginning of her last period as a potential expected day of her next period.[62] This is based upon the assumption that the average menstrual cycle follows a thirty-day cycle. This is called the "*onah beinonis*," the "average time (interval)." Accordingly, a *bedikah* is required on that day as it is on the day of an expected *vest*. The method of calculating the *onah beinonis* and its *halachos* are discussed in Chapter Fifteen.

3. Following a *hargashah*:

A woman who felt a *hargashah* (i.e., she felt a uterine or vaginal discharge) must immediately do a *bedikah* to ascertain whether or not any uterine bleeding accompanied that *hargashah*. The definition of a *hargashah*, as well as all *halachos* pertaining to *hargashah*, are explored in Chapter Three.

4. The three preliminary *bedikos*:

A woman who has no set *vest* (*vest kavuah*) is liable to start her period at any time. Since we do not know what actually stimulates the beginning of her flow, there is the remote possibility that cohabitation itself may cause her menstrual flow. For this reason, *halachah* requires that a woman do *bedikos* the first three times she cohabits with her husband after the earliest time her period normally comes.[63] Once this series of *bedikos* is concluded without the appearance of blood, she has established that cohabitation does not activate her menstrual cycle and she no longer requires *bedikos* before cohabitation. The rules of these *bedikos* are discussed in Chapter Fourteen.

B. When are *bedikos* not required?

Generally, if *bedikos* are not required, they should not be done. We noted above that although the Talmud[64] commends a woman who does additional *bedikos*, *Poskim* generally do not recommend unnecessary *bedikos*. The following is a list of situations where a woman may think it proper to do a *bedikah*, while in truth, it is neither required nor recommended.

---

62. 184:9, 189:4. See Chapter Fifteen where it is noted that, in the opinion of some *Poskim*, the thirty-first day is the *onah beinonis*.

63. 186:2.

64. *Niddah* 13a.

1. Upon finding a *kesem:*

There is a common misconception among women regarding *kesamim* (stains found upon a garment). Some women do a *bedikah* upon finding a questionable stain on their garment. Mistakenly, they believe that if the *bedikah* cloth is clear, the garment stain can be ignored. This is <u>not</u> so. A *kesem* and a *bedikah* are not relevant to one another. The *bedikah* may be spotless, but the *kesem* may nevertheless cause her to become a *niddah* and require the full *taharah* process, including a *b'rachah* on the *tevilah*. The fact is that a woman who finds a *kesem* should not do a *bedikah*. Often the *kesem* itself may be *tahor*, either because of its size or because of the color of the garment upon which it is found. The *bedikah*, however, will render her a *niddah* with even the smallest spot found upon it. One has nothing to gain and much to lose by doing a *bedikah* after finding a *kesem*. The *kesem* should be shown to a Rav. Similarly, a woman who finds a stain on a tissue used to clean herself after urination should not check herself, even externally, with another tissue. She should consult a Rav and inquire whether she is considered a *niddah*. **Incidentally, a woman should avoid looking at her tissues**. It is unnecessary and unwise. A stain found upon a tissue may render her a *niddah* or place the Rav in the uncomfortable position of relying upon lenient opinions which permit the stain.

2. After a gynecological examination:

A woman who underwent a gynecological examination is not required to do a *bedikah* afterwards. In the event that the doctor used an instrument that penetrated the uterus, she may be *temei'ah* even if no blood appears upon the *bedikah* cloth because of *pesichas hakever* (opening of the uterus, discussed in Chapter Twenty-Three). If, as is usually the case, the instrument did not penetrate uterus and no blood appeared, she is *tehorah*. *There is no reason for a bedikah*. A *bedikah*, rather than being beneficial, may be detrimental. The instrument may have grazed the vaginal tissue and caused slight bleeding. This blood is not uterine blood and would generally not cause her to become a *niddah*. Had the blood been noticed only on her garment, a Rav would have relatively little difficulty attributing it to the examination. However, once the blood is found upon a *bedikah* cloth, it is a more serious *halachic* problem. Thus, a woman has much to lose by making a *bedikah* after a gynecological examination. Nevertheless, a woman must consult a Rav after any gynecological examination.[65]

3. A second *bedikah* after a questionable one:
If a woman does a *bedikah* and finds a questionable color, she should not, as a matter of course, do a second *bedikah*. The second *bedikah* may be worse than the first and cause her to become a *niddah*, while the first may have been acceptable. This will be discussed in the following chapter.

V. A lost *bedikah* cloth

If a *bedikah* cloth is lost before the woman had a chance to inspect it, it is as if she had not done a *bedikah*. Thus, if the *hefseik taharah* or *bedikah* of the first or seventh day was lost, she should consult a Rav. If a *bedikah* that was not vital was lost, it may be ignored.[66] If, however, a suspicious color was noticed on the cloth before it was lost, one must be concerned that perhaps the color was red. A Rav should be consulted.[67]

---

65. See responsa *Avnei Neizer* (Y.D. 224) and *Shiurei Sheivet HaLeivi* 188:3[4], who require a *bedikah* after a gynecological examination performed with an instrument. However, most Rabbonim advise that one not do a *bedikah*.

66. If a woman does a *bedikah* on her *vest* day and subsequently the cloth is lost before inspection, *Chavos Daas* 184:11[b] is uncertain whether or not the *bedikah* may be ignored. See *Pischei Teshuvah* §18 who cites *Chavos Daas* as definitive *halachah* that she is *temei'ah*. Other *Poskim* disagree; see *Shiurei Sheivet HaLeivi* 184:9[6]. See Chapter Twenty-Two note 16 where this issue is discussed in detail.

67. See *Chochmas Adam* 111:3 and *Binas Adam* 5, that one must assume that the color was unacceptable. See, however, responsa *Maharsham* 3:214 and *Shaarei Taharah* p. 147. See *Sheivet HaLeivi* 3:119[9]. In a case regarding a lost *kesem*, *Chochmas Adam* 113:29 is lenient. See, however, *Pische Zuta* 190:47,48 who cites many opposing opinions. See also *Taharas Yisrael* 190:133. See also Chapter Six note 46.

CHAPTER SIX

בדיקות

Bedikos: Inspecting the *Bedikah* Cloth

- ☐ Inspection of the cloth.
- ☐ Asking a *sheilah.*
- ☐ Colors and shades.
- ☐ A change of colors.
- ☐ Repeating a *bedikah.*

I. The immediate inspection

A. The method of inspection

The *bedikah* cloth should be examined immediately after use. This inspection should be done with extreme care.

    1. The cloth may be inspected while still damp; one need not wait until it dries. If the color is acceptable at that time, the cloth may be discarded.[1] Even a cloth requiring close examination by a Rav may be examined by the Rav while still damp.[2] If, however, the stain is a color which is subject to a dispute among *Poskim* (e.g., a golden- or brown-colored stain), some authorities rule that it may not be examined until it dries.[3]

    2. Even the smallest red or black[4] speck, if visible to the naked eye, can render a woman a *niddah*.[5] This should not be confused with a *kesem*, which is insignificant when less than a certain size. This distinction causes much confusion. A *kesem* poses a problem only when it exceeds the size of a *gris* (roughly the size of a U.S. penny), whereas a stain on a *bedikah* cloth may be problematic, even if it is tiny and barely noticeable to the human eye (see an explanation of why this is so in Chapter Five, Section I). Even so, it is not necessary to inspect the cloth with a magnifying glass. *Halachah* recognizes only a stain which is visible to the naked eye.[6]

---

1. There may be an advantage to discarding the cloth, since a cloth that changes colors may create problems. See below section IV, D. If a woman's *bedikos* often change colors after they dry, some *Poskim* maintain that she should not discard them until they are inspected after drying, see below.

2. *Bach* 188 rules that one should not judge a stain while it is still damp since its color may change as it dries. *Taz* §1 and *Shach* §3 disagree. They argue that even though the color may change, we have no reason to assume that it will change to an unacceptable color. Later authorities follow this lenient opinion (see *Chochmas Adam* 111:2 and *Tzemach Tzedek*, Y.D. 127), as is common custom. However, many *Poskim* follow the opinion of *Bach* (see *Pardes Rimonim*, M.Z. 188:1, *Lechem VeSimlah* §3[s] and *Tiferes Tzvi* §1).

3. See *Pardes Rimonim*, M.Z. 188 end of §1, regarding a golden-colored stain and *Taharas Yisrael* §11, regarding a brown stain. See note 75 below.

4. In Section IV we will discuss which shades and colors render a woman a *niddah*.

5. See *Biur HaGra* 196:25.

6. See *Igros Moshe*, Y.D. 2:146. A Rav may, at times, examine a stain with a magnifying glass merely to examine its color carefully. He will not search for a speck which is invisible to the naked eye. See responsa *Eimek HaTeshuvah* 1:144 regarding whether the woman or the Rav is required to inspect the cloth for miniscule specks.

3. The entire surface of the cloth, including its outer edges, its back side and the attached string used to remove the cloth from the body, must be inspected carefully.

4. It is difficult to notice a small speck on a thin, translucent *bedikah* cloth. Therefore, one should fold the cloth or place it over a sheet of white paper.

5. If the stain itself is an acceptable color but is surrounded by a thin edge with an unacceptable color, it may be *tamei*. A Rav should be consulted.[7]

6. Occasionally, one may find tiny black specks or granules on the cloth. These may be dried blood and must be shown to a Rav who will determine whether they are blood or foreign matter.[8] One should not tamper with these specks by trying to move or remove them. Only an experienced Rav understands when and how to remove a speck. The cloth should be folded in a manner to ensure that the specks will not be lost. If they were lost, a Rav should be consulted.[9]

---

7. See *Bach* 188, *Shach* §3 and *Taz* §1. See responsa *Shvus Yaakov* 2:74 regarding a *kesem* that seemed to be an acceptable color when damp, but developed a red edge after it dried. The point of contention is only regarding the fact that the color originally seemed acceptable, but all agree that a stain with a red edge is *tamei*. See *Aruch HaShulchan* §15, who maintains that as a stain dries the color becomes more concentrated towards the edges. If one were to spread the color of the reddish edge over the entire area or the stain, it would not appear red at all. Thus, the color of the edge is not the actual color of the stain. Based on this assumption some Rabbonim are lenient regarding edges of certain, but not all, reddish shades.

8. See *Chochmas Adam* 111:7, who is very lenient regarding tiny specks. He assumes that these minuscule specks come from a foreign source. He, therefore, rules that only the *hefseik taharah* must be completely free of specks. All subsequent *bedikos* are *tahor* even if they have small black specks. One should be stricter with red specks during the first three days of the seven "clean" days. In a case of extreme difficulty, a Rav may be lenient even regarding red specks during the first three days. In all cases, the specks must be scratched away by the Rav to ensure that the fabric beneath the speck is not stained. See *Shiurei Sheivet HaLeivi* 188:4[3], who notes that *Chazon Ish* followed the opinion of *Chochmas Adam*. In 190:33[2], *Shiurei Sheivet HaLeivi* explains that any *bedikah* cloth is considered unchecked (*aino baduk*) in regard to these specks as one usually does not notice tiny specks when checking the cloth before the *bedikah* (this lenient argument seems to apply even to a speck which is embedded into the fabric). He notes that *Chazon Ish* held this view. Note that this leniency applies only to specks so tiny that they may have been on the cloth originally but went unnoticed in the initial inspection.

9. See *Sidrei Taharah* 188:8, *Chochmas Adam* 111:7, *Binas Adam* §6, responsa *Divrei Chaim* 2:73,74, *Chasam Sofer*, Y.D. 159, *Pischei Teshuvah* 188:9, *Pische Zuta* 188:11, *Taharas Yisrael* 188:54. Some *Poskim* are lenient, relying upon the multiple doubts in this case: Perhaps the granules were not blood, and even if they were, perhaps they were not uterine blood (they may have been caused by urinary tract infections, see *Taz* 191:4 and *Gilyon Maharsha* ad loc.). Even if the granules did originate

7. If the *bedikah* cloth is free of any questionable stains, it may be discarded. A woman is not required to show the cloth to her husband. He relies upon her competence and need not be concerned that she is unable to distinguish between acceptable and questionable colors.[10] If the woman is unable to decide, she should show the cloth to her husband. See Section II that neither the husband nor the wife should decide on any questionable color unless they are absolutely certain, from previous experience, that the color is acceptable without question. See Chapter Four, Section V regarding the circumstances under which a husband may rule on questions of *halachah* regarding his wife.

B. Inspection by day versus night

The proper time to inspect a *bedikah* cloth is during the day in natural light.[11] *Poskim* advise against examining a *bedikah* cloth at night under an electric light. Artificial light may change the appearance of the color. For example, incandescent bulbs unnaturally stress red; thus, brown stains may appear slightly reddish-brown. On the other hand, fluorescent light

---

from the uterus, they may have appeared without a *hargashah* (although a blood flow is assumed to appear with a *hargashah*, tiny granules are not necessarily accompanied by a *hargashah*). Those *Poskim* who take a lenient position regarding lost granules do so only if these granules were not found on any of the following types of *bedikos*: a) the *bedikah* of the day of her expected period, b) the *bedikah* of the thirtieth day from her last period (if she has no *vest kavuah*), c) the *hefseik taharah* or d) the *bedikos* of the first three of the seven "clean" days (see *Chasam Sofer* ibid.). Others are lenient during the first three days (see *Chochmas Adam* ibid.). The foregoing discussion applies only where the granule that was lost left no mark. If, however, one finds a red or black stain on the garment itself under the area where the granules had been, the woman is *temei'ah* (*Binas Adam* end of 6, see also *Shiurei Sheivet HaLeivi* 188:4[3]).

10. *Beis Yosef* 188 s.v. "ונאמנת."

11. See *Megillah* 14a. The Talmud *Niddah* 20b, instructs the individual examining a *bedikah* cloth to stand in sunlight and shade the cloth with his hand (see *Rashi* ad loc.). While *Rambam* (5:11) cites this as *halachah*, *Raavad* (ad loc.) disputes his ruling. *Raavad* argues that this was only required during Talmudic times when it was necessary to distinguish between varying shades of red. However, in subsequent generations, when all shades of red are disqualified, an exact examination is not as critical. *Raavad's* opinion is reflected in *Shulchan Aruch's* omission of this *halachah* (see *Toras HaShelamim* 188:1, *Sidrei Taharah* §1 and *Aruch HaShulchan* §11. See also *Sidrei Taharah* 190 end of §93). The discussion above pertains only to the Talmudic directive of standing in the sunlight and shading the light with one's hand. However, the basic rule that a *bedikah* cloth should be checked by day is accepted as *halachah* (*Rema* 196:4, see also *Aruch HaShulchan* 196:24). However, *Sidrei Taharah* 190, end of §93 differentiates between a *bedikah* of the seven "clean" days and certainly the *hefseik taharah*, which must be inspected by day, versus a *bedikah* done while the woman is in a *tehorah* status, which may be inspected by night.

does not properly accentuate some red shades and reddish-brown stains may appear brown.[12] However, there are circumstances when a *bedikah* cloth may be inspected by night.[13] The general guidelines are as follows:

1. A woman may examine the *hefseik taharah* and *moch dachuk* at night. If the cloth is clearly free of any problematic color, it may be discarded, and it need not be kept for further inspection by day.[14]

2. If the color on the cloth seems even slightly questionable, a woman should not rely[15] upon its appearance under artificial light. Rather, she should put it aside and examine it or show it to a Rav by day.[16]

3. Some Rabbonim do not rule on a questionable *bedikah* cloth at night.[17] Others will inspect *bedikos* at night. An experienced Rav can often take into consideration any variation in the color shade caused by unnatural light.[18] However, some colors or shades are very difficult to evaluate and must be seen in natural daylight.

4. When a decision is necessary that very night (e.g., a night of

---

12. *Shiurei Sheivet HaLeivi* 188:1[5] p. 96.

13. *Aruch HaShulchan* 188:12 contends that the Talmudic restriction against judging a stain at night was referring to viewing it in moonlight or starlight. Lamplight, however, is more closely comparable to sunlight and is acceptable. However, *Aruch HaShulchan* himself writes in §16 that preferably a *bedikah* should be checked by day. *Aruch HaShulchan* apparently considers the ruling of *Rema* 188:4, that a *bedikah* should be inspected by daylight not lamplight, as advice regarding the optimum procedure to follow. Alternatively, *Rema* may be referring to a case where close inspection is necessary. In summary, a Rav may inspect a *bedikah* by electric light, when necessary, relying upon the opinion of the *Aruch HaShulchan*. In addition, one may be lenient today since our electric lights are more effective than the lights earlier *Poskim* had available (see *Badei HaShulchan* 196:84). However, as noted above, one must be cautious since even electric lights affect the color somewhat.

14. *Shiurei Sheivet HaLeivi* 196:4[12]. Whatever disadvantage there may be in artificial light, it is nevertheless adequate for distinguishing between a color which is clearly non-problematic and one which may perhaps be problematic.

15. We noted in Chapter Four, Section III that a woman may judge the color on a *bedikah* if she is positive, from prior experience, that it is acceptable. Nevertheless, she may not do so at night unless the color is clearly non-problematic.

16. See *Pardes Rimonim, S.C.* 188 end of §4.

17. See *Aruch HaShulchan* 188:16, *Shiurei Sheivet HaLeivi* ibid. and *Darchei Teshuvah* §4.

18. In addition, we noted that our electric lights are brighter and clearer than the lights referred to by earlier *Poskim*.

tevilah or if the woman is currently in a *tehorah* status[19]), a Rav will, if possible, rule on a *bedikah* cloth using artificial light.[20] One should make every effort to bring a *bedikah* cloth to the Rav during the daylight hours to spare him the difficulty of ruling on a questionable *bedikah* at night.

When inspecting a cloth by day, it is not held in direct sunlight. A color seen in direct sunlight is difficult to judge.

II. Questionable *bedikos*

Often, a woman will find questionable stains on her *bedikah* cloth or garments. Most couples are unable to distinguish between varying shades and colors, and therefore must show the questionable stain to a Rav. In this regard, we reiterate that one should never assume that a color, ruled upon leniently in the past, is identical with the current stain unless one is absolutely certain. It may require years of experience to develop a "feel" for which color is acceptable and which is not. Furthermore, different standards are used for different *bedikos*. A *bedikah* of the seven "clean" days is subject to more lenient standards than that of a *hefseik taharah*. A couple must, therefore, be certain that a comparison between two stains is warranted, even if the colors are identical.

A. The impropriety of being needlessly strict

A married couple has a responsibility not to cause needless separation. We noted in the previous chapter that a woman should not do unnecessary *bedikos* which might cause her to become *temei'ah*. Any questionable *bedikah* should not be presumed unacceptable, but should be submitted to a Rav. All efforts should be made to ensure that a woman remain in a status of *taharah* and return to that status as quickly as possible after her *niddus* period. By the same token, a husband should not be needlessly strict in requiring *bedikos* when none are required and should accept the decision of a Rav who permits a *bedikah*, even if it seems questionable in his eyes. Nevertheless, *Poskim* note that a husband has the right, if he so

---

19. In this latter case, there are two reasons to be lenient and check the color at night: a) By not checking the color, one causes needless separation between the couple. b) Since she is presently in a permitted state there is reason to be lenient. See *Sidrei Taharah* 190 end of 93, *Pardes Rimonim* ibid. See *Daas Torah* 188:1 and *Darchei Teshuvah* §4. In the former case, only reason a applies.

20. *Aruch HaShulchan* 188:16. However, if the color is difficult to evaluate, the Rav has no choice but to keep the cloth for a daylight inspection. If the color is then found to be acceptable, the *tevilah* will be done the following night.

chooses, not to accept the ruling of a Rav who permitted a *bedikah* cloth. *Halachah* assumes that he is motivated by sincere piety and, further, that his wife is agreeable and is indeed proud of her devout husband.[21] The husband, however, should take note that the words *chasid* — pious — and *chesed* — considerate of others — share the same root, and carefully weigh his decision to adopt a strict approach and thereby infringe upon his wife's rights.[22]

In addition to the impropriety of needlessly assuming that a *bedikah* cloth is *tamei,* a woman should especially avoid assuming that a *bedikah* done during the seven "clean" days is not acceptable. At times, the mere assumption that the *bedikah* is not valid may invalidate the seven "clean" days.[23] This concept will be explained in Volume Two.

B. The danger of being improperly lenient

It is self-evident that a couple should not take *bedikos* lightly. We noted above that a *bedikah* may render a woman a *niddah* according to Torah law. One who erroneously dismisses a *bedikah* risks transgressing an *issur kares.* This should weigh heavily upon both husband and wife. They should not make any careless assumptions. While they may feel that the color of a stain is similar to one that had been previously approved by Rav, they must be absolutely certain that the colors are identical. In these matters, "almost" sure will not do.

C. Storing the cloth

If a woman wishes to show the *bedikah* cloth to her husband or Rav it must be stored properly. It should not be placed on any unclean surface, since it may become soiled. Left exposed, it may gather dust and dirt. When damp, it should not be placed on a tissue or in an envelope since it may adhere to the surface and become difficult, if not impossible, to

---

21. *Chasam Sofer, Y.D.* 149, cited in *Pischei Teshuvah* 188:2. *Pische Zuta* 188:9 notes that if, as a result of the husband's stringency, the wife went from a status of *tehorah* to *temei'ah,* she should probably not recite a *b'rachah* on her *tevilah.* However, if this *bedikah* was done during the seven "clean" days, she certainly recites a *b'rachah* over the *tevilah.* He also notes other applications where this *chumra* may lead to a *kula.* See *Pische Zuta* (ad loc. and 190 end of §7) regarding whether the wife also has the option of being stricter than required by *halachah.*

22. *Badei HaShulchan* 188:1, *Biurim* s.v. "ואין," is uncertain whether a husband who is not specially pious in other matters of *halachah* has the right to be pious in these matters and thereby infringe upon his wife's rights.

23. See *Pischei Teshuvah* 196:3, citing *Me'il Tzedakah.*

evaluate. A damp *bedikah* cloth should not be stored in a closed plastic bag since the color of the stain may change unnaturally. Ideally, a *bedikah* cloth should be placed on an open clean surface to dry and then placed in an envelope. If necessary it may be placed in an open plastic bag.

D. Keeping the cloth for an extended period

Under normal circumstances, one should not save the *bedikos* of several days to show them to a Rav all at once. *Bedikos* often change colors during the course of several days, e.g., a slightly reddish hue may turn brown, a dark brown may lighten and light clear stains may develop a dark border.[24] If one must save the *bedikos* of several days, they should be clearly marked and identified as either a *hefseik taharah, moch dachuk* or a simple *bedikah*. Even simple *bedikos* should be marked with the day and time on which they were done, e.g., 1A , 1AM or 1M (day one, first i.e., morning, *bedikah*), 3B or 3PM (third day, second, i.e., afternoon, *bedikah*).[25] Markings on a *bedikah* cloth should be done in blue or green ink, since red or black ink may smudge and compromise the *bedikah* (red and black are unacceptable stains). Alternatively, one can place each *bedikah* in a separate envelope that has been marked with the appropriate time and day.

E. Conduct in the interim

A questionable *bedikah* cloth must be assumed unacceptable until a Rav has determined otherwise. In the interim, the couple must conduct themselves as if the woman is actually a *niddah* regarding not only the exclusion of marital relations, but also all other forms of physical contact, and all the additional separations called *"harchakos"* which will be listed in Volume Two.[26] Furthermore, if the *bedikah* was done during the seven "clean" days, she should anticipate that the *bedikah* may be deemed unacceptable. The *hefsik taharah* should be repeated and she should prepare to begin counting the seven "clean" days anew. Many Rabbonim advise that the *moch dachuk* should not be repeated unless the *bedikah* is certainly invalid, i.e., it is stained with blood.

---

24. See *Shiurei Sheivet HaLeivi* 188:1[15] and 196:4[10].

25. This is extremely important. If any of the earlier *bedikos* is questionable, the Rav may permit the subsequent *bedikah* as a new *hefseik taharah*. If two cloths are marked "day 3" without an identifying mark as to which is first and which is second, an entire day may be unnecessarily lost.

26. See *Yoreh Deah* 195.

III. Asking a *sheilah*

A. Asking a *sheilah* personally

In order to accommodate the sensitivities of some women and their need for privacy, many Rabbonim allow women to leave problematic *bedikah* cloths marked with an identifying code in the Rav's mailbox. The Rav can then be called for an answer. Alternatively, the woman can leave her phone number on the envelope for the Rav to call her. While this approach is acceptable, it is not always optimal.

A Rav does not answer all questions in an identical manner. *Halachah* gives a Rav certain leeway in answering questions. A certain shade may be questionable under normal circumstances but acceptable in difficult situations. Consequently, when a Rav recognizes a woman as one who has had difficulty successfully completing her *bedikos* or one who is undergoing fertility treatment he makes every effort to judge the cloth leniently. A woman who does not identify herself to the Rav cannot avail herself of this benefit. There is also important information which a woman must share with the Rav regarding the *bedikah*. This includes: the type of *bedikah* being shown, whether *hefseik taharah, moch dachuk* or simple *bedikah,* the possible presence of *hargashah* or a sensation of pain at the time of the *bedikah.* While this information can and should be provided even if the woman remains anonymous, it is easier to communicate with the Rav when speaking to him personally. These issues have been discussed in Chapter One.

There is one final point. A Rav may render a decision on a *bedikah* or a question brought before him and subsequently wish to elicit additional information or he may realize that the party may not have understood him properly. If he is not aware of the identity of the party asking the question, it is impossible for him to contact her and alert her to the error.

Although the subject of this chapter is *bedikos,* the following section pertains to *kesamim* as well.

B. Providing the Rav with all relevant information

A Rav does not merely judge colors. He considers many other factors in reaching his decision.[27] It is therefore imperative that one draw the Rav's attention to any of the following:

---

27. Not all the factors listed here are applicable in all cases. Only a Rav is knowledgeable and experienced enough to weigh each of these factors as they apply to each individual case.

1. A small and difficult-to-locate spot:

Often, the questionable stain may not be apparent. For example, after careful examination, one may notice a tiny spot on the general stain. Unless he is otherwise alerted, a Rav may attend to the general stain only and overlook the small spot. Occasionally, a questionable spot may be on the outer edges, the handle or even the opposite side of the cloth. A Rav may not notice these unless they are brought to his attention. If the spot is extremely small and difficult to locate, one should mark it with either an identifying arrow or with a circle drawn around it, preferably with a blue or green pen.[28] Alternatively, one can stick a pin into the cloth near the area of the stain.

2. A cloth that was not checked well before the *bedikah:*

If a woman did not check the *bedikah* cloth thoroughly before inserting it, she should notify the Rav. The Rav may conclude that certain extremely small stains may be assumed to have been present before the *bedikah* was done.[29] <u>One should not make this assumption on their own.</u>

3. Identifying the type of *bedikah:*

The Rav should be informed whether a) the cloth being shown is a *hefseik taharah* or a *moch dachuk;* otherwise, he may assume that it is a *bedikah* of the seven "clean" days. A Rav judges a *hefseik taharah* and a *moch dachuk* with stricter standards than he does other *bedikos.* b) In addition, a Rav should be told which of the seven "clean" days the cloth is from. A *bedikah* done earlier in the seven days is judged more strictly than one done during the latter part of the seven days, since it is more likely then that some menstrual blood remained in the body. Moreover, a stain found towards the end of the seven days may be judged more leniently since it would cause more hardship for her to begin the seven "clean" days again. c) A woman should also inform the Rav if the *bedikah* is from the day of, or the days preceding, her expected period. At such times there is a considerable chance that a stain may actually mark the beginning of her expected period; while the color may be acceptable, or the *kesem* less than the required size, a stain at these times may signal an imminent flow.[30]

---

28. A red or black pen mark may smudge and seem like a questionable stain.

29. See *Pische Zuta* end of 188.

30. In such cases, the Rav may rule that although the woman is not *halachically* a *niddah,* they

4. A *hargashah*:

Occasionally, a woman may feel a *hargashah* (a sensation of an internal flow) before she does the *bedikah* or finds the *kesem*. While such a sensation should always be reported to a Rav, a woman must be particularly vigilant about doing so in connection with a *kesem*. Ordinarily, a *kesem* renders a woman a *niddah* by Rabbinic law only. However, a woman who finds a *kesem* that was accompanied with a *hargashah* may be a *niddah,* even according to Torah law. This means that even if the *kesem* is less than a *gris* or is found upon a colored garment (circumstances under which a *kesem* is normally *tahor*), the woman would be *temei'ah.* Accordingly, a Rav must be informed of such a *hargashah.* See Chapter Three regarding which sensations are considered *hargashos.* Similarly, the Rav should be notified if a *kesem* was found after cohabitation or immediately after urination. We are concerned that the sensation of cohabitation or urination may have masked the *hargashah.* Such a *kesem* may be treated similarly to a *kesem* found after a *hargashah* and render the woman a *niddah* by Torah law.

5. Possibility of attributing the stain to another source — *teliyah:*

If there is reason to believe that the stain on the cloth or on her garment came from another source (e.g., she has hemorrhoids, she has a vaginal or urinary tract infection or irritation, she had undergone a gynecological examination or she is using vaginal suppositories), the Rav should be told (see Section IV,C,4). The issue of *teliyah* (attributing blood to a *makkah* — a wound) is discussed in Chapters Eleven and Twenty-Three.

6. A sensation of pain:

If a woman felt pain at the time of the *bedikah,* she should notify the Rav.[31]

7. A pregnant or nursing woman:

A stain found upon a *bedikah* cloth of a pregnant or nursing woman renders her a *niddah.* The fact that these women usually do not experience a menstrual flow is no reason to ignore

---

should abstain for a day to ascertain whether or not the period is starting. See responsa *Mahari Steif* end of 188, *Shiurei Sheivet HaLeivi* p.95.

31. See responsa *Divrei Malkiel* 5:284 regarding whether one may attribute a stain on a *bedikah* cloth to a wound if she scratched herself internally in the course of the *bedikah.*

blood that is found. Nevertheless, a Rav shown a *bedikah* cloth or a *kesem* of a pregnant or nursing woman should be so informed. Since these women usually have no blood flow, in certain cases a Rav may assume that the stain came from another source.

8. A bride:

A Rav should be informed if the *sheilah* is from a bride before her wedding or a recently married woman. If a bride finds a blood stain, it may be attributable to hymenal bleeding which may be treated more leniently than regular blood.[32] In addition, if the woman is a bride, the Rav may be lenient in certain cases to enable a bride to be *tehorah* at the time of her wedding.

9. A problematic situation:

A woman who has had unusual difficulty producing a clean *hefseik taharah*, or who often finds stains during her seven "clean" days, should inform the Rav of this fact. A woman who has a vaginal irritation should also notify the Rav when she shows him her *bedikah* cloth. In these special circumstances, the Rav may see fit to rely on lenient opinions. He may recommend that the woman omit the *moch dachuk* or minimize the number of *bedikos* done during the seven "clean" days. Similarly, as noted in Chapter Five (Section III,8) a Rav may instruct a woman to do her *bedikos* in a different manner. One should never decide upon these questions without consulting a Rav.

A woman undergoing fertility treatment should inform the Rav. It is imperative that the *taharah* process be completed before her ovulation. A Rav may rely on more lenient opinions to facilitate a timely *tevilah*.

C. Asking a second opinion

Once a Rav rules that a *bedikah* cloth is *tamei*, one may not show it to another Rav, unless one informs the second Rav of the original decision.[33] This is true of any question in *halachah* upon which a Rav rules stringently. Under normal circumstances, the second Rav may not contradict the

---

32. See Chapter Five, note 44.

33. *Rema, Y.D.* 242:31.

first ruling.[34] Indeed, if the second Rav overturns the first ruling, his lenient judgment may be invalid.[35] If the second Rav feels that the original decision was erroneous, he must contact the first Rav and discuss the matter with him and try to convince him to change his ruling.[36]

IV. Colors and shades

A. General considerations

As noted in Chapter Two, according to Biblical law, only four types of red[37] qualify as *dam niddah*.[38] In addition, black fluid renders a woman a *niddah* since red blood may turn blackish. The *Mishnah*[39] rules that esrog color[40] or egg-yolk color[41] is not *dam niddah*.[42] The Torah[43] instructs that any

---

34. See details of this *halachah* in *Rema* ibid.

35. *Shach* ibid. §54.

36. *Rema* ibid. See also responsa *Divrei Chaim* 2:81.

37. As noted in the *Mishnah* (*Niddah* 19a). The *Mishnah* explains that deeper shades of each of the four colors are *tamei* while lighter shades are *tahor* (this is according to Biblical law. However, in post-Talmudic times we consider any shade of red *tamei*. There is no longer a difference between lighter and darker shades, 188:1). *Binas Adam* (*Issur Vehetar* 8[12]) notes that these four colors are different types of red, not merely lighter and darker shades of the same red. A similar position is concluded in responsa *Tzemach Tzedek*, *Y.D.* 124, and *Aruch HaShulchan* 188:5. It seems, however, from *Ramban* (*Niddah* 19a) and *Tosfos HaRash* (*Niddah* 20a) that the term "four types of red" refers to lighter and darker shades of the same red. It seems that *Rashi* (*Niddah* 19a, s.v. דמיה) follows a similar position. *Tosfos HaRash* explains that the Torah limited *tumas niddah* to the most common shades. Thus, although a lighter or darker shade may essentially be the same color, it is not the usual shade of *dam niddah*. *Tzemach Tzedek* finds this position difficult to understand. If (as postulated by *Rambam*) the four colors of which the *Mishnah* speaks are different shades of the same red, how can the *Mishnah* state that deeper shades of each color are *tamei* and lighter ones are *tahor*? The lighter shade of the darker color is the deeper shade of the lighter. Obviously, each of the colors cited by the *Mishnah* is a totally different type of red.

38. *Chinuch* 207 contends that all other shades do not originate from the uterus. This view is shared by *Tosfos Rid* (*Niddah* 22a). *Minchas Chinuch* (ad loc.) take issues with *Chinuch* on this point. He cites *Rambam* (*Issurei Biah* 5:6) who states clearly that even those colors excluded by *Chazal* originate from the uterus. A similar position is taken by *Terumas HaDeshen* 246. See also *Sidrei Taharah* 188:4, s.v. "אבל הא."

39. *Niddah* 19a.

40. *Tosfos* ibid.

41. *Rosh, Niddah* 2:4.

42. Although the *Mishnah* uses the term *yarok*, which is commonly translated as green, *Tosfos* ibid. notes that in the terminology of *Chazal*, "*yarok*" means esrog color unless they specified "*yarok kakarsi* — green as leek." See also *Rashi, Bava Basra* 4a, who defines "*yarok*" as beige.

43. *Devarim* 17:8,9. "If a matter of judgment is hidden from you, between blood and blood, ... you

questionable color be brought to a *Chacham* to determine whether or not it is *dam niddah*. In later Talmudic times, many *Chachamim* were not confident of their ability to discern properly between shades of red.[44] *Chachamim* of later generations[45] assumed that they, too, lacked the skills to properly differentiate between shades of red.[46] Thus, the *halachah* as practiced today considers any shade of red, whether light or dark, as well as black,[47] to be *dam niddah*.[48]

This work, as any work of its type, is not the proper medium from which to learn to differentiate shades and colors. Perception of colors is somewhat subjective. One individual's red may be another's orange or brown. This skill cannot be book learned;[49] rather, it can only be mastered

---

shall come to the Kohanim, the Levites and to the judge who will be in those days; you shall inquire and they will tell you the word of judgment."

44. See *Niddah* 20b; R' Yochanan and R' Zeira would not rule on shades of red.

45. *Graz* 188:2 writes that this is an ordinance of the late Talmudic era or Geonic era.

46. Responsa *Tzemach Tzedek, Y.D.* 124, is uncertain about the proper approach regarding a light colored red stain: Should we treat it as a *safek deOraisa* (a question of a Torah prohibition), no matter how light the color may be, since we are actually unable to properly distinguish between colors or perhaps it is a Rabbinic ordinance that we may not distinguish between any shade of red? *Graz* 188:2 seems to hold that it is a Rabbinic ordinance whereby even an individual who is able to distinguish between the four reds and other reds should not do so lest others who are less knowledgeable attempt to do the same. *Maharsham* 3:214, in a responsa about a lost *bedikah* cloth, seems to follow this view. He differentiates between a stain which is red and therefore may be one of the four reds that are *tamei* by Torah law and a color which is basically yellow but may have a reddish tinge. In the first case the stain is a *safek deOraisa* and in the second case it is only *deRabbanan*. If a cloth with a stain of the first type is lost, the woman is *temei'ah*; if it was of the second type, she is *tehorah*.

47. It seems from a simple reading of *Shulchan Aruch* 188:1 (although not convincingly so) that even light black is *tamei*. However, *Darchei Teshuvah* 188:5 cites opposing opinions on the matter. *Tevuas Shor* rules that light black is the equivalent of light red and is *tamei*. *Sidrei Taharah* 190, end of 52, is uncertain of this. While reluctant to permit light black on a *bedikah* cloth, he permits it regarding a *kesem*. *Pardes Rimonim* 188:1[sc] cites *Rishonim* in support of *Tevuas Shor*. Perhaps, one can logically differentiate between red and black regarding lighter shades. According to Biblical law many types of red are *tamei*. Of these types some are lighter than others (see discussion of this in note 37 above). Since we today are unable to differentiate between reds, we must necessarily consider all reds, even light reds, *dam niddah*. However, black according to Biblical law was certainly a dark black. Thus, although we cannot identify that particular type of black, we are certain that it was not light black.

48. *Y.D.* 188:1. See *Beis Yosef*, end of 183 s.v. "משרבו", who notes that we find no specific ruling of *Chazal* declaring all red shades as *dam niddah*. Rather, since *Chachamim* of the Talmudic era refrained from differentiating between reds, later *Chachamim* followed suit.

49. See responsa *Tzitz Eliezer* 13:81[3] who completely rejects a proposal to judge colors through a color chart.

through rigorous personal training and experience. Customarily, one who wishes to study and master subtle color variations and hues of *dam niddah* must serve an apprenticeship under the guidance of one who has mastered the field. This is called "*shimush.*" This chapter cannot substitute *shimush*, rather, it is to provide guidance to the layman as to what type of colors need to be shown to a Rav.

> An important note: A color is judged not only by its general color but by every shade and hue that may be present, regardless of how small. A seemingly innocent yellow may have a slight reddish hue in one area, a reddish border or a red or black dot and must be shown to a Rav.

Generally, colors may be divided between those that pose no problem, those that are certainly *tamei* and those that must be shown to a Rav. Newlyweds are not sufficiently acquainted with the color variations and are encouraged to show any shade to a Rav. Eventually, they will learn from experience to differentiate between those colors that are not questionable and those that must always be shown to a Rav. There are, however, colors which are difficult to clarify and should always be shown to a Rav, even if encountered by an experienced couple.

B. Colors

1. Red:
Any shade of red is *tamei*. There may, however, be certain shades which a Rav can ascertain bear no resemblance to blood and come from some other source (e.g., make-up or lipstick). These colors must be shown to a Rav.

2. Black:
Chazal consider black the *halachic* equivalent of red.[50] Blood may become very dark after it leaves the uterus[51] and thus appear black. Therefore, any black stain on a *bedikah* cloth or a

---

50. See *Darchei Teshuvah* 188:7, who notes that black renders a woman a *niddah* according to Torah law, even regarding an *issur kares* (see *Badei HaShulchan* 190:23, *Biurim*, s.v. "נתעסקה").

51. See responsa *Tzemach Tzedek, Y.D.* 125, who discusses the question of whether the blood turns black in the uterus itself or turns black in the vagina. It is clear from the Talmud (*Niddah* 19a) that black is not a color of *dam niddah*. *Chazal*, however, knew that black blood originally was red. Therefore, the question arises, when did the red blood turn black? If it turned black before it reached the *beis hachitzon* (the point at which *dam* renders the woman a *niddah*, see Chapter Twenty-Three), it should not render her a *niddah* since at that moment it was no longer *dam*. By this

garment is unacceptable.[52] Often a Rav may determine that a tiny black spot is actually a dust particle. A layman, however, should never assume so on his own.

3. Pink:
A pink stain must be shown to a Rav.[53]

4. Clear mucous:
Clear mucous is *tahor* and need not be shown to a Rav.

5. White or light grey:
White and light grey[54] are generally not problematic and need not be shown to a Rav. However, it is wise to show any *bedikah* that has any shade (besides clear mucous) to a Rav until one has gained sufficient experience.

6. Grey:
Some *Poskim* contend that a grey stain is *tamei* since grey is light black,[55] while others consider it *tahor* since grey is a color of its own.[56]

7. Brown:
Brown is the subject of much disagreement among *Poskim*.

---

reasoning, we must assume that the blood turned black in the *beis hachitzon*. Alternatively, *Tzemach Tzedek* considers the possibility that the blood turns black in the uterus; however, since it originally was red when it left the uterine lining, it renders her a *niddah* even after it turns black. *Tzemach Tzedek* seems to lean towards the first approach.

52. Different Rabbonim use different criteria in judging what is considered black. Some consider very dark brown as black, others consider even extremely dark brown as plain brown.

53. See *Shiurei Sheivet HaLeivi* p. 95, that some stains that seem pinkish when damp but turn white as they dry are permitted, but real pink is not acceptable.

54. See *Shach* §2.

55. Or a mixture of black and white, see *Darchei Teshuvah* §6 and following footnote.

56. The issues involved are two: a) Is light black *tamei*? and b) assuming that light black is *tamei*, is grey light black? Sidrei *Taharah* 190, end of §52, rules that grey is light black but contends that, unlike light red, light black is *tahor* with regard to a *kesem*. However, *Pardes Rimonim* 188:1[sc], *Beis Meir* §1, *Graz* §2 and *Chochmas Adam* 111:1 disagree with this contention (see *Darchei Teshuvah* §5). They maintain that light black is *tamei*. The question then remains: Is grey light black or is it a color of its own? The fact that the color grey is created by mixing black and white paint seems to be irrelevant. Darker yellow (which is acceptable) is produced by mixing yellow and black, and brown (which is often acceptable) is made by mixing red and green. Apparently, the method by which colors are produced is not the absolute criteria. R' Shlomo Kluger in *Shiyarei Taharah* 191 (cited in *Darchei Teshuvah* §7) and *Shiurei Sheivet HaLeivi* 5:106[6] contend that grey is not light black. Light black is a shade that is blackish, although not deeply so. Grey is a completely different color.

Some *Poskim* consider brown a lighter variation of black. Thus, since black is considered *dam niddah* because blood may turn blackish after it leaves the uterus, brown is similarly considered *dam niddah* since it turned brownish after leaving the uterus. Accordingly, when *Chazal* ruled that black is *tamei* they meant brown as well. Indeed, it is a fact that blood may become brownish when combined with fluids in the vagina. In addition, blood stains on *bedikah* cloths and garments eventually turn brown. Also, some browns have a clear reddish hue while some browns may border on black. For these reasons many authorities rule unequivocally that all browns are unacceptable.[57] Others differentiate between different shades of brown. The color of chestnut shells or coffee (with milk[58]) would be accepted, according to their opinion.[59] As noted, other authorities disagree. Some Rabbonim accept brown on a regular *bedikah* but not on a *hefseik taharah*. A *hefseik taharah*, being the *bedikah* which establishes that the flow has stopped, must be *tahor* beyond doubt.[60] The standards regarding brown are more lenient for *kesamim* than for *bedikos*.[61] Some Rabbonim are stricter regarding brown than others. One must show any brown to

---

57. *Beis Meir* §1, *Rosh Efraim* 38:59, responsa *Beis Shlomo*, Y.D. 2:4, *Pardes Rimonim*, 188:1[sc], *Lechem VeSimlah* §2[s], *Darchei Teshuvah* 188:3 and *Pische Zuta* §2.

58. Black coffee color is considered black (responsa *Levushei Mordechai*, Y.D. 1:110,111).

59. Responsa *Sheilas Yaavetz* 1:44, *Sidrei Taharah* 188:1 and 190 end of §52, *Chochmas Adam* 111:1, *Pischei Teshuvah* 188:1, seems to agree with *Sheilas Yaavetz. Aruch HaShulchan* 188:9, after explaining the lenient position of *Sidrei Taharah*, adds "חלילה להחמיר — (heaven) forbid to be strict (in this matter)." See also *Gilyon Maharsha* 188:1, responsa *Tzitz Eliezer* 6:22 and *Be'er Moshe* who cites the lenient opinion of responsa *Maharitz* (R' Y.Z. Dushinsky) 46, who ends "וכן ראוי להורות — this is the proper way to instruct." Responsa *Sheivet HaLeivi* 3:121 contends that *Aruch HaShulchan* exaggerated somewhat in his lenient opinion. *Sheivet HaLeivi* writes that although there is a sound basis to be lenient regarding brown, one should be cautious regarding *bedikos* during the beginning of the seven "clean" days and regarding a *bedikah* at the time of the expected period. In *Shiurei Sheivet HaLeivi* (end of 188:1), he contends that one may be lenient with stains on *bedikos* regarding a light-brown color, unless the woman usually finds brown discharges. He notes that often the period starts with brown discharges which eventually increase in reddishness. One must therefore be extremely cautious. A Rav may rule that a brown color is *tahor* but advise the couple to abstain for a day to ensure that the stain is not actually the beginning of her period.

60. *Igros Moshe*, Y.D. 2:78, is strict regarding brown, even during the first three of the seven "clean" days, unless it is a situation of difficulty.

61. *Aruch HaShulchan* 188:19 maintains that regarding any question we are more lenient with a *kesem* than with a *re'iyah*. *Pische Zuta* 188:2 argues that since there is a question about brown, one

a Rav. An experienced Rav is able to recognize a shade of brown that is indicative of faded blood.[62]

8. Blue or green:

Blue[63] and green[64] stains are not problematic since they bear no similarity to red. However, a very dark blue or green stain should be inspected carefully since it may contain a black area.[65] Some types of a purple hue are indicative of blood. An experienced Rav is able to recognize these colors.

9. Yellow:

Pale yellow is acceptable. Some deeper yellows or shiny yellows may be problematic (especially for a *hefseik taharah*) and should be shown to a Rav.

10. Gold, esrog, beeswax or egg-yolk colors:

A gold or beeswax color[66] or an esrog or egg-yolk color[67] are *tahor*.[68] However, they should be shown to a Rav since it is difficult to distinguish between some golden colors and a reddish hue.[69] Some *Poskim* do not permit a gold or wax-color stain on a *hefseik taharah*.[70] However, if the *hefseik taharah* itself was acceptable, they would accept these colors for a *moch dachuk*.[71]

---

should be strict regarding *bedikos* as it is a *safek deOraisa* — a doubt regarding Torah law. Similarly, *Igros Moshe*, Y.D. 2:78, is strict regarding a stain found after a *hargashah*. See also responsa *Chelkas Yaakov* 3:15 regarding a brown stain on a *bedikah* within forty or eighty days after childbirth.

62. It has been noted that immediately after *Tishah B'Av* and *Yom Kippur* women tend to find darker *kesamim* and *bedikah* stains. This is the result of reduced fluid intake due to the *taanis*. A Rav should be aware of this when judging *kesamim* during these times.

63. *Rema* 188:1.

64. *Shach* §5.

65. See *Shiurei Sheivet HaLeivi* 188:1[8] who notes that very dark blue is considered black.

66. 188:1.

67. *Shach* §4.

68. *Chochmas Adam* 111:1. See *Sidrei Taharah* §2, who cites opinion of *Shelah* that a beeswax or golden color is problematic. *Sidrei Taharah*, however, maintains that this opinion is not accepted by *Poskim. Aruch HaShulchan* §7 also writes that one should not be strict for others regarding these colors.

69. See *Aruch HaShulchan* ibid.

70. *Chochmas Adam* 117:9. See *Sheivet HaLeivi* 3:121 and *Shiurei Sheivet HaLeivi* 188:1[9] for a rationale to this *chumra*.

71. *Pische Zuta* 196:6. *Shiurei Sheivet HaLeivi* ibid. See, however, *Igros Moshe*, Y.D. 2:78 and 4:17[6], who is strict regarding these colors even during the first three of the seven "clean" days (i.e., three

11. Orange:
Some *Poskim* permit orange-colored stains;[72] nevertheless, they must be shown to a Rav.

C. Additional factors

1. The edge (rim) of the stain:
Often the stain on the cloth is a color which would be acceptable but the edge of the stain has a reddish hue. In the opinion of most *Poskim*, the *bedikah* is not acceptable. However, at times, a Rav may permit a *bedikah* with a questionable edging if, with his experience, he feels that the color of the edging is caused by the fabric.[73]

2. Tiny red spots:
Often a *bedikah* cloth has a tiny red spot which, upon close inspection (at times, with a magnifying glass), is nothing more than a thread. If the spot is undoubtedly a thread, it may be ignored.

3. Tiny black spots:
At times, a Rav may permit a *bedikah* with a tiny black spot if it is clear to him that the spot is only dust that had settled on the cloth. He may verify his assumption by gently removing the suspected spot. If the speck is removable without leaving a trace it may prove that the spot is not blood. A layman should never tamper with a *bedikah* cloth; rather, he must show it to a Rav.

4. *Teliyah* — attributing the stain to an external source:
Occasionally, a stain on a cloth may be attributable to another source. A stain may be caused by fecal matter, hemorrhoids or something she had been handling, e.g., lipstick or chocolate. A stain on a garment may be caused by the coloring of an outer

---

days after her *hefseik taharah*). He is lenient regarding a case of difficulty. He is also lenient regarding a woman who found these colors on the day of her expected period. As noted, other authorities disagree and are lenient in all cases except for a *hefseik taharah*.

72. Responsa *Levushei Mordechai* (R' M. Winkler), Y.D. 1:110.

73. See *Aruch HaShulchan* 188:15 and note 7 above. A Rav may permit a questionable edging if, based upon his experience, the edging is merely the color of the stain itself which tends to become darker at the edges. Thus, if the color of the stain itself is clearly acceptable, the edging may be accepted as well.

garment that "bled" onto an undergarment.[74] One should always discuss this with a Rav and never judge it alone. A Rav must weigh the many factors involved and judge accordingly.

5. Vaginal inflammation:
At times an experienced Rav can detect a vaginal inflammation due to the particular type of stain on a *bedikah* cloth. He may then advise the woman to be examined by a gynecologist. This should be done as soon as possible since the inflammation may heal and no longer be noticeable to the physician.

D. Changes of color

Colors often change as they dry. Yet, we noted above that one need not wait until the stain dries before judging its color.[75] Conversely, it is not necessary to show the *bedikah* cloth immediately to a Rav. One may wait until it dries without worrying that a reddish hue may turn to brown. However, one should not keep the cloth for a long period of time since colors fade with the passage of time. Generally, one tries to show a cloth to a Rav on the same or next day. If the *bedikah* cloth had a reddish stain which faded and turned brown, the Rav should be informed when shown the *bedikah*. The *halachos* regarding a stain that changes colors are as follows:

1. A clear stain that turns reddish:
Let us suppose that a Rav is shown a damp *bedikah* cloth and rules that the color is acceptable. Subsequently, the cloth dries and the stain appears reddish. *Poskim* disagree as to whether the original ruling is overturned. Some contend that the color of the stain at the time it left the body is the actual color and any subsequent change is the effect of the air or the material of the cloth.[76] Many other *Poskim* disagree and rule that we

---

74. See *Pischei Teshuvah* 190:31 and *Aruch HaShulchan* 190:70.

75. However, if the stain, even when damp, is a color which is subject to a dispute among *Poskim*, i.e., gold, some *Poskim* advise that one wait until it dries (*Pardes Rimonim*, M.Z. 188, end of §1. *Taharas Yisrael* §11 advises that one should not rule on a damp brown stain). See note 3 above.

76. Responsa *Chacham Tzvi* §46. He argues that since the *tumah* begins at the time the blood leaves the body, we are concerned with the color only as it appeared at that time. Since at that time it was acceptable, the woman is *tehorah*. (Actually, *Bach* 188 maintains that the color may have been reddish when it originally left the body and immediately turned yellow. Subsequently, when it dried, it returned to its original reddish color. This possibly deflects *Chacham Tzvi's* argument which assumes that the color of the discharge when it first leaves the body is the color of the stain as it first appears.) Furthermore, *Chacham Tzvi* argues, it is inconceivable that a decision to permit the

have no choice but to consider the woman a *niddah*.[77] It seems
that if the question concerned a *kesem*, not a *bedikah* cloth,

---

stain should be rescinded. The couple may have cohabited in the interim. Should we retroactively consider it cohabitation with a *niddah*? This certainly cannot be the Torah's intention ("its ways
are pleasant" — דרכיה דרכי נועם). Apparently the Torah expects us to judge a color by its appearance at the time it left the uterus. *Chavos Daas* 188:1[b] agrees with *Chacham Tzvi* as does *Sidrei
Taharah* §2, and seemingly, *Chochmas Adam* 111:2. See *Pischei Teshuvah* §3. Although the case cited
by *Chacham Tzvi* concerned a stain whose edges turned reddish, it is clear from his arguments that
the same principle applies to a stain that turned entirely red. Indeed, *Chavos Daas* and *Sidrei
Taharah*, when quoting and agreeing with *Chacham Tzvi*, make no mention of the fact that he was
referring to a case in which only the edges turned red. *Aruch HaShulchan* §14,14 is lenient for certain in a case of a red edge and perhaps even in a case where the entire color changed. Assuming
one were to follow *Chacham Tzvi's* lenient opinion, *Poskim* discuss the question of whether a Rav
may permit a *bedikah* with a reddish color if the woman claims that it was originally white. See
responsa *Chesed L'Avraham* cited in *Darchei Teshuvah* 188:1 and *Igros Moshe, Y.D.* 4:17[4].

77. Responsa *Shvus Yaakov* 2:74. Even *Sheilas Yaavetz* 1:12 (who was *Chacham Tzvi's* son) presumes
that his father's leniency in the matter was more speculative than practical. *Bach* quoted in *Taz* §1
certainly disagrees with *Chacham Tzvi*. Indeed, his concern regarding the possibility that the color
may change is such that he requires that one not rule on the cloth until it dries. It seems that since
Taz and *Shach* disagree with *Bach's* opinion merely by arguing that there is no basis to be concerned that the color may change, not by stating that a change of colors does not concern us, they
obviously disagree with *Chacham Tzvi*. *Pardes Rimonim* 188:1[mz],3[sc], also rejects *Chacham Tzvi's*
view as does *Tiferes Tzvi* 188:1. See also *Darchei Teshuvah* §1. This view is shared by *Tzemach
Tzedek, Y.D.* 127. This is also the view of R' Shlomo Kluger in *HaElef Lecha Shlomo* 224,225, who
maintains that if the woman's stains usually change colors after drying, even *Taz* would agree
that she must inspect her stains after they dry. Responsa *Maharsham* 3:250 cites responsa *R'Chaim
Or Zarua* §67 who clearly concurs with *Bach's* contention that the color may have been red origi-
nally, changed immediately to yellow and back to red when it dried (see previous footnote).
Interestingly, *Chasam Sofer, Y.D.* 145, follows the very same logic without citing any sources.
Maharsham feels that one cannot ignore the opinion of an authority of such stature as *R'Chaim Or
Zarua* and therefore rules like *Bach*. Responsa *Tiferes Tzvi* (R' Tzadok HaCohen) 2:10 also cites *R'
Chaim Or Zarua* but contends that one need not follow the opinion of *Bach* to the degree of waiting until the cloth dries. However, if the color actually changed to red, even responsa *Tiferes Tzvi*
seems, in conclusion, to disagree with *Chacham Tzvi*, although this is not entirely clear. However,
responsa *Avnei Neizer, Y.D.* 225, also quoting *R' Chaim Or Zarua*, reaches a different conclusion
entirely. He maintains that *R' Chaim Or Zarua* was referring to a case where the stain turned
entirely red. If however, it merely took a reddish hue or tinge, perhaps *Or Zarua* would agree
with *Chacham Tzvi* that she is *tehorah*. After a lengthy discussion, *Avnei Neizer* does not reach a
clear conclusion.

It is interesting to note that *Igros Moshe, Y.D.* 4:17[4], follows the lenient opinion of *Chacham Tzvi,
Chavos Daas* and *Sidrei Taharah*. He is surprised that *Sheilas Yaavetz* rejects his father's opinion. *Igros
Moshe* does not accept *Bach's* contention that the stain was originally red, then turned white and
finally returned to its original redness. He argues that the color that concerns us is the color of the
blood as it left the body; the color inside the body is immaterial. Thus, even if the color was originally red, since at the time it left the body, it was white, the woman is *tehorah*. In rebuttal of *Igros
Moshe's* logic, we might argue that according to *Bach*, the blood was red as it left the uterus,
changed colors in the vagina and subsequently returned to the original red. Thus, at the crucial

most *Poskim* would agree that she is *tehorah*.[78]

2. If only the edges turn reddish:

If the stain on the *bedikah* cloth was acceptable while it was damp, but the edges of the stain took a reddish tinge as it dried, some *Poskim* rule that she is *tehorah*.[79]

3. A reddish stain which becomes clear:

If a stain on a cloth appears reddish either to the woman or the Rav when damp but looks acceptable after it has dried, the woman is *temei'ah*.[80]

4. A stain seen originally at night:

a. A possibly reddish color:

If the stain, when originally inspected at night with a lamp, seemed reddish, but was difficult to judge with certainty, it should be rechecked by day. If, when the stain is rechecked at day, it appears definitely yellow, the woman is *tehorah*. We assume that the inferior light of the night gave the color an unnatural reddish hue.[81]

b. A definite reddish stain:

If, when seen at night, the stain certainly appeared

---

moment (at leaving the uterus), it was red. This seems to be the intent of *R' Chaim Or Zarua* as well. One should note that *Igros Moshe* is only lenient if the Rav himself saw the original acceptable color. However, if the Rav only saw the stain in its present reddish color but the woman claims that it was not red originally, she is *temei'ah*.

In summary: If the color of the stain changes from an acceptable to an unacceptable color: *Chacham Tzvi, Chavos Daas, Sidrei Taharah, Chochmas Adam, Aruch HaShulchan* (at least in a case where the edges turned red) and *Igros Moshe* are lenient, while *Shvus Yaakov, Sheilas Yaavetz, Pardes Rimonim, Bach, Taz, Shach* and *Chasam Sofer, Maharsham* and apparently, *R' Chaim Or Zarua*, are strict.

78. See *Chavos Daas* 188:1[b], *Avnei Neizer*, Y.D. 226, *Taharas Yisrael* §12, *Pische Zuta* §1 and 4.

79. *Aruch HaShulchan* 188:15 and *Taharas Yisrael* §15. *Aruch HaShulchan* contends that even those who disagree with *Chacham Tzvi* concede that if only the edges turned red, she is *tehorah*. This is difficult to accept since *Shvus Yaakov* is clearly referring to this very same case, as is *Bach, Taz* and *Shach*. All imply that if the color of the edges actually changed, she is *temei'ah* (see above). However, the proof to the *Bach's* opinion from *R' Chaim Or Zarua* cited above note 77 would not apply in a case where only the edges changed colors. See also *Avnei Neizer* cited above note 77.

80. See *Niddah* 20b, *Taz* 188:1 and *Chavos Daas* §1[b].

81. See *Rashi, Niddah* 20b, *Sidrei Taharah* 190 end of 93, cited in *Chochmas Adam* 111:2, *Sheivet HaLeivi* 3:121 and *Igros Moshe*, Y.D. 4:17[4,5]. *Sidrei Taharah* (190 end of 93) notes that a lamp may cause yellow to appear reddish. This is true with an incandescent bulb as well. Thus, a stain that may have a slight reddish hue at night when inspected with an incandescent bulb, but appears yellow or brown by daylight, is *tehorah* providing that one was not certain about the reddishness at night. We noted in I,B above that a fluorescent light does not stress red properly; thus, the same stain, when inspected under the two lights, may appear slightly reddish under the incandescent bulb

reddish, the woman is *temei'ah,* according to the opinion of most *Poskim,* even if it subsequently appeared yellow in daylight. In this case, since the color originally certainly appeared reddish, we must assume that the color changed in the interim.[82]

c. The Rav is told that the stain was reddish:

Occasionally, a woman may bring a *bedikah* cloth to a Rav and claim that when the cloth was damp, the stain appeared red. However, the Rav, upon inspecting the stain after it is dry, is convinced that the stain could never have been red. If the woman insists that originally the color was indeed red, the Rav has little choice but to rule that she is *temei'ah.* This follows the rule discussed in Chapter Four that one can create a prohibition upon oneself merely by stating a fact which effects the prohibition. However, if the woman is uncertain whether or not it was originally red, a Rav may, at times, assume that she was mistaken about its color. A Rav should approach this subject with caution and only be lenient where he is certain from experience that the color could not initially have been red.[83]

---

and brown under the fluorescent bulb. It may be that a stain which seemed reddish when seen with a fluorescent light, and subsequently appeared brown when viewed the following day in natural light, should not be approved. A fluorescent light minimizes redness more than natural light; therefore, if the stain appeared red under fluorescent light, it was surely red in natural light as well but faded with time.

82. *Chavos Daas* 188:1[b], *Sidrei Taharah* 190 end of §93, *Chochmas Adam* 111:2 and *Aruch HaShulchan* 188:16. *Pischei Teshuvah* 188:1 cites responsa *Givas Shaul* §63 and *Levushei Sarad* §78, who disagree and are lenient even in a case when the stain certainly appeared reddish. It is noteworthy that *Igros Moshe, Y.D.* 4:17[5], rules leniently in this case without citing the opinions mentioned above.

83. *Sheivet HaLeivi* 3:121, *Shiurei Sheivet HaLeivi* p. 95. If the woman originally saw the cloth at night, one may be lenient, as noted above. *Sheivet HaLeivi* argues that it is unusual for a color to change completely from an unacceptable to an acceptable color. It is much more reasonable to assume that the woman is mistaken in her recollection. It would seem that even if the woman claims that the color faded or changed, the Rav may nevertheless approve the *bedikah* if, according to his experience, the color before him could not have been *tamei* originally. The woman may be correct that the color changed, but it merely changed from a darker to a lighter hue of an acceptable color. As noted in the text, *Sheivet HaLeivi* cautions that one should approach this question with caution. Rav Y. Roth in *Beis Talmud LeHoraah* (vol 1:86) rules that if the stain is almost clear or pale yellow one may assume that the woman is mistaken if she claims it was red originally. Blood stains do not fade completely and turn yellow.

5. A possible change in colors:

If the stain was seen originally in daylight and seemed *tamei* but subsequently, when inspected a second time, it appeared yellow, we assume that the color changed and the woman is *temei'ah*.[84] However, if one was originally unsure about the color, and after a second inspection it appears acceptable, she is *tehorah*.[85]

6. A woman whose stains usually change colors:

If a woman is accustomed to finding yellow discharges that turn red after drying, *Poskim* disagree as to whether she is permitted to discard the cloth before it dries. Many authorities contend that, since this woman's stains usually change colors, discarding the cloth amounts to ignoring a possible problem.[86] In a similar case regarding a *kesem*, one may wash the garment before the color changes.[87]

V. Repeating a *bedikah*

One who does a *bedikah* and suspects that the color may be unacceptable cannot merely repeat the *bedikah*. This would depend upon the type of *bedikah* she had done. If she is in the middle of her seven "clean" days and she finds blood on her *bedikah* cloth, she must repeat the *hefseik taharah* and begin the seven "clean" days anew. Similarly, if she finds blood on a *bedikah* done while she is in a *tehorah* state, e.g., on the day of her expected period, she is a *niddah*, regardless of the result of a second *bedikah*. The second *bedikah* cannot negate the fact that blood was found

---

84. *Taharas Yisrael* 188:14.

85. *Shaarei Tohar* 8:3. It seems that there are three levels: a) a stain that originally certainly appeared red, b) a stain that seemed red and c) a stain about which one was unsure. In the first case, even if it was seen originally at night, she is *temei'ah*. This is the subject of *Chavos Daas* 188:1[b] and *Sidrei Taharah* 190:93, noted in 82 above. If the color originally seemed red, it depends upon whether it was seen by day or by night. If it was seen by night, she is *tehorah*. This is the subject of *Rashi, Niddah* 20b, and *Chavos Daas*, ibid. If it was originally seen by day, she is *temei'ah*. This is the *halachah* cited in the name of *Taharas Yisrael*. If one was unsure about the color and put it aside for further examination, she is *tehorah*, even if it was seen initially by day. This is the *halachah* cited from *Shaarei Tohar*.

86. See *Maharsham* 3:250 who is inclined to be stringent in this case. He cites the opinion of R' Shlomo Kluger (in responsa *Sheyarei Taharah*) who is lenient (it is odd that in responsa *HaElef Lecha Shlomo* 224,225, he takes the opposite position). See *Darchei Teshuvah* 188 end of §1. *Taharas Yisrael* §13 is stringent in this case; see also *Chasam Sofer, Y.D.* 145. See *Pische Zuta* 188:4.

87. Ibid.

on the first cloth. Nevertheless, a woman may find it advantageous to repeat a *bedikah* in the following instances.

A. After a *hefseik taharah*

A woman who attempted a *hefseik taharah* and finds blood on the cloth should do a second *bedikah*. In this case, the first *hefseik taharah* has no practical effect upon her status since she previously was *temei'ah*. Thus, she has much to gain by attempting a second *hefseik taharah* before sundown. Some *Poskim* note that a woman should wait a few minutes between *bedikos*.[88] If the first *hefseik taharah* was very bloody and the time remaining before sundown is short, the woman may choose to delay a second attempt until the following day. The chance of producing a clear *bedikah* is minimal, while continuous attempts may irritate the vagina and cause additional bleeding. However, if the original *hefseik taharah* was only slightly red, there is a chance that if she waits a few minutes she may be able to produce an acceptable *hefseik taharah* before sundown.[89] If the first *hefseik taharah* is a questionable color, (it should be put aside and shown to a Rav the following day and) she should attempt a second *hefseik taharah* in case the first is invalid. If the second *hefseik taharah* is clear, the first may be discarded since it is now irrelevant. If the second *hefseik taharah* is also questionable, both should be marked and shown to a Rav on the following day. At times, a Rav may permit the second only in conjunction with the first. For example, the second *hefseik taharah* may have a questionable color which is acceptable as a *bedikah* but not as a *hefseik taharah*. If the first *hefseik taharah* was discarded, the Rav must treat the second as a *hefseik taharah* and declare the woman *temei'ah*. However, if the first is shown to the Rav, it may be found acceptable and the second *hefseik taharah* will now be treated as a regular *bedikah* and accepted.

---

88. See *Chazon Ish, Y.D.* 81, regarding douching. *Chazon Ish* does not suggest a specific length of time to wait between douching and doing a *bedikah*. *Igros Moshe, Y.D.* 2:71, writes that one should wait fifteen minutes between douching and doing a *bedikah*. It would seem that one should also not do two *bedikos* immediately following one another. *Badei HaShulchan* 196:1, *Biurim* s.v. "שתפסק", notes that since none of the earlier *Poskim* mention either of these problems they apparently did not consider this a serious concern. See Chapter Five note 35

89. We noted above that perhaps one should wait between *bedikos*. In this case, however, if one were to wait, it would be impossible to do a second *hefseik taharah*. Thus, one should probably rely upon the fact that most *Poskim* make no mention of waiting between *bedikos*, as noted above.

B. A *bedikah* of the seven "clean" days

A woman who does a *bedikah* during the seven "clean" days and finds a questionable stain should attempt to show the *bedikah* to a Rav the very same day. If this is not possible, she should do another *hefseik taharah* before sundown so as not to lose an additional day. In this case she cannot merely redo the *bedikah* since if the first *bedikah* is unacceptable the entire process is invalidated. She must redo the *hefseik taharah* and begin counting the seven "clean" days again. If possible, she should wait a few minutes between *bedikos,* as noted above. Many Rabbonim advise that she should not do a *moch dachuk.*[90] The original *bedikah* should be shown to a Rav on the following day. If the Rav rules that the *bedikah* is acceptable, she may continue her original counting of her seven "clean" days. If the *bedikah* is not acceptable, she relies on the last *hefseik taharah* and starts the seven "clean" days again.

VI. *Teliyah:* attributing the stain to another source

At times, it may be possible to attribute a stain on a *bedikah* cloth to a foreign source, e.g., a woman suffering from hemorrhoids should consult with a Rav whether or not she may attribute blood found on a *bedikah* cloth to her condition. One should never assume that the blood on a *bedikah* cloth is from another source without consulting a Rav. This question is dependent upon the size of the stain, its shape, its color and the stage of the cycle in which the woman finds herself. These *halachos* are discussed at length in *Shulchan Aruch* and are among the more difficult issues in *Hilchos Niddah*. One should never attempt to rule upon such matters alone. The laws of *teliyah* regarding *kesamim* are discussed in Chapter Eleven.

---

90. A *moch dachuk* is not an absolute requirement. Hence, in a case of doubt where even a new *hefseik taharah* may not be required, one may omit the *moch dachuk.*

BOOK THREE

כתמים

Kesamim — Stains

Chapter Seven — General Principles
Chapter Eight — The Size Shape and Color
Chapter Nine — The Garment
Chapter Ten — The Location
Chapter Eleven — Attributing a Stain to
Another Source

כתמים, כללים

Kesamim: General Principles

□ The unique status of a *kesem.*

□ The difference between a *kesem* and a *bedikah.*

□ To whom the rules of *kesamim* apply.

□ A *kesem* that was lost.

□ Avoiding *kesamim* problems.

□ A *kesem* that precedes a menstrual period.

□ A *kesem* associated with a *hargashah.*

HALACHIC OVERVIEW
OF ALL THE CHAPTERS IN BOOK THREE

1. A *kesem* is a blood stain found upon an object (e.g., a sheet or blanket) or a woman's garment or body which is unattributable to any other source other than herself. A woman who finds a *kesem* becomes *temei'ah* and must observe all the *halachos* of a *niddah*. Although there are situations in which a *kesem* will be *tahor*, whenever the term "*kesem*" is used in this work it connotes a *kesem* that is *tamei*, unless noted otherwise.

2. A *kesem* differs from a *re'iyah* (an actual blood flow). A woman who finds a *kesem* becomes a *niddah* according to Rabbinic law only, while a woman who has a blood flow (a *re'iyah*) is a *niddah* according to Torah law. This difference is based upon two factors: a) A woman who had a blood flow felt, or is assumed to have felt, a *hargashah* (a sensation of a blood flow or a sensation usually associated with the beginning of menstruation) while a woman who merely found a *kesem* felt no *hargashah*. b) A blood flow certainly originated from the body while a stain may have come from an external source (although the source has not been identified). For these two reasons a *kesem* is excluded from the Torah law of *niddah*.

3. A woman who finds a *kesem* must wait the preliminary five days, do a *hefseik taharah*, count seven "clean" days, do a proper *tevilah* and recite the *b'rachah* on that *tevilah*. In short, she follows the very same procedure as a woman who has had a full menstruation.

4. The sole difference between a *re'iyah* and a *kesem* concerns the laws of *vestos*. *Vestos* do not apply to *kesamim*. A woman who finds a *kesem* three times on the same date of the Hebrew month or after the same three interval of days is not required to separate from her husband or do *bedikos* on the same date of the following month or after the similar interval.

5. Normally, a woman is not required to check her garments for *kesamim*. This does not constitute a willful evasion of the laws of *niddah* since *Chazal* did not require that she do a *bedikah* or check her garments.

6. During the seven "clean" days, a woman is required to ascertain that the menstrual period has completely ended. This is accomplished only by doing the required *bedikos* and wearing white garments to find any *kesem* that may appear.

7. The laws of *kesem* apply to any woman who finds a blood stain, even an unmarried woman (e.g., a *kallah* preparing for her wedding), a pregnant or nursing woman or a woman who is past menopause.

8. A *kesem* is not *tamei* unless it is a specific, minimum size. This is in contrast to a *re'iyah* which renders a woman a *niddah*, regardless of its size. *Chazal* ruled that a woman is not affected by a blood stain unless it is larger than the size of a bean, known as a "*gris*," which was common in their time. Most contemporary authorities agree that this is equivalent to the size of a U.S. penny. A *kesem* smaller than this size may be ignored.

9. A reddish stain, larger than a *gris*, that is found on a woman's body or garment renders her a *niddah*, regardless of its shape. It may be round, square or elongated; in all these cases, she is *temei'ah*. Even a streak across the width of her thigh renders her a *niddah*, even though it is extremely unusual for menstrual blood to fall this way.

10. An oblong *kesem* is measured in terms of its total area, not its length, width or circumference. If the *kesem* consists of several shades, some of an acceptable color and some reddish, one includes only those reddish parts of the stain in the measurement of the *gris*.

11. If a stain found upon a garment consists of two completely separate spots, each of which is smaller than a *gris* but, in combination, exceed a *gris*, the woman is *tehorah*. A *kesem* found upon the body is treated more strictly than one found upon a garment since, in all probability, it came from the uterus. Therefore, two small separate stains on the body, each smaller than a *gris*, render her a *niddah* if they combine to equal a *gris*.

12. A *kesem* that requires measurement should not be measured by a layman. Most *kesamim* are not perfectly round and must be measured by approximation. A Rav is experienced in measuring *kesamim*; a layman is not. Furthermore, a layman is not acquainted with different types of colors and shades. Only an experienced Rav is able to properly judge colors. One should not assume that a *kesem* larger than a *gris* is necessarily *tamei*, since part of the *kesem* may be an acceptable color and does not combine to the measurement of the *gris*. A woman should not be needlessly strict regarding a *kesem*, she should overcome her embarrassment and show any questionable *kesem* to a Rav. A Rav is an experienced professional who will deal with the situation in a discreet manner.

13. A woman who finds a stain on her body must measure it carefully and then remove it onto a cloth to show to a Rav.

14. One should not keep *kesamim* (or *bedikos*) for more than a day or two since colors fade and change. If a *kesem* is obviously *tahor*, the garment should be put aside and washed. If it is questionable, it should be shown to a Rav without unnecessary delay.

15. If a woman finds a questionable stain but loses (or washes) the garment before she is able to show it to a Rav, a Rav should be consulted.

16. A woman who finds a stain on the external opening of the vagina or who wipes the external vaginal area and finds a stain must consult a Rav, even if the stain is smaller than a *gris*.

17. The laws of *kesamim* do not apply to a stain found upon a colored garment, regardless of whether the garment is red or any other color. This is essentially true even if the stain is found on the day of her expected period, is red and larger than a *gris*. Nevertheless, under the circumstances described, a Rav should be consulted.

18. Common practice is to exempt any colored garment from the laws of *kesamim* even if it is not a dark color. However, it is difficult to classify extremely light pastel-colored garments as colored garments. Off-white or light beige colors are considered a variation of white and thus subject to the laws of *kesamim*.

19. If a garment is partially white and partially colored, the *kesem* is judged according to the part of the garment upon which it is found. If the stain is found upon the white part of the pattern, it is treated as a stain on a white garment, even though part of the garment is colored. If the *kesem* is partially on the white and partially on the colored part of the garment, the part on the colored area is ignored. Thus, if the stain on the white area is smaller than a *gris*, the woman is *tehorah*.

20. If the *kesem* overlaps onto both white sides of a colored area, the stain on the colored area is not added to the measurement of the *gris*, but the stain on the two white areas combine to a *gris* even though they are separated by the colored area.

21. Even a *kesem* found upon a white garment will not render the woman a *niddah* unless the garment had been previously checked for cleanliness. Otherwise, we assume that the stain was on the garment before she donned it and may be disregarded. Washed garments are assumed to be clean; thus, if a woman finds a *kesem* upon a white garment that was taken from the clothes dryer or the drawer and donned without inspection, she is a *niddah*.

22. *Poskim* advise a woman to avoid the problem of *kesamim* entirely by wearing colored garments during the time that she is *tehorah* (not during the seven "clean" days). This is not a willful evasion of the *halachah*. The same *Chazal* that declared a woman Rabbinically *temei'ah* if she finds a

kesem on a white garment specifically exempted colored garments from the laws of *kesamim*. Thus, a woman who wears colored undergarments is generally protected against *kesamim*. It is not necessary for a woman to wear black or navy blue garments; any color will do. She should, however, wear garments that are certainly considered "colored," not light beige or off-white colors. In addition, she should not wear a garment with a white lining. A *kesem* on the white lining will render her a *niddah* even though the garment itself is colored. Similarly, a woman who wears a colored undergarment to avoid *kesamim* problems, but wears white tights, is not completely protected against *kesamim*.

23. A woman who feels the external sensation of a flow (which may be considered a *hargashah*) while she is wearing a colored garment cannot dismiss a stain found afterwards on the garment. Even if she finds a stain smaller than a *gris* she may be *temei'ah*. A Rav must be consulted.

24. A *kesem* found close to the expected arrival of the period should not be dismissed, even if it was found on a colored garment. Although the woman is not rendered a *niddah* by the *kesem* itself, it may signal the imminent arrival of her period and precautionary steps are warranted. A Rav may advise the couple to abstain from cohabitation until her status becomes clearer. In addition, since a menstrual period is often preceded by a staining phase, the staining itself may be considered a *vest* (as explained in Chapter Eighteen) and the couple may be required to abstain upon the onset of the staining. The *halachah* will be discussed in Chapter Thirteen, Section II,B,4.

25. A stain found upon an object that is not *mekabel tumah* (not susceptible to *tumah*) will not render the woman a *niddah*, even if it certainly came from her body. Thus, a stain found upon the ground or anything connected to it, e.g., the floor of the shower stall, is *tahor*. However, a woman who finds a stain upon the plastic toilet seat or the toilet fixture itself should consult a Rav even though these fixtures are not *mekabel tumah*. Similarly, a woman who notices blood in the water after urination should consult a Rav.

26. A woman who finds a stain on toilet tissue which she used to clean herself or who finds blood in her urine should ask a *sheilah*. A woman should avoid looking at toilet tissues since, by doing so, she may cause unnecessary problems. If she does notice a red stain on the paper, she should not check herself again with a tissue or do a *bedikah*. She should ask a *sheilah*.

27. The *kesem* will not render a woman a *niddah* unless it is found in a location where it is reasonable that uterine blood may have fallen there

directly from the vagina. Thus, if blood is found upon a woman's shoulder or the top of her blouse, she is *tehorah*. Nevertheless, if it is possible that the garment moved, at some time, to a position where blood may have fallen upon it, she is *temei'ah*. These *halachos* are based on strict guidelines set forth in the Talmud. One should not attempt to reach conclusions based upon one's judgment without consulting a Rav.

28. A stain found upon a quilt renders the woman a *niddah* since quilts move in all directions during sleep. Similarly, a stain found upon a loose sheet renders her a *niddah*, regardless of its position, since the sheet may move during sleep. However, a stain found upon a tucked-in or fitted sheet that is found in position in the morning renders her a *niddah* only if it is found on an area that may have been near her waist had she changed positions completely during the course of the night. A woman who wore a tightly fitting undergarment during sleep is unaffected by any stains found on the sheet if the garment is found to be clean in the morning.

29. A woman who removes her robe and uses it to cover herself while sleeping at night and finds a *kesem* on any part of the robe is *temei'ah*. A robe used as a cover could move about at night and any part may have reached the vaginal area.

30. A woman who finds a *kesem* on her garment (or if her husband finds blood on his body) after cohabitation may be *temei'ah* according to Torah law, even if the stain is less than a *gris* and even on a colored garment. A stain found on the cloth with which either the woman or her husband used to clean themselves after cohabitation is more serious yet. A Rav must be consulted.

31. Since *kesamim* are only Rabbinic in origin, *Chazal* were lenient and permitted a Rav to attribute a *kesem* to any reasonable source other than the woman (this process is called *teliyah*). Examples of this are: a woman working with staining substances (e.g., she was salting meat or painting), or a woman who passes near those working with paints, or a woman with a wound or cut. In any of these cases the Rav may attribute any *kesem* that she finds to these sources. A stain may be attributed even to a partially healed wound if the scab could reopen when scratched a bit. Similarly, a *kesem* may be attributed to nose bleeds or hemorrhoids if the woman has a history of these problems. These *halachos* are complicated and lie entirely within the domain of a Rav. A woman who suspects that a *kesem* may be attributable to another source must discuss this with a Rav.

32. A woman who finds a *kesem* is not required to do a *bedikah*. If the *kesem* is unacceptable, she is *temei'ah* regardless of the result of the *bedikah*. If the *kesem* is acceptable, she needs no further support. A *bedikah* may cause her to become a *niddah* unnecessarily, since a small stain on a garment may be ignored, while even the smallest stain found upon a *bedikah* cloth renders her a *niddah*. Thus, she has nothing to gain and much to lose by performing a *bedikah*.

33. A woman who finds a *kesem* is not required to note the date. Even if she finds a *kesem* on the same date for three consecutive months, she is not required to treat that day as a *vest* day. This is true even if the *kesem* is certainly menstrual blood, larger than a *gris* and on a white garment. Even though she is *temei'ah,* the *kesem* does not establish a *vest*. Similarly, she is not required to abstain on the thirtieth day following the *kesem*. Indeed, the *kesem* is totally ignored regarding *vestos*. Thus, if she finds a *kesem* between two regular periods, she ignores the *kesem* and counts her interval between the two actual periods only.

I. The unique *halachic* status of a *kesem*

A. Introduction

One of the fundamental principles of *Hilchos Niddah* is the unique status of a *kesem* (a stain found upon an object, her garment or body)[1] as opposed to a *re'iyah* (an actual blood flow). Although we rule that a woman who finds a *kesem* becomes a *niddah,* and is essentially similar in status to a woman who had an actual blood flow, she is a *niddah* according to Rabbinic law only. By Torah law she is *tehorah*. A woman who has an actual blood flow is a *niddah* even according to Torah law. This difference is based upon two factors: a) A woman who had a blood flow felt, or is assumed to have felt, a *hargashah* (a sensation associated with the menstrual flow, see Chapter Three), while a woman who merely found a *kesem* felt no *hargashah*. b) A blood flow certainly originated from the body while a stain may have come from an external source. We will examine these two factors which set *kesamim* apart from a regular blood flow.

B. A *kesem* according to Torah law

1. The lack of *hargashah*:
According to Torah law, a woman cannot become a *niddah* unless she experiences a *hargashah* — a physical sensation attributed to

---

1. Which is definitely not accompanied by a *hargashah*.

the blood flow.[2] A blood flow without a *hargashah* will not, in the opinion of most *Poskim*, render her a *niddah* according to Torah law.[3] Accordingly, when a woman finds a *kesem*, she is not *temei'ah* according to Torah law. In this regard, a *kesem* is defined as any blood that appears without a *hargashah*.

2. The possibility of an external source:
Since a *kesem* may have originated from a source other than her body,[4] the Torah specifically[5] excludes it from the rules of

---

2. 190:1, See *Niddah* 57b.

3. See Appendix A, where the different opinions among *Poskim* are discussed in detail. In summary: *Sidrei Taharah* 190:93, s.v. "וכבר," contends that this is subject to a dispute among *Rishonim*. In the opinion of *Rashi, Tosfos* and possibly *Raavad*, if the blood certainly came from her body, even without a *hargashah*, she is a *niddah* according to Torah law. *Sidrei Taharah* maintains that *Rambam* disagrees, ruling that a *hargashah* is an absolute requisite. Even if the blood certainly came from her uterus, she is *tehorah* according to Torah law if the blood flow was not accompanied by a *hargashah*. Other *Poskim* disagree entirely with *Sidrei Taharah* (see *Binas Adam* 113[9], *Aruch HaShulchan* 183:47-54 and *Pardes Rimonim* pp. 11-14, who refute all *Sidrei Taharah's* arguments). In their view, even *Rashi* and *Tosfos* agree with *Rambam* that a *hargashah* is a requisite for *tumas niddah*. Even if the blood certainly came from her body, but there was no *hargashah*, she is *tehorah* by Torah law. They do, however, concede that if it is certain that the blood came from her body and there is the possibility that there was a *hargashah* (e.g. she did a *bedikah* and may have mistaken the *hargashah* for the sensation of the *bedikah*), she is a *niddah* according to Torah law. We assume that there must have been a *hargashah* since a blood flow is usually accompanied by a *hargashah*.

4. One should not confuse this concept with *teliyah* (discussed in Chapter Eleven). The rules of *teliyah*, in which the Rav attributes a stain to another source, apply only to a case in which the *kesem* can be attributed to another <u>identifiable</u> source. When no such identifiable source exists, *Chazal* instituted the *tumah* of *kesamim*. This *tumah*, however, is not based on Torah law since the <u>possibility</u> exists that the blood may be from another source unknown to us. In short: If the blood is certainly from the body, she may be *temei'ah* according to Torah law. If the blood may be from another source, but we cannot identify this source, she is *temei'ah* according to Rabbinic law. If the blood is attributable to an identified source, she is *tehorah* through the laws of *teliyah*.

5. The Talmud (*Niddah* 58b) cites R' Akiva who claimed that a *kesem* does not render a woman a *niddah* according to Torah law. R' Akiva derived this from the word "*dam*" which he understood to exclude a *kesem*. *Sidrei Taharah* 190:93 explains that, according to R' Akiva, "*kesem*" is defined as any blood that may have originated from a source other than her body, even if it may have been accompanied by a *hargashah* (see a similar approach in *Graz* 190:1 and *Binas Adam* 113[9]). *Chavos Daas* 196:3[b] explains R' Akiva in a slightly different manner. In his opinion, any blood flow that appears during the seven "clean" days, even if unassociated with a *hargashah*, invalidates the counting of "clean" days. The word "*dam*," according to R' Akiva, is required to exclude a *kesem* from invalidating the seven "clean" days. Accordingly, a woman who finds a *kesem* during the "clean" days may continue counting the seven days by Torah law according to *Chavos Daas'* explanation of R' Akiva. However, according to the Rabbinic law of *kesamim* (if the *kesem* is a type that *Chazal* deemed *tamei*) she is required to do a new *hefseik taharah* and begin the seven "clean" days anew.

niddah.[6] In this regard, a *kesem* is defined as any blood which may be attributed to another source.

In summary: The unique status of a *kesem* is due to one of two factors: a) the lack of *hargashah* and b) the possibility that the stain originated from another, though unidentified, source. Even when one of these factors does not apply, a *kesem* is still only Rabbinic in nature due to the other factor. See Chapter Eight, Section I,D,6, regarding a stain that certainly originated from the body. See Section VII, regarding a stain accompanied by a *hargashah*. If the stain certainly originated from her body and <u>may</u> have been accompanied by *hargashah*, she is *temei'ah* according to Torah law (see footnote 3).

C. A *kesem* according to Rabbinic law

Although a *kesem* is excluded from the laws of *niddah* by Torah law, *Chazal* decreed[7] that a woman who finds a *kesem* becomes a *niddah* according to Rabbinic law.[8] *Rishonim* offer two explanations as to why *Chazal*

---

6. *Sidrei Taharah* ibid., s.v. טרם אכלה, notes that since we have a rule of *safek deOraisa lechumra* (any doubt regarding a Torah law must be resolved in a strict manner), it may seem inappropriate to exclude a *kesem* from the laws of *niddah* merely because it may be from another source (since according to this reason we do not exempt a *kesem* because of the lack of *hargashah*). Rather, this should be a classical case of *safek deOraisa lechumra*: We should assume that indeed the blood is menstrual blood (not from some other source). Nevertheless, *Sidrei Taharah* explains, *kesamim* are permitted by Torah law. He further explains that we find other cases where the Torah specifically excludes certain *halachos* from the rule of *safek deOraisa lechumra*. For example: A *safek mamzer* (one whose status as a *mamzer* is in doubt) is permitted to marry a non-*mamzer* according to Torah law even though an actual *mamzer* is forbidden to marry anyone but another *mamzer*. The Torah specifically permitted a *safek mamzer*. Similarly, although any *kesem* may actually be a blood flow that renders her a *niddah* (since according to this reason we do not exempt a *kesem* because of the lack of *hargashah*), the Torah specifically excludes any blood that did not certainly originate from her body from the laws of *niddah*.

7. *Kesef Mishnah* (*Issurei Biah* 9:2) finds the Rabbinic prohibition of *kesamim* seemingly contradictory to the general principle that a *s'fek s'feika* (a double doubt) is permitted. Every *kesem* is a double *safek* since a) the blood may be from some source external to the body, and b) even if it did come from the woman, perhaps it is from some internal source other than the uterus. *Kesef Mishnah* offers two answers: a) The severity of the prohibition of *niddah* (the potential penalty of *kares*) mandates that we be strict, even in a case of *s'fek s'feika*. b) The chance that the blood may have come from an external source is not a significant consideration since we are not aware of any external source to which to attribute the blood. *Taz* 190:2 contends that since most blood comes from the uterus, the doubt that the blood may be from another source in the body (factor b) is not a serious consideration. See *Chavos Daas* 190:2[b] and *Sidrei Taharah* 190:2.

8. It is interesting to note that there is an opinion in *Rishonim* that the Rabbinic laws of *kesamim* were instituted only regarding laws of *tumah* and *taharah*, not regarding the prohibition of cohabiting

found it necessary to create the laws of *kesamim:* Some[9] explain that *Chazal* were concerned that a woman may have experienced a *hargashah* without noticing it. Others[10] explain that *Chazal* were concerned that women may not differentiate between blood that appears with a *hargashah* and blood that appears without a *hargashah* and mistakenly believe that both are *tahor.*

A woman who is rendered a *niddah* as a result of a *kesem* must wait the preliminary five days, do a *hefseik taharah,* count seven "clean" days,[11] perform a proper *tevilah* and recite the *b'rachah* on that *tevilah.*[12]

D. The practical difference between a *kesem* and a *re'iyah*

Although *Chazal* mandated that a *kesem* renders a woman a *niddah,* it is not the exact equivalent of a *reiyas dam.* The difference between the two relate to the situations in which they render a woman a *niddah* and consequences of her becoming a *niddah.*

> 1. The situations in which a *re'iyah* and a *kesem* render a woman a *niddah:*
> Any uterine blood flow[13] renders a woman a *niddah,* according to Torah law. As such, it is absolute and cannot be modified or limited in any manner (e.g., because of its size or where it is found) unless mandated by the Torah itself. A *kesem,* however, is Rabbinic

---

with a *niddah.* See *Raavad* (*Baalei HaNefesh,* beginning of *Shaar HaKesamim*) and *Ramban* (*Niddah* 19b, citing *R' Avraham Av Beis Din*) who cite this view and dismiss it. Responsa *Shoel U'Meishiv* 1:2:105 maintains that this is the opinion of *BeHaG* and *Rif;* see also *Aruch LaNer, Niddah* 58b and *Marcheshes* vol. 1 35:14. However, all *Rishonim* and *Acharonim* completely dismiss this view and *Shulchan Aruch* and *Rema* make no mention of it.

9. *Rashi, Niddah* 58a.

10. *Tosfos* (ibid.) argues that a *kesem* renders her a *niddah,* even if she is certain that she felt no *hargashah.* See *Sidrei Taharah* 190:7 and *Avnei Neizer, Y.D.* 243, in explanation of *Tosfos'* view.

11. 190:1.

12. *Aruch HaShulchan* 200:1. Indeed, *Aruch HaShulchan* rules that even if she immersed because a Rav ruled strictly on a questionable *kesem* out of doubt, nevertheless, since the woman is declared *temei'ah* and must perform a *tevilah,* she recites the *b'rachah* on the *tevilah* as well. *Shiurei Sheivet HaLeivi* 200:1[10] is uncertain about reciting a *b'rachah* on the *tevilah* for a questionable *kesem.*

13. Blood from a uterine wound does not render a woman a *niddah,* see 187:5 (although practically, the woman will become a *niddah* since it is difficult to determine that the bleeding is only from the wound. See Chapter Twenty-Three). There are some limitations even regarding menstrual blood: a) blood that was extracted from the uterus in an unnatural manner, e.g., through a tube, see 188:3. b) A uterine blood flow during certain weeks following childbirth will not render the woman a *niddah* according to Biblical law, see Chapter Two, Section VI. c) According to Torah law

in origin and governed by specific rules and standards which set it apart from a *reiyas dam*. These rules relate to the size of the *kesem*, the type and color of the object upon which it is found and the possibility of an identifiable source for the *kesem*. A *kesem* which is excluded by these rules will not render a woman a *niddah*.

2. The consequences of becoming a *niddah* through a *re'iyah* versus a *kesem*:

Although we noted that regarding all the *halachos* of *niddah* a *kesem* is the equivalent of a *reiyas dam*, there is one practical differerence between the two. The laws of *vestos* apply only to a *reiyas dam*, not to *kesamim*. Thus, a woman who finds a *kesem* three times on the same date of the Hebrew month or after having the same interval of days three times is not required to separate from her husband or do *bedikos* on the same date of the following month or after the similar interval.[14]

E. Checking for a *kesem*

Since a blood flow is normally accompanied by a *hargashah*, a woman who felt no sensation normally associated with menstruation need not worry that blood left her uterus. She need not be concerned that a *kesem* may be on her garment and is not required to check her garments for *kesamim*.[15] This does not constitute a willful evasion of the laws of *niddah* since *Chazal* (who instituted the laws of *kesamim*) did not require that she check her garments for *kesamim*. The sole exception to this principle is the seven "clean" days. During these days a woman is required to ascertain that the menstrual period has completely ended. This is accomplished (besides the required *bedikos*) by donning white garments so as to find any blood stains that may appear.

---

only five shades of blood render a woman a *niddah*. This is discussed in Chapter Two, Section II,C and Chapter Six, Section IV. However, for all practical purposes whenever a woman discharges uterine blood she becomes a *niddah*.

14. 190:54.

15. This can be explained in one of two ways. a) A *kesem* is *temei'ah* only according to Rabbinic law; thus, one may be lenient with a *safek*. Indeed, the fact that no *hargashah* was felt is, in itself, proof that no blood appeared. In addition, since one usually does not find *kesamim* on one's garments, one need not be concerned about the possibility. b) The *halachah* of *kesamim*, being a Rabbinic ordinance, is entirely dependent upon the manner in which it was decreed. *Chazal* mandated that only a *kesem* that is <u>found</u> renders a woman a *niddah*. If the *kesem* is never found, the woman is not a *niddah*. This does not constitute willful evasion of a prohibition since the prohibition takes effect only after a *kesem* is found.

II. Evaluating the *kesem*

A. Showing a *kesem* to a Rav

A *kesem* that requires measurement should not be measured by a layman. Most *kesamim* are not perfectly round and must be measured by approximation. A Rav is experienced in measuring *kesamim*; a layman is not. In addition, a layman is not experienced at distinguishing between colors and shades. Often a *kesem* consists of several shades, some *tahor* and some *tamei*. Only an experienced Rav is able to properly assess the sizes and colors that make up a *kesem*. One should not assume that a *kesem* larger than a *gris* is necessarily *tamei*, since part of the *kesem* may be an acceptable color in which case the *kesem* may be smaller than a *gris*. One should not be needlessly strict regarding a *kesem*. A woman should overcome her embarrassment and show any questionable *kesem* to a Rav.[16] A Rav is an experienced professional who will deal with the situation in a discreet manner.

B. Keeping a *kesem* for an extended period

One should not keep *kesamim* (or *bedikos*) for an extended period of time since colors fade and change. If a *kesem* is obviously *tahor*, the garment should be put aside and washed. If it is questionable, it should be shown to a Rav without unnecessary delay — preferably within the day.

C. A *kesem* that was lost

If a woman finds a questionable stain but loses (or washes) the garment before she is able to show it to a Rav, we are concerned that the stain may have been an unacceptable color and the size of a *gris* and she may, in fact, be *temei'ah*. A Rav should be consulted.[17] See Chapter Five, Section A,1, regarding a garment that was washed before she was able to determine whether the stain was in a location upon which uterine blood could have fallen.

---

16. See *Taharas HaBayis* vol. 1 pg. 373.

17. This question is possible in two forms: a) The stain was certainly the size of a *gris*, but she is uncertain of its color. b) The stain was definitely red, but she is uncertain whether or not it was the size of a *gris*. See *Chochmas Adam* 113:29, who contends, regarding case (a), that in general, doubts concerning a *kesem* fall into the category of a *safek deRabanan* (a doubt regarding Rabbinic law) in which we follow a lenient course. However, when a *kesem* is available for inspection, *Chazal*

III. To whom the laws of *kesamim* apply

The laws of *kesem* apply to any woman, even an unmarried woman (e.g., a *kallah* preparing for her wedding). Similarly, a pregnant or nursing woman or a woman who is past menopause[18] who finds blood on her garment becomes a *niddah*, even though these women normally experience no menstrual bleeding. The single exception to the *kesem* rule is a minor less than twelve years old.[19] A *kesem* found upon the garments

---

in Talmudic times required that we test it with the seven chemicals in the manner set forth in *Niddah* 62a, to see if it is blood. Today, we are ignorant of the proper method of testing. Thus, our *safek* pertaining to an available *kesem* is no longer a simple *safek deRabbanan,* but a *safek chisaron yediah* (a doubt based upon ignorance). A doubt of this nature is not considered a true *safek* since there may be someone, somewhere, who is more knowledgeable than we and knows how to test a *kesem* (see *Y.D.* 98:3). Such a doubt regarding a *kesem* renders a woman a *niddah.* However, once the *kesem* is lost, our ignorance is made irrelevant by the fact that the *kesem* is lost. No one in the world is able to test the *kesem* and our doubt has thus become a true *safek deRabbanan* and we may follow a lenient course. A similar position is taken by responsa *Divrei Malkiel* 4:67, who is lenient even regarding a *kesem* lost during the first three of the seven "clean" days. However, R' Akiva Eiger to *Shach* §61, citing *Tiferes LeMoshe,* argues that the moment the questionable *kesem* was noticed, the woman immediately became *temei'ah,* since it is a *safek chisaron yediah.* Subsequently, when the *kesem* is lost, her status cannot change. See also R' Shlomo Kluger in *Mei Niddah, Tinyana* 190:46, cited in *Daas Torah* 190:1, who contends that since most red fluids that flow from the body are menstrual blood, it is more reasonable to assume that the *kesem* was *tamei.* In this case we cannot use the principle of *safek deRabbanan lekula* since it contradicts the more reasonable assumption. Accordingly, if the doubt about the lost *kesem* pertains only to its color (case a), it must be assumed to be *tamei.* If, however, the doubt pertains to its size as well (case a and b combined), this would be a case of *s'fek s'feika,* and the woman is *tehorah.* It is unclear what position *Chochmas Adam* would take regarding a lost *kesem* that was surely red but may have been less than a *gris* (case b). See *Pische Zuta* 190:47,48, who argues that one cannot be lenient regarding a lost *kesem* which may have been less than a *gris* if it certainly was larger than the size of common body lice. By this reasoning, since body lice are extremely rare today, a woman who loses a *kesem* should be *temei'ah* even if the *kesem* may have been less than a *gris.* On the other hand, one may argue that today women find many stains on their garments that are bodily fluids, not *dam.* Indeed, most *kesamim* shown to a Rav are *tehorim.* Thus, perhaps R' Shlomo Kluger's conclusion should not apply today. See *Shiurei Sheivet HaLeivi* 190:46[6], who notes that *Poskim* are generally lenient regarding questions of lost *kesamim.*

18. See 190:52, and *Sidrei Taharah* 190:95, s.v. "ובשו''ת פנים מאירות", see also *Pischei Teshuvah* 191:2. *Shiurei Sheivei HaLeivi* 190:2[2] notes that it is common for women to find *kesamim* during the first phase after menopause. These *kesamim* render her a *niddah.* See responsa *Rav Pealim, Y.D.* 1:33, who rules that even a woman who has not experienced a menstrual flow for twenty years is subject to the laws of *kesamim.*

19. 190:2. Responsa *Rashba* 5:58. The age limit of twelve is based upon the assumption that by that time she has physically matured. Thus, the laes of *kesamim* apply to her even if she never had a menstrual period (*Rashi, Niddah* 5a). If, however, one ascertains that she has not physically matured by age twelve, the rules of *kesamim* would not apply until she actually matures (190:2). See *Shiurei Shevet HaLeivi* 190:2[3].

or even the body of a minor does not render her a *niddah*.[20] This is true even if her sheets are very soiled with blood and we are not aware of any source to which to attribute the blood.[21] We assume that she must have been in proximity to blood or paint although she was unaware of it. As farfetched as it may seem, this assumption is more reasonable than to assume that the blood came from her body, since minors have no menstrual periods.[22] *Chazal* therefore saw fit to exclude minors from their Rabbinic law of *kesamim*. However, a minor who had three separate blood flows[23] is considered an adult with regard to this *halachah*.[24]

Note that the above refers only to the case of a minor who finds a *kesem*.[25] However, the Torah law of *niddah* applies to a child of any age.[26] Thus, a minor who had a blood flow is considered a *niddah* regardless of her age.

IV. Avoiding *kesamim* problems

We will note in Chapter Nine, Section I,D that a woman should wear colored undergarments during the days that she is *tehorah* to avoid

---

20. See *Shach* §3, citing *Bach*, that a *kesem* found upon the body of a minor makes her a *niddah*. *Shach*, however, disagrees, as does *Toras HaShelamim* §5, *Graz* §4 and *Chochmas Adam* 113:5.

21. *Graz* §4, based on *Niddah* 5a.

22. *Graz* ibid. based upon *Rashi, Niddah* 5a.

23. See 190:3, regarding what is considered a "separate" flow. The wording above reflects *Rema's* ruling. Others contend that she is not considered an adult, regarding these rules, unless she experiences three actual periods. Even in the opinion of the latter *Poskim*, she need not set a *vest kavuah*. Any three separate cycles, even on different dates, removes her from the status of a minor (*Graz* §6).

24. 190:2. If ninety days pass without any additional flow, she reverts to her original status and is exempt from *kesamim*, 190:4.

25. *Poskim* disagree regarding a case where the *kesem* found by the minor is absolutely unattributable to any other source. For example, her garment was checked immediately before she donned it and moments later, before she had a chance to go anywhere or do anything, it was found to be stained with blood. A simple reading of *Rashi, Niddah* 5a, would indicate that she is *temei'ah*. This is indeed the conclusion of *Chavos Daas* 190:4. However, *Divrei Chamudos* (*Niddah* 1:8) interprets *Rashi* differently. He rules that, even in this case, she is *tehorah* since *Chazal* did not extend the laws of *kesamim* to minors. This opinion is shared by *Toras HaShelamim* §3 and *Shach* §3 (as understood by *Chavos Daas* and *Pischei Teshuvah* §8). *Sidrei Taharah* §7 ties this question to a dispute between *Rashi* and *Tosfos*. See also Responsa *R' Akiva Eiger* 62 and 81, who rules that if the blood certainly came from the body of the minor, she is a *niddah* according to Rabbinic law. He argues that *Chazal* exempted a minor only from the laws of *kesamim* (a *kesem*, in this sense, is defined as a stain which may be from another source). A blood flow without a *hargashah*, although *tamei* only according to Rabbinic law, is not a *kesem* and applies to a minor as well. In addition, R' Akiva Eiger argues, a minor has no sense of responsibility and no *halachic* believability. How can we rely upon her claim that she felt no *hargashah*? On the contrary, since the blood certainly came from her body and menstrual blood is usually accompanied by *hargashah*, we should assume that she felt a *hargashah* and indeed is *temei'ah* even according to Torah law.

26. *Niddah* 32a.

kesamim problems. Similarly, a woman who frequently finds problematic stains is advised to change her garments often during the course of the day to prevent the stains from becoming darker and larger and thereby becoming problematic.

V. Performing a *bedikah* after finding a *kesem*

A woman who finds a *kesem* is not required to perform a *bedikah*. If the *kesem* is unacceptable, she is *temei'ah* regardless of the result of the *bedikah*.[27] If the *kesem* is acceptable, she needs no further support. A *bedikah* may cause her to become a *niddah* unnecessarily, since a small stain on a garment may be ignored, while even the smallest stain found upon a *bedikah* cloth renders her a *niddah*. Thus, she has nothing to gain and much to lose by performing a *bedikah*.[28]

VI. *Kesamim* that precede a menstrual period

Many women begin their menstruation with a period of staining which gradually increases to a normal flow. There is an opinion that the *vest* is considered to have begun with the onset of the staining (even if less than a *gris*); thus, on the following month, she will abstain on

---

27. 190:1.

28. See *Shiurei Sheivet HaLeivi* 190:5[1], who notes that *Poskim* never required a woman who finds a *kesem* to perform a *bedikah*. He is somewhat uncomfortable with this and notes that it is preferable to do a *bedikah*. This position seems to be supported by the ruling of *Shulchan Aruch* 184:1 and 196:9, that a woman who performs many *bedikos*, even for no specific reason, is commendable. Obviously, if there is strong reason to suspect that there is blood in the vagina, it seems proper to check oneself. Thus, when a woman finds a *kesem*, it seems reasonable to assume that if she checks herself, she will find blood on the *bedikah* cloth as well. If a *kesem* is found on her *vest* day, *Sheivet HaLeivi* requires that a *bedikah* be done. *Chidushim U'Biurim, Niddah* 9:3, requires that a woman perform a *bedikah* after finding any *kesem*, regardless of when it was found and regardless of its size. While this position seems very logical, the fact that no earlier authority raises this issue suggests that previous *Poskim* did not share this view. It has been common for women to find *kesamim* since the times of the Talmud. Had *kesamim* less than a *gris* or on a colored garment required a *bedikah*, it is inconceivable that no mention of this would have been made by earlier authorities. See also *Shaarei Taharah* (R' Stern) §24. See *Taharas HaBayis* p. 402-403, who concludes that no *bedikah* is required. He concedes, however, that if the *kesem* on a colored garment is larger than a *gris* and not a common occurrence for the woman, it is advisable that she perform a *bedikah*. *Poseiach Shaar* 8:30 notes that it is common today that excessive *bedikos* cause irritation to the vaginal area; therefore, a woman should not perform *bedikos* unless she is *halachically* required to do so.

the day the staining began, not the day the actual flow began.[29] Other authorities disagree.[30] This question will be discussed in Chapter Thirteen, Section II,B,4.

A woman who usually begins menstruation with staining, even with small stains that will not render her a *niddah* or stains on a colored garment, should abstain once the staining begins. This is for two reasons: a) Even if one does not calculate a *vest* from the staining, the staining may be considered a *vest haguf* [31] (a physical sign that the menstruation is imminent, see Chapter Eighteen, Section I,A). b) Whenever a woman has a prolonged staining period (even if her menstruation is not due), it is prudent to abstain until her status is clarified.[32] If the staining passes without rendering her a *niddah* (i.e., the stains were less than a *gris* or were on colored garments) she may resume marital relations. See also Chapter Thirteen, Section II,B,4.

A woman should not wear very dark (navy blue or black) undergarments at the time her menstruation is expected. Her menstruation may begin in the form of staining which may go unnoticed due to the dark color of the garments.

VII. A *kesem* associated with a *hargashah*

We have noted that *kesamim* are not *tamei* according to Torah law for two reasons: a) the lack of a *hargashah* and b) the possibility that a *kesem* may originate from another source. A *kesem* associated with a *hargashah* cannot be treated as a normal *kesem*. The *hargashah* makes this *kesem* a possible *reiyas dam* according to Torah law and, thus, the leniencies of *kesamim* do not apply. This is possible in two ways: i) A *kesem* found after a <u>definite</u> *hargashah*, or ii) a *kesem* found after a <u>possible</u> *hargashah*. A *kesem* which is found after a <u>definite</u> *hargashah* is essentially not a *kesem*; it is a *re'iyah*. The fact that she felt a *hargashah* is, in itself, an indication that the blood came from the uterus. Thus both reason (a) and (b) do not apply. She is a *niddah*, even according to Torah law. If, however, the *hargashah* was not definite but only a <u>possible</u> *hargashah*, reason (a) no longer applies, since there may have been a *hargashah*, but reason (b) still applies. The following *halachos* illustrate the above principles:

---

29. *Igros Moshe, Y.D.* 2:46[2].

30. See *Shaarei Tohar* 4:27 and *Shiurei Sheivet HaLeivi* 190:54[7].

31. *Igros Moshe, Y.D.* 3:51.

32. There is the possibility that due to the staining she may find a stain immediately after cohabiting or her husband may find blood on his body. This would be a serious problem, see Chapter Fourteen, Section I,E.

A. A stain found after a definite *hargashah*

A woman who finds a blood stain after feeling a *hargashah* must consider that stain a regular blood flow. Both reasons (a) and (b) do not apply; therefore, the size of the stain, the color or type of garment are all irrelevant.[33] See Chapter Three, where the *halachos* of *hargashah* are discussed at length. A woman who feels a flow from her body (a sensation which may be considered a *hargashah*) and subsequently finds a *kesem* must consult a Rav, regardless of the size of the *kesem* or the type of garment.

B. A stain found after a possible *hargashah*

1. A stain found after cohabitation or urination:
A woman who finds a *kesem* on her garment after cohabitation or urination may have experienced a *hargashah* but failed to notice it. She may have erroneously attributed the *hargashah* to the sensation of the cohabitation or urination.[34] Thus, she may be *temei'ah* according to Torah law, even if the stain is less than a *gris* and even on a colored garment. On the other hand, the *kesem* may be from some other source and is not necessarily from her body. Thus, reason (a) does not apply but reason (b) does apply. This is the subject of much discussion in *halachic* literature. Common custom is to consider these stains normal *kesamim* unless they were found immediately after urination or cohabitation.[35]

> a. A *kesem* found on a tissue:
> A *kesem* found on the tissue that a woman used to clean herself after urination may also be problematic. This issue is discussed in Chapter Nine, Section II,4. A Rav should be consulted.[36]

> b. A stain found on the cloth used to clean themselves:

---

33. See *Binas Adam* 16 and *Tiferes Tzvi* cited in *Pischei Teshuvah* §190:3.

34. See *Niddah* 57b.

35. See *Chavos Daas* 183:2[c], who rules that she is *temei'ah* according to Torah law. *Sidrei Taharah* in 183:2 agrees. However, in 190:93, s.v. "ומעתה" and s.v. "נחזור," *Sidrei Taharah* concludes that a *kesem* found after cohabitation or urination is treated as any *kesem*. *Shaarei Tohar* 10:13 rules that she is *temei'ah* only if the garment was checked immediately before and after the urination or cohabitation; otherwise, she is *tehorah*. See also *Chazon Ish* 90:1, who rules that a *kesem* found after urination is similar in *halachah* to any *kesem*. See a discussion of the issues involved in Appendix A.

36. See Chapter Nine, note 48 where this subject is discussed at length. See also *Shiurei Sheivet HaLeivi* 190:10[3].

A stain found on the cloth with which either the woman or her husband used to clean themselves after cohabitation is more serious yet. A Rav should be consulted immediately. See Chapter Nine, Section III,4 and Chapter Fourteen, Section I,E.

c. A stain found on the toilet seat or in the water:
A woman who found blood on the toilet seat, the fixture or in the water, should consult a Rav.[37]

2. A stain found on a *bedikah* cloth.

We noted earlier that blood found upon a *bedikah* cloth is assumed to render a woman a *niddah*, even according to Torah law. Both reasons (a) and (b) for treating a *kesem* leniently do not apply to a *bedikah* cloth. The blood was found in her body (the vagina) and is unattributable to any other source. In addition, she may have felt a *hargashah* which she mistook for the sensation of the *bedikah* itself. Indeed, since blood usually appears with a *hargashah*, we must assume that there actually was a *hargashah*.[38]

---

37. See *Minchas Yitzchak* 9:93, and appendix to *Chezkas Taharah*.

38. See *Sidrei Taharah* 183:2, 190:93 (s.v. "ועוד כתבתי" at end), in explanation of *Rambam* 9:1. *Pleisi* 183:1, *Chavos Daas* 183:2[c], *Chochmas Adam* 113:30, *Pischei Teshuvah* 183:1 and *Aruch HaShulchan* 183:55. See Chapter Three note 7. If the woman was conscious of the possibility of *hargashah* at the time of *bedikah* but insists that she felt no *hargashah*, some *Poskim* maintain that she is not a *niddah* by Torah law. Others disagree and contend that a woman cannot differentiate between the sensation of the *bedikah* cloth and a real *hargashah*. See Chapter Three note 8.

CHAPTER EIGHT

כתמים, מהות הכתם

Kesamim: the Size, Shape and Color

□ The size of the stain.

□ Measuring a *gris*.

□ A black *kesem*.

□ A *kesem* on the body.

□ The color of the *kesem*.

□ The shape of the *kesem*.

Introduction

Since the *tumah* of *kesamim* is Rabbinic in nature, it is dependent upon guidelines set forth by *Chazal*. Accordingly, we find many limitations in the laws of *kesamim*. In the previous chapter, we have learned about the limitations pertaining to whom the laws of *kesamim* apply. In this chapter we will deal with limitations that apply to the size and color of the *kesem*. In the following chapters we will explain that a *kesem* is *tamei* only if it is found upon a white garment or object that is susceptible to *tumah*. This chapter is essentially devoted to the *halachah* that a *kesem* must be the minimum size of a *gris* (the size of a U.S. penny). A *kesem* smaller than a *gris* will not render a woman a *niddah*.

I. The size of the stain

A. The rationale of the *gris* size

A *kesem* is not *tamei* unless it is a specific, minimum size. This is in contrast to a *re'iyah* which renders a woman a *niddah*, regardless of its size. *Chazal* were lenient with regard to *kesamim* because, in their time, lice ("*ma'acholos*")[1] were commonplace. *Chazal* were reluctant to extend their decree of *kesamim* to a stain equal to or smaller than the blood of a *ma'acholes*. They were concerned that if even the smallest of stains were to render a woman a *niddah*, all women would be *niddos*, since, in their time, most bed sheets contained blood spots of dead lice.[2] Accordingly, *Chazal* never applied the laws of *kesamim* to a stain of the size that could result from the total blood of one *ma'acholes*. They permitted us to assume that any stain of this size or smaller is from a louse and ignore it.[3]

---

1. The Talmud (*Niddah* 19b) states that only the blood of head lice is similar to *niddah* blood, not body lice. However, *Tosfos HaRosh* (ad loc.) notes that this distinction pertained only to Talmudic times when *chachamim* were able to differentiate between different shades of red. Today that we are unable to do so, one can attribute a stain even to body lice. See also *Sidrei Taharah* 183:2 s.v. לפי.

2. See *Niddah* 58b.

3. Later *Poskim* raise an intriguing question regarding the exemption of a *kesem* that is less than a *gris:* Is the exemption of a stain less than a *gris* an independent qualification of the laws of *kesamim* (i.e., a *kesem* less than a *gris* is essentially excluded from the basic laws of *kesamim*) or is the exemption part of the general rule of *teliyah* (explained in Chapter Eleven) by which we may attribute a *kesem* to another source (i.e., a *kesem* less than a *gris* is included in the general law of *kesamim*, but is *tahor* based on a qualification in those laws)? The lenient opinion of *Chasam Sofer*, cited below (note 10), follows the first approach, while the *Sefer Yereim* (see note 11) follows the second approach. *Shiurei Sheivet HaLeivi* 190:5[1] notes that the wording of *Shulchan Aruch* 190:5, "תולין לומר דם כינה הוא," seems, at first glance, to support the second approach.

This is true even if the woman did not crush any lice.[4]

Chazal relate that the blood of a single *ma'acholes* would cover an area equivalent to the size of a bean known in their times as a *"gris."*[5] Accordingly, they ruled that a woman is not affected by a stain less than a *"gris v'od"* (slightly more than the size of that bean). *Chazal*[6] further defined a *"gris"* as equivalent, in size, to the area of nine lentil seeds, lined up in rows of threes, which, in turn, is equal to the area of thirty-six hairs as they are situated in a square of six by six hairs on the forearm.[7] *Poskim* of earlier generations used these guidelines to measure the minimum size of a *kesem* in relation to coins used in their time. Most contemporary authorities agree that the minimum size of a *kesem* is the area of a circle whose diameter is nineteen millimeters,[8] which is the size of a U.S. penny. A *kesem* smaller than that size may be ignored.[9]

Shiurei Sheivet HaLeivi 190:5[7] raises an interesting application of this question: Suppose one is able to differentiate between the shades of uterine blood and lice blood. May one be lenient regarding a *kesem* less than a *gris* which looks like uterine blood? This may depend on the previous question: Is a *kesem* less than a *gris* exempted entirely from the rules of *kesem*? If so, even if the stain is certainly not lice blood, it is *tahor* (one could, nevertheless, argue that since such a possibility existed even in the time of *Chazal*, they never exempted a *kesem* of this type. This is similar to the case of a black *kesem* cited below, Section D,1, note 31). However, if a *kesem* less than a *gris* is exempted because of *teliyah,* i.e. it is attributable to lice blood, it follows that it is *tamei* since in this case it cannot be attributed to lice blood.

One should note that there are cases where only one of the two approaches apply: a) A *bedikah* cloth that was not checked before use or not kept in a clean spot after use may not render a woman a *niddah* if a stain less than a *gris* is found upon it. See 190:35,36. In this case of a *bedikah* cloth there is the possibility of a *hargashah* and therefore the normal leniencies of *kesamim* do not apply. Accordingly, the small size of the stain can be used as a basis for *taharah* only using the approach of *teliyah.* Thus, if lice are not prevalent or their blood does not equal a *gris* or the stain does not resemble lice blood, there is no basis to be lenient. See responsa *Chasam Sofer, Y.D.* 150, *Lechem VeSimlah* 190:114[l],122[l] and *Shiurei Sheivet HaLeivi* 190:34[2]. b) A stain which certainly originated from the body (see D,6 below) cannot be attributed to lice. Obviously, in this case the approach of *teliyah* is not applicable. In the opinion of some *Poskim* she is *temei'ah.* Apparently, in their opinion, there is some aspect of *teliyah* in *Chazal's* exclusion of a stain less than a *gris.* Others contend that it is *tehorah.* Obviously, they argue that *Chazal* completely exempted a *kesem* less than a *gris.* See below, notes 11, 14, 31 and 45 regarding other applications of this question.

4. 190:5.

5. Literally, a *gris* is half of a bean split across its center, see *Chacham Tzvi* cited in *Pischei Teshuvah* §10.

6. *Negaim* 6:1.

7. *Pischei Teshuvah* 190:11. However, *Aruch HaShulchan* 190:23 contends that we measure with hairs as they grow on the head.

8. *Darchei Teshuvah* end of §40, see supplemental notes to *Badei HaShulchan* 190:5.

9. See Section D,5 and Chapter Seven, Section VII, where we note that a woman who experiences,

A *kesem* with an oblong shape or other shape is measured by its area, not its circumference. In the course of our discussion, we will use the terms "the size of a *gris*" (being *tamei*) or "smaller than a *gris*" (being *tahor*) because these are the terms used by *Poskim*. Actually, as noted above, a *kesem* is not *tamei* unless it is slightly larger than a *gris* ("*gris v'od*").

B. The applicability of the *gris* size today

Poskim note the apparent difficulty relating this *halachah* to modern times. Firstly, common lice today do not have enough blood to produce a stain the size of a *gris*. Secondly, in modern times, lice are uncommon. Thus, a stain less than a *gris* cannot, in reality, be attributed to lice. Nevertheless, *Poskim* explain that since the *halachah* of *kesamim* is of Rabbinic origin, it is limited to the exact guidelines set forth by *Chazal* in the original decree. Thus, since *Chazal* excluded a *kesem* less than a *gris*, the *halachah* cannot change. True, if we had authority to alter Rabbinic laws, it would seem reasonable to change the *halachah* to fit the present circumstances, but we lack that authority and must follow the original precepts, even if that results in our relying upon a seemingly inappropriate *kula*.[10]

---

or suspects that she may have experienced, a *hargashah* cannot ignore even a small *kesem*. A Rav must be consulted.

10. See responsa *Chacham Tzvi* 67, *Me'il Tzedakah* 27, *Chasam Sofer*, (Y.D. 150, 182), *Shoel U'Meishiv* 3,3:57, *Igros Moshe*, Y.D. 3:46, and *Chelkas Yaakov* 3, end of 80. *Chasam Sofer* adds a unique twist to this argument which would explain that we are not in fact relying on a *kula*. He contends (based upon *Raavad*) that the laws of *kesamim* were originally established regarding the *tumah* of *niddus* (that the *niddah* will make any foodstuffs she touches *tamei*). *Chazal* never intended these laws to apply to the <u>issur</u> (that she is prohibited to her husband). However, once *Chazal* instituted these laws regarding *tumah*, they were compelled to extend them to *issur* as well. Today, when the laws of *tumah* have no relevance, the *halachos* of *kesamim* should in fact be abolished, if we had the power to do so. While we have no legislative authority to annul any Rabbinic decree, we are certainly not required to extend their scope beyond its original parameters (i.e., a stain less than a *gris*), even if logic dictates that we do so. Accordingly, a *kesem* less than a *gris* is *tahor* even though *ma'acholes* are not common and today's lice do not have that much blood. No matter how one views the question, whether in terms of *Chazal's* original intent, or in terms of its applicability today, a *kesem* less than a *gris* should be *tahor*.

Lechem VeSimlah 190:12[s] develops a novel approach to the problem. He contends (based on *Rambam*) that *Chazal* never implied that a single *ma'acholes* can produce a *gris* amount of blood. Rather, *Chazal* attributed the stain to the blood of many *ma'acholos* that were crushed together. The reason they limited this to a stain less than a *gris* is merely because they felt that, under normal circumstances, a blood flow is never less than a gris. Thus, a stain less than a *gris* is easily attributable to any other source. Even today, when *ma'acholos* have less blood than in the time of *Chazal*, we can still attribute the stain to the blood of many *ma'acholos*. While this approach solves the

Some authorities are reluctant to exempt a *kesem* larger than the size of the blood of lice found today.[11] In their opinion, a *kesem* less than a *gris* is exempted only in a place where lice are common. Even then, only a stain with the circumference of 5-6 millimeters or less is exempt.[12] Common custom is to be lenient in all cases[13] and exempt any stain less than the size of a U.S. penny.[14]

C. Measuring a *gris*

The measurement of a *gris* is difficult in the following situations:

> 1. An oblong *kesem:*
> An oblong *kesem* is measured in terms of its total area, not its length, width or circumference.[15] If one is unable to measure the *kesem* properly, one may be required to consider it *tamei*. A Rav should be consulted.[16]

---

problem of the smaller lice found today, it is unclear how *Lechem VeSimlah* would resolve the second problem, namely, that lice are extremely uncommon today. See also *Pische Zuta* §7 and *Daas Torah* 5.

11. *Sefer Yereim,* cited in *Lechem VeSimlah* 190:12[s] and *Pischei Teshuvah* §9. *Shiurei Sheivet HaLeivi* 190:5[1] cites a similar opinion of *Kinas Sofrim*. Although *Lechem VeSimlah* finds justification for the lenient opinion, he notes that a punctilious individual should follow the stringent opinion. Essentially, this question depends upon the question noted above (note 3): Do we view the exemption of a stain less than a *gris* an independent qualification of the laws of *kesamim* or is it part of the general rule of *teliyah* by which we may attribute a *kesem* to another source?

12. Measurement taken from *Shiurei Sheivet HaLeivi* 190:5[1].

13. *Darchei Teshuvah* 190:40, *Igros Moshe*, Y.D. 3:46. *Shiurei Sheivet HaLeivi* 190:5[1] contends that since *Rambam* and many *Poskim* measured the size of a *gris* (not the size of lice prevalent in their time), they obviously felt that the measurement of a *gris* was absolute, not dependent upon the prevalence and size of lice. Nevertheless, in 190:5[5], on a practical level, he is more stringent and rules that if the *kesem* appears to be fresh blood, one should consider it *tamei* unless it is actually smaller than the blood of prevalent lice. See *Pische Zuta* 190:7, regarding whether the husband or wife has the right to be strict and follow the opinion of *Sefer Yereim*. *Shiurei Sheivet HaLeivi*, ibid., writes that they may be strict in the matter and the woman may even recite a *b'rachah* on the *tevilah*. However, if the *kesem* is certainly less than the size of prevalent lice, one should not be strict. *Taharas HaBayis*, vol. 1 p. 373 cautions that, in general, one should not be strict regarding the size of a *kesem*.

14. Essentially, we accept the view of *Chasam Sofer,* cited above, that a *kesem* less than a *gris* is permitted because *Chazal* never intended to include it in the original decree of *kesamim* and not merely because we attribute the stain to a *ma'acholes*. See note 3.

15. A practical method of measuring a *kesem* is to place a penny beneath the cloth and fold the cloth over the penny to estimate its relative area.

16. See Chapter Seven note 17.

2. A stain that spread:
If the spot itself is less than a *gris* but its color spread to an area more than a *gris*, the woman is *temei'ah*.[17] If, at the time the *kesem* was first noticed, it was less than a *gris* and spread to a larger area only afterwards, she is *tehorah*.[18]

3. A *kesem* with several shades:
A *kesem* may consist of several shades, some of an acceptable color and some of an unacceptable color. *Poskim* disagree whether the *gris* is measured in relation to the total area of the stain or only in relation to the part with the unacceptable color.[19] Common custom among Rabbonim is to include in the measurement of the *gris* only those parts of the stain which are an unacceptable color.[20] An example of the above is a *kesem* whose color is acceptable but is surrounded by a red edge. If the total area of the red edge is less than a *gris*, the woman is *tehorah* even though the entire area is larger than a *gris*.

4. A partially colored garment:
See Chapter Nine, Section I,B,3 regarding a stain larger than a *gris* that is found upon a garment that is partially white and

---

17. *Sidrei Taharah* end of §61, and *Pischei Teshuvah* §9.

18. *Shaarei Tohar* 10:5.

19. See *Taz* §41. *Chavos Daas* §9[b] rules that since it is one stain whose total area is a *gris,* the woman is *temei'ah* even though only part of that stain is red. The logic behind this view is simple. Essentially, even a small bloodstain should render a woman a *niddah*. The reason that a stain less than a *gris* is *tehorah* is only because it is attributable to a *ma'acholes*. A stain larger than a *gris* is certainly from her body, not from a *ma'acholes*. Thus, if any part of that stain is blood, it must certainly be attributed to her, not to a *ma'acholes*. Accordingly, she becomes a *niddah*. R' Akiva Eiger to 190:10, and *Sidrei Taharah* §93 s.v. להביא יש ועוד, and *Graz* 190:19, citing *Me'il Tzedakah* 20, oppose this view. *Me'il Tzedakah* argues that even if the larger stain is obviously one stain, and even if the part that is not blood certainly is a uterine discharge, she is *tehorah*. Although, logically, once it is established that the stain came from the uterus, we should attribute the red edge to her, nevertheless, we assume that some blood from a *ma'acholes* blended into the general stain and formed a red edge.

20. R' Akiva Eiger, *Sidrei Taharah* and *Graz,* cited above. However, all parts of the stain that are blood color combine to a measurement of a *gris* even though they are separated by an acceptable color. See R' Akiva Eiger 190:10. This is no contradiction to *Tzemach Tzedek* cited in *Darchei Teshuvah* §48 cited below (footnote 23). In our case, all the different shades are part of one large stain. In the case of the *Tzemach Tzedek* each spot seems like a separate stain, albeit connected by a thin line. It would seem that if a woman has several stains on her garment, one large yellow stain and two small red ones, and the stains appear not to be part of one large stain, each of the red stains is measured separately. However, if all the stains appear to be part of one stain, the two red spots combine to a *gris*. This is the case discussed by R' Akiva Eiger.

partially colored and the stain on the white area is less than a *gris*.[21]

5. Two smaller stains:

If the stain consists of two completely separate spots, each of which is less than a *gris* but, in combination, exceed a *gris*, the woman is *tehorah*.[22] However, if the spots seem separate but are connected by a thin line, *Poskim* are uncertain whether they should be considered one stain larger than a *gris* or several stains each smaller than a *gris*.[23]

6. A pleated garment:

Poskim disagree about the status of a stain on a pleated garment. The stain may, in totality, be a *gris* when viewed as one stain; however, when the pleats are opened, it appears as separate stains, each less than a *gris*. Most authorities rule that it is considered one stain the size of a *gris* and the woman is *temei'ah*.[24]

7. A stretchable garment:

A *kesem* found on a garment that stretches when worn but pulls together when removed poses a problem in measuring a *gris*. Should we measure the *kesem* as it appears less than a *gris* or should we measure it as it was worn stretched on the body? One must ask a *sheilah*.[25]

---

21. This question is similar in logic to that of a *kesem* that is partially red and partially an acceptable color, as noted in 3.

22. 190:8.

23. See *Darchei Teshuvah* §48 citing *Tzemach Tzedek*. *Shiurei Sheivet HaLeivi* 190:8[2] contends that one should not rely on this opinion. However, if when first noticed, there was one spot less than a *gris* and only later she noticed the additional spot connected to it, she is *tehorah*. See a similar case in *Shiurei Sheivet HaLeivi* 190:26[2].

24. See *Chochmas Adam* 113:19 cited in *Pischei Teshuvah* §16. In *Binas Adam* §9[15], he rules that if the pleats are not sewn together, the parts of the stain are not measured together. If the pleats are sewn in place, he is unsure of its status. *Aruch HaShulchan* §38 does not differentiate between sewn and non-sewn pleats. He rules that the entire stain is judged as one *kesem* and combines to a *gris*. He argues that it is completely illogical not to view the stain as one *kesem* since it certainly fell as one stain. *Pische Zuta* §14 follows a similar view. *Shiurei Sheivet HaLeivi* 190:8[3] shares this view if the stain appears as actual blood. He also notes that *Binas Adam* was lenient only regarding a pleat on a sleeve. Perhaps even *Binas Adam* would concede regarding an undergarment. *Sheivet HaLeivi* also notes that an undergarment may be woven in the form of ridges and, at times, the stain may seem like separate stains but, in actuality, it is one stain. He considers this question similar to that of the pleats.

25. See *Sheivet HaLeivi* 3:119[6], regarding a question of a stretchable garment that separates when stretched, separating the *gris* into separate parts. He rules that the *kesem* is considered one *kesem*. The issues in our question are different.

8. A stain that passes through two garments:
If a bloodstain passes through two garments (e.g., an undergarment and tights), leaving a stain less than a *gris* on each, the stains are not measured in combination. Each stain is less than a *gris* and is therefore dismissed.[26] If one of the stains is a *gris* by itself, she is *temei'ah*. If a woman wears two garments, one colored and one white, and a stain passes through both, the stain on the colored garment is ignored but the stain on the white garment renders her a *niddah* if it equals the size of a *gris*.

9. A thick, absorbent garment:
A stain found upon a thick, absorbent garment which, due to the absorbency of the fabric, appears less than a *gris*, will not render the woman a *niddah* since, in appearance, it is less than a *gris*. The fact that the stain contains enough blood to produce a larger stain on a thinner fabric is irrelevant.[27]

10. A thick stain:
If a woman finds a thick stain on her garment, it should be shown to a Rav. Some *Poskim* speculate that if the stain contains enough blood to spread over an area more than a *gris*, even though the stain itself is less than a *gris*, she is *temei'ah*.[28] Most *Poskim*, however, are lenient.[29]

D. Situations where the *gris* measurement may not apply

1. A black stain:
In the opinion of some *Poskim*, a black stain that is less than a *gris* cannot be attributed to lice. Lice blood, unlike menstrual blood, does not turn black.[30] Thus, in their opinion, if a woman finds a

---

26. *Daas Torah* 190:5 and *Pische Zuta* §14 citing *Pachad Yitzchak*.

27. *Pische Zuta* 190:14. This case is essentially similar to the previous one, see *Pische Zuta* endnotes to 190 no. 6.

28. *Sidrei Taharah* 190 end of §61 does not reach a clear conclusion on this question, and leaves it to the discretion of the individual Rav. See also *Pischei Teshuvah* §9.

29. *Aruch HaShulchan* §34 claims that this is the position of later authorities. From the manner in which *Lechem VeSimlah* §21[l] cites *Sidrei Taharah*, it seems that he, too, is lenient. See also *Pische Zuta* §14.

30. *Raavad* cited in *Sidrei Taharah* §10. See also R' Akiva Eiger 190:5, *Pischei Teshuvah* §12 and *Graz* §9. *Aruch HaShulchan* §22, based on *Sidrei Taharah* ibid., rules that a black *kesem* which is less than

black spot on her garment, she is *temei'ah* even if the stain is less than a *gris*. Other *Poskim* are lenient regarding a black stain less than a *gris*.[31]

2. A stain found only upon the body:

Some *Poskim* contend that a stain found only upon the body[32] renders a woman a *niddah*, even if it is less than a *gris*.[33] A *kesem* found upon the body is treated more strictly than one found upon a garment since, in all probability, it came from the uterus.[34] Most *Poskim* are more lenient and equate a *kesem* found upon the body with one found upon a garment.[35] However, even they concede that two small separate stains[36] on the body are measured in combination to equal a *gris* and thus render her a

a *gris* is *tahor*. However, *Aruch HaShulchan* was referring to a place where fleas (who have black blood) are common. *Be'er Moshe* 4:70 follows this stricter view.

31. *Sheivet HaLeivi* 5:109[3] notes that most blackish stains are from foreign matter, not blood; however, if the black stain appears to be actual blood, the woman is *temei'ah* even though the stain is less than a *gris*. *Igros Moshe, Y.D.* 3:142[4], rules that the woman is *tehorah* in any case. The issue of a black stain may depend upon the general question of whether the limitation of less than a *gris* depends upon the actual possibility of the blood coming from lice or whether it is an absolute restriction; see *Igros Moshe* ibid. See note 3. However, one may argue that even *Raavad* agrees that the limitation of less than a *gris* is absolute, not because of *teliyah*. Nevertheless, *Raavad* maintains that even in the time of *Chazal* there was no reason to exclude a black stain from *kesamim*, therefore the *halachah* does not change today.

32. See Chapter Ten that the *kesem* must be found on a place where blood may have fallen directly from the vagina. Otherwise, the *kesem* cannot render her a *niddah*.

33. *Rambam* (*Issurei Biah* 9:6) and *Shulchan Aruch* 190:6 in his second opinion. *Shulchan Aruch* cites two conflicting opinions without offering a definitive ruling. *Shach* §10 cites the lenient opinion of *Bach*, although *Shach* himself is strict on the matter. *Aruch HaShulchan* §30 rules definitively like the stricter view. See *Lechem VeSimlah* §13[s], who rules that a *kesem* on the body is *tamei* even if it is less than a *gris*. He notes that even one who follows the lenient opinion should do so only if the stain is less than the blood of those lice that are actually prevalent at that time and place. Thus, according to his opinion, there is no basis to be lenient today since lice are not prevalent today at all. *Shiurei Sheivet HaLeivi* 190:6[6] concurs with this view.

34. *Chavos Daas* §6[b] and *Graz* §14. See note 39.

35. *Rashba, Raavad* and the first opinion in *Shulchan Aruch*, ibid. *Toras HaShelamim* §9 and *Sidrei Taharah* §12,16 follow this view. *Igros Moshe, Y.D.* 4:17[7], notes that common custom is to follow the lenient (first) opinion of *Shulchan Aruch* which is the opinion of most *Rishonim*.

36. See *Pische Zuta* §15, regarding two completely separate stains on parts of the body that are far from one another, e.g., each stain is on a separate leg. *Cheiker Halachah, Niddah* §23, is uncertain whether they combine to a *gris*, while *Chavos Daas* §11[c] and R' Shlomo Kluger in *Tuv Taam Vodaas* 3:263, and *HaElef Lecha Shlomo, Y.D.* 230, rule that they combine. Both stains must certainly be situated in a place where uterine blood could fall directly; see Chapter Ten. *Pische Zuta* cites proof to the stricter opinion of R' Shlomo Kluger. However, *Shiurei Sheivet HaLeivi* 190:8[2] rules that one may be lenient if necessary.

niddah.[37] A woman who finds a stain on her body must measure it carefully, remove it onto a cloth and show the color to a Rav. A stain found on the external opening of the vagina or found upon a cloth that was placed there is stricter yet. See 7 below.

3. A stain found on the body and on a garment:

Those *Poskim,* cited above, who contend that a *kesem* less than a *gris* on the body is *tamei,* concede that if part of the stain is on a garment as well as the body,[38] and each is less than a *gris,* the woman is *tehorah.*[39]

4. A stain on the hand:

A woman who finds a bloodstain on her hand that is less than a *gris,* or several stains smaller than a *gris,* even though in totality they equal a *gris,* is *tehorah.* Stains on the hand, unlike stains elsewhere on the body, do not combine. Each stain on the hand is considered separately. We are more lenient regarding a stain on the hand since one's hand is constantly in motion and inadvertently comes in contact with many potential sources of stains.[40] These *halachos* are discussed in detail in Chapter Ten, Section B,1.

5. A stain found after a *hargashah:*

A woman who finds even a minute stain after experiencing a *hargashah* is *temei'ah.* The presence of a *hargashah* transforms the *kesem* into a possible *re'iyah;* thus, all the limitations of *kesamim* do not apply. This stringency may apply even in an instance where

---

37. 190:8, see *Shach* §13, *Chochmas Adam* 113:7 and *Sidrei Taharah* 190:16.

38. Even if the stain on the garment is not directly opposite the stain on her body. A garment moves around. Therefore, the stains may be from one source even though they are not in close proximity; see *Sidrei Taharah* §13 citing *Tiferes LeMoshe,* see also *Pischei Teshuvah* §14. It would seem that if the garment involved is a tightly fitting garment (e.g., an undergarment), we cannot be lenient if the stains are not close to one another.

39. A *kesem* found only upon the body, not on the garment, indicates that the source of the *kesem* must be the body itself. A stain from an external source would certainly have soiled the garment as well. If, however, the *kesem* is found on the body and the garment, we no longer have any proof that it originated from the body. This is the logical basis of *Tiferes LeMoshe's* view, see *Graz* §14. This lenient view is supported by R' Akiva Eiger ad loc. and on *Taz* §24. However, *Chavos Daas* §6[b] disagrees. He does not differentiate between a *kesem* found on the body alone and one found on both the garment and the body; in either case, according to *Rambam* (cited above note 33), she is *temei'ah.* As noted, other *Poskim* disagree with *Chavos Daas.* In addition, we noted above that many *Poskim* do not follow the *Rambam's* opinion. It would seem that even if the stain is on a colored garment, the woman is *tehorah.*

40. *Chochmas Adam* 113:12.

the woman merely suspects that <u>perhaps</u> there may have been a *hargashah*. These cases are discussed in Chapter Seven, Section VII.

6. A stain that certainly originated from the body:
There is disagreement among *Poskim* regarding a *kesem* less than a *gris* that certainly[41] came from her body[42] but appeared on a white garment without a *hargashah*.[43] Some authorities contend that since the *kesem* appeared without a *hargashah*, it may be disregarded as is any other *kesem* less than a *gris*.[44] Others rule that a *kesem* less than a *gris* is disregarded only because it is attributable to a *ma'acholes*.[45] A *kesem* that certainly originated from the body cannot be attributed to a *ma'acholes* and is therefore *temei'ah*, even if it is less than a *gris*.[46] There is no clear consensus among *Poskim* regarding this question.[47]

7. A stain on a cloth used to wipe the vaginal opening:
A woman who wipes the external vaginal area and finds a stain

41. *Badei HaShulchan* 190:104 cites the following example: A woman checked a garment carefully and found it spotless. She donned the garment and found a stain on it a short time later. She remembers everything she did and everywhere she went during that short interval and cannot attribute the stain to anything but herself.

42. In Appendix A we noted that according to *Sidrei Taharah*, some *Rishonim* (*Rashi* and *Tosfos*) hold that blood which certainly came from the body renders a woman a *niddah* according to Torah law, even without a *hargashah*. Most *Poskim*, however, dispute this theory. In their opinion, any *dam* that flows without a *hargashah* cannot cause *niddus* according to Torah law. Our case above accepts the fact that she is only *temei'ah* according to Rabbinic law. The question is whether or not one can exempt a *kesem* less than a *gris* from that Rabbinic law.

43. See Appendix A, citing *Binas Adam* [9], and other *Poskim* that a stain that certainly came from her body and <u>may</u> be associated with a *hargashah* (i.e., immediately after cohabitation or a *bedikah*, either of which may mask a *hargashah*) renders her a *niddah* even according to Torah law. This is because menstrual blood usually flows with a *hargashah*. However, if there is no reason to suspect *hargashah*, she would be *tehorah* if the *kesem* had been found upon a colored garment. In this case, the *kesem* was found on a white garment, but it was less than a *gris* and therefore is subject to the dispute cited in the text.

44. *Me'il Tzedakah* 20, and *Toras HaShelamim* 183:1, cited in *Sidrei Taharah* 190:61, see also *Pleisi* 183:1.

45. This question is not dependent upon the question noted above (note 3) regarding the basis of the limitation of a *kesem* less than a *gris*. In this case, perhaps even in the time of *Chazal* this *kesem* would have been *temei'ah*.

46. *Sidrei Taharah* ibid. and *Pleisi* 183:1.

47. *Shiurei Sheivet HaLeivi* 183 on *Shach* §2 contends that all later authorities follow the stricter view. *Minchas Yitzchak* 6:83 rules that one should follow the stricter opinion unless there are additional lenient factors.

need not be concerned about the possibility of *hargashah*. The sensation of an external wiping cannot be confused with the sensation of a menstrual flow.[48] Nevertheless, some authorities rule that she is *temei'ah* even if the stain is less than a *gris*.[49] In their opinion, since this blood certainly came from the body, it renders her a *niddah* even when less than a *gris*; others disagree.[50] In the opinion of those *Poskim*, cited above, who maintain that even a stain that certainly came from the body requires a *gris*, she is *tehorah* in this case as well. See Chapter Seven, Section VII, B, regarding a stain found after cohabitation or urination. See Chapter Nine, Section II,4, regarding a stain found on toilet tissue.

8. A stain found on a diaphragm:
A woman using a diaphragm (with Rabbinical consent)[51] who finds a speck of blood on it cannot treat it as a *kesem* since there may have been a *hargashah* of *dam* which she mistook for the sensation of the diaphragm. Nevertheless, since a woman often irri-

---

48. See *Pleisi* 183:1, *Chavos Daas* 183:2[c] and *Sidrei Taharah* §2.

49. See *Sheivet HaLeivi* 3:118. This is based upon the *Sidrei Taharah* and the *Pleisi* cited in note 46 above.

50. An additional problem is the assumption that no lice are found at the opening of the vagina; thus, one cannot attribute the stain to a *ma'acholes*. Accordingly, even a stain less than a *gris* should be *temei'ah*. See *Badei HaShulchan* 190:64. Indeed, it seems from *Sidrei Taharah* §57 that even a stain found in the general area of the vaginal opening cannot be attributed to a *ma'acholes* (this seems difficult to reconcile with *Sidrei Taharah's* position in 183:2 s.v. לפי, that today, since we cannot differentiate between the colors of head lice and body lice blood, one can attribute a stain found in the vaginal area to lice). However, *Igros Moshe, Y.D.* 4:17[16], rules that a stain less than a *gris* found on a cloth used to wipe the vaginal area is *tehorah*. R' Moshe Feinstein concedes that had the cloth been confined to the actual vaginal opening, the *kesem* would be *tamei* since it cannot be attributed to a *ma'acholes*. Thus, a woman performing a *bedikah*, who is usually careful to confine the cloth to the actual vaginal area, cannot attribute any speck to a *ma'acholes*. However, a woman cleaning herself usually wipes the surrounding area as well. Thus, in his opinion, any stain less than a *gris* found upon the cleaning cloth is *tahor*. R' Moshe Feinstein seems to maintain this view even if she inserted the cloth a bit into the vaginal opening as well. Since her purpose was for cleaning, we assume that she also cleaned the surrounding area. Responsa *Cheishev HaEifod* 2:75 is very strict on this issue. He rules that even if she wiped herself with a colored cloth, she is *temei'ah*. See *Taharas HaBayis* vol. 1 p. 24, who objects strongly to *Cheishev HaEifod's* position.

51. One should not use a diaphragm or any contraceptive device without discussing the matter with a Rav. There are many serious *halachic* questions that pertain to the use of any contraceptive device. The woman's specific condition must be discussed with the Rav (who may need to discuss the matter with her physician) to determine if any contraception is permissible, the type of method which may be permitted and the duration of the *heter*. Any change in the woman's condition which may impact upon the *heter* must be brought to the attention of the Rav.

tates her vaginal area in the process of inserting and removing the diaphragm, at times the blood may be attributable to an abrasion. A Rav must be consulted.[52]

E. Preventing *kesamim* from reaching a *gris*

A woman who suffers from a staining problem should be advised to wear colored garments. A woman who is concerned about finding *kesamim* during her seven "clean" days (during which, she must wear white), should change her undergarments often so that successive stains do not combine in size to a *gris,* and in depth to an unacceptable color.

II. The color of the stain

A *kesem* is only *tamei* if its color resembles blood. Thus, even a stain larger than a *gris* which is found on a white garment that is *mekabel tumah,* even if the stain certainly came from the body, renders a woman a *niddah* only if it is the color of blood. In this sense, a *kesem* is similar to a *bedikah.* We noted, in Chapter Six, Section IV, that we consider any shade of red as *dam* regarding *bedikos.* So too, regarding *kesamim,* any shade of red, or any black stain, larger than a *gris* found on a white garment renders a woman a *niddah.* The reader is referred to Chapter Six, where the status of various shades and colors are discussed. A Rav may be more lenient regarding the color of a *kesem* than he would be regarding a *bedikah.* The reason for this is obvious: A *kesem* is merely Rabbinic while a *bedikah* can cause *niddus* according to Torah law.[53]

1. A stain not similar to uterine blood:
A stain which is an unacceptable color of red renders a woman a *niddah,* even if its color is completely different from the color of her usual menstrual blood.[54] At times, an experienced Rav may permit even a red *kesem* (or even a red stain on a *bedikah* cloth) if, according to his experience and knowledge, it is not menstrual blood.

2. A black stain:
We noted in I, D,1 above that, in the opinion of some *Poskim,* a black stain renders a woman a *niddah,* even if it is less than a *gris.*

---

52. See *Igros Moshe, Y.D.* 4:17[end of §16]. Some Rabbonim differentiate between blood found on the edges of the diaphragm, which is attributable to irritation, and blood found on the center, which is more difficult to attribute to irritation.

53. *Aruch HaShulchan* 188:19.

54. See *Darchei Teshuvah* §8.

III. The shape of the stain

A reddish stain, larger than a *gris,* that is found on a woman's body or her garment,[55] renders her a *niddah* regardless of its shape.[56] It may be round, square or elongated; in any case, she is *temei'ah.*[57] Even a stain formed in the shape of ring,[58] or as dots either in a straight line[59] or at random[60] (each dot being at least the size of a *gris*), renders the woman a *niddah.* Even a streak across the width of her thigh,[61] or a stain which appears to have fallen on her leg from the ground upwards, renders her a *niddah,* even though it is extremely unusual for menstrual blood to fall this way.[62]

---

55. See *Badei HaShulchan* 190:95.

56. Ibid. §94.

57. 190:5.

58. *Rashi, Niddah* 58a. *Graz* 190:19 notes that the area of the hollow center does not combine to the size of the *gris.*

59. *Tosfos* ibid.

60. *Graz* §20.

61. *Niddah* 58a. Normally, a stain that originated from her uterus would fall along the length of her thigh.

62. 190:9.

CHAPTER NINE

כתמים, דיני הבגד
Kesamim: the Garment

□ Wearing colored garments.

□ Lightly shaded fabrics.

□ Partially colored garments.

□ A *kesem* found upon the ground.

□ A *kesem* found on a tissue.

□ A blood stain in the urine.

□ A non-checked garment.

Introduction

As discussed in Chapter Seven, the Torah laws of *niddah* apply only to a *re'iyah* (a flow associated with a *hargashah*). The laws of *kesamim* are Rabbinic in nature. *Chazal* applied these laws only to stains that are at least the size of a *gris*, as was discussed in Chapter Eight, and only to stains on garments that fit certain criteria. The garment must be 1) white, not colored, 2) susceptible to *tumah* and 3) pre-checked for cleanliness. This chapter will examine these three criteria.

I. A colored garment

The laws of *kesem* do not apply to a stain found upon[1] a colored[2] garment,[3] regardless of whether the garment is red or any other color.[4] A stain found upon a colored garment will not render a woman a *niddah*,

---

1. If the stain was found on a colored garment but is subsequently wiped onto a white garment, the woman is *tehorah* since it was originally found only on the colored garment (responsa *Betzeil HaChochmah* 6:125).

2. An interesting point raised by *Poskim* concerns a material that is naturally colored but dyed white, e.g., white leather. Is the criterion the fact that the material is colored or that it is not white? Responsa *Beis Shlomo, Y.D.* 2:33, rules that the critical factor is that the shade of blood is not easily evaluated on a colored garment. Thus, if the garment is colored white, it is subject to all the rules of *kesamim*. A similar position is taken in responsa *HaElef Lecha Shlomo, Y.D.* 229. See note 23 regarding the reverse situation.

3. 190:10. It is interesting to note that when referring to a *kesem* on something colored, *Chazal* used the term "*beged tzavua*" — a colored garment. However, when referring to a *kesem* on something that is not susceptible to *tumah*, they said "*davar she'aino mekabel tumah*" — an object that is not susceptible to *tumah*. This modification from "garment" to "object" would seem to imply that the exclusion of "colored" refers to garments only. This would be understandable in light of the fact that a garment is absorbent and thus affects the color of the stain, while an object is usually non-absorbent and does not affect the color of the stain. This would explain the Talmud (*Niddah* 57b) regarding a woman who sat on the ground (which is usually not white) and found a *kesem*. Or a woman who found a *kesem* on an olive leaf (*Niddah* 60b). See C,1, regarding non-absorbent materials. *Rambam* 9:7 uses the term "*kli tzivonim*" which could apply equally to garments or objects. See responsa *Shoel U'Meishiv, Tlisai* 1:362. Perhaps *Chazal* used the term "*beged*" not to exclude a *kesem* found upon other objects but to exclude a *kesem* found upon the body. Skin color would normally be classified as colored, especially skin of a darker-colored person. Nevertheless, the Talmud (*Niddah* 58a) discusses a *kesem* on the body without ever specifying that it is referring to the unusual case of someone with white skin. Apparently, the limitation of *beged tzavua* applies only to garments or perhaps other objects, not the skin. If this is true, a woman who finds bloodstains on her colored fingernails or toenails cannot dismiss it as a *kesem* on a *davar tzavua*.

4. *Graz* 190:23 and *Chochmas Adam* 113:9.

even if it is found on the day of her expected period.[5] Even a stain that is larger than a *gris*,[6] red and is obviously blood will not render her a *niddah*,[7] even if it certainly originated from her body.[8]

A. Why colored garments are excluded

Poskim explain that *Chazal* exempted a stain on a colored garment from the laws of *kesamim* because it is difficult to evaluate the shade of a stain on colored fabric. A woman, or even a Rav, inspecting a *kesem* on a colored garment would be faced with difficulty in deciding whether or not the color of the *kesem* is red. *Chazal*, therefore, chose to completely exempt colored garments from the laws of *kesamim*.[9] See section E,2 below regarding a *kesem* found on the day of the expected period or at a time that a woman feels that her period is approaching.

The obvious difficulty with this explanation is that one can easily differentiate between red stains and stains of another color on most colored fabrics (with the exception of extremely dark fabrics). Why, then, do we permit *kesamim* found on <u>all</u> colored garments? *Poskim* resolve this difficulty by noting that, according to Torah law, not all shades of red render a woman a *niddah*. In the time of *Chazal*, when Torah law was applied, even the slightest variation in shade could differentiate between a red that is *tamei* and one that is not.[10] Since any colored garment will, to some

---

5. *Badei HaShulchan* 190:109. *Shiurei Sheivet HaLeivi* 190:10[3] notes that punctilious individuals ("בעלי נפש") are strict regarding a *kesem* that appears to be actual blood if found on the day of the *vest*, even on a colored garment. Although this strict ruling is not generally accepted, it is prudent to abstain from marital relations until it becomes clear whether or not the stain is the beginning of the menstrual cycle. See Section E,2 below.

6. Even a stain found during the first three of the seven "clean" days (*Me'il Tzedakah* cited in *Pischei Teshuvah* 196:12). See Chapter Eleven, Section G.

7. *Dagul Marevavah* 190:10 cites the view of *Rishonim* who maintain that even a *kesem* on a colored garment renders a woman a *niddah*. He is therefore hesitant to be lenient regarding colored garments. However, most *Poskim* reject his view, see *Pischei Teshuvah* §21 and *Shiurei Sheivet HaLeivi* 190:10[7].

8. See *Sidrei Taharah* 190 end of §36.

9. An alternate explanation: The laws of *kesamim* were instituted even though any *kesem* is, by definition, a *safek* (a doubt). Perhaps the blood is not uterine blood (see Chapter Seven). A *kesem* on a colored garment always involves an additional *safek* since we cannot be certain that the color is *tamei*. Therefore, *Chazal* were lenient and excluded it from the laws of *kesamim*.

10. To illustrate the subtlety of the differentiation between a shade of red that the Torah considers *dam niddah* and a shade which is not considered *dam niddah*, see *Niddah* 19b. The Talmud explains that if a woman has a blood flow the color of a blood from the wound on the little finger of an

degree, affect the shade of the stain it is difficult to evaluate a stain on a colored garment.[11] Therefore, *Chazal* chose to completely exempt colored garments from the rules of *kesamim* rather than present us with the difficult task of diagnosing the effect of the fabric color upon the stain.[12]

Today, the criterion of acceptable and unacceptable colors has changed from what it was in early Talmudic times. *Chachamim* of later Talmudic generations felt themselves unqualified to distinguish between different shades of red. Accordingly, we consider any reddish stain to be *tamei*. Examining a stain today is merely a question of determining whether or not it appears reddish. Since this is usually not affected by the color of the garment, the exemption of all colored garments from the laws of *kesamim* seems strained. Nevertheless, since we are not empowered to revise the laws of *kesamim* in any way the original exemption as decreed by *Chazal* remains in effect.[13]

B. Defining a colored garment

1. The depth of the fabric color:
There are contemporary opinions which maintain that only darkly colored garments that actually affect the color of blood are excluded from the rule of *kesamim*.[14] However, common practice is to exempt any colored garment. Indeed, some Rabbonim frown upon the custom of women who regularly wear black undergarments. A black garment hides any stain. There are times when it may be important to note the color of a stain. A woman who feels a *hargashah* and finds a red stain cannot dismiss it merely because it is on a colored garment. A Rav must be consulted. A very large red stain, even on a colored garment, may indicate the beginning of her menstruation, and a Rav should be consulted.[15] A woman nearing her expected menstru-

---

unmarried man younger than twenty years old that was stubbed, healed and stubbed again, she is *temei'ah*. If the blood is the color of blood from the first stubbing, from a finger other than the little finger, from a man older than twenty or a man who was married, she is *tehorah*.

11. See *Rashi, Niddah* 61b, cited by *Graz* 190:23.

12. See *Malbushei Taharah* 190:27[37] and *Chezkas Taharah* 190:51.

13. See responsa *Cheishev HaEifod* 2:92.

14. See *Sheivet HaLeivi* 2:87, who rules that a pale yellow garment is not considered a "colored" garment. In *Shiurei Sheivet HaLeivi* 190:10[4], he rules that any pale color, besides pale red, is not considered "colored." However, *Taharas HaBayis*, vol. 1 pg. 391, rejects this view.

15. See note 33.

ation will certainly want to know if any bleeding has begun. In all these cases, a black garment may mask the true color of the stain. It is more advisable to wear a garment that is certainly colored (see 2 below) and therefore exempt from *kesamim* but not dark enough to mask a real bloodstain.

2. Extremely light shaded fabrics:
Some garment colors are so light (i.e., extremely light pastel colors) that it is difficult to classify them as colored garments.[16] One who wishes to avoid *kesamim* should not wear such garments. It is assumed that off-white or light beige colors are a variation of white and thus subject to the laws of *kesamim*.[17]

3. A partially colored garment:
If a *kesem* is found upon a garment that is partially white and partially colored, its status would depend upon the following:

> a. If the stain is completely on the white part of the garment, it is considered a stain on a white garment, even though part of the garment is colored.[18]

> b. If the *kesem* is partially on the white and partially on the colored part of the garment, most *Poskim* maintain that the stain on the colored part is ignored. Thus, if the stain on the white area is less in area than the size of a *gris*, the woman is *tehorah*. If the stain on the white area alone is a *gris*, she is *temei'ah*.[19]

---

16. *Chazal* gave no guideline other than the term *"beged tzavua,"* leaving the definition open to the normal understanding of that term. It would seem, on one hand, that any garment that would commonly be called a "colored" garment should be excluded from the laws of *kesamim*. On the other hand, the reason colored garments were excluded is because the fabric color affects the stain shade. It would logically follow that a lightly colored fabric, which does not affect the color of the stain, should not be excluded from *kesamim*. See *Tzitz Eliezer* 6:23, who rules that any garment called "colored" is exempt from the laws of *kesamim*. It would seem that a garment whose color is so light that it is only noticeable when compared to a white garment should not be considered "colored."

17. In earlier times, white garments were not as white as those today. Thus, *Chazal* would probably consider off-white the equivalent of white.

18. See *Tzitz Eliezer* 6:23[16].

19. Responsa *Me'il Tzedakah* cited by R' Akiva Eiger, 190:10, *Sidrei Taharah* §21 and *Pischei Teshuvah* §20. *Chavos Daas* §9[b] disagrees. He maintains that since the stain is obviously one stain, we cannot attribute the part on the white to lice. Thus, if in totality the stain is larger than a *gris* the woman is *temei'ah*. *Pischei Teshuvah* ibid. cites responsa *Tiferes Tzvi* and *Teshuvah MeAhavah* who agree with *Chavos Daas*. *Graz* 190:23 and *Chochmas Adam* 113:10 agree with the lenient position of

c. If the *kesem* overlaps onto both white sides of a colored area, the stain on the colored area is not added to the measurement of the *gris*, but the stain on the two white areas may combine to a *gris* even though they are separated by the colored area.[20]

d. A garment that is woven of white woof and colored warp threads (or the reverse) is judged by the general appearance of the garment. If it looks white, it is considered a white garment.[21] Thus, a stain found upon this type of garment that is the size of a *gris* renders the woman a *niddah*, even though some of the stain is on colored threads.[22]

4. A naturally colored garment:
Even a *kesem* found upon a garment that is naturally colored will not render a woman a *niddah*, e.g., a leather garment.[23]

C. Issues pertaining to colored garments

1. A *kesem* found on a non-absorbent garment:
Colored garments are exempt from *kesamim* only because a stain may change shades when absorbed into the colored fabric; thus, a non-absorbent fabric should not be exempt. Nevertheless, *Poskim* contend that the color of a *kesem* is somewhat affected by

---

Me'il Tzedakah, as is the common custom. *Igros Moshe*, Y.D. 3:53, follows the opinion of *Chavos Daas*, whose argument, he feels, is more compelling. He is lenient in a case of difficulty, e.g., that of a couple who have not yet had children. *Shiurei Sheivet HaLeivi* 190:10[6] also rules that one should follow the stringent opinion of *Chavos Daas*, while *Taharas HaBayis* vol. 1 p. 395 contends that one may follow the lenient opinion of most *Poskim*.

20. *Me'il Tzedakah*, R' Akiva Eiger, *Sidrei Taharah* and *Chochmas Adam* cited above. *Me'il Tzedakah* explains that since the stains are all part of one stain, they combine to the size of a *gris*. See *Tzemach Tzedek* 190:10 who assumes that the *Graz* disagrees with these *Poskim* and maintains that the stains on the two white areas do not combine.

21. See *Shaarei Tohar* 10:13, who notes that if both colors are visible on the fabric, she is a *niddah* if the stain on the white fibers alone is the size of a *gris*. Thus, if a fabric is woven with thick yarn (e.g., a knitted sweater), one would treat each part according to its individual color.

22. *Chochmas Adam* 113:10. The logic to this is that *Chazal* exempted a "colored garment"; hence, the appearance of the garment is the decisive factor.

23. See responsa *Shoel U'Meishiv* cited in *Darchei Teshuvah* §63 and Chochmas Adam 113:10, who are strict with regard to this question. However, *Lechem VeSimlah* §16[s], R' Shlomo Kluger cited in *Sheivet HaLeivi* 2:87, *Shaarei Tohar* 10:[12] and *Taharas Yisrael* 190:53 take a lenient position. See note 2 above regarding the reverse situation.

any material. Therefore, even a stain found on a colored, non-absorbent garment will not render a woman a *niddah*.[24]

2. A thick *kesem*:

Most contemporary *Poskim* rule that even a thick *kesem* which is obviously blood and, because of its thickness, is unaffected by the fabric color is *tehorah*; others are more strict.[25]

3. A garment worn close to the body:

In the opinion of most *Poskim*, a *kesem* found on a colored garment is *tehorah* even if the garment is worn tightly against the body.[26] Thus, a woman who wears colored undergarments is generally protected against *kesamim*.

D. Wearing colored garments to avoid *kesamim* problems

1. When to wear colored garments:

Poskim advise a woman to avoid the problem of *kesamim* entirely by wearing colored garments during the time that she is *teho-*

---

24. See *Lechem VeSimlah* 190:16[s] who contends that a *kesem* found upon a leather garment is *tahor*. He contends that even a stain on leather is somewhat affected by the color of the leather. See *Badei HaShulchan* 190, *Tziyunim* §197, citing *Shiyarei Taharah* 191:2.

25. It seems that *Lechem VeSimlah*, noted above, exempts leather only because he assumes that the leather changes the shade of the stain. However, if the *kesem* is very thick and totally unaffected by the fabric, it seems that he would not exempt the *kesem*. *Lechem VeSimlah* cites *Rashi* (*Niddah* 61b) who explains that a colored garment generally changes the shade of the stain. Thus, if it does not change the shade, the woman is *temei'ah*. *Darchei Teshuvah* §62 citing *Makor Chaim* and *Beis Hillel* seems to share this view as does *Be'er Moshe* 4:65. See *Badei HaShulchan* 190:10, s.v. וכן כתם, regarding a dry piece of blood found upon a colored garment. However, *Sheivet HaLeivi* 2:87 cites *Rishonim* who contend that any stain (even a thick stain) on a colored garment is *tehorah*. *Chazal* exempted colored garments in all cases. The only exception is a lightly colored garment since it was never the intention of *Chazal* to include this in the term "colored garment." An application of this question in the reverse regards a white garment that is treated with chemicals so that any blood absorbed into it will change colors. If the main criterion is the fact that a colored garment affects the color of the stain (and for this reason a thick non-absorbed stain on a colored garment is *tamei*), this white fabric may have the status of a colored fabric. If, however, the main criterion is the fact that the fabric is colored (and for this reason a thick non-absorbed stain on a colored garment is *tahor*), this garment is considered white.

26. *Chasam Sofer*, Y.D. 161, seems to be strict in this case. See, however, responsa *Maharsham* 1:81,82. *Darchei Teshuvah* 190:66, *Pische Zuta* §21 cite opposing opinions. *Taharas Yisrael* 190:56 follows the opinion of *Chasam Sofer* in advising that initially one should not wear colored garments tightly fitted to the body. *Minchas Yitzchak* 4:118 accepts this position. However, *Chazon Ish*, Y.D. 89:4, rejects *Chasam Sofer's* view entirely; see also *Tzitz Eliezer* 6:23[19]. *Sheivet HaLeivi* 2:87 accepts *Chazon Ish's*

rah.[27] This is not a willful evasion of the *halachah*, since *Chazal*, the originators of the laws of *kesamim*, specifically exempted colored garments from the laws of *kesamim*.[28] Thus, even a woman who constantly finds *kesamim* on her garments may avoid the problem by wearing colored garments.[29]

2. How to wear colored garments:

A woman who wishes to protect herself from *kesamim* by wearing colored garments should follow these guidelines:

> a. The color:
> The woman should wear undergarments that are certainly considered "colored," not light beige or off-white colors. It is preferable to avoid wearing black or navy blue garments, see 1 above.
>
> b. A garment with a white lining, or tights:
> A woman should not wear a garment with a white lining. A *kesem* on the white lining will render her a *niddah* even though the garment itself is colored. Even if she reverses the garment and wears the white lining on the outside, she will become a *niddah* if a *kesem* is found on the lining.[30] Similarly, a woman who wears a colored undergarment but wears white tights is not protected against a *kesem* found on the tights.

3. When not to wear colored garments:

We noted in Chapter Seven I,E that during the seven "clean" days a woman is required to wear white garments.[31] This is to

---

lenient conclusion (however, in *Shiurei Sheivet HaLeivi* 190:10[5], he contends that if the stain seems to be real blood, one should be strict). *Sidrei Taharah* 190, end of 36, maintains that even a blood stain that certainly came from her body is *tahor* if it is found on a colored garment (providing that there was no *hargashah*). Apparently, he would disagree with *Chasam Sofer*.

27. *Rambam* (*Issurei Biah* 9:7) writes that *Chazal* established that a woman <u>should</u> wear colored garments. *Kesef Mishnah* (ad loc.) and *Beis Yosef* 190 note that the Talmud (*Niddah* 61b) seems to indicate that a woman <u>may</u> wear, not <u>should</u> wear colored garments. *Rema* 190:10 seems to follow *Rambam's* opinion that women <u>should</u> wear colored garments. However, *Toras HaShelamim* §14 explains that *Rema* merely <u>advises</u> that a woman wear colored garments to prevent *kesamim* problems. *Chochmas Adam* 113:9 and *Chasam Sofer, Y.D.* 161, seem to follow *Toras HaShelamim's* approach.

28. See responsa *Maharsham* 1:81, 82, and *Tzitz Eliezer* 6:23[19].

29. *Maharsham* ibid.

30. *Taharas HaBayis* vol. 1, p. 396.

31. See *Pischei Teshuvah* §22, citing *Amudei Kesef*. *Amudei Kesef* also writes that a woman should not wear colored garments on her "*niddah* days." His intent is unclear. *Badei HaShulchan* (*Tziyunim* 190:205)

ascertain that the menstrual flow has stopped completely. If the woman wears colored garments she cannot be certain that the flow stopped. In a case of difficulty, a Rav should be consulted.[32]

E. Problems that may be encountered even when wearing colored garments

1. A *kesem* found on a colored garment after a *hargashah:*
A woman who feels a sensation of a flow while she is wearing a colored garment cannot dismiss a *kesem* found afterwards on the garment. Similarly, if a stain is found after cohabitation or immediately after urination, one must be concerned that there may have been a *hargashah.* See below Section II,4 and Chapter Seven, Section VII.

2. A *kesem* found when the expected period is approaching:
A *kesem* found close to the expected arrival of the period (the *yom havest* or the thirtieth interval day) should not be dismissed lightly, even if it was found on a colored garment. Although the

interprets this to mean her expected *vest* day. Thus, a woman is required to don white during the days that she expects her period. *Igros Moshe* also suggests that a woman wear white during her *vest* day as a means of effecting a constant *bedikah.* However, since all other authorities make no mention of this *halachah* which relates to all women, they seem to disagree.

32. A Rav may advise a woman with a vaginal irritation to wear colored garments. The requirement to wear white is in order to ascertain that the uterine bleeding has stopped. Her wearing colored garments is not an evasion of that requirement since the staining that may appear is not from uterine blood. If she wears white we will be compelled to attribute the blood to the irritation, which at times may be done with hesitation. However, it is more difficult to permit a woman with mid-cycle bleeding to wear colored garments. The blood that may appear is uterine blood and nullifies the counting of seven "clean" days. Wearing colored garments and ignoring that bleeding is contrary to the whole purpose of wearing white, i.e., to ascertain that the uterine bleeding has stopped. Nevertheless in a case of extreme difficulty a Rav may permit a woman to wear colored garments even during the seven "clean" days. See *Maharsham* ibid., who permits a woman to wear colored garments during the seven "clean" days when necessary. A similar position is taken in *Responsa R' Akiva Eiger, Tinyana* 32. *Shiurei Sheivet HaLeivi* 190:10[9] contends that this is permitted only on the intermediate days, not on the first and seventh day. *Igros Moshe, Y.D.* 2:78, does not differentiate and permits colored clothes during all the days, providing that the woman felt no *hargashah* and performs a *bedikah* on the first and seventh day. See also *Taharas HaBayis* vol. 1 p. 397-400. A woman should <u>never</u> don colored undergarments during the seven "clean" days without consulting a Rav who will approach this question with proper caution and restraint. In addition, one who was given permission to wear colored garments should assume that permission was granted on a "one-time" basis only unless she was told otherwise. See *Shiurei Sheivet HaLeivi* ibid.

woman is not rendered a *niddah* by the *kesem* itself, it may signal the imminent arrival of her period and precautionary steps are warranted. A Rav may advise the couple to abstain from cohabitation until her status becomes clear. In addition, a menstrual period is often preceded by a staining phase which may be considered a *vest haguf* (as explained in Chapter Thirteen, Section II,B,4 and Chapter Eighteen, Section I,A). Therefore, the couple may be *halachically* required to abstain from any physical contact upon the onset of the staining. In either case, although they may be required to abstain, the *kesem* is essentially *tahor* since it was found on a colored garment and they need not observe all other rules of *harchakos* (e.g., not handing an object from one to another).

3. A very large stain:
If a woman finds a very large[33] red stain on a colored garment, a Rav must be consulted.

II. An object not susceptible to *tumah*

A stain[34] found upon an object[35] that is not *mekabel tumah* (not susceptible to *tumah*)[36] will not render the woman a *niddah*,[37] even if it almost

---

33. It is difficult to define "large." There are some who maintain that a stain the size of a half-dollar is *tamei* even when found upon a colored garment. There seems to be no source for this in *halachic* literature. However, a stain as large as those stains a woman finds on her garments before menstruation is difficult to dismiss even if found on colored garments and even if she is unaware of any *hargashah*. This stain may be the beginning of her menstruation.

34. Or even a piece of dried blood, see *Badei HaShulchan* 190:102.

35. *Sidrei Taharah* 190:93, s.v. מזה יצא, contends that a *kesem* found on an object that is not *mekabel tumah* but is lying on or held by something or someone that is *mekabel tumah* is *tamei*. This is the subject of much controversy in *halachic* literature. See responsa *Divrei Chaim* 2:80, *Minchas Chinuch* 161, *Pri Deah* (introduction, §4) and *Pische Zuta* 190:16. It has been noted that *Graz* (*Kuntres Acharon* 183:2) and responsa *Chasam Sofer* 6:81 seem to disagree with *Sidrei Taharah*. See *Shaarei Taharah* (R' M. Stern) 15 and *Badei HaShulchan* (*Biurim* 190:10, s.v. דבר). See also *Badei HaShulchan* 190:100, regarding objects that are susceptible to *tumas negaim* only.

36. There is a difference of opinion among *Poskim* regarding a *kesem* found on an object that is *mekabel tumah* only according to Rabbinic law, not Torah law, e.g., glass. *Noda B'Yehudah, Y.D.* 2:109 contends that the *kesem* is *tamei*. This seems to be the opinion of *Sidrei Taharah* §20 and *Malbushei Taharah* §23, as well. However, *Pri Deah* (S.L. §16) and responsa *Divrei Chaim* 2:80 prove from *Rambam* otherwise. *Taharas Yisrael* 190:47 rules that one may safely follow the lenient view.

37. *Sidrei Taharah* 190:93, s.v. ועל פי זה, cites the explanations of *Tosfos* and *Ran* (*Niddah* 58a) to this *halachah*. He interprets *Ran's* explanation in the following manner: Menstrual blood in itself is *tamei* regardless of the status of the woman. This is known by the Talmudic (*Niddah* 16a) term —

certainly came from her body,[38] and even if found on the day of her expected *vest*.[39] Some *halachic* issues regarding a stain found upon an object that is not *mekabel tumah* are:

1. A stain found upon the ground:
The ground or anything attached to it is not *mekabel tumah*.[40] Thus, a woman who finds a stain upon the floor (e.g., of the shower stall) is *tehorah*.

2. A stain found upon the toilet:
A woman who finds a stain upon the toilet seat or the toilet fixture itself should consult a Rav, even though these fixtures, being attached to the ground,[41] are not *mekabel tumah*. Similarly, a woman who notices blood in the water should consult a Rav.[42] In these cases, there may be reason to assume that the blood appeared with a *hargashah* which was masked by the sensation of urination.[43]

3. A stain found upon a small piece of cloth:
The exclusion of an object that is not *mekabel tumah* applies equal-

---

"מקור מקומו טמא" — the uterus itself (and all blood that passes through) is *tamei*. Thus, if some menstrual blood leaves the uterus even without causing a *hargashah*, and falls upon an object, the object is *tamei* since it came in contact with *tumah*. The woman, however, is *tehorah* by Torah law since she felt no *hargashah*. *Chazal* were concerned that one may erroneously assume that if the woman is *tehorah*, the object is *tahor* as well. This prompted *Chazal* to establish the laws of *kesamim* whereby the woman is also *temei'ah*. (See a similar idea in Chapter Eight note 10.) If, however, the object is not susceptible to *tumah*, there is no reason to bring *tumah* upon the woman, since the object cannot become *tamei*. Accordingly, *Chazal* exempted a *kesem* found upon an object that is not susceptible to *tumah*. A similar view is found in *Tosfos* (ibid.). *Sidrei Taharah*, however, explains *Tosfos* in a slightly different manner.

38. I.e., we assume that it almost certainly came from her body, not that we actually saw it come. The source of this rule is the case in *Niddah* 57b of a woman who checked the cleanliness of the ground, sat on it and, when she rose, found a *kesem*. Based upon this, *Sidrei Taharah* 190:36, *Pleisi* 183:1 and *Graz* 190:1 and §21 rule that a *kesem* found upon an object that is not *mekabel tumah* or a colored garment is not *tamei*, even if it almost certainly came from her body.

39. See *Badei HaShulchan* 190:103. And even if found during the first three of the seven "clean" days, *Chemdas Shlomo* 20, cited in *Pischei Teshuvah* 196:12.

40. A possible exception to this is a *kesem* found upon the wall in *Eretz Yisrael* which is susceptible to *tumas negaim*; see *Badei HaShulchan* 190:100.

41. See *Aruch HaShulchan* 190:40.

42. See responsa *Minchas Yitzchak* 9:93, *Cheishev HaEifod* 3:105 and appendix to *Chezkas Taharah*.

43. Blood that is accompanied by a *hargashah* is not subject to all the leniencies of *kesamim*. Even if it is found upon a colored garment or an object that is not *mekabel tumah* and even if it is less than a *gris*, the woman is *temei'ah*. See 9 below.

ly to a case where the material (of which the object is made) is unfit for *tumah* or a case where the size of the object excludes it from *kabalas tumah*. For example, a cloth less than three finger-widths wide (approximately 2.5-3 inches, see footnote)[44] is not *mekabel tumah*. Thus, a *kesem* found upon a piece of cloth this size does not render the woman a *niddah*.[45] One should be reminded that this refers to a *kesem* only. A bloodstain found upon a *bedikah* cloth renders the woman a *niddah*, regardless of the size of the cloth.

4. A stain found on paper or a tissue:
Many *Poskim*[46] contend that paper is not *mekabel tumah*.[47] This would apply to a woman who sat on paper or wore a paper garment and found a stain on it. However, a woman who found a stain on toilet tissue which she used to clean herself should ask a *sheilah*.[48] A woman should avoid looking at toilet

---

44. The measurement of a finger-width is subject to the same fundamental dispute as other standards of measure. In the opinion of *Chazon Ish*, a finger-width is 2.5 centimeters; see *Chazon Ish, Kuntres HaShiurim*, §9 (or, more exactly, close to 2.4 cm., see *Shiurim Shel Torah* 3:2). According to this opinion, a *kesem* on a cloth less than the width of 7.5 cm. — 2.95 inches (or, more exactly, 7.2 cm. — 2.83 inches) — is not *tamei*. However, *Chazon Ish* (*Kuntres HaShiurim* end of §15) states that his measurement is to be used only *lechumra* (a strict application), not *lekula* (a lenient application). Thus, perhaps one must be strict in a case of *kesamim* and follow the opinion of R' Avraham Chaim Naoh (*Shiurei Torah* p. 76) that a finger-width is 2 cm. Accordingly, a *kesem* on a cloth 6 cm. (2.36 inches) wide is *tamei*. Perhaps, since *kesamim* are Rabbinic in nature, one may follow the *Chazon Ish's* measurement even *lekula*. In reality, this question is of limited practical importance since *kesamim* are usually not found on such small cloths.

45. *Shach* §16.

46. *Shiurei Sheivet HaLeivi* 190:10[3] maintains that this is the opinion of most *Poskim*.

47. See *Sidrei Taharah* 190:19 and responsa *Chasam Sofer* 6:81, who rule that paper is not *mekabel tumah*. However, *Noda B'Yehudah* 2:105 and *Chochmas Adam* 113:8 contend that paper is *mekabel tumah* (*Chasam Sofer* had a version of *Chochmas Adam* who ruled leniently). See *Pischei Teshuvah* §18, *Pische Zuta* §17 and *Chazon Ish* 89:2. See responsa *Maharsham* 1:2, regarding a paper garment. *Igros Moshe, Y.D.* 3:53 and 4:17[14], essentially follows the stringent opinion of *Noda B'Yehudah* that paper is *mekabel tumah*; however, he concedes that thin paper, and certainly tissue paper, which is not washable in the manner of other fabrics, is not *mekabel tumah* since it is discarded whenever soiled. (It seems from *Igros Moshe, Y.D.* 3:53, that the tissue loses its status of *kabalas tumah* only after it became soiled. However, since at the time the *kesem* came on the paper, the paper is essentially soiled, the *kesem* is *tahor*.)

48. As noted above, *Igros Moshe* argues that even those who contend that paper is *mekabel tumah* concede that tissue paper is not *mekabel tumah*. Nevertheless, a stain found on tissue paper used to clean oneself after urinating is more complex for the following reasons:
a) There may have been a *hargashah* at the time, which she mistook for the sensation of urination, See *Sidrei Taharah* 183:2 and 190 end of §36, who initially takes a stringent position. However, in

tissues since, by doing so, she may cause unnecessary problems.[49] If she notices a red stain on the paper, she should not

187:3 and 190:93, he reverses himself and concludes with a lenient view. See *Chavos Daas* 190:1[b], who differentiates between a stain found soon (סמוך) after urination and one found later. In the first case, we must suspect that there may have been a *hargashah* and thus she is *temei'ah*, even according to Torah law. In the second case, the stain is merely considered a *kesem* since we do not associate the *hargashah* with the stain. *Chavos Daas*, however, does not define the period of time which is considered "soon" other than to refer to 190:51. *Shiurei Sheivet HaLeivi* 190:10[3] assumes that if the stain is found one minute after the end of the urinal flow, we need not be concerned about a *hargashah*. It would seem that since most people do not wait a full minute after urination before they clean themselves, according to *Shiurei Sheivet HaLeivi*, the woman is *temei'ah*. However, this seems hard to accept since the time referred to in 190:51 is the time required to do a *bedikah* in all crevices. This seems to be less than a full minute. *Igros Moshe, Y.D.* 4:17[13], rules that if the woman was not in an unusual rush to leave the bathroom (e.g., her baby was not crying and the phone was not ringing), we assume that she waited somewhat before cleaning herself and we are not concerned about *hargashah*. See also *Pischei Teshuvah* §18, citing responsa *Chemdas Shlomo* who is lenient regarding this question. See also *Badei HaShulchan* 190:10 (*Biurim* s.v. כיצד) who cites opinions that if the woman is certain that she felt no *hargashah* of *dam*, one need not worry that she confused the sensation of urination with that of *dam*.

b) A tissue used to clean oneself after urination is placed against the vaginal opening. This is referred to as "קנוח" (an external wiping). *Sidrei Taharah* 190:57 rules that in this case one cannot be lenient with a stain that is less than a *gris*. A *kesem* less than a *gris* is only disregarded because it can be attributed to lice. However, *Chazal* note that body lice are not found in the vaginal area; thus, even a *kesem* less than a *gris* renders her a *niddah*. *Igros Moshe, Y.D.* 4:17[16], takes a more lenient view. He argues that *Sidrei Taharah* was referring to a woman who wiped only the vaginal opening. A woman who cleans herself after urination usually cleans the general area including areas that were, in times of *Chazal*, prone to body lice. Thus, in his opinion, a woman who finds a stain less than a *gris* on a bathroom tissue is *tehorah*. See Chapter Eight, note 50.

c) Another issue raised by *Sidrei Taharah* §93, s.v. מזה, is that an object that is not *mekabel tumah* but is held by something (in this case, the person) that is *mekabel tumah* is subject to the rules of *kesamim*. *Shiurei Sheivet HaLeivi* 190:10[2] contends that most *Poskim* do not share *Sidrei Taharah's* view. See also *Badei HaShulchan* 190:10 (*Biurim* s.v. דבר), who notes that *Chasam Sofer* and *Graz* disagree with *Sidrei Taharah*. See also *Pische Zuta* 190:16. See note 35.

d) Perhaps the *kesem* found upon the tissue is considered a *kesem* on the body (which is *mekabel tumah*) since the stain was wiped onto the cloth directly from the body (thus, the *kesem* was not essentially "found" on the cloth). See responsa *BeZeil HaChochmah* 6:125 and *Badei HaShulchan* 190:33 (*Biurim* s.v. אפילו) who are strict regarding this point. See also responsa *Cheishev HaEifod* 2:75 and *Poseiach Shaar* 8:23, *Miluim* 3:10. See Chapter Eight, note 50. *Igros Moshe, Y.D.* 4:17[16], does not seem to take this point into consideration. Apparently, he considers it a *kesem* on the tissue which is not *mekabel tumah*. Even according to the stricter view, if the *kesem* is less than a *gris* she is *tehorah*. We essentially follow the view that even a *kesem* on the body that is less than a *gris* is *tehorah*.

Common custom among *Rabbonim* is to be lenient regarding a red stain less than a *gris* found on toilet tissue. Others are lenient even if the stain is more than a *gris* since paper is not *mekabel tumah*. While these issues would apply to tissue of any color, there is a slight advantage to colored tissue, especially a darker color which masks the shade of the stain. Responsa *Minchas Yitzchak* 5:111[3] takes a strict position even regarding colored tissue paper.

49. See *Shiurei Sheivet HaLeivi* 190:10[3].

check herself again with a tissue, since if she finds a stain again, it may be more problematic than the first.[50] She is similarly advised not to do a *bedikah*.

5. A *kesem* found upon nylon and synthetic materials:
Poskim disagree about the status of a *kesem* found upon a garment made of nylon, rayon or any synthetic fiber.[51] One should consult a Rav.

6. A *kesem* found on cotton:
A *kesem* found on a wad of cotton is *tahor*, since cotton that was not formed into cloth is not *mekabel tumah*.[52]

7. A stain found on a sanitary napkin or a tampon:
A woman who finds a stain on a sanitary napkin or pad must ask a *sheilah*, even if the pad is made of a material that is not *mekabel tumah*.[53] A stain found upon a tampon is stricter yet; it is the equivalent of a stain on a *bedikah* cloth[54] and renders her a *niddah*. A woman who is apprehensive about her garments possibly being soiled by a discharge but wishes to avoid *kesamim* problems should, in addition to wearing a colored undergarment, place soft, darkly colored tissues in her undergarment (if she finds a large stain on the tissues, she should consult a Rav).

---

50. The second stain may be more problematic than the first since she was actually examining her body with the paper; thus, perhaps there is more reason to consider it a stain on the body rather than on the paper (as in footnote 48(d)). If the stain is a *gris*, she may be *temei'ah*. A Rav should be consulted.

51. *Minchas Yitzchak* 4:118 rules that a *kesem* on a nylon garment is *tamei*; *Shiurei Sheivet HaLeivi* 190:10[3] rules that it is not. *Igros Moshe, Y.D.* 3:53, differentiates between nylon produced from vegetative matter, which is *mekabel tumah,* and nylon produced from oil which is not. He does not differentiate between nylon sheets and woven fabrics. See *Badei HaShulchan* 190:10 (*Biurim* s.v. כל דבר) regarding a *kesem* found upon a plastic chair.

52. *Shiurei Sheivet HaLeivi* ibid.

53. *Shiurei Sheivet HaLeivi* ibid. is strict regarding a *kesem* found upon a wad of cotton used as a sanitary napkin. There is no consensus among contemporary authorities as to the status of sanitary napkins. It seems that most pads are not *mekabel tumah*. However, a woman usually wears a pad when she expects heavy staining. A pad may absorb much of the stain and cause a larger flow to seem less than it actually is. Thus, the period may actually begin but seem like a stain. If one dismisses any stain on a pad, a woman could theoretically experience a period and not realize that she is *temei'ah*.

54. She may have experienced a *hargashah* and have mistaken it for the sensation of inserting the tampon. This is similar to a *kesem* found upon a *bedikah* cloth. We noted in Chapters Three and Five that any stain on a *bedikah* cloth is treated as if it would have appeared with *hargashah*.

8. **Blood found in the urine or stool:**
A woman who finds blood in her urine should consult a Rav.[55] Blood found on her stool, however, does not render her a *niddah* since stool is certainly not *mekabel tumah*.[56]

9. **A stain found upon an object that is not *mekabel tumah*, after a *hargashah*:**
A woman who felt a sensation of a flow and subsequently finds a *kesem* upon an object that is not *mekabel tumah*, or a woman who finds a very large *kesem*[57] upon an object that is not *mekabel tumah*, should consult a Rav. A *kesem* accompanied with *hargashah* may render her a *niddah*, even if found upon an object that is not *mekabel tumah*.

III. A pre-checked garment

Even a *kesem* found upon a white garment renders the woman a *niddah* only if the garment had been previously checked for cleanliness.[58]

---

55. *Poskim* disagree whether urine is *mekabel tumah*. However, if the woman urinated, we are concerned that some uterine blood may have been expelled with the urine and accompanied by a *hargashah* which was masked by the sensation of urination. These *halachos* are discussed in *Y.D.* 191. See *Shiurei Sheivet HaLeivi* 190:10[3]. See Chapter Seven, VII, B.

56. *Shiurei Sheivet HaLeivi* ibid.

57. See note 33 above.

58. 190:39. *Rishonim* define three types of *bedikah* cloths (and garments) with regard to prior checking: a) an *"eid habaduk"* (a pre-checked *bedikah* cloth) or a *"chaluk habaduk"* (a garment that was checked before wearing), b) an *"eid she'aino baduk"* (an unchecked cloth) or a *"chaluk she'aino baduk"* (an unchecked garment), c) an *"eid beinoni"* (an intermediate cloth) or a garment that is neither checked nor assumed to be soiled. The definition of these terms is as follows: a) *Baduk* is something that was checked for cleanliness and used immediately afterwards or was put, after checking, in a place where its cleanliness was neither specifically preserved nor compromised until its use (see *Badei HaShulchan, Biurim* 190:35 s.v. כל שבדקתו. See *Shiurei Sheivet HaLeivi* 190:38[1] regarding the length of time that may elapse between the original checking and its use for *bedikah*). b) *Aino baduk* is defined as something that is assumed to be soiled, even if it was checked for cleanliness at some earlier time; for example, a clean garment that was piled together with soiled laundry. c) *Beinoni* is defined as something that we have no reason to assume as either clean or soiled; for example, a garment that was never checked but was found among clean clothes. *Taz* § 29 and *Toras HaShelamim* §38 are of the opinion that with regard to *kesamim*, even an intermediate-type garment (type c) is considered *baduk*. Most other *Poskim* disagree. *Bach, Shach* §46, R' Akiva Eiger, ad loc., *Chochmas Adam* 113:38, *Sidrei Taharah* 190:67, *Pleisi* §20 and *Graz* §76 maintain that only type (a) is considered *baduk* regarding *kesamim*. However, according to *Taz*, a garment is only considered *aino baduk* if it was never checked (and never washed, see below). It is difficult to envision such a garment in modern times except in the case cited by *Sidrei Taharah* 190:67, i.e., a woman who wore a garment that she got from another woman and is unable to inquire whether or not it was clean before.

Otherwise, we assume that the stain was on the garment before she donned it and may be disregarded.[59] This leniency is due to the Rabbinic origin of *kesamim*.[60]

> ### 1. Pre-washed garments:
> Washed garments are assumed to be clean;[61] thus, a bloodstain[62] found upon a white garment that was taken from the clothes dryer, put in a closet or drawer and subsequently donned without inspection or donned immediately without inspection renders the woman a *niddah*.[63]

> ### 2. A garment worn during *niddus*:
> If a woman dons, without checking, a garment that was previously worn while she was a *niddah*, she may assume that the stain found upon the garment is from her *niddus* period.[64] See Chapter Eleven, Section E.

---

59. *Beis Yosef* 190. Responsa *Sheivet HaLeivi* 3:119[5] notes that if the stain seems to be actual blood, it is difficult to disregard the *kesem* even on an unchecked garment. He contends that our dwellings, unlike those of generations past, are generally clean. It is therefore hard to imagine a garment being stained for no apparent reason. It is difficult to dismiss this point. In addition, *Sheivet HaLeivi* argues, if the stain is large, it is inconceivable that she had not noticed it when donning the garment. For these reasons, he is very critical of one who is lenient in this matter. See also *Shiurei Sheivet HaLeivi* 190:39[2].

60. There are lenient rules regarding an unchecked *bedikah* cloth as well. However, since a stain on a *bedikah* cloth involves Torah law, these leniencies are much more limited in scope. See 190:36,37.

61. Although, in previous generations, washing did not remove all stains (see 190:46), today, clothes are washed more thoroughly (*Graz* 190:93) and with detergents (*Lechem VeSimlah* 190:54[s]). See also *Badei HaShulchan* §354.

62. I.e., a stain that looks fresh. There are stains that are not removed by laundering. These are usually recognizable and do not render a woman a *niddah*.

63. *Shiurei Sheivet HaLeivi* 190:39, end of 2. He notes, however, that laundry which was hung outdoors to dry is not assumed to be clean unless it was checked before it was worn. See a similar view in *Beis Lechem Yehudah* to 190:18.

64. 190:44. Even though it was checked before she wore it the first time (*Shach* §60). See *Chochmas Adam* 113:40, who notes that if the *kesem* is found during the first three days of the seven "clean" days, she cannot assume the *kesem* is from her *niddus* unless she knows that the garment became partially stained during the *niddus* period.

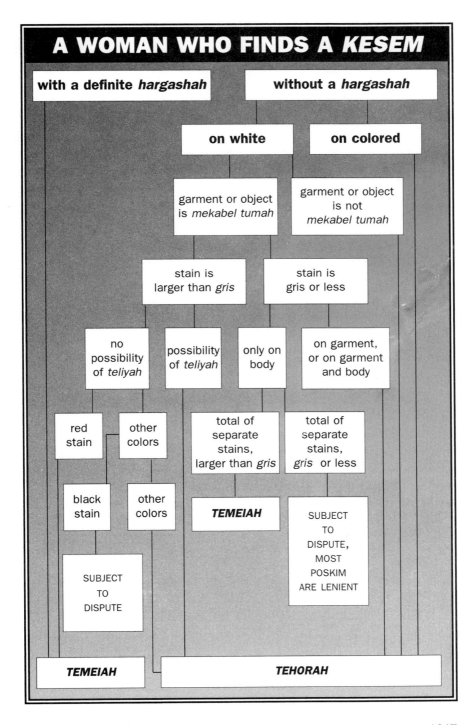

A WOMAN WHO FINDS A *KESEM*

with a definite *hargashah* | **without a *hargashah***

on white | **on colored**

garment or object is *mekabel tumah* | garment or object is not *mekabel tumah*

stain is larger than *gris* | stain is gris or less

no possibility of *teliyah* | possibility of *teliyah* | only on body | on garment, or on garment and body

red stain | other colors | total of separate stains, larger than *gris* | total of separate stains, *gris* or less

black stain | other colors | *TEMEIAH* | SUBJECT TO DISPUTE, MOST POSKIM ARE LENIENT

SUBJECT TO DISPUTE

TEMEIAH | *TEHORAH*

CHAPTER TEN

כתמים, המקום

Kesamim: the Location

- [ ] What locations are subject to *kesamim.*
- [ ] A garment which may have moved.
- [ ] A *kesem* found on the sleeve.
- [ ] A *kesem* found on a quilt or sheet.
- [ ] A *kesem* found on an outer garment.
- [ ] A *kesem* found on the hand.
- [ ] A *kesem* found on the leg or foot.
- [ ] A *kesem* found on her husband.

Introduction

In previous chapters we have learned that the size of a stain, its color, and the color and type of garment upon which it is found are key factors in determining whether or not a *kesem* is *tamei*. Another such key factor is the location of the stain. This is the subject of this chapter.

Only a stain found in a location (upon the woman's garment or body) where uterine blood may have dripped there directly from the vagina can render a woman a *niddah*. Thus, if blood is found upon a woman's shoulder or the top of her blouse, she is *tehorah*. The fact that we cannot identify any other source to which we may reasonably attribute the stain is completely immaterial since it is equally impossible to attribute the stain to uterine bleeding.

A. Stains on a garment or object

Note: Whenever the terms "stain" or "*kesem*" are used in this chapter they refer to red stains larger than the size of a *gris* that were found on a white garment or her body.

We noted above that a stain renders a woman a *niddah* only if found in a location where uterine blood may have dripped. However, if it is possible that the garment moved, at some time, to a position where uterine blood may have fallen, she is *temei'ah*. This general principle will be illustrated with specific examples below.

1. A stain found upon her robe or dress:

A woman who finds a stain upon her robe or dress below, or at the waist, is *temei'ah*.[1] Even though the waist is above the vaginal area, the garment could easily move near (or below) the vaginal area if she bends slightly forward.[2] If the stain is found above the waist,[3] she is *tehorah* unless she remembers bending deeply forward.[4] If the garment was washed before she could determine whether the

---

1. 190:12.

2. *Aruch HaShulchan* §57. The source for this is in *Beis Yosef* p. 62b, citing *Raavad*.

3. I.e., above the navel, see *Sidrei Taharah* 190:52.

4. She is *tehorah* regardless of whether or not the robe had a belt, unless she distinctly remembers bending over deeply; *Sidrei Taharah* §31 cited in *Chochmas Adam* 113:17. However, in a later view (§35), *Sidrei Taharah* seems to hold that the requirement that she must remember bending over deeply applies only if the robe has a belt. A robe with a belt does not hang as loosely as a robe without a belt. Therefore, if the robe has no belt, any stain found above the waist renders her a *niddah* if it could potentially reach her vaginal area when she bends over deeply. This is true even

stain was above or below the waist, she should consult a Rav.[5]

2. A garment that is pulled upwards:
A stain found upon a garment that is donned by inserting one's legs into the collar or waist, or taken off in that manner, is *tamei*, regardless of where the stain is found.[6]

3. A garment that may have moved:
A stain found on the back of a robe is *tamei* if the robe is loose fitting and could move from back to front.[7] Similarly, a stain found upon her undergarment is *tamei* if it is found on a location that may have moved to the vicinity of the vaginal area. This depends on the tight or loose fit of the garment.

4. A stain found upon a sleeve:
A stain found upon the sleeve of a garment is *tamei* even if it is situated on an area that may have reached below her waist only while she was bending deeply forward.[8] This applies exclusively to a woman wearing long sleeves[9] or very wide sleeves that hang down.[10]

---

if she is unaware of bending over deeply. *Pischei Teshuvah* §27 is critical of *Chochmas Adam* for omitting *Sidrei Taharah's* later words. Actually, it is not perfectly clear that *Sidrei Taharah* in §35 rejected his earlier view of §31. This may explain *Chochmas Adam's* position. See *Tzemach Tzedek, Piskei Dinim* §12, who follows the latter view and differentiates between a robe with a belt and a robe without a belt. In the former case, a *kesem* found above the waist is *tamei* only if she remembers bending deeply, while in the latter case, a *kesem* above the waist is *tamei*, even if she is unaware of doing so. *Aruch HaShulchan* §59 concurs with *Chochmas Adam's* lenient position as does *Taharas Yisrael*.

5. *Darchei Teshuvah* §79 cites the ruling of responsa *Nachlas Avos* that she is *temei'ah*. This seems to contradict the opinion of other authorities regarding a *kesem* that was lost before one was able to measure it; see Chapter Seven note 17. *Darchei Teshuvah* himself seems aware of this as he refers the reader to §37. Perhaps this case is different since the stain was certainly red and certainly a *gris*. Additionally, since there is nothing to which to attribute the *kesem*, we must assume that the blood came from the uterus (see *Niddah* 3a) and the *kesem* must have been below the waist.

6. *Cheiker Halachah, Niddah* §31, see *Shiurei Sheivet HaLeivi* 190:12[4].

7. *Rema* 190:12.

8. 190:13. Apparently (see *Beis Yosef*), we are concerned that she may have bent over excessively without being aware of doing so. *Shach* §58 is troubled by the fact that we are concerned about her bending over deeply with regard to a stain on her sleeve but not regarding a stain on her robe above the waist (see note 4, that this is subject to a difference of opinion). *Aruch HaShulchan* §59 answers that with regard to the upper robe, we are not concerned about her bending over excessively since, in that case, the robe would move away from the body and blood is less likely to fall upon it. However, the sleeve may reach the vaginal area without moving away and be in a position where uterine blood could reach it. See §64, where *Aruch HaShulchan* cites another rationale for this *halachah*.

9. *Shiurei Sheivet HaLeivi* 190:13.

10. *Chochmas Adam* 113:19.

5. A woman that did a somersault:

If a woman does a somersault or stands on her head and then finds a *kesem* on her upper body or garment, she may be *temei'ah*. These *halachos* are discussed in *Shulchan Aruch*.[11] A Rav should be consulted.

6. A covering used during sleep:

A stain found upon a quilt renders a woman a *niddah* regardless of its position since a quilt moves in all directions during sleep.[12] Similarly, a stain found upon a loose sheet renders her a *niddah*, regardless of its position, since the sheet may move during sleep.[13] A stain found upon a tucked-in or fitted sheet that is found in position in the morning renders her a *niddah* only if it is found on an area that was near her waist or even may have been so had she changed positions completely during the course of the night.[14] Thus, the woman is *tehorah* only if the stain is found at the upper or lower ends of the bed.[15] However, a woman who wore a tightly fitting undergarment during sleep is unaffected by any stains found on the sheet if the garment is found clean in the morning.[16]

7. A stain found upon the mattress:

A stain found upon the mattress or mattress cover, but not upon the sheet, is *tahor* if the sheet did not move off the mattress during the course of the night.[17]

8. A garment used as a covering at night:

A woman who used her robe to cover herself while sleeping at night[18] and finds a *kesem* on any part of the robe, including the

---

11. 190:11.

12. See 190:14.

13. *Taz* §37.

14. See *Pischei Teshuvah* §26. See, however, *Shiurei Sheivet HaLeivi* 190:14[1], who contends that this applies only to a woman who tends to completely change positions during sleep.

15. See *Shach* §68.

16. *Shiurei Sheivet HaLeivi* 190:12[2].

17. *Taz* § 37, *Chochmas Adam* §18. I.e., the sheet remained tucked in throughout the night.

18. *Poskim* discuss the case of a woman who used the garment during sleep at night. Perhaps a woman who covered herself during a daytime nap need not be concerned that the garment changed positions. A daytime nap is of much shorter duration and the robe is less likely to move about. If this is true, if she used the garment as a covering during a short nighttime nap she need not be concerned that it may have changed positions. This needs further study.

outer surface, is *temei'ah*. The robe could move about at night and any part may have been near the vaginal area.[19]

9. A stain on a kerchief:

A woman who finds a *kesem* on a kerchief that she wore on her head at night is *temei'ah*. If, however, the kerchief is still tied tightly to her head when she awakened, she is *tehorah*.[20]

10. A stain found on an outer garment:

A woman wearing only a slip and a skirt who finds a stain only on the skirt is *temei'ah*[21] since the slip may have folded or rolled upwards enabling the blood to fall directly on the skirt. If, however, she is wearing a tightly fitting undergarment which is free of any stain, and she finds a *kesem* on her slip or skirt, she is *tehorah*[22] unless it is conceivable that blood dripped onto the garment while she was dressing or undressing (either in the morning or evening or when she was in the bathroom).[23] A Rav should be consulted.

1. A stain found on the outer surface of a garment:

Even a stain found only on the outer surface of a skirt renders a woman a *niddah*,[24] since the outer surface may have momentarily folded inwards. A stain found on the outer surface of a garment that cannot fold inwards (e.g., undergarments or tights) is *tahor*[25] if she is certain that the blood did not come onto the garment while it was being put on or removed.[26]

12. A woman using a tampon:

If a woman had a tampon inserted throughout the time that she wore the garment, she need not be concerned about any *kesem* she finds on the garment if the tampon is clean.[27]

---

19. 190:14. See *Badei HaShulchan* §169, that this is true even if the robe was found in the morning in the exact same position that it was in the evening. We are nevertheless concerned that the top may have moved to the bottom and then been returned to its original position.

20. 190:14.

21. *Niddah* 58b.

22. See *Sidrei Taharah* 190:45 s.v. ודע, *Shiurei Sheivet HaLeivi* 190:11[3], 12[2], 18[5] and *Badei HaShulchan* §153.

23. See responsa *Maharsham* 6:99, *Shiurei Sheivet HaLeivi* 190:11[3] and *Badei HaShulchan* 190:152. If she lifts her skirt before lowering the undergarment, blood could not have fallen on the skirt.

24. 190:12.

25. *Sidrei Taharah* 190:45 s.v. ודע and *Shiurei Sheivet HaLeivi* 190:11[3], 12[2].

26. Responsa *Maharsham* 6:99, *Shiurei Sheivet HaLeivi* 190:11[3] and *Badei HaShulchan* 190:152.

27. *Shiurei Sheivet HaLeivi* 190:18[5].

B. Stains on the body

We noted in Chapter Eight (Section I,D,2) that some *Poskim* maintain that a stain found only[28] upon the body (and not upon the garment) renders the woman a *niddah* even if it is less than a *gris*[29] since, in all probability, it came from the uterus (a stain from an external source would have soiled the garment as well). Most *Poskim* are more lenient and equate a *kesem* found upon the body with one found upon a garment.[30] However, even they concede that (unlike the case of a garment where two small stains do not combine) two small separate stains on the body are combined to equal a *gris* and render her a *niddah*.[31] A woman who finds a stain on her body must measure it carefully, then remove it onto a cloth to show its color to a Rav.

Bloodstains found upon the body will render a woman a *niddah* only if they are on an area upon which blood may have fallen <u>directly</u> from the vagina. Otherwise, she will not become a *niddah*. Even though there is no identifiable source to which to attribute the stain, the fact that it could not have come directly from the vagina precludes her from *niddus*. We are left with no alternative but to assume that she does not recall that she was working with blood or paints, or that she was in close proximity to those that were doing so without being aware of it.[32] The following cases illustrate this principle:

> 1. A *kesem* found upon the hand:
>> a. A *kesem* found on the palm of the hand[33] or the fingers is *tamei*.[34] We suspect that perhaps she touched her vaginal area[35] or her legs beneath the vaginal area and blood

---

28. If the stain is found upon both the body and her garment, the *halachah* is more lenient; see Chapter Eight, Section I,D,3.

29. *Rambam* and *Shulchan Aruch* in second opinion 190:6. See Chapter Eight for more extensive footnotes.

30. *Rashba, Raavad* and first opinion in *Shulchan Aruch* ibid.

31. 190:8, *Shach* §13.

32. See *Pri Deah* to *Shach* §19, who explains why it is more logical to assume that she came into the proximity of paints without being aware of it than to assume that she inadvertently touched the vaginal area and then touched the area in which the *kesem* was found (see C below). He concludes that perhaps both positions are equally illogical; however, since *kesamim* are merely *deRabbanan*, we choose the lenient alternative.

33. See *Sidrei Taharah* end of §26. *Taharas Yisrael* §64 seems to be lenient in this case; however, the sources he quotes were actually referring to the back of the hand.

34. 190:11.

35. Ibid.

dripped onto her hand at that moment.[36] *Poskim* add that even if she is unaware of touching these areas, we suspect that she may have inadvertently done so.[37] If, however, she is certain that she had not placed her hand in those areas since last washing her hands, she is *tehorah*.[38]

b. A *kesem* found on the back of the hand is *tahor*.[39] We assume that blood could not have reached there directly from the uterus.

c. Similarly, a *kesem* found on the wrist or forearm is *tahor*.[40]

Poskim note that even according to those opinions that a *kesem* less than a *gris* found upon the body is *tamei*, a *kesem* less than a *gris* found upon the hand is certainly *tahor*.[41] This is true even if many small spots found upon the hand equal a *gris* in total, providing that no one stain is the size of a *gris*.[42] However, if she is certain that she touched the vaginal area and that she did not wash her hands, these leniencies do not apply.[43]

A woman working in the kitchen may often be able to attribute a *kesem* found upon her hands to the foods with which she was working (e.g. meat or ketchup).[44] The laws of *teliyah* are explained in Chapter Eleven.

---

36. *Beis Yosef* citing *Magid Mishnah*. Our concern is not that her hand may have become soiled from blood that was on the leg, since no blood is presently found on the leg. Our concern is that the blood may have fallen directly onto the hand; see Section C below.

37. *Shach* §18, see *Sidrei Taharah* §25. *Shiurei Sheivet HaLeivi* 190:11[3] notes that perhaps a woman wearing tightly fitting undergarments is not affected by a *kesem* on her hand unless she remembers touching that area and not washing her hands since. Thus, she need not be concerned that she may have touched the area when in the bathroom since she routinely washes her hands after using the bathroom.

38. *Sidrei Taharah* §26, *Lechem VeSimlah* §44[l], *Chochmas Adam* 113:12 and *Aruch HaShulchan* §50.

39. *Sidrei Taharah* ibid. and *Aruch HaShulchan* §50. *Chochmas Adam* 113:12, cited in *Pischei Teshuvah* §23, is lenient only if there are additional lenient factors.

40. *Sidrei Taharah* §26, citing *Ran, Tzemach Tzedek, Piskei Dinim*, 11.

41. *Sidrei Taharah* ibid.

42. *Chochmas Adam* 113:12.

43. *Badei HaShulchan* §129. *Shiurei Sheivet HaLeivi* 190:11[2] notes that if she did a *bedikah* and found a spot on her hand, but the cloth itself was clean, she is *tehorah*.

44. *Shiurei Sheivet HaLeivi* ibid.

2. A *kesem* found upon the leg:

A woman who finds blood on the inside surface of the thigh,[45] calf or leg is *temei'ah*. If the blood is found on the outside or on the front or back surface of the thigh or calf, she is *tehorah*. The inside surface is defined as those parts of the thigh and calf that touch when one stands and presses thigh to thigh and calf to calf.[46]

3. A *kesem* found on the foot:

a. A woman who finds a *kesem* on the top of the foot is *temei'ah* since uterine blood may have fallen there while she was walking.[47]

b. Similarly, if a *kesem* is found on her big toe, she is *temei'ah*.[48]

c. If a *kesem* is found on one of the other toes, some *Poskim* rule that she is *tehorah*;[49] others disagree.[50]

d. If the stain is found on her heel, she is *temei'ah* since she may have sat cross-legged with her heel under her body. Some *Poskim* contend that this applies only in those cultures where people sit in this position.[51] Others rule that this applies to all cultures since we suspect that she may have inadvertently sat in this manner.[52]

---

45. Even on the very top of the thigh which is slightly higher than the vaginal opening (see *Aruch HaShulchan*190:48 and *Shiurei Sheivet HaLeivi* 190:11[1]).

46. 190:11. *Tosfos* (*Niddah* 58a, s.v. מקום) cites the interpretation of *Aruch* that the inside surface is that area of the thigh and calf that touch one another when one squats and presses calf to thigh.

47. *Rema* 190:11, *Taz* §11.

48. 190:11.

49. *Taz* §11, *Toras HaShelamim* §16, *Graz* §26 and *Lechem VeSimlah* §43[l].

50. *Shach* §17, citing *Drishah*. *Shiurei Sheivet HaLeivi* maintains that *Shach's* position is more logical since the big toe is so close to the other toes.

51. *Taz* §10, citing *Prisha*, implies that if she did not sit in this manner, she is *tehorah*. Indeed, *Chochmas Adam* 113:11 states so clearly.

52. *Pische Zuta* §22 and *Taharas Yisrael* §60 rule that this *halachah* applies even in our societies. *Pri Deah* ibid. seems less than certain on this point. *Aruch HaShulchan* §46 explains that it is possible for blood to fall on the heel while one sits on a chair or stool; thus, the *halachah* applies even if she did not sit cross-legged. It would seem that if she wore a tightly fitting undergarment (as is usually the case) which is found to be clean, she should be *tehorah*. The reason for this is as follows: We noted in A,10 that a woman wearing a tightly fitting undergarment is unaffected by *kesamim* if her garment is clean. She would only be *temei'ah* if the staining may have occurred while she was

4. A woman who did a somersault:
A woman who stood on her head or did a somersault and then found a *kesem* on a part of her body where uterine blood could not normally fall should consult a Rav.[53]

C. Indirect contact

An axiomatic principle in the laws of *kesamim* is the rule that we do not assume that a stain has been indirectly transmitted from the vaginal area. For example, if blood is found on a woman's shoulder, we are not concerned that she may have touched the vaginal area and then touched her shoulder.[54] Even if she remembers touching the vaginal area, she is *tehorah* if no blood was found on her hands.[55] It is unreasonable to assume that blood came from the vaginal area to her hands and then to her shoulder since no blood is found on her hands.

D. A stain found on her husband

In the opinion of some *Poskim*, a stain found upon her husband's body or garment will not render a woman a *niddah*, even though it may have conceivably come from her body. These *Poskim* contend that since the stain was found on his, but not her, clothes or body, it is an indication that it must be from some other source.[56] We assume that he must have been in close proximity to blood or paint without being aware of

---

dressing or undressing. In the case under discussion, *Poskim* explain that a *kesem* on the heel is *tamei* only because the woman may have sat cross-legged. Thus, if a woman was wearing an undergarment and found a *kesem* on her heel, she would be *temei'ah* only if it is conceivable that she was dressing or undressing while she sat cross-legged. Obviously, this is almost impossible. It is questionable whether or not *Aruch HaShulchan's* explanation is applicable in this case. See *Badei HaShulchan*, 190:11, *Biurim*, s.v. נמצא, regarding a woman who claims that she certainly did not sit cross-legged.

53. See 190:11.

54. *Taz* §12 and *Shach* §19.

55. *Pri Deah* to *Taz* §12. It would seem that if there is blood on her hands and on her shoulder, she would be *temei'ah*. See *Pri Deah* to *Taz* §14. This seems to be the opinion of *Sidrei Taharah* §95, see also §28. *Sidrei Taharah* seems to render her a *niddah* even if no blood is found on her hand if she definitely touched both the vaginal area and the spot where the *kesem* is found. See *Badei HaShulchan* 190:131.

56. *Sidrei Taharah* 187:3, 190 end of 61, citing responsa *Panim Meiros* 2:127. See also *Chochmas Adam* 113:4. *Panim Me'iros* exempts a *kesem* found on the husband's garment even if that garment was worn during cohabitation (unless he used it to clean himself afterwards). See also responsa *Maharsham* 1:163, regarding this case. *Maharsham* notes that *Divrei Chaim* followed the lenient

it.[57] Other *Poskim* do not differentiate between a *kesem* found on his or her garment.[58]

One should note that this difference of opinion applies only to a stain that he finds on his body or garment. However, if he cleaned himself after cohabitation and found blood on the cloth, the woman is a *niddah*. This may be a serious matter and a Rav should be consulted. See Chapter Fourteen, Section I,E.

---

opinion and scoffed at anyone following the strict opinion. Responsa *Beis Shlomo, Y.D.* 10, follows *Panim Mei'ros'* lenient conclusion. *Pische Zuta* §2 and *Shaarei Tohar* 10:4 maintain that if her husband checked his garment immediately before contact with his wife and found it clean, and immediately after contact with her, he finds a *kesem* on that garment, she is *temei'ah*. In this case, we cannot assume that the stain came from another source. If, however, the *kesem* is noticed only after some time has passed, *Shaarei Tohar* is lenient.

57. Unlike a woman who is more sensitive to the problems that stains may cause and is therefore more likely to be aware when she is in proximity to staining substances.

58. See *Lechem VeSimlah*190:4[s], who cites a *Tosefta* that seems to contradict *Panim Mei'ros* (cited in footnote 56 above). *Pischei Teshuvah* §2 cites this *Tosefta* as well. However, *Darchei Teshuvah* §6 and *Pische Zuta* §2 reconcile the *Tosefta* with the lenient opinion. See *Shiurei Sheivet HaLeivi* 190:1[5], who rules that if the stain on the husband's garment seems like actual blood, one should consider the woman a *niddah*. In 190:39[2], *Shiurei Sheivet HaLeivi* rules that if the husband's garment was not checked before it was worn, even though it was machine washed, one may consider it an unchecked garment and the woman is *tehorah*. It is unclear what his position would be regarding a combination of both factors, i.e., an unchecked (or machine-washed) garment with a stain that seems like actual blood.

CHAPTER ELEVEN

תליית הכתם
Attributing a *Kesem* to Another Source

☐ The requirements for *teliyah*.

☐ A retroactive *teliyah*.

☐ Causing a *teliyah*.

☐ A *kesem* found on the body.

☐ Attributing a *kesem* to a wound.

☐ Attributing a *kesem* to her *niddus* period.

☐ Attributing a *kesem* during the first three of the seven days.

Introduction

Since *kesamim* are Rabbinic[1] in origin, *Chazal* were lenient and dismissed any *kesem* that can be attributed to a reasonable source other than the woman herself.[2] Attributing a *kesem* to another source is called *"teliyah."* If the *kesem* can reasonably be attributed to the other source, the woman is *tehorah*. Although it may seem that *teliyah* is a matter of simple logic and probability, it is governed by specific regulations set forth in the Talmud. One must present any question of *teliyah* to a Rav to determine whether *teliyah* is appropriate.

A. The required conditions for *teliyah*

1. Similarity of colors:

One cannot attribute a *kesem* to another source if the color of the *kesem* is not similar to that of the source. For example: If the *kesem* is red and the possible source is black[3] (or the reverse), the woman is *temei'ah*.[4] Even if both colors are red, but completely dissimilar shades of red, the *kesem* cannot be attributed to that source.[5] However, all reds or all blacks are considered similar in

---

1. *Lechem VeSimlah* 190:23[s] notes that in some cases, one may be lenient even regarding a Torah prohibition and attribute a cause to a reasonable source. For example, at times, one may assume that a blemish found in a slaughtered animal occurred after the *shechitah,* not before, even though the issue is the Torah prohibition of *treifah*. However, this is limited to a case where the assumption is very probable. A *kesem,* being Rabbinic, may be attributed even to a less probable source. An example of this is the case in A,7,c below, where we assume that a garment folded outwardly.

2. 190:18. Even if the *kesem* is found during the expected day of her *vest* (*Taz* 190:41).

3. Our discussion is limited to red and black stains since these are the only colors which render a woman a *niddah*. *Pische Zuta* 190:42 wonders why we cannot attribute a black stain to a red source. The reason a black stain is *tamei* is only because red blood may turn black. By this reasoning, the black stain should be attributable to the red source which subsequently may have turned black on the garment. *Shiurei Sheivet HaLeivi* 190:23[2] answers that red blood turns black only while in the vagina. Once it leaves the body, it cannot turn black. Thus, a black stain is attributable to the woman, not to a red source. See Chapter Six, note 51.

4. 190:23.

5. *Shiurei Sheivet HaLeivi* 190:30 notes that if a stain certainly does not resemble paint, one cannot attribute it to paint. In 190:18[3], he contends that if the *kesem* looks like actual blood, one cannot attribute it to paint. Similarly, if the *kesem* looks like black dried blood, it cannot be attributed to black paint since they are completely dissimilar. He notes that an experienced Rav is able to differentiate between the two. Therefore, he maintains, if one has the option of showing the *kesem* to an experienced Rav, one may not choose to show it to one unfamiliar with the subtle differences. See *Badei HaShulchan* 190:18 s.v. יש לה, regarding attributing a stain to blood from a wound which is not similar in color to uterine blood.

shade unless they are noticeably dissimilar. *Poskim* note two reasons for this: a) Different specimens of the same substance may acquire different shades, b) the shade of a substance is affected by the fabric into which it is absorbed.[6] Thus, even if the shades are slightly different, one may attribute the change to the effect of the fabric.[7] One is not required to place the colors next to one another for comparison,[8] even if one can easily do so.[9] Indeed, a *kesem* may be attributed to a source even if one is uncertain whether it resembles the possible source in any way. For example, one may attribute a red or black *kesem* even to a source of uncertain color.[10] Thus, a woman who passed near painters and later found a red stain on her garment may attribute the stain to the paints, even if she is unaware of what color was being used at the time (obviously, if she knows that the painters were using only green paint, she cannot attribute a red stain to them).

2. The size of the *kesem* must be attributable to the source: One cannot attribute a *kesem* to a source incapable of producing a stain the size of the *kesem*.[11] However:

> a. If the difference in size is merely a *gris* or less,[12] we may attribute the excess to a *ma'acholes*. For example, if the paint she was using is accountable for a stain the size of a quarter, while the *kesem* is the size of a quarter plus a dime, we attribute the quarter-size stain to the paint and the dime-size stain to a *ma'acholes*.[13] This is true even if

---

6. *Sidrei Taharah* 190:45.

7. *Aruch HaShulchan* 190:74, *Tzemach Tzedek, Piskei Dinim* 190:23. If, however, it is demonstrated that the color does not change even when absorbed into a fabric, one cannot attribute the *kesem* to the substance if their shades are dissimilar (however, one is not required to check whether the substance in fact changes color when absorbed into the garment). In addition, if the shades are completely dissimilar, the difference cannot be assumed to be caused by the fabric (*Aruch HaShulchan* ibid., *Shaarei Tohar* 10:[24]).

8. 190:30.

9. *Sidrei Taharah* 190:50 citing *Prishah*. See *Shiurei Sheivet HaLeivi* 190:30.

10. *Badei HaShulchan* 190:243.

11. 190:26.

12. We noted in Chapter Eight that in these chapters we refer to the minimum size of a *kesem* as a "*gris*"; in truth, a *kesem* is *tamei* only if it is slightly larger than a *gris* (the area of a U.S. penny is considered larger than a *gris*). A *kesem* only the exact size of a *gris* can be attributed to a *ma'acholes*. Thus, in our case if the difference is a *gris* the *kesem* may be attributed to the paint and a *ma'acholes*.

13. 190:26.

the entire *kesem* appears to be one large stain, i.e., a perfect circle.[14]

b. If we do not know the exact amount of paint that was used, one may attribute a *kesem* of any reasonable size to the paint.[15]

3. There should be no indication that the *kesem* is from the body: If there is indication that the *kesem* came from the body, not from the possible source, the woman is *temei'ah*. For example, a woman finds a yellow discharge, surrounded by a red edge,[16] on her garment. The discharge certainly came from her body[17] and the red edge is certainly part of the same stain; thus, it cannot be attributed to another red source.[18] Some *Poskim* maintain that even if it is not certain that the red edge is part of the stain (but <u>may</u> be part of it), the stain cannot be attributed to another source since the discharge certainly came from her body.[19]

4. A *teliyah* must be definitive:
A *kesem* cannot be attributed to a foreign source unless the exposure to the source is definitive, i.e., she <u>certainly</u> was using stains or dyes or she <u>certainly</u> passed in close proximity to others using stains. If, however, she <u>may have</u> used stains, or <u>may have</u> been in close proximity to others using stains, she cannot attribute a stain to them.[20]

---

14. R' Akiva Eiger ad. loc., citing *Me'il Tzedakah,* see also Chapter Eight I,C,3.

15. *Rema* 190:27. See *Shiurei Sheivet HaLeivi* 190:26[1].

16. Which, in itself, is larger than a *gris* in total area.

17. *Graz* 190:19 contends that this refers only to a yellow stain that is certainly a discharge from the body (e.g., a vaginal discharge). However, if the yellow stain is probably, but not certainly from her body, the woman is *tehorah.* The red area may be attributed to the foreign source. *Lechem VeSimlah,* end of 190, disagrees. He contends that since there is nothing to which to attribute the yellow stain, we must assume that it came from her body. Since both stains seem to be from one source, we are left with no alternative but to assume that the red stain is also from her body and the woman is *temei'ah.* This differs from case 2,a, where the blood is attributable to a *ma'acholes.* See note 24 below.

18. *Taz* 190:41. *Shach* ad loc. in *Nekudos HaKesef. Graz* 190:19 seems to lean towards this opinion, as does *Lechem VeSimlah,* end of 190.

19. Responsa *Rema* cited in *Taz* ibid. In this case, even *Lechem VeSimlah,* cited above, note 17, would agree with *Graz* that if the yellow stain did not certainly come from her body, she is *tehorah.*

20. 190:22. *Poskim* cite *Or Zarua* 34 (351), who explains that this is a case of *s'fek s'feika lechumra* (a stringent double doubt) since even if she has a definite *teliyah,* it permits the *kesem* only based on a doubt. Thus, a doubtful *teliyah* is even less of a viable reason to consider her *tehorah. Beis Shlomo,* Y.D. 2:14, explains that the uterus is a definite source of blood, while the *teliyah* source is an uncertain

5. A *teliyah* cannot be retroactive:

One cannot attribute a *kesem* to a source unless that source certainly existed at the time the *kesem* was found. If, however, the source was noticed only later, the *kesem* cannot be attributed to it retroactively. Essentially, this is an extension of the previous rule. In this case, too, the *teliyah* is not definite since we are uncertain whether the external source existed at the time.[21] For example:

> a. A woman finds a *kesem,* and only later notices that she has a wound. The wound may or may not have been present at the time the *kesem* was found. Accordingly, the woman is *temei'ah.*[22]

> b. A woman sat on a chair and subsequently found a *kesem* on her garment. Later, she notices a lipstick smear on the chair, but she has no idea of how or when the chair became soiled. The woman is *temei'ah* since she is uncertain whether the smear was on the chair while she sat there.[23]

6. Attributing a *kesem* to several sources:

A woman working with paints on two separate occasions who finds a *kesem* attributable only to both sources combined (e.g., the brush was dipped into paint twice and the stain is the size of two paint drips) may attribute the stain to the paint only if the *kesem* appears as two separate stains. If, however, the *kesem* appears as

source since she is uncertain if she came into proximity to the external source. One should note the subtle difference between the case cited in no. 1 above and this case. We stated in no. 1 that one may attribute a stain to a source even if one did not compare the colors. In the present *halachah* we learn that the source must be definite. This may seem contradictory since in both cases there is doubt whether one can attribute the *kesem*. However, one can differentiate between the two: *Chazal* only mandated that the source must be defined, they did not mandate that it must be verified. In case 1 the source is identified but not verified; in the present case the source is not even identified with certainty. However, according to *Or Zarua* who explains our *halachah* in terms of a *s'fek s'feika lechumra*, it is difficult to differentiate between the two cases.

21. *Beis Shlomo, Y.D.* 2:14.

22. See *Mei Niddah, Kuntres Acharon* 190:52, regarding a woman who notices that she has hemorrhoids. See responsa *Maharsham* 3:369, regarding a woman who had a hemorrhoid problem in the past, but more recently had no bleeding episodes. If she finds a *kesem* and subsequently notices bleeding hemorrhoids, perhaps this is not considered a retroactive *teliyah* since in the past her hemorrhoids bled at times. See also *Pische Zuta* 190:60.

23. *Beis Shlomo, Y.D.* 2:14.

one stain (i.e. a perfect circle), it cannot be attributed to the paints.[24]

7. The *teliyah* must be logical:

If the *kesem* is in a location such that it could not conceivably have come from any foreign source (e.g., it is only on the inner surface of her undergarment or it is on both surfaces, but the inner stain is larger, or she was wearing tights over the undergarment and the tights are clean), there can be no *teliyah*. She cannot attribute the *kesem* to the blood or stains she was handling.[25]

> a. A *kesem* found upon an inner garment:
> A woman wearing a dress and a slip who finds a *kesem* only on an inner garment may attribute the *kesem* to another reasonable source.[26] The outer garments may have lifted momentarily or blood may have splattered from the ground in an upward manner.[27] *Poskim* note that although this is the *halachah*, common custom is to be strict in this case.[28]

> b. A *kesem* found only on the body:
> A woman who was working with blood (e.g., salting meat) and finds a bloodstain <u>only</u> on her body cannot attribute that stain to the blood.[29] Since the bloodstain was found only on her body,[30] not on her garment, one

---

24. R' Akiva Eiger on 190:26, citing *Me'il Tzedakah*. This case is different than the case in *Rema* 190:27 (cited in 2,a above) because, in the previous case, it is conceivable that the two sources combined into one stain since lice are attracted to dirt. However, it is unreasonable to assume that two separate drops formed one perfect circle. *Shiurei Sheivet HaLeivi* 190:26[2], is uncomfortable with this explanation, since today we cannot actually attribute stains to lice. We merely follow *Chasam Sofer's* theory that *Chazal* exempted all stains less than a *gris* (see Chapter Eight note 10). Thus, while we may exempt the part of the stain that is less than a *gris*, we have no logical explanation as to why a stain caused by both a paint drip and lice should appear as one stain. He nevertheless concedes that *Poskim* do not seem to differentiate in 2,a between a case where lice are prevalent and a case where they are not. In either case we assume that the two sources combined to form one stain.

25. *Shiurei Sheivet HaLeivi* 190:18[5].

26. 190:18.

27. *Beis Yosef*. The former interpretation citing *Tosfos* and the latter citing *Rashba*. See note 31 below.

28. *Lechem VeSimlah* 190:80[l], citing *Hagahos Maimoni*.

29. 190:11.

30. If the stain was found on her hands as well as her body, she may attribute the stain on her body to her hands and the stain on her hands to the blood. This double *teliyah* is only possible if she was actually working with blood, since it is then certain that the blood on her hands came from

assumes that it came from her body, not an external source. A stain from an external source would have stained her garment as well.[31]

c. A *kesem* found on the body and a garment:
If a *kesem* is found upon her body and her garment, we may attribute the *kesem* to the blood the woman was

---

the foreign source. If, however, she was not working with blood but merely passed among those working with blood, we cannot attribute the stain on the body to her hands since it is not established that the blood on her hands came from the external source. While the stain on her hands itself may be attributed to the external source since it possibly originated from that source, we cannot extend this questionable *teliyah* to the stain on her body. *Teliyah* is only possible from a definite source, not from a source which is itself dependent upon a *teliyah*. If she was actually working with blood we may extend the *teliyah* to her body since the blood on her hands is certainly from the source (*R' Akiva Eiger* on *Taz* §14, in interpretation of *Rashba*, although *R' Akiva Eiger* himself feels that it is more logical to be lenient in all cases). See footnote 36.

31. *Niddah* 57b, *Yoreh Deah* 190:18. There are two possible explanations for this *halachah:* a) A technical approach: A stain from an external source could not possibly reach the body without soiling the garment first. This is the approach we followed in the text. b) A statistical approach: It is more reasonable to assume that the stain originated from her body since blood was found on her body, not on any of her garments. Had the stain originated from an external source, it would probably leave a stain on her garment as well.

A practical difference between these two approaches occurs in a case where the *kesem* is found on a part of her body that is not covered by a garment, e.g., her hand or foot, if she was barefoot. According to position a), she is *tehorah* since the stain could easily have come onto her hand without soiling a garment. According to position b), it is still unreasonable to assume that blood from an external source would splatter onto her hand without soiling any of her garments.

Responsa *Beis Shlomo*, *Y.D.* 2:14, attributes position (a) to *Tosfos* and position (b) to *Rashba*. *Tosfos* and *Rashba* both ask the same question: If a woman is wearing three overlapping garments, why may we attribute a stain found on the outside of the inner garment to an external source, while if a woman is wearing even only one garment, we cannot attribute a stain on her body to an external source? *Tosfos* (*Niddah* 57b, s.v. על) uses a technical approach: A stain found on an inner garment may be from an external source since she may have lifted the two outer garments and exposed the inner garment. However, she would never lift all her garments and expose her body. *Rashba* (cited in *Beis Yosef* 190 p. 62) rejects *Tosfos'* answer. He uses a statistical approach and maintains that we cannot attribute a stain found on the body to an external source is because since it was found on her body it is more statistically likely to have originated from her body. Thus, explains *Beis Shlomo*, if a stain is found on the hand of a woman who passed near painters, according to *Tosfos* she is *tehorah* (since the stain could technically have originated from an external source without staining her clothes), and according to *Rashba*, she is *temei'ah* (since it is statistically likely to have come from her body). Responsa *Beis Shlomo* concludes that even *Tosfos* would concede that she is *temei'ah*. He maintains that *Chazal* did not differentiate between the different cases; they ruled that any *kesem* found only on the body cannot be attributed to an external source. *R' Akiva Eiger* to *Taz* §14 rules leniently in this case (although apparently *Taz* ibid. disagrees as does *Shiyarei Taharah* cited in *Darchei Teshuvah* 190:70,104). Since *R' Akiva Eiger* seems to be explaining the position of *Rashba*, he apparently disagrees with *Beis Shlomo*. *Taharas Yisrael* 190:72 writes that a Rav may safely follow the lenient view, in this case, when ruling for others.

handling.[32] In this case, the objection cited above does not apply since the stain was found on her garment as well.[33] She is *tehorah* even if the stain is found on her body and only the inner surface of the garment.[34] We assume that, perhaps, either the garment folded outwardly and blood splattered on its inner surface and on her body, or blood which was on the ground splattered in an upward manner under her garments.[35]

8. The *teliyah* must be direct:

As noted above, a *kesem* cannot be attributed to a source unless it is in a location where blood could have fallen directly from that source, e.g. on a robe, below the waist. *Chazal*, who enacted the laws of *teliyah*, limited it to a case of possible direct contact, i.e., a case where the blood could have fallen directly from the external source to the *kesem*. One cannot use *teliyah* in a case where the

---

32. 190:11. See *Sidrei Taharah* §40, regarding a stain found on her garment in an area totally unrelated to the *kesem* on her body. *Badei HaShulchan, Biurim* s.v. ואפילו, contends that this question should depend upon the opposing views of *Tosfos* and *Rashba* cited above.

33. This *halachah* may be understood in two ways: a) The fact that a stain was also found on her garment proves that it <u>certainly</u> came from the external source, or b) we need not be certain that the stain came from the external source; we must merely eliminate the proof (as in note 31) that the stain must have come from the body. Hence, it is sufficient to merely demonstrate that the stain <u>possibly</u> came from an external source. A difference between these two positions is found in a case where the garment upon which the stain was found was never checked for cleanliness beforehand. If we require proof that the stain is from an external source (position a), a stain on an unchecked garment does not provide that proof. If, however, we must merely demonstrate the possibility that the stain originated from another source (position b), even a stain on an unchecked garment provides that possibility. *Sidrei Taharah* §35 raises this issue and rules that we merely require the possibility that the stain came from the external source. See also *Aruch HaShulchan* §63. Another example of the difference between position (a) and (b) is found in *Cheiker Halachah, Niddah* §28: The stain on the body was the size of a *gris*, while the stain on the garment was less than a *gris*. If we require a positive indication that the source of the stain is external (position a), she is *temei'ah*. The stain on the garment, being less than a *gris*, is attributable to a *ma'acholes* and proves nothing. If we merely require the possibility that the stain may have come from an external source (position b), she is *tehorah*. Even a stain less than a *gris* on the garment permits us to speculate that the *kesem* on the body came from an external source. *Badei HaShulchan*, ibid., cites yet another example: The garment she was wearing at the time was washed before it was inspected for stains and was subsequently found to be clean. According to position (a), she cannot attribute the *kesem* to an external source, since there is no proof that there was a stain on the garment before washing. According to position (b), she can.

34. 190:12.

35. *Lechem VeSimlah* 190:59[1]. This second reason follows the explanation of *Rashba* cited above note 31.

kesem is indirectly linked to the source. One cannot, for example, assume that blood fell from her shoulder onto her hand which in turn stained the robe. This is true even if she finds blood on her hand as well as the robe.[36] One may not assume that she touched the wound with her hand and subsequently touched and stained her garment. She is *temei'ah* unless both: a) blood is found on her hand and b) she knows that she touched the wound. However, we may assume that the stain came from the wound if: a) she <u>knows</u> that she touched the wound and b) her hand is bloody. In addition, if the wound is a type that would certainly soil the hands if touched, she can attribute the bloodstain to the wound if she knows that she touched the wound. She may have inadvertently touched and soiled any part of her body or garments.[37] This is true even if her hand is not presently bloody if it may have been bloody earlier (i.e., she washed her hands in the interim).[38]

9. One may not cause a *teliyah*:

Although one may attribute a *kesem* to a reasonable source, a woman may not purposely cause a *teliyah* for the purpose of avoiding *kesamim* problems. For example, a woman who anticipates a staining problem may not purposely involve herself with paints in order to have a basis for *teliyah*.[39]

---

36. *Chochmas Adam* 113:15 is lenient when blood is found on her hand only if it is certain that she touched the wound. See R' Akiva Eiger on *Taz* §14 who explains (regarding a similar case) that even though the stain on the hand may be attributed to the wound and the stain on the body may be attributed to the blood on the hand, since the blood on the hand is not definitely from the external source (only attributed to it), we cannot extend the leniency of *teliyah* further by making two assumptions (i.e., attributing the blood on the hand to the wound and the stain to the hand). R' Akiva Eiger, has difficulty with the logic of this approach. He feels that one should be lenient even if the hand did not touch the wound for certain. See also note 30.

37. *Sidrei Taharah* §28, R' Akiva Eiger to *Taz* §14.

38. *Chochmas Adam* 113:15. *Aruch HaShulchan* 190:56 is uncertain in this case. See *Sidrei Taharah* §95, regarding a case where it is not certain that the wound would bloody her hands, but she remembers touching both the wound and the place where the *kesem* was found. *Sidrei Taharah* is undecided whether she may attribute the *kesem* to her hand and the wound if no blood is presently found on her hand.

39. *Mei Niddah*, cited in *Pische Zuta* 190:21 and *Taharas Yisrael* §57. This is unlike wearing colored garments, which is permitted. A colored garment is completely exempt from the laws of *kesamim* whereas *teliyah* is a situation in which *Chazal* were lenient based upon a doubt; one may not artificially create that doubt. Similarly, a woman may be advised to change her undergarment often to ensure that stains do not combine to equal a *gris*. This is also permissible since a stain less than a *gris* is completely exempt from the laws of *kesamim*.

B. Examples of *teliyos*

The classical cases of *teliyah* cited by *Chazal* and *Shulchan Aruch* are: a woman who passes through a meat-slaughtering market, a woman involved with staining substances and a woman with a bleeding wound. *Teliyah,* however, is not limited to those cases. Any situation in which it is possible to attribute a *kesem* to a foreign source saves a woman from *tumas kesamim.*[40]

1. Attributing a stain to a slaughtering market or involvement in stains:

A woman who passes through a meat-slaughtering market may attribute a bloodstain to the blood found in the market. A meat-slaughtering market is an area assumed to be full of blood splatters. Anyone passing through the market could easily have their clothes soiled by splattering blood.[41] Similarly, a woman who was working with blood or paint, e.g., she was salting meat, or painting with red paint, or even if she herself was not involved with the blood or paints but stood or passed near people who were, may attribute a stain to the blood or the paint.[42] We noted above (A,1) that one is not required to visually compare the two colors. If, however, the shades are completely dissimilar, the stain cannot be attributed to the paint, even if both are red. In addition, the stain must be in a position where it may have come from the assumed source (A,7).

2. Attributing a stain to a wound:

A woman with a wound or cut[43] may attribute any *kesem* that she finds[44] to that cut. One may attribute a stain even to a par-

---

40. *Aruch HaShulchan* 190:70 cites the following examples: a woman who diapered a child and may have soiled her garments, a woman was wearing red clothes whose color may have "bled" onto her garment through sweat or a woman had not cleaned herself properly from fecal matter.

41. This refers to a slaughtering market, not a modern-day meat market. See *Shiurei Sheivet HaLeivi* 190:11[5] and *Chezkas Taharah* 190:72.

42. 190:11,18.

43. Even if she is unaware of its tendency to bleed (*Shach* 187:27), since it is common for a wound to bleed at times (*Graz* 187:29). If she is unaware of any wound but feels a pain, *Noda B'Yehudah, Y.D.* 2:100, contends that she may attribute a stain to the assumed wound, providing that she has a *vest kavuah* and the *kesem* is not found during the time of her expected *vest*. See *Badei HaShulchan* 187:5, *Biurim* s.v. בכל.

44. Even on the day of her expected period (*Rema* 187:5, *Shach* §27).

tially healed wound if the scab could reopen when scratched a bit.[45] Even a *kesem* found only on her body, not on a garment, may be attributed to a wound.[46] In A,7 above we stated that a *kesem* found only on the body cannot be attributed to an external source. This provision does not pertain to a *kesem* attributable to a wound since blood from a wound could stain her body without soiling her clothes.[47] We noted above that only a Rav may determine whether any *teliyah* is appropriate.

A wound must be in a position so that its blood could fall <u>directly</u> to the *kesem*. If the blood could not fall there directly from the wound, she is *temei'ah*.[48] *Poskim* note the following examples:

> a. A wound on the neck:
> A woman with a wound on the back or side of her neck[49] who finds a *kesem* is *temei'ah*. The *kesem* is in a position where the blood may have fallen directly from the uterus but cannot have fallen from the wound. If, however, the wound is on the front of her neck, she is *tehorah* since blood from the wound may have dripped while she was bending forward.[50] If the garment was worn only while she was lying, the stain cannot be attributed even to a wound on the front of the neck since, in that position, blood from the wound could not fall on the lower part of her robe.[51] If the robe was used as a blanket to cover herself while she slept, a *kesem* found upon any part of the robe may be attributed to the wound on her neck.[52] This is similar to the *halachah* discussed in Chapter Ten, Section A,6.

> b. A nosebleed:
> A woman who is susceptible to nosebleeds whenever her

---

45. 190:18. Perhaps she inadvertently scratched it (*Lechem VeSimlah* 190:86[1]). This applies even if the wound is presently covered with a scab (*Chochmas Adam* 113:15).

46. Ibid.

47. This is possible according to each of the explanations cited above (note 31); see responsa *Beis Shlomo, Y.D.* 2:14.

48. 190:11. Providing, of course, that the *kesem* is in a position where blood could flow directly from the uterus; see Chapter Ten.

49. *Shach* §29, *Toras HaShelamim* §19.

50. *Shach* §29.

51. *Toras HaShelamim* §21.

52. *Sidrei Taharah* 190:37, see also *Shiurei Sheivet HaLeivi* 190:16.

nose is even slightly hit may attribute a *kesem* to a nose-bleed, provided that it is found in a location where the blood may have fallen directly from her nose.[53]

c. Hemorrhoids:

A woman who occasionally suffers from hemorrhoids may attribute a *kesem* to hemorrhoids, even if she was not aware that they were bleeding at the time.[54] Some *Poskim* rule that she may attribute a *kesem* to hemorrhoids even if it is found at a time when the hemorrhoids do not usually bleed.[55] Others disagree.[56] If the hemorrhoids rarely bleed, she cannot attribute a *kesem* to them unless she felt pain.[57] A woman suffering from hemorrhoids should discuss the *halachic* ramifications of her particular situation with a Rav.[58]

C. Attributing a stain to her husband or child

If the woman herself was not involved with any blood or stains, but her husband or child was, she may attribute any *kesem* to them since a woman is often in close proximity to her husband or child.[59] However, this is contingent upon one of the following conditions being met:

> 1. She is certain that there was blood or stains on her husband or child. For example, she saw blood on their hands,[60] garment or body,[61] or they were involved with staining substances that would certainly soil their hands or garments.[62]

---

53. See *Pischei Teshuvah* §31 and *Badei HaShulchan* §209.

54. Responsa *Beis Shlomo, O.C.* 75, *Aruch HaShulchan* 190:70.

55. *Responsa R' Akiva Eiger* 56. This seems to be the opinion of R' Shlomo Kluger (*HaElef Lecha Shlomo, Y.D.* 221) as well.

56. *Beis Shlomo, O.C.* 75. See also *Pische Zuta* 190:60. Responsa *Maharsham* 8:369 cites responsa *Rashba* who rules that one may only attribute a *kesem* to hemorrhoids during the time of the month that they usually bleed (hemorrhoids can be affected by the body's hormones). *Taharas Yisrael* 190:97 notes that one may safely follow the lenient view, regarding others (המקיל לא הפסיד).

57. *Beis Shlomo, Y.D.* 2:14. See responsa *Mahari Assad, Y.D.* 232, regarding a woman who was straining herself while relieving herself and subsequently finds a stain.

58. See *Shiurei Sheivet HaLeivi* 190:18[3].

59. 190:19.

60. See 190:19.

61. Even if presently there is no blood on them, but we know that there was blood previously on them; *Shach* §33.

62. This is similar to the *halachos* cited in A,8; see *Badei HaShulchan* 190:219.

2. No blood is found on them, but they were handling substances that would splatter on her had she been in close proximity to them.[63] Even if she is unaware of being in close proximity to them while they were involved with the staining substances, she can attribute the stain to them. We assume that she was near them, since a woman is often in close proximity to her husband or child. However, she cannot attribute a *kesem* to strangers who were working with staining substances unless she is certain that she passed in close proximity to them.[64]

3. If her husband or child had a wound on their hands, she may attribute the stain to that wound,[65] even if the wound is partially healed.[66] Similarly, if they have a wound on other parts of their body, the *kesem* may be attributed to them if they slept in the same bed with her.[67]

4. As noted above, these *halachos* are based upon the assumption that a woman usually comes into close contact with her husband or child. Where this cannot be assumed, these *halachos* do not apply. Thus:

> a. An older son is not usually physically close to his mother; thus, she can no more attribute a *kesem* to him than to any other person.[68]
>
> b. A stain found during the seven "clean" days cannot be attributed to her husband since they are forbidden to have physical contact at that time.[69]
>
> c. If the woman usually does not come into physical contact with her husband or child, she cannot attribute a stain to them.[70]

---

63. *190:19. Sidrei Taharah* §43 notes that, in this case, she can attribute a *kesem* to them only if the *kesem* is found on her garment as well. In the previous case, she can attribute the *kesem* to them even if it is found only on her body.

64. *Lechem VeSimlah* 190:28[s].

65. *190:19.*

66. As in B,2 above. See *Chasam Sofer* cited in *Pischei Teshuvah* 190:32. *Lechem VeSimlah* §88[l] cites an opposing opinion. *Shiurei Sheivet HaLeivi* 190:19[1] cites other *Rishonim* who follow the lenient opinion.

67. See *Badei HaShulchan* 190:221.

68. *Aruch HaShulchan* 190:71. Perhaps *Aruch HaShulchan* would agree that case 2 could apply to an older son as well.

69. *Badei HaShulchan* 190:223. Case 2 should apply in this situation as well.

70. *Shaarei Tohar* 10:20.

d. If the woman is certain that she did not come into physical contact with them throughout the time that she wore the stained garment, the stain cannot be attributed to them.[71]

D. Attributing a *kesem* to another woman

If two women sat on the same bed or wore the same garment (e.g., a woman and her daughter both wore the same pair of socks), and a *kesem* is found on the bed or garment, we are faced with a dilemma. Who is *temei'ah*? Both, one, or neither? There are many aspects to this question which are discussed in *Shulchan Aruch*.[72] Generally, if there is no logical basis to attribute the *kesem* to one rather than the other, both are *temei'ah*. At times, we may conclude that the *kesem* is logically more attributable to one woman. In such cases, only one woman is *temei'ah*. This conclusion may be due to the sitting or lying position of one woman as opposed to the other,[73] whether they actually wore the garment or used it as a cover while sleeping, or how the garment fit each of them (if one woman is tall and the garment does not reach below her waist it would be less logical to attribute the stain to her).[74] It may be due to factors intrinsic to the women themselves: which woman is more liable to have a menstrual flow,[75] which has more to lose by becoming a *niddah*[76] or who demonstrated through *bedikos* that she is either *temei'ah* or *tehorah*.[77] These issues are complex and must be presented to a Rav.

E. Attributing a stain to her *niddus* period

If a woman wore a garment during her *niddus* period[78] and subsequently wore it again while she was *tehorah* without washing it or check-

---

71. *Badei HaShulchan* 190:222 citing *Meiri* (*Niddah* 57b).

72. 190:15.

73. 190:50,52.

74. 190:48.

75. 190:41,42,49,52.

76. 190:42.

77. 190:51.

78. Or during her seven "clean" days following a *niddus* period. However, even if she can attribute the *kesem* to her "clean" days, she gains nothing. If the *kesem* actually occurred during the "clean"

ing it beforehand, she may assume that any *kesem* found upon the garment is from the *niddus* period.[79] This is true only if she originally wore the garment while she was a *niddah* due to an actual menstrual flow. However, if she originally wore it while she was a *niddah* because of a *kesem*, she cannot attribute any subsequent *kesem* to the previous *niddus*.[80] See Section G regarding a case where the *kesem* was found during the first three days of the seven "clean" days.

F. Attributing a *kesem* to an unknown source

An interesting *halachah* in the rules of *kesamim* pertains to a woman who found a *kesem* that would normally render her a *niddah*. In this unusual case, in addition to the *kesem*, she finds another stain that, because of its position, is not attributable to menstrual blood. For example, she finds one stain on her skirt below the waist and one stain on her upper sleeve. Although we are not aware of any possible source to which to attribute either stain, we assume that both stains came from the same external source. The logic to this is simple: The upper stain cannot be uterine blood and certainly came from an outside source. Apparently, she was exposed to paints, stains or an external source of blood. We may therefore assume that the lower stain came from that source as well.[81] This *halachah* is subject to the following conditions:

> 1. The colors must be similar:
> Both stains must be the same, or similar in color and shade. If one is red and one is black, they are irrelevant to one another and the woman is *temei'ah*.[82]

days, the days were invalidated, her *tevilah* is invalid and she remains a *niddah*. See *Badei HaShulchan, Biurim* 190:44 s.v. לבשה.

79. 190:44.

80. See *Shiurei Sheivet HaLeivi* 190:44[2] and *Badei HaShulchan* 190:408.

81. 190:17. R' Akiva Eiger notes that this *teliyah* is stronger than other *teliyos*. In this case, we are certain that the upper stain came from a foreign source. Accordingly, he feels that the lower stain may be attributed to a foreign source even during the first three of the seven "clean" days. He is, however, hesitant to rule so definitively. See *Shiurei Sheivet HaLeivi* 190:17[3]. If the upper stain is on her garment and the lower stain is on her body, *Sidrei Taharah* §40 is uncertain whether she is *temei'ah*. R' Akiva Eiger rules that she is *temei'ah* in this case. See also *Shaarei Tohar* 10:15.

82. *Be'er HaGolah* ibid., *Sidrei Taharah* §41 and *Chavos Daas* §11[b]. *Chazal* limited this *halachah* to a case where it is possible that both stains came from the same source. However, if the stains could not have been derived from a single source (i.e., they are not similar in color), the *kesem* cannot be attributed to a foreign source (see *Shiurei Sheivet HaLeivi* 190:17[2]). One cannot argue that just as

2. The upper stain must certainly be from a foreign source:
This *halachah* is based upon the logic that the top stain definitely came from a foreign source while she was wearing both garments. If, however, this is not certain, e.g., the top garment was not checked before it was worn, then the bottom stain renders her a *niddah*.[83] Similarly, she must be certain that she did not do a somersault or stand on her head; otherwise, the stain may be from her body, not the foreign source.[84]

3. The upper stain must be larger than a *gris:*
Similarly, if the upper stain is less than a *gris*, we have no proof that the stain came from a foreign source since it may be from a *ma'acholes* (while the bottom stain is more than a *gris* and therefore unattributable to a *ma'acholes*).[85] If, however, the upper stain is larger than a *gris*, the woman is *tehorah* even if the lower stain is considerably larger.[86]

G. A stain found during the first three of the seven "clean" days

The general rule of *teliyah* does not apply to a stain found during the first three of the seven "clean" days. One may not attribute a

---

one stain came from an unknown foreign source, the other stain came from another unknown source as well. We have proof for one unknown source, not two (see *Rosh, Niddah* 8, end of §8). Basically, the guidelines to this *halachah* are similar to those in Section A,1. We assume that all reds or blacks are similar unless they are visibly dissimilar. See *Badei HaShulchan* 190:17, *Biurim* s.v. טהורה, regarding a case where one stain is damp and the other dry and obviously did not both happen simultaneously.

83. *Chavos Daas* 11[b], *Sidrei Taharah* end of 35. This *halachah* differs from that discussed in footnote 33. In this case, we require a positive indication.

84. 190:17, see *Shach* §30.

85. 190:17, *Shach* §31. See Chapter Eight, Section I,B, where we noted the difficulty of applying the exclusion of a small *kesem* in modern times given that lice are no longer prevalent. As noted, *Poskim* explain that since *Chazal* did not impose *tumah* on a *kesem* less than the size of a *gris*, we are not required to do so, even if their reason (i.e., the prevalence of lice in their times) no longer applies. The exclusion of a small *kesem* is not because we today actually attribute it to lice, but because *Chazal* specifically excluded it from their edict of *kesamim*. In our case, however, the issue does not pertain to the woman becoming *temei'ah* but rather to the question of whether the upper stain came from lice or whether it came from an outside source. Thus, it does not fall within the scope of *Chazal's* original decree, but depends upon the actual possibility of the stain coming from lice. Accordingly, the woman should be *tehorah*. The upper stain certainly came from the outside source, not from lice that, in reality, do not exist. See *Badei HaShulchan* 190:17, *Biurim* s.v. כגריס. While this seems very logical, it is difficult to dismiss a *halachah* cited in *Shulchan Aruch*.

86. *Lechem VeSimlah* 190:69[l], citing *Tosefta*.

kesem found during these days to any external source[87] since it has not yet been established that her menstrual period has completely ended.[88] The purpose of these days is to prove that the flow has come to an end. If a woman finds a *kesem* during these days she cannot be certain that the flow has ended. True, the *kesem* may be from another source, but we cannot dismiss the fact that it may have come from her body. Thus, these days do not provide the necessary proof that the flow has ended.

One should note that this limitation applies only to the laws of *teliyah;* however, the other limitations of *kesamim* apply even during the first three days. Thus, a *kesem* found upon a colored garment or a garment that is not susceptible to *tumah*[89] or a *kesem* less than a *gris* may be disregarded even if found during these days.[90]

> 1. When do the three days begin:
> The three days begin from the evening following the *hefseik taharah.* Thus, if a woman did a *hefseik taharah* at 3 p.m. on Sunday, she cannot attribute a *kesem* found before nightfall Wednesday evening to an outside source.[91] *Poskim*[92] suggest a possible[93] solution for a woman who must work or who has many cuts and

87. *Rema* 190:41, 196:10. This is a *chumra* established by the *Rishonim* and has no real basis in the Talmud (see *Darchei Moshe* 196:1 and *Beis Lechem Yehudah* 196:10. However, *Chasam Sofer, Y.D.* 165, tries to find a Talmudical basis). *Lechem VeSimlah* 196:18[s] contends that if she did not do *bedikos* during each of the first three days, she cannot attribute a stain to an outside source even if found after the three days. See *Shiurei Sheivet HaLeivi* 196:10[10] and *Badei HaShulchan* 196:138, regarding this question.

88. *Darchei Moshe* 196 citing *Mordechai*. See responsa *Chasam Sofer, Y.D.* 165.

89. *Pischei Teshuvah* 196:12. *Shiurei Sheivet HaLeivi* 196:10[8] is strict regarding a stain found upon an undergarment that is larger than a *gris* and is obviously blood.

90. *Rema* 196:10. *Pischei Teshuvah* 196:13 cites an opinion that if she could have avoided lice and did not, she cannot attribute the stains to lice. We noted in Chapter Eight, note 3, that there are two ways to understand the limitation of *kesamim* to a *kesem* larger than a *gris:* a) It functions as a form of *teliyah* (i.e., we actually attribute the stain to lice). b) It is a limitation in the basic rule of *kesamim* (i.e., that because of the prevalence of lice, *Chazal* never extended their ordinance of *kesamim* to a *kesem* less than a *gris*). This opinion cited by *Pischei Teshuvah* seems to support view a). This makes our utilization of this limitation today, when lice are not prevalent, difficult to understand. This problem is discussed earlier in note 85. See *Pischei Teshuvah* 190:38, regarding a stain less than a *gris* found during the first three days upon a *bedikah* cloth that was not kept adequately clean.

91. See *Darchei Teshuvah* 196:13 and *Badei HaShulchan* 196:137.

92. *Toras HaShelamim* 196:13 and *Sidrei Taharah* 190:74 and 196:33. See *Gilyon Maharsha* 196:10, regarding the opposing opinion of responsa *Tzemach Tzedek*. See also *Chasam Sofer* cited in *Pischei Teshuvah* 196:10. *Beis Lechem Yehudah*, to 196:10, doubts the advisability of recommending an earlier *hefseik taharah*.

bruises[94] and is concerned about finding *kesamim* during the first three days. Normally, a woman must wait five days before she begins counting her seven "clean" days.[95] However, a *hefseik taharah* is valid even if done before the fifth day (providing that she completes the remainder of the five days before beginning the seven "clean" days).[96] In this case, the three days would begin from the earlier *hefseik taharah,* although the actual counting of the seven "clean" days begins on the sixth day. For example, if her period starts on Sunday afternoon and the *hefseik taharah* is done in the late afternoon on Monday, the seven "clean" days do not begin until Thursday evening. However, a *kesem* found Thursday night[97] may be attributed to a foreign source since three full days have passed since the actual *hefseik taharah.* The fact that Thursday night is only the first night of the actual seven "clean" days is irrelevant.

2. When are *teliyos* applicable even during the three days:
The restriction against attributing *kesamim* to another source during the first three days is based upon the assumption that, logically, a *kesem* at that time should rather be attributed to the menstrual flow. There are cases[98] where this logic would not apply. Accordingly, *teliyos* would be applicable.

    a. Seven "clean" days following a *kesem*:
    A woman who found a *kesem* that rendered her a *niddah*

---

93. Depending on whether her menstrual bleeding and residual staining stop before the fifth day.

94. Of the type that are not constantly bleeding (*Toras HaShelamim* 196:13). Otherwise, she can attribute a *kesem* to them even during the first three days. See 2,d,ii, below.

95. *Rema* 196:11.

96. See 196:2, under which circumstances the *hefseik taharah* is valid even when done on the first day of the period.

97. She must, however, avoid any questionable *kesamim* even between Monday afternoon and Thursday night. Any *kesem* found in between cannot be attributed to another source and necessitates a new *hefseik taharah.* The *kesamim* found within three days of this new *hefseik taharah* are subject to the dispute noted in 2,a, below. *Toras HaShelamim* §14 follows his lenient opinion in that case as well.

98. In addition, *Shiurei Sheivet HaLeivi* 196:10[5] notes that some women are unusually strict regarding any stain on a *bedikah* cloth. They would consider themselves a *niddah*, without consulting a Rav, even upon finding a brown spot on the cloth (this is being needlessly strict and may not be an advisable practice, see Chapter Six, Section II,A). In this case, we should accept a *teliyah* even during the first three days after finding the brown stain. Accordingly, a Rav should inquire as to exactly how the woman became a *niddah* before dismissing a *teliyah* during those days.

must wait five days and count seven "clean" days. Nevertheless, since we are not certain that any blood actually came from her body, she may attribute any subsequent *kesem*, even if found during the first three days, to a foreign source.[99] However, if she originally had a regular menstrual flow, started the seven "clean" days, found a *kesem* which required that she restart the seven "clean" days and subsequently found a second *kesem*, *Poskim* disagree whether or not the second *kesem* may be attributed to an external source.[100]

b. Seven "clean" days following *dam besulim:*
Hymenal bleeding is not *dam niddah* since it is caused by a wound, not menstrual blood. Nevertheless, *Chazal* required that a *besulah* count seven "clean" days after her first cohabitation. These *halachos* are explained in *Shulchan Aruch* and will be discussed in Volume Two. However, since this is only a Rabbinic ordinance, *Poskim* rule that if she subsequently finds a *kesem* during the first three days, it may be attributed to any reasonable source.[101]

c. Seven "clean" days following *dam chimud:*
A woman who set a date for her wedding is required to count seven "clean" days, even if she was in a *tehorah* status beforehand. *Chazal* were concerned that the emotional trauma of setting a wedding date could cause a blood flow. This is called *"dam chimud."* *Chazal* required that she count seven "clean" days even if no blood is actually noticed. Indeed, if the wedding date had been previously determined and she counted seven "clean" days but the wedding was put off without setting a new date, when a new date is set, she must repeat the seven "clean" days. These *halachos* are discussed in *Shulchan Aruch* and will be discussed in Volume Two. *Poskim* rule

---

99. *Beis Shmuel, Even HaEzer,* 63:3, cited in *Dagul Mervavah* 196:10 and *Pischei Teshuvah* 196:10.

100. *Beis Shmuel,* ibid., rules that it may not be attributed to a foreign source. *Toras HaShelamim* 196:14 rules that it may. *Sidrei Taharah* 190:74 agrees with *Beis Shmuel,* while *Beis Lechem Yehudah* 196:10 seems to agree with *Toras HaShelamim. Tzemach Tzedek, Piskei Dinim* 196:20, adds that even if this continues endlessly, she cannot attribute the *kesem* to the foreign source.

101. *Beis Shmuel* ibid. *Chochmas Adam* 117:17.

here, too, that if she finds a *kesem* during the first three days, it may be attributed to any reasonable source.[102]

d. A stain attributable to a wound:

i. A bleeding wound:

If a woman has a bleeding wound, she may attribute a *kesem* to that wound (subject to the conditions noted in B,2, above) even during the first three of the seven "clean" days.[103] A woman who suffers constantly from bleeding hemorrhoids may attribute a stain, even during the three days, to that condition if it is found on a garment near the affected area.[104] See the principles of attributing a *kesem* to hemorrhoids in Section B,2,c.

ii. A wound not presently bleeding:

Even though one may usually attribute a *kesem* even to a non-bleeding wound if it would bleed when scratched or bruised, one may not

---

102. *Beis Shmuel* ibid. *Dagul Mervavah* ibid.

103. *Rema* 196:10. However, in *Darchei Moshe* (after proving that one may attribute a *kesem* to a bleeding wound) he advises that, initially, one should not do so if the wound will heal in a few days. In *Shulchan Aruch, Rema* omits this reservation. *Taz* 196:4 takes issue with *Rema* and rules that a woman is required to prevent blood from a bleeding wound from soiling her garments. This is comparable to waiting for the wound to heal. If she was able to but did not do so, she cannot attribute a *kesem* to that wound. *Shach* 196:13 (and briefly, in 190:51) is also critical of *Rema's* conclusion and rules that one cannot attribute a *kesem* to a bleeding wound unless it is a type of wound that cannot be prevented from soiling her garments. *Toras HaShelamim* 196:14 cites responsa *Tzemach Tzedek* who follows *Rema's* lenient opinion. Although *Toras HaShelamim* cites *Shach's* opinion as well, it is clear from his addition in parenthesis to note §13 that he agrees with *Rema*. Responsa *Panim Me'iros* 2:170 refutes all *Shach's* objections to *Rema* and supports *Rema* as does *Pleisi* 196:5. Although *Sidrei Taharah* 196, end of 34, rejects *Panim Me'iros'* arguments and withholds judgment regarding the dispute between *Rema* vs. *Taz* and *Shach*, he notes that most *Poskim* follow *Rema's* lenient opinion. In addition, *Chochmas Adam* 117:17 and *Aruch HaShulchan* 196:33 both follow *Rema's* lenient opinion. *Shiurei Sheivet HaLeivi* 196:10 also notes that most *Poskim* follow *Rema's* opinion.

104. See *Pische Zuta* 190:60 and *Shiurei Sheivet HaLeivi* 190:10. *Shiurei Sheivet HaLeivi* adds that even if they do not bleed constantly but bled that day and the area was not cleaned properly, she may attribute the stain to them. *Taharas Yisrael* 196:97 rules that if she knows that the hemorrhoids are presently bleeding, a stain may be attributed to them. See responsa *HaElef Lecha Shlomo, Y.D.* 221, who is strict regarding the first three days. However, he seems to be referring to hemorrhoids that do not usually bleed during this time. He recommends that a woman suffering from hemorrhoids not look at her garments during the first three days so as to avoid the problem.

attribute a *kesem* found during the first three days to such a healed wound or to one that was never known to bleed.[105]

iii. A stain found on a *bedikah* cloth:
A woman who did a *bedikah* and found a bloodstain on the cloth cannot attribute the stain to an outside source during the first three days, even if she has a bleeding wound in the vaginal area. We are lenient only regarding a *kesem*, which is Rabbinic, but not regarding a *bedikah*, which may render her a *niddah* even according to Torah law.[106]

e. A *niddus* caused by a small speck:
A woman who notices a small speck of blood leaving her body or finds a small speck of blood on a *bedikah* cloth becomes a *niddah* and requires seven "clean" days. However, if she subsequently finds a *kesem* during the first three days, it may be attributed to any reasonable source. A small speck of blood is not a normal uterine flow; therefore, there is no logical reason to attribute the *kesem* to a continuation of a flow rather than a possible external source.[107]

3. Questionable cases of *teliyah*:

a. A *kesem* which may not be from the first three days:
A woman wore a garment on the third and fourth day of the seven "clean" days and finds a *kesem* upon it when removing it on the fourth day. *Poskim* disagree whether or not the *kesem* may be attributed to another source.[108]

---

105. *Rema* 196:10.

106. *Responsa R' Akiva Eiger* 78. See *Darchei Moshe* cited below. Nevertheless, *Shiurei Sheivet HaLeivi* 196:10[7] rules that if it is obvious that the stain on the cloth is from the wound, i.e., she continually finds the stain on the same area, she may attribute a stain on a *bedikah* cloth to the wound, even during the first three days.

107. *Chochmas Adam* 117:17. Apparently, if she finds more than a mere speck on a *bedikah* cloth, it is considered a *reiyas dam* and the three-day limitation to *teliyos* applies.

108. See *Pischei Teshuvah* 196:11 citing opinions of responsa *Tiferes Tzvi, Y.D. 24 Panim Me'iros* 2:170 and *Beis Efraim*. *Sidrei Taharah* end of 190:74 leans toward the lenient opinion but reaches no definite conclusion. *Shiurei Sheivet HaLeivi* 196:10 notes that most *Poskim* are lenient in this case. The issues involved are the contradictory concepts we use regarding *kesamim*: On one hand, we assume

b. A *kesem* attributable to her *niddus* days:

A woman who finds a *kesem* on a garment that she had previously worn during her menstrual period may normally attribute the *kesem* to her past menstrual period.[109] *Poskim* disagree whether a *kesem* found during the first three of the seven "clean" days can be attributed to the previous *niddah* days. Most authorities rule that it cannot be attributed to the previous *niddah* days.[110]

---

assume that a *kesem* actually appeared when it was found, not earlier. On the other hand, we find that, at times, *Chazal* were concerned that a *kesem* may be from an earlier date. See *Sidrei Taharah* ibid., cited in *Tzemach Tzedek, Piskei Dinim* 196:18, who rules that only if she found the *kesem* after she had already done a clean *bedikah* after the three days may the *kesem* be attributed to another source. See *Badei HaShulchan* 196:144, regarding a case where the supposed source is only relevant to the first three days, e.g., she was salting meat on the third day, but first found the *kesem* on the fourth day.

109. 190:44.

110. *Shach* 190:51 argues that according to *Rema,* the stain should be attributed to her *niddah* days. *Mishneh LeMelech* (*Issurei Biah* 9:29) takes issue with *Shach.* Although *Sidrei Taharah* 196:34 refutes *Mishneh LeMelech's* argument, he feels himself unworthy to dispute his conclusion. He explains the difference between attributing a stain to a wound and attributing it to her *niddus* in the following manner: A woman cannot prevent stains from a wound, but she can avoid wearing a *niddus* garment during the seven "clean" days. *Shach,* who, as noted above (note 103), disagrees with *Rema* even with regard to the case of a bleeding wound, is certainly stringent in this case as well, see *Shach* 190:51. A similar position is taken in *Toras HaShelamim* 190:45, who, although he agrees with *Rema* regarding a bleeding wound, contends that even *Rema* would concede that a *kesem* cannot be attributed to the *niddus* period. *Shiurei Sheivet HaLeivi* 196:10[6] follows the strict opinion in this case. *Pischei Teshuvah* 196:14 cites *Beis Efraim, Y.D.* 45, and *Panim Me'iros* 2:170, regarding a woman who wore a garment during her *niddus* and then mistakenly donned it during the first three of the seven "clean" days, but only noticed it after the three days had passed. The question is: If we assume that a stain on the first three days cannot be attributed to *niddus,* then this stain, although found later than the three days, cannot be attributed to the *niddus* unless we assume that it was on the garment during the first three days as well. *Panim Me'iros* is lenient because, in his opinion, one can attribute a *kesem* to *niddus* even during the first three days. In 190:73, *Sidrei Taharah* cites *Me'il Tzedakah,* that although she cannot attribute the *kesem* to her *niddus* period, if she is certain that the garment was stained during *niddus* but is uncertain as to the amount of stains, she may attribute all stains to the *niddus,* even if found during the first three days.

BOOK FOUR

Vestos: Establishing a Pattern

Chapter Twelve — Vestos Made Simple
Chapter Thirteen — General Principles
Chapter Fourteen — Vest Kavuah and Sheaino
                  Kavuah
Chapter Fifteen — The Three Basic Vestos
Chapter Sixteen — Unusual Vestos
Chapter Seventeen — Uprooting a Vest
Chapter Eighteen — A Physical Manifestation
Chapter Nineteen — Induced Vestos
Chapter Twenty — Exemptions
Chapter Twenty One — Starting a Vestos Calendar
Chapter Twenty Two — Yom Havest

CHAPTER TWELVE

Vestos Made Simple

□ A beginner's guide to the basic concepts of *vestos.*

Vestos made simple? This seems like an oxymoron. The reader has surely noted that this volume has eleven chapters devoted to the subject of *vestos*. There is probably nothing more complex in the *halachos* of *niddah* than the principles of *vestos*. A beginner is usually intimidated by the myriad details this subject entails. However, the essential laws of *vestos* are relatively quite simple. Most of the complicating factors in *vestos* are due to unusual occurrences which one rarely encounters. In this short chapter, we will attempt to present the most basic concepts of *vestos* and direct the reader to other sections of this book in where the basic ideas are set forth in a simple manner. The reader can choose to tackle the more complicated issues when he feels he has mastered the basic principles.

The laws of *vestos* is the method by which we calculate when to expect the next menstruation in order to abstain from relations and do *bedikos* on that day. In these few pages, we will explain the three basic *vestos* that apply to almost every woman: *vest hachodesh*, *vest haflagah* and *onah beinonis*.

When a woman menstruates once, she encounters the *vest hachodesh*. This is simply a matter of noting the date of the Hebrew month when the menstruation began on one's calendar and marking the same day of the next month as the day of the *vest* (the *yom havest*). One should also note

ADAR-NISSAN-IYAR

Sunday	Monday	Tuesday	Wednesday	Thursday	Friday	Shabbos
28 Adar	29	1 Nissan	2 ● day	3	4	5
6	7	8	9	10	11	12
13	14	15	16	17	18	19
20	21	22	23	24	25	26
27	28	29	30	1 Iyar	2 ✗ day yom hachodesh	3

Marking the Yom HaChodesh

whether the menstruation began during the day or during the night. One must abstain from relations and do *bedikos* on the same date of the following month during the corresponding day or night. For example, a woman menstruated on Wednesday afternoon, the second of *Nissan*. She marks that day on her calendar and marks the daytime of Friday, the second of *Iyar*, as the *yom havest*. This is the *vest hachodesh*.

see calendar on previous page

The next calculation which must be made is the *onah beinonis*. Essentially, this is the thirtieth interval day. When the woman menstruated on Wednesday, the second of *Nissan*, she must count thirty days starting from and including Wednesday itself. The thirtieth day is Thursday, the first of *Iyar*. She must abstain from relations and do *bedikos* on that day in addition to the *vest hachodesh*. This is the *onah beinonis*. The *onah beinonis* is always four weeks after the onset of the menstruation and one day later in the week.

ADAR-NISSAN-IYAR						
Sunday	**Monday**	**Tuesday**	**Wednesday**	**Thursday**	**Friday**	**Shabbos**
28 Adar	29	1 Nissan	2 ● day	3	4	5
6	7	8	9	10	11	12
13	14	15	16	17	18	19
20	21	22	23	24	25	26
27	28	29	30	1 Iyar ✗ onah beinonis	2 ✗ day yom hachodesh	3

Marking the Onah Beinonis

Let us assume, for example, that her next menstruation occurs on the afternoon of Tuesday, the twenty-ninth of *Nissan*. She then counts the days between Wednesday, the second of *Nissan*, and Tuesday, the twenty-ninth of *Nissan*, inclusive of both days. This totals twenty-eight days. This is the interval of days which is called *vest haflagah*. She marks the interval day on her calendar, notes the interval number and whether the menstruation began during the day or during the night. She then counts twenty-eight interval days from Tuesday, the twenty-ninth of *Nissan*, starting from Tuesday itself. The interval day is Monday, the twenty-sixth of *Iyar*. She must abstain from relations and do *bedikos* during the daytime of Monday. This is the *vest haflagah*. She must also abstain on Wednesday, the twenty-eighth of *Iyar* which is the *onah beinonis* and Thursday the twenty-ninth which is the *vest hachodesh*.

NISSAN-IYAR-SIVAN

Sunday	Monday	Tuesday	Wednesday	Thursday	Friday	Shabbos
27 Nissan	28	29 ● day 28 interval	30	1 Iyar	2	3
4	5	6	7	8	9	10
11	12	13	14	15	16	17
18	19	20	21	22	23	24
25	26 X day interval	27	28 X onah beinonis	29 X day vest hachodesh	1 Sivan	2

Marking all the Vestos.

A reader who wishes to learn more about *vestos* but does not, as yet, feel competent enough to tackle the more difficult areas of *vestos* should read the following chapters.

Chapter Thirteen, Sections I and III.
Chapter Fourteen, Section I, A through D,2,a and Section III.
Chapter Fifteen, Section I, A through B,2, Section II,A and Section IV, A through C,1.
Chapter Seventeen, Section I.
Chapter Twenty-One.
Chapter Twenty-Two, Section I, A through B,2.

CHAPTER THIRTEEN

כללי וסתות
Vestos: **General Principles**

☐ The concept of *vestos.*

☐ Terms used in *hilchos vestos.*

☐ The different types of *vestos.*

☐ From what is a *vest* calculated.

☐ When the *vest* day passes.

I. Introduction

תָּנוּ רַבָּנָן וְהִזַּרְתֶּם אֶת בְּנֵי יִשְׂרָאֵל מִטּוּמְאָתָם (ויקרא טו) אָמַר רַבִּי יֹאשִׁיָה (יִרְמִיָה)
אַזְהָרָה לִבְנֵי יִשְׂרָאֵל שֶׁיִּפְרְשׁוּ מִנְּשׁוֹתֵיהֶן סָמוּךְ לְוֶסְתָּן. וְכַמָּה? אָמַר רַבָּה עוֹנָה
(שבועות יח: נדה סג:)

The Rabbis taught: "You shall separate the Children of Israel from their impurity" (*Yayikra* 15:31). R' Yoshiyah said: From here is derived a warning to the Children of Israel that they should separate from their wives close to the expected time of their menstruation. And how much before must one separate? Rabbah said: One time period (*Shevuos* 18b, *Niddah* 63b).

A. The concept of *vestos*

One of the fundamental and pertinent aspects of *hilchos niddah* is the issue of *vestos*.[1] A *vest*[2] is the pattern according to which the woman menstruates. The *yom havest* is the day during which we expect the menstrual bleeding to begin. The *onas havest* is the part of that day (either daytime or nighttime) in which we expect the onset of the period. It is of utmost importance to identify the day in which to expect the period, for one who is unaware of the onset of the period could easily transgress the prohibition of *niddah*. Our concern is twofold: a) The menstrual flow may suddenly begin[3] during cohabitation,[4] or b) the flow may begin with a minute, barely noticeable discharge. One may be unaware of this flow and cohabit after the *vest* day has passed. Either of these would constitute a transgression (although unintentional) of a cardinal prohibition. Accordingly, two steps must be taken: a) One must refrain from cohabitation during the time that the period is anticipated (the *onah* or *yom havest*)[5] and b) one

---

1. The correct pronunciation of *vest* should be "*veses*" in singular and "*vesasos*" in plural. However, we chose to use the colloquial pronunciation of "*vest*" and "*vestos*," since the reader is more acquainted with those terms.

2. Literally translated: "a set pattern" or "a routine." In this case, it is the set pattern of her menstrual cycle. We find *vest* also used in the Talmudic saying "שינוי וסת תחילת חולי" – a change of routine is the beginning of sickness." This term is used in *Bava Basra* 146a, regarding a dietary change, and in *Kesubos* 110b, regarding a change of dwelling.

3. *Reah, Bedek HaBayis (Shaar HaPrishah)*, explains that cohabitation itself may cause her to menstruate. See a similar explanation in *Bach* end of 184.

4. See 185:4 and Chapter Two, Section IX, regarding the proper conduct in this event.

5. This is in anticipation of possibility (a) that the menstruation may begin at the time of cohabitation. Thus, even one who did a *bedikah* and found it to be clean must abstain during the duration of the *onas havest*.

must do a *bedikah*[6] during this time to determine whether or not the period has begun.[7] There is a dispute in the Talmud[8] whether the laws

---

6. Although, essentially, a woman is required to do one *bedikah* on the *vest* day, some *Poskim* require two (or more) *bedikos*. See Chapter Twenty-Two.

7. This is to ensure that not even a minor discharge has occurred (possibility b). This *bedikah* permits cohabitation after the *onas havest* has passed.

8. See *Niddah* 9a, regarding whether one is Biblically obligated to do a *bedikah* on the day of a *vest kavuah* (see *Rashi* ibid.). See *Niddah* 15a and 16a, regarding whether a woman is considered a *niddah* if she did not do the required *bedikah*. With regard to these questions regarding *bedikos*, we follow the opinion that *vestos deRabbanan*, i.e., they are not Biblically required (see *Beis Yosef* 184 s.v. ודוקא and *Shulchan Aruch* 184:9). Thus, if a woman did not do a *bedikah* on her *vest kavuah* day, she may do so at a later time. However, she must abstain until the *bedikah* is done.

Since *vestos* are *deRabbanan* regarding *bedikos*, one would logically deduce that the requirement to abstain on the *onas havest* is also *deRabbanan*. Indeed, this is the opinion of *Raavad* (*Baalei HaNefesh, Shaar Tikun Vestos*) and *Rashba* (*Toras HaBayis, Shaar HaPrishah* and *Shaar HaVestos*). Nevertheless, in the opinion of *Reah* (*Bedek HaBayis, Shaar HaPrishah*) and many *Poskim*, the requirement of abstaining from cohabitation on the day of the *vest* is *deOraisa*. At first glance, this seems illogical: either the Torah accepts the concept of *vestos* or not. Why should we be concerned about the possibility that a *vest* will arrive on a given day and not worry after the day passed that the *vest* has actually arrived? However, *Noda B'Yehudah*, Y.D. 1:55,56 and 2:103, resolves this difficulty in a novel manner. He explains that the reason *vestos* are not *deOraisa*, with regard to a *vest* that passed, is because the *chazakah* (the presumption) that she menstruated is balanced by the *chazakah* that her halachically permitted status (חזקת טהרה) did not change. He compares this to the Talmudic axiom (*Gittin* 28b) שמא ימות חיישינן שמא מת לא חיישינן. We do not suspect that a person died (שמא מת) since all people are presumed not to have changed their status of living (חזקת חי), but we must consider the possibility that a person may die in the near future (שמא ימות), since all people do eventually die. Thus, the presumption of continued life (חזקת חי) can be projected to the past, not to the future. Similarly, the presumption that the woman's permitted status has not changed (חזקת טהרה) cannot be projected into the future since most women do eventually menstruate (שמא תראה). Thus, argues *Noda B'Yehudah*, a woman is Biblically required to abstain on the day of her *vest*, since we must presume that she may menstruate. Once the day passes, we do not assume that she actually menstruated, since she has a prior permitted status (חזקת טהרה). *Chasam Sofer*, Y.D. 170 and 179, commends this approach and notes that this was the opinion of his mentor R' Nassan Adler (see *Pischei Teshuvah* 184:3) as well. A similar explanation is found in *Beis Meir* 184:9 and *Chidushei R' Chaim HaLeivi* (*Issurei Biah* 4:12). *Aruch HaShulchan* 184:4,5 reaches the same *halachic* conclusion albeit with a different rationale. He contends that since we have a presumption (חזקה) that a woman feels a *hargashah* (a sensation) when she menstruates, if the *vest* day passes without a *hargashah*, we have the presumption (חזקה) that she did not menstruate (without sensation) to counter the presumption that she did menstruate on her *vest* day. However, during the day of the *vest* itself, we have no basis for countering the presumption that the *hargashah* and menstruation will begin that day. Thus, the requirement of separation on the *onas havest* is certainly *deOraisa*. Although this is the opinion of *Reah, Ritva* (*Shevuos* 18b regarding the exact time of the *vest*), *Noda B'Yehudah* and *Chasam Sofer, Shach* 184:5 notes that most *Poskim* and *Acharonim* maintain that even the requirement to abstain on the *onas havest* is *deRabbanan*. Among the *Rishonim* who follow this lenient view are: *Raavad, Tosfos* (*Yevamos* 62b), *Rashba, Rezah, Rosh* (*Hilchos Niddah* 1:1, 9:2, however, in *Tosfos HaRosh, Yevamos* 62b he seems to contradict himself, see *Maharsham* of *vestos*[9] are Biblical — *vestos deOraisa,*[10] or Rabbinic — *vestos deRabbanan.*[11] The *halachos* concerning the day of the *vest* will be discussed in Chapter Twenty-Two. In this chapter, we will discuss the basic principles of *vestos*. In the following chapters we will discuss the various types of *vestos* and the manner in which a *vest* is established and uprooted.

Rishonim stress the importance of familiarity with the laws of *vestos*. They note that both women and men must be acquainted with these laws so as not to transgress the prohibition of *niddah*.[12] *Poskim* advise that one keep a written record of all menstrual periods in order to avoid *vestos* problems.[13] In Chapter Twenty-One, we will describe the appropriate manner in which to keep a *vest* calendar.

Essentially, *vestos* is an issue of probability based upon the Talmudic principle of *chazakah* — presumption of a pattern. When something occurs once or twice, it may be a chance happening. If it occurs three times, we assume it to be a natural or behavioral pattern. For example: When an ox gores once or twice, it is considered an aberration; thus, the owner is only partially responsible for any damage inflicted. But if the ox gores three times, it has demonstrated a destructive behavioral pattern. If the owner subsequently fails to properly control the ox, he is fully responsible for any damages inflicted. Similarly, if a woman begins menstruation on a

---

5:47), *Magid Mishnah* (*Issurei Biah* 4:12) and *Tur*. Among the *Acharonim* who follow this lenient view are *Rema* 184:10, *Shach* 184:5, *Tosfos Yom Tov* (*Niddah* 9:9), *Toras HaShelamim* 184:12, *Biur HaGra* 184:22, *Chavos Daas* 184:3[b],10[b], *Chochmas Adam* 108:1, *Pardes Rimonim* p.9,10 and *Chazon Ish* 80:14.

9. This discussion relates to a *vest kavuah*. A *vest she'aino kavuah* is certainly not *deOraisa*.

10. *Rosh* (*Niddah* 1:1) notes that according to the opinion that *vestos* are *deOraisa*, it is of Sinaiatic origin. *Rosh* and *Tosfos* (*Niddah* 15a) contend that according to this opinion, when the time of the *vest* arrives, we assume that she <u>certainly</u> menstruated. Even if she noticed no blood, we assume that she experienced a minute flow that went unnoticed. *Rashi* (ad loc.) seems to be of the opinion that even though *vestos* are *deOraisa*, we merely <u>suspect</u> that she menstruated; we are not certain that she did.

11. *Chazon Ish* 80:1, 2,7 is troubled by the view that maintains *vestos deRabbanan*. Why should *vestos* be different than all matters of Torah law where we follow the concept of *chazakah*? He offers two explanations: a) Since a woman usually feels a *hargashah* at the time that she menstruates, the fact that she felt no sensation on the *vest* day proves that she did not menstruate. b) Menstruation is affected by food, drink and climate. Since these are variables, one cannot project a *vest* into the future. *Chazon Ish* seems to accept the latter explanation.

12. See *Ramban* (*Hil. Niddah*) 6:14. *Chavos Daas,* cited in *Taharas Yisrael* 184:39, notes that studying the laws of *vestos* should take precedence over any speculative study.

13. See *Chochmas Adam* 112:40. He ends with the following statement: "כן קבלתי מרבותי וכך הייתי נוהג כל ימי ולא אנה לי כל און . ברוך השם המקדש עמו — So I received from my masters, and such was always my custom and no wrongdoing has befallen me. Blessed is *Hashem* Who sanctifies His nation."

particular date once or twice, it is considered a chance happening. If, however, she menstruates on the very same date for three consecutive months, she has demonstrated a pattern in her physical nature. Accordingly, whenever this date arrives, one expects the period to recur.

It may seem that the issue of *vest* is a simple matter of probability; thus, an expert in the laws of probability should be an expert in *vestos* as well. This is not so. *Chazal* set many guidelines as to what is significant with regard to *vestos* and what is not.[14] The laws of *vestos* are complex and are firmly rooted in many passages of the Talmud.

It is worthwhile for the reader to acquaint himself with the following terms that appear often in the following chapters:

- Day: has two connotations: the calendar day and "day" as opposed to "night." In this chapter, "day" refers to the calendar day of the Hebrew month unless noted otherwise. Regarding *vestos*, this begins at sundown of the previous evening and ends at the following sundown. "Day," as opposed to "night," begins at sunrise and ends at sundown of that same day.[15]

- Night: regarding the *halachos* of *vestos*, begins at sundown and ends at sunrise.[16]

- Month: when used in these chapters, refers exclusively to the Hebrew month. The civil date has no relevance whatsoever to the *halachah* of *vestos*.[17]

- *Onah*: a complete day or night. Thus, the *onas havest* is the day or night during which one expects the period to begin. See Chapter Twenty-Two regarding the *halachic* status of the *onah* preceding the actual *onas havest*.

- *Vest kavuah*: a *vest* that is established when a woman menstruates three times in a distinct pattern, e.g., on the same calendar day or after an equal interval of days.

---

14. Indeed, *Chazon Ish, Y.D.* 99:4, is uncertain whether or not a non-Jewish woman who established a *vest* before conversion keeps that *vest* after conversion.

15. *Chavos Daas* 184:5[b]. This is different than the normal laws regarding day and night. Regarding other *halachos*, we consider day to begin at dawn (עלות השחר) and end at dusk (צאת הכוכבים). See *Megillah* 20b. The laws of *vestos* are different: They depend upon the actual position of the sun. Thus, once the sun sets, the day is over and does not begin again until the sun rises the next morning. See note 36. below.

16. *Chavos Daas* ibid.

17. The Hebrew date is rooted in nature (the phase of the moon, or the power of *Beis Din* to affect nature, see note 20 below); however, the civil date is a matter of convention and cannot conceivably affect menstruation.

- *Vest she'aino kavuah:* a tentative *vest,* when a woman menstruates once or twice on the same calendar day or after the same interval of days. A woman who menstruates many times without a fixed pattern has a *vest she'aino kavuah,* not a *vest kavuah.*

- *Vest haflagah:* a *vest* based upon equal intervals of days between the onset of her periods (a *vest haflagah* may be either a *vest kavuah* or a *vest she'aino kavuah*).

- *Vest hachodesh:* a *vest* based upon her menstruations beginning on a particular day of the Hebrew month (this may be either a *vest kavuah* or a *vest she'aino kavuah*).

- *Vest haguf:* a *vest* based upon physical sensations or that occurrences take place before the onset of her period.

- *Onah beinonis:* the average *vest.* This is the *vest* that *halachah* assumes to be normal for any woman who has not established a *vest kavuah.*

- *Akirah* or *ne'ekar:* a *vest* that is eliminated by passing the *vest* day without incident. *Akirah* (pl. *akiros*) is a noun translated as "uprooting." *Ne'ekar* is an adjective translated as "uprooted."

These are the most common terms used throughout these chapters. Other terms will be defined as they appear in the text.

Where necessary, we will use diagrams to illustrate *vest* situations. The reader should acquaint himself with the meaning of our diagrams and symbols.

●	connotes a menstrual period.
○	connotes an expected day of the *vest.*
3	connotes a period that creates a *vest hachodesh.* The number in the box represents the day of the month.
☐	connotes an expected period on the *yom hachodesh.*
↕←28→◀	connotes the interval between periods. The number represents the amount of days in the interval between the onset of the two periods (including the days of the onset itself).
↕←28→⏀	connotes the interval between a period and the expected period on the interval day (including both days).

B. A tentative *vest* (*she'aino kavuah*) and an established *vest* (*kavuah*)

Although we explained the concept of *vestos* in terms of patterns, one should not assume that the rules of *vest* apply only to a *vest* that has an established pattern. Whenever a woman menstruates, even once, on a given day, we suspect that perhaps she has begun to establish a permanent *vest* for that day.

Vestos are divided into two types: a tentative[18] *vest* (a *vest she'aino kavuah*) and an established *vest* (a *vest kavuah*). In previous times, most women established a *vest kavuah*. Today, a *vest kavuah* is unusual. The practical differences between a *vest kavuah* and a *vest she'aino kavuah* will be explained in detail in Chapter Fourteen, Section I.

C. The duration of a *vest*

The oans *havest* lasts one complete *onah*, i.e., a complete day or night. "Day" begins at sunrise and ends at sunset; "night" begins at sunset and ends at sunrise, regardless of the length of the day or night.[19] Thus, a woman whose *vest* is on a July night has a *vest* of approximately nine hours, while a *vest* on a January night would last approximately fifteen hours. The exact period of time during which one must abstain from cohabitation will be explained in Chapter Twenty-Two.

D. The types of *vestos*

Vestos are divided into two types: a) causative *vestos*, i.e., *vestos*, that are considered the cause of the menstruation, and b) symptomatic *vestos* i.e., *vestos* that herald the arrival of the menstruation.

1. Causative *vestos*:
The concept of *vestos* is based upon the assumption that natural forces outside of the woman's body may affect and control her

---

18. Some translate *vest she'aino kavuah* as an "irregular *vest*." The translation "tentative" used above seems more accurate. The *vest* is not irregular, the woman is. "Tentative" is a more accurate translation since the rationale of a *vest she'aino kavuah* is the chance that it may become established as a *vest kavuah*. See *Rashi, Niddah* 63b, *Rosh, Niddah* 63a and *Hilchos Niddah* §2, and *Graz* 187:42. Responsa *Beis Shlomo* 2:27 notes that it is clear from all *Rishonim* that this is the underlying rationale of a *vest she'aino kavuah*. See also *Chavos Daas* 189 end of 14[b] וכל שאינה קובעת בסופו ודאי שאין לו בתחילתו — "one is not required to abstain on a *vest she'aino kavuah* day if that *vest* cannot, in the future, become *kavuah*."

19. *Taz* 184:2 and *Toras HaShelamim* §6. See Chapter Twenty-Two for different opinions.

menstruation. Primary among these factors is the day of the month. *Chazal* assumed that a woman's cycle may follow the cycle of the moon, i.e., that a certain phase in the lunar cycle causes her menstruation to begin. This is not dependent upon the actual phase of the moon; rather it is dependent upon the particular day of the lunar calendar.[20] Furthermore, *Chazal* assumed that the sun influences whether the *vest* is confined to the daylight hours or the nighttime hours of the particular day. In addition to the solar and lunar influences described, menstruation could be caused by the interval of days between periods or even by physical activity. The following is a list of causative *vestos*:

> a. *Vest hachodesh:*
> One of the most common causative *vestos* is the *vest hachodesh*, the *vest* based upon the day of the Hebrew month. Whenever a woman has a menstrual period, she must suspect that the period may have been brought upon by the particular day of the month. Thus, she is required to refrain from cohabitation and do a *bedikah* on the same day of the following month. The *halachos* of this *vest* are explained in Chapter Fifteen.

> b. *Vest haflagah:*
> A second common *vest* is the *vest haflagah*, a *vest* based upon the interval of days between onsets of the two periods. If a woman menstruated twice twenty-nine days apart, we suspect that perhaps her menstruation follows a cycle of twenty-nine days. When twenty-nine days pass from the onset of the last period, she must consider that day a *vest* day. This is also a causative *vest* since the menstruation is caused by the buildup of the endometrium (the lining of the uterus) over the passage of a specific period of time. At the end of this specific period, the bodily hormones cause the uterus to shed the endometrium. Unlike a *vest hachodesh*, a *vest haflagah* is only possible after two periods have passed, since two

---

20. This is an example of where the *halachah*, or more accurately, *Beis Din* affects the course of nature. The onset of the woman's menstruation is dependent upon the deliberations of *Beis Din* whether or not to add a day to the month. *Rashba* (*Mishmeres HaBayis, Shaar HaVestos*) compares this to the *Talmud Yerushalmi* (*Nedarim* 6:8) who finds a basis for this concept in the verse (*Tehillim* 57:3) לקל גומר עלי. *Reah* (*Bedek HaBayis* ad loc.) contends that *vestos* follow the actual *molad* of the new moon. However, this is not the accepted view.

periods create one interval. The rules of *vest haflagah* and the difference between it and a *vest hachodesh* are discussed in Chapter Fifteen.

c. *Onah beinonis:*

A variant of the *vest haflagah* principle is the *onah beinonis* — the average cycle. This principle assumes that the typical woman functions on a thirty-day menstrual cycle, i.e., that her *vest haflagah* is based upon an interval of thirty days. Therefore a woman who has not demonstrated that her menstruations follow a different cycle must assume that she functions according to the average cycle. The rules of this *vest* are explained in Chapter Fifteen.

d. *Vest hadilug:*

Either a *vest hachodesh* or a *vest haflagah* may function in a manner that it increases each cycle in equal increments. For example, a woman may menstruate on the fifth, sixth, seventh and eighth of four consecutive months or after intervals of twenty-five, twenty-six, twenty-seven and twenty-eight days. In this case, she establishes a *vest* to continue her pattern and to menstruate on the ninth and then the tenth of the following months or after twenty-nine and then thirty interval days. This phenomenon, which is unusual, is explained in Chapter Sixteen.

e. *Vest haones:*

Menstruation may also be brought on by physical activity or by foods eaten. This is called a *"vest haones"* and is discussed in Chapter Nineteen.

2. Symptomatic *vestos* — *vest haguf:*

A second type of *vest* is that which does not cause the menstruation but heralds its appearance. This is called *vest haguf* — a *vest* based upon a physical manifestation that the arrival of the period is imminent. For example, a woman experiences distinct aches or pains before menstruation. These aches may constitute a *vest*, and immediately upon their onset, she must refrain from cohabitation and must do the necessary *bedikah*. This *vest* is discussed in Chapter Eighteen.

3. Complex *vestos* — *vest hamurkav:*

At times, a woman may acquire a *vest* comprised of a combination of two other *vestos*. For example, her menstruation may begin whenever she feels stomach cramps on the fifth of the month, but not on the fifth of the month when cramps do not occur and not when cramps occur on other days of the month. This woman has a *vest hamurkav*, a complex *vest*, one that is a combination of two factors. Whenever she experiences stomach cramps on the fifth day of the month, she must treat that day as a *vest* day. This will be discussed in Chapter Eighteen.

E. Uprooting a *vest: akiras vest*

Once a *vest* is established, it remains effective until it is demonstrated that the woman's cycle no longer functions according to that *vest*. This is called *akiras vest* — uprooting a *vest*. The rules by which one uproots a *vest* vary depending upon the type of the *vest* and whether the *vest* is a *vest kavuah* or a *vest she'aino kavuah*. This will be discussed in Chapter Seventeen.

II. The beginning of the cycle

Before discussing the types of *vestos* in detail, we must determine what type of menstrual bleeding requires that one calculate a *vest*. We learned previously that a woman may become a *niddah* either through a blood flow, a stain found on a *bedikah* cloth or a *kesem* found upon her garments. Which of these types of bleeding establishes a *vest*? A second issue that must be clarified is how the *vest* relates to menstruation: Is it calculated from the day of the onset, from its end or is the *vest* related to each day of menstruation? Finally, the onset of menstruation must be specifically defined. For example, a woman finds a stain on her garments before her menstrual flow, or she finds a stain on a *bedikah* cloth prior to the flow or she has two flows which follow one another after a pause of a day or two. Should she calculate the *vest* based upon the *kesem*, the *bedikah*, the first or second flow?

A. From what does one calculate the *vest*: a flow, a *bedikah* or a stain?

1. *Vestos* are based only upon a *re'iyah*:
Vestos apply only to a *reiyas dam*, a menstrual flow, regardless of the amount,[21] intensity or duration of the flow.

---

21. Responsa *Chasam Sofer*, Y.D. 166[2], notes that even the minutest amount of *dam* establishes a *vest*. It is interesting to note that *Chasam Sofer*, ibid. 168, maintains that a woman who has established a *vest* of normal menstrual flows expects a similar flow on her *vest* day, not a mere speck of blood.

2. A *vest* is not based upon *kesamim*:

A woman who finds a *kesem*,[22] even if it is an actual bloodstain larger than a *gris* and on a white garment, does not calculate *vestos* from the *kesem* though she becomes a niddah.[23] Even if a woman finds a *kesem* on the fifth of three consecutive months, she is not required to treat the fifth of the month as a *vest* day. Similarly, the *kesem* in no way affects the calculation of the interval days. The interval is calculated from the onset of the last blood flow to the onset of the next flow, regardless of any *kesamim* found in the interim. Thus, if she finds a *kesem* between two regular periods, she ignores the *kesem* and counts her interval only between the two actual periods.[24] If she has two regular periods on the fifth of months A and B and finds a *kesem* on the fifth of month C, the *kesem* will not create a *vest kavuah* or even a *vest she'aino kavuah*.[25] Similarly, she is not required to abstain on the

---

These two responsa of *Chasam Sofer* are not contradictory. Although even a speck of blood can create a *vest*, if her previous periods were complete flows, we expect a flow, nothing less. See responsa 168 for the *halachic* implications.

22. We are referring to a *kesem* that is not accompanied by a *hargashah*. Such a *kesem* has the *halachic* status of a *re'iyah* and is not relevant to the laws of *kesamim*. *Be'er Moshe* 3:158 maintains that if the woman feels an internal (vaginal) flow and finds a *kesem* afterwards, the *kesem* is considered a *re'iyah* regarding *kesamim*.

23. 190:54.

24. Ibid.

25. I.e., the fifth of month D is not a *yom havest*. See *Prishah* 190:91. However, *Be'er Moshe* 5:148 rules that one should consider that she has a *vest kavuah* regarding stringent applications, not lenient applications. *Shaarei Tohar* 4[29] contends that a woman who had a *vest kavuah* for the fifth of the month and for three months has no menstrual flow on the fifth of the month, but finds a *kesem* on each of those days, has not uprooted the *vest*. It seems that *Shaarei Tohar* considers the *kesem* a possible *re'iyah* and as such it cannot uproot a *vest*. However, since *Prishah*, and all who follow him, interpret the words of *Shulchan Aruch* in a different, more complicated manner, apparently they do not agree with *Shaarei Tohar*. Furthermore, if *Shaarei Tohar* were correct, one could argue that even if she found a *kesem* on those days on a garment that is not susceptible to *tumah*, the vest is not uprooted since it is a possible *re'iyah*. If this were true, we would be faced with a strange phenomenon: The woman is *tehorah* but the day is not considered having passed without *dam*. (Incidentally, *Shaarei Tohar* must be referring to a woman who did a *bedikah* on the day of the *vest*; otherwise, the *vest* is not uprooted in any case, see *Chavos Daas* 184:10[b].)It seems that *Shaarei Tohar* would maintain that even a *vest she'aino kavuah* is not uprooted if she finds a *kesem* on the *yom havest*. Thus, if a woman menstruated on the fifth of the month and on the following month, she does not menstruate on the fifth of the month, but finds a *kesem*, the *vest* is not uprooted. A similar *halachah* is found in *Chavos Daas* 184:10[b], regarding a woman who is assumed to have bled

thirtieth day following the *kesem*[26] or on the *vest hachodesh* of the *kesem*. The *kesem* is totally ignored regarding *vestos*.

3. A *vest* based upon a flow without a *hargashah*:

In the opinion of some *Poskim*, even if she experienced an actual blood flow without a *hargashah*,[27] she is not required to abstain on the same day of the following month;[28] others disagree.[29] One should follow the stricter latter opinion.

4. A *vest* based upon a stained *bedikah* cloth:

A woman who performs a *bedikah* and finds a bloodstain on the cloth does not calculate a *vest* from the *bedikah* (although she becomes a *niddah*) unless this occurs three times on the same monthly date or after the same number of interval days.[30] If this

---

without a *hargashah* on the day of her *vest*. According to *Sheivet HaLeivi's* interpretation (see note 29 below) the *vest* is not uprooted even though such a flow cannot establish a *vest*.

26. *Badei HaShulchan* 190:505.

27. See Chapter Three note 15, that we normally assume that any blood flow is accompanied by a *hargashah* unless a woman is absolutely sure that she felt no *hargashah*.

28. *Graz* 190:122 and *Tzemach Tzedek, Piskei Dinim* 190:54.

29. *Chazon Ish, Y.D.* 80:16, is uncertain about the status of this flow regarding *vestos*. *Igros Moshe, Y.D.* 3:46, maintains that it is considered a *vest*. If she previously established a *vest* through regular menstruations and then has a blood flow without *hargashah* on her *yom havest*, *Chavos Daas* 184:10[b] rules that the *vest* is not uprooted. This can be interpreted two ways: either *Chavos Daas* maintains that a blood flow without *hargashah* can establish a *vest* (this is the view of R' Meir Bransdorfer cited in *Sheivet HaLeivi* 2:86) or *Chavos Daas* holds that although a flow without *hargashah* cannot create a *vest*, if a woman experiences such a flow on the *yom havest* the *vest* is not uprooted (this is the view of *Sheivet HaLeivi* himself). *Sheivet HaLeivi* (ibid.) essentially agrees with *Graz's* lenient opinion (noted in previous footnote), but concludes that one should be stringent and consider the flow a *vest*. In *Shiurei Sheivet HaLeivi* 190:54[4] he contends that one should follow the stricter ramifications of both views, i.e., that the *vest* is established, but it cannot uproot another *vest*. *Be'er Moshe* 3:118 maintains that *Graz's* opinion is based upon Talmudical sources. However, since it is common today that women menstruate without a *hargashah*, a woman must abstain on the *yom havest*.

30. According to *Shulchan Aruch* 190:54, one must calculate *vestos* from a stained *bedikah* cloth. However, later authorities explain that this applies only in a case that it has become a *vest kavuah*, e.g., she found a stain on a *bedikah* cloth on the fifth day of three consecutive months or after three equal intervals. This is the accepted custom. See *Darchei Teshuvah* 190:270, *Pische Zuta* §102, *Shiurei Sheivet HaLeivi* §54[7], *Be'er Moshe* 3:119 and *Badei HaShulchan* §513. Responsa *Eimek HaTeshuvah* 2:75 explains that although a stain on a *bedikah* cloth is the equivalent of a normal *re'iyah*, nevertheless, since a woman usually menstruates with a full flow not a small stain, we do not associate the stain with a *vest* unless it occurs three times. *Badei HaShulchan* 190:54, *Biurim* s.v. והרי הן is uncertain of the status of a woman who menstruates twice on *Rosh Chodesh* and finds a stain on a *bedikah* cloth on the third *Rosh Chodesh*. Can the *bedikah* cloth combine with the first two periods to establish a *vest kavuah*?

occurs three times on the same date she establishes a *vest kavuah*.[31]

5. A menstruation preceded by a *kesem* or a stained *bedikah* cloth:
If a woman menstruates soon after finding a *kesem* or finding a
bloodstain on a *bedikah* cloth, the *vest* is normally calculated from
the actual menstruation, not the *kesem* or the *bedikah* cloth. At
times, it may be calculated from the *kesem* or the *bedikah*. See
Section B,4-5.

B. From when does one calculate the *vest*?

1. The onset versus the duration:
Although a period may last several days, the *vest* day is determined by the day the menstrual flow begins; the duration of the
flow is irrelevant[32] with regard to *vestos*.[33] The uterus begins to
shed its lining at a certain point in the woman's cycle. Even
though the uterus requires several days to completely expel the
lining, *halachah* regards the time when the uterus opens (*pesichas
hamaayon*, i.e., the beginning of the menstruation) as the main
cause of the flow; the duration of the flow is merely a continuation
of the flow due to the remaining blood in the uterus.[34] Accordingly,
a woman need only be concerned about the day of the following

---

31. It would seem that a woman should note on her calendar any day during which she finds a
stain on a *bedikah* cloth, otherwise she will never know that she has established a *vest kavuah*
through *bedikos*. However, this does not seem to be the custom. Apparently, we consider it unlikely that she will find a stain on a cloth on the same day of three consecutive months.

32. 184:6. Although this is the accepted view in *Shulchan Aruch*, one should note that *Ramban* and
Raavad disagree. In their opinion, cited in *Tur* 184, a woman considers each day of flow as a separate *vest* day. Thus, if in the following month she does not menstruate on the day corresponding to
the onset, she must nevertheless abstain on all the days corresponding to the duration of the flow.

33. Even in a case where she would establish a *vest kavuah* if we were to consider the continuation
of the flow. For example, a woman menstruated the fourth and the fifth of month A, the fifth of
month B and the fifth of month C. The menstruation of the fifth of month A is completely irrelevant and cannot be used to establish a *vest kavuah*. One could make a logical case that the flow of
the fourth of month A was an independent flow, not part of her menstrual cycle, and the real flow
was on the fifth. Nevertheless, she has not established a *vest kavuah* for the fifth of the month. See
Badei HaShulchan 189:126. See appendix D.

34. 184:6. See *Taz* §9 and *Shach* §16, citing *Bach*. There are differing opinions regarding when a flow
is considered a continuation of the previous flow and when it is considered a new flow. This
depends upon several opinions and upon whether the flows were separated by one full day without a flow or whether they were separated by eight days. The underlying concepts are explained
in Appendix D. There are situations where even a continuation of a flow may be considered a separate *vest*. An example would be in a case that a woman menstruated on day three of months A

month (or the interval) which corresponds to the day of the menstrual onset. There is, however, one exception to this rule. A woman who experiences only a short flow which starts in one *onah* and continues for a short while into the next *onah* and then stops completely keeps a *vest* corresponding to the entire first *onah* plus the segment that continues into the next *onah*.[35]

2. The day and *onah* of the *vest*:

The *vest*, regardless whether it is a *vest haflagah* or a *vest hachodesh*, is the day corresponding to the day on which the period began. "Day" is defined here as the twenty-four hour period from sunset to sunset.[36] However, one must also note the *onas havest*, i.e., whether the flow began by day or by night. These two factors together determine the *vest*. The day factor determines the actual

---

and B and day one and three of month C. In this case, day three was an initial flow day twice. We therefore assume that it was the initial flow day of month C as well. The earlier flow of day one was merely additional blood not relevant to her flow. This principle has a Talmudic source in *Niddah* 39b. If the flows of month C were not separated by a full day, i.e., she menstruated day three of months A and B and days two and three of month C, *Poskim* disagree whether or not she has established a *vest kavuah*. If the second flow begins eight days after the first flow, it is considered a new *vest*. See Appendix D.

35. 184:5. In this case, since the continuation of flow into the following *onah* was very short, one keeps the *vest* on the full *onah* of the day of the onset plus the time period in which the flow extended into the second *onah*. For example, a woman had a short flow on the day *onah* of the fifth of the month and the flow continued for three hours into the night of the sixth of the month. On the following month, she keeps a *vest* on the entire day *onah* of the fifth of the month and for the first three hours of the night of the sixth of the month. Similarly, regarding a *vest haflagah*, if her flow started on the twenty-fifth interval day and continued for only three hours into the night of the twenty-sixth, on the following month she keeps a *vest* on the entire twenty-fifth interval day plus the first three hours of the night of the twenty-sixth interval day. If, however, the flow continued through the twenty-sixth day, she keeps the *vest* only on the twenty-fifth interval day.

36. See *Rambam, Issurei* Biah 4:13. *Sidrei Taharah* 184:6 (see also §3) finds this view of *Rambam*, that *vestos* depend upon sunrise and sunset, difficult. *Halachically*, he argues, day and night depend upon dawn and dusk (עלות ושחר וצאת הכוכבים), not sunrise and sunset. However, the accepted view is that of *Chavos Daas* 184:5[B], who rules that *vestos* actually do depend upon sunrise and sunset. This view is followed by *Graz* 184:7, *Chochmas Adam* 108:4, *Lechem VeSimlah* §5[s], *Pardes Rimonim* §7[sc] and *Pri Deah* (introduction *Shaar* 7). See also *Shiurei Sheivet HaLeivi* 184:4[2]. In §[3] *Sheivet HaLeivi* speculates that perhaps even *Rabbeinu Tam*, who considers the second *shkiah* (which is fifty-eight and one half minutes after sundown) the *halachic shkiah*, would concede that with regard to *vestos*, we follow the first *shkiah* (sundown). *Aruch HaShulchan* 184:27 finds it very difficult to accept the view that *vestos* depend upon sunrise and sunset, rather than dawn and dusk. He rules that one should follow the strict aspect of each position. Thus, in his opinion, if a woman menstruates between sundown and dusk she should consider both the day and the night as her *onas havest*. Common custom follows the view of *Chavos Daas* and other *Poskim* that *vestos* depend

day of the *vest* (the day of the month regarding the *vest hachodesh* or the amount of days regarding the interval of the *vest haflagah*). The *onah* factor determines which time period, day or night, of that day is the actual *onas havest*.

Therefore, when a woman marks the onset of her period on her calendar, it is most important that she note whether the period began by day or by night. She must also be aware that "day" and "night" depend upon sunrise and sundown.

3. A case of doubt:

If a woman is uncertain[37] whether menstruation began before or after sunrise or sunset, she considers the later *onah* (time period) as the beginning of her menstruation.[38] This is because the later *onah* is certainly part of her menstruation, while the earlier *onah* may not be.[39] For example, a woman did not notice the exact time of the onset of her period. It may have been several minutes before or after sundown (or several minutes before or after sunrise). She considers the *onah* after sundown (or sunrise) as her *onas havest*. Other *Poskim* rule that although we assume that the menstruation began during the later *onah*, she should abstain the following month on the earlier *onah* as well.[40] A woman who, upon awakening in the morning, notices that her period began, considers the

---

only on sunrise and sunset. See responsa *K'sav Sofer, Y.D.* 90, regarding a woman who began menstruating after both she and the community recited *tefillas arvis* before sundown. *K'sav Sofer* rules that nevertheless the menstruation is considered a day menstruation. In view of the above, this seems elementary. *Vestos* depend upon the actual sundown and sunset, not upon *halachic* day or night. *Tefillas arvis* may determine that it has *halachically* become night but it cannot replicate the effect of actual sundown.

37. *Sugah Bashoshanim* 2:[26] maintains that this refers only to a case where she was uncertain at the time of the flow. However, if at the time of the flow she did note the time, but forgot it at a later date, she cannot assume that it started on the later *onah*. It seems that this view is not accepted by all *Poskim*; see *Levanon Nota* cited in *Darchei Teshuvah* 184:25.

38. 184:4.

39. *Shach* 184:13.

40. The first opinion cited in *Tur* (it is unclear, according to this opinion, whether the *vest* is also calculated from the earlier *onah*). *Bach* cited in *Shach* §14 rules that one should follow the stricter opinion and abstain during both *onos*. *Shach* accepts his opinion based upon the requirement of the *Or Zarua* (see Chapter Twenty-Two) that one must always abstain on the *onah* before the *onas havest* — the *Or Zarua's onah* (it seems that this was the intention of *Bach* as well). This view is followed by *Toras HaShelamim* §10 and *Aruch HaShulchan* §26. See responsa *Eimek HaTeshuvah* 1:124, who (besides presenting the issues involved in a most clear manner) explains that *Shach* essentially agrees with the lenient opinion (that one is required to abstain only during the later *onah*), but accepts the stricter opinion only because one should follow *Or Zarua* in any case. It is unclear

onah in which she first notices the flow[41] as her *onas havest,* even though the flow may have actually begun earlier.[42]

4. A flow preceded by *kesamim:*

Often a menstrual period is preceded by a staining period which may last for several hours or more than a day. For example, a woman finds *kesamim* on Monday and is rendered a *niddah,*[43] but the actual flow begins on Tuesday. Although *kesamim* alone cannot establish a *vest* (see A,2 above), in this case, in the opinion of some authorities, the *kesem* represents the beginning of the actual menstruation that followed. According to these authorities, the woman considers that her *vest* began at the onset of the staining. However, even in their opinion, if the staining stopped for a full day before the actual menstruation began or if she did a *bedikah* in between and found the cloth clean, she calculates the *vest* from the actual flow, not the *kesamim.*[44] Other authorities contend that the *vest* is always calculated from the beginning of the flow itself, not the *kesamim.*[45] This is the commonly accepted view. Nevertheless, if she usually finds *kesamim* before the onset of

whether, according to *Shach, Toras HaShelamim* and *Aruch HaShulchan,* one who does not usually keep the *Or Zarua vest* must keep it in this case (we will note in Chapter Twenty-Two, Section I,B,2 that in the opinion of many authorities, one is not required to abstain on the *Or Zarua's onah*).

41. She must note the time she awakened and the actual time of sunrise. If sunrise is at 7:10 a.m. and she awakens at 7:00 a.m. and finds a flow, the *vest* is a night, not a day, *vest.*

42. *Sefer HaEshkol* 32, cited in *Badei HaShulchan* 184:31. Rav Y. Roth, in *Beis Talmud LeHora'ah* vol. 1 §80, maintains that if a woman established a tendency to menstruate at night and, on one occasion, notices a flow upon awakening, she should assume that the flow began at night.

43. If the *kesem* is larger than a *gris* and is found on a white garment, see Chapters Eight and Nine.

44. *Igros Moshe, Y.D.* 3:51. He differentiates between a case where the actual flow is also without *hargashah* and a case where the flow itself is accompanied by a *hargashah.* In the former case we have no clear indication when the *re'iyah* began and must therefore assume it began with the stains. In the latter case, since the flow itself is accompanied by a *hargashah,* the flow is considered the actual beginning of the menstruation. Since most women today do not notice a *hargashah* at the time of menstruation, we presented the *halachah* in the text accordingly. In additiom *Igros Moshe* notes that if menstruation usually begins with staining the *vest* is calculated from the staining. Responsa *Eimek HaTeshuvah* 3:72 concurs with this view. *Igros Moshe* is certainly referring to *kesamim* that are larger than a *gris* and on a white garment; otherwise, the woman is still *tehorah* and the *kesem* cannot be considered the beginning of her period.

45. *Shiurei Sheivet HaLeivi* 190:54[7] and *Taharas HaBayis* vol. I p. 470. They note that: a) Though in the opinion of *Rashi* (*Niddah* 53b), the *vest* starts from the *kesamim,* most *Rishonim* disagree and contend that the *vest* begins from the actual flow. b) Furthermore, even the interpretation of *Rashi's* opinion is subject to dispute. *Be'er Moshe* 4:80 follows this view with the exception of a case where she finds a *kesem* on the *vest* day and menstruates within twenty-four hours. In this last case he assumes that the *kesem* was the beginning of her period.

menstruation, she must abstain from cohabitation when such staining occurs on the following month close to her *yom havest*.[46] Even if the staining itself does not render her a *niddah* (e.g., if the stain is less than a *gris* or on a colored garment), it heralds the beginning of the period. This may be considered a *vest haguf*,[47] see Chapter Eighteen, Section I,A.

In summary, a flow preceded by *kesamim* is relevant to two questions: a) When did the period start, with the *kesamim* or the flow? Should one calculate the interval from the *kesamim* or the flow? b) If in the future she again finds such *kesamim*, should she consider it a *vest haguf* and abstain? In regard to question (a), common practice is to calculate the interval from the flow itself. In regard to question (b), one may be required to abstain when the staining recurs.

5. A flow preceded by a stained *bedikah* cloth:
The actual flow may, at times, be preceded by a stain found on a *bedikah* cloth. For example, a woman performs a *bedikah* on Monday and finds it stained. She is *temei'ah* immediately but the actual flow begins on Tuesday. There is an opinion that the *vest* is calculated from Monday, the day of the *bedikah*.[48] Other *Poskim* consider the *vest* to have begun on Tuesday, the day of the actual flow.[49] This is the common custom.

---

46. Some Rabbonim advise that whenever recurrent staining occurs (even less than a *gris* or on colored garments), one should abstain until the staining stops. A Rav will base his decision upon the frequency and color of the staining.

47. *Igros Moshe, Y.D.* 3:51. He maintains that even in a case where the *kesamim* are not considered the beginning of the actual period, e.g., they stopped for a full day before the actual flow began and even if they are less than a *gris* and perhaps even if they are brown, not red, they are considered a *vest haguf*. Thus, when the staining begins on the following month, she must abstain and do a *bedikah* as is required during any *vest haguf*. As with any *vest haguf*, if the menstruation usually begins a fixed number of days after the manifestation of the *vest haguf*, one is required to abstain only after the fixed amount of days. See Chapter Eighteen, Section III,B,4. Responsa *Eimek HaTeshuvah* 1:125 is uncertain whether staining should be considered *vest haguf*. In any case, whenever the stains are such that they do not render her a *niddah*, all authorities agree that the calculation of the *vest* is done from when the actual flow began, not the stains.

48. *Shaarei Tohar* 4:27. Responsa *Eimek HaTeshuvah* 2:75 leans towards this opinion.

49. *Sheivet HaLeivi* 4:99 implies that the main *yom havest* is the day of the actual flow. See also *Sheivet HaLeivi* 2:75[2] and *Shiurei Sheivet HaLeivi* 184:6[3], 190:54[7], where he is less certain and notes that one should calculate the *vest* from both days. It seems that one who calculates a *vest* from both days should do so only regarding the *yom hachodesh* and the *onah beinonis*, not regarding a *vest haflagah*. If one would calculate the interval from both days, future calculations would be confusing.

6. Two close consecutive flows:

If a menstrual flow[50] begins on Monday, stops on Tuesday and begins anew on Wednesday, most *Poskim* consider it a continuation of the first *vest*. Thus, in the following month she must abstain and do *bedikos* only on the day corresponding to Monday.[51] If the second flow begins eight days after the first, e.g., the first flow was on Monday afternoon and the second flow is during Sunday night or any time thereafter, the flows are considered two separate menstruations.[52] This is true even if the original flow lasted seven days, stopped completely, and continued again, even momentarily, on the eighth day.[53]

III. When the *vest* day passes

A woman who passes the *yom havest*, whether *vest haflagah, hachodesh* or any *vest*, is *halachically* free of any further limitations, provided that she has made a *bedikah* and found it to be clean. There is no reason to assume that menstruation will begin on any particular day. We certainly cannot prohibit a couple from marital relations indefinitely. Nevertheless, it is difficult to ignore the fact that she will probably menstruate very soon. She should therefore be especially conscious of any feeling normally associated with her menstruation.[54] Some authorities advise that one do a *bedikah* before cohabiting.[55] If there is any reason to suspect that her *vest* is imminent, they should abstain.

---

50. This refers to an actual menstrual flow. However, if the first flow was a mere drop of blood, *Sheivet HaLeivi* 4:99 seems to consider it the equivalent of a stain found on a *bedikah* cloth discussed in 5 above.

51. *Chavos Daas* 184:7[b],15[c], see note 33 and Appendix D. See also *Sheivet HaLeivi* 2:75[2] and *Chazon Ish, Y.D.* 85:43.

52. Ibid. See *Graz* 189:112. In this case *Chazon Ish* rules that the *haflagah* is calculated from the later flow.

53. See *Misgeres HaShulchan* (appended to *Kitzur Shulchan Aruch*) 155:63.

54. See *Shiurei Sheivet HaLeivi* 184:6[3], who notes that many unfortunate situations of women who menstruated during cohabitation are a result of a lack of awareness of this problem. He suggests that one wait an additional day after the *yom havest* and also do a *bedikah* before subsequent cohabitations. Although it is not commonly accepted to wait an additional day since earlier *Poskim* make no mention of this requirement, it is prudent to do a *bedikah* before cohabiting. This *bedikah* should not be done in the presence of her husband, 186:1.

55. *Shiurei Sheivet HaLeivi* ibid. and *Igros Moshe, Y.D.* 3:50. *Igros Moshe* requires that she do a *bedikah* after cohabiting as well.

CHAPTER FOURTEEN

וסת קבוע ושאינה קבוע
Vest Kavuah and *She'aino Kavuah*

□ The difference between a *vest kavuah* and *aino kavuah*.

□ The requirement of *bedikos* at the time of cohabitation.

□ A woman who finds blood after cohabitation.

□ A *vest hashaos* — a *vest* dependent upon hours.

Introduction

All types of *vestos* fit into one of two categories: a *vest kavuah*, an established *vest* or a *vest she'aino kavuah*, a tentative *vest*, one that has not yet established itself.[1] Each of the different types of *vestos* becomes a *vest kavuah* in a unique manner befitting that particular type of *vest*, whether a *vest haflagah*, *vest hachodesh*, *vest hadilug* or *vest haguf*. However, every *vest kavuah* is similar in concept. A *vest* becomes *kavuah* (established) when the pattern of the *vest* repeats itself three times, be it a specific day, a specific interval, a *dilug* or specific physical symptoms.

I. The difference between a *vest kavuah* and a *vest she'aino kavuah*

A. *Akiras vest*: eliminating a *vest*

A *vest kavuah* and a *vest she'aino kavuah* differ in the manner in which they are uprooted. A *vest kavuah* is more significant than a *vest she'aino kavuah* since it has established itself three times, thereby creating a *chazakah*, a presumption that the cycle is a permanent part of her physical nature which will not change. A *vest she'aino kavuah* can be eliminated quite easily, i.e., by passing the *vest* day even once. A *vest kavuah*, however, is more difficult to uproot.

1. A *vest kavuah*:

There are three aspects to the distinctive manner in which a *vest kavuah* is uprooted:

a. A *vest kavuah* cannot be uprooted unless the *vest* day is passed three times without incident.[2]

b. A *vest kavuah* can never become completely uprooted unless it is exchanged for another *vest kavuah*. This will be explained in Chapter Seventeen.

c. Even if the *yom havest* passes three times without menstruation, a *vest kavuah* is only uprooted if the woman did a *bedikah* on the *yom havest*. This will be explained later in this section.

---

1. The adjective "tentative" is used because a *vest she'aino kavuah* is only noteworthy because it may be the beginning of a *vest kavuah* (see Chapter Thirteen, note 18).

2. 189:2.

2. A *vest she'aino kavuah*:

A *vest she'aino kavuah* is completely uprooted when the woman passes the *vest* day once without incident even if she does not do a *bedikah*. Even a woman who menstruates twice either on the same calendar day or after the same interval of days is no longer required to keep the *yom havest* if she passes the *vest* day the third time without incident.[3]

B. *Onah beinonis*

Another difference between a woman who has a *vest kavuah* and one who does not regards the principle of *onah beinonis*. The basis of *vestos* is our concern that the woman may unexpectantly menstruate. This may occur at any time. If she has a *vest kavuah*, we know when to expect her period and there is no need to be concerned that she may menstruate at any other time. However, if a woman has not established a *vest kavuah*, we do not know when to expect the menstruation. This eventuality cannot be ignored since she certainly will menstruate in the future.

Since most women menstruate after an interval of thirty days, *Chazal* considered this the average, or common, *vest* and called it "the *onah beinonis*," the "average" *vest*. They required that a woman who has no *vest kavuah* keep this day as her *vest*. However, a woman who has a *vest kavuah* knows when to expect her menstruation and is therefore exempt from *onah beinonis*.[4] The *halachos* of *onah beinonis* are discussed in detail in Chapter Fifteen.

C. The requirement of a *bedikah* on the *vest* day

Chazal instituted a system of *bedikos* whereby a woman ensures that she has not experienced a blood flow unknowingly. The manner in which *bedikos* are done and the times when they are required are explained fully in Chapter Five. With regard to our discussion, the following should be noted:

A woman must do a *bedikah* during the *onah* of the *vest*. This is to ensure that not even a speck of blood has appeared. The *halachos* of this requirement differ between a *vest kavuah* and a *vest she'aino kavuah*.

1. A *vest kavuah*:

The Talmud mandates that a woman who has a *vest kavuah* <u>must</u>

---

3. 189:2.

4. 189:1.

do a *bedikah* on the day of her *vest*. This *bedikah* is vital since otherwise we must assume that she experienced a blood flow without noticing. There is an opinion that if a woman omitted the *bedikah* on the *vest* day, she is automatically considered a *niddah*, even if a subsequent *bedikah* is found clean.[5] Others are more lenient and accept a *bedikah* done later.[6] However, even the latter *Poskim* agree that the woman must consider herself *temei'ah* until she performs the *bedikah*.[7] On the basis of her established *vest*, we must assume that she menstruated until she shows otherwise. A third group of *Poskim* are still more lenient and rule that once the *vest* has passed, no *bedikah* is required.[8] In their opinion, the woman retains her *tehorah* status. The accepted *halachah* follows the second opinion.[9] Thus, she may, and must, do a *bedikah* even at a later time.[10] It is important to note that the *onah beinonis* is similar to a *vest kavuah* with regard to these *halachos*.[11]

In addition, a *vest kavuah* cannot be uprooted unless a *bedikah* was done on the day of the *vest*.[12] If the day passed without a

---

5. See *Niddah* 16a and *Shach* 184:23.

6. Logically, once several days pass, the *bedikah* proves nothing and should be ineffective. Nevertheless, these *Poskim* set no limit as to how late the *bedikah* may be done. It is noteworthy that Taz §12 states that even a *bedikah* delayed for a "long time" (זמן הרבה) is accepted. *Shach* §23, however, cites the *Beis Yosef* as permitting the *bedikah* although it was delayed for "some time" (זמן מה). The exact wording of the *Beis Yosef* (כמה זמן) seems to support Taz. *Shiurei Sheivet HaLeivi* on *Shach* notes that the original print of *Shach* conformed to the version in *Beis Yosef*. *Shiurei Sheivet HaLeivi* on Taz maintains that even if her period usually lasts only four days and she delays her *bedikah* until five days after the *yom havest*, the *bedikah* is valid.

7. *Tosfos* (*Niddah* 16a s.v. ורב נחמן) and *Rashba* (*Toras HaBayis*, end of 7:3) cited as second opinion in 184:9. *Sidrei Taharah* 184:13 cites *sefer Tiferes LeMoshe* who maintains that they must abstain from intimate physical contact as well, i.e., hugging and kissing (*chibuk v'nishuk*). *Sidrei Taharah* himself disagrees. He contends that since these forms of contact are *halachically* permissible even during the *onas havest*, they are certainly permissible after the *onas havest* has passed.

8. *Ran* (Hil. *Niddah*, *Rif Shavuos* 5a) citing *Rif* and *Rambam*.

9. Second opinion in 184:9.

10. However, she should do the *bedikah* without delay. In addition, the *bedikah* should not be done immediately before cohabiting since, at that time, she may rush the *bedikah* and not check all crevices properly (*Sidrei Taharah* 183:13).

11. 184:9, 189:4.

12. *Chavos Daas* 184:10[b]. *Sugah Bashoshanim* 3:11 notes that if she did not do the required *bedikos* on the *vest* day, but on the following day, the *vest* is not uprooted. This seems to be the opinion of *Chavos Daas* as well. This view seems supported by *Raavad* (p. 34 in Kapach edition). However, *Shaarei Tohar* 4:20 rules that the *vest* is uprooted. He argues that it is illogical to assume, by merit of the *bedikah* on the following day, that she remains *tehorah* which implies that she did not men-

bedikah,[13] we assume that there was an unnoticed flow on that day and the *vest* is not eliminated.[14]

2. A *vest she'aino kavuah*:

A *vest she'aino kavuah* is much weaker than a *vest kavuah* since it has never been established. Even those who hold that *vestos* are Biblical (*deOraisa*) concede that a *vest she'aino kavuah* is merely Rabbinical in origin (*deRabbanan*).[15] Therefore, if the day passes without menstruation, one may assume that no blood appeared. No further *bedikah* is required.[16] Nevertheless, in the opinion of many *Poskim*, a *bedikah* should be done on the day of the *vest*.[17] This is the accepted custom.

---

struate and yet in terms of the *vest*, to assume that the *vest* was not uprooted which implies that she did menstruate. However, *Chavos Daas* explains that we assume she did not menstruate because she has a status of *taharah* (*chezkas taharah*) and even if she did menstruate, it was without *hargashah* and thus only *deRabbanan* (while regarding uprooting the *vest* we face the *chazakah* that she did menstruate and the *vest* is not uprooted). It would seem that if she found a bloodstain when she did the *bedikah* on the following day, all would agree that the *vest* is not uprooted.

13. *Chavos Daas* 184:11[b] is uncertain about the status of a woman who did a *bedikah* on the *vest* day but subsequently lost it. He considers the possibility that the woman is *temei'ah*. He contends that the reason a woman is *tehorah* after the *vest* day passes is because since she had no *hargashah*, we assume that she did not menstruate. However, if a *bedikah* was performed, we can no longer assume that there was no *hargashah*. She may have had a *hargashah* of *dam* at the time of the *bedikah* and confused it with the sensation of the *bedikah*. Therefore, she is *temei'ah*. *Pischei Teshuvah* §18 contends that according to *Chavos Daas* she is *temei'ah* even if a second *bedikah* is done after the *vest* in place of the lost *bedikah*. *Pardes Rimonim* (on *Taz* §13) disagrees with *Chavos Daas* as does *Chazon Ish* 80:22. *Chazon Ish* adds that even if she douched before the *bedikah*, the *bedikah* is valid; we are not concerned that she may have washed away a trace of blood. See Chapter Twenty-Two note 17.

14. *Raavad* (pp. 34 and 47 in Kapach edition), *Ramban, Hilchos Niddah* 5:19, cited in responsa *Beis Shlomo, Y.D.* 15, 27. See *Chavos Daas* 184:10[b] who contends that even if during the *vest* days of the three consecutive months no *dam* was found but no *bedikah* was performed, the *vest* is not uprooted. He adds that even if she did a *bedikah* on the *vest* days of months A,B and D but forgot to do so on month C, the *vest* is not uprooted. There may have been some *dam* on the *vest* day of month C which went unnoticed. *Beis Shlomo* 27 disagrees with *Chavos Daas* on this last point, as does *Divrei Chaim, Y.D.* 2:78.

15. *Chasam Sofer, Y.D.* end of 179, *Lechem VeSimlah* 184 end of §7[s].

16. 189:4, implied in 184:9 and *Ramban* ibid. *Taz* 189:38 and *Divrei Chamudos* (*Niddah* 9:11) contend that if the *vest she'aino kavuah* is a *vest haguf*, the woman is required to do a *bedikah* even if the day passes without incident. *Taz* explains that since she felt a physical manifestation of the *vest*, we suspect that there may have been *dam* even though she felt no *hargashah*. *Shach* (*Nekudos HaKesef* ad loc.), however, seems to disagree. *Graz* § 88, citing the lenient opinion of *Raavad,* also disagrees with *Taz*. However, *Chochmas Adam* 112:30 and *Pischei Teshuvah* 184:21 cite *Taz's* position as if it were the accepted *halachah*.

17. *Beis Yosef*, end of 184, cites *Rashba* that a *bedikah* is not required. However, in *Shulchan Aruch*

If a woman passes the *vest she'aino kavuah* day and finds no *dam*, the *vest* is uprooted, even if she did not do a *bedikah*[18] on the *vest* day.[19]

D. *Bedikos* at the time of cohabitation

1. A woman with a *vest kavuah*:
If a woman has a *vest kavuah*, we expect her period to begin on the day of her *vest* and we are not concerned that she may menstruate at any other time. She is not required to do any *bedikos* before or after cohabitation since there is no reason to be concerned that she will have a menstrual flow at that time. Indeed, she should not do *bedikos* at that time since this may cause her husband to be apprehensive. He may suspect that she is performing a *bedikah* because she felt a *hargashah*. This will cause him to abstain needlessly either at that time or in the future.[20]

2. A woman without a *vest kavuah*:
If a woman has not established a *vest kavuah*, we cannot ignore the possibility that she may menstruate at any time. In addition, since we do not know what actually stimulates the beginning of her flow, there is the remote possibility that cohabitation itself may precipitate her menstrual flow.[21] Therefore, there is an opinion in

---

184:9 he seems to require a *bedikah*. This is also the opinion of *Graz* 184:28, citing *Bach* (189 s.v. פיהקה) and *Prishah* (184:18). *Shiurei Sheivet HaLeivi* 184:9[2] notes only the stricter opinion. *Badei HaShulchan* 184:58 maintains that, if possible, a *bedikah* should be done.

18. *Responsa Beis Shlomo, Y.D.* 27, based upon *Taz* ibid., contends that a *vest haguf*, even *she'aino kavuah*, is not uprooted without a *bedikah*. It is questionable whether the other *Poskim* cited above, who follow *Taz's* view, agree with *Beis Shlomo*.

19. *Ramban* ibid. 5:18, cited in *Beis Shlomo, Y.D.* 15. See also *Pischei Teshuvah* 184:18. *Chavos Daas* 184:10[b] cites an interesting application of this issue. A woman had a period twice on the first of the month. On the third month, she forgot to do a *bedikah* on the first of the month, but experienced no blood flow. If she subsequently finds *dam* on the first of the fourth month, *Chavos Daas* rules that she has set a *vest kavuah*. Although we cannot establish a *vest kavuah* based on the third month since we have no proof that she had a blood flow on that day, we nevertheless have no right to assume there was no *dam* since she did no *bedikah*. In effect, the third month is neutral. However, when she menstruates on the first of the fourth month, the third month cannot serve as an *akirah*. *Beis Shlomo, Y.D.* 27, disagrees. He contends that since *Ramban* rules that a *vest she'aino kavuah* is uprooted when it is passed without an appearance of *dam*, even if no *bedikah* is performed, the *vest* was uprooted after the third month and cannot be established without three new menstruations. A similar position is taken by *Divrei Chaim* 2:78 and *Taharas Yisrael* 184:70, see also *Pische Zuta* 184:12.

20. First opinion in 186:1, and *Rema* ad loc. *Rema* 184:1, regarding a *bedikah* after cohabitation.

21. Indeed, this is the very reason that one may not cohabit on the day of the *vest*: There is reason

the Talmud[22] that a woman without a *vest kavuah* is forbidden to cohabit since she may menstruate at the time of cohabitation. The couple must seek a divorce since they cannot live together normally as man and wife. This is not the *halachah*. The couple may remain married but must perform *bedikos* at the time of cohabitation. There is an opinion among *Rishonim*[23] that she is always required to do two *bedikos* one before and one after cohabiting. This is also not the accepted *halachah*.[24]

a. The *halachah* as practiced today:
According to accepted practice, both husband and wife must do *bedikos* the first three times they cohabit[25] to prove that cohabitation is not a cause of menstruation.[26] (See c below regarding who is exempt from this requirement and d below as to on which days these *bedikos* are required.) On each of these occasions, the woman must do two thorough[27] *bedikos:* one before cohabitation[28] (which is inspected immediately)[29] and

---

to suspect that the cohabitation itself may cause menstruation. See *Bach* 184 s.v. ופרישה.

22. *Niddah* 12b.

23. *Rabbeinu Chananel* cited in *Tur* 186 and *Rambam* (*Hil. Issurei Biah* 4:16).

24. Following opinion of *Rashi, Rashba* and *Ran,* all cited in *Beis Yosef* 186.

25. *Darchei Teshuvah* §6 cites *Mekor Chaim* who maintains that these *bedikos* are valid only if they were done on three separate nights. A couple that cohabits more than once on the same night before completing the series of three *bedikos* require *bedikos* each time. The *halachah* regarding this case is found in *Rema* 186:2.

26. This is the opinion of *Shulchan Aruch* in 186:2. However, *Shach* §1 disagrees and contends that no *bedikos* are required. *Pleisi* §3 rejects *Shach's* lenient opinion. *Toras HaShelamim* §1 rules that one should follow the stringent opinion of *Shulchan Aruch* unless there is an established custom to follow the lenient opinion. *Graz* §7 seems to follow the stringent opinion of the *Shulchan Aruch*; see *Tzemach Tzedek, Piskei Dinim* vol. 3 p.10. *Chasam Sofer* (ad loc.) also follows the ruling of *Shulchan Aruch*. This seems to be the opinion of *Lechem VeSimlah* §6[l], as well. *Chochmas Adam* 109:1 cites *Shulchan Aruch's* stringent opinion without comment.

27. *Churin u'sedakin, Graz* §6 citing *Rashba* and *Ran. Chavos Daas* §1[b] rules that a *kinuach* is sufficient.

28. *Lechem VeSimlah* 196, end of §11[s], rules that the *bedikah* need not be done immediately before cohabiting. It may be done when she finishes any other involvement and decides to be with her husband. *Pische Zuta* 187:7 rules that the *bedikah* may be done up to one half an hour before cohabiting. Thus, a woman may do the *bedikah* at a time that if she finds a questionable stain it may be still brought to a Rav. If the woman did a *bedikah* but fell asleep before cohabiting, she must do the *bedikah* again (*Shaarei Tohar* 2:[2]).

29. *Graz* §7 and *Lechem VeSimlah* §10[l]. However, *Chavos Daas* §1[c],2[b] maintains that one may check the cloth the following day. At first glance, this seems illogical. If we require a *bedikah* before

one immediately[30] afterward and the husband cleans himself with a cloth[31] and checks the cloth.

These *bedikos* should be consecutive. However, they are valid even if they are not consecutive. Therefore, if the couple checked themselves twice and forgot to do so on the third occasion, they are not required to begin the series anew.[32] However, if they find blood on one of the *bedikah* cloths, they must begin the series anew. Whenever a woman finds blood after cohabiting, she must consult a Rav, see Section E below.

b. If the series of *bedikos* was not done:

A couple that did not do this series of *bedikos* as newly-weds should do them as soon as they become aware of this *halachah,* even if many years have passed. Similarly, a woman who had a *vest kavuah* for many years and was exempt from these *bedikos* is required to do them if she ever uproots the *vest kavuah.*

c. Women who are exempt from this requirement:

Certain women are exempt from this requirement of *bedikos* even though they have no *vest kavuah:*

> i. A *kallah* is not required to do these *bedikos* until after the initial cohabitation, since at that time she can attribute any blood to the *besulim.*[33]

---

cohabitation, how can the inspection be delayed until the following day? *Poskim* explain that the first *bedikah* is not a real necessity; however, since she needs a *bedikah* afterwards, *Chazal* required a *bedikah* before as well. *Shiurei Sheivet HaLeivi* 186:2 §11 maintains that one should follow the view of *Graz.* However, if there is no light available by which to inspect the cloth (e.g., on Friday night), one is not required to abstain; the cloth may be checked the next day.

30. *Graz* §3. Therefore, a woman should not go to the bathroom to do the *bedikah,* and certainly not urinate before the *bedikah* was done. She should prepare a cloth near her bed. *Shiurei Sheivet HaLeivi,* end of 186:2, rules that if the *bedikah* was not done immediately, it can be done up to one half hour afterward.

31. The husband's checking need not be done immediately after cohabitation (see *Shach* 187:4) but it should be done before any blood that may be on his body is wiped away.

32. *Eimek HaTeshuvah* 1:126. It would seem that this is true even if she menstruated in between. For example, they did *bedikos* on the twenty-seventh and twenty-eighth interval day after one menstruation and cohabited on the twenty-ninth day without doing *bedikos.* After the next menstruation they did the third *bedikah* on the twenty-seventh interval day.

33. *Badei HaShulchan* 186:7 rules that following the first cohabitation, these *bedikos* are required, even if she experiences pain at the time. The fact that any blood found on the *bedikah* cloth may be

ii. Pregnant[34] or nursing[35] women are not required to perform these *bedikos* since they do not usually menstruate. Accordingly, if a couple did the *bedikos* and subsequently realized that the woman is pregnant, the *bedikos* are not valid. After weaning the child, they are required to do the series of three *bedikos*.[36]

iii. A woman who established a *vest haguf* (see Chapter Eighteen regarding what constitutes a *vest haguf*) is considered a woman with a *vest* and is exempt from these *bedikos*.[37] Even if she has not established a definite *vest haguf*,[38] but she always feels cramps before she menstruates, she is not required to do these *bedikos* if she does not feel any cramps.[39] Thus, many women are exempt from this requirement.

d. A negative *vest*:
With regard to this requirement of *bedikos, Shulchan Aruch*[40] notes an intermediate status between a *vest kavuah* and a

---

attributable to *dam besulim* is no reason to omit the *bedikah*. However, many Rabbonim advise that these *bedikos* should be delayed until it is established that the *besulim* are completely healed.

34. *Toras HaShelamim* §3, citing *Maharam Padua. Shiurei Sheivet HaLeivi* §2[2] rules that although, *halachically,* a woman is considered "pregnant" regarding *vestos* only after three months of pregnancy have passed, with regard to this *halachah,* if her pregnancy is medically confirmed, one may be lenient once she misses one expected period. However, responsa *Eimek HaTeshuvah* 1:126 rules that *bedikos* are required until three months of pregnancy have passed.

35. *Graz* §7 rules that even if she is not actually nursing, she is exempted from these *bedikos* for twenty-four months, since *halachically* a woman is not expected to menstruate for twenty-four months after childbirth. However, *Shiurei Sheivet HaLeivi* 186:2[2] rules that since today non-nursing women menstruate shortly after childbirth, one should not rely on this leniency. Accordingly, once she resumes her menstrual cycles, she must do the series of *bedikos* if she has not completed them beforehand. He contends that one certainly cannot follow the lenient opinion after a miscarriage since most women menstruate shortly after a miscarriage.

36. If they did the *bedikos* both at the beginning of pregnancy and after childbirth it would seem that no further *bedikos* are required. Either the three *bedikos* of the beginning of pregnancy or the *bedikos* done during the post-partum twenty-four months are valid.

37. See *Graz* 186:2.

38. For instance, she has no set time to menstruate after the cramps; rather, sometimes she menstruates the same day, other times she menstruates after a day or two.

39. *Eimek HaTeshuvah* 1:126, *Badei HaShulchan, Biurim* 186:2 s.v. ולהרמב"ם.

40. 186:3.

vest she'aino kavuah. This can best be described as a "negative" *vest*.[41] A woman who has no set day for her menstruation, but does not menstruate before a certain day,[42] is considered to have a "negative *vest*" until the earliest possible menstruation day. For example, a woman usually menstruates between the twenty-sixth and thirtieth interval day without any set pattern, but never before the twenty-sixth day. We consider her to have a *vest kavuah* regarding the days before the twenty-sixth day (since we know that she will not menstruate before that day) but not regarding day twenty-six and onward (since we do not know on which day to expect her menstruation). Thus, a newlywed couple who requires *bedikos* the first three times they cohabit should do so the first three times they cohabit only from day twenty-six onward. If any of the *bedikos* are done before the twenty-sixth day, it may not be counted as one of the three preliminary *bedikos*.[43] One should note that this unique type of a "negative" *vest* is applicable only in this case.[44]

e. Following the three *bedikos:*

Once this series of three *bedikos* is concluded without the appearance of blood, the woman has established that cohabitation does not activate her menstrual cycle and

---

41. This *vest* is known as "the *Terumas HaDeshen's vest*" since its source is found in *Terumas HaDeshen* 247. The reason he accepts this *vest* in this case is because, in the opinion of many *Rishonim*, a woman is not even required to do these three *bedikos*. See also *Chavos Daas* 186:3[b].

42. I.e., she has passed those days the last three months without menstruating, see *Minchas Yitzchak* 3:80[2]. For example, if, in the last months, she menstruated after intervals of 24, 25, 27 and 29 days, she needs no *bedikah* before day 24. If at a later date she menstruates (even twice) after an interval of 22, she has not uprooted her negative *vest*. She requires *bedikos* only from day 25 onward (besides abstaining on day 22); see *Chavos Daas* 189:2[b] and *Lechem VeSimlah* 186 end of §8[s].

43. *Chasam Sofer* 186:2 rules that the *bedikos* are not valid. See *Badei HaShulchan, Tziyunim* §14, who is troubled by this ruling. He argues that since *Chavos Daas* explains that the negative *vest* is relied upon (to exempt the couple from *bedikos*) only because the requirement of these *bedikos*, it itself is subject to controversy. Thus, the concept of a negative *vest* is used only for lenient purposes. Accordingly, *Badei HaShulchan* argues, in *Chasam Sofer's* case, we have no right to use the concept in a stringent manner. *Shiurei Sheivet HaLeivi* §2[4] and *Eimek HaTeshuvah* 1:126 rule that although initially the *bedikos* should be done after the time that her menstruation is usual, if they were done earlier, they are valid.

44. For example, see Chapter Fifteen, Section IV,D,2 that a negative *vest* is not applicable regarding an *onah beinonis*.

the couple no longer require *bedikos* before cohabitation.[45] Some *Poskim* require that even after the series of *bedikos* are completed, when the days of the "negative" *vest* pass,[46] she should do a *bedikah*[47] or at least wipe herself externally and check the cloth before each cohabitation.[48] One should consult their Rav regarding which opinion to follow.

E. A woman who finds blood after cohabitation

A woman who finds blood on her garment or body (or if the husband finds blood on his body) after cohabitation[49] should consult a Rav immediately. There is the remote possibility that cohabitation itself is the cause of that menstrual bleeding. This is a serious problem which must be addressed immediately. She should be examined by a gynecologist as soon as possible to see if there is any external (vaginal or external cervical) wound. This would eliminate the concern that cohabitation causes menstrual bleeding. If she is not examined, or if no other source of bleeding is found, she may be required, in the future, to do *bedikos* before and after cohabitation to determine whether or not the cohabitation causes

---

45. 186:2.

46. See Chapter Twenty-Two, Section II regarding the problematic days.

47. *Pleisi* 186:3.

48. *Taharas Yisrael* 186:3 and *Shiurei Sheivet HaLeivi* end of 186:2 citing *Chavos Daas*. However, *Eimek HaTeshuvah* 1:126[22] contends that *Chavos Daas* never required external wiping (*kinuach*) when *bedikos* are not necessary (i.e., after the series of *bedikos* is completed); rather, he sanctioned *kinuach* in the place of *bedikos* (i.e., during the first three times). *Kineh Bosem* (on 186:2) cites two reasons why a woman should always do a *bedikah* after the negative *vest* passes: a) Since she usually menstruates in this span of days, we noted in Chapter Twenty-Two, Section II, that in the view of some *Poskim* she should abstain during all the days. Therefore, even one who follows a more lenient opinion (where applicable) should at least do a *bedikah* beforehand. He notes that many unfortunate cases of women who began menstruating during cohabitation could have been avoided had they done a *bedikah* beforehand. b) If a woman menstruates during cohabitation, her status of *shogeig* (unintentional transgression) or *ones* (blameless transgression) depends upon whether she did a *bedikah*. If she did not do a *bedikah*, she is partially guilty and needs atonement. If she did a *bedikah*, she is blameless (see *Beis Yosef* end of 184). It may be that since most women today feel symptoms before their period begins, one may follow the lenient opinions, see c,iii, above. Nevertheless, it is meritorious to do a *bedikah* or at least a *kinuach* before cohabiting (see *Graz* §7).

49. I.e. she finds blood any time that night even if it is much later than the cohabitation. In regard to the *halachah* that a couple who find blood three times after cohabiting must divorce, the blood must be found on the woman immediately after cohabitation or on the man even later, see 187:1. See Chapter Three note 10.

menstrual bleeding. If she has a *vest kavuah,* she is required to do a pair of *bedikos* only once. If she has no *vest kavuah,* she must do these *bedikos* three times in a manner similar to that noted in D,2,a above.[50]

F. Ruling out other *vestos*

A woman who has no *vest kavuah* does not definitively know whether her menstrual flow is caused by the day of the month or the interval. Therefore, she must consider each of these possibilities and regard both the date and the interval as a possible cause of the flow. Accordingly, she must abstain on both those days as on any *vest she'aino kavuah.*[51] However, once she establishes a *vest kavuah* of either type, she recognizes the true cause of her menstruation and is no longer required to consider any other *vest* as a possible cause.[52] If, in the future, she menstruates on a day incompatible with the *vest kavuah,* we are concerned that perhaps she is in the process of changing to a new *vest kavuah.* Hence, she must keep both the old *vest kavuah* (which has not yet been eliminated since it was not uprooted three times) and the new *vest she'aino kavuah.*[53] See Section III below and Chapter Seventeen.

G. Bleeding which can be attributed to a wound — *teliyah*

We noted in Chapter Six (III,B,5) that a bloodstain on a *bedikah* cloth may at times be attributed to a wound. This depends upon, among other considerations, whether or not the wound is known to bleed, whether or not she has a *vest kavuah* and whether or not the stain was found on the day of her *vest.* It is easier to attribute a bloodstain to a wound if the woman has a *vest kavuah* and the bleeding occurs on a day other than the *yom havest.* See Chapter Twenty-Three, Section II,A.

H. Unusual *vestos*

Another example of the significance of a *vest kavuah* relates to unusual *vestos.* Certain *vestos* are considered unusual occurrences that are not expected to recur. A *vest she'aino kavuah* is not applicable to such *vestos.*

---

50. *Chavos Daas* 186:2[b] cited in *Pischei Teshuvah* §2.

51. *Rema* 189:13.

52. Ibid.

53. 189:14. This *vest she'aino kavuah* is similar to any *vest she'aino kavuah.* Thus, she must keep both the *vest hachodesh* and the *vest haflagah* aspect of the *vest.*

However, if the *vest* repeats itself three times, we assume that this woman menstruates according to a unique *vest*. For example: If a woman menstruates on the fifteenth of month A and the sixteenth of month B, she need not be concerned that perhaps she is starting a *vest hadilug* (an incremental *vest*) since a *vest hadilug* is unusual. Therefore, if the sixteenth of month C passes without incident, she is not required to keep the seventeenth as a *yom havest she'aino kavuah*.[54] However, if she menstruates on the seventeenth of month C she establishes a *vest hadilug kavuah* and treats it as any *vest kavuah*.[55] This *vest* is discussed in Chapter Sixteen. Similarly, a woman who menstruates due to physical exertion (*vest haones*) need not be concerned that she will menstruate again if she repeats the same exertion at a later date. However, if this phenomenon repeats itself three times, it must be treated as a *vest*. The unique *halachos* of this *vest* are discussed in Chapter Nineteen.

I. When the *onas havest* passes

If the *onas havest* passes and the husband does not know whether or not the period arrived, he is required to suspect that his wife is *temei'ah*. In regard to this *halachah* there is a difference between a *vest kavuah* and a *vest she'aino kavuah*.

> 1. If a *vest kavuah* or the *onah beinonis* pass, the couple may not cohabit until the husband inquires of his wife whether or not she did the required *bedikah*.[56] He may not rely upon the fact that she is awake and acts as if she is *tehorah*,[57] since she may not realize that a *bedikah* was required.

> 2. If only a *vest she'aino kavuah* passes, her husband need not ask her specifically if she menstruated or if she did a *bedikah*. In the opinion of many *Poskim* this applies only if she is awake. However, if she is sleeping he is forbidden to cohabit with her.[58] These issues are discussed more thoroughly in Chapter Four, Section I,A.

---

54. 189:11.

55. 189:5.

56. 184:11, see *Aruch HaShulchan* §46 and *Darchei Teshuvah* §60.

57. *Chavos Daas* 184:14[b], 32[c].

58. *Pardes Rimonim* 184:30[sc] and *Aruch HaShulchan* §46. *Chavos Daas* §1[b] disagrees. He rules that even if she is sleeping he may assume that she is *tehorah*. *Taharas Yisroel* §95 follows the stricter position.

In summary: A woman who has a *vest kavuah* differs from a woman who has a *vest she'aino kavuah* with regard to the following:[59] a) She need not be concerned about *onah beinonis,* b) she is not required to do a *bedikah* before or after cohabitation, c) she <u>must</u> do a *bedikah* at the time of the *vest* and is forbidden to have marital relations even after the *yom havest* passes until a *bedikah* is performed, d) they may not cohabit until the husband inquires whether this *bedikah* was done, e) she need not be concerned about any other previous *vest she'aino kavuah,* f) she must keep the *vest* until it is uprooted three times and g) there is a difference between a woman with a *vest kavuah* and one without a *vest kavuah* regarding attributing bleeding to a wound and regarding certain unusual *vestos.*

II. A *vest hashaos* — a *vest* dependent upon hours

There is a unique *vest* which is, essentially, a combination of a *vest kavuah* and a *vest she'aino kavuah.*[60] This is a *vest hashaos* — a *vest* dependent upon hours, i.e., a woman who menstruates without a set pattern, on different days each month and on unequal interval days, but always at the same time of day. For example, she menstruates after intervals of twenty-nine, twenty-seven and twenty-six, but each time she begins menstruating at noon. This woman must observe a *vest she'aino kavuah* the following twenty-sixth day, but her *vest* time is limited to the hour of noon.[61] Normally, we do not limit *vestos* to hours; rather, the entire *onas havest* is prohibited. In this case, however, the twenty-sixth day is merely a *vest she'aino kavuah,* while the limitation of the hour is *kavuah* since it was repeated three times. Therefore, the *vest kavuah* aspect of hours overpow-

59. Other possible differences include: a) A woman with a *vest kavuah* should abstain for the twelve hour period preceding her *onas havest.* This is commonly called the *onah* of the *Or Zarua.* In the opinion of some *Poskim,* a woman who has a *vest she'aino kavuah* is not required to abstain during the preceding *onah.* See *Sugah Bashoshanim* 2:2[5]. b) A *vest kavuah* requires abstaining the entire *onah,* even if the menstruation always begins at a set time of the day. A *vest she'aino kavuah* which always begins at the same hour requires that one abstain only during that hour (see Section II, below). *Lechem VeSimlah* 189:13[l].

60. While this *vest* is not mentioned in the Talmud, *Raavad* in *Baal HaNefesh* derives it from Talmudic sources. We have followed the interpretation of *Chavos Daas* 189:1 and *Pleisi* §2, which seems closest to *Beis Yosef's* explanation; *Shiurei Sheivet HaLeivi* §3[2] notes that *Meiri* (*Niddah* 63b) explains *Raavad* in this manner. See a completely different interpretation of *Raavad* in *Chidushei Haflaah* (ad loc.).

61. 189:3.

THE DIFFERENCES BETWEEN A VEST KAVUAH AND A VEST SHE'AINO KAVUAH

	Akiras vest	Onah Beinonis	Required Bedikah	Bedikos related to cohabitation	Finding blood after cohabitation	Ruling out other vestos	Attributing a stain to a wound	Unusual vestos
Vest Kavuah	A vest kavuah is uprooted only if: a) it was passed on three consecutive occasions, b) a bedikah was done on each occasion and found clean.	A woman with a vest kavuah is exempt from keeping onah beinonis.	A bedikah must be done on a vest kavuah day. If it is omitted it must be done at a later time. The couple must abstain until the bedikah is done.	A woman with a vest kavuah requires no bedikos at the time of cohabitation. No bedikah should be done.	A woman with a vest kavuah who finds blood after cohabitation requires one set of bedikos at time of next cohabitation.	A woman with a vest kavuah is not required to consider any other vest as the possible cause of her menstruation.	It is easier to attribute a stain found on a bedikah cloth to a wound, if the woman has a vest kavuah and the stain is not found on the vest day.	A vest hadlug or vest haseirug that is established as a vest kavuah is treated as any other vest kavuah.
Vest She'aino Kavuah	A vest she'aino kavuah is uprooted even if: a) it was passed only once, b) a bedikah was not done on the vest day.	A woman without a vest kavuah must keep onah beinonis.	A bedikah should be done on a vest she'aino kavuah day. If the bedikah was omitted it is no longer necessary.	A woman without a vest kavuah requires a series of bedikos the first three times she cohabits.	A woman without a vest kavuah who finds blood after cohabitation requires a series of bedikos the next three times she cohabits.	A woman without a vest kavuah must consider each possible cause of her menstruation. She must observe yom hachodesh and yom haflagah days.	If the woman has no vest kavuah, additional factors are required to permit a Rav to attribute the stain to a wound.	A vest hadlug or seirug need not be observed if it is only a vest she'aino kavuah.

ers[62] the *vest she'aino kavuah* of days and limits the *vest* to the exact hour of expected menstruation.[63] When the hour of noon passes, the day is no longer considered *onas havest* and she is permitted to cohabit even without a *bedikah*.[64]

III. A woman who has both a *vest kavuah* and a *vest she'aino kavuah*

A woman who has a *vest kavuah* and passes the *vest kavuah* day without menstruating, but menstruates on another day, has both a *vest kavuah* and a *vest she'aino kavuah*. On the following month, she must treat both the *vest kavuah* and the *vest she'aino kavuah* days as *yom havest*.[65] Therefore, she must keep all the suitable applications of the *vest she'aino kavuah*, i.e., both its *yom hachodesh* and its *yom haflagah*. In effect, she treats the *vest she'aino kavuah* as if she does not have a *vest kavuah*.[66] Each individual *vest* is treated according to its particular *halachos*, i.e., its *akirah* and the requirement of *bedikos*. Since she has a *vest kavuah,* she is not required to keep *onah beinonis*.[67] If the *vest kavuah* is uprooted three times, she must begin to keep *onah beinonis*.

---

62. We know, by merit of the *vest kavuah* of hours, that she will menstruate at noon, not another time of the day.

63. It is difficult to define the exact parameters of the hour. *Chazon Ish, Y.D.* 85:74, contends that the hours are determined by dividing the day into twelve segments, this is usually referred to as *"shaos zemanios." Chazon Ish* rules that if she usually menstruates in the beginning of the fifth hour she is permitted until the very end of the fourth hour even though it is only minutes away from the fifth hour. Similarly, she is forbidden the entire span of the fifth hour even though she normally menstruates at the beginning. In conclusion, *Chazon Ish* is hesitant and seems less than certain about his theory.

64. 189:3, according to *Chavos Daas'* interpretation. *Chavos Daas* explains that normally, when a *vest kavuah* passes without incident, the woman needs a *bedikah*. In this case, however, the hour was *kavuah* but the day was not. Therefore, the basis to expect the period was essentially a *vest she'aino kavuah*. *Poskim* do not elaborate on how this *vest* is uprooted. It would seem that it can only be uprooted if she menstruates on three occasions after the usual hour. However, if she menstruates only once on a different hour the *vest hashaos* remains intact. *Sugah Bashoshanim* 4:5, however, contends that if she menstruates at any other time of the day, she must keep *yom havest* on the corresponding following day and abstain the entire day, not just at noon. He explains that just as one who has a *vest kavuah* and menstruates on a different day is required to keep the *vest she'aino kavuah* as well, so, too, in this case, she retains the *vest kavuah* of noon, but must observe a *vest she'aino kavuah* as well. The *vest she'aino kavuah* is not oriented to a particular hour (since it was not repeated three times at that hour). Therefore, she must abstain all day.

65. 189:14.

66. See *Graz* 189:41.

67. *Graz* 189:41.

CHAPTER FIFTEEN

וסת הפלגה, וסת החודש ועונה בינונית
The Three Basic *Vestos*

- ☐ The *vest haflagah.*
- ☐ Computation of the *vest haflagah.*
- ☐ The *vest hachodesh.*
- ☐ The differences between a *vest haflagah* and a *vest hachodesh.*
- ☐ The *onah beinonis.*
- ☐ The thirtieth or thirty-first day.
- ☐ Situations in which the *onah beinonis* is subject to controversy.

Introduction

There are three *vestos* which apply to any woman who has no *vest kavuah*: the *vest haflagah*, the *vest hachodesh* and the *onah beinonis*. A woman who has a *vest kavuah* keeps only the *vest kavuah*, be it *vest haflagah* or *vest hachodesh*. Since most women today have no *vest kavuah*, the three aforementioned *vestos* apply to almost all women. These *vestos* will be examined in this chapter.

I. *Vest haflagah:* a *vest* based upon the interval between periods

A. What is a *vest haflagah?*

One of the two most common *vestos* is the *vest haflagah*, a *vest* based upon the interval between periods. The hormonal changes which causes the body to expel the uterine lining function according to a biological clock, resulting in a pattern based upon a set interval. Thus, if, a woman menstruates twenty-nine days after the previous period, we assume that this is her set pattern and we expect her to continue to menstruate according to this pattern. Therefore, when a woman has two menstrual periods, she counts the number of days between the onset of the two periods (the interval) and then calculates the day of her next expected period. Once that day is identified, precautionary measures must be taken. The interval between these two periods constitutes a *vest she'aino kavuah*, which, although less established than a *vest kavuah*, cannot be ignored. If the pattern continues for the next three occasions, she has established a *vest haflagah kavuah* for an interval of twenty-nine days. Since the interval (the *haflagah*) is identified only after two periods, a woman requires four periods to determine three intervals and establish a *vest haflagah kavuah*.

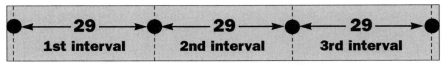

Four periods are required to create three intervals.

The three twenty-nine day intervals which constitute a *vest* must be free of any intermediate menstrual flow. For example, if during any of the intervals the woman had a menstrual flow on the seventeenth interval day and then had a normal menstruation after a thirteen day interval, which is twenty-nine day from her previous normal menstruation, she has not established a *vest kavuah*. The interval is calculated from the immediately preceding previous flow (the seventeenth interval day) and is considered an interval of thirteen, not twenty-nine days.

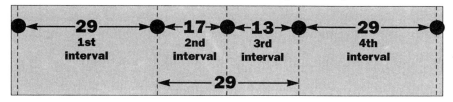

B. Computation of a *vest haflagah*

1. The conventional method:

The conventional method of calculating a *vest haflagah* is to count the days from the onset of first menstruation through the onset of the second menstruation. The length of the actual menstruation is irrelevant.[1] For example, a woman began to menstruate on a Sunday (day a, in diagram) and began her second menstrual period four Sundays later (day b). This interval is considered an interval of twenty-nine days. She therefore assumes that her next period will recur after the same interval (again four Sundays later — day c) which is twenty-nine days from the second menstrual period. The fact that the first period may have lasted six days and the second only four days is irrelevant. One should note that actually only fifty-seven days have passed between the first and third periods because the twenty-ninth day is counted

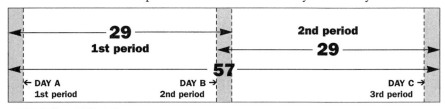

---

1. While this is the opinion of almost all *Poskim* and the nearly universally accepted custom (see *Chasam Sofer, Y.D.* 166[3]), it is noteworthy that *Graz* 184:22 and 189:3 disagrees. He contends that one counts the interval from the end of the first period to the beginning of the second. Thus, if a woman had a longer blood flow during the first period and a shorter flow in the second, her expected third period will be closer to the beginning of the second than the second was to the beginning of the first. *Poskim* almost unanimously disagree. Responsa *Beis Shlomo, Y.D.* 15, notes that *Ramban* (*Hil. Niddah* 5:5) writes that *onah beinonis* is calculated from the beginning of menstruation. He considers this proof against *Graz's* position. However, *Graz* himself (189:1) concedes that regarding *onah beinonis*, one calculates from the beginning of the flow; thus, one cannot disprove *Graz's* position from *Ramban*. *Beis Shlomo* contends that although most *Poskim* disagree with *Graz*, a punctilious individual should compute the *vest* according to *Graz* in addition to the conventional manner, but one should not compute it solely according to *Graz*. *Shiurei Sheivet HaLeivi* 189:2[2] notes that common custom is to follow *Chasam Sofer's* opinion exclusively.

twice: once as the twenty-ninth day of the first period and again as the first day of the second period.[2]

2. The requirement for uniform *onos:*
A *vest haflagah* cannot become established unless all the menstruations began in the same *onah,* i.e., either all during the daylight hours or all during the night.[3] If one period began during the day and the other two during the night, the *vest* is not *kavuah.*[4] One can only set a *vest kavuah* if all the periods are uniformly in the same *onah.* The discrepancy of the change from day to night disturbs the uniformity of the intervals. Indeed, there is an opinion that perhaps even the very first of the four periods that create the *vest haflagah* must be during the same *onah* as the following three, even though this period merely serves as a starting point from which to count the intervals but is actually not one of the three periods that create the *vest kavuah.*[5] Most *Poskim* do not seem to share this view.[6]

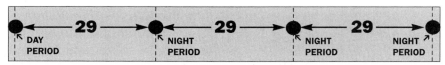

This case may not be a vest kavuah.

3. Computation through *onos:*
There is an opinion that a woman can set a *vest* through equal intervals of multiples of *onos* — twelve hour segments.[7] According to this opinion, if she menstruates on one day *onah* (a) and menstruates again twenty-nine days later on the (earlier)

---

2. A woman should be careful when she charts her interval. For example, she might mistakenly count twenty-nine days inclusive of both the first period (day a) and the second (day b), and then plot twenty-nine days from the second period counting from the following day, not the day of the period itself (day b). She would thus erroneously keep the thirtieth day instead of the twenty-ninth. Similarly, she will miscalculate the thirtieth day of the *onah beinonis.*

3. While it is true that according to the opinion cited in 3 below, that a *vest haflagah* is calculated from the *onos,* not the days, a woman could set a *vest haflagah* even if some periods began during the day and some at night, as noted below, this is not the accepted *halachah.* It is our practice to follow the ruling of most *Poskim* that *vestos* are calculated by days.

4. Even though the interval of *onos* are equal (*Noda B'Yehudah* 2:83).

5. See *Chazon Ish, Y.D.* 85:72.

6. See *Badei HaShulchan, Tziyunim* 189:94.

7. *Graz* 189:36, a similar view is quoted in *Noda B'Yehudah* 2:83, in the name of R' Dovid Tevle. See also *Pischei Teshuvah* §9 and *Pri Deah* (S.L. 189:13).

night *onah* (b), twenty-eight days later on the day *onah* (c), and twenty-nine days later on the (earlier) night *onah* (d), she has set a *vest* for every fifty-sixth *onah*. Most *Poskim*, however, reject this view,[8] as is common practice. Accordingly, she has no *vest kavuah* since the periods were not in the same interval. Furthermore, they were not in the same *onah*.

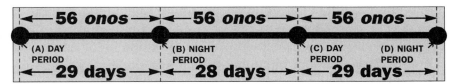

Computation through onos vs. computation through days

4. Calculating *yom havest* following a missed period:
A woman who misses a period on her *haflagah* day need not be concerned about the next *haflagah* day, even if she had established a *vest kavuah*, until she experiences another blood flow. For example, a woman who has a *vest kavuah* for an interval of twenty-eight days and passes that interval day without incident has no *vest haflagah* day until she menstruates again. She does not (in the opinion of most *Poskim*)[9] count twenty-eight days from the twenty-eighth day on which she was expected to menstruate. A *vest haflagah* is counted only from an <u>actual</u> blood flow, not from an <u>expected</u> flow. Indeed, the day after the expected twenty-eighth day is not day two but day twenty-nine, followed by day thirty. Thus, day twenty-eight from the expected day is actually day fifty-five. Day twenty-eight will not return until twenty-eight days after the <u>next</u> period.[10]

---

8. See *Noda B'Yehudah* ibid. (*Aruch HaShulchan* §26, seems to interpret *Noda B'Yehudah* differently). See also *Chazon Ish, Y.D.* 85:59,60, *Igros Moshe Y.D.* 3:48, *Sheivet HaLeivi* 3:125. The theory of *Graz* regarding counting the intervals by *onos* seems, at first, most logical. The interval between menstruations should be exact. This can only be accomplished by calculating through *onos*. However, this is not necessarily so. Even *Graz* concedes that we calculate according to *onos*, not hours and minutes, although that would seem more exact and logical. Apparently, the exact interval span is not the vital factor. Therefore, the opinion of other *Poskim* who calculate the interval through days is no less acceptable a position than that of the *Graz* who calculates through *onos*. In their opinion, the *vest* is based upon the interval day factor but is limited to the exact *onah*. Indeed, *Chazon Ish* contends that even the original of the four menstruations must be in the same *onah*, as noted above.

9. *Bach* 189 p. 54b. This is the opinion of most *Poskim* (see *Sidrei Taharah* 189:19), as opposed to *Beis Yosef* and *Taz* §18, see also *Taz* §30.

10. See *Maharshal* cited in *Taz* §31 and *Graz* 189 end of §65.

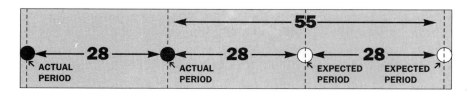

5. Calculating *yom havest* following an early period:

One calculates a *vest haflagah* from the last menstruation. Thus, in the opinion of most *Poskim*, a woman with a *vest haflagah kavuah* who menstruates earlier than expected readjusts her calendar to reflect the change. She counts her interval from the last menstruation.[11] Thus, she may erase a *vest* day that was previously registered on her calendar. For example, a woman has a *vest haflagah kavuah* for the thirty-second day interval. She had a period on day (a), marked the next interval of thirty-two days (c) on her calendar, completed her *taharah* process and was *tovel*. She then unexpectedly menstruated early on the eighteenth day (b). She completed her *taharah* process and is *tovel* again. She may now erase the original day thirty-two (c) from her calendar, since it is no longer day thirty-two but day fifteen from the last period (b).[12] Instead, she now marks the thirty-second day (d) from day (b).[13] Although this is the opinion of most *Poskim*, many *Poskim* maintain that she must keep the original *yom havest* (c).[14] Accepted *halachic* practice follows the first view.[15] The reader should note

---

11. *Chazon Ish* 85:43 notes that this applies only if the second menstruation is at least seven days after the beginning of the first menstruation. Otherwise, the second menstruation is considered a continuation of the first. See Chapter Thirteen, Section II,B,1 and Appendix D.

12. *Bach* 189 p. 52b, *Prishah* §28, *Sidrei Taharah* §14 shows that this is the opinion of *Raavad* and *Rosh* as well. See also *Beis Meir* ad loc., *Pleisi* §16, *Graz* §43 (who notes that this is also the opinion of *Rambam*) and *Lechem VeSimlah* §34[l]. See *Chavos Daas* §21[c],14[b], *Chazon Ish* 85:33,34 and *Badei HaShulchan, Biurim* 189:13 s.v. ראתה בא' באייר, regarding a woman who established a *vest kavuah l'haflagah* with three equal intervals but has an additional period in between. For example, she menstruated in the following sequence of intervals, ten, ten, twenty and twenty. If we could ignore the second interval of ten, she would have established a *vest kavuah*. See ibid. for several variations of this question.

13. In the opinion of *Shach* §31 and §40, if the original *vest* of thirty-two had been a *vest she'aino kavuah*, she would not keep the *yom havest* of day d either since the *vest* of thirty-two was uprooted by the earlier interval of eighteen. See Chapter Seventeen III,A,3. In regard to our case, *Shach's* opinion is unclear; see *Nekudos HaKesef* on *Taz* §18.

14. *Rema* 189:13, *Taz* §18 and *Toras HaShelamim* §22.

15. This is the opinion of *Raavad, Ramban, Rosh* and most *Acharonim*. Responsa *Sheivet HaLeivi* 2:81 (at end) rules that if the period of day b was not a full menstruation, e.g., a flow lasting two or three days, but was a short flow, it would be logical to keep the day c *vest*.

that this discussion relates to a *vest haflagah* only. A *vest hachodesh* is unaffected by any menstruation on another day.[16]

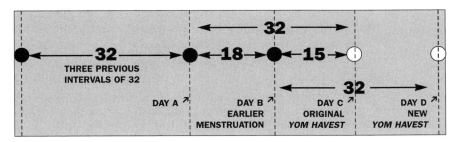

II. *Vest hachodesh:*
a *vest* based upon the day of the month

A. What is a *vest hachodesh?*

We noted that a woman who menstruated on three consecutive months on the same day of the Hebrew calendar has established a permanent *vest*. This is true even if one month is a full month (*malei:* of thirty days) and one a deficient month (*chaseir:* of twenty-nine days), with the result that the interval of days are not equal.[17] For example, a woman who menstruates on the fifth of *Nissan*, the fifth of *Iyar* and the fifth of *Sivan* has a permanent *vest* to menstruate on the fifth of each month. To avoid confusion, in the future, we will refer to the months by a number or letter, instead of by name. When a woman menstruates on the fifth of month a, we assume that this day is her normal menstruation date and she will probably continue to menstruate on the fifth day of each following month. This constitutes a *vest hachodesh she'aino kavuah,* which, although less definite than a *vest kavuah,* cannot be ignored. Accordingly, precautionary measures must be taken.[18] If the pattern continues two more times, it becomes a *vest kavuah.* Although a *vest haflagah* requires four periods to produce three intervals, a *vest hachodesh* becomes established with only three periods if they occurred on the same date for three consecutive months. Also, as opposed to a *vest haflagah,* a *vest hachodesh* can become established even if she experienced a flow during the intermediate days. A *vest hachodesh* is determined by the menstrual flows on similar dates of the months; any flow in between is immaterial.[19]

---

16. See *Prishah* §28.

17. 189:6, *Shach* §13 and *Chochmas Adam* 112:6.

18. 189:2.

19. *Prishah* §28.

B. Unusual cases

1. Two independent vestos:

A *vest hachodesh* is based upon the rationale that the particular day of the month causes menstruation, regardless of the time interval between periods. Thus, theoretically, a woman can have two independent *vestos hachodesh*. For example, a woman who menstruates on the fifth and the eighteenth of month One, Two and Three has a *vest hachodesh* to menstruate on both the fifth and the eighteenth of each month.[20] These *vestos* are independent of one another. Thus, if one is uprooted, e.g., she passes the fifth and eighteenth day of month Four and Five and the fifth day of month Six without incident, she uprooted the *vest* of the fifth but not that of the eighteenth unless she passes the eighteenth of month Six without incident.

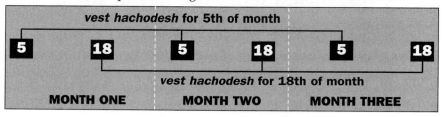

Two independent vestos

2. An alternating vest hachodesh:

A woman can set a *vest hachodesh* on alternating months. For example, a woman menstruated on the fifth day of months One, Three and Five but not on months Two, Four and Six. She has a *vest kavuah* on the fifth of all odd-numbered months but not on even numbered months.[21] This *vest* is discussed in Chapter Sixteen B. Alternatively, a woman may have a *vest* combining both this factor (an alternating *vest*) and the previous factor (two independent *vestos* as in 1 above). She may menstruate on the fifth of months One, Three and Five, and on the twentieth of months Two, Four and Six. She has a *vest kavuah* for the fifth of odd-numbered months and the twentieth of even-numbered months (see chart, following page).

3. Uniformity of either day or night flows:

A *vest hachodesh* cannot be established unless all three periods began during the daylight hours or all three during the night-

---

20. 189:32.

21. 189:12. Obviously, after a lunar leap year, the order will change and her *vest* will be for even numbered months.

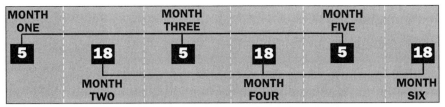

Two independent vestos on alternating months

time.[22] Thus, even if she menstruates for many years on the fifth day of each month but changes from day to night without a set pattern, she has no *vest kavuah*[23]. If, however, she alternates from day to night with a set pattern, e.g., one month during the day and the following month during the night, she establishes two independent *vestos:* one on the fifth day of the odd-numbered months during daylight hours and one on the fifth night of the even numbered months.[24]

4. The thirtieth of the month:

The thirtieth day of the month presents a unique problem. Only full months (*melei'im*) have thirtieth days; deficient months (*chaseirim*) do not. Therefore, if a woman has a *vest hachodesh* for the thirtieth of the month, what does she do on a month that has no thirtieth day? One may argue that since months usually alternate between those having and not having a thirtieth day, every *vest* for the thirtieth day is actually a *vest haflagah* for the sixtieth interval day. However, this would not solve the problem of the first month. Furthermore, the presence of a thirtieth day does not necessarily follow a fixed pattern. At times, two, or even three full months or two or three deficient months may follow one another. Thus, the *vest* does not always follow a definite interval pattern. *Poskim* suggest three possible solutions to this problem:

> a. Perhaps a *vest* of the thirtieth day of the month should be viewed as a *vest* for the last day of the month. Thus, a woman who menstruates on the thirtieth of *Nissan* should consider the twenty-ninth of *Iyar* the *yom*

---

22. 189:13.

23. See, however, *Igros Moshe* cited in Chapter Twenty-Two note 54. *Chidushei Haflaah* 189, end of §4, ponders the status of a woman who menstruates one *onah* later each month. For example, she menstruated on the night of the fifteenth of the month, the day of the fifteenth, the night of the sixteenth and the day of the sixteenth of consecutive months. Is this considered a *vest hadilug* (see Chapter Sixteen)? Perhaps, since *vestos* are not based on intervals of *onos*, a *dilug* of an *onah* is not considered a *dilug*.

24. *Mekor Chaim* §59. Therefore, each *vest* is not affected by the *akirah* of the other.

havest (since *Iyar* has no thirtieth day and the twenty-ninth is the last day of the month).[25] According to this view, if a woman menstruates on the thirtieth of *Nissan*, the twenty-ninth of *Iyar* and the thirtieth of *Sivan*, she has established a *vest kavuah* for the last day of the month.[26] Most *Poskim* dismiss this view.[27]

b. Since the thirtieth of *Nissan* is called *Rosh Chodesh Iyar* (although it is the last day of Nissan), perhaps one should assume that she has a *vest she'aino kavuah* for *Rosh Chodesh* and treat the first day of *Sivan* as *yom havest*. *Poskim* reject this possibility as well.[28] See 5 below, regarding a *vest kavuah*.

c. Perhaps she should assume that she has a *vest* for the thirtieth day of the month. Thus, whenever a month has thirty days, she should consider the thirtieth day as her *yom havest*. There is an opinion that if this occurs three times (i.e., she menstruates on the thirtieth of *Nissan*, *Sivan* and *Av*), she has set a *vest kavuah* for the thirtieth of the month.[29]

In view of the above and since *Poskim* have not reached a clear resolution of this question, it would seem that a woman who menstruated on the thirtieth of the month should observe *yom havest* on the twenty-ninth of the following month since that is her *onah beinonis*. In a case of two consecutive months with thirty days (*melei'im*), she observes the thirtieth of the following month in addition to the twenty-ninth.[30]

---

25. *Pri Deah* (189:17[tc]) raises this possibility without reaching a definite conclusion.

26. It would seem that this is the logical conclusion according to *Pri Deah* cited above. Indeed, in this case, the *vest* repeated itself three times.

27. *Aruch HaShulchan* 189:12 contends that if this were true, earlier *Poskim* would have noted this *halachah*. *Shiurei Sheivet HaLeivi* 189:6[4] concurs with *Aruch HaShulchan's* view.

28. *Pri Deah* (ibid.) deduces from *Bach* that if this occurs only once, the twenty-ninth day is not considered *Rosh Chodesh* regarding *vestos*. See *Bach* p. 52b.

29. See *Be'er Moshe* 3:119. See a discussion of the issues involved, in *Badei HaShulchan* 189:6 s. v. באחד בניסן. In 189:13 s.v. חוששת לאחד באייר, *Badei HaShulchan* contends that a woman who only menstruates once on the thirtieth day of a month should consider the following thirtieth day her *yom havest* even if a "*chaseir*" month passed in between.

30. If she menstruates only on the thirtieth of each *chodesh malei* for many months and is then faced with two consecutive *chadashim melei'im* or two *chadashim chaseirim*, it is unclear whether or not she ignores the *vest haflagah* aspect of the *vest*.

5. Rosh Chodesh:

A *vest hachodesh* on *Rosh Chodesh* also poses a problem. Can a woman establish a *vest kavuah* for *Rosh Chodesh* even if not all of her three periods were on the first of the month? For example, a woman menstruates on the first of *Nissan*, the thirtieth of *Nissan* and the first of *Sivan*. In this case, not all the days are similar in their dates but all are *Rosh Chodesh* (the thirtieth of *Nissan* is the first day of *Rosh Chodesh Iyar*). Authorities rule that this constitutes a *vest kavuah*[31] for *Rosh Chodesh*.[32] Accordingly, she must treat both days of *Rosh Chodesh Tammuz* as *yom havest*.[33]

---

31. *Bach* 189 p. 52a and 52b. He explains that although the periods did not all occur on the same *yom hachodesh,* the fact that two of the periods were on the actual *Rosh Chodesh* day (the first of the month) leads us to assume that the period of the thirtieth of *Nissan* was also *Rosh Chodesh* related, since that day is called *Rosh Chodesh* as well. See also *Aruch HaShulchan* 189:28. *Badei HaShulchan* 189:48 contends that similarly, if she menstruates on the thirtieth of *Tishrei*, the first of *Kislev* and the first of *Teives* or she menstruates on the first of *Iyar*, the first of *Sivan* and the thirtieth of *Sivan*, she established a *vest kavuah* for *Rosh Chodesh*. In both of these cases she menstruated twice on the actual *Rosh Chodesh* day. He further claims, that if she menstruates on the thirtieth of *Nissan*, the first of *Sivan* and the thirtieth of *Sivan*, she also establishes a *vest kavuah* for *Rosh Chodesh*. It is not certain whether *Aruch HaShulchan* cited above agrees in this last case since two of the three menstruations were not on the actual *Rosh Chodesh* day. However, according to the theory which *Aruch HaShulchan* presents in §12 and §28, that any day which carries the name *Rosh Chodesh* is considered *Rosh Chodesh* regarding *vestos*, he should agree to this case as well. *Bach* p. 52b concedes that we consider the thirtieth of the month *Rosh Chodesh* regarding *vestos* only when she menstruates more than once on days that are called *Rosh Chodesh*. However, when she menstruates once on *Rosh Chodesh Nissan*, she need not treat the thirtieth of *Nissan* as *yom havest* even though it is called *Rosh Chodesh* since it is not the first of the month. See 4,b above.

32. *Bach* ibid. Indeed, *Bach* contends that even if she did not establish a *vest kavuah* but menstruated only on the first of *Nissan* <u>and</u> the thirtieth of *Nissan*, she must observe *yom havest* on *Rosh Chodesh Sivan* (which is thirty-one days later). Even though the two periods were not on similar dates, the fact that both days are called *Rosh Chodesh* leads us to suspect that perhaps she will set a *vest kavuah* for *Rosh Chodesh*. As noted in previous footnote, *Bach* (p. 52b) concedes that if she menstruates only on the first of *Nissan*, she is not required to observe *yom havest* on the thirtieth of *Nissan* (the first day of *Rosh Chodesh Iyar*) as a *vest hachodesh*, but she must expect her period on that day as the *onah beinonis*, if applicable (i.e., she did not menstruate between the first and thirtieth of *Nissan*). *Bach* explains that we normally attribute the period of *Rosh Chodesh* to the monthly date (the first of the month), not the aspect of the day (*Rosh Chodesh*). However, if she menstruates twice on two days that share the *Rosh Chodesh* aspect but not the date (i.e., the first and thirtieth of *Nissan* are both called *Rosh Chodesh* although they are on different month days), we assume that the *Rosh Chodesh* aspect is the cause of the period. Thus, she must observe *yom havest* on *Rosh Chodesh Sivan*.

33. *Bach* ibid. Apparently she continues observing *yom havest* on both days of *Rosh Chodesh* during those months that have a two-day *Rosh Chodesh* and observes the single day *Rosh Chodesh* of those months that have a one-day *Rosh Chodesh*. It would seem that this status continues as long as she continues to alternate between the first and second days of *Rosh Chodesh*. However, if she menstruates three consecutive times on the first of the month, perhaps the *vest* should change to a regular *vest* for the first of the month only. This question remains unclear. *Badei HaShulchan* 188:48 speculates that perhaps even a woman who never menstruated on the first day of *Rosh Chodesh* but established a *vest kavuah* for the second day of *Rosh Chodesh* (which is the first of the month — the "actual" *Rosh Chodesh*) must observe *yom havest* on both days of *Rosh Chodesh*. This is difficult to accept, since no earlier authority mentions this possibility even though this case is frequently mentioned in *Shulchan Aruch*.

III. Differences between a *vest haflagah* and a *vest hachodesh*

Among the differences between a *vest haflagah* and a *vest hachodesh* are the following:

1. A *vest haflagah* needs two periods to create one *haflagah;* thus, it can only become *kavuah* with four periods. A *vest hachodesh* is created with one period and becomes *kavuah* with three.

2. A woman cannot have two *vestos haflagah;* one *vest haflagah* inherently contradicts another. However, a woman can have two *vestos hachodesh* since each day of the month may cause her to menstruate independently of one another.

3. We noted in A,4 above that a woman who misses a period on her *haflagah* day need not be concerned about her next scheduled *vest haflagah,* even if she has established a *vest kavuah,* until she experiences a blood flow again. A *vest haflagah* is counted only from an actual blood flow, not from an expected flow. However, a woman who passes her *vest hachodesh kavuah* day without incident must nevertheless expect a *vest* on the following month. A *vest hachodesh* is determined by the date of the month and is not dependent upon what occurred the previous month.

4. Similarly, as we noted in A,5 above, a woman with a *vest haflagah kavuah* who menstruates earlier than expected readjusts her calendar to reflect the change. She counts her interval from the last menstruation. Accordingly, she may erase a *vest* day that was previously registered on her calendar. However, a woman with a *vest hachodesh kavuah* continues to expect her *vest* on that day of the month even though on the previous month she menstruated on a different day. The month date is unaffected by the change (unless it occurs three times).

IV. *Onah beinonis:* the median *vest*

A. The underlying logic

Chazal recognized the fact that a woman will certainly menstruate eventually. If she has a *vest kavuah,* we expect her period on the day of her *vest* and we need not be concerned that she will menstruate at any other time. However, even a woman who has not established a *vest kavuah* will certainly menstruate at some time;[34] therefore, we cannot ignore the possibility that she may suddenly menstruate. Chazal assumed that since she has not established a *vest kavuah* of her own, she will probably menstruate according to the average *vest* of most women. This is called the *onah beinonis*, the median *vest*. Chazal assumed this to be the thirtieth day from her last menstruation.[35]

An *onah beinonis* is treated as a *vest kavuah*; thus, a woman is required to do a *bedikah* on the *onas havest*. If she forgot to do a *bedikah* during the *onah beinonis*, she must abstain until a *bedikah* is done.[36] See Chapter Twenty-Two regarding the *halachos* of the *onas havest*.

Any woman who has no permanent day on which to expect her period is subject to *onah beinonis*.[37] An *onah beinonis* is always calculated from the last menstruation. Thus, if a woman menstruated eighteen days after her previous menstruation, she keeps the *onah beinonis* thirty days from the eighteenth day. She need not, in the opinion of most *Poskim*, abstain twelve days after the eighteenth day, even though this had originally been set as the *onah beinonis* from the earlier period.[38]

---

34. To quote the term used by *Rishonim;* "וכי לעולם לא תראה — will she never menstruate"?

35. *Niddah* 9b. It is noteworthy that the *onah beinonis* is always calculated from the last menstruation, since its basis is similar to that of a *vest haflagah*, not a *vest hachodesh* (see *Sidrei Taharah* 189:12). In addition, any menstrual blood flow necessitates an *onah beinonis*, even if it was caused by unnatural factors, e.g., a fall. Thus, when thirty day pass from the menstrual flow caused by the fall, she must observe the *onah beinonis* (see 184:12, *Shach* §32, *Sidrei Taharah* 189:12 and *Chavos Daas* 189:22[b]).

36. 189:4.

37. 189:1. *Graz, Kuntres Acharon* §1, notes that *Rif, Rambam, Raavad* and *Reah* do not accept the entire concept of *onah beinonis*. *Rashi* and *Ramban* accept *onah beinonis* only with regard to requiring a *bedikah* before cohabitation. In their opinion, once a *bedikah* is done, cohabitation is permitted. However, *Shulchan Aruch* 189:1 and all later *Poskim* follow the opinion of *Rashba* that *onah beinonis* is comparable to any *yom havest*. This is the accepted *halachic* tradition.

38. *Chavos Daas* 189:13[b]. He explains that even according to those opinions (*Rema* 189:13 *and Taz* §18 noted above footnote 14) that, regarding a *vest haflagah*, we calculate from the previous menstruation even though there was an intermediate flow, regarding an *onah beinonis*, we should certainly calculate from the last menstruation. The *raison d'etre* of an *onah beinonis* is that she certainly will menstruate in the future, therefore, once she menstruates, there is no reason to expect another menstruation before thirty days. A similar view is held by *Sidrei Taharah* §13 and R' Akiva Eiger to *Taz* §17. See also *Sugah Bashoshanim* 5:[5]. However, *Taz* himself §17 and *Graz* §42 disagree.

B. The thirtieth or thirty-first day

In the opinion of most[39] *Poskim, onah beinonis* is the thirtieth day from her previous period.[40] Other *Poskim* maintain that the *onah beinonis* is the thirty-first day,[41] while still others consider it to be the day of the month of the last period.[42] The basic *halachah* follows the opinion that *onah beino-*

---

39. Term used by *Pri Deah* in introduction to 189, §8.

40. *Beis Yosef* 189 s.v. לשון הרמב"ן, *Bach* ad loc., *Taz* 189:14,17, *Prishah* §23, responsa *Chacham Tzvi* 114, *Pleisi* 189:15 and *Graz* §1.

41. *Chavos Daas* 189:12 [b] and *Lechem VeSimlah* §1 and 23. *Graz, Kuntres Acharon* 189:1 notes that this is the opinion of *Rashi*. They explain that when *Chazal* used the term "thirty days" or "thirtieth day" they were referring to the days between one menstruation and the next, not including the day of the expected period. A woman is not required to abstain until the thirty days pass. Thus, the actual day to abstain is the thirty-first day. *Chasam Sofer, Y.D.* 166, s.v. ואחד, seems to follow this view. It is noteworthy that although *Chavos Daas* holds *onah beinonis* to be the thirty-first day, in §1[c] and 20[c] he concedes that one should keep the thirtieth day as *onah beinonis* as well as the thirty-first. However, *Igros Moshe, Y.D.* 3:50, follows *Chavos Daas'* view exclusively to the thirty-first. He does not require that one separate on the thirtieth day. This is a unique view among contemporary *Poskim* and is not the accepted custom.

42. *Shach* §1,30 and *Toras HaShelamim* §21. *Aruch HaShulchan* reaches no final conclusion but he leans toward *Shach's* position. *Shach's* opinion may, at first glance, seem difficult since one is required to keep the *yom hachodesh* anyway. However, *Poskim* note several differences between the two: a) *Sidrei Taharah* §12 notes that a *yom hachodesh* that is not *onah beinonis* differs from one that is in the following manner: a woman who did not do the required *bedikah* on the *vest* day, if the *vest* were only *yom hachodesh*, she is no longer required to do the *bedikah* since it is a *vest she'aino kavuah*. However, if the *yom hachodesh* is an *onah beinonis* as well, it has the status of a *vest kavuah* and she must do a *bedikah*. b) Similarly, if her husband was away from home and returns after the *yom hachodesh* (she'aino kavuah) has passed, he is not required to ask whether or not the period arrived. He may rely upon the fact that she does not inform him that she is *temei'ah*. However, if the *yom hachodesh* is considered the *onah beinonis* as well, he is required to ask whether or not the period arrived. c) *Pleisi* 189:15 notes another difference. He contends that the *onah beinonis* is a complete twenty-four-hour period from sunset following the twenty-ninth day to the sunset following the thirtieth day (this opinion is shared by *Graz* 189:1, see Section C). Thus, a *yom hachodesh* that is not the *onah beinonis* extends for only the twelve-hour period (day or night) in which she menstruated on the previous month.

Another problem regarding *Shach's* position is: If the *onah beinonis* and *yom hachodesh* are one and the same, why do *Poskim* refer to them as two separate entities? How is it possible for the *yom hachodesh* not to be *onah beinonis* and how could *onah beinonis* not be the regular *yom hachodesh*? *Sidrei Taharah* (ibid.) resolves this problem. He explains that it is possible to find a *yom hachodesh* that is not *onah beinonis*. A woman menstruated on the first of the month and again on the twentieth of the same month. The following first of the month is her *yom hachodesh* but not her *onah beinonis* since it is only the twelfth day from the last period. *Sidrei Taharah* cites yet another example: A woman has a *vest kavuah* on the first of the month. One month she menstruates on the fifth of the month instead of the first. On the following month she keeps a *vest kavuah* on the first of the month and a *vest hachodesh she'aino kavuah* on the fifth. The *yom havest* of the fifth is a simple *vest nis* is the thirtieth day from the last period.[43] However, *Poskim* note that it is proper to keep the *onah beinonis* on both the thirtieth and the thirty-first day.[44] This includes the *yom hachodesh* as well, since the *yom hachodesh* is either the thirtieth or thirty-first day. In cases of difficulty, one should consult a Rav.

C. The duration of the *onah beinonis*

A normal *yom havest* extends only to the *onah* of the *vest* itself, i.e., the twelve-hour period, i.e., either a full day or a full night in which the period last occurred. Thus, a woman who menstruated after an interval of twenty-five days on the day *onah* of the fifth of the month must primarily keep an *onas havest* on the day *onah* of the following twenty-fifth interval day (and on the day *onah* of the fifth of the following month for *vest hachodesh*). However, in the opinion of some *Poskim*, an *onah beinonis* extends a full twenty-four hours, from sundown following the twenty-ninth day to sundown following the thirtieth day. Thus, the woman must abstain the full night and day of the fourth (if the first month was a *chodesh malei*) or the fifth of the following month (if the first month was *chaseir*).[45] Other *Poskim* disagree; they contend that *onah beinonis* is similar to all other

---

hachodesh, not an *onah beinonis*, since a woman with a *vest kavuah* need not keep *onah beinonis*. The reverse case of an *onah beinonis* that is not a *vest hachodesh* is found in a case where a woman menstruated on the first of the month after strong physical exertion. This is called a *vest haones*, a *vest* caused by an external factor, as explained in Chapter Nineteen. She is required to keep a *vest hachodesh* on the following first of the month only if the conditions at the time replicate those of the first month, i.e., she exerts herself again in a similar manner, otherwise, she need not keep *yom hachodesh* as *vest hachodesh*. However, she must keep it as *onah beinonis*, since she has no *vest kavuah*. See also responsa *Eimek HaTeshuvah* 1:132 for further analysis of *Shach's* position.

43. See *Graz* 189:1, who proves that *Ramban* disagrees with *Shach*. He notes that *Shach* stands alone in his opinion that *onah beinonis* is *vest hachodesh*.

44. *Pische Zuta* 189:1 citing *Pri Deah*. See *Shiurei Sheivet HaLeivi* on *Shach* §30.

45. *Pleisi* 189:15, *Graz* §1 and *Cheiker Halachah, Niddah* §1. *Cheiker Halachah* explains that since an *onah beinonis* is based upon the normal interval for the average woman, the time of the period of the individual woman's last period is irrelevant. *Badei HaShulchan* 189:13, s.v. אין האשה explains that the rationale of limiting a *vest* to the *onah* of the previous menstruation is simply because we assume that the cause of the flow was that particular *onah*. However, the *onah beinonis* is not based on what caused her previous flow; rather, it is based upon the assumption that she is like most women who menstruate on the thirtieth day. We have no reason to limit this to the day or night alone. *Cheiker Halachah* adds an interesting addendum to this *halachah*. He contends that even if she set a *vest kavuah* for the thirtieth day, she is required to keep both the night and day *onos* as her *onas havest*, regardless of when the original period began and regardless of whether or not she usually keeps the *Or Zarua vest*. A woman who establishes a different day as a *vest kavuah* replaces the *onah beinonis* with the *vest*

vestos and one must abstain only on the primary *onah* of the last menstruation (in this case, the day *onah*).[46] We will note in Chapter Twenty-Two that many *Poskim* rule, with regard to <u>all</u> *vestos,* that one should abstain during the twelve-hour period before the primary *onas havest* Commonly called the *"Or Zarua's vest."* Contemporary authorities rule that even one who normally does not follow this opinion[47] should follow the stricter opinion regarding the *onah beinonis* of the thirtieth day if the last menstruation took place by day.[48] In a situation of difficulty, one should consult a Rav. The basic issues with which one must contend are two: When does one abstain the full twenty-four hours[49] and when does one abstain on the thirty-first day?[50] We will discuss several situations:

> 1. A woman must abstain and do *bedikos* on the thirtieth day. If her previous menstruation was during the night, the night of the thirtieth is certainly the *onas havest.* If the previous menstruation was by day, the day of the thirtieth is the *onas havest;* however, she should abstain on the previous night as well.

> 2. Regarding the thirty-first day, it depends if the previous month was *malei* or *chaseir.* If the previous month was *malei,* the thirty-first *onah beinonis* day will be the *vest hachodesh* in any case. One must abstain on that *onah* even if it would not be *onah beinonis.* The only leniency could be in a case where the previous menstruation was by day. In that case, the night preceding the thirty-first day may be permitted if one usually does not abstain during the *"Or Zarua's vest."* However, if one keeps the *Or Zarua vest,* one would abstain the night before the thirty-first because of the *vest hachodesh.*

kavuah. The *onah beinonis* is no longer relevant. However, a woman who establishes a *vest kavuah* for a thirty-day interval actually turned her *onah beinonis* into a *vest kavuah;* thus, she has an *onah beinonis kavuah* which must be treated with the stringencies of an *onah beinonis* as well. See also *Badei HaShulchan* 189:13, s.v. אין האשה.

46. *Sidrei Taharah* 189 end of 31. *Pri Deah,* 189 introduction to §8, contends that most *Poskim* seem to accept this lenient view. *Pische Zuta,* who cites this in 189:5, also seems to accept this view. See also responsa *Cheishev HaAifod* 1:141.

47. Even one who normally follows the *Or Zarua* is not required to add the *Or Zarua's vest* onto the *Pleisi's* twenty-four hours. If the previous menstruation was during the day, one is not required to abstain a total of thirty-six hours. *Shiurei Sheivet HaLeivi* 189:1[5].

48. See *Shiurei Sheivet HaLeivi* 189:1[5] and *Badei HaShulchan* 189:7. The opinion of *Or Zarua* regarding all *vestos* and that of *Pleisi* regarding *onah beinonis* are not based on the same principle. Nevertheless, in this case we have a convergence of two independent reasons to abstain earlier: the *Or Zaruah's vest* and the twenty-four-hour duration of the *onah beinonis.*

49. As is the opinion of *Pleisi* and *Graz.*

50. As is the opinion of *Chavos Daas.*

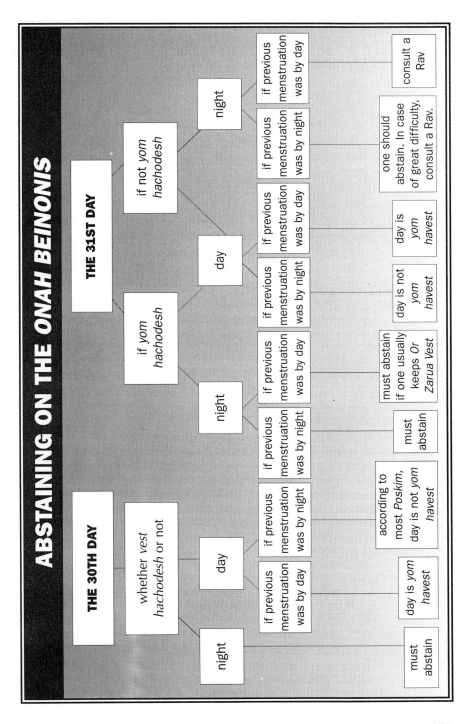

ABSTAINING ON THE *ONAH BEINONIS*

THE 30TH DAY

whether *vest hachodesh* or not

night

must abstain

day

if previous menstruation was by day

day is *yom havest*

if previous menstruation was by night

according to most *Poskim*, day is not *yom havest*

THE 31ST DAY

if *yom hachodesh*

night

if previous menstruation was by night

must abstain

if previous menstruation was by day

must abstain if one usually keeps *Or Zarua Vest*

day

if previous menstruation was by night

day is not *yom havest*

if previous menstruation was by day

day is *yom havest*

if not *yom hachodesh*

night

if previous menstruation was by night

one should abstain. In case of great difficulty, consult a Rav.

if previous menstruation was by day

consult a Rav

3. If the previous month was *chaseir,* the *yom hachodesh* and *onah beinonis* are both on the thirtieth day. Thus, the thirty-first day is considered *onah beinonis* only according to a minority opinion.

a. If the previous period was at night, one should abstain on the night of the thirty-first. In a case of great need, one must consult a Rav.[51]

b. If the previous period was during the day, there is additional reason that one not be required to abstain on the night before; nevertheless a Rav should be consulted.[52]

4. If a *tevilah* night[53] coincides with the *onah beinonis:*

a. If the *tevilah* is on the night before the thirtieth day after a day period a Rav must be consulted.[54]

b. If the *tevilah* is scheduled on the thirty-first night, and the previous period was during the day, one may follow the lenient opinion.[55]

c. If the *tevilah* is scheduled on the thirty-first night, and the previous period was at night, the *tevilah* may have to be postponed. One should consult a Rav.[56]

D. Situations in which the *onah beinonis* is subject to controversy

1. If a woman passes the *vest kavuah* day:

A woman who has a *vest kavuah* for an interval of thirty-one days or more is not subject to *onah beinonis* since she expects her period

---

51. *Shiurei Sheivet HaLeivi* on *Shach* §30.

52. In this case, we may not be required to follow *Pleisi's* opinion to abstain on the night *onah.* In the opinion of most *Poskim,* the thirty-first day is not the *onah beinonis.* Thus, although we follow *Chavos Daas'* opinion to consider the thirty-first day the *onah beinonis,* we do not extend this to the *Pleisi's* opinion regarding the night of the *onah beinonis.* Briefly stated, we follow each *chumra* (those of *Pleisi* and *Chavos Daas*) independently of one another; we do not follow them in combination. See *Be'er Moshe* 1:47.

53. See Chapter Twenty-Two regarding the issues involved in a *tevilah* on the *onas havest.* Generally, it is accepted that a woman must abstain on the *onas havest* even if it is her *tevilah* night. Many *Poskim* are lenient regarding the *Or Zarua's vest.*

54. See *Shiurei Sheivet HaLeivi* 189:1[5]. In this case, the *Or Zarua's* view would not be an impediment, since we normally push aside his view when a *tevilah* is involved. The question of *onah beinonis* is more serious.

55. *Shiurei Sheivet HaLeivi* ibid., as in note 52 above.

56. *Shiurei Sheivet HaLeivi* ibid.

on her normal *vest* day, not earlier.[57] If a woman has a *vest kavuah* for an interval of less than thirty days and passes the *haflagah* day without incident, some *Poskim* contend that she is subject to the rules of *onah beinonis* on the thirtieth day.[58] The logic to this is simple: Any woman who has no permanent day on which to expect her *vest* must observe *onah beinonis*. The reason we exempt a woman with a *vest kavuah* from *onah beinonis* is only because she has a set time to menstruate and we are not concerned that she may menstruate on another day. She is therefore not subject to the median period of other women. However, once she passes her *vest kavuah* without menstruating, she must expect her period on the *onah beinonis* since there is no other specific day on which to expect her period.[59] Other *Poskim* disagree; they do not differentiate between a *vest haflagah* that is shorter and one that is longer than thirty days.[60] Some later authorities rule that it is proper to follow the first, stringent view. However, they are lenient regarding anything but the basic *onah beinonis*. Thus, she keeps only the thirtieth day as *onah beinonis*, not the thirty-first (see Section B), only the exact *onah*, not the full twenty-four-hour day and not the previous twelve-hour *onah* (see Chapter Twenty-Two).[61]

2. A woman who consistently passes the *onah beinonis* without incident:

There is an opinion that a woman who never menstruates before the thirty-first day is not subject to *onah beinonis*.

---

57. 189:1. See *Lechem VeSimlah* §2[s]. *Beis Yosef* 189 cites *Ran* who notes the opinion of *Rashi* that even a woman with a *vest kavuah* is subject to *onah beinonis*.

58. The original source for this is *Ramban* in his commentary to *Niddah* 15a. *Ran* (*Shavuos,* Chapter Two) concurs with this opinion, while *Rashba* (*Niddah* 15a) considers this an excessive *chumra*. *Taz* 189:5, as interpreted by *Chavos Daas* §2[b] and 20[b], follows *Ramban's* stringent opinion (it seems odd that *Taz* in §31 cites the opposing lenient opinion of *Levush* without comment). *Lechem VeSimlah* §3[b] seems to accept *Ramban's* opinion although in §2[s] he cites *Rashba's* lenient opinion as well. *Sugah Bashoshanim* 5:24 cites many lenient sources among the *Rishonim,* but concludes that one should follow the stringent opinions.

59. One should remember that the underlying principle of *onah beinonis* is: Will she never have a period? וכי לעולם לא תראה? See *Badei HaShulchan* 189:1, *Biurim* s.v. ואם יש, regarding a *vest hachodesh*.

60. *Rashba, Niddah* 15a. *Maharshal,* cited in *Taz* 189:31, clearly follows *Rashba's* lenient opinion. *Badei HaShulchan* 189:1, *Biurim* s.v. ואם יש, notes that *Shulchan Aruch* 189:1 and 14 also seems to follow this lenient view.

61. *Sugah Bashoshanim* 5:24. *Shiurei Sheivet HaLeivi* 189:1[5] seems to lean towards this view. However, *Taharas Yisrael* 189:15 follows the lenient opinion and rules that one need not keep *onah beinonis* at all.

According to this opinion, the fact that she never menstruates before the thirty-first day gives her a status of a woman with a *vest kavuah* during those days (we find a similar idea in Chapter Fourteen, Section I,D,2,d). Nevertheless, almost all *Poskim*[62] disagree. They contend that she is subject to *onah beinonis* since she has no set day on which to expect her period.[63]

---

62. The wording of *Toras HaShelamim* 189:4 seems to imply that an *onah beinonis* is uprooted even when passed only once. *Toras HaShelamim* takes issue with *Levush* (cited by *Shach* §30) who (*Toras HaShelamim* claims) contends that an *onah beinonis* is uprooted only after it is passed three times. However, this is not necessarily the intention of *Toras HaShelamim*. See *Pri Deah* on *Shach* §30 for an entirely different interpretation of *Toras HaShelamim* and *Levush*. However, *Chavos Daas*, end of §12, interprets *Levush* as being of the opinion that a woman who passed the *onah beinonis* three times without incident is no longer subject to *onah beinonis*. He contends that *Shach* § 30 soundly disagrees with *Levush*. See also *Pri Deah* on *Shach* §30. *Chavos Daas* 186:3[b] considers the lenient position of *Levush* absurd. The opinions of *Levush* and *Toras HaShelamim* are subject to interpretation. *Shach, Chavos Daas* and *Pri Deah* are certainly of the opinion that *onah beinonis* is never uprooted. *Sidrei Taharah* 189:20 is undecided on the issue, and seems to lean towards the stricter view. Among the later *Poskim* who take a lenient view are: *Taharas Yisrael* 183:13 and *Igros Moshe, Y.D.* 2:72. Most other contemporary *Poskim* follow the stricter view. See *Minchas Yitzchak* 6:82, *Shiurei Sheivet HaLeivi* on *Shach* 189:30, s.v. ולהלכה, *Be'er Moshe* 1:47, *Chelkas Yaakov* 2:74, *Eimek HaTeshuvah* 1:128 and *Badei HaShulchan* 186:25. The author was told by R' Yaakov Kaminetsky *zt"l* that in Lithuania the lenient view was not accepted.

63. A woman who has a *vest kavuah* differs in two aspects from one who has none: a) She has a definite day on which to expect her period and b) she is assured that she will not menstruate on any other day. Therefore she is exempt from *onah beinonis*. A woman who has no *vest kavuah* has no day on which to expect her period and must be concerned that she may menstruate at any time. She is therefore subject to *onah beinonis*. A woman who never menstruates before a certain interval but has no specific day on which she menstruates (for example, she never menstruates before the thirty-second day) is similar to a woman with a *vest kavuah* with regard to aspect b) because she is sure that she will not menstruate before the thirty-second day, but not with regard to aspect a) since she has no specific day on which to expect her period. It seems clear from *Poskim* that the criterion that excludes a woman with a *vest kavuah* from *onah beinonis* is that she expects her period on a particular day other than the thirtieth. This woman, who has no specific day on which to expect menstruation, must therefore keep *onah beinonis*.

CHAPTER SIXTEEN

וסת הדילוג

Unusual Patterns in *Vestos*

- □ *Vest haflagah bedilug.*
- □ *Vest hachodesh bedilug.*
- □ *Vest haseirug.*
- □ *Vest hashavuah.*

Introduction

In the previous chapter, we discussed the common *vestos* that apply to almost all women: *vest haflagah, vest hachodesh* and *onah beinonis*. In this chapter, we will discuss *vestos* that follow an unusual pattern. It is very rare for a woman to maintain these unusual *vestos* for a longer period. However, they may appear over a span of several months. It is therefore necessary that one be acquainted with the concept of these *vestos* so that one can recognize them if and when they appear. We will discuss three types of unusual patterns: a *vest hadilug* — a *vest* that increases or decreases in increments, a *vest haseirug* — an alternating *vest,* and a *vest hashavuah* — a *vest* dependent upon the day of the week. This last case is actually not an instance of an unusual pattern; rather, it is an unusual type of a *vest,* as will be explained.

A. *Vest hadilug:* an incremental *vest*

A woman may set a *vest* in a pattern of incrementation e.g., n, n+1, n+2.[1] This is possible in both *vest haflagah* and *vest hachodesh*. For example, a woman menstruates on day five of month A, on day six of month B and day seven of month C. Similarly, she may menstruate after an interval of twenty-four days, followed by an interval of twenty-five days and then an interval of twenty-six days. Two factors set apart *vest hadilug* from other *vestos:* a) Since a *vest hadilug* is unusual, one need not suspect that a *vest hadilug* will repeat itself (even if it occurs twice). A *vest hadilug* is significant only after it is repeated three times and becomes a *vest kavuah*.[2] b) Every *vest kavuah* is a phenomenon that repeated itself three times; similarly, a *vest hadilug* may not become *kavuah* until after the *dilug*, the incrementation itself, is repeated three times. *Vest hadilug* differs from other

---

1. These numbers are used merely as an example. The *vest* may also increase in increments of 2 (n, n+2, n+4), 3 (n, n+3, n+6) or any amount; 189:5, *Aruch HaShulchan* §19. *Badei HaShulchan* 189:5, *Biurim* s.v. שבכל ענין, explores the possibility of a *vest* with increments in the amount of increments. For example, she menstruates in a progression of 30, 31, 33 (which is 2 days later than the previous interval) and 36 (which is 3 days later than the previous interval). This is n, n+1, n+3 and n+6. Certainly, in this case, we cannot consider this a *vest,* even according to *Rav,* until she menstruates after an interval of 40 (4 days later than the previous interval, n+10), since this particular type of increment is not noticeable until the third period.

2. 189:11. This applies equally to a *vest hachodesh bedilug* and a *vest haflagah bedilug;* see *Lechem VeSimlah* §17[s]. For this reason R' Y. S. Eliashiv (cited in *Shevilei Taharah* [R' Stern] 25) rules that since, in basic *halachah,* a woman is not subject to *vestos* during the twenty-four-month period following childbirth, any consideration of *vestos* at that time is merely a *chumra*. Therefore, one need not be concerned with any *vest hadilug* during that time.

vestos in that it cannot become *kavuah* with merely three periods since three periods can never form three *dilugim*. Using a *vest hachodesh* as an example, a woman who menstruated on the fifth of month A and on the sixth of month B has two periods but only one *dilug*. Thus, a woman cannot establish a *vest hachodesh, bedilug, kavuah* unless she has a minimum of four periods. A *haflagah bedilug*, an incremental interval, also[3] needs three periods to establish one *dilug*, since two periods create only one simple interval. For example, a woman menstruates twenty-four days after her previous period. She now has one interval. If, after twenty-five days, she menstruates again, she has one *haflagah bedilug*. She needs five periods to establish a *vest haflagah, bedilug, kavuah* since three *dilugim* require four intervals which, in turn, require five periods.[4] This is the opinion of *Shmuel*.[5] However, *Rav* disagrees. He contends that both a regular *vest* and a *vest hadilug* require the same amount of periods to establish a *vest kavuah*. Thus, according to *Rav*, a *vest hachodesh bedilug* requires only three periods while a *vest haflagah bedilug* requires only four periods.[6] There is a difference of opinion among *Rishonim* as to which opinion to follow. *Shulchan Aruch*[7] rules that we follow the stringent aspect of either position.[8] This will be explained during the course of our discussion.

1. *Vest haflagah bedilug:*

A woman who menstruated after an interval of twenty-four days

---

3. This is the opinion of *Shach* 189:15, who contends that *Shmuel* applies his principle to *vest haflagah bedilug* as well. This opinion is followed by most *Poskim*. However, it is noteworthy that *Lechem VeSimlah* §10[s] contends that it seems from *Rambam* and *Raavad* that *Shmuel* concedes that a *vest haflagah bedilug* is similar to a regular *vest haflagah* and requires only four periods. *Chazon Ish, Y.D.* 86:1, assumes the exact opposite (see also *Reshash, Niddah* 64a). According to his understanding of the *Rishonim*, even *Rav* concedes that a *vest haflagah bedilug* requires five, not four, periods. Both *Lechem VeSimlah* and *Chazon Ish* concede that their view is at variance with that of other *Poskim*.

4. These five periods would suffice even if the first of the five was part of a pre-existing *vest kavuah*. For example, if she had a *vest kavuah* for the twenty-fifth interval and, on the following four occasions, menstruated on the twenty-sixth, twenty-seventh, twenty-eighth and twenty-ninth intervals, it is considered a *vest hadilug kavuah*, even according to *Shmuel* (189:7, see also *Niddah* 64a).

5. Cited in *Niddah* 64a , regarding a *vest hachodesh*.

6. *Rav* concedes that if the first period was part of a previous *vest kavuah*, for example, she previously had a *vest kavuah* for the fifth of the month, she cannot use the last menstruation of the fifth of the month as one of the periods that establish a *vest hadilug* (see *Niddah* 64a).

7. 189:7.

8. *Sidrei Taharah* §6, notes that although *vestos* are Rabbinic (*deRabbanan*), we do not use the usual rule of *safek deRabbanan lehakel* (one may follow the lenient option when dealing with laws of Rabbinic origin). *Lechem VeSimlah* §15[s] explains that this is because, in this case, either view is both a *kula* and a *chumra*.

and subsequently menstruated after twenty-five days has experienced one *dilug*. Since one *dilug* is insignificant, it is ignored. On the following month, she is required to keep an *onah* on the twenty-fifth day only (besides the thirtieth — the *onah beinonis*).[9] If no blood appears on that day, she need not suspect that the *vest* will skip another day and arrive on the following day, the twenty-sixth. If the next period does arrive on the twenty-sixth day, she has experienced two *dilugim* but must nevertheless keep an *onah* only on the following twenty-sixth (and thirtieth) interval day. She is not required to keep an *onah* on the twenty-seventh (the possible *dilug*) day since she has not yet established a *vest kavuah* for *dilug*. If the next period arrives on the twenty-seventh day, she has established a *vest haflagah, bedilug, kavuah* according to *Rav,* but not according to *Shmuel.* Accordingly, she must keep her *onah* the following twenty-seventh day (as a *vest she'aino kavuah,* in *Shmuel's* view), the twenty-eighth day (as a *vest kavuah,* in *Rav's* view) and *onah beinonis* on the thirtieth day[10] (according to *Shmuel,* since she has not as yet established a *vest kavuah*). If her next period arrives after an interval of twenty-eight days, she has established a *vest haflagah, bedilug, kavuah* according to all opinions.[11] She now expects the next period only on the twenty-ninth day, not the twenty-eighth. She no longer keeps the *onah beinonis,* since she has a *vest kavuah.*[12] If the following period arrives on the thirty-second day instead of the twenty-ninth, she should expect her next period on the thirtieth day (and the thirty-second day)[13] from the menstruation of the thirty-second day.[14]

---

9. In addition to the proper *vest hachodesh.*

10. In addition to the *vest hachodesh.*

11. However, if the period arrives on the twenty-ninth day, she has not established a *vest hadilug.* Her potential *dilug* was for an increment of one day; instead, she had a two-day increment. See 189:10.

12. Had the period not arrived on the twenty-eighth day but on the thirty-second, according to *Rav,* she must expect her period on the twenty-ninth interval day from the menstruation of the thirty-second (see note 14). According to *Shmuel,* she would expect it on the thirty-second interval day from the thirty-second.

13. Since she has both a *vest kavuah* and a *vest she'aino kavuah.*

14. *Mekor Chaim* 189:22, as explained in *Badei HaShulchan* 189:5, *Biurim* s.v. לדילוג. See also *Sheivet HaLeivi* 2:83. See a similar case regarding a *vest hachodesh,* in *Chavos Daas* 189:5[b]. In this case, she effected one *akirah* of her *vest.* However, since she has a *vest kavuah,* she must continue to expect her periods on the *dilug* days. One should note that a *vest hadilug* does not determine that the following period will be one day (in this case) later than the last. Rather, it follows the predetermined system that was set by her *vest* (i.e., 24, 25, 26, 27, 28, 29, 30 and 31). Thus, her expected day is not

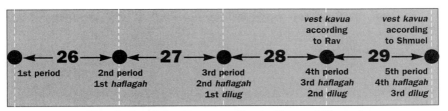

Vest haflagah bedilug according to Rav and Shmuel

2. *Vest hachodesh bedilug:*

A woman menstruated on the fifth day of the month and on the following month menstruates on the sixth day of the month. She has thus far experienced only one *dilug*, which may be ignored. She therefore expects the next period only on the sixth of the next month. If the period arrives on the seventh of the month instead, she has established a *vest hachodesh, bedilug, kavuah* according to *Rav* but not according to *Shmuel*. Since we follow the stringent aspect of both *Rav* and *Shmuel*, she must keep her *onah* on the seventh (as a *vest she'aino kavuah,* according to *Shmuel*) and the eighth (as a *vest kavuah,* according to *Rav*) of the following month. In addition, she must keep the *onah beinonis*.[15] If, on the following month, she menstruates on the eighth of the month,[16] she has a *vest hachodesh, bedilug, kavuah* according to both *Rav* and *Shmuel*, and keeps only the ninth of the following month,[17] not the eighth and not the *onah beinonis*. If the period does not arrive on the ninth or any day of that month, she must observe *yom havest* only

_____

the thirty-third (which is one day later than her present *vest*), but the thirtieth. *Badei HaShulchan* (ibid.) raises an interesting question: if she menstruated on the twenty-eighth day instead of the expected twenty-ninth, should she expect her next period on the twenty-ninth or the thirtieth?

15. And the proper *vest haflagah* if applicable.

16. However, if the period arrives on the ninth of the month, she has not established a *vest hadilug;* see 189:10.

17. 189:7. *Poskim* grapple with the question of how to deal with this *vest* once she reaches the thirtieth of the month. Should the *vest* continue to the first of the month after four weeks? Or perhaps since her *vest* increases in date, not decreases, the *vest* should no longer apply? *Pische Zuta* 189:9 cites *Pri Deah*, introduction *Shaar* 8, who rules that the *vest* continues to the first of the month, the second, etc. However, he is less than certain. *Lechem VeSimlah* §17[s] seems to follow this view. *Chidushei Haflaah* 189:2 rules that the *vest* is eliminated when it reaches the end of the month. A similar ruling is found in *Sugah Bashoshanim* 4:12, and attributed to *Chazon Ish* in *Imrei Avraham* (R' Auerbach) 2. See also *Minchas Yitzchak* 10:77[1]. *Badei HaShulchan* 189:7, *Biurim* s.v. עד שתראה , notes that the phrase "וכן לעולם — and so forever" used by *Shulchan Aruch* seems to imply that the *vest* does not come to an abrupt end. Obviously the *vest* continues to the first of the month.

on the tenth of the following month.[18] If the period does not arrive for three months, the *vest hadilug* is uprooted.[19]

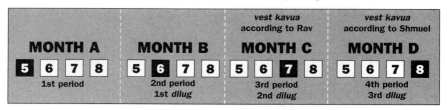

Vest hachodesh bedilug according to Rav and Shmuel

Shulchan Aruch[20] cites another example of *vest hachodesh bedilug* in a case of a recurring cycle of increments. A woman who menstruates on the 15th of month A, the 16th of month B, the 17 of month C, the 15th of month D, the 16th of month E, the 17 of month F, the 15th of month G, the 16th of month H and the 17 of month I[21] has established a *vest* of recur-

---

18. *Chavos Daas* 189:5[b].

19. See *Pri Deah* §8 who is uncertain whether this *vest* remains dormant and can be revived with one menstruation on the *vest* day (see Chapter Seventeen, Section I,C). For example, If she menstruates at a later date on the expected *dilug* day, can the *vest* be reestablished? If it can be reestablished, *Pri Deah* is uncertain whether the expected *dilug* day is calculated according to the projected *dilug* had she not uprooted the *vest*, or does the last number become frozen in place? For example, she had a *hadilug* of intervals of 15, 16, 17 and 18 and thereby established a *vest hadilug*. In the following three months, she did not menstruate (or menstruated on different days). On the fourth month, she menstruated on a 19th interval day. Would this reestablish her *vest hadilug*? *Pri Deah* is inclined to conclude that the *vest* is not reestablished since her expected *vest* for this month (had she continued her *dilugim*) should be the 22nd not the 19th interval day; however, he reaches no positive conclusion. Another possible solution is that the *vest* is reestablished whenever she menstruates again with a one-day increment. *Minchas Yitzchak* 10:77[1] notes these two possibilities. A similar question is raised in *sefer Shvilei Taharah* (R' Stern) 25, regarding a woman with a *vest hadilug* for 15, 16, 17 and 18 who became pregnant. After childbirth, should she expect her *vest* to resume on the 19th or must she calculate the increment for each month of pregnancy? He proposes that perhaps this case is different than that above since no menstruation is expected during pregnancy; thus, the entire span of time is completely out of the picture. *Sefer Pischei Migadim* p. 379 cites an opinion of R' Gedaliah Nadel that a *vest hadilug* that is uprooted three times is completely uprooted and cannot be reinstated even if she menstruates again on the *yom havest*. He explains that when a *vest kavuah* that was uprooted and made dormant is reestablished, it functions in the following manner: The *vest* recurs once and is immediately a *vest she'aino kavuah*; since this *vest* was once a *vest kavuah* and was never completely uprooted, it immediately is elevated into a *vest kavuah*. However, a *vest hadilug* that occurs once is insignificant, it is not even considered a *vest she'aino kavuah* until it occurs three times. Therefore, the one occurrence cannot be elevated into a *vest kavuah*.

20. 189:8 (according to *Shach* §20). This *dilug* is interesting in that even *Shmuel* would agree that the first level of the *vest* is based upon only three months of 15, 16 and 17. One could argue that, according to *Shmuel*, we require four menstruations of 15, 16, 17 and 18 in the first level (followed by 16, 17, 18, 16, 17, 18). Indeed, this is the opinion of *Bach* (cited in *Shach*). However, for the sake of simplicity, we followed the opinion of *Shach*.

21. *Chidushei Haflaah* examines several novel variations of this *vest*. For example, if she menstruates

ring *dilugim*.[22] This vest can also manifest itself in two-month cycles, i.e., the 15th of month A, the 16th of month B, the 15 of month C, the 16 of month D, etc.,[23] or four-month cycles.[24]

3. A decreasing *vest hadilug*:

A woman may establish either a *vest haflagah* or a *vest hachodesh* in a decreasing *dilug*.[25] For example, she menstruates in intervals of twenty-eight, twenty-seven, twenty-six and twenty-five. She establishes a *vest hadilug* and subsequently keeps her *onah* one day earlier each cycle. Similarly, if she menstruates on the eighth of month A, the seventh of month B, the sixth of month C and the fifth of month D, she establishes a *vest hachodesh, bedilug*. These two *vestos* depend upon the respective opinions of *Rav* and *Shmuel*.

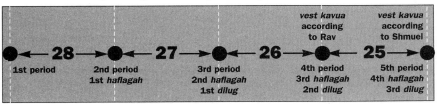

A decreasing Vest haflagah, bedilug according to Rav and Shmuel

A decreasing Vest hachodesh bedilug according to Rav and Shmuel

---

in the following manner, 15, 15, 16, 16, 17 and 17 of consecutive months. He also speculates whether this type of *vest* is possible in a *vest haflagah*. For example, if she menstruated after intervals of 20, 30, 40, 20, 30, 40, 20, 30 and 40. He is certain, however, that if her intervals followed a pattern of 20, 30, 20, 30, 20 and 30, it would not be a *vest* since this *vest* is only possible as a *vest haseirug* which cannot apply to a *vest haflagah*.

22. This *vest* can be understood as one large *vest* comprised of nine menstruations or three separate *vestos* of three menstruations each. This is especially relevant to the manner in which they are uprooted. See *Shiurei Sheivet HaLeivi* 189:8[2] and *Badei HaShulchan, Biurim* 188:8.

23. *Taz* §10 and *Shach* §21.

24. I.e., 15, 16, 17, 18, 15, 16, 17, 18 and 15, 16, 17, 18, of consecutive months, *Taz* ibid.

25. *Shach* §9, *Graz* §19. This *vest* is most unusual because it cannot continue indefinitely. Once the *vest haflagah* reaches the lowest numbers, e.g., three, two, it must stop decreasing. See *Pleisi* §6. *Aruch HaShulchan* §19, however, notes (as does *Graz*) that *Shach's* opinion is supported by *Raavad*.

B. *Vest haseirug:* an alternating *vest*

Another example of an unusual *vest* is a *vest haseirug*, an alternating *vest*. We discussed earlier that a woman may set a *vest hachodesh* on alternating months. For example, a woman menstruated the fifth day of months One, Three and Five but not on months Two, Four and Six. She has a *vest kavuah* on the fifth of all odd numbered months but not on even numbered months.[26] This is a *vest haseirug*.[27] A *vest haseirug* is only possible in terms of a *vest hachodesh*, not a *vest haflagah*. This *vest* is unusual and odd, for, if the fifth day of the month causes her menstruation, we would expect it to do so every month. For this reason, a *vest haseirug* shares the *halachic* status of a *vest hadilug*. One does not suspect a *vest haseirug* until it is established as a *vest kavuah*.[28] There is a difference of opinion if a *vest haseirug* also shares the nature of a *vest hadilug* regarding the *halachah* that, according to *Shmuel*, a *vest haflagah* needs five periods and a *vest hachodesh* needs four periods to become a *vest kavuah*.[29] Most *Poskim* follow the view that, in this case, even *Shmuel* concedes that the first period is counted and only three periods are required to establish the *vest*.[30]

MONTH A	MONTH B	MONTH C	MONTH D	MONTH E
5	5	5	5	5

Vest haseirug

---

26. 189:9. However, if she menstruated on the fifth of months 1, 2 and 4, she has not established a *vest haseirug*, ibid.

27. See *Badei HaShulchan, Biurim* 189:9 s.v. "באחד," regarding a woman who menstruated on the fifth of months 1, 2, 3, 5 and 7. Should the menstruation of month 3 be used to establish a normal *vest hachodesh* or should it be combined with 5 and 7 to create a *vest haseirug*? See also s.v. "קבעה" regarding a woman who menstruated on the fifth of months 1, 3, 5, 6 and 7. Should the menstruation of month 5 be combined with that of 6 and 7 to create a regular *vest hachodesh*?

28. 189:12. For similar reasons, *Shaarei Tohar* 4:6, rules that if the *vest haseirug* takes place in the summer (when the months follow the schedule of one *chaseir* and one *malei*) and continues four times, i.e., she menstruates on the fifth of month 7, the *vest* turns into a *vest haflagah* of sixty days, since a *vest haflagah* is more common than a *vest haseirug*. Thus, all the differences between a *vest haflagah* and a *vest hachodesh* apply; see also *Shiurei Sheivet HaLeivi* 189:9. Nevertheless, this *halachah* applies for the seventh month (the *vest* becomes a *vest kavuah* after three periods. Thus, she must abstain on the fifth of the seventh month). The *halachah* may also apply during the winter months if the months follow the normal pattern of one *chaser* and one *malei*, or if she had a minor menstrual flow in between these periods.

29. See *Prishah* §14 and *Taz* §12 (see *Aruch HaShulchan* §25, who understands *Taz* in a different manner), who rule that, according to *Shmuel*, an extra period is required. However, *Shach* §26, citing *Raavad*, disagrees, as does *Toras HaShelamim* §15 and *Chavos Daas* §14[c].

30. The simple understanding of *Shulchan Aruch* 189:12 supports this view (see, however, *Taz* §12). See *Taharas Yisrael* §59.

C. *Vest hashavuah:* a *vest* based upon days of the week

A woman may set a *vest* based upon the particular day of the week.[31] A woman may menstruate on three Sundays[32] or every third or fourth Sunday and thereby show that Sundays activate her menstrual cycle. This is essentially similar to a *vest hachodesh* and needs only three occurrences to establish the *vest*.[33]

1. Types of *vest* hashavuah:
Poskim offer two examples of a *vest hashavuah:*

a. A woman who menstruated on three consecutive Sundays has established a *vest* to menstruate each and every Sunday.[34] The obvious problem with this *vest* is that it seems completely irrelevant since she will not be able to count seven "clean" days by the following Sunday. Thus, she will be *temeah* and must abstain regardless of the *vest*. *Poskim* explain that this *vest* can be relevant if she passes one Sunday without incident. She then may be able to immerse in a *mikveh* the following Thursday night. She will then be required to abstain the

---

31. One should note that the day of the week, according to *halachah,* starts on the previous evening. With regard to *vestos,* it starts exactly at sundown of the previous evening, as has been explained in Chapter Thirteen.

32. *Tur* and *Shulchan Aruch* add that this *vest* can be established even if she menstruates on unequal days of the week. Apparently, this means that a woman who menstruated on a Sunday, Tuesday and Thursday establishes a *vest hashavuah bedilug* and must expect her *vest* two days later of each week. *Sidrei Taharah* §4 finds this difficult. Why, he asks, isn't every *vest haflagah* established after three periods since every *vest haflagah* can be presented as a *vest hashavuah bedilug*? *Sidrei Taharah* concludes that since a *vest hashavuah bedilug* is unusual, we normally assume a *vest* to be a *vest haflagah* rather than a *vest hashavuah bedilug*. However, if the *vest* cannot be viewed as a *vest haflagah*, i.e., she had a minor flow between the regular flows, we are forced to assume the unusual: that the *vest* is a *vest hashavuah bedilug*. This is also the view of *Chavos Daas* §4[b]. However, *Graz* (*Kuntres Acharon,* end of §3) seems to hold that there is no such thing as a *vest hashavuah bedilug* (he is referring to the second type of *vest hashavuah,* noted in b below, not a *vest hashavuah* of consecutive weeks). He contends that we have a source in Talmud only for *vest haseirug* (which is similar to this case of *vest hashavuah*) or *vest hadilug,* not both combined. This is also the final position taken by *Sidrei Taharah* in §31 and *Haflaah* 189:2. Thus, when *Shulchan Aruch* refers to a *vest hashavuah bedilug,* he means only one that recurred three consecutive weeks. *Badei HaShulchan* §47 maintains that one may follow this lenient view.

33. 189:6.

34. *Prishah* §8 and *Graz* §22.

following two Sundays since her *vest kavuah* must be uprooted three times.

b. A woman who menstruated every third Sunday has also established a *vest hashavuah*.[35] This *vest* is similar to a *vest hachodesh beseirug* in that it can be established with only three periods (see above regarding *vest haseirug*).[36]

2. The difference between a *vest hashavuah* and a *vest haflagah*:

Every *vest hashavuah* is also a *vest haflagah* since the periods are separated by an equal number of days. However, *Poskim* note several differences.[37]

a. A *vest haflagah* needs a minimum of four periods to establish itself, while each of the types of *vest hashavuah* is established with three periods.[38]

b. Another example of the particular nature of the *vest hashavuah* is in a case where the woman passed Sunday and menstruated on Tuesday instead. Had the Sunday *vest* been a *vest haflagah*, she would count a *haflagah* to the next Tuesday (or in case b, the following third Tuesday), since a *vest haflagah* is always calculated from the last menstruation. However, since the Sunday *vest* is a *vest hashavuah*, she must keep *yom havest* on Sunday, in addition to the following Tuesday.

c. If a woman had an additional minor blood flow between two regular *vestos* of Sunday, the *vest haflagah* aspect would no longer be an interval of eight (or twenty-two) days since the last interval was between the minor flow and the last Sunday period. However, the *vest hashavuah*, similar to a *vest hachodesh*, is unaffected by any intermittent flow. Thus, she continues to keep the corresponding Sunday as her *yom havest* (in addition to any *vest* caused by the intermittent minor flow).[39]

---

35. *Shach* §14 citing *Bach*.

36. *Toras HaShelamim* §9 citing *Beis Yosef*.

37. See *Pleisi* §8, *Chavos Daas* §4[b] and *Sidrei Taharah* §4.

38. *Toras HaShelamim* §9.

39. *Chavos Daas* §4[b] and *Sidrei Taharah* §4.

d. If she passed three of her *vest* Sundays without incident, the *vest hashavuah* is uprooted. However, the *vest haflagah* is not uprooted until she passes the *vest haflagah* day after three separate actual menstruations without incident.

e. If she passes one Sunday without incident, the *vest haflagah* aspect is ineffectual until she menstruates again; otherwise, there is no period from which to calculate the *haflagah*. However, the *vest hashavuah* aspect is still operative. She must therefore treat the following Sunday as a *yom havest*.[40]

f. A woman who had a *vest hashavuah* for Sundays, and uprooted it, restores that *vest* any time that she menstruates again on Sunday. However, the *vest haflagah, kavuah* is not reestablished again until she has two periods separated by the previous amount of days.[41]

g. If, on the third Sunday, the flow started a day or two earlier, i.e., the flow started on Friday and continued into Sunday, she has not established a *vest kavuah* with regard to the *vest haflagah* aspect, since the last *haflagah* was two days earlier. However, regarding the *vest hashavuah*, she has a *vest kavuah* since she menstruated on Sunday as well.[42]

3. The unique nature of a *vest hashavuah*:
A *vest hashavuah* is unusual and therefore subject to these *halachos:*

a. A *vest hashavuah* is most unusual; therefore, it cannot retain its status if the periods fit a more common pattern. We assume that her periods are regulated by a more common cause. Thus, if a woman menstruates on three Sundays, thereby establishing a *vest hashavuah*, and subsequently menstruates the following Sunday,[43] the *vest hashavuah* is transformed into a regular *vest haflagah* since she now has four periods separated by three

---

40. *Sidrei Taharah* §4.

41. Pleisi §8 and *Sidrei Taharah* ibid.

42. *Shiurei Sheivet HaLeivi* §6[2] citing *Pleisi* although it is not that clear in *Pleisi*. This is similar to the *halachah* of a *vest hachodesh* noted in Chapter Thirteen note 24 and Chapter Seventeen note 42.

43. Without any other menstrual flow in between, see *Chavos Daas* §4[b].

equal intervals.[44] The ramifications of this change from a *vest hashavuah* to a *vest haflagah* have been explained above.[45]

b. A woman does not suspect a *vest hashavuah* unless it is established as a *vest kavuah*. Thus, a woman who menstruates on a Sunday need not expect a period on any following Sunday, even if this occurs twice.[46]

---

44. *Chavos Daas* §8[c], 4[b]. However, *Pleisi* §8 is uncertain in this case. *Sidrei Taharah* §4,31 cites *Rashba* and *Ramban* who seem to support *Chavos Daas'* view. However, *Sidrei Taharah* himself is uncertain. He feels that a punctilious individual should keep the stringent applications of both views. *Chochmas Adam* 112:15 follows *Sidrei Taharah's* view. *Shiurei Sheivet HaLeivi* §6[3] notes that most *Poskim* follow *Chavos Daas'* view. According to *Chavos Daas'* view, this type of a *vest* is difficult to understand. The rationale of a *vest* is that we expect the woman to continue following this cycle. This *vest*, however, is self-destructing. If she continues it for a fourth time, it changes into a simple *vest haflagah*. See *Igros Moshe, Y.D.* 1:122, for various cases regarding this question.

45. See *Chavos Daas* §4[b].

46. See *Graz* §22.

CHAPTER SEVENTEEN

עקירת וסת

Akiras Vest: **Uprooting a Vest**

- □ Uprooting a *vest kavuah.*
- □ Uprooting a *vest she'aino kavuah.*
- □ A dormant *vest.*
- □ Uprooting a *vest haflagah.*
- □ A shorter interval uprooting a longer interval.
- □ Uprooting a *vest hachodesh.*

Introduction

We noted in the previous chapters that all *vestos* can be uprooted. This is called *"akiras vest."* The exact manner by which *vestos* are uprooted differ from *vest* to *vest*. In this chapter, we will examine, in detail, *akiras vest,* the manner in which *vest kavuah* and a *vest she'aino kavuah,* a *vest haflagah* and a *vest hachodesh* are uprooted. The manner in which *vest hadilug, vest haguf* and *vest haones* are uprooted will be explained in their respective chapters.

I. Uprooting a *vest kavuah* or a *vest she'aino kavuah*

A. A *vest kavuah:*

An established *vest* remains effective until it is demonstrated that the woman's cycle no longer follows that *vest.* The rules by which a *vest* is uprooted vary depending upon whether the *vest* is a *vest kavuah* or a *vest she'aino kavuah.*

A *vest kavuah* is more significant than a *vest she'aino kavuah* since the *vest* has established itself three times and created a *chazakah,* a presumption that the cycle is a permanent part of her physical nature which will not change. There are three aspects in which a *vest kavuah* is distinct in the manner of its *akirah:*

> 1. A *vest kavuah* is uprooted only if it is passed three times. A woman who has a *vest kavuah* must continue to consider herself subject to that *vest,* even if she passes the *vest* day once or twice without menstruating.[1] We consider the passing of the *vest* day without a flow a mere chance happening. Once she passes the *vest* day three times without menstruating, she has established a *chazakah* that her physical nature is no longer subject to that cycle and she is no longer required to keep the *vest.*[2]

> 2. A *vest kavuah* can never become completely uprooted unless it is replaced by another *vest kavuah.* See C below where this concept is explained in detail..

---

1. 189:2,13.

2. 189:2, see also 189:13-16.

3. A *vest kavuah* day is considered passed without incident only if the woman does a *bedikah* on the *vest* day.[3]

B. A *vest she'aino kavuah:*

A *vest she'aino kavuah* has not established itself permanently; it is merely conjecture that the *vest* may, in the future, establish itself. Therefore, once the *vest* passes without incident, we assume that, in reality, the *vest* was never about to become *kavuah* and the woman is no longer subject to the *vest*. Among the *halachos* regarding uprooting a *vest she'aino kavuah* are the following:

> 1. Even a woman who menstruates twice on the same calendar day or after the same interval may ignore the *vest* day if she passed it the third time without incident.[4] Thus, the provision of three occurrences is both a minimum and a maximum standard regarding *akiros*, i.e., two occurrences are no more significant than one and ten occurrences are no more significant than three. A *vest* that occurred fewer than three times is uprooted by one *akirah* and even a *vest* repeated on tens of occasions is uprooted by only three *akiros*.
>
> 2. Although a woman should do a *bedikah* on her *vest she'aino kavuah* day, if she omitted that *bedikah*, the *vest she'aino kavuah* is uprooted. No further *bedikah* is required.[5] Indeed, even if she menstruates (or finds blood on a *bedikah* cloth) the following day, the *vest* of the previous day is uprooted.[6] The new *vest she'aino kavuah* is the day on which the flow actually began.

C. A dormant *vest:*

A *vest kavuah* is unique in that it can never become completely uprooted unless it is replaced by another *vest kavuah*. Otherwise, the *vest*

---

3. *Rambam, Hil. Issurei Biah* 5:19. We noted in Chapter Fourteen (note 14) the opinion of *Chavos Daas* 184:10[b], that if a *bedikah* was missed even on only one of the three days, the *vest* remains intact. We also noted (note 12) the opinion of *Sugah Bashoshanim* 3:11, that even if she performed the *bedikah* on the following day and it was found clean, the *vest* remains intact.

4. 189:2.

5. See Chapter, Eighteen, note 26, where we noted that according to *Taz* 189:38, if a woman passes a *vest haguf she'aino kavuah,* she is required to do a *bedikah* even after the *vest* passes. *Shach* (ad loc.) and *Graz* §88 disagree.

6. See *Badei HaShulchan* 189:14, *Biurim* s.v. ושינתה.

becomes dormant, i.e., it is neither active nor eliminated. It is deactivated in that the woman is not required to keep the *vest* day. It is not eliminated since it can be reactivated when she returns to the *vest*, even once. This is possible in two cases.

1. She menstruates on other days:

A woman had a *vest kavuah* to menstruate on the twentieth interval day and subsequently menstruates on the thirty-first, the thirty-fourth and the thirty-sixth interval instead. The *vest kavuah* of the twentieth interval day is uprooted, but not completely; it lies dormant. If, in the future, she ever menstruates after an interval of twenty days,[7] even only once, even after many years,[8] the *vest* is reactivated and immediately becomes a *vest kavuah* (and eliminates any *vest she'aino kavuah*). It then cannot be uprooted unless it is passed another three times without incident.[9]

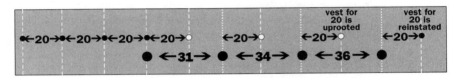

This *halachah* applies to a *vest hachodesh* as well. If she had a *vest kavuah* for *Rosh Chodesh* and menstruates the following three months on other days of the month, e.g., the third, fourth and the sixth, the *vest* for *Rosh Chodesh* is uprooted. If, in the future, she

Month A	Month B	Month C	Month D	Month E	Month F	Month G
1	1	1	3	4	6	1
				vest for Rosh Chodesh is uprooted X	vest for Rosh Chodesh is reinstated X	

---

7. See *Sugah Bashoshanim* 5:7 regarding a case where she menstruated a day or two earlier than the twentieth but the flow continued into the twentieth.

8. Regarding after a year, see *Ramban* 6:5. Regarding many years, see *Chasam Sofer, Y.D.* 166, *Sugah Bashoshanim* 5:(21).

9. 189:15. This *halachah* is based on *Raavad* (*Baalei HaNefesh* p.34, Kapach edition). However, *Sidrei Taharah* §19 and *Lechem VeSimlah* §33[s], note that *Ramban* (*Hilchos Niddah* 6:3,4) seems to disagree with *Raavad*. *Lechem VeSimlah* contends that *Rashi*, *Ramban* and *Rezah* all disagree with *Raavad*. He, therefore, rules that one may follow their lenient opinion and assume that the original *vest* is completely uprooted. *Tiferes Tzvi* §22 is also troubled by this *halachah*. Therefore, in *Mekor Chaim*

menstruates again on *Rosh Chodesh*, the *vest* is reinstated as a *vest kavuah*.[10]

2. She skips three menstrual periods:

If a woman has a *vest haflagah kavuah* of, for example, twenty day[11] intervals and passes three twenty day segments[12] without menstruating, she uproots the *vest haflagah* of twenty.[13] When she menstruates in the future, she is no longer required to keep a twenty day *vest haflagah*[14] since that interval was uprooted.[15] If, in the future, she ever[16] menstruates again after a twenty day interval,[17] the twenty day interval is reinstated as a *vest kavuah*.[18]

---

§91, he rules that the *vest* is only reinstated *lechumra* — regarding strict applications, not *lekula* — regarding lenient applications. Thus, although the *vest* of twenty becomes a *vest kavuah*, one is nevertheless required to keep *onah beinonis* as well. *Sugah Bashoshanim* 5:[21] disagrees. He rules that the *vest* is completely reinstated; therefore, one need not keep *onah beinonis*. *Badei HaShulchan, Biurim* 189:15, s.v. ואם ראתה, contends that if there is an additional lenient consideration, one may follow the lenient opinions that the original *vest kavuah* is not reestablished. It would seem that *Sugah Bashoshanim* cited above would not agree, since he applies the reestablishment *lekula* as well. In addition, since all later *Poskim* cite this *halachah* without comment, it seems that they consider the *vest* reestablished as a *vest kavuah* without reservation. See below note 35.

10. See *Graz* §68.

11. Similarly, if her *vest haflagah* was for thirty-five days, it would be uprooted by passage of one hundred and five days (actually one hundred and three days, see below). Passage of ninety days is insufficient even though it constitutes three median *vestos* (see *Shach* 189:65). This is unlike the *halachah* by which an older woman becomes exempt from *vestos* by passing three *onos*, see Chapter Twenty D,2,a.

12. This would total fifty-eight days. Day twenty of the first segment and day one of the second segment are the same day, as is day twenty of the second segment and day one of the third segment.

13. 189:15. This is a unique type of *akirah*. The *vest* is not uprooted by passing three times since, in reality, the *vest* was passed only once. A *haflagah* is calculated only from an actual period (see Chapter Fifteen). Thus, the second segment is not a *haflagah* since there is no period from which to calculate it. Rather, since she passed a time span which equals three of her periods, her menstruation routine is interrupted (סילוק דמים) and she no longer needs to be concerned with that *vest*.

14. She keeps no *vest haflagah* from that menstruation besides the *vest hachodesh* and *onah beinonis*, *Graz* §64.

15. There is a difference of opinion among *Poskim* whether or not she must keep the large *haflagah* (e.g., for fifty-eight days) as well. In the opinion of *Maharshal* cited in *Taz* §31, she is not required to keep the large interval since it was not actually a *vest* interval, but a סילוק דמים — an interruption in her menstrual process. *Chavos Daas* §20[b] disagrees. He maintains that one must keep a *vest haflagah* for fifty-eight days as well. *Shiurei Sheivet HaLeivi* 189, end of 15, notes that if the *vest haflagah* for twenty is reestablished, it eliminates the *vest* for fifty-eight.

16. Even after a year, *Ramban* 6:5; or many years, see note 8, above.

17. *Taz*, end of §31, contends that, in this case, whenever she menstruates, even once, she must keep the *vest haflagah* of twenty. However, almost all *Poskim* disagree. They maintain that she is not required to keep a *vest haflagah* for twenty until she menstruates twice with an interval of twenty days in between.

18. 189:15. Even *Ramban*, who disagrees with the previous *halachah* (a), agrees, in this case, that the

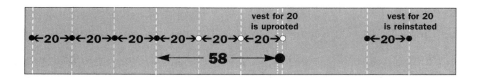

However, once a woman establishes a new *vest kavuah*, it totally eliminates the first *vest* and assumes its place.[19] Thus, once a woman establishes a *vest kavuah*, she retains a *vest kavuah* for the rest of her life, either in the active or the dormant state.[20]

II. Uprooting a *vest she'aino kavuah* through establishing a *vest kavuah:*

A woman who has no *vest kavuah* does not know whether her menstrual flow is caused by the day of the month or the interval of days. She must, therefore, consider each of these possibilities and treat both the date and the interval as a possible cause of the flow.[21] Once she establishes a *vest kavuah* of either type, she now recognizes the true cause of her menstruation and no longer needs to consider any other *vest* as a possible cause.[22] Similarly, if a woman has two simultaneous *vestos she'ainon kavuos*, e.g., she menstruated four times: two after the same interval and two on the same

---

original *vest* is not totally uprooted. In the opinion of *Ramban,* the difference between the two cases is as follows: In case (a), the *vest* is completely uprooted because she menstruated three times on another date. The fact that she did not establish another *vest kavuah* is irrelevant. In case (b), she not only did not establish another *vest kavuah,* she did not even menstruate on another day. This is not a full *akirah.* See *Ramban (Hilchos Niddah* 6:4,5).

19. *Shach* §41.

20. However, there is a possibility for a woman to negate a *vest kavuah* without establishing another *vest kavuah.* A woman with a *vest haflagah kavuah* for a twenty-five day interval uproots it by menstruating on the fifth, sixth, seventh and eighth of the month, thereby establishing a *vest hachodesh bedilug.* When the *dilug* reaches the end of the month, it is questionable whether it continues into the next month. Similarly, if she menstruates on intervals of twenty-seven, twenty-eight, twenty-nine and thirty, she establishes a *vest haflagah bedilug.* If she then uproots the *vest hadilug* by not menstruating on the expected days, the *vest hadilug* is uprooted. It is very questionable whether a *vest hadilug* can be reestablished again by one menstruation. In either of these two cases she is left without any *vest kavuah.* See a discussion of these cases in Chapter Sixteen, notes 17 and 19 respectively.

21. *Rema* 189:13.

22. Ibid.

date of the month, which ever of the *vestos* becomes *kavuah* uproots the other. If her fifth period occurs on either the same interval day or the same monthly date as the two previous periods, the interval or date becomes a *vest kavuah* and the other *vest* is eliminated.[23] See Section III,A,3 regarding whether an earlier interval can uproot a later interval.

One should note that although a *vest kavuah* can eliminate a *vest she'aino kavuah* that preceded it, it cannot overrule a *vest she'aino kavuah* that follows it. For example, a woman establishes a *vest kavuah* and then menstruates on a day that is incompatible with the *vest kavuah*. She must keep both the *vest kavuah* (which has not yet been eliminated since it was not passed three times) and the new *vest she'aino kavuah*. We are concerned that perhaps she is in the process of changing to a new *vest kavuah*.[24]

III. Uprooting different types of *vestos*

A. Elimination of *a vest haflagah:*

A *vest haflagah* is eliminated in several ways:

1. Establishing a *vest kavuah:*

A *vest she'aino kavuah* is uprooted when a woman establishes a *vest kavuah*. This *vest kavuah* sweeps away any previous *vest she'aino kavuah* that she tentatively set in the past. For example, a woman menstruated on the fifth day of month A and the fifth

---

23. *Rema* 189:13. Regardless of whether the *vest haflagah* or the *vest hachodesh* becomes established (*Graz* 189:46). *Chavos Daas* 189:15[b] and 18[b] rules that this pertains to a *vest haflagah* versus another *vest haflagah* or versus a *vest hachodesh* only. If, however, she had two *vestos hachodesh,* the one that becomes *kavuah* does not uproot the *aino kavuah*. He argues that a *vest haflagah* inherently excludes any other *vest* since one interval *vest* cannot coexist with another interval *vest* or with a monthly date *vest*. She will either menstruate according to one interval or the other, not both. However, a *vest hachodesh* is not exclusive. A woman can have two *vestos hachodesh* each on a different day of the month. Thus, when one *vest hachodesh* becomes *kavuah* it does not necessarily exclude another *vest hachodesh she'aino kavuah*. A similar view is held by *Beis Meir* 189:13. However, *Mekor Mayim Chaim* (to *Rema* 189:13) disagrees. He contends that there is no difference between two *vestos hachodesh* and a *vest hachodesh* versus a *vest haflagah*. In either case, a *vest kavuah* uproots the *vest she'aino kavuah*. The logic seems to be that we do not assume that there are two independent causes of her menstruation. *Graz* ibid. and *Noda B'Yehudah,* Y.D. 1:61, seem to disagree with *Chavos Daas*. See a lengthy discussion of this issue in *Badei HaShulchan, Biurim* 189:14, s.v. ואם לאחר, who contends that one may follow the lenient opinion.

24. 189:14. If, and when, she menstruates again on the *vest kavuah* day, the *vest* is automatically eliminated even though she had not yet passed the day without a flow (*Maadanei Melech* cited in *Shach* §40 and *Taz* §28 see 3b below). The dispute between *Graz* and *Chavos Daas* cited above regarding a *vest hachodesh* applies to this case as well.

and the twentieth days of month B. If she menstruates on the fifth of month C, the fifth becomes a *vest kavuah*. She need not keep the interval of fifteen days from the fifth of month C on the nineteenth of the month, even though the interval between the twentieth of month B and the fifth of month C was fifteen days.[25]

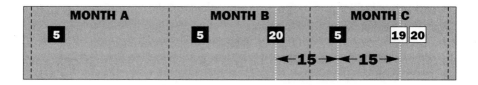

2. Passing the *vest* day:
A *vest she'aino kavuah* can be uprooted even without the establishment of a *vest kavuah* if the *vest* day is passed once without any appearance of *dam*.

3. A smaller interval:
If a woman does not pass her interval day but menstruates on an earlier day, it is questionable whether or not the *vest* is uprooted. There are several variations of this question:

> a. A *vest she'aino kavuah* uprooting another *vest she'aino kavuah*:
> There is a difference of opinion among *Poskim* regarding a woman who menstruated earlier than her expected interval. For example, a woman menstruated after an interval of twenty-eight days and subsequently menstruated after an interval of twenty-five days. Some *Poskim* contend that this constitutes an *akirah* since she menstruated on a different day.[26] Others contend that this is not considered an *akirah* since the *vest* day was not passed without incident.[27] In their opinion, if she men-

---

25. If month C was *chaseir* (a month of only twenty-nine days). She is also not required to keep the *vest hachodesh* on the 20th of month C since it was uprooted by the establishment of the *vest kavuah*. This depends upon the dispute between *Chavos Daas* and other *Poskim* cited above, note 23.

26. *Shach* §31, 40. This is also the opinion of *Maharsha* (*Niddah* 64a). *Igros Moshe, Y.D.* 1:122, seems to follow this lenient view.

27. See *Taz* §18, *Beis Meir* (ad loc.), *Pleisi* §16, *Graz* §43, *Lechem VeSimlah* §34[1] and *Sugah Bashoshanim* 5:3. This is also obviously the opinion of *Rema* 189:13. *Sidrei Taharah* §19 deduces this from *Ramban* (*Hil. Niddah* 6:2). In §14, he shows this to be the view of *Raavad* as well. *Toras*

struates after an interval of twenty-nine, twenty-eight, twenty-six, twenty-four and twenty-three, she must abstain in the future on all the intervals[28] until she passes each without menstruating.[29] Most authorities follow this latter stringent view.[30]

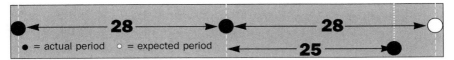

● = actual period   ○ = expected period

A woman may experience an unusually long interval, e.g., one of forty days. Subsequently, she continues her normal intervals ranging from twenty-eight to thirty-three days, without setting a *vest kavuah*. It is unclear from *Poskim* how long she must keep account of the forty-day interval. Must she continue to mark off that day on her calendar?[31] Even if over the course of many years, she will never exceed an interval of forty.

It is interesting to note that this latter position is relevant with regard to establishing a *vest kavuah* as well. For example: A woman menstruated with intervals of thirty, twenty, thirty and thirty. If a shorter interval (in this case, twenty) can eliminate a longer interval (thirty), she has no *vest kavuah*. The first thirty interval was eliminated

---

HaShelamim §22 and *Chazon Ish, Y.D.* 85:34, also cite *Raavad* to support this view. (It is noteworthy that the section of *Raavad* cited by *Chazon Ish* is not found in the manuscript of *Baalei HaNefesh* used by R' Yosef Kapach. See Kapach edition p. 48 note 86. Presumably, this would not trouble *Chazon Ish*; see *Kovetz Igros Chazon Ish* 1:32.)

28. She should keep each *yom havest* according to the *onah* in which it originally started. Thus, if the menstruation of 29 was by day, 28 by night, 26 by day etc., she would abstain the day of the 29th, the night of the 28, the day of the 26th etc. from her last period.

29. She must abstain during all the *vestos hachodesh* as well (*Graz* 189:44). See *Sheivet HaLeivi* cited in 31 below.

30. Since this is the opinion of most *Acharonim*, and especially since this is the view of *Raavad* and *Ramban*. Nevertheless, *Shiurei Sheivet HaLeivi* 189, end of 14, rules that young couples may follow the lenient opinion during the first year of marriage. *Be'er Moshe* 6:142 rules that if a woman had a longer interval, then a shorter interval, passed the shorter interval and was found to be pregnant, she is not required to observe the longer interval. Although a woman who is pregnant for less than three months is not *halachically* considered pregnant regarding *vestos* (see Chapter Twenty, B,1), in this case one may be lenient since some *Poskim* consider a shorter interval an *akirah*.

31. *Chazon Ish* 85:37 assumes that *Ramban* would consider this completely illogical. Responsa *Sheivet HaLeivi* 5:107 speculates that perhaps if a woman had three shorter intervals, she is no

leaving only two intervals of thirty. According to the first opinion, this is comparable to a woman whose intervals were: thirty, thirty-five, thirty and thirty. However, according to the latter, accepted view, the first interval of thirty was not eliminated and combines to establish a *vest kavuah*.[32]

According to first opinion, vest is not kavuah, according to second opinion, it is.

b. A *vest kavuah* uprooting a *vest she'aino kavuah*:

If the shorter *haflagah* becomes a *vest kavuah*, it certainly uproots the longer *haflagah she'aino kavuah*. This is possible in three cases: a) She had an interval of twenty-nine followed by three intervals of twenty, or b) she previously had a *vest kavuah* of twenty, she passed it twice and menstruated on the twenty-ninth day instead and then menstruated on the twentieth day. In each of these cases, the twentieth interval day uproots the twenty-ninth day since it became a *vest kavuah*.[33] c) If she had a *vest kavuah* for the twentieth day and uprooted it by menstruating on three different days, e.g., the twenty-sixth, twenty-eight and twenty-ninth, the *vest kavuah* for twenty was never fully uprooted, but put in a dormant state (see Section I,C above). If she subsequently menstruated after an interval of twenty, the interval of twenty becomes

---

longer required to keep the longer interval. He is reluctant to issue a definite ruling. Actually, she is affected by this longer interval only once. If she ever reaches it, she will either uproot it or confirm it. The issue here is whether to continue with the bother of marking it on the calendar.

32. See *Chazon Ish, Y.D.* 85:34, and *Eimek HaTeshuvah* 1:131. However, *Taharas Yisrael* 189:94, is lenient in this case. It is unclear in this case as well, if there is any limit to this *halachah*. For example, a woman menstruates once on the thirty-fifth interval day and for a year or two menstruates before the thirtieth day. She then menstruates twice on the thirty-fifth day. Does she have a *vest kavuah*?

33. *Maadanei Melech* cited in *Shach* §40 and *Taz* §28. *Ramban* (*Hil. Niddah* 6:2), *Raavad* who contends that in this case, the later *vest* of twenty-nine is not uprooted. *Ramban* deduces from this that *Raavad* would take a similar position, even if she had three intervals of twenty; indeed, even if she continues so for several years. *Ramban* considers this absurd. *Sidrei Taharah* 189:19 cites *Rosh* who seems to agree with *Raavad* in the case of when she menstruates on day twenty only once. However, as noted in note 37 below, according to *Rosh*, if she menstruates three times on twenty she uproots a longer *haflagah* even if it was a *vest kavuah*.

kavuah immediately and uproots the *vest she'aino kavuah* of twenty-nine.[34] There is an opinion that, even in this case, the *vest* of twenty-nine is not uprooted.[35]

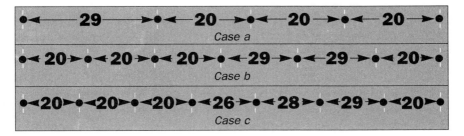

Case a

Case b

Case c

c. A *vest kavuah* uprooting a *vest kavuah*:
A woman with a *vest kavuah* for intervals of twenty-nine who menstruates three times after an interval of twenty, has not, in the opinion of some *Poskim*, uprooted the *vest kavuah* for twenty-nine.[36] Others disagree

---

34. See *Malbushei Taharah* 189:42 (cited in *Taharas Yisrael* 189:98) who maintains that the *vest* of twenty-nine is uprooted. However, he cites no source.

35. It seems from *Chochmas Adam* 112:23 that, in his opinion, the *vest* of twenty-nine is not uprooted. Responsa *Mishnas R' Aharon* §22 takes issue with *Chochmas Adam*. He explains that *Chochmas Adam* felt that the reactivation of the *vest* of twenty is less than certain and, thus, is used only *lechumra* — for stringent applications — not *lekula* — for lenient applications. R' Aharon dismisses this view. We noted earlier (note 9) that other *Poskim* do actually maintain that the *vest* is reactivated only *lechumra*, not *lekula*. One could make an argument that the *vest* should not be uprooted since the view that the *vest* of twenty is reactivated is that of *Raavad*. However, *Raavad* himself maintains that even in the earlier case, the *vest* does not uproot the later *vest*.

36. It seems from *Beis Meir* that even if the shorter interval becomes a *vest kavuah*, it would not uproot the longer *vest kavuah* interval. A shorter interval cannot uproot a longer *vest kavuah* interval, even if the shorter interval becomes a *vest kavuah*. See *Chazon Ish*, Y.D. 85:35-37, who discusses *Beis Meir's* opinion and reaches no clear conclusion. It seems clear that those *Poskim* who maintain that a shorter *haflagah she'aino kavuah* uproots a longer *haflagah she'aino kavuah*, i.e., *Shach* §32,40, would surely agree that a shorter *vest kavuah* uproots a longer *vest kavuah*. The question is whether those who hold that a shorter *vest she'aino kavuah* does not uproot a longer *vest she'aino kavuah*, i.e., *Taz* §18, would concede that a *vest kavuah* uproots a *vest kavuah*. The logic may be as follows: A *vest she'aino kavuah* is based upon the principle that the woman <u>may</u> be about to establish a fixed pattern of menstruating after a certain interval. When she passes that day without menstruating, she demonstrates that the interval is not about to become established. If she menstruates on an earlier interval, she did not demonstrate that the later interval is not a potential *vest kavuah*. However, a *vest kavuah* is based upon the logic that she established a fixed pattern and will continue to follow that pattern. This, in itself, constitutes an *akirah* of any other pattern (even *kavuah*), since a woman cannot have two *vestos haflagah kavuah*.

and rule the *vest* for twenty-nine is uprooted.[37]

4. Calculating the *haflagah* from the last period:

Although, in the opinion of most authorities, a smaller *haflagah* does not uproot a longer *haflagah*, must a woman continue to count the interval from the earlier period? For example, a woman had one interval of thirty-five days on day b (see chart below). Subsequently, she menstruates after an interval of twenty days on day c. After another twelve days, she is able to complete her *taharah* process. Must she count the thirty-five interval day from day b or must she keep the thirty-five interval day only from day c? We noted in Chapter Fifteen Section I, B, 5 that this is subject to a dispute among *Poskim*. Some contend that since the thirty-five interval from day b was set prior to the period on day c, it cannot be ignored.[38] Most *Poskim* rule that every *vest haflagah* is calculated only from the last menstruation. Thus, she must count the intervals of the *vest haflagah* only from day c.[39] Common custom is to follow this latter opinion.

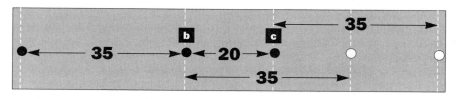

37. This seems to be the opinion of *Rosh* (*Kitzur Hil. Niddah* §2) and certainly of *Shach* §31, 40, cited above note 26 who is lenient even regarding a *vest she'aino kavuah*. We noted in previous footnote that *Chazon Ish* also considers this option. *Graz* 189:58 (and *Kuntres Acharon*, end of 4) takes a very unique position. He contends that the *vest* for twenty-nine is uprooted and placed in a dormant state (similar to the *halachah* noted in Section I,C). Thus, she need no longer be concerned about the twenty-nine day *vest*, but if, in the future, she ever menstruates after an interval of twenty-nine days, it immediately is revived into a *vest kavuah*. *Graz* explains that a full *akirah* consists of two factors: passing the *vest* three times without a flow and substituting another *vest kavuah* in its place. If only one factor takes place, the *vest* becomes dormant. If she passes the *vest* three times without substituting another *vest kavuah*, the *vest* lies dormant as was noted above I,C. Similarly, *Graz* argues, if she substitutes another *vest kavuah* without passing the *onas havest* without a flow, the *vest* is not completely uprooted and lies dormant. This is the present case.

38. *Rema* 189:13 (we assume that the menstruation of day c was an additional flow, totally irrelevant to her sequence of thirty-five intervals, *Taz* §18). *Taz* and *Toras HaShelamim* §22 agree with *Rema's* position.

39. *Bach* 189 p. 52b, *Prishah* §28, *Shach* 189:31, *Sidrei Taharah* §14 shows that this is the opinion of *Rosh* and *Raavad* as well. See also *Beis Meir* ad loc., *Pleisi* §16, *Graz* §43 and *Lechem VeSimlah* §34[1]. This is totally independent of the question of whether the *vest haflagah* of thirty-five is uprooted.

B. Elimination of *vest hachodesh*

A *vest hachodesh* is eliminated in a manner similar to other *vestos*. The date of the month that the period started in previous months must be passed without an appearance of blood. If the *vest hachodesh* is not *kavuah*, it is eliminated by passing the date on <u>one</u> month without a blood flow. If the *vest* is *kavuah*, she must pass the date on <u>three consecutive</u> months without a blood flow. Unlike a *vest haflagah* (in which there is a difference of opinion, see A,3,a above), a *vest hachodesh* is certainly not eliminated by a menstruation on a different day of the month.[40] She must actually pass the original date without a blood flow.[41] For example, in month A, a woman began menstruating on the twenty-fifth of the month. If, in month B, she menstruates on the tenth, she must still keep the *yom havest* on the twenty-fifth. If she menstruates again on the twenty-fifth of month B, she must keep both the tenth and the twenty-fifth of month C as *vest* days.

Similarly, a *vest hachodesh* is only uprooted if a woman passed it without any blood flow. Thus, if the period began earlier than the *vest hachodesh* day and the flow continued on the *vest* day, the *vest* is not uprooted. For example, a woman menstruates on the fifth day of month A and on month B the period begins on the third day but continues into the fifth day of the month,[42] the *vest* for day five is not eliminated, since she actually had a blood flow during that day.[43] The fact that the blood flow on the fifth was merely the continuation of the flow that began on the third is irrelevant in this case. Thus, the following month, she will keep the fifth (which was not uprooted) as well as the third of the month (which was the actual beginning of the new *vest*) as her *vest* days.

Therefore, in the of opinion these *Poskim,* even if she were to keep the *vest haflagah* of thirty-five, it would be calculated from day c only, which is the last menstruation. See *Pleisi* §16.

40. *Prishah* §28.

41. Nevertheless, if she menstruates earlier on a different day of the month, the original *vest hachodesh* will not have the additional status of *onah beinonis,* even if it falls on the thirtieth day from the previous *yom hachodesh.* See *Sidrei Taharah* 189:12.

42. This *halachah* is relevant to a *vest hachodesh* only. It cannot apply to a *vest haflagah* for two reasons: a) In the opinion of *Taz* and most *Poskim,* cited above, even if the earlier menstruation did not overlap the later *vest* day, it does not uproot the *vest.* b) Once the woman menstruates, we begin a new calculation of the interval from that day. For example, if a woman had a *vest haflagah* for twenty-eight days and menstruates on the twenty-seventh, the next day is called day two, not day twenty-eight. Thus, the continuation of the flow into that day is irrelevant with regard to the *vest haflagah* of twenty-eight.

43. *Graz* 189:38 rules that a menstruation on the night before the *vest* day does not uproot the *vest* day of even a *vest she'aino kavuah.* In §68, he rules that a *vest kavuah* is not uprooted by a previous menstruation if it continued into the *vest* day. *Igros Moshe, Y.D.* 1:122, rules that even a *vest she'aino kavuah*

One should note that this principle relates only to uprooting a *vest*. In order to uproot a *vest*, the day must be free from any uterine blood flow, even a blood flow that is merely a continuation of a previous flow. However, in terms of setting a *vest*, only the onset of the flow has any relevance. The continuation of the flow is not considered regarding *vestos*. Thus, if a woman menstruates on the fifth of month A, the fourth and fifth of month B and the fifth of month C, she has not established a *vest hachodesh* for the fifth of the month. This concept is explained in detail in Chapter Thirteen.

A *vest haguf* is uprooted in a manner which is unique to the type of *vest haguf* and is explained in Chapter Eighteen.

---

is not uprooted by a menstruation even several days earlier if its flow continued into the *vest* day. Responsa *Minchas Yitzchak* 8:74 shares this view, as does *Shiurei Sheivet HaLeivi* 189:13[14], responsa *Sheivet HaLeivi* 5:107 and responsa *Eimek HaTeshuvah* 1:130. Responsa *Mishnas R' Aharon* 22[7] also leans towards this view. However, *Shaarei Tohar* 4:21 rules that the *vest* is uprooted. See also *Ohalei Yosef* §16[96], who interprets *Graz* in a manner that only a menstruation of the night before will not uproot the day *vest* since the earlier flow is very short. However, if the menstruation was a day or more earlier than the *onas havest*, the *vest* is uprooted even though the flow continued into the *onas havest*. This view seems contradicted by *Graz* 189:68. See *Poseiach Shaar* (R' S. Friedman) p. 25, citing author of *Cheishev HaEifod*, who differentiates between a *vest she'aino kavuah* and a *vest kavuah*. The former is uprooted by an earlier flow which continues into the *onas havest*; the latter is not. Responsa *Eimek HaTeshuvah* 1:131 does not differentiate between *vest kavuah* and *vest she'aino kavuah*. In either case the *vest* is not uprooted. He notes that this is relevant to establishing a *vest* as well. For example, if she menstruates on the fifth of the month, then on the fourth and fifth of the month. Each opinion cites arguments in support of their position. It would seem that the question hinges on one point: What is necessary for *akiras vest*? Is it the lack of a positive menstruation or is positive proof required that the day is no longer a cause of menstruation? Thus, a woman who menstruates on the fifth of the month and menstruates on the fourth and fifth of the following month has not reaffirmed the *vest* of the fifth since the flow on the fifth is only a continuation of the flow that started on the fourth. She has not eliminated the *vest* either. A *vest* is eliminated only when it is demonstrated that the day does not cause menstruation. This is accomplished when she passes the day without a blood flow. Passing the day with a flow that can be attributed to other causes is neither an affirmation of the *vest* nor an elimination. A similar example may be found in the case of a woman who was in hiding during her *vest* day. We do not expect her to menstruate that day since fear inhibits the onset of a menstrual flow (184:8). It does not seem that the *vest* is uprooted. Another similar case could be that of a woman who menstruated on the thirtieth of the month and passes the following month, which has only twenty-nine days, without menstruating. If we require positive proof that the day does not cause menstruation, it is not there. However, if we need the *vest* to be affirmed, it has not been affirmed either.

CHAPTER EIGHTEEN

Vest Haguf: a Physical Manifestation

- □ The different types of *vest haguf.*
- □ The unique quality of a *vest haguf.*
- □ *Vest hamurkav.*
- □ The duration of the *vest.*
- □ *Onah beinonis* with regard to *vest haguf.*
- □ Uprooting a *vest haguf.*

Introduction

Most women experience a physical sensation before the onset of their menstruation. Often, this sensation is not unique to the onset of menstruation but may occur at other occasions unrelated to menstruation. In this case the sensation is not a *vest haguf*. However, some women experience a very unique physical sensation[1] prior to their menstruation. This is called *vest haguf*. A *vest haguf* is not a causative *vest* but a symptomatic *vest* (see Chapter Thirteen, Section I,D). The physical manifestation is the symptom, not the cause, of the *vest*.[2] We do not know the cause of the flow, but we do know when it is about to begin.

I. The basic *halachos* of a *vest haguf*

A. What constitutes a *vest haguf*

1. The sensations that are considered *vest haguf*:
Among the sensations enumerated by *Chazal*[3] as *vestos haguf* are women who experience a stretching or yawning spell,[4] a belching spell,[5] a sneezing spell[6] or a spell of flatulence.[7] More common today are other symptoms[8] (some also noted by *Chazal*). Many women feel aches or cramps in the stomach,[9] the lower abdomen[10]

---

1. The subject of this chapter are those general symptoms (e.g., sneezing, cramps, muscular aches, etc.) which may occur prior to menstruation. These are not to be confused with the specific sensation (*hargashah*) that a woman feels when her menstruation actually begins. Those sensations are discussed in Chapter Three. See Chapter Three, Section I,B.

2. *Rashba* (*Toras HaBayis* 7:3 p. 13b) and *Ran* (*Niddah* 63a).

3. *Niddah* 63a.

4. פיהוק, in *Yoreh Deah* 189:19. According to *Rashi*, *Niddah* 63a, פיהוק is stretching and yawning is גוסה (63b).

5. Ibid. see *Taz* §33 and *Shach* §52.

6. עיטוש, according to *Rambam* cited in *Shach* §53.

7. עיטוש, according to *Shulchan Aruch* ibid.

8. It would seem that any unusual physical manifestation is considered a *vest haguf*, even if it is not noted by *Chazal*. See *Rambam, Pirush HaMishnah* (*Niddah* 9). However, responsa *Pnei Yehoshua*, Y.D. 1, seems to have understood differently. See also *Chezkas Taharah* 189:19, *Moreh Derech* §1.

9. חוששת בפי כריסה, 189:19.

10. בשפולי מעיה, ibid.

or limbs, headaches,[11] hot flashes,[12] a shivering spell[13] or nausea.[14] A woman can also set a *vest haguf* if she usually finds stains (even stains less than a *gris* or lightly colored stains which do not render her a *niddah*) before menstruation.[15] These symptoms may be a sign that the period is about to begin and may be considered a *vest haguf*. For the sake of simplicity, we will use the example of cramps when discussing a *vest haguf* in this chapter, since it is common for women to experience cramps before menstruation.

2. The similarity of the symptoms:
A *vest haguf* is established only if the woman experiences the same symptom on each of the three occasions. However, if on one occasion she had a sneezing spell, on one occasion a yawning spell and on one a belching spell, she has not established a *vest kavuah*.[16]

3. The uniqueness of the symptoms:
A woman considers her symptoms a *vest haguf* only if those symptoms are unusual. Therefore, the headache which establishes a *vest haguf* refers to a headache which is unusual and is always associated with menstruation. Similarly, a woman who experiences unusual cramps before her menstruation may have a *vest haguf*. The sneezing which establishes a *vest haguf* refers to an extended[17] sneezing fit which is not associated with a cold or allergies. A simple sneeze prior to menstruation is not considered a *vest haguf* since it is common to sneeze.[18] Even an extended sneezing fit is not considered a *vest haguf* if the woman has a cold or allergies since it is common to sneeze often when one has a cold or allergies. Since it may be difficult

---

11. ראשה ואיבריה כבדים עליה, ibid.

12. צירי הקודחות, ibid.

13. רותתת, in *Niddah* 63b.

14. גוסה, in *Niddah* 63b, according to *Rashba, Toras HaBayis* 7:3 13b.

15. See *Aruch HaShulchan* 189:53 and *Igros Moshe*, Y.D. 3:51. See Chapter Seven, Section VI and Chapter Thirteen, Section II,B,4.

16. 189:23.

17. *Toras HaShelamim* cites *Tosfos* (*Niddah* 63a) that this implies a sneezing spell lasting an hour or two. *Tosfos Yom Tov* (*Niddah* 9:8) seems to assume that any excessive sneezing is considered *vest haguf*. This is also reflected in the words of *Shulchan Aruch* 189:19. *Aruch HaShulchan* 189:54 explains that *Shulchan Aruch* means to exclude a case where she sneezed only two or three times. The underlying principle is that the sneezing spell should be unusual, but not necessarily lasting an hour or two.

18. 189:19, *Shach* §54.

to establish what constitutes an unusual symptom, a woman who suspects that she has a *vest haguf* should consult a Rav.[19]

4. A feeling that the period is imminent:
Some women have a distinct feeling that their period is about to begin. A woman must then abstain, even if this feeling is not one of the sensations identified by *Poskim* and even if this sensation appears when her period is not expected.[20]

5. Other types of sensations:
It should be noted that a woman may feel many types of sensations during the course of her menstrual cycle due to the hormonal change in her body. Some sensations may come as early as a week or two before the menstruation. These sensations are not associated with the actual blood flow and are not the subject of this chapter. A woman need not take any precautionary steps based upon these sensations.[21] In addition, mood changes which may precede menstruation, such as depression and irritability, are not considered a *vest haguf*.[22]

B. A *vest haguf* as compared to other *vestos*

While a *vest haguf* is similar to other *vestos* in its *halachos*, it differs in some aspects.[23] It is similar to other *vestos* in that: a) One must take note of a *vest haguf*, even if it happens only once. b) The *vest* is eliminated through the usual rules of *akiras vest* as will be explained in Section V. c) The time of the *vest* is treated as any other *onas havest:* One must abstain and do *bedikos*.[24] However, the duration of time that one must abstain varies according to the type of *vest haguf*, as will be explained in Section II. d) The *vest* is established when she menstruates three times after experiencing a particular symptom. If, in between the three occurrences, she

---

19. These *halachos* are discussed in 189:19.

20. See *Shiurei Sheivet HaLeivi* 189:19[10], s.v. ויש לפעמים, who notes that this is more severe than a regular *vest haguf*. This sensation is an actual indication that the menstruation is about to begin. According to *Beis Yosef* and *Lechem VeSimlah* cited below note 37, this is certainly so.

21. See *Shiurei Sheivet HaLeivi* 189:19[10]. In addition, we will note below, note 68, that, in the opinion of some *Poskim*, if the *vest haguf* is separated from the onset of the menstruation by more than a day, it is not considered a *vest haguf*.

22. Ibid.

23. 189:26.

24. 189:19,26.

experienced the symptoms without menstruating, the *vest* is not established.[25] In some respects a *vest haguf* is unique:

> 1. When a woman feels a symptom of her *vest*, it is a clear indication that her menstruation is about to begin. Therefore, in the opinion of some *Poskim*, a woman who feels the sensation of a *vest haguf* must do a *bedikah*, even if the *vest* is not *kavuah*. She is not permitted to cohabit even after the sensation subsides until a *bedikah* is performed.[26] In the case of a regular *vest she'aino kavuah*, a woman is not required to do a *bedikah* once the *onas havest* passes.

> 2. A *vest haguf* is established as a *vest kavuah* even if the three menstruations occurred in different *onos*, i.e., she menstruated once during the night and on another occasion during the day. In a regular *vest* all the menstruations must occur on the same *onah*, otherwise the *vest* cannot become a *vest kavuah*.[27]

II. A "simple" *vest haguf* and a *vest hamurkav*

There are two types of *vest haguf*: one that is not dependent upon any other factor, which we will call a "simple" *vest haguf*, and one that is dependent upon another factor, i.e., the day of the month or the interval from the last menstruation. *Poskim* call this second type a "*vest hamurkav*."

A. A simple *vest haguf*

A woman who establishes a *vest haguf* independent of any set monthly date or interval day must abstain whenever the symptoms of the *vest haguf* occur. See Section III below regarding at which stage of the symptoms she must begin to abstain and whether or not she is required to continue to abstain even after the symptoms stop. Although a woman with another

---

25. 189:26.

26. *Taz* 189:38 and *Divrei Chamudos* (*Niddah* 9:11). *Taz* explains that since she felt a physical manifestation of the *vest*, we suspect that there may have been *dam* even though she felt no *hargashah*. *Shach* (*Nekudos HaKesef* ad loc.), however, seems to disagree. *Graz* § 88, citing the lenient opinion of *Raavad*, also disagrees with *Taz*. However, *Chochmas Adam* 112:30 follows *Taz's* view, and *Pischei Teshuvah* 184:21 cites *Taz's* position as if it were the accepted *halachah*. Among contemporary authorities, *Be'er Moshe* 1:53 rules that one should follow *Taz's* opinion.

27. *Shiurei Sheivet HaLeivi* 189:19[10].

type of *vest kavuah* is not subject to *onah beinonis*, a woman with a <u>simple</u> *vest haguf kavuah* is required to keep *onah beinonis*. Since we do not know when to expect her *vest haguf*, we are required to assume that she will experience the symptoms and menstruate on the thirtieth day.[28] However, she is not required to abstain on the *vest hachodesh* or the *vest haflagah* of the previous menstruation unless the symptoms recur on those days.[29]

B. A *vest haguf hamurkav* — a complex *vest*

A woman may establish a *vest kavuah* which is a combination of a physical manifestation *vest* and a day *vest*.[30] Essentially, this is a causative *vest*. We know that menstruation is caused by a particular day. But, in addition, we have an indication that the menstruation is about to begin. The day aspect may be either a *vest haflagah* or a *vest hachodesh*. For example: She may usually menstruate after cramps that occur on the first of the month or she may usually menstruate after cramps that occur on the twenty-eighth interval day.[31] In either case, she has established a *vest hamurkav* for cramps that occur on that particular day.[32]

---

28. *Chavos Daas* 189:2[c], see below Section IV.

29. Unless the flow usually begins before the onset of the cramps, *Shaarei Tohar* 4:[9]. See also responsa *Tzemach Tzedek, Y.D.* 131.

30. *Sugah Bashoshanim* 7:4 maintains that a *vest hamurkav* can also be established with a combination of two physical manifestations. For example, a woman experiences a sneezing spell, then a belching spell and subsequently menstruates. She must, at first, suspect that each manifestation alone may be a cause and she must abstain if, in the future, she has <u>either</u> a sneezing or belching spell (this is similar to the *halachos* cited in Section III,3 below). If, subsequently, on <u>two</u> separate occasions, she has <u>either</u> a sneezing spell or a belching spell and menstruates, she establishes a *vest* for either sneezing or belching. However, *Aruch HaShulchan* 189:61 is uncertain whether a woman who menstruates after <u>both</u> sneezing and belching is required to abstain if, in the future, she only sneezes <u>or</u> belches. If the combination occurs three times at the time of menstruation, she establishes a *vest kavuah* for sneezing and belching combined. She is certainly no longer required to abstain after either sneezing or belching alone.

31. *Sugah Bashoshanim* 7:2 contends that even the first menstruation from which the first interval is calculated must be associated with cramps. *Badei HaShulchan, Tziyunim* 189:223, notes that this is implied in the words of *Shulchan Aruch* 189:22. See Chapter Nineteen, note 11.

32. One should note that there is a disagreement among *Poskim* whether a *vest haguf hamurkav* can be established if a woman menstruates three times on the day following the cramps. For example, she experiences cramps three times on the first of the month but only menstruates each time on the second of the month. Should we assume that the cramps of the previous day are associated with the menstruation (as we do in the case of a *vest haguf* that is not *murkav* (see III,B,4 below)? *Sugah Bashoshanim* 7:4 (based on *Chavos Daas* 189:23[b]) contends that the *vest* is a simple *vest hachodesh*, not a *vest haguf murkav*. We assume that the cramps are unrelated to the menstruation. Thus, she is required to keep *yom havest* on the second day of the month even if she experienced

A *vest hamurkav* may be divided into a "positive" *vest hamurkav* and a "possible" *vest hamurkav*.[33]

1. A "positive" *vest hamurkav:*

If a woman feels cramps and menstruates on three successive occasions on the first of the month, she has established a *vest hamurkav* to menstruate on the first of the month with a warning sign of cramps.[34] The <u>cause</u> of this *vest* is certainly the first of the month. The <u>warning sign</u> is the cramps. Similarly, she may establish a *vest hamurkav* to menstruate after an interval of twenty-eight days combined with a warning sign of cramps.[35] Her *vest kavuah* is dependent upon both factors, the day and the cramps. If only one factor is manifest, it may be considered a *yom havest*, depending upon which of the factors is manifest:

a. A manifestation of cramps alone:

If she experiences cramps on a different day of the month (e.g., the fifth of the month), she need not treat it as a *yom havest*. Her *vest haguf* was established only by the combination of the cramps and the *yom hachodesh*. The sensation of cramps alone gives us no reason to suspect that her period is imminent. Similarly, in the case of a *vest hamurkav* of an interval and cramps, if she experiences cramps on any day other than the twenty-eighth interval day, she need not keep a *yom havest*.[36] There is an opinion that she should treat the cramps as a *vest she'aino kavuah* and abstain for the duration of the cramps.[37]

---

no cramps on the previous day. However, responsa *Chasam Sofer, Y.D.* 183, s.v. וכ' ב"י, seems to maintain that one can establish a *vest haguf murkav* for the day following the cramps. Responsa *Sheivet HaLeivi* 3:124 contends that even *Chavos Daas* (cited by *Sugah Bashoshanim*) would agree to this. He maintains that *Chavos Daas* was referring to a *vest hakefitzos* only, not a *vest haguf*.

33. The words "positive" and "possible" are not being used to modify the word "murkav." The *vest* is certainly *murkav*. However, with the former we are "positive" that the period will arrive. With the latter we suspect that the period "possibly" may arrive.

34. 189:19.

35. In either of these cases, the *vest* is unaffected by any menstrual bleeding that occurs in between the three occasions. The *vest* is comprised of menstrual bleeding combined with cramps. Bleeding without cramps is not relevant to the *vest*. See *Chavos Daas* 189:24[b] and note 31 above.

36. 189:19 and *Rema*. She need not even treat the cramps as a *vest she'aino kavuah, Taz* §36, *Shach* §56 and *Toras HaShelamim* §39, as opposed to the stricter opinion of *Beis Yosef* (cited in following footnote). *Lechem VeSimlah* §42[s] notes that *Rambam* (*Hil. Niddah* 6:12) seems to follow the lenient opinion. *Lechem VeSimlah* himself follows the stricter opinion.

37. *Beis Yosef* cited in *Taz* §36. *Lechem VeSimlah* §42[s] finds the lenient opinion of most *Poskim* difficult

b. The arrival of the day alone:

When the first of the month (or the twenty-eighth interval day) arrives, we assume that she is about to menstruate even though the cramps have not yet begun. In this respect, the day factor of the *vest* differs from the cramps factor. The day is the <u>cause</u> of the *vest*, while the cramps are merely a <u>symptom.</u> Thus, when the symptom appears on a different day, we can ignore it since it has never established its association with the menstruation on any day other than the first of the month. The day factor, however, cannot be ignored. When the first of the month arrives, even without cramps, we assume that she certainly will menstruate since that is her *vest kavuah* day. The lack of cramps is not sufficient proof that menstruation is not imminent since the cramps may begin at any moment, even during cohabitation. This is true even if she usually does not menstruate until an hour after the cramps begin.[38]

Therefore, when the *yom havest*[39] arrives, she must abstain for the duration of the day, even if she feels no cramps.[40] However, if the day passes without the appearance of cramps, it retroactively is no longer considered a *yom havest* since the second factor (i.e., the cramps) never actualized.[41] Therefore, she does not require a *bedikah*[42] to permit her to resume relations after the day has passed.[43] Similarly, if she established a *vest hamurkav* to menstruate

---

to accept. He argues that although the woman usually experiences the cramps and menstruates on a particular monthly or interval day, if these very same cramps appear a day earlier, how can they be ignored? *Chavos Daas* §23[b] notes that according to the opinion of *Beis Yosef*, we are not certain that the *vest* is actually a *vest hamurkav*; it may really be a regular *vest* or a simple *vest haguf*. Therefore, she is required to abstain even if only one factor occurs. According to *Rema*, we are certain that it is a *vest hamurkav*. Therefore, she is not required to abstain if only one factor occurs.

38. We suspect that menstruation may begin earlier than usual because of cohabitation, *Graz* §97.

39. However, she is not required to abstain on the previous *onah*, even though she usually observes the *Or Zarua vest*; *Sheivet HaLeivi* 3:124, *Shiurei Sheivet HaLeivi* 189:25.

40. *Shach, Nekudos HaKesef* on *Taz* 189:39, *Toras HaShelamim* §47 and *Graz* §97, as opposed to *Taz* §39 who contends that she need not keep *yom havest* until the cramps begin. *Shach* in §56 seems to contradict his own ruling in *Nekudos HaKesef*; see *Chavos Daas* §26.

41. We required that she keep it as a *yom havest* only in anticipation that she may experience cramps. Since no cramps appeared, we realize in retrospect that it actually was not a *yom havest*.

42. *Chavos Daas* 189:26[b].

43. *Graz* 189:83,97. *Sugah Bashoshanim* 7:[3] and 16 understands this to mean that she does not even require a *bedikah* on the day of the *vest* itself unless cramps begin. He argues that the only

after an interval of twenty-eight days combined with cramps, she must treat every twenty-eighth interval day as a *yom havest,* regardless of whether or not she feels cramps. If she feels cramps on a different day, it may be ignored.[44] In this respect, a *vest hamurkav* is no different than any *vest hachodesh* or *vest haflagah.*[45]

2. A "possible" *vest hamurkav:*

If a woman both feels cramps and menstruates three times on the first of the month on non-successive months (or after non-successive twenty-eight day intervals), she has not established a *vest* to menstruate on the first of the month. In this case, it is clear that the first of the month is not the cause of the *vest* since she has passed the first of the month without incident. However, she has established a *vest* that whenever menstruation occurs on the first of the month, it is accompanied by cramps.[46] When the first of the month arrives without cramps, or if she experiences cramps on a different day of the month, it is not considered a *yom havest*[47] and she is not required to abstain. If she feels cramps on the first of the month, she must treat the remainder of the day[48] as a *yom havest.*

---

reason that they must abstain is out of concern that she may begin having cramps and immediately menstruate during cohabitation. This concern does not apply to the *bedikah* requirement. See, however, *Ran, Niddah* 63b and *Chavos Daas* 189:34[b] where it seems that the reason she must abstain the entire day is because any *vest* associated with a fixed day applies to the entire day.

44. 189:19.

45. 189:25.

46. See *Chavos Daas* end of 184, 189:34[b]. However, *Graz* 189:91 contends that a woman cannot establish a *vest hamurkav* unless it appears on three consecutive cases of a *yom hachodesh* or *yom haflagah.* His argument appears to be the following: A *vest hamurkav* is based upon recognition of the day aspect of the *vest* as a causative *vest.* This being the case, if the *yom hachodesh* passed without cramps and without menstruation, it is considered an *akirah* since she has demonstrated that the day does not cause menstruation. Therefore, if she menstruates once on the first of the month with cramps and passes the next first of the month without cramps and without menstruating, the *vest she'aino kavuah* is uprooted and cannot be combined with any subsequent menstruations on the first of the month to effect a *vest kavuah.* As noted, *Chavos Daas* disagrees.

47. See *Badei HaShulchan, Biurim* 189:19 s.v. ואם בא (at end), who notes that, according to *Chavos Daas,* this is true only if she had previously experienced cramps on other days without menstruating. However, if she never experiences cramps on other days, only on non-successive first days of the month, she establishes a *vest* for cramps regardless of when they occur.

48. If her flow usually continues after the cramps end. However, if the flow is usually limited to the duration of the cramps, she is not required to abstain once the cramps stop (see *Raavad* cited in *Beis Yosef* end of 184) and *Badei HaShulchan* 189:273. See Section III,B,1 below.

3. An *onah beinonis:*

Another difference between a "positive" and a "possible" *vest hamurkav* regards the *onah beinonis*. A woman with a positive *vest hamurkav* is not required to observe *onah beinonis* since we know when to expect her menstruation. A woman with a possible *vest hamurkav* is required to observe the *onah beinonis* since there is no definitive established day for menstruation.[49]

III. The duration of the *onas havest*

The rules regarding the *onas havest* of a *vest haguf* are unique. A normal *vest* is day oriented — either the monthly date or the interval day. A woman must abstain and do *bedikos* on her *onas havest*. This begins at the beginning of the *onah* and ends at the end of the *onah*. A *vest haguf*, however, is dependent upon the physical manifestation. Should she abstain at the onset of the cramps or at the beginning of the day or night *onah* (in the case of a *vest hamurkav*) of the cramps? Should she continue to abstain even after the cramps have stopped and no *dam* appeared? Should she continue to abstain if the cramps continue into another *onah?*

Poskim differentiate between a simple *vest haguf* and a *vest hamurkav*, between a woman who usually menstruates at the beginning of the cramping, one who menstruates only after the cramps have continued for a while, one whose flow continues after the cramps have ended and one whose flow continues only during the duration of the cramps. However, there is no difference regarding these *halachos* between a *vest haguf kavuah* and a *vest haguf she'aino kavuah.*

A. A *vest hamurkav*

We noted above that a woman who has a *vest hamurkav*, e.g., she experienced cramps and menstruated on the first of three successive months, must keep *onas havest* as soon as the first of the month arrives (even before cramps begin).[50] As explained above, her *vest* is essentially dependent upon the day of the month; thus, we are concerned that she may begin to

---

49. *Sugah Bashoshanim* 7:16.

50. 189:25. This follows the interpretation of *Shach* (*Nekudos Hakesef* ad loc.) as opposed to *Taz* §39 who contends that a woman who has a *vest hamurkav* (like a woman with a simple *vest haguf*) is not required to abstain before the cramps begin. In the opinion of *Taz*, the sole difference between a simple *vest haguf* and a *vest hamurkav* regards a case where the flow is limited to the duration of the cramps. In the case of a simple *vest haguf*, she is permitted after the cramps pass. In the case of a *vest hamurkav*, she must abstain for the remainder of the day or night *onah*.

menstruate at any time during the day. This is true even if she usually experiences cramps two hours before the flow begins and even if the flow is limited to the duration of the cramps.[51] Nevertheless, we cannot assume that she will have a two-hour warning before the flow begins.[52]

B. A simple *vest haguf*

A woman with a simple *vest haguf* is certainly not required to abstain before the cramps begin since she cannot know when they are about to begin.[53] However, if she experiences cramps, on any day, she is required to abstain. Most women today do not have a *vest kavuah* for a particular interval or monthly date. Therefore, whenever a woman feels the particular type of physical manifestation usually associated with her menstruation, and always related to it within a similar time frame (see 1,b below), she is required to abstain, even if the day is not the date of her last menstrual period. The duration of the time in which she must abstain depends upon the nature of the *vest haguf*[54] as follows:

_____

51. *Sugah Bashoshanim* 7:16.

52. As noted previously, cohabitation itself may cause the flow to come earlier (*Graz* 189:97); see note 38.

53. This reason is needed only in a case of a flow which continues after the cramps have stopped. If the flow is restricted to the duration of the cramps, she would not be required to abstain beforehand, even if we were to know that she will feel cramps that day, as explained in the following note.

54. The underlying principle of these *halachos* is the following: A simple day-related *vest,* either a *vest hachodesh* or a *vest haflagah,* depends upon the day. We expect the flow to begin that day. Therefore, she must abstain the entire day. A *vest haguf* however, is possible in two forms: a flow completely limited to the duration of the cramps and one which continues after the cramps have stopped. In the former case, the *vest* has no relation whatsoever to the day; it is limited to the phenomenon of the cramps. Thus, the cramps are the equivalent of the "day" in a day *vest.* However, this comparison is not completely accurate. A "day" *vest* applies to the entire day, even though she usually menstruates only at a certain hour. In contrast, a *vest haguf* applies only to the part of the cramping in which the flow usually begins, not earlier. For example, if the menstruation usually begins an hour after the cramps begin, she is only required to abstain after an hour of cramping. If the comparison of "cramps" to "day" were accurate, she would be required to abstain the entire cramping time just as she is required to abstain the entire day of a day *vest. Rashba* (cited in *Beis Yosef* 189 p.56) and *Raavad* (cited in *Beis Yosef* 184 p.44a) explain that regarding *vest haguf,* we accept the position of R' Yosi (*Niddah* 63b) that a *vest* can be limited to a particular hour, even though regarding a normal day *vest,* we reject his position. A woman with a *vest haguf* limited to the duration of the cramps is required to abstain only when she reaches that phase of the cramps during which the flow usually begins (for example, after one hour). Following this logic, if she usually menstruates at the beginning of the cramps, one would expect that if the flow does not begin immediately, she is no longer bound by the *vest* even while she still experiences cramps, since the flow did not begin at the expected time. Nevertheless, *Chavos Daas* 189:30[b] explains, since she

1. A flow limited to the duration of the cramps:
If the flow usually lasts no longer than the cramps themselves, i.e.,
the flow is limited to the duration of the cramps, the duration is
compared to a *yom havest*. Thus, she must abstain only during the
term of the cramps. Once the cramps end, her *onas havest* is over.[55]

a. An immediate flow:

If the flow is limited to the duration of the cramps and
usually begins immediately with the onset of the
cramps,[56] the woman must abstain the moment she experiences that type of cramping. Even if the flow does not
begin at the beginning of the cramping, she must abstain
during the entire duration of the cramps.[57]

b. A delayed flow:

If the flow usually does not begin immediately with the
onset of the cramps, but some time after the cramps
begin, e.g., one hour,[58] she is required to abstain only[59]
after one hour has passed.[60] This *halachah* is unique to a
regular *vest haguf* since it is not dependent upon the day.

---

continues to experience cramps, we suspect that perhaps the beginning of the cramps were not the
actual cramps associated with the flow; rather, each successive cramp may be the cramp associated
with the flow. The above pertains to a flow limited to the duration of the cramps. However, if the flow
usually continues after the cramps have ended, the flow relates to the day as well and is treated as a
"day"-oriented *vest*. Thus, regardless of when the flow usually begins, she must abstain for the duration of the cramps and until the end of the day or night *onah*, even after the cramps have ended (see
Chavos Daas §31[b]). Indeed, she should be required to abstain even at the beginning of the day if we
could predict on which day the cramps will begin. The *halachos* that follow reflect these principles.

55. 189:24.

56. See *Sugah Bashoshanim* 7:14, and *Igros, Moshe Y.D.* 1:84, regarding a woman who sometimes
menstruates with the beginning of the cramping and sometimes at the end. See also *Badei
HaShulchan* 189:263 and *Biurim* s.v. לראות בסופו.

57. 189:24. Perhaps the later phases of the cramps, not the first phase, are the cramps associated
with the flow. *Chavos Daas* §30[b] and *Aruch HaShulchan* 189:62.

58. See *Sugah Bashoshanim* 7:14 who uses an example of a flow delayed half-an-hour.

59. If she wishes to cohabit during the first hour, she should do a *bedikah* beforehand (see *Bach* 189
p.56a and *Sheivet HaLeivi* 3:117).

60. 189:24. *Lechem VeSimlah* 189:42[s] notes a fascinating *halachah*. A woman has a *vest hamurkav*
and her flow usually begins an hour after onset of the cramps on *Rosh Chodesh*. When the last hour
of *Rosh Chodesh* arrives and she has not yet experienced any cramps, she is no longer required to
abstain that day. Even if the cramps will begin, she will not menstruate today since she never
menstruates before an hour has passed. *Badei HaShulchan, Biurim* 189:25 s.v. ואז אי, notes that
according to this position, she is not even required to abstain the following night since it is no
longer her *vest* day. *Pischei Migadim* (R' Meisels) 25:12 cites an opposing opinion. It seems that if
the *vest* is not a *vest hamurkav* she must abstain after the hour although it extends into the next *onah*.

However, a *vest haguf murkav*[61] or a regular *vest hachodesh* or *vest haflagah* that is not related to a *vest haguf* applies to the entire *onas havest*. When the day of the *vest* arrives, she must abstain regardless of whether the flow usually begins in the beginning of the *onah* or later in the day.

If the flow of a regular *vest haguf* is delayed for more than a day after the cramping, she is required to abstain on the day of the expected menstruation only; see 4 below.

2. A continued flow:

If the flow usually continues after the cramps subside, even for a short while, the *vest* is not limited to the duration of the cramps. This *vest* is treated as a "day"-oriented *vest*. Therefore, she must abstain from the onset of the cramps, even if the flow usually begins an hour after the cramps have begun.[62] She must also continue to abstain until the end of the day or night *onah*, even though the cramps have ended.[63] If the cramps continue into the night, she must abstain for the remainder of the night.[64]

3. A flow that begins after the cramps end:

If the flow usually begins only after the cramps end, she is required to abstain from the beginning of the cramps to the end of the day or night *onah*.[65] This *vest* is also a "day"-oriented *vest* as in 2 above.

---

61. A *vest hamurkav* requires that she abstain the entire day even before the cramps begin as explained in A above.

62. 189:24. *Chavos Daas* §31[b] explains that since the flow continues after the cramps have stopped, the *vest* is considered day oriented. *Shiurei Sheivet HaLeivi* 189:24[3] explains that, essentially, she should abstain from the beginning of the day since the entire day is her *vest*. However, since we do not know which day to expect the cramps, she is permitted to cohabit until the cramps begin.

63. 189:24.

64. This is similar to the *halachah* cited in 1,a, that a woman must abstain for the duration of the cramps even though she usually menstruates at the beginning of the cramps. We suspect that the last stage of the cramps may be the cramps associated with the flow. In this case, even if the cramps end during the course of the night, she must abstain for the remainder of the night, since this is the *onas havest*; see *Badei HaShulchan* 189:266.

65. *Chavos Daas* §31[b] and *Levush* cited in *Badei HaShulchan* 189:267. *Chavos Daas* notes that, in the opinion of *Rashba*, if the flow usually begins after the cramps end, she is required to abstain only after the cramps end. *Graz* (end of 184) seems to follow *Rashba's* lenient view he uses the words"או אחר יורי."

4. A flow that begins on a following *onah:*

If the flow usually begins on the following *onah*, her *vest* is the *onah* following the *onah* of the cramps.[66] Thus, she is not limited in any way on the *onah* of the cramps and requires no *bedikah*.[67] Similarly, if the flow usually begins three days after the onset of the cramps, cohabitation is permitted during the first two days but is prohibited on the third day.[68] A woman who usually menstruates three hours after the onset of the cramps and begins to feel cramps two hours before sundown is not required to abstain until sundown since she does not expect to menstruate on the day of the cramps.[69] If the interval between the cramps and the flow is irregular, i.e., at times, the flow begins the following day and, at times, it begins after three days, one should consult a Rav whether or not this is considered a *vest haguf*.[70]

5. A flow that begins before the cramps:

If the flow usually begins before the onset of the cramps but does not continue after the cramps have subsided, she is required to

---

66. *Sugah Bashoshanim* 7:4. However, *Mishnah Acharonah* (*Niddah* 9:8) is uncertain whether this case is a *vest haguf* since the menstruation does not follow the cramp immediately. See note 32 regarding a *vest hamurkav*. See also *Chavos Daas* 189:23[b] regarding a similar case in a *vest hakefitzos*. *Vest hakefitzos* is explained in Chapter Nineteen.

67. If a woman usually feels cramps at noon and menstruates eight hours later in the evening and on one occasion feels cramps in the morning, it seems that one should assume the *vest* is in the evening, not in the afternoon, even though that is after eight hours. However, it is not clear if a woman who menstruated once in the evening after eight hours of noon-time cramps and subsequently feels cramps in the morning should abstain after eight hours or in the evening.

68. *Darchei Teshuvah* 189:78 and *Sheivet HaLeivi* 3:117, citing responsa *Riva* (of Faksh). This seems to be the opinion of *Igros Moshe*, Y.D. 1:84 and 3:51, as well, though his wording in the latter responsa is unclear. Nevertheless, *Sheivet HaLeivi* advises that she do a *bedikah* before cohabitation during these two days. However, *Sugah Bashoshanim* contends that if the menstruation is more than a day after the cramps, it is not attributed to the cramps; thus, she has no *vest haguf* at all. In this sense, a *vest haguf* is similar to a *vest haones* (see Chapter Nineteen note 20). In summary, in the opinion of *Mishnah Acharonah* (note 66) if the menstruation begins a day after the cramps, it may not be considered a *vest haguf*. In the view of *Sugah Bashoshanim* even if the menstruation occurs on the following day it is a *vest haguf*. However, if the menstruation follows by more than a day, it is not considered a *vest haguf*. In the view of other *Poskim*, even a menstruation that follows the cramps by several days is a *vest haguf*.

69. *Lechem VeSimlah* 189:42[s].

70. *Shiurei Sheivet HaLeivi* 189:19[10] rules that, in this case, she should abstain after the earliest possible time to expect the flow. For example, if the flow sometimes begins two days and sometimes three or four days after the cramps, she should abstain two days after the cramps. Even during the first two days, she should do a *bedikah* before cohabitation. This is similar to the *halachah* of a woman whose *vest* alternates within a span of a few days; see Chapter Twenty-Two.

abstain whenever she experiences cramps even if the flow did not begin. *Poskim* are uncertain whether she is required to continue to abstain after the cramps subside.[71]

IV. A *vest hamurkav she'aino kavuah*

A woman who menstruates on any day in conjunction with cramps must keep all of the *vest* possibilities as a *vest she'aino kavuah*. Therefore, she must abstain on the same day of the following month,[72] the next corresponding interval of days,[73] the *onah beinonis*[74] and the next time that she experiences similar cramps.[75] On each of these *vest* possibilities, she should do a *bedikah*. If she did not do a *bedikah* on the corresponding day of the month or the interval day, a *bedikah* is no longer required. If she did not do a *bedikah* on the *onah beinonis*, she must abstain until the *bedikah* is performed. If she did not do a *bedikah* while experiencing cramps,[76] she must, in the opinion of some *Poskim*, abstain until she performs the required *bedikah*.[77] Other *Poskim* do not require a *bedikah* once the cramps subside.[78] When the *vest hachodesh*, *vest haflagah* and *vest haguf* pass without incident, she is no longer required to keep those

71. See *Shach* §61 and *Sugah Bashoshanim* 7:15.

72. 189:22.

73. Ibid.

74. *Graz* §91.

75. 189:21. If, in the previous menstruation, the flow continued after the cramps ended, she must, on this second occurrence, abstain the remainder of the day. If, in the original occurrence, the flow was limited to the duration of the cramps, she is required to abstain only for the duration of the cramps (see *Graz* §87). If she usually does not menstruate until an hour after experiencing cramps, she may cohabit during the first hour after performing a *bedikah*.

76. It would seem that she should do a *bedikah* after the cramps end since the last stage of cramps are those associated with menstruation.

77. *Taz* §38, *Lechem Chamudos* (*Niddah* 63a, 9:11), *Sidrei Taharah* 189:27 and *Chochmas Adam* 112:30. *Taz* explains that a *vest haguf* is more serious than a regular *vest* since she actually felt a bodily symptom. *Badei HaShulchan, Biurim* 189:21 s.v. ואם בדקה, notes that according to this view, if she did a *bedikah* later and found a bloodstain on the cloth, the *vest haguf* is not uprooted.

78. *Bach* 189 p. 55b, 56a. *Shach, Nekudos Hakesef* ad loc. also dismisses *Taz's* view. He nevertheless differentiates between a day *vest* and a *vest haguf*. When a day *vest she'aino kavuah* passes without incident, she may cohabit immediately. However, when a *vest haguf* passes, i.e., the cramps stop, she may not cohabit immediately afterward without performing a *bedikah*. Once a considerable amount of time (זמן מופלג) passes, a *bedikah* is no longer required. *Shach* gives no hint as to what is considered a considerable amount of time. *Graz* §88 follows *Shach's* opinion and implies that זמן מופלג is certainly no longer than the time left to the end of the *onas havest*. *Aruch HaShulchan* seems to follow *Shach's* opinion. He notes that if she waits several hours, a *bedikah* is no longer required.

vestos.[79] If the *vest haguf* occurs three times on the same monthly or interval day, she has established a *vest murkav kavuah* as described above.

V. A *vest hamurkav* that concludes as a simple *vest*

If a woman menstruates twice on the first of the month with cramps but on the third month menstruates on the first of the month without cramps,[80] she has demonstrated that her *vest* is a simple *vest hachodesh* unrelated to the cramps. Similarly, if, on the third month, she menstruates on the second of the month with cramps, she has demonstrated that her *vest* is a simple *vest haguf* based upon cramps, regardless of the day.[81] In both of these cases, we assume that the factor that repeated itself three times is the main factor, while the factor that did not repeat itself is merely coincidental.[82]

VI. *Onah beinonis* with regard to a *vest haguf*

A woman with a *vest haguf kavuah hamurkav,* whether combined with a *vest hachodesh* or a *vest haflagah,* is not subject to *onah beinonis* since she has a *vest kavuah.* We noted in II,B,3 above that this refers to a "positive" *vest hamurkav* only, not a "possible" *vest hamurkav.* However, a *vest haguf* that is not day oriented is not, in a certain respect, a *vest kavuah* since

---

79. 189:22.

80. See 189:20 regarding a case where, on the third occasion, she experienced the cramps on the previous day but only menstruated a day later, on the first of the month.

81. 189:20, *Shach* §57,58. See *Shaarei Tohar* 4:10, who contends that if she menstruates both on the first of the month without cramps and on another day with cramps, she established two independent *vestos,* one for the first of the month and one for cramps. It seems from *Shaarei Tohar* that, in this case, she has no *vest hamurkav.* Thus, if she experiences cramps three times without menstruating and passes the first of the month three times without cramps and without menstruating, she uproots both *vestos* (as *Shaarei Torah* himself notes).

82. However, once the *vest* has established itself as a *vest hamurkav,* any subsequent menstruation cannot alter the nature of the *vest.* For example, if, after she menstruated three times on the first of the month with cramps, she menstruates on the fifteenth of the month with cramps, we do not assume that her *vest* is a simple *vest haguf.* Rather, she retains the original *vest hamurkav kavuah* for the first of the month. Nevertheless, she must, in addition, consider any appearance of cramps a *vest she'aino kavuah* and abstain, regardless on which day it occurs. This is similar to the case of any woman with a *vest kavuah* who menstruates on a day incompatible with her *vest kavuah.* See *Chavos Daas* 189:23[b] and *Shaarei Tohar* 4:[11].

we have not determined what actually causes the menstruation. Menstruation may take place any day, albeit combined with cramps. We must suspect that the menstruation may take place on the thirtieth day since that is the average interval, the *onah beinonis*.[83] Thus, a woman who has a simple *vest haguf* is an example of a woman with a *vest kavuah* who must also keep the *onah beinonis*.[84] If the *onah beinonis* passes without cramps, she is not required to do a *bedikah*.[85]

VII. Uprooting a *vest haguf*

A *vest haguf* is uprooted according to the same principles and in the same manner as any other *vest*. Thus, a *vest she'aino kavuah* is uprooted with one *akirah* and a *vest kavuah* with three. In addition, a *vest kavuah* cannot be uprooted without a *bedikah*, while a *vest she'aino kavuah* is uprooted even without a *bedikah*.[86] The exact manner depends upon the individual type of *vest haguf*.

A. A simple *vest haguf*

A woman who has a simple *vest haguf*, e.g., she established a *vest kavuah* to menstruate whenever she experiences cramps, uproots that *vest* when she experiences similar cramps on three occasions without menstruating.[87]

---

83. *Chavos Daas* 189:2[c] contends that this applies only if the menstruation usually begins immediately with the onset of the cramps or the blood flow continues after the cramps have stopped (in which case the *vest* is not limited to the duration of the cramps, see B,2 above). However, if the menstruation begins only after the cramps have continued for a while and does not continue after the cramps have stopped, she need not keep the *onah beinonis* since she has sufficient warning before the flow actually begins. A similar view is found in *Graz* 184:45. However, *Sugah Bashoshanim* 7:[34] contends that, in any case, she must abstain the entire *onah beinonis*.

84. See *Shach* 184:32.

85. Her status is similar to that of a woman with a *vest hamurkav* who passes the day without cramps and requires no further *bedikah* as noted in *Graz* 189:83. This is because we know that she did not menstruate, since all her menstruations are accompanied by cramps. However, her husband must inquire whether or not she experienced cramps.

86. See 189:26. However, she may require a *bedikah* to permit cohabitation, see notes 77,78. *Responsa Beis Shlomo*, Y.D. 27, based upon *Taz* 189:38, contends that a *vest haguf*, even *she'aino kavuah*, is not uprooted without a *bedikah*. See Chapter Fourteen note 16, that many *Poskim* disagree with *Taz*, they certainly disagree with *Beis Shlomo*. It is questionable whether even those *Poskim* who follow *Taz's* view agree with *Beis Shlomo*.

87. 189:26. *Badei HaShulchan* §281 notes that it seems that even if a woman experiences three separate spells of cramps on one day without menstruating, the *vest* is uprooted.

B. A *vest haguf hamurkav:*

The *halachos* of uprooting a *vest haguf* combined with a physical manifestation (e.g., cramps) and a particular day (e.g., the first of the month or
the twenty-eight interval day) are as follows:

1. The *vest* is uprooted only when both factors appear without
causing menstruation (i.e., she experienced cramps on that day
without menstruating).[88]

2. If she experiences cramps on three other days without menstruating, the *vest* remains intact since only the combination of
both factors is expected to cause the *vest.*[89]

3. If the day passes three times without cramps and without menstruation, the *vest* is partially uprooted. She has demonstrated
that the day alone does not necessarily cause menstruation; thus,
when the day appears, she need not keep a *yom havest.* However,
when both factors appear (i.e., she experiences cramps on the
first of the month), she must expect the *vest.* In effect, her *vest*
changed from that of a "positive" *vest hamurkav*, explained in
II,B,1, above, to that of a "possible" *vest hamurkav*, explained in
II,B,2.[90]

4. If she menstruates three times on the first of the month without experiencing cramps, it becomes apparent that the prime factor of her *vest* is the *vest hachodesh*, not the *vest haguf.* The *vest*
hamurkav is transformed into a regular *vest hachodesh.* If, in the
future, she passes the first of the month for three consecutive
months without menstruating, the *vest hachodesh* is uprooted. If,
thereafter, she experiences cramps on the first of the month, she
is not required to abstain, since the original *vest hamurkav* was
previously uprooted.[91]

---

88. 189:26.

89. Ibid.

90. *Chavos Daas* 189:42[c] and *Aruch HaShulchan* 189:64.

91. This seems apparent from *Aruch HaShulchan* 189:65. *Aruch HaShulchan* is uncertain regarding
a case where, after establishing a *vest hamurkav* for cramps on the first of the month, she menstruates on the first of the following three months without cramps but on each of the days she experienced a different type of *vest haguf*, e.g., she experienced a headache, a sneezing spell, etc.
Perhaps this would not be considered an *akirah* of the original *vest hamurkav*. Although the different types do not combine with one another to establish a *vest haguf*, they are, nevertheless, similar in nature and perhaps one is not an *akirah* for another.

5. If a woman established a *vest hamurkav* and uprooted it, but in the future experiences cramps on the same *vest* day and menstruates, the *vest* may be reestablished as a *vest kavuah*.[92] This *halachah* is not unique to *vest haguf;* it applies to any *vest kavuah* and is discussed in Chapter Fourteen.

see chart on next page

---

92. *Be'er Moshe* 1:56. See *Badei HaShulchan, Biurim* 189:26 s.v. בן הוא. A *vest kavuah* that was uprooted without establishing a new *vest kavuah* is reestablished when she menstruates even once on the *yom havest*, see Chapter Seventeen, Section I,C.

THE DURATION OF A VEST HAGUF

VEST HAGUG KARUA

the day of the last occurrence arrives without cramping → not required to abstain

cramping occurs on any day
- if flow is usually limited to the duration of the cramping
  - if flow is usually delayed some time after cramping begins → After time of usual delay, must abstain for duration of cramping
  - if flow is usually immediate → must abstain immediately for duration of cramping
- if flow usually continues after cramping ends → must abstain for remainder of day

VEST HAGUF HAMURKAV

the day arrives without cramping → must abstain entire day

cramping occurs on another day → not required to abstain according to most poskim

CHAPTER NINETEEN

וסת האונס

Induced *Vestos*

□ The unique status of a *vest haones.*

□ *Vest haachilos.*

□ Hormonal regulation of a *vest* .

Introduction

The subject of this chapter are *vestos* that are not caused by nature, such as the monthly date and the interval from the last period (discussed in Chapter Fifteen), or physical manifestations that signal the imminent arrival of her period such as *vest haguf* (discussed in Chapter Eighteen). We will discuss *vestos* that are self-imposed: *vestos* that are caused by the woman herself, whether willingly or unwillingly. We will discuss three such types of *vestos:* Two have a source in the Talmud itself and one is a fairly modern application of this Talmudic law. The Talmud discusses the case of a woman who jumped and subsequently had a uterine flow. The Talmud also mentions the case of a woman who ate sharp foods and subsequently had a uterine flow. This is usually referred to as a *"vest haachilos,"* a *vest* of "eatings." Later *Poskim* discuss the case of a uterine flow brought about through medicinal means. The subject of this chapter is these three *vestos*.

A. *Vest haones* — a *vest* induced by external physical factors

Chazal note a unique type of *vest:* a menstruation caused by external physical factors. For example, a woman who jumped from a high position,[1] was hit or exerted herself physically, e.g., by carrying a heavy load,[2] and menstruates soon afterwards.[3] This is known as a *"vest hakefitzos"* — a *vest* of jumping — or a *"vest haones"* — an induced *vest*. We will use the term *vest haones* in our discussion.

One should understand the essential difference between a *vest haones* and a *vest haguf*. A *vest haguf* is a symptomatic *vest:* The sneezing is a symptom of the menstruation, not its cause. A *vest haones* is a causative *vest:* The jumping is the actual cause of the menstruation.[4] Also, a *vest haguf* is natural, while a *vest haones* is unnatural. A *vest haones* is somewhat illogical. Is it possible that she will menstruate whenever she jumps (even every

---

1. *Rambam, Peirush HaMishnah, Niddah* 1:6.

2. *Rezah, Shaar HaVestos* §25 (Kapach edition).

3. *Sugah Bashoshanim* 6:[7] maintains that even a woman who menstruates after three different physical exertions (i.e., she jumped on one occasion, was hit on another and lifted a heavy load on a third) has established a *vest* for any type of physical exertion. In this manner a *vest haones* differs from a *vest haguf* which cannot become *kavuah* unless all components are similar, see Chapter Eighteen.

4. *Rashba* (*Toras HaBayis* 7:3 p. 13b) and *Ran* (*Niddah* 63a).

day)?[5] Therefore, a *vest haones* is treated differently than other *vestos*. We will use the example of a woman who jumps and subsequently menstruates, since this is the case discussed in the Talmud[6] and *Shulchan Aruch*.[7]

1. A woman who jumps and menstruates soon afterwards is rendered a *niddah* but is not required to assume that she will menstruate each time she jumps.[8] Thus, if she jumps again in the future, she need not abstain and is not required to do a *bedikah*.

2. If she jumps on the fifth of month A and menstruates afterwards, she is not required to observe a *vest hachodesh* on the fifth of month B since we assume that the menstruation was caused (at least partially) by her jump, not by the fifth of the month alone. Similarly, if she jumped on the twentieth interval day from her last period and menstruated, she is not required to observe a *vest haflagah* on the following twentieth interval day.[9] Nevertheless, she must observe an *onah beinonis* on the thirtieth day from the last menstruation, even if that menstruation was caused by jumping.[10]

3. If both factors recur in combination, i.e., she jumps again on the fifth of month B or any subsequent month or she jumps again on the twentieth interval day,[11] she is required to abstain.[12]

---

5. Furthermore, if she never jumps in the future, will she never menstruate? Apparently, jumping cannot actually cause a menstrual period; it merely hastens the arrival of a flow that is about to begin, *Malbushei Taharah* 189:46.

6. *Niddah* 11a.

7. 189:17.

8. *Shach* §48 and *Chochmas Adam* 112:35. However, *Prishah* §59 contends that she must abstain whenever she jumps. See *Pleisi* §21 and *Sidrei Taharah* §21, who contend that this pertains only to the opinion of *Tur* (cited in note 13) that a *vest haones* can become a *vest kavuah* even if it is not time oriented (i.e., it does not always occur on the same monthly date or after the same interval). However, according to *halachic* consensus that a *vest haones* cannot become *kavuah* unless it is time oriented (see 4 below), a woman need not abstain for a *vest haones* that occurred only once or twice.

9. 184:12 according to interpretation of *Shach* §32.

10. *Chavos Daas* 189:22[b] and *Sidrei Taharah* §12. This is also apparent from *Shulchan Aruch* 184:12 and *Shach* 184:32 citing *Rashba*.

11. It seems from *Shach* 189:48 that this is true only if the first menstruation of the interval was also associated with a jump. However, if she menstruates without jumping and jumps on the following twentieth interval day and menstruates, she is not required to keep a *yom havest* even if she jumps again on the next twentieth interval day. We assume that the second menstruation was caused by the jump alone. We do not consider it a twenty day interval since the two components of the interval (the two menstruations) are not similar; one was caused by jumping and the other was not (*Graz, Kuntres Acharon* 187:12 and *Avnei Neizer, Y.D.* 229:8).

12. *Shach* 189:48. *Shiurei Sheivet HaLeivi* (ad loc.) explains that there are several possible causes of

This *vest she'aino kavuah* is uprooted only when both factors recur, i.e., she jumps again on the fifth of the month and does not menstruate (it is then uprooted and if she jumps on the next *yom havest* she is not required to abstain). If she jumps on another day or passes the *yom havest* without jumping and does not menstruate, the *vest* is not uprooted.

4. A *vest haones* never becomes a *vest kavuah* (even if repeated many times) unless it is associated with another *vest*,[13] e.g., a day of the month or an interval.[14] Nevertheless, a *vest haones* that repeats itself three times becomes the equivalent of a *vest she'aino kavuah*.[15] Thus, if she jumps three times on unrelated days and menstruates each time,[16] she has established a *vest she'aino kavuah* not a *vest kavuah*. A

---

her previous menstruation: The jumping alone may be the cause, the day of the month (or *haflagah*) alone may be the cause or the menstruation may be caused by the combination of the two. Thus, if she jumps again on the same day of the month, she must keep a *yom havest* since all three possibilities were replicated. Whereas, if she did not jump on that day, there are two possibilities that she need not keep a *yom havest* on that day: Perhaps the jumping alone is the cause of the menstruation or perhaps the combination of the two. The possibility that the day alone is the cause is only a minor probability, which may be ignored.

13. 189:17, following opinion of *Rambam* (*Hilchos Issurei Biah* 8:5) and *Rashba* (*Toras HaBayis* 7:3, p.13b). However, in the opinion of *Ramban* (*Hilchos Niddah* 6:12), *Rezah* (*Shaar HaVestos* §25) and *Tur, a vest haones* becomes *kavuah* after three occurrences even without the combination of another *vest*.

14. *Pleisi* §23 raises an interesting question. Could a *vest haones* become a *vest kavuah* when combined with a *vest haguf*? For example, if, on three occasions, she felt stomach cramps, jumped and menstruated, can this become a *vest kavuah*? *Pleisi* reaches no definite conclusion.

15. *Shulchan Aruch* 189:17 implies that a *vest haones* may be ignored even if it repeats itself three times. However, *Rema* (ad loc.) rules that it has the status of a *vest she'aino kavuah*. *Chavos Daas* §1[b] and 22[b] maintains that if, on these three occasions, she menstruated a fixed time after jumping, e.g., three hours later, she is required to keep the *vest* only after that period of time. She is permitted to cohabit up to three hours after she jumps and is permitted to cohabit after the fourth hour has passed. However, if the *vest haones* is combined with a specific day or interval, she must keep the *vest* for the entire day, *Shach* §50.

16. *Chavos Daas* §23[b] maintains that if, on each of the three occasions, she menstruated on the day following the jump, she establishes a *vest she'aino kavuah* (since a *vest haones* cannot become *kavuah*) for the day following a jump. However, if all three periods occurred on the same interval or monthly date, we consider the *vest* a regular *vest* unrelated to the jumping. *Sugah Bashoshanim* 6:5 contends that if she menstruates three times two days after a jump, it cannot create a *vest*. He maintains that we cannot associate a menstruation to the jumping which preceded it by two days. See also *Noda B'Yehudah, Y.D.* 2:93. Responsa *Sheivet HaLeivi* 3:124, s.v. א״רשב״א והרשב״א, is uncertain regarding a woman who jumped towards evening and menstruated in the beginning of the night. Is this considered a menstruation on the same day or on the following day? Logically, it should be considered the same day and the *vest* should be a regular *vest hakefitzos*. However, it seems from *Poskim*

vest haones is elevated after three occurrences, from a non-*vest* to a *vest she'aino kavuah* (unlike a regular *vest* which is elevated after three occurrences from a *vest she'aino kavuah* to a *vest kavuah*). Accordingly, whenever she jumps she must abstain and perform a *bedikah*. Once the *onas havest* passes she may cohabit even if she did not perform the *bedikah*. If, in the future, she jumps, even once, without menstruating, the *vest* is uprooted.[17]

5. If she jumped and menstruated on the same date of three months,[18] or after three equal intervals,[19] she has established a *vest kavuah* for that monthly date or that interval day, in combination with a jump.[20] Thus, if she jumps (and only if she jumps) on that day, she is required to abstain[21] and do a *bedikah*. If the day passes without a flow but she did not do the required *bedikah*, she is forbidden to cohabit until she does a *bedikah*. This *vest kavuah* is uprooted only when she jumps three times on the specific *vest* day without menstruating.[22]

6. *Shulchan Aruch*[23] discusses the case of a woman who menstruated three times on, for example, the fifth of the month. On the first

that it is considered the following day and subject to the same standards as the case of a woman who jumped on one day and menstruated on the next day.

17. *Chochmas Adam* 112:35.

18. See *Graz* 189:75 as to whether the three months must be consecutive. See also *Badei HaShulchan* 189:17, s.v. שאינו קבוע.

19. *Chavos Daas* §24[b] maintains that the intervals are measured from one menstruation due to jumping to another menstruation due to jumping. Any intermediate menstruation not due to jumping will not interrupt the interval. A *haflagah* of jumping is only measured from another menstruation caused by jumping. This view seems supported by *Shach* §48, see note 11. Thus, even the first of the four menstruations that cause the *vest haflagah* must be from a menstruation caused by jumping.

20. We noted, in note 16 above, the opinion of *Chavos Daas* §23[b] that if she did not menstruate on the actual day of the jump, but the following day, we attribute the menstruation to the day alone without the jumping. One should note that *Chavos Daas* differentiates between a simple *vest hakefitzos* and a *vest hakefitzos* on an established date. In the former case, the *vest* can become established as a *vest she'aino kavuah* (since a *vest* for *kefitzos* never becomes *kavuah*) even if the menstruations were always the day after the jumping. However, the latter case (which can become a *vest kavuah*) will not become *kavuah* if the menstruations were the day after a jumping. Since the *vest* occurred three times on a certain day, we assume that the day alone caused the menstruation, not the jumping of the previous day.

21. As noted above note 15, in this case, she must abstain the entire *onah*, even if the menstruation usually occurs at a specific time after jumping, *Shach* §50.

22. *Shach* §50.

23. 189:17.

two occasions she menstruated immediately after jumping, but on the last occasion she jumped on the fourth but menstruated on the fifth of the month. Does she establish a *vest hakefitzos* linked with a *vest hachodesh* or does she establish a simple *vest hachodesh*?

B. *Vest haachilos:* a *vest* caused by eating certain foods

A woman may also menstruate due to certain foods that she eats. *Chazal*[24] note the *vest* of a woman who menstruates after eating sharp foods, e.g., garlic, onions or hot peppers. Among the unique *halachos* of this *vest* are the following:

1. A *vest haguf* must usually be comprised of similar components; different components cannot create a *vest haguf kavuah*. For example, a woman who had three different types of physical sensations (e.g., a sneezing, a yawning and a hiccupping spell) prior to her *vest* cannot establish a *vest haguf*. However, a *vest haachilos* can become established even if, on each occasion she ate a different food, all the foods were of a similar type.[25] For example, if she ate garlic once, onions once and hot peppers once, she establishes a *vest kavuah* for menstruating whenever she eats sharp[26] foods.[27]

2. *Poskim* disagree whether a *vest haachilos* is compared to a *vest haguf* or a *vest haones*. For example, on three occasions a woman ate garlic and menstruated afterwards. Some *Poskim* compare it to a *vest haones;* thus, she has a *vest she'aino kavuah* only, not a *vest kavuah*, unless it is set in combination with a *vest hachodesh* or a *vest haflagah.*[28] Others maintain that this case is similar in *halachah*

---

24. *Niddah* 63b.

25. We noted above (note 3) that in the opinion of *Sugah Bashoshanim* 6:4, a *vest haones* can also be established with three different types of physical exertions.

26. *Sugah Bashoshanim* 8:6 rules that if the *vest* was set in this manner, she must observe the *vest* even when she eats other sharp foods. He notes many variations of this theme.

27. *Rema* 189:23. *Biur HaGra* (ad loc.), however, maintains that, in this regard, a *vest haachilos* is no different than a *vest haguf*. Thus, three different types of sharp food cannot establish a *vest kavuah*. R' Akiva Eiger (ad loc.) agrees with *Rema* but contends that if she ate only garlic on all three occasions, she has no *vest* regarding other sharp foods. Thus, if she subsequently eats onions, she is not required to abstain. In addition, if she ate garlic twice and onions once, she has no *vest*. See *Badei HaShulchan, Biurim* 189:23 s.v. אכלה בצל.

28. First opinion in *Rema* 189:23. This is the opinion of *Raavad* (*Baalei HaNefesh*, end of *Shaar Tikun Vestos* p. 52 in Kapach ed.). This seems to be the view of *Rashba* as well.

to a *vest haguf* and becomes a *vest kavuah* by itself.[29] Some *Poskim* rule that one should follow the strict application of each opinion.[30]

3. Another application of this disagreement pertains to a woman who ate garlic once and menstruated afterwards. According to the first opinion above, if she eats garlic in the future, she is not required to abstain. According to the second opinion, she must abstain and do a *bedikah*.[31]

C. A menstruation regulated medically

The previous sections regarding a *vest haones* and *vest haachilos* are not very relevant on a practical level. These *vestos* are unusual. However, the principles of *vest haones* and *vest haachilos* are relevant to the case of a woman who is regulating her menstrual cycle through medical means. A physician may prescribe hormonal therapy, usually in pill form. Sometimes pills commonly called "birth-control pills" are used for this purpose.

1. Reasons for hormonal treatment:
Hormones may be prescribed to rectify several medical conditions that may result in *halachic* problems.[32]

---

29. Second opinion in *Rema* ibid., which is the view of *Tosfos* (*Niddah* 63b). *Tosfos* explains that, unlike jumping which is an externally induced cause, a flow caused by eating is more natural. It seems that, according to *Tosfos*, a *vest* caused by eating is considered natural because it functions through the normal menstrual system. The sharp foods somehow induce the body to expel the uterine lining. A *vest haones*, however, is an intervention completely external to the menstrual system. The jumping shakes and loosens the uterine lining (see *Badei HaShulchan* 189:252). Alternatively, a *vest haachilos* is a direct influence on the menstrual system, while *vest haones* is indirect (see *Shiurei Sheivet HaLeivi* 189:23[4]. *Rezah* (*Shaar HaVestos* §19) offers another explanation. He contends that a *vest* of eating is not considered a *vest haones* since she eats these foods of her own free will and for enjoyment. He apparently defines *vest haones* as something imposed upon the body unwillingly. It is unclear how *Rezah* would classify the case of a woman who jumped for pleasure or ate garlic unwillingly. Would these be considered *vest haguf* or *vest haones*?

30. *Toras HaShelamim* §43. He adds that, according to the first opinion, even if a *vest haachilos* occurs three times, she is required to keep *onah beinonis*. *Sugah Bashoshanim* 8:[5] disagrees; he maintains that according to both opinions she must keep *onah beinonis*.

31. *Sugah Bashoshanim* 8:[1].

32. One should note that often, if hormonal treatment continues for several months, the physician may advise that a woman not become pregnant for a month or two after completing the treatment. The woman would then wish to use some contraceptive device. We will note later in this section that any contraceptive method involves serious *halachic* issues. Therefore, if a physician prescribes hormonal treatment, a woman should inquire about the long-time implications and discuss the matter with her Rav.

a. A woman may have fertility problems, e.g., she does not ovulate (anovulation) or ovulates irregularly (oligo-vulation) or her menstrual flow lasts too long and she is unable to complete her seven "clean" days before ovu-lation.

b. A woman may have only a few days between her *tevilah* and her next menstruation due to an exceptional-ly long period, pre-menstrual staining, continuous bleeding or an unusually short cycle.

c. She may experience mid-cycle bleeding.

In addition to these conditions, a woman may be using hormones for the following reasons:

d. A *kallah* (a bride) may use hormonal treatment to ensure that she is *tehorah* during her wedding night. However, one should note that although there is good reason, both *halachic* and practical, to do everything pos-sible to ensure that a bride is *tehorah* for her wedding, there are serious reservations about using hormonal treat-ment for this purpose. Any hormonal therapy is invasive of the body's natural functions and should be approached with caution. In addition, the hormonal treat-ment may result in staining problems which may persist even after termination of the treatment.[33] Therefore, a bride who is concerned about the possibility of being a *niddah* during her wedding should discuss the matter with her *kallah* teacher or Rav. If she still wishes to regu-late her menstruation medically, she should do so only after consultation with both her Rav and her physician.[34]

e. A woman may receive Rabbinic sanction to use hor-monal pills as a means of contraception. It should be noted that there are serious *halachic* questions regarding the use of any contraceptive method. One may never use any contraceptive method without prior consultation with a Rabbinical authority.

---

33. See responsa *Be'er Moshe* 6:137.

34. *Shiurei Sheivet HaLeivi*, addendum to p. 33, writes that a bride should only use pills if she pass-es the last menstruation before the wedding and it seems that she will menstruate again shortly before the wedding.

2. The effect of hormones on the menstrual cycle:
We will present the *halachos* of *vestos* as they are relevant to a woman undergoing hormonal treatment.

a. Some hormonal treatments do not directly affect the menstrual cycle. Most medications used to induce or regulate ovulation (Clomiphene, Pergonal, Metrodin, Factrel or Lutrepulse) do not directly induce or retard menstruation and are irrelevant to the questions of *vestos*.

b. A woman undergoing other types of hormonal therapy will menstruate according to use of the hormonal treatment, not her natural menstrual cycle. This may be in pill form. For example, a woman may take estrogen/progesterone pills which inhibit the shedding of the uterine lining. When she discontinues use of these pills, the estrogen/progesterone level drops and causes the uterine lining to shed and thus brings on menstruation. The interval between the time that she discontinues the pills and the onset of menstruation is usually about two or three days. This varies from woman to woman. Most women are consistent in their intervals. Thus, a woman may know from past experience that her menstruation begins two days after she stops taking the pills.

c. Another form of hormonal treatment is through progesterone injections. This injection brings on menstruation after three to five days or as late as two weeks. This depends on when in her cycle the injection is given. Thus, it may vary from month to month even in the same woman. A woman being treated through injections would find it more difficult to predict when her period is expected.

d. A woman with a mid-cycle bleeding problem may be treated with estrogen during the mid-cycle days. Thus, although she may have a *vest hachodesh* from the previous month's mid-cycle bleeding, she is assured that, due to the estrogen, it will not be repeated this month. Similarly, a woman with continuous bleeding or an irregular cycle may be treated with estrogen/progesterone cycling. Her menstruation will be completely controlled by these hormones.

3. The *halachos* of *vestos* regarding hormonal treatment:

a. The issues involved:

When a woman's cycle is controlled by hormonal treatment, is she nevertheless required to follow the normal rules of *vestos*? The issues are twofold:

i. Must a woman abstain and perform *bedikos* on the *yom hachodesh* or *yom haflagah* of a menstruation induced by these pills, even though she knows that the reason that she menstruated was because of the pill, not because of its being the *yom hachodesh* or *yom haflagah*?

ii. Must she abstain and perform *bedikos* on the day that she expects her period due to the pills if it is neither the *yom hachodesh* or the *yom haflagah*?

iii. Must she abstain on a *yom havest* of a previously established natural period or the *onah beinonis* if she knows that she will not menstruate due to hormonal treatment?

b. The practical *halachah*:

Menstruation induced by hormonal therapy is comparable to a menstruation induced by eating sharp foods. It is neither a natural menstruation, since it is induced unnaturally, nor a *vest haones*, which is caused in a manner completely external to the natural functions of the menstrual cycle. A hormonally induced menstruation is caused by outside intervention, but it replicates the body's natural process. This is essentially similar to a *vest haachilos* in which eating certain foods induces a menstrual flow. However, in one aspect this *vest* may be stronger than a *vest haachilos*. The effect of hormonal intervention has been clinically tested and proven. It may not be necessary for the woman to actually demonstrate that her menstruation is controlled by hormonal treatment. Contemporary authorities have provided the following guidelines regarding these issues.

i. Calculating a *vest* from a period induced by the pill:

A woman who menstruates as a result of hormonal therapy is not required to calculate a *vest hachodesh* or a *vest haflagah* from that menstruation unless she replicates the circumstances. For example, a woman stops taking the pills on the fifth of the month and menstruates on the following day, which is the twenty-eighth interval day. She is not required to keep *vest hachodesh* or *vest haflagah* on the following month[35] unless she stops taking the pill on the same day of the month or the same interval day.[36]

ii. Keeping a *yom havest* based on the pill:
A woman who stopped taking the pill and menstruates the following day must keep a *yom havest* when she stops taking the pill on the following month, even though it is neither the *yom hachodesh* or the *yom haflagah*. If she usually menstruates several days after stopping the pill, she is not required to abstain until the corresponding time passes on the following month after cessation of the pill. Some authorities maintain that she should abstain for twenty-four hours preceding the expected onset of the menstruation.[37]

iii. Keeping *yom havest* if she is not expected to menstruate:
Poskim disagree concerning a woman who is taking a pill to withhold menstruation and reaches a *yom havest* or an *onah beinonis* from a natural

---

35. We noted above that a woman must keep an *onah beinonis* after a *vest* caused by jumping. It would seem that this applies to this case as well. See iii below regarding a case where she knows that, because of the therapy, she will not menstruate on the *onah beinonis*.

35. We noted above that a woman must keep an *onah beinonis* after a *vest* caused by jumping. It would seem that this applies to this case as well. See iii below regarding a case where she knows that, because of the therapy, she will not menstruate on the *onah beinonis*.

36. If she stops taking the pill, she must abstain the following day, even if it is not the *yom havest*, and perform a *bedikah*. Responsa *Sheivet HaLeivi* 3:124 on *Rema* 189:23 speculates that perhaps even if the period did not arrive on that day, she must abstain until she performs a *bedikah*. He compares this to the view of *Taz* 189:38 regarding a *vest haguf*.

37. *Shiurei Sheivet HaLeivi* 189:23[5].

period. One should discuss this question with a Rav. [38]

4. Uprooting a *vest* through the pill:

A woman who had a *vest she'aino kavuah* and uprooted it as a result of the hormonal therapy, i.e., she did not menstruate on the *vest* day because of the therapy, need not keep that *vest* even after she stops the therapy.[39]

5. A *vest* established through the pill:

A woman who establishes a *vest kavuah* through hormonal therapy keeps that *vest* only as long as she continues the therapy. Once she stops the therapy, she is not required to keep the *vest*.[40]

---

38. The earliest source for this question is responsa *Radvaz* 8:136, regarding a woman who took a potion to withhold her menstruation. See *Shiurei Sheivet HaLeivi* 184:8[2], who rules that although *Radvaz* required that the potion prove its effectiveness by withholding her *vest* on three occasions, a hormonal drug is assumed to be more effective. These drugs have proven their effectiveness on thousands of women. Nevertheless, *Shiurei Sheivet HaLeivi* is lenient only in a pressing situation. He is lenient regarding a wedding night that coincides with a *yom havest* and the bride is not expected to menstruate because of hormonal treatment. In 189:23[5], he seems even more lenient. *Sheivet HaLeivi* bases his opinion on *Radvaz* cited above. However, his interpretation of *Radvaz* is disputable, see responsa *Tzitz Eliezer* 13:103. Responsa *Be'er Moshe* 6:137 is lenient regarding a *vest she'aino kavuah*. He contends that even if she has no previous experience with the pill, she may assume that it completely withholds her menstruation, since such pills have proven their effectiveness. She is not required to abstain or do a *bedikah* on the *onas havest*. However, regarding a *vest kavuah* or *onah beinonis*, he contends that she cannot rely on the pill unless she knows from personal experience that the pill effectively withholds her menstruation. If the pill is effective for her, even once, she need not observe either a *vest kavuah* or *onah beinonis*. *Be'er Moshe* is less lenient regarding hormonal treatment through injection. He maintains that since the dosage is regulated differently for each woman, one cannot assume with certainty that it is effective until it has withheld at least one period. Responsa *Minchas Yitzchak* 1:127 takes a completely different approach. He maintains that we have no right to assume that any treatment completely withholds menstruation. Therefore, a woman under any type of hormonal treatment must abstain and perform *bedikos* on her normal *vest* day. Responsa *Tzitz Eliezer* 13:103 concurs with this stricter position. He maintains that the above-mentioned *Radvaz* supports this view.

39. *Kineh Bosem* on 189:23. It seems that a *vest kavuah* is not uprooted even if this occurred three times.

40. *Kineh Bosem* ibid.

CHAPTER TWENTY

מעוברת ומניקה

Women Who Are Exempt From *Vestos*

□ A minor.

□ A pregnant woman.

□ A nursing woman.

□ An elderly woman.

□ After menopause.

Introduction

V̶estos are based upon the assumption that a woman will menstruate according to her usual cycle. Therefore, it is reasonable to assume that women who are not expected to menstruate should not be subject to the usual rules of *vestos*. If one of these women happens to menstruate, they should not be required to abstain on the following *vest hachodesh, onah beinonis* or any *vest haflagah* that may develop. The Talmud[1] notes four women who are normally not expected to menstruate: a) *besulah,* a minor,[2] b) *me'uberes,* a pregnant woman, c) *meinikah,* a nursing woman, and d) *zekeinah,* an old woman. In addition, the Talmud[3] notes that, at times, even a normal woman with a *vest* may not be expected to menstruate on her usual time. For example, a woman in hiding (e.g., from bandits) is not expected to menstruate because fright inhibits the onset of menstruation. *Rishonim* derive from these sources that the women listed above are exempt from the laws of *vestos* since they are not expected to menstruate.[4]

A. *Besulah* — a minor

A young girl is not expected to begin menstruation before she physically matures. *Halachically,* a woman is considered mature only when she attains physical maturity after the age of twelve.[5] A young girl is, therefore, exempt from the laws of *vestos* unless she establishes that it is usual for her to menstruate. A young girl differs from a mature woman in two aspects of *vestos:* A) A young girl is not subject to a *vest she'aino kavuah,* i.e., if she happens to menstruate, she need not abstain on any of the *vest* days until the *vest* is established as a *vest kavuah.* b) Even if she establishes a *vest kavuah,* if she passes three *onos beinonios*[6] without menstruating, the *vest* is uprooted. Since the *halachos* regarding a *ketanah* have little practical relevance today, we will not discuss them in this work.[7]

---

1. *Niddah* 7a regarding retroactive *tumah,* מעת לעת. See *Niddah* 9a regarding *vestos* for a pregnant woman.

2. Normally, *besulah* connotes a virgin. With regard to this *halachah, besulah* is defined as a woman who never menstruated, regardless of whether or not she is married. See *Niddah* 7b.

3. *Niddah* 39a.

4. See discussion of the various opinions in *Beis Yosef* 189 p.58b.

5. I.e. she must both reach the age of twelve <u>and</u> physically mature (189:27) afterwards (see *Even HaEzer* 155:4).

6. See D,2 below.

7. They are discussed in *Shulchan Aruch, Yoreh Deah* 189:27.

B. *Me'uberes* — a pregnant woman

Under normal conditions, a pregnant woman is not expected to experience uterine bleeding. Accordingly, she is exempted from some laws of *vestos*.

> 1. The application of this *halachah* today:
> In previous times, a woman would usually continue to menstruate normally during the first three months[8] of pregnancy. However, after three months, she would stop menstruating and would be exempt from *vestos*. The Talmud[9] explains that, after three months, the burden of the pregnancy causes her menstrual cycle to stop.[10] Today, it is common for menstruation to stop immediately after conception. *Poskim* disagree whether the *halachah* today should reflect this change in nature. Perhaps today a woman should be exempt from *vestos* even during the first three months of pregnancy. In the opinion of most *Poskim*, this is not so.[11] Therefore, regarding the *halachos* of *vestos*, a woman is not considered "pregnant" until she is three months pregnant.[12] However, there is an opinion that once the pregnancy is medical-

---

8. The months are measured according to the monthly date, regardless of whether the months are *malei* (thirty-day months) or *chaseir* (twenty-nine day months), *Tosfos Yom Tov, Niddah* 1:5.

9. *Niddah* 9a.

10. Thus, the factor is not the pregnancy itself, but the burden of the pregnancy, which begins only after three months.

11. This position is taken by responsa R' Akiva Eiger §128, s.v. לענ"ד, and *Avnei Neizer, Y.D.* 238, who note that, even in their time, women stopped menstruating immediately after conception. Nevertheless, they assume that the *halachah* does not change. See responsa *Chasam Sofer, Y.D.* 169, who contends that a woman's menstrual cycle is affected immediately after conception; any bleeding thereafter is minimal. However, the complete cessation of menstrual activity takes place only after three months as a result of the burden of pregnancy. See also responsa *Sheivet HaLeivi* 3:114 and *Be'er Moshe* 1:48, who cite many sources that the status of "pregnant" regarding this *halachah* is achieved only after three months. It is noteworthy that although *Shiurei Sheivet HaLeivi* 189:33[2] does not accept the *halachic* implications of the immediate cessation of menstruation during pregnancy regarding a lenient application, he accepts it regarding a stringent application. Therefore, if a woman had a *vest kavuah* before pregnancy and uprooted it three times during the first three months, the *vest* is not uprooted. We assume that the *vest* is still active but was restrained because of pregnancy. *Sheivet HaLeivi* 186:2[2] is nevertheless lenient regarding the *bedikos* required for a woman without a *vest kavuah* before and after the first three cohabitations. During the first three months of pregnancy, this is not necessary (if she passed at least one *vest* date) since we know that she will not menstruate. See Chapter Fourteen note 34.

12. It is difficult to determine exactly when the three months begin since we do not know exactly when she became pregnant. Perhaps one should not calculate from the last *tevilah* since she may have conceived at a later date. She may have also conceived even a month earlier and the last menstruation took place during pregnancy. *Pardes Rimonim* 10:4 contends that if she is visibly

ly confirmed, the woman is *halachically* considered "pregnant." According to this opinion, she should performs a *bedikah* (as an added precaution); if cloth is found clean, she is not required to abstain on her *onas havest*.[13] However, one should follow the more stringent opinion which is an accord with most *Poskim*.[14]

2. The status of a pregnant woman:
The unique status of a pregnant woman is relevant to two *vestos* situations: a pre-established *vest* day that arrives during pregnancy and a new *vest* that is established during pregnancy.

a. Pre-existing *vestos:*
A woman with a *vest kavuah* which was established before her pregnancy is not required to abstain or perform *bedikos* on the *onas havest* during pregnancy. We noted that, according to the Talmud and *Shulchan Aruch*,[15] this applies only after three months of pregnancy have

---

pregnant, "הוכר עוברה," one assumes that three months have passed. However, if we know that three months have not passed, e.g., she is married less than three months, she is not *halachically* considered "pregnant" even if the pregnancy is visible and even if she shows other signs of pregnancy, e.g., loss of appetite. If three months have certainly passed since conception, she is considered "pregnant" even if it is not visibly evident. *Chazon Ish, Y.D.* 101:2, seems uncertain about this last point. *Shiurei Sheivet HaLeivi* 184:7[1] and 189:33[2] contends that one normally calculates the three months from the last *tevilah*. One should note that physicians often calculate the pregnancy from the beginning of the last period. Thus, one cannot rely on the physician's statement that she is three months pregnant since she actually became pregnant at least twelve days later. See also Responsa *Eimek HaTeshuvah* 1:135 and 3:70.

13. *Igros Moshe Y.D.* 3:52. In *Y.D.* 4:17[1] he takes note of the opposing opinions of R' Akiva Eiger and *Avnei Neizer*. Although he essentially disagrees with their opinion, his conclusion in the latter responsa is unclear.

14. Most contemporary authorities follow the stricter opinion. The final position of *Igros Moshe* in 4:17[1] is unclear. The question is essentially two-fold: a) Perhaps *Chazal* only required that the woman be three months pregnant to confirm her pregnancy. Thus, if, today, a pregnancy can be confirmed earlier, she should be considered *halachically* pregnant. b) Even if we concede that in Talmudic law it is not the pregnancy *per se* which exempts a pregnant woman from *vestos*, but the three months of pregnancy, perhaps this was so only in Talmudic times when women menstruated for the first three months. However, today women stop menstruating immediately after conception. Obviously, nature has changed (נשתנו הטבעים) Shouldn't *halachah* change accordingly? Responsa *Chasam Sofer* and *Sheivet HaLeivi*, cited above note 11, address point a, while responsa R' Akiva Eiger and *Avnei Neizer* address point b. See responsa *Be'er Moshe* 1:48[3] who elucidates this distinction. He explains that the lenient opinion (one assumes that he is referring to *Igros Moshe*) is based on point b which he essentially accepts but withholds final judgment. Perhaps one may be lenient regarding the *Or Zarua vest*, see Chapter Twenty-Two.

15. 189:33,34.

passed.[16] We noted, too, that there is a second opinion that this applies today as soon as the pregnancy is verified. According to this opinion, when a woman passes her *onas havest* without menstruating and medically confirms her pregnancy, she is no longer required to abstain or perform *bedikos* on her *vest* days. In the opinion of most *Poskim*, she must keep the *vestos* during the first three months. Practically, the difference between these opinions is minor: Once a woman conceives, she will no longer menstruate and will observe only one *vest haflagah* since she has no day from which to count another interval.[17] Similarly, she must observe only one *onah beinonis* from her last menstruation since *onah beinonis* is calculated only from an actual flow. However, according to the first opinion, which one should follow, she must observe *vest hachodesh* (if it is *kavuah*) for another two months.[18] Once the first three months pass, she no longer keeps the *vest hachodesh* for two reasons: a) She is *halachically* considered pregnant and is no longer subject to *vestos* and b) according to the second opinion, she has uprooted the *vest hachodesh* on three occasions.[19] Today, most women do not have a *vest kavuah*. Therefore, even according to the first opinion, a woman keeps only one *vest hachodesh* day[20] after becoming pregnant. Once that day passes, her *vest hachodesh she'aino kavuah* is uprooted. Thus, she is not concerned with either *vest haflagah, vest hachodesh* or *onah beinonis*.

---

16. We will note that this exemption was relevant in previous times when women menstruated during the first three months. Thus, a woman who menstruated normally during her third month of pregnancy was not required to keep any *vestos* from the fourth month on. However, if the woman actually does not menstruate during the first three months, her exemption of the following months will have little practical application. (see *Shiurei Sheivet HaLeivi* 184:7[1], 189:33[2]) The sole example of the relevance of this *halachah* would be in a case where she established a *vest haflagah* with an interval in excess of ninety days.

17. A *vest haflagah* is calculated only from a day that she actually had a blood flow, not from a day that she <u>expected</u> her period. See Chapter Fifteen.

18. A woman usually becomes aware of her pregnancy only after passing one *vest hachodesh*.

19. According to the second opinion, the *vest kavuah* is not uprooted since the reason she did not menstruate on her *vest* day was because of her pregnancy. Therefore, when her pregnancy (and nursing) is over she may be required to keep the *vest kavuah*, see Responsa *Eimek HaTeshuvah* 3:70.

20. Which usually passed already. A *vest she'aino kavuah* is uprooted during the first three months of pregnancy, see Responsa *Eimek HaTeshuvah* ibid.

b. Establishing a *vest* during pregnancy:

A woman who experiences uterine bleeding three times during pregnancy[21] on the same monthly date or after the same interval of days cannot establish[22] a *vest kavuah*.[23] Even if she bleeds on a *vest kavuah* day that was established before pregnancy, the *vest* is not treated as a *vest kavuah*.[24] Nevertheless, in either case, she must treat the *vest* as if it were a *vest she'aino kavuah* and abstain on the following monthly or interval day,[25] even if the flow occurred only once.[26] However, she is not required to keep the *onah beinonis* from the day she began bleeding.[27]

---

21. Or even if she menstruates twice before being three months pregnant and once after, she cannot establish a *vest kavuah* (*Sugah Bashoshanim* 10:5).

22. One should note that a *vest* established during pregnancy is not considered a *vest kavuah* even during and after the twenty-four months following childbirth (see *Sidrei Taharah* 184:10).

23. 189:33. *Shach* §73 notes that although this is the accepted ruling of *Shulchan Aruch, Ramban* disagrees. He holds that a woman can establish a *vest kavuah* during pregnancy and during the twenty-four month post-partum period. *Shiurei Sheivet HaLeivi* 189:33[6] cites responsa *Chasam Sofer, Y.D.* 164, who contends that a woman who is not actually nursing (see C,2 below) should follow *Ramban's* stricter view.

24. 189:34. Thus, if the next *vest* day passes without a flow, the *vest* is uprooted and she is permitted to cohabit even without performing a *bedikah* (*Graz* 189:115, see *Shiurei Sheivet HaLeivi* 189:34[2]). Nevertheless, she may assume the leniencies of a *vest kavuah*. Thus, she must abstain only on the day of her original *vest* type, whether *vest hachodesh* or *vest haflagah*. For example, if she originally had a *vest hachodesh* and menstruated on her *vest hachodesh* day, the *vest* remains *vest hachodesh she'aino kavuah*. She must abstain the month date of the following month, but not on the interval day. In addition, she is not required to keep *onah beinonis* from that menstruation (*Sugah Bashoshanim* 10:1). See note 27 where we noted the difference of opinion whether a pregnant woman is ever required to keep *onah beinonis*.

25. Ibid. Nevertheless, the *vest* has the leniencies of a *vest kavuah*. For example, if she menstruated three times on the same monthly date, she treats the *vest* as a *vest hachodesh* and is not required to consider the last interval of days, *Sidrei Taharah* 189:36.

26. *Sidrei Taharah* 184:10, 189:36, *Chavos Daas* 189:50[c] and *Graz* §113, citing *Raavad* and *Rashba*. However, *Maharshal* (cited in *Shach* 184:19), *Pleisi* 189:31 and *Toras HaShelamim* 184:16 seem to hold that a pregnant woman need not be concerned with a *vest she'aino kavuah*. Even according to the stricter view, one is not required to keep the *Or Zarua vest* (see Chapter Twenty-Two) if the flow occurred only once (*Sugah Bashoshanim* 10:1).

27. *Sidrei Taharah* 189:36. However *Chavos Daas* §50[c] and *Graz* §114, citing *Maharam Padua* contend that she must keep *onah beinonis*. *Pardes Rimonim* 10:1 requires that one keep *onah beinonis* on the thirtieth day and only do a *bedikah* on the thirty-first day. *Shiurei Sheivet HaLeivi* 189:33[5] rules that one may follow the lenient view and not abstain on the *onah beinonis*.

C. *Meinekes* — a nursing woman

Another woman exempt from *vestos* is a *meinekes*, a nursing woman. Today, a woman usually does not begin menstruating soon after childbirth. A woman who nurses usually begins menstruating even later. When discussing the exemption of a woman after childbirth, *Chazal* referred to her as a *meinekes* — a nursing woman. Nevertheless, she is exempt from the laws of *vestos* during this period even though she is not actually nursing.[28] *Chazal* assumed that the trauma of childbirth[29] itself affects the menstrual process so severely that normal menstruation does not resume for twenty-four months.[30] This is true even if she weaned the child or even if she never even began to nurse the child.[31] Even if the child did not survive or was stillborn or even if a woman had a miscarriage,[32] she is exempt from *vestos* for the next twenty-four months.[33]

> 1. The status of a *meinekes:*
> A post-partum woman is governed by the same *halachos* as a pregnant woman. She cannot establish a *vest kavuah* but she must treat any uterine flow (one[34] or even three) as a *vest she'aino kavuah.*[35] The bleeding that accompanies childbirth is not part of the menstrual cycle and has no relevance to *vestos.* A woman is not required to

28. Conversely, if she continues to nurse beyond twenty-four months, she is subject to the laws of *vestos* (R' Akiva Eiger 184:7 and *Graz* §24).

29. Regardless of whether the child was born naturally or through caesarean Section (*Shiurei Sheivet HaLeivi* 184:7[4], *Badei HaShulchan, Biurim* 184:7 s.v. הולד, is uncertain on this question.

30. 189:33. There is a difference of opinion regarding a leap year. For example, if a woman gave birth on the first of *Adar* I of year A which was a leap year, does she end the twenty-four months on the first of *Adar* of year C or the first of *Shevat*? See *Shach* 184:18, *Pleisi* §8 and *Graz* §24.

31. See *Daas Torah* 189:33, as opposed to *Shiyarei Taharah* cited ibid.

32. If she carried the embryo for at least forty days (see footnote 12 regarding from when one calculates the conception), she is exempt from *vestos*, see *Pleisi* §31 and *Sidrei Taharah* §36. A pregnancy of less than forty days is subject to different standards, see Chapter Two, Section VI,C.

33. 189:33.

34. See note 26 where it was noted that most *Poskim* rule that she must keep a *vest she'aino kavuah* even if she menstruates only once.

35. 189:33. *Sidrei Taharah* §36 rules that a *meinekes* is not required to keep an *onah beinonis* from a menstruation that occurs during the twenty-four months. *Chavos Daas* §50[c] disagrees. *Graz* §114, citing *Maharam Padua*, also disagrees with the lenient position of *Sidrei Taharah*. *Shiurei Sheivet HaLeivi* 189:33[5] rules that one should follow the stricter ruling of *Graz* and *Maharam Padua*, especially since the leniency of *meinekes* hardly applies today (as will be explained). *Sugah Bashoshanim* 10:1 and *Pische Zuta* §29 contend that it is sufficient to abstain on the *onah beinonis* of the thirtieth day only, not the thirty-first. Rav Y. Roth in *Beis Talmud LeHoraah* (vol 1:85) rules that one need not treat the

keep *onah beinonis* from the bleeding due to childbirth. Similarly, when she menstruates some time after childbirth, she does not calculate an interval from the flow accompanying childbirth.[36]

2. The application of the *halachah* today:

There is a problem adapting the *halachah* of *meinekes* to modern times. Almost all women menstruate within twenty-four months following childbirth. A woman who is not actually nursing often menstruates within several weeks of childbirth. Even nursing women (who generally do not menstruate while nursing) will usually begin their menstrual cycles well before twenty-four months pass. Therefore, *Poskim* disagree about the application of this *halachah* today. Many authorities rule that once a woman's menstrual cycle returns, she is subject to all the rules of *vestos*.[37] However, since this is essentially a *chumra* (a stricter view), it cannot be used *lekula* (for a lenient application). For example:

> a. If a woman establishes a *vest kavuah* during the post-partum period, it cannot uproot a *vest* that was established before pregnancy.[38]

> b. If she had a *vest kavuah* before pregnancy it is not uprooted even if she began menstruating during the

---

onah beinonis as a *vest kavuah*. Thus, if she did not do a *bedikah* on the *onah beinonis* she is no longer required to do so once the day passes. *Be'er Moshe* 4:67 rules that during the *yemei tohar* (see Chapter Two) after childbirth one need not observe the *onah beinonis*.

36. See *Badei HaShulchan, Biurim* 189:33, s.v. שתראה.

37. *Igros Moshe*, Y.D. 3:52, 4:17[2], rules that once she menstruates, she must keep all *vestos* including *onah beinonis*, regardless of whether or not she is actually nursing. However, she is not required to abstain, even on her *vest hachodesh, kavuah* day from before pregnancy, until she experiences her first menstruation. See *Shiurei Sheivet HaLeivi* 184:7[4], who cautions that one should be especially careful regarding *vestos* after childbirth since the menstrual periods at the time follow no pattern and she is liable to menstruate at any time. He urges that one be particularly prudent after a miscarriage since menstruations are liable to begin even earlier. He advises that a *bedikah* always be done before cohabitation. One should discuss this question with a Rav. A woman should be especially sensitive to any sensation that may forewarn that she is about to menstruate. We noted above (note 23) the view of *Chasam Sofer*, Y.D. 164, that a woman who is not actually nursing should follow *Ramban's* view that a *vest* can be established during the post-partum months.

38. *Shiurei Sheivet HaLeivi* 189:34[3]. It would seem that, in this case, she need not keep the earlier *vest* during the post-partum period. Either way you look at it, the earlier *vest* may be ignored. If we follow the *halachah* as presented in *Shulchan Aruch,* she need not keep the *vest kavuah* since she is within twenty-four months of childbirth. On the other hand, if we follow the present nature of women, the *vest* was uprooted. *Shiurei Sheivet HaLeivi's* wording seems to support this argument.

post-partum period and passes the *vest kavuah* day three times without menstruating.[39]

3. When the twenty-four months pass:
When a woman passes the twenty-four months, she is subject to all the rules of *vestos*. As noted, most women menstruate before the end of twenty-four months. However, if a woman did not menstruate throughout the twenty-four months, there is a difference of opinion among *Rishonim* regarding when she is required to begin being concerned about *vestos* that were established before her pregnancy.

a. *Vest hachodesh:*
In the opinion of many *Poskim*, she is not required to begin keeping *vestos* until she menstruates at least once.[40] However, *Shulchan Aruch*[41] rules that she must keep the very next[42] *vest hachodesh* day even if she had not yet menstruated. This dispute has little practical significance today.[43]

---

39. It would seem that if she did not menstruate on the *vest kavuah* day either during the first months of pregnancy or during the post-partum period, the *vest* should be uprooted. Either way one looks at it, the *vest* is uprooted. If we follow the *halachah* as presented in *Shulchan Aruch*, the *vest* was uprooted during the first three months of pregnancy; if we assume נשתנו הטבעים, the *vest* was uprooted during the post-partum period.

40. *Ramban* cited in *Tur*, *Raavad* cited in *Beis Yosef* 189. *Shach* §75 is troubled by *Shulchan Aruch's* omission of this opinion. It seems that *Shach* follows this lenient opinion. *Chavos Daas* §52[c] and *Graz* §116 cite *Shach* without comment. One assumes that they too share his lenient view. *Chochmas Adam* 112:38 cites the lenient view as that of most *Poskim*.

41. 189:34.

42. See *Badei HaShulchan, Biurim* 189:34 s.v. וכן כל, regarding a *vest hadilug* or *vest haseirug*. For example, she has a *vest hachodesh bedilug* with one day increments each month. If her last menstruation before pregnancy was the twenty-fifth of the month, does she observe *vest hachodesh* on the twenty-sixth day or should she calculate all the months that passed and add a day for each month? A similar question applies to a *vest haseirug*. See a discussion of this point in Chapter Sixteen, notes 14 and 19.

43. Most women menstruate during the course of the twenty-four post-partum months. Nevertheless, all *Poskim* agree that during this period she does not keep any of the *vestos* until she actually menstruates once. Once she menstruates, she must keep her previous *vestos*, either as *vest she'aino kavuah* or (in the opinion of many contemporary authorities) as *vest kavuah* (if we assume that נשתנו הטבעים). Either way, when the twenty-four months end, she must keep the very first *vest hachodesh* whether or not she menstruates again. For example, if she had a *vest kavuah* for *Rosh Chodesh* and ends the twenty-four months on the fifth of *Nissan*, she must keep *yom havest* on the first of *Iyar* even though she has not yet menstruated since the fifth of *Nissan*. One could certainly construct cases where the above-mentioned *halachah* would apply, but they are uncommon.

b. *Vest haflagah* and *onah beinonis:*
She certainly cannot keep her *vest haflagah* or *onah beinonis* until she experiences her first menstruation.

c. *Vest she'aino kavuah:*
In the opinion of many *Poskim*,[44] if she had no *vest kavuah* before pregnancy (as is the case with most women today), she is not required to keep any of her previous *vestos she'ainon kavuos*.[45] When she does menstruate, she is required to keep only *onah beinonis*.

D. *Zekeinah* — an elderly woman

Chazal exempted an elderly woman from the *halachos* of *vestos*. Although this status is commonly called "post-menopause," the terms are not similar and should not be confused.[46] Menopause is the physical condition in which a woman's hormonal balance changes and causes to her stop menstruating. *Zekeinah* is the *halachic* status that exempts a woman from the rules of *vestos*. The exemption of *zekeinah* is dependent upon two conditions: a) The woman must fit the definition of "*zekeinah*," an elderly woman, and b) she must demonstrate that her menses has ended. Once these two conditions are met, even if she happens to menstruate, it is considered a chance happening and, although she is *temei'ah*, she is not required to keep either *vest hachodesh, vest haflagah* or *onah beinonis*.

1. The definition of *zekeinah:*
Chazal defined "*zekeinah*" as a woman who reached an age when

---

44. *Noda B'Yehudah* 2:86, cited in *Pischei Teshuvah* 189:32. *Lechem VeSimlah* §57[s] is uncertain on the matter and *Haflaah* in responsa *Givas Pinchas* §54 disagrees with *Noda B'Yehudah*. However, *Shiurei Sheivet HaLeivi* 189:34[4] contends that one follows the lenient view of *Noda B'Yehudah*.

45. Thus, if she menstruated once before the end of three months of pregnancy after an interval of twenty-eight days, but the fourth month of pregnancy began before the next interval of twenty-eight (or according to the opinion that she may disregard *vestos* as soon as she becomes pregnant, she had a twenty-eight day interval before conception and conceived before the next twenty-eight day interval), she need not keep a twenty-eight day interval. Although the *vest* was not actually uprooted, the pregnancy itself uproots any *vest she'aino kavuah*.

46. *Sugah Bashoshanim* 9:[14] entertains the possibility that a woman who reaches menopause is certainly included in the *halachah* of *zekeinah* since her menstrual process has completely ended. He relies on this assumption regarding the *halachah* (according to some opinions, see Chapter Fourteen) that a woman without a *vest kavuah* requires *bedikos* before cohabitation. Thus, in his opinion, once she reaches menopause, she requires no *bedikos*.

an average woman[47] would no longer object to being called[48] *"ema"* (a term used in Talmudic times to refer to an old woman).[49] There is a difference of opinion whether we require that she does not <u>mind</u> being called "old" or whether, even if she does mind, she does not <u>object</u> to that name.[50] It seems that in today's terms, the name *"savta,"*[51] *"bubby"* or *"granny"* when not used by one's grandchildren, but by a stranger, would be comparable to the term *ema*. It is difficult to judge at what age women would not mind being called "old."[52] Certainly, a woman in her fifties would mind being called "old," even though that is the average age when women reach menopause. Although *Poskim* give no clear ruling as to the age of *"zekeinah,"* they assume that a woman in her mid-sixties should be considered a *zekeinah*.[53]

2. Demonstrating that the menses has ended:
When a woman reaches the age that renders her a *zekeinah,* she is subject to all rules of *vestos* unless her menses has completely ended. This is accomplished when she passes three *onos* without menstruating.

There is a similarity between a *zekeinah* demonstrating that she no longer menstruates and a regular woman who uproots her *vest* by passing the *onas havest* three times.[54] In either case, the passing of the *vest* three times establishes that one is no longer required to be concerned with the *vest*. However, the similarity ends there. The *akirah* of a *vest* merely uproots that particular *vest*. The passing of three *onos* by a *zekeinah* demonstrates that her menses has ended. Therefore, the *halachos* of these *akiros* are essentially different.

---

47. If she reaches an age where the average woman would not object, but she objects, or she did not reach that age, but objects, her personal feelings are inconsequential (*Rema* ad loc., *Toras HaShelamim* §53 citing *Beis Yosef*).

48. As a title added to her name, i.e., *ema* so-and-so. See *Rambam, Pirush HaMishnah, Niddah* 1:5. See, for example, *B'rachos* 16b.

49. 189:29.

50. *Taz* §46 requires that she not even mind being called old. *Gra* §47 and *Graz* §109 contend that even if she <u>minds,</u> but does not <u>object,</u> she is considered a *zekeinah*.

51. See *Shiurei Sheivet HaLeivi* 189:29[3].

52. See responsa *Beis Shlomo* 2:8, 28 and *Shiurei Sheivet HaLeivi* ibid.

53. See *Noda B'Yehudah* 1:55, *Shiurei Sheivet HaLeivi* ibid.

54. The discussion here pertains to a unique aspect of *akiras vest* whereby a woman who stops menstruating uproots her *vest haflagah* even though she passed only one interval day. For example, a

a. The *akirah* of the *vest* of a younger[55] woman is effected by passing the *vest* interval three times, regardless of whether the interval is less or more than thirty days.[56] However, in order for a *zekeinah* to establish that her menses has ended, she must pass three *onos beinonios* of thirty days each.[57] Similarly, a younger woman with an alternating *vest hachodesh*, i.e., she menstruated the first of months A, C and E, but not months B and D, cannot uproot that *vest* unless she passes the first of three alternating months (i.e., months G, I and K) without menstruating. A *zekeinah* with a similar *vest* would establish that she no longer menstruates by passing ninety days without menstruating.[58]

b. If a younger woman uprooted her *vest* by passing it three times without menstruating, and then she happens to menstruate again, she must keep a *vest she'aino kavuah* of the monthly date and *onah beinonis*.[59] However, a *zekeinah* who menstruates after an interval of ninety days or more is not required to keep the original *vest kavuah*,[60] the present *vest she'aino kavuah* or the *onah beinonis*.[61] If she happens to menstruate three times on unrelated days, she must begin to keep *vestos*. Similarly, if she menstruates, even once, on the original *vest hachodesh* day or

---

woman with a *vest kavuah* of twenty day intervals who passes the twentieth day without menstruating has effected only one *akirah* and her *vest* is intact. As time passes without any menstruation, she has no additional *akiros* since an interval is calculated only from a menstruation. However, if she passes a total of fifty-seven days, which, in this case, would have been three intervals, her *vest* is uprooted. This is a unique type of *akirah* by which she uproots a *vest* by an interruption of her menstrual routine; a degree of סילוק דמים. This type of *akirah* is explained in Chapter Seventeen.

55. The term "younger" is used here in contradistinction to a *zekeinah* and should not be confused with a *ketanah* (a minor) who is governed by other *halachos*.

56. See *Shach* 189:65.

57. In the opinion of some *Poskim*, this totals eighty-seven days, since the day between the *onos* is counted twice, once with each *onah*. Others maintain that she must pass ninety days (including the first day of her last menstruation) without menstruating. See *Chacham Tzvi* §114 and *Graz* 189:103.

58. *Shach* §65 regarding a *besulah*.

59. *Graz* 189:64.

60. Even if she did not actually uproot the *vest kavuah*. For example, she had a *vest haflagah* of thirty-five day intervals or a *vest hachodesh beseirug*, i.e., every other month (*Toras HaShelamim* §50).

61. See 189:30.

menstruates twice separated by her original interval of days, her menses is considered reactivated and her *vest kavuah* is reestablished.[62]

3. The menopausal process:

Today, women do not suddenly stop their menses. The menopausal process may take many months. A woman may begin menopause by menstruating every other month, then every three months and then continuing to experience longer and longer intervals between periods. The process may be irregular. She may menstruate after twelve weeks and then after eight weeks. For this reason, some authorities advise that a menopausal woman do a *bedikah* before cohabitation until she passes at least a half a year without any menstruation.[63]

Although we noted in this section the similarities between a *besulah, zekeinah me'uberes* and *meinikah,* one should note differences in their *halachos.*[64] A *besulah* and *zekeinah* have both a lenient *halachah* and a stringent *halachah* as opposed to a *me'uberes* and a *meinikah.* A *besulah* and *zekeinah* are not required to keep any *vest she'aino kavuah.* Thus, if they menstruate, they are not required to abstain on the *onas havest.*[65] A *me'uberes* and *meinikah* are required to keep *vest she'aino kavuah.*[66] A *me'uberes* and *meinikah* who menstruate three times on the same monthly date or interval day cannot establish a *vest kavuah.*[67] A *besulah* and *zekeinah* who menstruate three times on the same day establish a *vest kavuah.*[68]

---

62. 189:31. In this aspect, a *zekeinah* is different than a *besulah* who is not affected by a menstruation that occurs on the previous *vest kavuah* day unless it occurs three times (189:27).

63. See *Taharas Yisrael* 184:43.

64. See *Aruch HaShulchan* 189:83,84, who notes these differences and explains their reasons.

65. 189:28.

66. 189:33.

67. Ibid..

68. 189:27,30.

CHAPTER TWENTY-ONE

לוח וסתות
Starting a *Vestos* Calendar

Step-by-step instructions to set up a *vestos* calendar.

A woman who menstruates for the first time, or (as in the case of a *kallah* preparing for her wedding) a woman who has no record of any previous menstruations, must be aware of several basic principles in establishing a *vestos* calendar. The purpose of a *vest* calendar is to establish the days that one must abstain and do *bedikos*. This can be confusing for someone not accustomed to these *halachos*. It is common that a newly married couple finds it difficult to organize a *vest* calendar. One should bring one's calendar with all pertinent information to a Rav who will gladly advise how this is done. This should preferably be done personally, not over the phone. The following are step-by-step instructions in setting up a calendar. This is based upon the principles set forth in the previous chapters.

1. All *vestos* based upon a monthly date follow the Hebrew calendar. The civil date has no bearing on a *vestos* calendar other than identifying the *yom havest* in terms that are easy to relate to.

2. The day of the past menstruation is the day in which the menstruation began. The length of the flow, whether one hour, one day or five days, has no bearing on the calculation of *vestos*.[1] The time of the menstruation is the time that the actual flow began.

3. All *vestos* are calculated by days and then limited to *onos* (an *onah* is a day or a night), as will be explained. The calculation of the day, with regard to determining the monthly date or the interval day of the last period, is determined by the twenty-four-hour day. With regard to the laws of *vestos*, a day begins at sundown (not the appearance of three stars, as in other *halachos*) and ends at sundown of the following day. Shabbos candle-lighting time or Shabbos ending time are irrelevant for this purpose (unless used to calculate sundown time).[2] Similarly, when calculating when the next menstruation is expected (the *yom havest*), one considers that day as beginning at sundown and ending at the following sundown.

4. After the day of the previous period and the day of the expected period have been identified, one must determine the *onah* of the previous *vest*. An *onah* is the night or daylight part of the day. These could be ten, twelve or fourteen hours depending upon the season. A night *onah* starts at sundown and ends at sunrise. A day *onah* begins at sunrise and ends at sundown. If, for example, the

---

1. This is the opinion of most *Poskim* as explained in Chapter Thirteen.

2. Candle-lighting time is usually eighteen minutes <u>before</u> sundown. *Shabbos* ending time is between forty-two to seventy-two minutes <u>after</u> sundown, depending upon one's custom.

previous period started at night, then the night of the *"yom havest"* is the *"onas havest."* If the previous period started by day, then the day of the *"yom havest"* is the *"onas havest."* We have now chosen the *yom havest* and limited its scope to the *onas havest.*

5. When calculating a *vest hachodesh,* one must be aware that the first day of *Rosh Chodesh* is the thirtieth day of the previous month, not the first day of the following month. The particular *halachos* of that day are discussed in Chapter Fifteen, Section II,B.

6. The first period that a woman experiences or the first period that she can recollect is identifiable, regarding *vestos,* only by its calendar date. There is, as yet, no interval to calculate. Thus, when a woman menstruates, she should note the date on a Hebrew calendar and note whether the menstruation began during the day *onah* or during the night *onah.* She should then mark off the corresponding day (and *onah*) of the next month on her calendar. This is the *yom hachodesh.*

7. In addition to the *yom hachodesh,* she should calculate the thirtieth day from the beginning of her menstruation and mark it on her calendar. This is the *onah beinonis.* These days are counted inclusive of both the menstruation day and the *onah beinonis* day. On a practical note: Instead of actually counting the days, one can find the day of the beginning of the menstruation on the calendar, count four weeks and add one more day of the week. That will be the thirtieth day — her *onah beinonis.* For example, if she began menstruation on Monday, her *onah beinonis* is Tuesday, four weeks later.

8. Some *Poskim* rule that in addition to the thirtieth day, one should also keep the thirty-first day as *onah beinonis.* Thus, in the previous case, Wednesday will also be considered *onah beinonis.* A couple should consult with their Rav as to which opinion to follow.

9. The *vest hachodesh* will always coincide with either the thirtieth or thirty-first day. This will depend upon whether the previous month was *malei* (a month of thirty days) or *chaseir* (a month of twenty-nine days). If the previous month was *malei,* then *yom hachodesh* will be on the thirty-first day; if the month was *chaseir,* the *yom hachodesh* will coincide with the thirtieth day. Put another way, if the present month has a one-day *Rosh Chodesh,* the *vest hachodesh* is the thirtieth day. If the month has a two-day *Rosh Chodesh,* the *vest hachodesh* is the thirty-first day.

10. A woman should mark these days immediately after the onset of her menstruation. Often couples who do not mark their calendars immediately lose count of the days and forget when the menstruation was.

11. Thus far, a woman has one[3] (or two)[4] days only as *yom havest*. When she menstruates the second time, she has an interval (called a *haflagah*) as well. The interval is the span from the beginning of one menstruation to the beginning of the next menstruation, inclusive of both days.

12. She now notes the date of the new menstruation and marks the *yom hachodesh* and *onah beinonis* from this new menstruation on her calendar. She must also mark the *yom haflagah*. Assuming that she did not menstruate on her previous *yom hachodesh* day, she now has two (or three) days of *yemei havest*: the *yom hachodesh*, the *yom haflagah* and perhaps an extra day of *onah beinonis*.

13. One must now determine whether the original *vest hachodesh* still applies. This depends upon whether the new period was earlier or later in the month than the previous period or on the same date. There are four possible situations: a) If the new period is later in the month, then the first *vest hachodesh* passed without incident and was uprooted since it is a *vest she'aino kavuah*. b) If the new period was on an earlier day in the month and her flow continued into the original *yom hachodesh* day, then the *yom hachodesh* was not uprooted. c) If the new period was on an earlier day of the month and the flow did not continue into the original *yom hachodesh* day, the original *vest hachodesh* is uprooted when it is passed without incident. d) If the second menstruation falls on the same monthly date (and *onah*) as the first, the date is certainly not uprooted, but strengthened. Nevertheless, it is not a *vest kavuah* and can yet be uprooted if she passes the day without a flow.

14. In the event of either case a) or c) above, the woman keeps only the new *vest hachodesh*. In the event of cases b) or d), she keeps both the original and the new *vest hachodesh*.[5] She may now have

---

3. If the *vest hachodesh* is on the thirtieth day and her Rav advised her not to abstain on the thirty-first day.

4. If either the *vest hachodesh* coincides with the thirty-first day or her Rav instructs her to abstain on the thirty-first day because of *onah beinonis*.

5. She keeps each *vest hachodesh* according to its respective *onah*.

two to four days of *yemei havest*: one (or two) *yom hachodesh*, the *yom haflagah* and perhaps an extra day of *onah beinonis*.

15. Assuming that her next (third) menstruation falls on neither of the days noted above, she proceeds to mark her calendar in the following manner: First, she marks the *onah beinonis* as explained above (either the thirtieth or both the thirtieth and thirty-first day). Next, she marks the *vest hachodesh*, which is either the thirtieth or thirty-first day. She must then determine whether any or both of the previous *vest hachodesh* apply. This is done in similar manner as is described in 13 above. If the new menstruation was at a later monthly day than the previous two, both are uprooted; if it is later than one, that one is uprooted.[6] If the new menstruation was at an earlier monthly date than the previous two, the earlier *vest hachodesh* may or may not be uprooted depending upon whether the flow continued into those days, as explained above. She may now have one, two or three *vestos hachodesh*.

16. Next, she must determine whether or not the previous *vest haflagah* was uprooted. This, too, depends upon whether or not the new interval is the same, shorter or longer that the first one. If the new interval is longer, then the previous *yom vest haflagah* was uprooted and is forgotten. If the second interval is shorter than the first, regardless of whether or not the flow continued into the original *yom havest*, in the opinion of some *Poskim*, the original *vest haflagah* is not uprooted. Although others disagree and contend that the original *vest* is uprooted, one normally follows the first, more stringent opinion. If the second interval is the same as the first, the *vest haflagah* is strengthened but not yet a *vest kavuah*. She may now have one or two *vestos haflagah*.

17. She may now have one (or two) *onah beinonis*, one (two or three) *vest hachodesh* and one (or two) *vest haflagah* for the following month.

18. If all three menstruations were on the same monthly date,[7] she has set a *vest hachodesh kavuah* and keeps neither the *onah beinonis*[8] nor the *vest haflagah*.

---

6. If the *vest hachodesh* is passed without incident, it is uprooted even if she menstruated twice on the same monthly date.

7. And the same *onah* period, see Chapter Fifteen, Section II,B,3.

8. We noted above Fifteen, Section IV,D that if the *vest kavuah* is less than thirty days, some *Poskim* contend that she must still keep the *onah beinonis*.

19. Assuming no *vest hachodesh kavuah* was set, after the fourth menstruation, she repeats steps 15 to 18. In addition, if all three menstruations were on the same interval day,[9] she has set a *vest haflagah kavuah*. She now keeps only the *vest haflagah*, not the *onah beinonis*[10] or the *vest hachodesh*.

20. She continues in this manner through all her periods. If she establishes a *vest kavuah* but subsequently menstruates on a different day, she must continue to keep the *vest kavuah* day, since it was not uprooted three times, but must also keep all the ramifications of the new day, i.e., she keeps both the *yom hachodesh* and the *yom haflagah* of that day. She follows all the instructions above from 6 onward with one notable exception. She does not keep any *onah beinonis*. A woman who has a *vest kavuah* does not keep *onah beinonis* even for the *vest she'aino kavuah* days.[11]

21. If she passes the *vest kavuah* days three successive times in a manner that the *vest* is uprooted, see 13 above regarding a *vest hachodesh* and 16 above regarding a *vest haflagah*, her *vest kavuah* is uprooted.[12] This can be in one of two ways: either she sets a new *vest kavuah* or she merely uproots the *vest kavuah* without setting a new *vest kavuah*. In the first case, the old *vest kavuah* is completely eliminated and its place is taken by the new *vest kavuah*. If no new *vest kavuah* is set, the old *vest kavuah* is not eliminated, it merely lies dormant. If she ever menstruates on that day in the future, even once, the *vest* is reestablished as a *vest kavuah*. Therefore, the date should be noted on her calendar.

In addition to marking one's dates on a calendar, a woman may find the following chart useful. After each menstruation she marks the day of the week, the month, day of the month, the *onah*, the interval and any additional comments, such as the duration of the period. Any pattern whether in the monthly dates or the intervals will be easily noticed. This chart may be photocopied.

---

9. And the same *onah* period, see above.

10. And perhaps, the *onah beinonis* if the *vest kavuah* is less than thirty days.

11. Unless her *vest kavuah* is a *vest haflagah* of less than thirty day intervals.

12. See Chapter Fourteen, Section I,C that this is only true if she performed a *bedikah* on the *onas havest* and found it clear of any questionable stain.

Day of Week	Hebrew Month	Date	Onah		Interval from last period	Additional Comments
			N	D		
✍ Monday	Nissan	14		✔	28	period lasted 6 days

CHAPTER TWENTY-TWO

יום הוסת

The day of the *vest*

□ The prohibitions of the *yom havest.*

□ The required *bedikos* on the *yom havest.*

□ Bathing on the *yom havest.*

□ The opinions of *Or Zarua* and *Aviasaf.*

□ *One who embarks on a journey.*

□ *Tevilah* on the *onas havest.*

□ The problematic days.

□ One who loses their calendar.

Introduction

אָמַר רַבִּי יוֹחָנָן מִשּׁוּם רַבִּי שִׁמְעוֹן בֶּן יוֹחַאי כָּל שֶׁאֵינוֹ פּוֹרֵשׁ מֵאִשְׁתּוֹ סָמוּךְ
לְוֶסְתָּהּ אֲפִילּוּ הַוְיָין לוֹ בָּנִים כִּבְנֵי אַהֲרֹן מֵתִים. דִּכְתִיב וְהִזַּרְתֶּם אֶת בְּנֵי
יִשְׂרָאֵל מִטֻּמְאָתָם וְהַדָּוָה בְּנִדָּתָהּ. וּסְמִיךְ לֵיהּ אַחֲרֵי מוֹת. אָמַר רַבִּי חִיָּיא
בַּר אַבָּא אָמַר רַבִּי יוֹחָנָן כָּל הַפּוֹרֵשׁ מֵאִשְׁתּוֹ סָמוּךְ לְוֶסְתָּהּ הַוְיָין לוֹ בָּנִים
זְכָרִים דִּכְתִיב (ויקרא יא) לְהַבְדִּיל בֵּין הַטָּמֵא וּבֵין הַטָּהוֹר וְסָמִיךְ לֵיהּ אִשָּׁה
כִּי תַזְרִיעַ וְיָלְדָה זָכָר. רַבִּי יְהוֹשֻׁעַ בֶּן לֵוִי אָמַר הַוְיָין לוֹ בָּנִים רְאוּיִין
לְהוֹרָאָה דִּכְתִיב (ויקרא י) לְהַבְדִּיל וּלְהוֹרֹת

שבועות יח: –

R' Yochanan said in the name of R' Shimon bar Yochai: Whoever does not separate from his wife close to the expected time of her period, even if he has children as righteous as the sons of Aharon, they will die. For it is written: "And you shall separate the Children of Israel from their contamination .. And the *niddah* in her state of separation..." and in proximity to this verse it is written: "And Hashem spoke to Moshe after the death of Aharon's two sons." R' Chiya bar Abba said in the name of R' Yochanan: Whoever separates from his wife close to the expected time of her period will merit to have male children. For it is written: "To distinguish between the contaminated and the pure," and in proximity to this verse it is written: "When a woman conceives and gives birth to a male." R' Yehoshua ben Levi said: He will merit to have sons who are fit to render judgment; for it is written: "In order to distinguish ... between the contaminated and the pure... and to teach the Children of Israel."

— *Shevuos* 18b

We noted in Chapter Thirteen that when a woman's day of *vest* arrives, two steps must be taken: a) *perishah:* One must refrain from cohabitation since the menstruation may begin at any moment, and b) *bedikah:* One must perform a *bedikah* since some menstrual blood may have appeared already.[1]

We noted as well that one calculates the *vest haflagah* and *vest hachodesh* with days to determine the *yom havest.* However, the *vest* itself is observed on the *onas havest,* i.e., the twelve-hour period, either the daytime or nighttime, in which the menstruation occurred the previous month. Regarding this *halachah,* day begins at sunrise and ends at sundown of that day.[2] Night begins at sundown and ends at sunrise.[3]

---

1. This is discussed in Chapter Thirteen, Section I,A.

2. *Chavos Daas* 184:5[b]. This is different than the normal laws regarding day and night. In regard to other *halachos,* we consider day to begin at dawn and end at dusk.

3. *Chavos Daas* ibid.

I. *Halachos* pertaining to the *onas havest*

A. The prohibitions and requirements

The Talmud derives from the Torah that one is required to separate — *perishah* (from cohabitation) — from one's wife close to the time of the expected period.[4] The Talmud interprets this to extend to the entire *onas* (the twelve-hour period of day or night) *havest.*

When the *vest* arrives, whether a *vest haflagah*, a *vest hachodesh*, a *vest haguf*, whether a *vest kavuah* or *aino kavuah* or even the *onah beinonis*, there are two general *halachic* requirements: separation and *bedikos.*

1. The separation (*perishah*):
When a woman actually becomes a *niddah* she is required to separate from her husband. This separation has three applications: a) separation from marital relations, b) separation from physical contact and c) separation from intimate conduct which may lead to transgressing the prohibition of *niddah* (this last type is called *harchakos*). During the *yom havest* a woman is not yet a *niddah* but we expect the onset of her menstruation. While the couple must separate, some, but not all, of the stringencies of *niddah* apply.

a. Marital relations:
We noted in Chapter Two that one who cohabits with a *niddah* transgresses the cardinal prohibition of *niddah*. If the act is committed knowingly, both the man and his wife are punished by *kares*. If they do so unknowingly (i.e., the husband and wife are unaware that she was a *niddah*), each is liable for a *korban chatas*. *Halachah* cannot permit cohabitation during a time that she is accustomed

---

4. *Rishonim* disagree whether, and to what degree, this *perishah* is a Biblical requirement. *Tosfos* (*Yevamos* 62b, *Pesachim* 72b), *Ritva* (*Shevuos* 18b) and *Reah* (*Bedek HaBayis* 7:2) contend that the requirement to abstain is a Biblical requirement, i.e., the verse "you shall separate the Children of Israel from their contamination" is an actual *derashah*. We noted in Chapter Thirteen note 8, that *Noda B'Yehudah, Chasam Sofer* and *Aruch HaShulchan* each explain that this is true even according to the Talmudic opinion that *vestos* are of Rabbinic origin (*deRabbanan*). However, *Raavad* (*Baalei HaNefesh* beginning of *Shaar Vestos*), *Rashba* (*Toras HaBayis* 7:3) and *Ran* (*Shevuos* 1b in *Rif*) are of the opinion that the requirement of separation is only Rabbinic in origin. The verse cited in the Talmud is merely an *asmachta* — a Biblical allusion to the Rabbinic law. Those *Rishonim* who maintain that this *perishah* is a Biblical requirement disagree regarding the extent of the period of abstention required. *Binas Adam* 108:1 contends that requirement to separate on the exact time that she usually menstruates is Biblical (this is also the view of the Ritva cited above). However, *Graz* 184:5 rules that even the separation on the exact time that she usually menstruates is Rabbinic.

to menstruate since she may begin to menstruate during relations[5] and they will both violate the prohibition of *niddah*.[6] Therefore, a husband and wife are prohibited from having marital relations on the *onas havest*. This is the essential *halachah* of *vestos*. If a couple cohabit during the *onas havest*, even if she did not menstruate, they transgressed a prohibition and need to repent.[7]

b. Physical contact:
We noted in Chapter Two that the prohibition of *niddah* extends to any personal, physical contact between a *niddah* and any man. In the opinion of most *Rishonim*, pleasurable contact, e.g., hugging or kissing (*chibuk v'nishuk*), is Biblically prohibited, and punishable by *malkos* (flogging). Indeed, any personal bodily contact, whether pleasurable or casual, between the two is prohibited. There is an opinion that *chibuk v'nishuk* is prohibited during the *onas havest* as well.[8] However, *Shulchan Aruch*[9] rules that a couple is not required to avoid physical contact during the *onas havest*.[10] Other *Poskim* maintain that although *chibuk v'nishuk* is not prohibited, it is meritorious to refrain from such contact.[11] Later authorities maintain that it is proper to follow the strict view.[12] *Poskim* note that sleeping together in one bed even when both are fully clothed is similar

---

5. See *Reah* (*Bedek HaBayis*, beginning of *Shaar HaPrishah*) and *Bach* (184 s.v. פרישה) who explain that since it is common for cohabitation to bring on menstruation there is reason to prohibit cohabitation any time that menstruation is expected.

6. The *halachos* regarding such an event are found in 185:4.

7. *Toras HaShelamim* §3 citing *Shach*. If a couple realize during cohabitation that it is the *onas havest*, they must separate. See *Chavos Daas* 185:7[b], responsa *Maharam Shick*, Y.D. 176, and *Pardes Rimonim* [mz], end of 185, regarding the manner in which to separate.

8. *Terumas HaDeshen* cited in *Beis Yosef* and *Bach* ibid. and *Taz* §3.

9. 184:2. Following opinion of *Ramban*, *Rashba* and *Raavad*, all cited in *Beis Yosef*.

10. According to *Reah* and *Bach* cited above (note 5) it is understandable why the prohibition applies only to cohabitation, not physical contact. Another possible explanation is that we are more concerned about a prohibition punishable by *kares*. See another explanation in *Chasam Sofer* to 184:2[5], citing R' Nassan Adler, that we are more concerned regarding cohabitation because if she has a blood flow during cohabitation they may not disengage immediately, whereas if she has a blood flow during other physical contact they can immediately disengage.

11. *Bach* ibid.

12. But it is not binding that one do so.. See *Shiurei Sheivet HaLeivi* on *Shach* 184:6. He notes that one who accepts the stricter view as a *chumra* and finds it too difficult may be *matir neder* (annul his vow).

to *chibuk v'nishuk* and should be avoided.[13] Similarly, one should avoid light-headed or intimate talk which may lead to intimate behavior.[14]

c. *Harchakos:*
One is not required to refrain during the *onas havest* from other types of behavior that are prohibited during *niddus*, e.g., eating or drinking together, or handing to one another.[15]

2. The requirement of *bedikos:*
When the *onas havest* arrives a woman is required to do a *bedikah.*[16] This *bedikah*, if found free from any bloodstain, will not permit her to cohabit on the *onas havest* itself, but if found clean, it will permit cohabitation after the *onas havest* passes and eliminate the *vest (akiras vest)*. See b below regarding the amount of *bedikos* that are required.

a. A *vest kavuah* and a *vest she'aino kavuah:*
There is a difference between a *vest kavuah* and a *vest she'aino kavuah* regarding the stringency of the *bedikah* requirement.

i. A woman with a *vest kavuah* is required to perform *bedikos* on the *onas havest* to ensure that no blood appeared. She should be careful not to lose the cloth before checking it. If the cloth is lost, she may repeat the *bedikah.*[17] If she omitted the *bedikah* entirely during the *onas havest* there is an opinion that we must assume that some blood appeared.

---

13. *Graz* 184:6.

14. *Darchei Teshuvah* 184:10 citing *Malbushei Taharah*.

15. See *Terumas HaDeshen* cited in *Bach* ibid. *Chochmas Adam* 108:1.

16. The *bedikah* cloth must be inserted into all crevices of the vagina (*churin u'sedakim*); an external examination (*kinuach*) does not suffice (*Chavos Daas* 184:22[c] and *Sidrei Taharah* §13). See Chapter Five regarding the manner in which a *bedikah* must be performed.

17. *Chavos Daas* 184:11[b] maintains that if a *bedikah* was done on the *vest* day and subsequently lost, the woman may be *temei'ah*. He contends that a woman is *tehorah* after the *vest* day passes only because she had no *hargashah* and we may therefore assume that she did not menstruate. However, if a *bedikah* was done and lost, we cannot be certain that there was no *hargashah*. She may have had a *hargashah* of *dam* at the time of the *bedikah* and confused it with the sensation of the *bedikah*. We, therefore, have no choice but to consider her a *niddah*. *Aruch HaShulchan* 184:39 follows this view. *Pischei Teshuvah* §18 contends that according to *Chavos Daas* she is *temei'ah* even

She is, therefore, automatically a *niddah,* even if she is subsequently able to produce a clean *bedikah.*[18] A second group of *Poskim* accept a *bedikah* done later. However, even they agree that the woman must consider herself *temei'ah* until she performs the *bedikah.*[19] Other *Poskim* are still more lenient and rule that once the *vest* has passed no *bedikah* is required. The accepted *halachah* follows the second opinion.[20] Thus, she must abstain[21] until she does a *bedikah.* The *bedikah* should be done without any further delay but it is valid even if it is done at a later time.[22] It is important to note that the *onah beinonis* is similar to a *vest kavuah* with regard to these *halachos.*[23] These *halachos* are explained in Chapter Fourteen, Section I,C,1.

The stringency of the *bedikah* requirement on the *onah* of a *vest kavuah* is such that the couple

---

if a *bedikah* is done afterwards (it seems from *Pischei Teshuvah* that this is true only if the second *bedikah* was done after the *onas havest* passes, but if she did another *bedikah* during the *onas havest* she is *tehorah.* See a similar view in *Be'er Moshe* 1:55). *Pischei Teshuvah* also maintains that, according to *Chavos Daas,* if the woman urinated during the *onas havest* she is also *temei'ah* since she may have confused the sensation of urination with *hargashah.* However, *Imrei Binah* (responsa §6) maintains that even according to *Chavos Daas* urination will not render her a *niddah.* He argues that it is almost impossible for a woman not to urinate during her *onas havest* (perhaps *Pischei Teshuvah* expects a woman to check the urine for blood or he ws referring to a woman who normally menstruates at a distinct time of the day). Among *Poskim* who reject *Chavos Daas'* view (even regarding a lost *bedikah* cloth) are: *Imrei Binah, Pardes Rimonim* (on *Taz* §13), *Maharam* Shick (end of introduction to *Y.D.*), *Beis Shlomo* 2:27, *Cheiker Halachah* (*Niddah* §2), *Daas Torah* 184:9 and *Chazon Ish* 80:22. *Imrei Binah* explains that the only reason to suspect that there was blood on the *bedikah* cloth is because a woman usually menstruates on her *vest* day. However, a woman usually menstruates with a full flow, not a mere drop of blood. Therefore, it is illogical to make two contrary assumptions: a) that since she usually menstruates on her *vest,* she must have menstruated today and b) that even though she usually menstruates with a full flow, this time only a small drop of blood appeared. One should note that although *Poskim* reject *Chavos Daas'* view, a woman should be careful not to lose the *bedikah* of the *onas havest.* If the *bedikah* cloth is lost she should repeat the *bedikah.*

18. See *Niddah* 16a and *Shach* 184:23.

19. Second opinion in 184:9.

20. *Rema* ad loc.

21. *Sidrei Taharah* 184:13 cites *Tiferes LeMoshe* who maintains that they must abstain from intimate physical contact as well, i.e., hugging and kissing (*chibuk v'nishuk*), *Sidrei Taharah* himself disagrees.

22. The *bedikah* should not be done immediately before cohabiting since at that time she may rush the *bedikah* and not check all crevices (*Sidrei Taharah* 183:13).

23. 184:9, 189:4.

may not cohabit until the husband inquires whether or not his wife did the required *bedikah*.[24] He may not rely upon the fact that she is awake and acts as if she is *tehorah*. He must specifically ask whether a *bedikah* was done.[25] If sufficient time has passed to allow the expected period to end, for her to count five and then seven "clean" days and to immerse herself in a *mikveh*, he may assume that she did so and is *tehorah*, even if she is sleepy and not alert.[26] These *halachos* are discussed in greater detail in Chapter Four Section I,A,2.

ii. A *vest she'aino kavuah* is weaker since it was not established three times. Therefore, in the opinion of some *Rishonim* a *bedikah* is not required on the *onas havest*.[27] The fact that she felt no *hargashah* and found no *dam* is sufficient proof that no *dam* appeared. Others maintain that a woman should perform a *bedikah* even on a *vest she'aino kavuah* day.[28] Nevertheless, all agree that if she did no *bedikah* in the course of the day, no further *bedikah* is required. Her husband need not ask her specifically if she menstruated or if she did a *bedikah*.[29]

b. The number of *bedikos*:

Although only one *bedikah*[30] is necessary on the *yom havest*,[31] common custom is to perform two *bedikos*. If the

---

24. 184:11, see *Aruch HaShulchan* §46 and *Darchei Teshuvah* §60.

25. *Chavos Daas* 184:14[b], 32[c].

26. 184:11.

27. See *Beis Yosef* end of 184 and *Pardes Rimonim* 184:12[mz],22[sc].

28. *Prishah* 184:18, *Bach* 189 s.v. פיהקה בר"ח and *Graz* §28.

29. There is a difference of opinion among *Poskim* whether this applies only if she is awake or even if she is sleeping. See Chapter Four, Section I,A,2.

30. *Chavos Daas* (184:9[b]) maintains (and *Aruch HaShulchan* 184:38 seems to agree) that if a woman has no set time to begin the menstruation, she is required to keep a *moch dachuk* inserted throughout the *onas havest*. However, responsa *Imrei Binah* §6 and *Shiurei Sheivet HaLeivi* 184:9[4] note that most *Poskim* reject *Chavos Daas'* view. One is advised not to follow *Chavos Daas'* view since it may cause vaginal irritation.

31. *Shiurei Sheivet HaLeivi* 189:9[4] notes that it seems from *Shulchan Aruch* that only one *bedikah* is necessary.

onas havest is during the night, she does one *bedikah* after nightfall and one upon awakening. On a daytime *onas havest* she does one *bedikah* upon awakening and another before sundown.[32] Some *Poskim* advise that she do three *bedikos*.

3. Bathing during the *onas havest*:

Since we expect a woman to menstruate on her *onas havest*, some *Poskim* maintain that a woman may not bathe or swim (and cer-

---

32. See *Be'er Moshe* 2:57 and *Badei HaShulchan* 184:54. The *bedikah* for a day *onah* should not be done before dawn (perhaps not even before sunrise, see *Be'er Moshe* ibid.) and before sundown (or dusk). *Shiurei Sheivet HaLeivi* 184:9[4] rules that a woman should do three *bedikos* for a daytime *vest*: one upon awakening, one at noon and one before nightfall. Regarding a nighttime *vest*, he rules that she should do a *bedikah* after sundown, another before retiring and another upon awakening (if she wakes before sunrise, and even if she wakes afterwards it is proper to do a *bedikah*). *Be'er Moshe* 6:138 agrees that a woman should do three *bedikos* if she has a *vest kavuah* or during the *onah beinonis*. However, if she merely has a *vest she'aino kavuah*, two *bedikos* suffice. *Shiurei Sheivet HaLeivi* requires that she do one *bedikah* even in the *Or Zarua's onah* (i.e., the *onah* preceding the primary *onas havest*). *Be'er Moshe* (ibid.) disagrees. After the *vest*: *Shiurei Sheivet HaLeivi* also requires that she do a third *bedikah* after the *onas havest* passes unless the last *bedikah* was done close to the end of the *onah*. *Badei HaShulchan* contends that she should do a *bedikah* after the *onas havest* even if the second *bedikah* was done close to the end of the *onah*. He argues that the main *bedikah* should be done at the actual hour of the *vest*. Since women today do not have a set hour, a *bedikah* done any time during the day does not fully qualify as the *bedikah* of the *onas havest*. A similar view is held by *Kineh Bosem* 184:16. He maintains that the main *bedikah* should be done at the very end of the *onah*. Therefore, a woman should do one *bedikah* during the *onah* and one afterwards. If she has difficulty doing many *bedikos*, she should do a *bedikah* only after the *onah*.

The *onah beinonis*: *Sheivet HaLeivi* maintains that the *bedikah* for the *onah beinonis* should be done on the *onah* of her last menstruation on both the thirtieth and thirty-first day (we noted in Chapter Fifteen that in the opinion of some *Poskim*, the thirty-first interval day is the *onah beinonis*). If her last menstruation was during the day she should do a *bedikah* on the day of the thirtieth and one *bedikah* on the night before. He is uncertain whether she must do a *bedikah* on the night before the thirty-first. In 184:9[9] he rules that if she did not do a *bedikah* on the thirty-first day she is not required to abstain until she does the *bedikah*. *Badei HaShulchan* maintains that on the *onah beinonis* a woman should do one *bedikah* at the beginning of the night, one upon rising and one before sundown.

Igros Moshe, Y.D. 3:48, notes an alternative method of *bedikos* on the *onas havest* (this would be useful for someone traveling): She should wear a white undergarment that holds tightly to her body and do a *bedikah* at night (even if it is past the *onas havest*).

It should be noted, that although *Poskim* maintain that one should do as many as three *bedikos* during the *onas havest*, one must consider whether the excessive *bedikos* irritate her vagina and whether they are advisable considering her emotional state. One should bear in mind that a *vest she'aino kavuah* perhaps requires no *bedikos* and that essentially one *bedikah* suffices even for a *vest kavuah*.

tainly not douche) during her *onas havest*[33] of a *vest kavuah* or *onah beinonis*.[34] We are concerned that perhaps a minute amount of menstrual blood may wash away unnoticed. Indeed, some *Poskim* rule that a woman who bathed on the *onas havest* is considered a *niddah*.[35] Others rule that she may do a *bedikah* afterwards and is *tehorah*.[36] Some authorities permit a woman to bathe during the *onas havest* if she does a *bedikah* beforehand and inserts a *moch dachuk* for the duration of the bath.[37] Others maintain that even so a woman should preferably avoid bathing during that *onah*.[38] Some permit a woman to bathe or swim on the *onas havest* of a *vest she'aino kavuah*.[39] All agree that a shower is permitted.[40]

In summary: A woman may shower during her *onas havest* regardless of whether it is a *vest she'aino kavuah*, *vest kavuah* or *onah beinonis*. She should preferably not swim or bathe during the *onas havest* of a *vest kavuah* or *onah beinonis*. If she must swim, she should do a *bedikah* beforehand and insert a tampon. She may swim during the *onas havest* of a *vest she'aino kavuah* but preferable do a *bedikah* beforehand.

---

33. *Be'er Moshe* 2:60 is more lenient regarding the *onah* before the *onas havest* or the thirty-first day as opposed to the thirtieth. He permits her to swim if she does a *bedikah* beforehand.

34. Since there is the possibility that some blood may appear at any moment during the *onas havest* and according to some *Poskim* a *bedikah* is no longer valid. See *Kineh Bosem* 184:15 (and responsa 1:63) who maintains that a woman who must be *tovel* on the night following her *onas havest* (e.g., if she had an exceptionally early menstruation or she found a mid-cycle *kesem*) should do the preparatory bathing at night, not during the day of her *onas havest*. However, if her scheduled *tevilah* is Friday night she may do the preparatory bathing on Friday which is her *onas havest*. Responsa *BeTzeil HaChochmah* 3:19 also permits the preparatory bath on Friday if she does a *bedikah* beforehand.

35. Similarly, if she did no *bedikah* on the *onas havest* and bathed before doing a *bedikah* afterwards, or if she wiped the external area and did not inspect the cloth, she is considered a *niddah* (*Prishah* 189:18, *Kitzur Shulchan Aruch* 155:9). *Pardes Rimonim* §12[mz] maintains that this question is dependent upon a disagreement between *Ramban* and *Rashba*. *Be'er Moshe* 2:60 differentiates between a hot bath and bathing in cool water (i.e., swimming); in the former case she is considered a *niddah*, in the latter case she should do a *bedikah* afterwards. In 3:140 *Be'er Moshe* is lenient regarding a woman who always feels cramps or aches before menstruating. Since she felt no cramps on the *onas havest* we may assume that she had no flow even though she lost the *bedikah* cloth.

36. *Bach* (*Kuntres Acharon*), *Chazon Ish* 80:22, see also *Pische Zuta* 184:11.

37. *Be'er Moshe* 2:60.

38. *Shiurei Sheivet HaLeivi* on *Taz* §184:13.

39. *Be'er Moshe* ibid.

40. *Be'er Moshe* and *Shiurei Sheivet HaLeivi* ibid.

4. A *kesem* found during the *onas havest:*

A *kesem* found during the *onas havest* is governed by the same *halachos* as any *kesem*.[41] A stain less than a *gris* or found upon a colored garment will not render a woman a *niddah,* even if it is found on the day of her expected period.[42] Nevertheless, the *kesem* should not be dismissed lightly. There are two reasons for concern. First, while the woman is not rendered a *niddah* by the *kesem* itself, the *kesem* may signal the imminent arrival of her period and precautionary steps are warranted. A Rav may advise the couple to abstain from cohabitation until her status becomes clearer. Second, a menstrual period is often preceded by a staining phase. In this case, the staining itself may be considered a *vest haguf* and the couple may be required to abstain upon the onset of the staining. The *halachah* was discussed in Chapter Eighteen. In either case, since the *kesem* is essentially *tahor,* they need not observe all the other rules of *harchakos,* (e.g., handing to one another).

A woman nearing her expected period will certainly want to know if any bleeding has begun. Therefore, a woman should not wear very dark (navy blue or black) undergarments at the time her menstruation is expected.[43] Her menstruation may begin in the form of staining which may not be noticed due to the dark color of the garments.

---

41. See *Daas Torah* 184:9, citing *Tashbatz,* that a woman who did not do a *bedikah* on the *onas havest,* finds a *kesem* less than a *gris* and then does a *bedikah* is *tehorah* if the *bedikah* is clear. *Shiurei Sheivet HaLeivi* 184:9[5] is very strict regarding a *kesem* found during the *onas havest.* He contends that although *halachically* a *kesem* found during the *onas havest* is no different than any other *kesem,* it is very difficult to be lenient. He argues that since today many women feel no sensation at the time of the *vest,* we cannot ignore even a *kesem* less than a *gris* if it looks like blood even though she felt no *hargashah.* Although a woman who finds a *kesem* requires no *bedikah* afterwards, in this case he requires that the woman do a *bedikah. Sheivet HaLeivi* is generally strict regarding a *kesem* that is certainly blood even when it is not found on the *onas havest.* Although *Sheivet HaLeivi's* arguments are sound, common custom is to treat a *kesem* on the *onas havest* as any other *kesem.* The reason for this may be that a woman usually menstruates with a heavy flow, not a small spot on her garment. Thus, if the *kesem* is associated with her *vest* it should be a flow, not a mere *kesem.* A similar idea is noted in footnote 17. In addition, earlier *Poskim* do not mention a difference between a *kesem* found on the *onas havest* and one found at other times. However, a woman who finds a small *kesem* on her *onas havest* should be prudent and abstain even after she does a *bedikah* and the *onas havest* passes until she is confident that the menstruation is not about to begin.

42. *Badei HaShulchan* 190:109. However, *Shiurei Sheivet HaLeivi* 190:10[3] notes that punctilious individuals ("בעלי נפש") are strict regarding a *kesem* that appears to be actual blood if found on the day of the *vest,* even on a colored garment. Although this strict ruling is not generally accepted, as noted above, it is prudent to abstain from marital relations until it becomes clear whether or not the stain is the beginning of her menstrual cycle.

43. *Pischei Teshuvah* 190:22 cites *Amudei Kesef* that a woman should not wear colored garments on

5. *Hargashah* during the *onas havest*:

A woman must be conscious of any *hargashah* that she may feel during the *onas havest*. Even those sensations that do not qualify as *hargashah* (see Chapter Three) are suspect during an *onas havest*.[44] A woman who feels a *hargashah* or even only a sensation of fluid leaving her body[45] must do a *bedikah* to ascertain whether or not the discharge is blood.[46]

B. The duration of the prohibition

1. The *onas havest*:

Essentially, one is required to abstain only on the *onas havest* itself, i.e., the daytime or nighttime on which the *vest* falls. If she usually menstruates shortly after sunrise, she may cohabit the night before and must abstain during the day. If she usually menstruates shortly before sundown, she must abstain all day, but may cohabit the following night.[47] If a woman has two *vestos she'ainon kavuuos* she abstains on the *onah* of each particular *vest*. For example, in the previous month, she menstruated on the night of the third and on the day of the fifteenth, she abstains the following month on the night of the third and the day of the fifteenth.

---

her *"niddah* days." His intent is unclear. *Badei HaShulchan* (*Tziyunim* 190:205) interprets this to mean her expected *vest* day. Thus, a woman is required to don white during the *yom havest*. *Igros Moshe* Y.D. 3:48, although he does not require that a woman don white during the *onas havest,* he considers it proper. However, since all earlier authorities make no mention of this *halachah* which affects all woman, apparently, they disagree. While it is customary to permit wearing colored garments during the *onas havest,* as noted, a woman should not wear dark colors that could hide a bloodstain.

44. See *Cheiker Halachah* (*Niddah* §2) who maintains that even a *hargashah* of a vaginal flow, (i.e., she feels a flow in the vagina which is *halachically* not considered *hargashah*, is considered a *hargashah* on the *onas havest*. Therefore, he rules that if a woman feels such a sensation on the *onas havest* she is *temei'ah* even if she does a *bedikah* and finds nothing, *Shiurei Sheivet HaLeivi* 184:9[6] accepts this view but maintains that a feeling of an external flow (i.e., she feels fluid leaving her body) is not considered *hargashah* even on the *onas havest*. It would seem that according to *Sheivet HaLeivi* if she does a *bedikah* and finds nothing, she is *tehorah*. However, she certainly is required to do a *bedikah* even if she usually has similar sensations during the month.

45. Even if she is accustomed to feeling such discharges.

46. See *Maharsham* 1:188, *Divrei Chaim* 1:34, 2:66, *Pische Zuta* 190:3, *Imrei Yosher* cited in *Darchei Teshuvah* 190:21 and *Chazon Ish,* Y.D. 89:1.

47. 184:2. This is based on the principle that the day itself is the cause of the menstruation.

2. The *Or Zarua:*

Rishonim[48] cite the opinion of *Or Zarua*[49] who maintains that besides the actual *onas havest,* one must abstain on the preceding *onah* as well.[50] Thus, if the *onas havest* is during the daytime, one must abstain the previous night and if the *onas havest* is during the night, one must abstain the preceding day. *Shulchan Aruch*[51] rejects this view as do many *Poskim.*[52] However, other *Poskim*[53] maintain that one should follow *Or Zarua's* view.[54] Since there are varying traditions regarding this question, the reader is advised to discuss the matter with their Rav.

There are situations when many authorities agree that even one who usually follows the *Or Zarua's* view may be lenient.

> a. When there is a doubt regarding the *vest* itself (see Section IV), one is required to abstain only on the *onas havest* itself, not the preceding *onah.*

---

48. See *Beis Yosef* 184.

49. R' Yitzchak ben Moshe of Vienna.

50. *Shach* in §7 and in *Nekudos HaKesef* explains that although the Talmud states clearly that one is required to abstain only one *onah*, *Or Zarua* maintains that today one must abstain two *onos*. He explains that in earlier times, women usually began menstruation each month at the same time of the day. Thus, it was sufficient to abstain for the *onas havest* only. Today, women do not have an exact time in which they begin to menstruate. Accordingly, one must extend the prohibition to the previous *onah. Chochmas Adam* 108:3 seems to understand from *Shach* that this depends in the individual woman. If she has a set time of the day in which she usually menstruates, she is required to abstain only on the *onas havest*. If she has no set time, she must abstain the earlier *onah* as well.

51. 184:2.

52. *Taz* §2, *Toras HaShelamim* §6, *Chavos Daas* §3[b], *Sidrei Taharah* §3, *Beis Lechem Yehudah* ad loc., *Chochmas Adam* 108:3, *Aruch HaShulchan* 184:20 and *Chazon Ish* cited in *Taharas Bas Yisrael.*

53. *Bach* 184 maintains that although essentially *halachah* requires that one abstain only one *onah,* one should follow *Or Zarua's* view as a *chumra. Shach* §7 and in *Nekudos HaKesef* supports *Or Zarua's* view and cites other *Rishonim* who follow his view. It is interesting that responsa *Maharsham* 3:258 comments that it is clear from *sefer Or Zarua* that *Or Zarua* never intended to state a *halachah*, he merely advised that one follow a *chumra* and abstain an additional *onah. Shiurei Sheivet HaLeivi* on *Taz* 184:2 uses this comment of *Maharsham* for an opposite effect. He maintains that those who rejected *Or Zarua's* view did so only because the Talmud states clearly that one need not abstain for more than one *onah*. Since it is now clear that *Or Zarua* meant to state a *chumra*, not a *halachah*, his words do not contradict the Talmud. Therefore, there is no basis to reject his view.

54. *Chasam Sofer, Y.D.* 179, strongly supports *Or Zarua's* view. *Igros Moshe, Y.D.* 3:48, maintains that one should follow *Or Zarua* unless that would cause difficulty. In addition, he rules that if she usually alternates her period between day and night, both day and night are considered one *onah. Shiurei Sheivet HaLeivi* on *Taz* 184:2 notes that it is proper to follow *Or Zarua's* view and that this was the custom in most countries. He doubts whether one whose custom it was to follow *Or Zarua* may be *matir neder* and follow the lenient view.

b. Some *Poskim* rule that regarding a *vest she'aino kavuah*, one is not required to abstain on the *Or Zarua's vest*.[55] Others do not differentiate between *vest kavuah* and *vest she'aino kavuah*.[56]

c. If a *vest haflagah she'aino kavuah* was uprooted by a shorter interval, one is required to abstain only on the *onas havest* itself of the longer interval. For example, a woman menstruated during the day after a twenty-eight day interval and then menstruated during the day after a twenty-six day interval. In the opinion of some *Poskim*, the *vest haflagah* of twenty-eight was not uprooted, see Chapter Seventeen, Section III,A,3. Therefore, she must now abstain on the day and night of the twenty-sixth interval day but only the day of the twenty-eighth interval day.

d. If the *onah* of the *Or Zarua* coincides with the evening before her husband is leaving on a trip or the evening of a scheduled *tevilah*, the couple may not be required to abstain; a Rav should be consulted. See Section C.

e. A woman who usually menstruates within a span of a few days may be required to abstain for several days, see Section II. However, if she usually menstruates during the day, she is only required to abstain during the *Or Zarua's onah* of the actual *yom havest*.[57]

f. Even one who abstains during the *Or Zarua's vest* need not refrain from *chibuk v'nishuk* — hugging and kissing.[58]

One should note that in the opinion of many *Poskim* the *onah beinonis* is a always a complete day.[59] Thus, if the last menstruation was during the day, the *onah beinonis* will be on the thirtieth day <u>and</u> the evening before. We noted in Chapter Fifteen, Section IV,B that in the opinion of some *Poskim* the *onah beinonis* is the thirty-first interval day. Even one who keeps *onah beinonis* both

---

55. Responsa *Teshuras Shai* 1:275.

56. See *Chasam Sofer*, Y.D. 179, who is lenient only in a case of dire necessity. In §170 it seems he was lenient only regarding one who is leaving on a trip. *Shiurei Sheivet HaLeivi* to *Taz* §2 contends that common custom is to abstain on the *Or Zarua's onah* even for a *vest she'aino kavuah*.

57. *Chochmas Adam* 108:6. See below note 100.

58. *Be'er Moshe* 4:62.

59. *Pleisi* 189:15; however, *Sidrei Taharah* 189:31 is lenient even regarding *onah beinonis*.

the thirtieth and thirty-first days need not abstain on the night between the two, unless the thirty-first is also the *yom hachodesh*[60] and he usually follows the *Or Zarua's* view.[61]

3. The *Aviasaf's* view:

Rishonim cite another unusual view regarding calculation of the *onas havest;* this is the view of *Aviasaf.*[62] He maintains that *onos* and *vestos* do not depend on sunrise and sunset of the individual day, but on those of the median day. Thus, if sunrise during the equinox is, e.g., at 6 a.m. and sunset at 6 p.m., the span between those hours is called "day" or "night." A woman who menstruated during the day of a winter month must abstain until 6 p.m. of the same day of the following month even though nightfall was at 5 p.m. This has a lenient application as well. If this were a summer month she would abstain only until 6 p.m. even though sundown is at 8 p.m.. *Aviasaf's* view applies to the determination of date of the menstruation as well. If she menstruated on the fifth of the month at 5:50 p.m. during the winter, it is considered a "day" period even though nightfall was at 5 p.m. On the following month she will abstain on the day of the fifth of the month, not the night of the sixth. Some *Poskim* note that a punctilious individual should follow the strict applications of both opinions and abstain both the day of the fifth and the night of the sixth.[63] However *Poskim* generally[64] reject *Aviasaf's* view[65] as is common custom.

4. A change in time zones:

A woman traveling from the United States eastward to *Eretz Yisrael* on the day before her *onas havest,* arriving there after sundown (of her night *vest*), must observe her *vest* even though her *onas havest* has not yet begun in the United States. This is true of a *vest haflagah* as well as a *vest hachodesh.*[66]

---

60. The *yom hachodesh* is always either the thirtieth or the thirty-first interval day.

61. He would then be required to abstain on the night before the thirty-first day because of the *vest hachodesh,* not the *onah beinonis.*

62. *RAVYaH (R' Eliezer ben Yoel HaLeivi,* d. circa 1225).

63. *Chochmas Adam* 108:2, *Lechem VeSimlah* 184:10[l].

64. Excluding *Bach* 184, who follows *Aviasaf's* view. *Shach* §7 also seems to support his view.

65. *Beis Yosef, Taz* §2 and *Graz* §12. *Pleisi* §4 tries to defend the view of *Aviasaf* but concludes that *halachah* follows the view of the majority of *Poskim* who disagree with *Aviasaf. Graz* notes that the view of *Aviasaf* seems contrary to the theory that *vestos* are caused by the sun.

66. *Be'er Moshe* 7:3[YD 189]. See *Sheivet HaLeivi* 4:98[3] regarding a woman traveling during her night *onas havest* who arrives in *Eretz Yisrael* after sunrise. He is uncertain whether she is required

C. *Onas havest* under special circumstances

Poskim discuss the requirement for *perishah* during the *onas havest* of a *vest kavuah*, a *vest she'aino kavuah* as well as the *Or Zarua's vest* under the following special circumstances:

1. One who embarks on a journey:
The Talmud[67] (according to the interpretation of most *Rishonim*)[68] states that one who is about to embark[69] on a journey[70] is required to[71] cohabit with his wife the night before.[72] This is required even if that night[73] is the *onas havest*.[74] Although this *halachah* is cited in

---

to continue to observe the *vest* until the night at the point of her departure has ended. This case is perhaps different than that above. In this second case the *onas havest* had already begun at the time of her departure. This should bring on her menstruation. Her arrival at her destination where the *onas havest* has passed may not stop an internal process which has already begun. If this difference is true, *Sheivet HaLeivi* would agree in the first case that she follows the time in *Eretz Yisrael*. One should note that regarding the seven "clean" days one certainly follows the time zone at the point of destination. For example, a woman who began her seven "clean" days on Monday night in New York and travels to *Eretz Yisrael* may be *tovel* on nightfall the following Monday night even though it is still daytime in New York.

67. *Yevamos* 62b.

68. As opposed to *Rabbeinu Tam* in *Tosfos* ad loc.

69. See *Darchei Teshuvah* 184:46 regarding the night of one's return from a journey or the night before the woman is embarking on a journey. He is not lenient in either of these cases. It is questionable whether one may be lenient in these cases even on the *Or Zarua's onah*. See also *Shiurei Sheivet HaLeivi* 184:10[2].

70. Regarding this *halachah*, a journey is any trip that will cause his absence during a time of their normal *onah*, i.e., the time that they normally cohabit (*Yaavetz* gloss to *Yevamos* 62b). However, *Shiurei Sheivet HaLeivi* 184:10[3] maintains that one who travels a great distance (e.g., out of the country) or one who reports for hazardous military duty is considered "leaving for a journey" even if he plans to return before their usual *onah*. He adds that if one is presently away from home and wishes to leave on a journey from there, he should return home beforehand for a night if possible.

71. If the journey was for a *mitzvah*, he is not required to cohabit, *Rema* ad loc. We are concerned that he may neglect the *mitzvah*, see *Rashi*, *Yevamos* 62b.

72. *Poskim* struggle with the apparent contradiction between this *halachah* and that stated in *Orach Chaim* 240:15 that one should not cohabit on the day that one plans to embark upon a trip. Some differentiate between one who is traveling by foot and one who rides (one who plans to travel by foot should not cohabit since such travel is strenuous), or between cohabiting on the day itself (which one should not) and the night before, or that the *halachah* in *Orach Chaim* is based upon medical considerations, not actual *halachah*. See *Shach* §25 and *Toras HaShelamim* §18 among others.

73. See *Badei HaShulchan* 184:68 regarding a woman who usually menstruates at a certain time of the day; may one, according to these *Poskim*, cohabit even during that period of the day?

74. The requirement overrides the Rabbinic *halachah* of *vestos*.

Shulchan Aruch,[75] *Rema* adds that it is a meritorious act[76] to find other expressions of affection[77] but to refrain from cohabitation.[78] Later authorities are stricter yet and rule that one is *halachically* required to abstain on the *onas havest* itself.[79] This is the accepted view today.

a. The *Or Zarua's onah:*

In the opinion of some *Poskim* one embarking on a journey need not abstain on the *Or Zarua's onah.* One should discuss this question with a Rav.[80] If the *onas havest* is for a *vest she'aino kavuah,* not a *vest kavuah* or *onah beinonis,*[81] one may be lenient regarding the *Or Zarua's onah.*[82]

b. Intimate physical contact:

Although *Poskim* require that one abstain from cohabitation on the *onas havest* even when the husband is about to embark on a journey, they permit intimate physical contact (*chibuk v'nishuk*).[83] Normally one should refrain from such contact during the *onas havest.*

---

75. 184:9. *Poskim* note the unusual fact that *Rambam* omits this Talmudic *halachah* from his compendium. *Toras HaShelamim* §18 claims this is because of the problem of cohabiting before embarking on a journey, see note 72. *Aruch HaShulchan* §42 claims that *Rambam* shares *Rabbeinu Tam's* view (see note 68).

76. *Maharshal,* cited in *Toras HaShelamim* §19, is uncomfortable with one being strict and meritorious in a manner that infringes on his wife's marital rights. He, therefore, suggests that one try to delay his departure. *Graz* §33 suggests that the husband should, through comforting and reassuring words, convince her to absolve him of his obligation to her.

77. But only such talk which is permitted while she is a *niddah* (*Pardes Rimonim* on *Taz* §15). It is interesting to note that, according to *Tiferes LeMoshe* 184:10 and *Pardes Rimonim,* even if one's wife is actually a *niddah,* he should soothe her with expressions of affection before leaving on a journey. One must, nevertheless, be cautious not to indulge in intimate talk which is prohibited while she is a *niddah.*

78. 184:9.

79. *Chasam Sofer, Y.D.* 180, and *Igros Moshe, Y.D.* 3:58. It is not clear whether or not one may be lenient regarding a *vest she'aino kavuah.*

80. *Sheilas Yaavetz* 2:10 is lenient. *Pri Deah* on *Shach* 184:26, *Malbushei Taharah* 184:11, *Shaarei Tohar* 3:5 and *Taharas Yisrael* 184:81 follow this view. *Chasam Sofer, Y.D.* 170, seems to be lenient, albeit with some reservation. *Lechem VeSimlah* 184:31[l] is not only lenient but contends that one may not abstain. However, *Igros Moshe, Y.D.* 3:58, maintains that although it is *halachically* permitted to cohabit, one should preferably abstain. *Shiurei Sheivet HaLeivi* 184:10[2] is lenient about the *Or Zarua's vest* even regarding a *tevilah* night; he would certainly be lenient regarding one leaving on a journey.

81. The *onah beinonis* has the legal status of a *vest kavuah* (189:4), thus the requirement to follow the *Or Zarua's* view is stronger. In addition, see Chapter Fifteen, Section IV,C where we noted the opinion of many *Poskim* that one is normally required to abstain the full twenty-four hours of an *onah beinonis.*

82. One can certainly rely on the lenient opinions in this case.

83. *Shach* §27. *Beis Lechem Yehudah* (ad loc.) is strict even regarding *chibuk v'nishuk* based on two

2. A woman whose *tevilah* night coincides with her *onas havest:* *Poskim* discuss the question of applying the previous discussion to the case of a woman whose seven "clean" days end on the evening of her *onas havest*. Some *Poskim* contend that this case is comparable to that of one who is about to embark on a journey. Thus, according to *Shulchan Aruch* she may be *tovel* and need not abstain on the *onas havest*.[84] However, even these *Poskim* concede that the case of a *tevilah* night is no better than the case of one embarking on a journey. Thus, all the stricter opinions noted above certainly apply here. In addition, most *Poskim* reject this lenient view entirely[85] and do not permit cohabitation on an *onas havest* even if it is a *tevilah* night. Indeed, *Poskim* do not even permit her to be *tovel* for the purpose of other forms of physical contact.[86] If the *tevilah* coincides with the *Or Zarua's onah* one should consult a Rav.[87]

---

reasons: a) Most journeys are for the purpose of a *mitzvah* (which includes one's livelihood) and therefore since there is no requirement to cohabit one cannot compromise the *yom havest* in any way. b) According to *Taz* abstaining from *chibuk v'nishuk* on the *onas havest* is not a mere *chumra* but a requirement according to *halachah*. Therefore, we cannot be lenient regarding *chibuk v'nishuk* just as we are not lenient regarding cohabitation itself.

84. *Knesses Yechezkel* §33 cited in *Baer Heitev* §14 and *Pischei Teshuvah* §22. If she has a distinct hour in which she usually menstruates, she is required to abstain that hour only (ibid.). *Toras HaShelamim* 187:29 is uncertain whether one may cohabit on an *onas havest* which is *tevilah* night. See also *Malbushei Taharah* 184:10,12 who concurs with *Knesses Yechezkel*.

85. *Tevilah* can easily be delayed one day (*Chavos Daas* §13[b], *Sidrei Taharah* §14 and *Sheilas Yaavetz* 2:10). In addition, the leniency of one embarking on a journey is based on the fact that cohabitation before a journey is a requirement (*chovah*). However, cohabitation on a *tevilah* night may be only a *mitzvah* rather than an obligation and therefore not sufficient reason to disregard the *onas havest* (*Noda B'Yehudah*, Y.D. 2:117). *Chochmas Adam* 108:7, *Lechem Vesimlah* 184:29[l] and *Pardes Rimonim* 184:27[sc] follow the strict view. *Pleisi* 187, end of §10, rules that one cannot be lenient even regarding a *vest she'aino kavuah*. Responsa *Givas Shaul* §62 (cited in *Pischei Teshuvah* §22) notes that the rationale of *Knesses Yechezkel's* view to permit *tevilah* on the *onas havest* is that it is a *mitzvah* to be *tovel* in the proper time (טבילה בזמנה מצוה). Thus, explains *Givas Shaul*, one may think that we reject *Knesses Yechezkel's* view only because we assume that this *tevilah* is after a *kesem* that she found in middle of her cycle. Since a *kesem* mandates a *tevilah* only by Rabbinic law, the *mitzvah* of *tevilah* in this case is a minor one. However, if she had a mid-cycle flow, which renders her a *niddah* and requires *tevilah* by Torah law, one may think that the *mitzvah* of *tevilah* would override the *vest*. Nevertheless, *Givas Shaul* maintains, she must abstain the night of the *onas havest*. The reason we reject *Knesses Yechezkel's* view is for the reasons stated by *Chavos Daas* and *Noda B'Yehudah*.

86. Responsa *Even Shoham* §14 (cited in *Pischei Teshuvah* §22) permits the *tevilah* for the purpose of other intimate contact (*chibuk v'nishuk*). However, *Aruch HaShulchan* §43 reject this view. See also responsa *Mahari Steif* §182.

87. *Tiferes Tzvi* 189:15, *Kitzur Shulchan Aruch* 155:2 and *Malbushei Taharah* 184:12 are lenient in this case as is *Shiurei Sheivet HaLeivi* 184:10[2]. In his notes on *Taz* 184:2, *Shiurei Sheivet HaLeivi* stipulates

3. A *kallah* whose wedding night coincides with the *onas havest:*
Poskim do not permit even a *chasan* and *kallah* to cohabit on their wedding night if it coincides with the *onas havest.*[88]

4. A *tevilah* that coincides with the husband's departure on the *onas havest:*
Poskim do not permit actual cohabitation even if the *onas havest* coincides with <u>both</u> a *tevilah* night and the husband's departure. Although in this case there are two independent leniencies, *Poskim* do not permit cohabitation.[89]

5. Additional considerations:
In any of the abovementioned situations that cohabitation is permitted on the *onas havest*, one should do a *bedikah* beforehand.[90] Similarly, is any situation where cohabitation is permitted on the *Or Zarua's onah*, a *bedikah* should be done first.[91] In addition, in any of these cases if the woman feels any of those sensations associated with the beginning of her menstruation she must certainly abstain.[92]

II. The problematic days

It is very common that a woman has no specific day on which she menstruates. The menstruations may begin at some point during a span of several days without any set pattern. There is a difference of opinion

---

that if she feels any sensations that usually precede menstruation they must abstain. We noted above note 80 that *Igros Moshe* maintains that one should preferably abstain even in a case of a journey. He would certainly rule so in the case of a *tevilah* night. It would seem that in a case of a *vest she'aino kavuah* one may be lenient regarding the *Or Zarua's onah* that coincides with a *tevilah* night.

88. *Noda B'Yehudah* ibid. He explains that the consummation of the marriage, the *biyas mitzvah*, is a *mitzvah* whenever it is done, not necessarily the first night. Although *Sefer HaMiknah, Kiddushin, Kuntres Acharon, Hilchos Kiddushin*, 61:1, raises the possibility that a *chupah* night may be analogous to the night of departure, *Pardes Rimonim* 184:27[sc] seems to reject his view. *Shiurei Sheivet HaLeivi* 184:10[2] is lenient regarding the *Or Zarua's onah.*

89. *Chasam Sofer, Y.D.* 170.

90. *Tiferes LeMoshe* 184:10.

91. *Shaarei Tohar* 3:5.

92. *Pardes Rimonim* on *Taz* §14. *Shiurei Sheivet HaLeivi* 184:10[2] explains that this applies even to those cases where these sensations would not constitute a *vest haguf*, e.g., if they are combined with a specific day (*vest hamurkav*). Nevertheless, since, in this situation, she wishes to cohabit on the *onas havest* we are concerned about any sign that the menstruation is imminent. However, if the menstruation usually begins several days after the sensations begin, she needs to abstain only twenty-four hours before the usual arrival of the menstruation. These concepts are explained in Chapter Eighteen.

among *Poskim* about how to deal with this common situation.[93] On one hand the woman has no *vest kavuah*, thus, one could argue that she need to abstain only on the day of her last menstruation following all the normal rules of *vestos*. On the other hand, since her periods usually fall within a specific group of days, it is difficult to completely ignore the possibility that menstruation may begin at any time.

93. This discussion is based upon *Rema* 184:2, which is, in turn, based upon *Hagahos Maimonis* (*Issurei Biah* 8:1). *Rema* rules that a woman who "changes her *vest* by menstruating two or three days earlier or later must abstain two or three days before or after her *vest* day." It is unclear what this means. *Shach* 189:39 interprets *Rema* in a manner irrelevant to our discussion. Thus, according to *Shach* (and *Biur HaGra* 184:6 and *Graz* 189:53 who follow *Shach's* interpretation) there is no requirement for a woman to abstain on any day besides her current *vest* day. Later *Poskim* present two other interpretations of *Rema* which are the basis for the *halachah* currently under discussion. *Noda B'Yehudah, Y.D.* 1:46 s.v. ובזה נלע"ד, contends that a woman who always menstruates within a span of several days must consider all those suspect days as *vest* days and abstain the entire period. For example, a woman never menstruates before the twenty-sixth interval but menstruates between day twenty-six and twenty-nine without a set pattern. This woman must abstain from day twenty-six through day twenty-nine. *Noda B'Yehudah* s.v. ומעתה explains that this is the flip side of the so called "*Terumas HaDeshen's vest*" cited in 186:3. *Terumas HaDeshen* contends that a woman who never menstruates before fourteen day pass is considered a woman with a *vest kavuah* not to menstruate before fourteen days pass. We referred to this *vest* previously as a "negative *vest*" (see Chapter Fourteen, Section I,D,2,d). *Noda B'Yehudah* argues that if the *vest* is valid for the negative it is also valid for the positive (and especially so since the positive is a *chumra*). Accordingly, she must abstain during all the days of this *vest kavuah*. A similar position is found in *Shiltei Giborim* (*Rif, Hilchos Niddah* 2a) who discusses the issue without reaching a definite conclusion. *Pleisi* 184:5 interprets *Rema* in a manner similar to *Noda B'Yehudah*. *Noda B'Yehudah* sets no limit to the amount of days that a woman must abstain. *Chavos Daas* 184:4[b] argues that the seven days cited in *Noda B'Yehudah* are arbitrary, since the same logic applies to a woman with a twenty-day span. *Chavos Daas* considers this completely illogical. He argues that the comparison to *Terumas HaDeshen's* case is flawed. The woman may have a negative *vest* for the fourteen days since she has a definite nature not to menstruate during those fourteen days. This is as effective as any *vest kavuah*. However, she has no positive *vest* afterwards since there is no day that can be singled out as a *vest* day. *Chavos Daas*, therefore, offers another interpretation of *Rema* based upon *Raavad, Baalei HaNefesh* p. 38 in Kapach ed. (However, it seems difficult to base *Rema* on this *Raavad* since *Raavad* uses this approach as a basis for his view, cited in *Tur* 184, that one must abstain during all the days of the duration of the previous *vest*, see Chapter Thirteen, Section II,B. However, this view is not accepted in *halachah*, thus it is difficult to assume it to be the basis for *Rema*.) *Chavos Daas* explains that since this woman's menstruations occur within a span of a few days, there is reason to suspect that all the days became *vestos kavuos*. For example, the woman may have menstruated on the third of months A, B and C, then menstruated on the second and third of months D, E and F, and on the first, second and third of months G, H and I. If this occurred, she has three independent *vestos*, for the first, second and third of each month (in this case the earlier menstruations do not uproot the later *vestos hachodesh* as explained in Chapter Seventeen, Section III,B). *Chavos Daas* contends that we must suspect that may have occurred. She is, therefore, required to abstain all three days. *Sidrei Taharah* also explains *Rema* based on *Raavad*, but explains his view in a different manner. In his opinion, since the beginning of her menstruations vary within a span of a few days, we suspect that what seems to have been the beginning of the menstruation may have actually

1. There is an opinion that a woman must treat all those days as *yom havest* and abstain on all those days.[94] There is a difference among these *Poskim* as to the maximum limit of days to which we extend this prohibition. Some would apply the prohibition even if her menstruations vary within a span of seven days. Others apply it only if the span is four days or less and some apply it only to a span of three days or less.[95]

2. Other *Poskim* are more lenient and do not require that one abstain except for the *vest* of the last menstruation.[96] The following points should be noted:

    a. If the span of questionable days is more than three days, one may be lenient and abstain only on the normal *vest* day.

    b. If the span is three days or less, some *Poskim* require that one abstain for the duration of the three days. This

---

been premenstrual bleeding, not the actual beginning of the menstruation. Thus, since we do not know which day is the actual beginning of the *vest*, she should abstain all the days in question.

94. *Noda B'Yehudah Y.D.* 1:46, *Chavos Daas* 184:4[b], *Sidrei Taharah* 184:4, *Chochmas Adam* 108:6 (who was a disciple of *Noda B'Yehudah*) and *Aruch HaShulchan* 184:25.

95. *Noda B'Yehudah* sets no limit on the span of days. He discusses a case where the woman must abstain for seven days. *Shiltei Giborim* discusses a span of five days. A position similar to that of *Noda B'Yehudah* is found in *Leket Yosher* (by R' Yosef ben Moshe, a disciple of *Terumas HaDeshen*), *Y.D.* p.18. He rules that the maximum span of days is seven. If her menstruations vary over a period of more than seven days, the days cannot be considered a *vest*. The logic of this position seems to be that there must be some limit to the amount of days which one could consider a *vest*. Every woman has a period of days in which she will not menstruate. If we consider all the other days as *vest* days, a woman could theoretically be required to abstain most of the month. This is impossible. There must be some point at which we consider her to have no *vest* since the span of possible days is too great. Logically, it should be seven days, since, according to Torah law, *niddus* lasts seven days (see *Shiurei Sheivet HaLeivi* 184:2[9]. If one were to interpret *Rema's* words "a woman who menstruates two or three days earlier or later" as one case, i.e. the same woman menstruates either before or after, then *Rema* is alluding to a seven-day span. *Shaarei Tohar* 3:7 sets the limit at four days. He interprets *Rema* in an "either — or" manner, she menstruates either within three days before or three days after. *Shaarei Tohar*, nevertheless, notes that a punctilious individual should abstain for up to a seven-day span. He explains that *Noda B'Yehudah* interpreted *Rema* in an "and," not an "either — or" manner. He also notes that we cannot assume a variance of more than three days from the base day. *Be'er Moshe* 4:68, citing R' Yonasan Steif, rules that one is not required to abstain if the span is more than three days.

96. *Shach* 189:39, *Biur HaGra* 184:6 and *Graz* 189:53. *Sugah Bashoshanim* 2:15 rules that although one should follow the stricter view, one who wishes to follow the lenient view may do so. An argument posed in support of the lenient opinion is the fact that *Shulchan Aruch* 189:13 rules that if a woman always menstruates on the same monthly date, at times during the daytime and at times

could cause undue hardship and strain for many couples. One should consult a *Rav*.[97]

c. Some *Poskim* contend that one should abstain all the questionable days only in a case where she menstruated three times on each of the days in question. For example, if her menstruations alternate between day twenty-six and day twenty-seven, and she menstruated in the course of six months, three times on each of those days. Or if her menstruations alternate between day twenty-six, twenty-seven and twenty-eight, and she menstruated in the course of the past nine months, three times on each of those days.[98]

d. Some *Poskim* rule that a woman who alternates her periods between day and night (without a set pattern) must abstain on both day and night of her *yom havest* since they are both considered one *onah*.[99]

e. *Poskim* note that even one who follows the stricter view may be lenient regarding the following applications:

> i. Even one who normally keeps the *Or Zarua vest* is required to do so only on the normal *vest* day. Thus, if the last menstruation started during the day she should abstain on the night and day corresponding to the last menstruation but only on the day of the other two days.[100]

---

during the night, without establishing any pattern, she needs to abstain only on the last *onas havest*. If *Noda B'Yehudah* and *Chavos Daas* were correct in their interpretation of *Rema*, *Rema* should have noted that the woman must abstain on both day and night.

97. See responsa *Minchas Yitzchak* 5:135, who notes that one should certainly not impose the stricter view on newlyweds. He is generally lenient as well in regard to advising others although he seems to deem it proper for one to be strict with oneself.

98. *Shiurei Sheivet HaLeivi* 184:2[9] and responsa *Eimek HaTeshuvah* 1:125. *Shiurei Sheivet HaLeivi* is somewhat hesitant regarding this leniency.

99. *Taharas Yisrael* 184:25,27 and *Igros Moshe*, Y.D. 3:48. Someone who abstains on the *Or Zarua's onah* is essentially not affected by this opinion since they abstain the night before a day *onah* and would normally not cohabit on the day of a night *onah* (see *Orach Chaim* 240:11).

100. *Chochmas Adam* 108:6 and *Sugah Bashoshanim* 2:15. *Shaarei Tohar* 3:7 disagrees. Although *Chavos Daas* 184:8[c] states clearly that one must observe the *Or Zarua vest* even in this case, we who merely follow *Chavos Daas* as a *chumra* (at best) need not follow the additional *chumra* of the *Or Zarua vest*.

ii. If a *tevilah* night occurs on one of the additional days, one need not delay the *tevilah*.[101]

iii. A woman in the twenty-four months following childbirth may rely on the lenient opinions.[102]

iv. If the first days of the span were passed in the last three months without menstruation, it is no longer included in the span of questionable days.[103] This has both a lenient and a strict application (see footnote).[104]

3. *Poskim* maintain that even one who follows the lenient view should perform a *bedikah* before and after cohabiting on the questionable days.[105]

---

101. Ibid. *Shaarei Tohar* 3:7 disagrees in this case as well. He rules that if the span is limited to four days, one cannot be lenient even in the case of a *tevilah* night.

102. Responsa *Minchas Yitzchak* 3:80. It seems from *Minchas Yitzchak* that although many authorities do not rely upon the leniency of the twenty-four-month post-partum period today (see Chapter Twenty, Section C), in this case the leniency may be used as additional support for the lenient view cited above. *Minchas Yitzchak* in 10:87 is lenient regarding a pregnant woman as well.

103. *Shaarei Tohar* 3:10. He also maintains that if she never established a *vest kavuah* on the first day (or days), the day can be uprooted by passing it only once without menstruating. Thus, if she varies her periods from twenty-six to twenty-eight-day intervals and menstruated on day twenty-seven, she is not required to abstain the following month on day twenty-six. Responsa *Minchas Yitzchak* 3:80 disagrees with this last point. He requires that she pass day twenty-six three times, even if it never became a *vest kavuah*. One should note that these *halachos* apply only to the first day (or days) of the span. The middle days cannot be uprooted without the first since the flow of the first day will usually continue into the others.

104. If the periods usually fluctuate within a span of three days, e.g., day twenty-five, twenty-six and twenty-seven, but in the last three cycles she passed day twenty-five without menstruating, her span is narrowed to two days, day twenty-six and twenty-seven. If her periods usually fluctuate within a span of four days, e.g., twenty-four, twenty-five, twenty-six and twenty-seven, but she passed twenty-four three times without menstruating, her span is narrowed to three days. In the process, she becomes subject to the stricter ruling by some *Poskim* that she is required to abstain all three days. Had the span remained a span of four days, she would be required to abstain only on the last *yom havest*, according to their opinion.

105. *Pleisi* 186:3, *Igros Moshe*, Y.D. 2:67, and *Minchas Yitzchak* 3:80, 5:135. This is not an actual *halachic* requirement since we follow the lenient opinions cited in *Shulchan Aruch* 186, see Chapter Fourteen, Section I,D. See *Poseiach Shaar* 24:10, based on *Chavos Daas* 186:1, who notes that an actual *bedikah* is not required. It is sufficient to merely perform a *kinuach*, i.e., wiping the external area. This should not be done while lying on one's back. However, It may be that even those *Poskim* who rule that a woman without a *vest* needs no *bedikos* at the time of cohabitation concede that in this case a *bedikah* is required. This view is noted in *Haflaah* in gloss to 184:2. This seems to be the opinion of responsa *Maharil* (*HaChadoshos* §93:5, *Machon Yerushalayim* edition) as well. *Igros Moshe*

One should discuss the question with a Rav and seek his guidance[106] as to which opinion to follow.[107]

III. When the *onas havest* passes

When the *onas havest* has passed, one is no longer required to abstain. We noted above that if one did not do the required *bedikah* for a *vest kavuah,* one must abstain until the *bedikah* is done. We noted as well that the husband is required to ask his wife whether or not she is *tehorah* and whether she did a *bedikah.* Once these matters are settled, they are not required to abstain any longer. Nevertheless, there is an opinion that the woman should do a *bedikah* before and after cohabitation.[108] She must also be especially conscious of any sensations normally associated with her menstruation.[109]

IV. One who loses her calendar

If a woman loses her calendar and/or forgets the date of her last menstruation she cannot calculate the day of her expected *vest.* We are then faced with a difficult problem. Should we require that she abstain during all the days that may be her *vest* day or should we permit cohabitation

---

also notes that this *bedikah* requirement is basic *halachah,* not a mere *chumra.* Thus, *Poseiach Shaar's* contention is debatable since *Chavos Daas'* acceptance of a *kinuach* in place of a *bedikah* is perhaps not applicable in this case. Nevertheless, a woman who is tense about every dot, hue and shade on a *bedikah* cloth should perhaps be advised to perform a *kinuach* instead or not perform any *bedikah,* only checking her undergarment.

106. Since there is no clear consensus on the matter, it is difficult to guide the reader more specifically than to advise consultation with their Rav. A Rav who knows the couple can judge whether they should follow the stricter or more lenient opinions. It seems that there is a strong basis to be lenient when necessary providing that *bedikos* are performed. A Rav should always ask to see the *vestos* calendar and study it carefully to find some pattern in the periods (*Minchas Yitzchak* 5:135[4]).

107. Among later authorities, *Chazon Ish, Y.D.* 85:23, *Igros Moshe, Y.D.* 2:67, and *Minchas Yitzchak* 5:135 (although in an earlier responsa 3:80, he is less lenient) follow the lenient opinion of *Shach* and require that a woman abstain only during the actual *vest* days. *Igros Moshe* requires that one performs a *bedikah* before cohabiting on these questionable days. *Shiurei Sheivet HaLeivi* 184:2[9] rules that if the span of days is three or less, one should follow the stricter opinions. Otherwise, one may follow the lenient view. He contends that despite *Chazon Ish's* lenient written position, he advised privately that one follow the stricter view.

108. *Igros Moshe, Y.D.* 3:50.

109. See *Shiurei Sheivet HaLeivi* 184:6[3].

during all the days?[110] Many authorities rule that one need not keep any *vest* even if she had a *vest kavuah*.[111] Other authorities rule that she must abstain on all those days in which there is a doubt.[112] One should discuss the problem with their Rav. There are many aspects and variations of this question.

---

110. There are several approaches to solve this problem. We can use the concept of *bitul*. Thus the *vest* day (which is essentially *assur*) is *batel* (nullified) in the majority of days (which are *mutar*)). This approach is used by *Darchei Teshuvah* 189:2. If this approach is used then if only two days are in question she must abstain on both, see below. Another approach uses the concept of *safek deRabbanan lekula* — one may be lenient regarding doubt pertaining to Rabbinic ordinances. This is the approach of *Chavos Daas* 184:4[b] and *Mahari Assad Y.D.* 190. *Chasam Sofer* rejects this view because he maintains that regarding abstaining, *vestos* are *deOraisa*. An additional problem with this approach is that we cannot use *safek deRabbanan lekula* if by doing so we eliminate the *halachah* entirely (see *Ran* on *Rif, Pesachim* 23a). However, if there is a logical reason to attribute the period to a particular day, e.g., because that day is certainly part of the vest, one can use the concept of תולין הקלקלה במקולקל (one attributes a deficiency to that which is known to be deficient). See *Taz* 184:7. This is the approach of *Levanon Nota* cited below. *Darchei Teshuvah* 189:2 contends that perhaps if one sets aside one day for the *vest*, one can be lenient regarding all the other days. He compares this to the *halachah* regarding one who forgets which day is *Shabbos, Orach Chaim* 344.

111. *Chavos Daas* and responsa *Mahari Assad* as cited in the previous footnote. *Mahari Assad* rules that she must abstain only on the thirtieth day from her last period. This assumes that she remembers the last period day. If she does not even remember the last period day, one assumes that according to *Mahari Assad* she is not required to abstain on any day. It is odd that *Mahari Assad* notes responsa *Chasam Sofer* which contradicts his view. *Maharsham* in *Daas Torah* 184:2 assumes that *Mahari Assad* rejected *Chasam Sofer's* stricter view. See *Sheivet HaLeivi* cited above. *Darchei Teshuvah* 184:25 cites an interesting view of *Levanon Nota* who maintains that if the span of questionable days is seven or less she should abstain only on the last day since that day was certainly within the *niddus* days of the previous menstruations. This is similar to the *halachah* stated in 184:4 regarding a woman who is uncertain whether her menstruation started before or after sunrise. If the span of the doubt is more than seven days, she is required to abstain all the days since there is no day that was certainly included in her *niddus* days. *Sugah Bashoshanim* 2:(26) explores this approach but rejects its lenient application. *Darchei Teshuvah* 189:2 seems to lean toward the lenient position.

112. See *Chasam Sofer, Y.D.* 166, regarding a woman who usually menstruates after intervals of 26, 27 or 28 and does not remember if any were established as a *vest kavuah* or which were *ne'ekar*. *Chasam Sofer* rules that even if the days were *vestos she'aino kavuah*, she must treat all the days as *yom havest*. A similar view is held by *Sugah Bashoshanim* 2:10. *Chasam Sofer's* view is in accord with oft-stated position (see note 4) that *vestos* are of Biblical origin regarding the obligation to abstain on the day of the *vest*.

There are several reasons why we may be permitted to follow the more lenient views in this case: a) Responsa *Eimek HaTeshuvah* 1:124 notes that most *Rishonim* disagree with *Chasam Sofer* (one should note that *Eimek HaTeshuvah* is nevertheless hesitant to dismiss *Chasam Sofer's* view). b) *Sheivet HaLeivi* 5:103[5] speculates that perhaps *Chasam Sofer* was strict only in the case of a woman who usually menstruates within a span of several days and forgot the exact date of her last menstruation. However, in a case where she has no recollection of when her period began, he may concede that she is not required to abstain. In addition, *Sheivet HaLeivi* 184:2[2] and *Kineh Bosem*

1. A woman who remembers the date of her last menstruation but forgot the normal interval of the *vest haflagah* or the normal day of the *vest hachodesh*.

> a. If she had no *vest kavuah*, perhaps she is required to abstain only on the *onah beinonis* from this last period.[113]

> b. If she has a *vest hachodesh kavuah*, but cannot remember the usual day of the month, perhaps she may assume that the last menstruation was on her regular monthly date and abstain only on the same date of the following month.[114]

> c. If she has a *vest haflagah kavuah*, but cannot remember the usual interval, if she usually experiences symptoms before menstruating, perhaps she may rely on the lenient opinions and need not abstain until *onah beinonis* or until she feels those symptoms.[115]

2. If she forgot the date of her last menstruation, she has no day from which to calculate her *vest* or even her *onah beinonis*.

> a. If she had a *vest kavuah* but usually menstruates during the daytime, perhaps she need not abstain during the nights of the questionable days.[116]

---

to 184:4 maintain that *Chasam Sofer* partially based his view on *Raavad*, however, according to the Kapach edition of *Baalei HaNefesh*, it is clear that *Raavad* held that *vestos* are *deRabbanan*. c) *Darchei Teshuvah* 189:2 notes that since most women feel physical sensations before the onset of their period (as noted by *Mahari Assad*), perhaps even *Chasam Sofer* would concede that she need not abstain prior to the onset of those sensations. d) Most women today only have a *vest she'aino kavuah*. Thus, all *Poskim* agree that the *vest* is only *deRabbanan*, see *Yad Yosef* noted below. Indeed, *Chasam Sofer* himself (*Y.D.* 179) differentiates between a *vest kavuah* and a *vest she'aino kavuah*.

113. According to *Chavos Daas* one can certainly be lenient regarding the other days. As noted above, perhaps even *Chasam Sofer* would concede regarding a *vest she'aino kavuah* (*Yad Yosef* cited below). In addition, since she abstains on the *onah beinonis* day, she has set aside one day and may be lenient on the rest, as noted in *Darchei Teshuvah* ibid.

114. See responsa *Har Tzvi*, *Y.D.* 150, who apparently is referring to a *vest hachodesh*.

115. I.e., *Chavos Daas*, *Mahari Assad* and *Darchei Teshuvah*.

116. *Yad Yosef* (cited below). If the last three menstruations were by day, *Chasam Sofer* and *Sugah Bashoshanim* are both lenient and permit cohabitation on the preceding nights. Although *Shach* 184:7 rules that one abstain on the *onah* preceding the *onas havest*, in this case one may be lenient. *Sugah Bashoshanim* rules that regarding the last day of the questionable days, one must abstain on the night before as well.

b. If she had a *vest kavuah* and usually menstruates at night but usually feels bodily symptoms before menstruation, some contemporary authorities rule that if she feels no symptoms she may cohabit even at night.[117] It would be proper to abstain on the one night which seems most likely to be the *yom havest*.[118]

c. If she does not feel any physical sensations before her period, it may be sufficient to abstain only on the last of the days, provided that there are three or more days in question.[119]

d. If she does not feel any physical sensations before her period and there are only two *onos* in question, e.g., her *vest* is either Sunday or Monday night, perhaps she should abstain both nights.[120]

3. If she is within the twenty-four post-partum months, perhaps she is not required to abstain during the days in question.[121]

4. If she had no *vest kavuah* perhaps she need not abstain during the questionable days.[122] It may be proper to abstain on a day which seems likely to be the *yom havest*.[123]

---

117. In this case we have only *Chavos Daas* to rely upon. Nevertheless *Yad Yosef*, Y.D. 66, cited in *Pische Zuta*, *Tinyana* 189:1, would be lenient in this case. See also *Be'er Moshe* 2:55.

118. This is in accordance with the view of *Darchei Teshuvah* 189:2 comparing this case to that of one who forgets which day is *Shabbos*.

119. *Yad Yosef*, see also *Kineh Bosem*, *Birurei HaShitos* 184:3.

120. *Kineh Bosem* ibid. He contends that in this case we cannot use the *bitul* concept since this is *bitul chad bitrei* — a "mixture" of two equals, i.e., one *onah* that is prohibited and one *onah* that is permitted. However, according to *Levanon Nota* (cited above note 110) she could abstain on the second day only since that day is certainly part of her *vest*. As noted, according to *Chavos Daas* she is not required to abstain at all.

121. *Chazon Ish*, Y.D. 87:3. He explains that a) it is considered a *vest she'aino kavuah* and b) according to *Rashba* a nursing woman is not required to keep any *vest*. One assumes that *Chazon Ish* was aware of the fact that today women menstruate before the end of the twenty-four-month period.

122. *Yad Yosef* ibid. Even *Chasam Sofer* who maintains that *vestos* are *deOraisa* concedes (Y.D. 179) that a *vest she'aino kavuah* is *deRabbanan*.

123. As in 118 above.

5. In any case where cohabitation is permitted during the questionable days, she should perform a *bedikah* beforehand.[124]

This outline is presented as a general guide. One should discuss the individual situation with a Rav. The difficulties presented should serve as a reminder of the importance to immediately register on the calendar any day on which a woman menstruates.[125]

---

124. *Mahari Assad* ibid.

125. *Eimek HaTeshuvah* ibid. maintains that if a woman is negligent in recording her period, perhaps she should be penalized.

BOOK FIVE

ענייני רפואה
Gynecological Issues

Chapter Twenty-three — The Principles Involved
Chapter Twenty-four — Gynecological Procedures

Gynecological examinations: the Issues Involved

☐ A description of anatomical terms.

☐ *Teliyah b'makah* — attributing bleeding to an injury.

☐ Relying on a physician in matters of *halachah*.

☐ *Pesichas hakever* — the opening of the uterus.

☐ General guidelines regarding gynecological examinations.

☐ Scheduling gynecological procedures.

HALACHIC OVERVIEW

This is a difficult chapter and must be studied carefully. We cannot, therefore, present an overview in the manner that was done in the earlier chapters. There are, however, several most important points which one should be aware of.

A woman undergoing a gynecological examination or a procedure may be rendered a *niddah* even if no blood appears. Conversely, she may find blood and nevertheless not become a *niddah*. This determination must be made by a Rav. One may never rely solely upon the physician's claim that the blood is not uterine in origin. In all cases, one must discuss the matter with a Rav. All information regarding the procedure must be forwarded to the Rav. The Rav may wish to discuss the matter with the physician who will provide him with more detailed information. The relationship between a Rav and a physician is that of two professionals with mutual respect for one another.

There are several advantages in using an observant Jew as one's gynecologist. Statements made by a Torah-observant physician are *halachically* more readily acceptable. In addition, a Torah observant physician will be more accessible to and cooperative with a Rav who wishes to discuss the procedures performed on a patient. Also, an observant physician can more easily empathize with the problems that the *niddus* status places upon a Torah observant couple.

One should never tell a physician "don't tell me if you see blood." This is a willful disregarding of an established fact. However, one is not required to ask the physician whether or not he saw blood or do a *bedikah* after the procedure.

A woman undergoing an examination or procedure should establish the name of the procedure. If bleeding is present, she should inquire as to its source and whether or not the source is visible to the physician. If there is no bleeding at the time of the examination, she should ask whether bleeding is to be expected and from what source. All this information should be forwarded to the Rav.

A woman who must undergo a gynecological procedure should consult a Rav as to the proper time during her monthly cycle to schedule the procedure.

Introduction

This chapter will discuss the *halachic* issues relevant when a woman undergoes a gynecological examination or procedure. We will begin with a brief review of the anatomy of the female reproductive organs, followed by a halachic overview of the issues involved. The following chapter will briefly outline common gynecological procedures. The information presented in this chapter should greatly enhance the lay person's understanding of the *halachic* ramifications of these procedures and the type of information that must be provided to the Rav. It should be clear that this chapter does not and cannot serve as a basis for a lay person to make his own *halachic* determinations. These complex issues must <u>always</u> be discussed with a Rav.

I. Anatomical terms

It is important to identify the various organs involved in our discussions by their biological and Hebrew names (see also the introduction to Chapter One).

A. The vulva

This refers to the external area: the mons veneris, labia majora (lips, two large folds of adipose tissue), labia minora (two reddish folds of skin), clitoris (a cylinder-shaped body at the top of the labia minora). The area between the labia minora and the vaginal opening is called the vestibule.[1] The vaginal opening is guarded by the hymenal ring (a skinlike membrane which covers the vaginal opening). Until the hymen is broken, menstrual blood flows through a small opening in the hymen. The urethra (through which the urine flows) opens into the upper portion of the vestibule and the vagina (through which menstrual blood flows) opens to the lower portion. Thus, both urine and menstrual blood flow out by way of the vestibule.

B. The vagina

The vagina is an elastic flattened tube extending from the vaginal opening to the cervix. It averages eight centimeters in length, although its size varies with age, ovarian function and parity. In *halachic* literature, the vagina is called the *"beis hachitzon"* (the external chamber) or the *"prozdor"* (the vestibule — not to be confused with the term "vestibule" used in medical literature as described above).[2]

---

1. It seems from *Noda B'Yehudah E.H.* 2:23, that this is the *"prozdor hachitzon"* ("outer vestibule") referred to in *Chullin* 68a. See *Tosfos* s.v. אדם and *Tosfos Niddah* 42b s.v. שהוציא for a slightly different interpretation of the outside *prozdor*. This should not be confused with the term *"prozdor"* used in *halachic* literature which refers to the vagina or cervix.

2. *Noda B'Yehudah* (ibid.) notes that the Torah refers to this area as *"makor"*, even though the actual

C. The uterus

The uterus is a pear shaped muscular organ which consists of two parts: 1) the narrow neck of the uterus called the cervix and 2) the uterine body or corpus.

> 1. The cervix: the *"tzavar harechem,"* the "neck" of the uterus which projects into the upper end of the vagina. It is usually 2 to 3 cm in length. The cervix has two ostia (plural of os — openings): The external os opens into the vagina and the internal os opens into the uterus. The internal os of a woman who has not given birth usually is open to a width of 1mm, while that of a woman who has given birth is open up to 3mm. The area between the two ostia, which measures two to three centimeters in length, is called the endocervical canal.
>
> 2. The *uterine corpus* the uterine body, referred to by *Chazal* as the *"makor"* or the *"kever,"* which is approximately six centimeters long and lined with a tissue called the endometrium. The endometrial lining may vary from two to ten millimeters in thickness, depending upon the stage of the menstrual cycle.

D. The Fallopian tubes

Above either side and leading into the uterus are two tubes called the Fallopian tubes. The egg (ovum), released from the ovaries, travels down the Fallopian tubes and, if fertilized, is implanted into the uterine endometrium where it develops as an embryo. If fertilization does not take place, and no implantation occurs, the ovum is expelled and the uterus sheds its lining. Menstruation is the result of this shedding. Menstrual blood flows through the cervix and leaves the body by way of the vagina. Menstruation typically results in a blood loss of one to three ounces and generally lasts four to five days.

There is much controversy in *halachic* literature regarding the status of the cervix. Is it *halachically* considered part of the uterus proper or not? Does the *makor* (uterus) begin at the external os (the external entrance to the cervix), the internal os (the entrance from the cervix to the uterus proper) or at some other point?[3] This question has several *halachic* ramifi-

---

makor is the uterus.

3. Much of the difficulty in determining the *halachic* status of the various anatomical sites stems from our inability to properly identify sites mentioned in Talmudic literature. The Mishnah (*Niddah*

cations: a) *Chazal*[4] state that a woman becomes a *niddah* even while the blood is still in her body once the flow has reached a certain anatomical point.[5] Does she become a *niddah* when the flow reaches the internal os, the external os or some other anatomical location? b) *Halachah* rules that if the *kever* (the *makor* — uterus) opens, the woman becomes a *niddah* because we assume that there was a blood flow. This is called *"pesichas hakever"* (the opening of the uterus). Does this refer to an opening of the external or internal os?

It should be noted that the anatomic point at which blood is *halachically* considered to have left the uterus, thus rendering the woman a *niddah* does not necessarily coincide with the rule of *pesichas hakever*.[6]

Another important issue is whether cervical bleeding is considered *dam niddah*. It is commonly accepted that even if the external os is the *halachic* beginning of the *makor*, cervical bleeding does not render a woman a *niddah*. The cervix has no endometrium and does not shed its lining in the

---

17b) describes the inner organs in terms unfamiliar to present-day anatomical knowledge. The Mishnah (*Niddah* 40a) rules that a woman becomes a *niddah* when menstrual blood passes into the *beis hachitzon*. The Talmud uses the terms *cheder, prozdor* and *beis hachitzon*, which are difficult for us to identify. Rambam (*Hil. Issurei Biah* 5:2-5) provides us with a detailed description of the inner organs based upon the above-mentioned Talmudic texts. However, commentators differ in their understanding of his words. *Cheder* certainly includes the uterus, but that may include the cervix as well. If this is the case, the vagina must be the *prozdor* and the *beis hachitzon* must be more externally located in the area medically known as the "vestibule." Alternatively, *"cheder"* may be the uterus alone, in which case the cervix is the *prozdor* and the vagina is the *beis hachitzon*. It is indeed possible that neither of these assumptions is correct; the *beis hachitzon* may start at some other point.

4. *Niddah* 40a.

5. I.e., when it passes through *bein hashinayim*.

6. *Niddus* begins when menstrual blood passes the *bein hashinayim*. *Pesichas hakever* (which also results in *niddus*) is defined as an opening of the *makor* (uterus). These two anatomical sites (i.e., the *bein hashinayim* and the opening of the *makor*) may not correspond, see opinion of *Noda B'Yehudah* and *Chasam Sofer* cited in note 7 below. Furthermore, even if these points do anatomically correspond (i.e., the point at which the blood must pass to render a woman a *niddah* and the opening of the *makor* are identical), it may be that *halachically* we distinguish between the two. This is due to the many uncertainties regarding *pesichas hamakor*: a) There is a basic disagreement among *Rishonim* whether or not the opening of the *makor* renders a woman a *niddah* b) there is a disagreement among *Acharonim* whether an externally induced opening is considered *pesichas hakever* (as noted below). Accordingly, perhaps, one may take a lenient view and follow the opinion of those *Poskim* who consider the internal os (rather than the external os) the *pesach hakever*. (The issue of *pesichas hakever* will be discussed more fully in Section II,C.) However, regarding the question of when a woman becomes a *niddah*, perhaps we follow the view that she becomes a *niddah* when the blood passes the external os. In conclusion: Even if we assume that a woman becomes a *niddah* only when the blood leaves the <u>external</u> os, we may nevertheless assume that only an opening of the <u>internal</u> os renders her a *niddah*.

manner of the uterus. Accordingly, any bleeding originating in the cervix is not menstrual bleeding and does not render a woman a *niddah*.[7]

See footnote 7 for a detailed analysis of the issues and opinions.[7]

---

7. The *Mishnah* (*Niddah* 40a) rules that a woman becomes a *niddah* when the menstrual blood reaches the *beis hachitzon*. The Talmud (*Niddah* 41b) explains that the *beis hachitzon* is external to the *bein hashinayim* (the *bein hashinayim* may be either the internal or external os, a point in between or some point in the vagina. The surface of the cervix and, to a lesser degree, the vagina have ridges which may fit the description of *shinayim* — teeth). An alternative description in the Talmud defines the internal border of the *beis hachitzon* as the spot where the male organ reaches at the time of cohabitation. The male organ certainly does not normally penetrate beyond the external os. This would seem to indicate that according to the second definition the internal os cannot be considered the *bein hashinayim*.

Another related question is the definition of the *prozdor*. We know that the point of demarcation at which a blood flow renders a woman a *niddah* is the *bein hashinayim*. This is where the *beis hachitzon* (which is located external to the *bein hashinayim*) ends. We do not know whether this is one of the two ostia or some other point. Even if we were to know the point at which the *beis hachitzon* begins, we would still be unable to identify the *prozdor* since we do not know if the terms *"beis hachitzon"* and *"prozdor"* are exclusive of one another. Perhaps they overlap. Thus, the *prozdor* itself may be considered part of the *beis hachitzon* or it may be a site closer to the *cheder* — the uterus.

Among the earliest *Poskim* who discuss these problems are the *S'ma* (R' Yehoshua Falk), responsa *Masos Binyamin* §49, R' Feivish of Cracow and *Bach*. R' Feivish (in responsa to *S'ma*, cited in responsa *Bach HaChadoshos* §34) contends that, according to *Rambam*, the uterus is the *cheder*, the cervix is the *prozdor* and the *bein hashinayim* is the internal os. Thus, the cervix itself is external to the *bein hashinayim*. Accordingly, when uterine blood enters the cervix, the woman is *temei'ah*. Also, an opening of the internal os is considered *pesichas hakever*.

R' Feivish explains that according to other *Rishonim*, the *bein hashinayim*, the point at which the *beis hachitzon* begins and at which a blood flow renders her a *niddah*, is the external os. Thus, the uterus and the cervix are one organ and both are considered *"cheder."* According to their opinion, the vagina is the *prozdor* and is also called the *beis hachitzon*. It seems, according to this view, that the external os is the *pesach hamakor*. R' Feivish contends, based upon testimony of midwives and well-reasoned arguments, that this latter opinion is more correct. He argues that acceptance of *Rambam's* opinion would necessitate two difficult presumptions: a) that the male organ penetrates into the cervix and b) that a *bedikah* should preferably be inserted into the cervix. Both of these are difficult to accept. R' Feivish, concluding, speculates that perhaps even *Rambam's* words lend themselves to interpretation similar to the other *Rishonim*.

Bach (ibid. responsa 35) disagrees. He contends that the internal os is certainly the boundary between the *rechem* and the *beis hachitzon*. The cervix, which is the *prozdor*, is part of the *beis hachitzon*. According to this opinion, the internal os is the *pesach hamakor*. This is also the view of *S'ma* cited in *Bach* §34 and in responsa *Masos Binyamin* §49.

Noda B'Yehudah, Y.D. 1:55, maintains that the *bein hashinayim* is the external os or some site nearby. Nevertheless, he contends that the *pesach hamakor* is the internal os. A similar position is taken by responsa *Masos Binyamin* §49. Thus, according to them, a woman becomes a *niddah* when the uterine blood flows past the *bein hashinayim* — the external os area, but *pesichas hakever* requires opening of the internal os.

It is interesting to note that *Noda B'Yehudah's* assumption that the *pesach hamakor* (the anatomical site which determines *pesichas hakever*) is different from the *bein hashinayim* (which determines the

II. The *halachic* issues involved

There are three *halachic* issues which must be resolved regarding gyne-cological examinations and procedures: a) the question of *teliyah b'makah* — whether or not any bleeding may be attributed to trauma (injury) to the organs involved; b) the issue of *ne'emanus* — trust, whether one may rely upon a physician's statement that the bleeding is a result of trauma, not uterine bleeding; c) the question of *pesichas hakever* — whether the examination or procedure resulted in opening of the *kever* (the *makor* — uterus) which may render a woman a *niddah* regardless of whether or not there has been visible bleeding.

---

beginning of *niddus*) is his proof that a sensation of a vaginal flow constitutes a *hargashah*. *Noda B'Yehudah* argues that since the word "בבשרה" teaches us that *tumas niddah* takes effect when the blood passes the *bein hashinayim* (see *Niddah* 40a) and the same word teaches us that a woman must have a *hargashah* בבשרה (*Niddah* 57b), both must be referring to the same site (the external os). Thus, *hargashah* cannot be at the *pesach hamakor* which is at a different site. Responsa *Masos Binyamin* 49 also appears to maintain that although the internal os is the *pesach hamakor,* the *bein hashinayim* is in the area of the external os.

Sidrei Taharah 194:26 also contends that the *bein hashinayim* is not the internal os itself. According to *Sidrei Taharah*, the *bein hashinayim* is some site between the external and internal ostia. Nevertheless, it seems from *Sidrei Taharah* that the *pesach hamakor* is the internal os.

Chasam Sofer, Y.D. 145,167 and 171, takes a position similar to that of R' Feivish of Cracow. He claims that according to *Rambam*, *bein hashinayim* is very close to the internal os, although he con-cedes that in the opinion of *Rashi* and *Tosfos*, the *bein hashinayim* is closer to the external os. He con-tends that medical knowledge supports *Rambam's* view. *Chazon Ish Y.D.* 92:28, questions *Chasam Sofer's* conclusions. He also deduces that R' Akiva Eiger did not consider the internal os the *bein hashinayim*. In either case, *Chasam Sofer* seems to assume that the internal os is the *pesach hamakor*. Like *Noda B'Yehudah*, *Chasam Sofer* considers the possibility that the word בבשרה may refer to one site regarding the *bein hashinayim* and another site regarding the rule of *hargashah*, although he dis-agrees with *Noda B'Yehudah* regarding the question of whether a vaginal flow is considered a *har-gashah*. See responsa *Chasam Sofer, Y.D.* 167.

Tiferes LeMoshe 188 proves that an externally induced opening is not considered *pesichas hakever* (as opposed to *Noda B'Yehudah*) from the fact that the penetration of the male organ is not consid-ered *pesichas hakever*. This indicates that *Tiferes LeMoshe* considers the external os the *pesach hamakor*. *Binas Adam* 13(23) uses a similar argument against *Noda B'Yehudah*. Apparently, he too considers the external os the *pesach hamakor*. Responsa *Beis Shlomo, Y.D.* §39, seems to hold that the internal os is the *pesach hamakor* as does responsa *Beis Yitzchak, Y.D.* 2:14.

In conclusion: According to *Masos Binyamin, Bach, S'ma, Noda B'Yehudah, Chasam Sofer, Beis Shlomo* and *Beis Yitzchak*, it seems that the internal os is the *pesach hamakor*. According to R' Feivish, *Tiferes LeMoshe* and *Binas Adam*, it is the external os. Among contemporary authorities, responsa *Har Tzvi Y.D.* 152, *Igros Moshe, Y.D.* 1:83, and responsa *Cheishev HaEifod* 2:7 contend that (at least regarding questions of *pesichas hakever*) the internal os is the *bein hashinayim* and is thus the beginning of the *makor*. R' S. Z. Auerbach, in a lengthy appendix to *Sefer Imrei Avraham* (by his brother R' A. D. Auerbach) section 4, interprets many of the above mentioned *Poskim* in a different manner. He con-tends that the external os is the *pesach hamakor*. *Shiurei Sheivet HaLeivi* 188:3[4] also follows this

A. Teliah b'makah — attributing bleeding to an injury

The status of a *niddah* is brought about only by menstrual bleeding. Other bleeding, even if it exits the body through the vagina, will not render a woman a *niddah*. Lacerations, ulcerations, inflammations (e.g., cervicitis or vaginitis) and cervical erosion are examples of such bleeding. Thus, if it can be established that vaginal bleeding is caused by an injury to the vulva, vagina or cervix, the woman is not a *niddah*. Indeed, even bleeding from the uterus, if caused by fibroids, polyps or an injury to the uterine wall, rather than by bleeding from the endometrium, does not render the woman a *niddah*.[8] However, it is very difficult to determine

stricter view. Thus, in their opinion, even an opening of the external os renders a woman a *niddah*. See also *Maadanei Yom Tov* on *Rosh, Niddah* 10:5 §8.

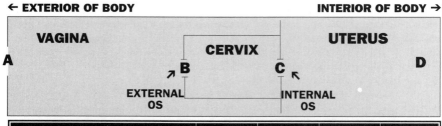

← **EXTERIOR OF BODY** | **INTERIOR OF BODY** →

		Cheder	Prozdor	Bein Hashinayim	Pesach Hamakor	Beis Hachitzon
R' Feivish	according to Rambam	C-D	B-C	C	C	A-B
	according to other Rishonim	B-D	A-B	B	B?	A-B
Bach		C-D	B-C		C	A-C
Noda B'Yehudah		C-D		B or nearby	C	A-near B
Sidrei Taharah		C-D	B-C	between B/C	C	A-B/C
Chasam Sofer		C-D	B-C	close to C	C	

8. *Shach* 187:17, *Toras HaShelamim* §15, responsa *Maharam Lublin* 110, cited in *Pischei Teshuvah* §22. See letter from *Chazon Ish*, published originally in the monthly *Hapardes* vol. 35 no. 6, and reprinted in his biography *P'er HaDor* vol. 4 page 131. *Chazon Ish* categorizes *dam makkah* (which is *tehorah*) as blood which flows from the uterus when it is lacerated in a manner that blood would flow from any other organ when it is lacerated. However, if the uterus is merely shaken or hit and some menstrual blood is loosened and emitted, she is *temei'ah*. See *Nishmas Avraham, Y.D.* 187, p. 81, citing R' S. Z. Auerbach, that even if the blood flows from the very same blood vessels that emit menstrual blood, if the cause is a wound, the woman is *tehorah*. A similar position is found in *Chazon Ish, Y.D.* 81, s.v. אבל מה.

whether blood flowing from the uterus is from polyps, from an injury to the organ wall or from bleeding from the endometrium. Therefore, for all practical purposes, any gynecological procedure resulting in uterine bleeding will render a woman a *niddah*.[9] The case to consider the woman a *niddah* is even stronger if the bleeding is the result of a procedure performed on the uterus close to the time of her expected menstrual period. In such a case, it is highly questionable whether the blood can be attributed solely to a wound. The possibility exists that the procedure caused her menstruation to begin early.[10] If a doctor claims that the bleeding is from polyps or a uterine wound, a Rav must be consulted. A woman should never rely solely upon the information provided by a physician as a basis to consider herself *tehorah*. A Rav must be consulted.

If a woman has a blood flow and suspects that it may be from a wound, there are several factors that must be clarified. a) A *re'iyah* vs. a *kesem*: Is she experiencing a blood flow or did she merely find a *kesem* on her garment or body? b) When did the *re'iyah* or *kesem* take place: at the time of her *vest* (her expected period, see Chapter Twelve), the thirtieth day from her last period (if she has no *vest kavuah*), or some other time? c) The source of the bleeding: Is the bleeding definitely from the uterus or may it be from the cervix?[11] d) The type of wound: Is it a wound that is certainly bleeding or a wound that may bleed?[12] e) The status of the woman: Does she have a *vest kavuah*? f) The current stage in her menstrual cycle: Is she currently *tehorah* and the bleeding may render her a *niddah*, is she currently *temei'ah* and the bleeding has appeared on her *hefseik taharah* or *bedikos*, or did the bleeding occur during the first three of seven "clean" days?

1. If one can clearly establish[13] that the woman has a bleeding

---

9. See *Rambam, Hil. Issurei Biah* 5:5.

10. See ruling of R' S. Z. Auerbach cited in *Nishmas Avraham, Y.D.* p.103.

11. If the bleeding is certainly from the uterus, we noted above that it is difficult to rule out bleeding from the endometrium. However, if the bleeding may be cervical or vaginal, there is more of a basis to consider her *tehorah*.

12. At times, a vaginal or cervical wound may *halachically* be considered a "bleeding" wound if it is prone to bleeding, although it is not bleeding at the moment. This determination must be made by a Rav.

13. *Rema* 187:5 is lenient even regarding a wound that is not <u>known</u> to be bleeding, but <u>may</u> be bleeding (i.e., it was not examined to see if it is bleeding and we do not know whether or not it usually bleeds), if she has a *vest kavuah* and is presently not at the time of her expected *vest* (or even if she has no *vest kavuah*, but never menstruates before a certain day, which has not yet arrived — *Chavos Daas* §13[c], see Chapter Fourteen, I,D,2,d for discussion of this particular *vest*). *Lechem VeSimlah* §38[l] extends *Rema's* lenient rule to a nursing woman, while responsa *Maharam Shick, Y.D.* 181, extends it to a woman after menopause. In either case, since she is not expected to menstruate, one may attribute the bleeding to a wound, even if it is not known to bleed.

wound[14] in the vagina or cervix (whether on the inner or outer surface of the cervix) and she is currently in a *tehorah* state, she

One must note that the subject of the *Shulchan Aruch* and *Rema* is a woman who bleeds during cohabitation. This is a severe problem which, if not solved in some acceptable manner, may ruin her marriage. We will call this "question a." The goal of *Poskim* in this case is to somehow demonstrate that the bleeding is due to a wound, not cohabitation, thus permitting the couple to remain married. Another directly related issue is the question of whether the woman requires a *hefseik taharah*, seven "clean" days and *tevilah*. This pertains to any woman who finds blood which may be attributable to a wound. We will call this "question b." The case in question in *Shulchan Aruch* relates to both issues. Is the woman permitted to remain married and, if so, does she require *tevilah*? A simple reading of *Rema* would seem that his lenient position applies to question (b) as well as (a). Thus, any woman may attribute bleeding to a wound, even if it is not bleeding for certain, providing that she is presently not at the time of her expected *vest*. However, *Shach* §20, *Toras HaShelamim* §18 and *Chavos Daas* §6[b] contend that *Rema* was only lenient regarding whether she is permitted to remain married (question a), but not regarding whether to dismiss the bleeding completely without counting seven "clean" days and undergoing *tevilah* (question b).

Shach and R' Akiva Eiger differ in their explanations of the above distinction: *Shach* §20 explains that we are lenient regarding question (a) only in order to save their marriage. R' Akiva Eiger (ad. loc.) contends that we are lenient regarding question (a) because it is a question of a *vest* (the woman seems to have a *vest* to bleed during every cohabitation; thus, she may not cohabit). Since we rule that *vestos* are *deRabbanan* (Rabbinic), one may be lenient. However, the question of requiring *tevilah*, argues R' Akiva Eiger, is *deOraisa* and thus is more severe. See *Chazon Ish* (Y.D. 82:1) who clarifies the distinction between the viewpoint of *Shach* and R' Akiva Eiger. Following *Shach's* approach, we may be lenient regarding a woman with a chronic bleeding condition and permit her without *tevilah*. In this case, too, her marriage is jeopardized, see *Graz* §23 and *Aruch HaShulchan* §58. Consistent with R' Akiva Eiger's approach, we cannot be lenient in a case of chronic bleeding since the issue is *deOraisa*.

As noted above, *Shach*, *Toras HaShelamim* and *Chavos Daas* contend that a woman who bleeds or finds blood on a *bedikah* cloth (case b) is *temei'ah*. She cannot attribute the blood to a wound unless the wound is known to be bleeding or known to be the type that usually bleeds. *Noda B'Yehudah* Y.D. 1:41[1] (cited in *Pischei Teshuvah* §27), understands that *Rema* is lenient even regarding case b, i.e., permitting a woman without seven "clean" days and *tevilah*. Nevertheless, *Noda B'Yehudah* himself ibid. [3] and most other *Poskim* do not permit one to attribute a blood flow (or a *bedikah*) to a wound unless the wound certainly is bleeding. See *Pischei Teshuvah* ibid. and *Graz* §23. However, *Aruch HaShulchan* §57 contends that one may safely follow the lenient view ("לא הפסיד"). One should note that this discussion pertains only to a wound that is not bleeding for certain. If the wound is certainly bleeding, all *Poskim* agree that one may attribute blood to the wound and dismiss it entirely. The woman requires no *tevilah*, providing that it is not the day of her *vest* or the thirtieth day since her last period.

14. See *Chazon Ish*, Y.D. 82:1, who defines a bleeding wound as a wound which, when touched with a cloth, will leave a stain on the cloth (even if only when the cloth is pressed against the wound. It may be that *Chazon Ish* was lenient in a case where it bleeds only when the cloth is pressed against the wound only in the case of a woman who bleeds during cohabitation because the pressing of the cloth replicated the situation of cohabitation. This question remains unclear). A woman who finds a bloodstain on a *bedikah* cloth and suspects that it is from a wound should be able to ascertain whether the wound is a bleeding wound by applying similar pressure to the area as she applies when making a *bedikah*. She should then consult a Rav.

will not be rendered a *niddah* by any bleeding,[15] by stains found on a *bedikah* cloth or by any *kesem* found on her garments.[16] It is normally assumed that if the physician can <u>see</u> a wound that he <u>knows</u> usually bleeds, she is not a *niddah*.[17] However, if the bleeding takes place during the time of her *vest*, it cannot be attributed to the wound unless the physician can actually see cervical or vaginal bleeding at the time.[18]

2. If a woman undergoes a procedure that usually causes trauma to the cervix or uterus and she felt pain,[19] it may be that she is not rendered a *niddah* if that type of procedure normally causes bleeding. Indeed, a Rav may rule that the woman is *tehorah* even if she felt no pain if, according to his information, it is clear that this procedure usually causes bleeding.[20] We

---

15. Even heavy bleeding (*Gilyon Maharsha* 187:5).

16. *Rema* 187:5 is lenient provided that the wound is certainly bleeding (i.e., it certainly bleeds, even if she is not certain that this flow is from that wound — *Shach* §24). He differentiates between: a) an actual blood flow (or blood found on a *bedikah* cloth) and a *kesem*. b) between bleeding found at the time that her period is not expected and bleeding found at a time that her period is expected. The various *halachos* are as follows: a) If she has no *vest kavuah*, she may attribute the flow to the wound provided that the bleeding does not take place on the thirtieth day (or after the thirtieth day — *Chavos Daas* 187:10[b]) from her last period. If she has a *vest kavuah*, she can attribute the blood to a bleeding wound, providing that the bleeding does not take place on the actual day of her *vest*. b) If the bleeding takes place on the day of her *vest* or on (or after) the thirtieth day (if she has no *vest kavuah*), she cannot attribute the blood to the wound even if the wound is a type that is known to bleed unless she knows that the flow is from the wound (*Shach* §26, *Aruch HaShulchan* §57). c) If she had no blood flow but merely found a *kesem* (even the size of a *gris* on a white garment), *Rema* is lenient in any case, even if the wound is not presently bleeding and even if the *kesem* is found on the day of her *vest* (*Shach* §27). *Taz* §10 expands upon the concept of a bleeding wound. He adds that she may attribute the blood even to a wound that is not certainly bleeding under any of the following circumstances: i) She does several internal examinations (*bedikos*) and always finds blood in the same spot (as in Y.D. 187:7), ii) if, at the time of the bleeding, she experiences pain (see also *Pischei Teshuvah* §27), or iii) if other women who have a similar wound usually bleed. In each of these cases, it is considered as if she knows the wound is bleeding.

17. The cautious tone of this statement is due to the fact that the issue of relying upon the physician in a case based on medical generalities and theories without visual evidence has not been resolved with certainty. See below Section B.

18. As in *Shach* §26, see *Shiurei Sheivet HaLeivi* (ad loc. s.v. ולכן).

19. The presence of pain indicates that the wound is bleeding. However, *Poskim* are reluctant to rely upon the mere presence of pain to indicate that there is a wound present. See *Aruch HaShulchan* 187:62.

20. Based on *Taz* §10, cited above.

emphasize again that under no circumstances should one reach such conclusions without Rabbinic guidance.

3. If the procedure was done on the day[21] of her *vest kavuah*[22] day or on the thirtieth day from her last period (if she has no *vest kavuah*), one cannot attribute the blood to the wound unless the physician actually sees the blood flowing from the wound.[23]

4. If no actual bleeding was noticed and no blood was found on a *bedikah* cloth, but the woman found a bloodstain on her undergarments, the question involves only a *kesem*, which is less serious. *Poskim* rule that the *kesem* may be attributed to the wound even if the wound is not presently bleeding[24] and even if we are not aware of the tendency of this type of wound to bleed.[25] This is true even if the *kesem* is found on the day of her expected period[26] and even if the wound is partially healed if it is still prone to bleed when irritated.[27]

5. One should note that this discussion pertains to a woman who finds a blood flow or a stain during the time period in which she is *tehorah*. The stain is attributed to the wound and is ignored. Similarly, a *bedikah* may be ignored under such circumstances if the wound is known to be bleeding.[28] However, a woman who must establish a status change through a *bedikah* cannot rely on a *bedikah* with a stain, even if the stain may be attributed to another source. While we can ignore the negative effect of the stain by attributing it to a wound, we cannot use the *bedikah* in a positive manner, i.e., to prove that there is no longer any bleeding from the uterus. Thus, a woman with a wound who must do a *hefseik taharah* and start

---

21. *Shiurei Sheivet HaLeivi* 187:5[4] is uncertain regarding bleeding from a wound during the twelve-hour period before the actual *vest* (commonly called "the *Or Zarua onah*").

22. However, one may attribute bleeding to a wound on the day of *vest she'aino kavuah* (*Chezkas Taharah* 187:68).

23. *Shach* §26, *Aruch HaShulchan* §57.

24. *Rema* 187:5.

25. *Shach* §27.

26. *Rema* and *Shach* ibid.

27. 190:18.

28. See *Shach* 187:19 and *Pischei Teshuvah* §24.

the seven "clean" days is faced with a serious problem. The *hefseik taharah* must be *tahor* beyond any doubt. Even if the blood on the cloth is attributable to a bleeding wound, it is essentially as if the *hefseik taharah* was not performed. Indeed, even the validity of the first *bedikah* of the seven "clean" days is questioned by *Poskim* if blood is found on the cloth, though the blood is attributable to a wound.[29] A woman who finds it difficult to do these *bedikos* should consult a Rav.

6. If blood is found during the first three of the seven "clean" days, it is more difficult to attribute it to a wound since, during this period, we suspect that any bleeding may be a continuation of her menstrual flow. *Poskim* discuss the various conditions under which one may attribute blood to a wound even during those three days (see footnote).[30] It is therefore advisable that if a woman must have a procedure done during the seven "clean" days, it should preferably be delayed at least until after the first three days.[31] A woman who must undergo a medical procedure during the seven "clean" days should consult with a Rav whether or not she should do all of the normally required *bedikos* and whether she should wear white or colored garments during those days. A Rav may advise her to do only one *bedikah* on the first and one on the seventh of the seven "clean" days. Depending upon the circumstances, he may advise that she wear colored garments.

29. *Chavos Daas* 196:3 and responsa *Avnei Miluim,* end of 23, rule that at least one *bedikah* of the seven "clean" days must be free of any blood. *Chasam Sofer, Y.D.* 177, rules that in a case of extreme necessity, one may be lenient with the *bedikah* of the seven "clean" days provided that the *hefseik taharah* was clean and free of any bloodstain. *Shiurei Sheivet HaLeivi* 187:5[3] rules that one should not be lenient. *Igros Moshe, O.C.* 3:100, is also strict regarding the *hefseik taharah* and the *bedikah* of the first day. Some *Poskim* differentiate between a case where the *hefseik taharah* is required after a normal menstruation and a case where the *hefseik taharah* is required after she was rendered a *niddah* by a flow on her *vest* day which may have actually come from the wound. See *Taharas HaBayis* vol. 1 page 252.

30. Regarding a *kesem,* see Chapter Eleven, note 103. Regarding blood found upon a *bedikah* cloth, responsa R' Akiva Eiger §78 rules that the stain cannot be attributed to the wound even if she has a *vest kavuah* and the *bedikah* was not done on the *vest* day. *Shiurei Sheivet HaLeivi* 196:10[7] rules that if the woman can ascertain that the blood was from the wound, i.e., she always finds blood on the same spot, she is *tehorah. Igros Moshe, Y.D.* I:95, is lenient if the physician inserted an instrument and claims that the bleeding is caused by trauma of the instrument. It is unclear if *Igros Moshe* is referring to a *kesem* or even to a blood flow. This refers to a woman who happened to find blood on a *bedikah* cloth. However, if she has a chronic condition, *Poskim* are lenient even regarding the first of the seven "clean" days.

31. *Igros Moshe, Y.D.* I:83, *O.C.* 3:100.

One should not take any of these steps without Rabbinic approval.

7. A woman who finds a bloodstain on a *bedikah* cloth, notices that she consistently finds the stain on a particular spot and suspects that it is due to a vaginal wound, should consult a Rav.[32]

B. Ne'emanus — halachic acceptability of a doctor's claim

There is much discussion in *halachic* literature[33] regarding the issue of whether one may rely upon a physician in matters pertaining to *halachah*.[34] The question is twofold:

---

32. See *187:7. Poskim* disagree whether *Shulchan Aruch,* in this case, is referring to a woman who is aware of a wound in the vagina. In the opinion of responsa *Noda B'Yehudah* 1:46 (cited in *Pischei Teshuvah* §37), *Chavos Daas* §7[b], §20[c], *Chochmas Adam* 110:11 and R' Akiva Eiger 1:61, *Shulchan Aruch* is referring to a case where the woman is aware of a wound in the vagina. Otherwise, she cannot attribute the stain to a wound, even if she consistently finds the stain on the same area of the cloth. *Graz* §33, responsa *Tzemach Tzedek, Y.D.* 113, and *Aruch HaShulchan* §66 contend that, in the opinion of *Shulchan Aruch,* she may attribute the stain to a wound even if she is not aware of a wound in the vagina. The fact that she finds blood only on one spot is itself proof that she must have a wound. Among contemporary authorities, responsa *Sheivet HaLeivi* 5:105, *Badei HaShulchan* 187:118 follow the strict opinion. *Taharas HaBayis* vol. 1 pages 244-247, after exhaustive citation of all relevant texts, reaches a lenient conclusion.

An important consideration, although not necessarily a deciding factor, is whether or not the woman experiences pain at the time of the *bedikah.* Some *Poskim* require that she test the surrounding area to establish that there is no blood in any other place in the vagina and check the suspected area three times to determine if it is actually bleeding. If blood is found in another area of the vagina, it raises the suspicion that the bleeding is from a uterine source, not from a wound. These three tests should not be performed one after another since blood found the second and third time may be residue from the earlier blood and will not prove that there is a bleeding wound (see *Badei HaShulchan* §116). Some *Rabbonim* advise the woman to see a gynecologist to ascertain whether she has a wound in the vagina. This should be done as soon as possible, since the wound that stained the cloth one day may heal by the next. The closer the examination is to the time of the *bedikah,* the easier it may be to determine whether the wound was there at the time of the *bedikah.* At times, a gynecological examination may not be a practical option. In any case, a Rav must be consulted. It is worthwhile for a Rav to know of an observant physician (preferably female) to whom he can refer women who need to be examined.

33. See *Pischei Teshuvah* 187:30, *Darchei Teshuvah* 187:98, 188:30, 194:19. See also introduction to responsa *Maharam Shick, Y.D.*

34. See *Tur* 187, *Beis Yosef* ibid., s.v. התרומות בספר כתב, who cites *Sefer HaTerumos, S'mag* and *S'mak,* who are uncertain whether one may rely even upon a Jewish physician. *Ritzva* (cited ibid.) is lenient only regarding an observant physician. See also responsa *Shvus Yaakov* 1:65.

1. May one accept a medical assessment as fact? *Poskim* were wary that some physicians (even individuals who are reliable and trustworthy in matters not relevant to *halachah*) may reach conclusions and make statements based upon conjecture and presumption, rather than upon fact.[35] This may be sound medical practice, but *halachah* demands more concrete proof.

2. If the physician is a non-Jew or a non-observant Jew, may one rely even on a statement of fact that he may make? One of

---

35. This question applies even to a Jewish physician who is observant. *Chasam Sofer*, in several responsa (*Y.D.* 158,175) seminal to this issue, raises two points: a) the efficacy of the testimony: A physician can create a doubt, not a fact. *Chasam Sofer* cites the view of *Me'il Tzedakah* that the sources in the Talmud which serve as a basis for relying upon a physician were referring to cases of endangerment of life (i.e., eating on *Yom Kippur*). In such cases, even a testimony that creates only a doubt regarding the danger to life is sufficient to permit one to eat on *Yom Kippur*. However, where positive fact is required, perhaps a doctor's testimony is not equal to fact. b) The basis of claim: fact or theory. *Chasam Sofer* contends that doctors' opinions are reliable only in a general sense, i.e. they have the expertise to know that certain ailments may cause vaginal bleeding. However, their opinions (unless backed by objective evidence) have no reliability in a specific case, i.e., to ascertain that <u>this</u> woman is bleeding for this particular reason. He argues that doctors often make judgments based upon conjecture and presumption, not hard, visual fact. *Halachah* cannot be based upon such speculation. If, however, the doctor claims to actually see the wound, he is believed since that statement is based upon fact, not speculation. Responsa *Maharsham* 1:24, 2:72 explains that the physician is believed since the presence or absence of the wound can be confirmed, the physician places his reputation in jeopardy if his presentation of the fact is inaccurate. *Shiurei Sheivet HaLeivi* 187:8[3] notes that, in this regard, the situation today is better than it was in previous times. Medicine, in earlier times, was more a matter of theory and conjecture. Today, it is often based upon visual evidence and techniques proven reliable through extensive research.

Igros Moshe, Y.D. 4:17[17], follows *Chasam Sofer's* basic premise, albeit with slight modification (which *Chasam Sofer* himself may agree with). He contends that if we know that the woman has a wound and the doctor claims that this type of wound usually bleeds, one may accept his opinion even though it is based upon assumption. *Igros Moshe* contends that since the existence of the wound is a fact, the claim that it bleeds is not far fetched. If, however, we are not aware of the existence of the wound without the information provided by the doctor, we cannot rely upon his opinion that this type of wound is likely to bleed unless he actually saw the wound (in which case one may rely upon a non-Jew as well). In addition, R' Moshe contends that if the doctor predicts that the woman will bleed after the examination as a result of the trauma of the examination, he is believed. In this case, we are assured that the doctor's assessment is correct since he actually predicted the bleeding. He takes this position in *Igros Moshe, Y.D.* 2:69, as well.

In short, in the opinion of *Igros Moshe*, we accept a physician's claim that blood is from a wound if either a) we know beforehand that there is a wound, b) the physician actually sees the wound or c) the physician predicted that there will be bleeding. Responsa *Eimek HaTeshuvah* 3:73 rules that if the physician claims to actually see the wound, we rely upon his claim. However, if he claims the source of the bleeding is a wound that can no longer be seen, we cannot accept his claim since it is not verifiable. See also *Aruch HaShulchan* 188:64-72.

the axiomatic principles in *halachah* is that one cannot rely upon the testimony of a non-Jew or a non-observant Jew in matters pertaining to *halachah*. This in no way denigrates the character of the non-Jew or non-observant Jew; rather, it is a question of value judgment. The seriousness and importance of Torah and *mitzvos* is, to the observant Jew, the primary consideration. We believe that the performance of a *mitzvah* or the violation of an *aveirah* has deep significance which affects not only the spirituality of the individual but which impacts upon the cosmos in a manner that can be properly appreciated only by one who accepts and shares in our beliefs. A non-Jew, or indeed even a non-observant Jew[36] however honest and trustworthy he may be, cannot appreciate the enormous import of the information he provides. He may, out of the goodness of his heart, anticipate the desire of a woman not to become *temei'ah* and wish to assure her that a blood flow is not menstrual blood. This *halachic* concern is countered by the fact that *halachah* views the physician as a medical expert with high professional standards who would not risk his reputation by providing inaccurate information.[37] The question of whether to rely upon the statements of a non-Jewish or non-observant gynecologist is based upon the conflict between these two opposing truths.

One generally needs information from the physician regarding whether or not an instrument was used, the type and width of the instrument if used, the frequency of bleeding following such a procedure, the source of the bleeding and whether the doctor visually verified the source of the bleeding. One <u>may not</u> rely solely upon the physician's impression that the blood is not uterine in origin.[38] In all cases, <u>one must discuss the matter with a Rav</u> and inform him whether or not the physician is an observant Jew. If necessary, the Rav will discuss the matter with the physician who will provide him with more detailed information. The

---

36. See *Mei Niddah* (*Mahadura Tinyana,* end of 187) responsa *Maharsham* 1:13.

37. This is in accord with the general principle that even one whose testimony is suspect is nevertheless trusted regarding a fact which can easily be verified (מילתא דעבידא לגלויי). See responsa *Divrei Chaim* 2:77, *Maharsham* 1:24, 2:72. In addition, we assume that any professional will not risk his professional standing, see *Tosfos, Chullin* 97a, s.v. סמכינן.

38. One certainly cannot give any credibility to his statement that the bleeding is "not menstrual." The doctor may merely intend to state that it is not her monthly menstrual cycle, although it may be uterine blood . See *Igros Moshe, Y.D.* 2:69.

relationship between a Rav and a physician is that of two professionals with mutual respect for one another.

There are several advantages in using an observant Jew as one's gynecologist. If the physician is Torah observant, the problems of *ne'emanus* are avoided. In addition, a Torah observant physician will be more accessible to and cooperative with a Rav who wishes to discuss the procedures performed on a patient. Also, an observant physician can more easily empathize with the problems of a woman with staining problems. He is aware of the emotional strain that a prolonged and frequent *niddus* state places upon a Torah observant couple. He sympathizes with their difficulty in conceiving due to an irregular cycle. This is not necessarily true of a non-observant physician. A non-observant physician may not fully grasp why his observant patients "pester" him with seemingly trivial questions about minute blood specks and stains.

Another noteworthy point: A Torah-observant woman should realize that her concern about any irregular blood flow gives her a medical advantage as well. Some irregularities on the menstrual cycle may be indications of a medical situation which requires treatment. While this is rare, it may give a Torah observant woman the advantage of earlier treatment.

C. *Pesichas hakever* — the opening of the uterus

We noted in Chapter Two that a woman may acquire a *niddah* status even without any visible appearance of *dam*. This is true because of the Talmudic[39] ruling that whenever the uterus opens (in the terminology of *Chazal*, this is called *"pesichas hakever"*), one must assume that some *dam* was discharged into the vagina, thereby rendering the woman a *niddah*. Accordingly, any time a substance[40] of sufficient size[41] is emitted from the

---

39. *Niddah* 21b. *Rambam* (*Hil. Issurei Biah* 5:13) follows the opposing view in the Talmud that a uterine opening does not necessarily cause a blood discharge. However, most other *Rishonim* follow the stricter opinion (see *Magid Mishnah* ibid., *Beis Yosef, Y.D.* 188, p.50a). This is also the view of *Shulchan Aruch, Y.D.* 188:3.

40. See responsa of *Noda B'Yehudah* cited in *Teshuvah MaAhavah* 1:116, that this applies only if some solid substance is expelled from the body. A mere opening without discharging any substance does not render her a *niddah*. *Noda B'Yehudah* contends that even if fluid is discharged, it does not constitute *pesichas hakever*. Accordingly, a woman whose water breaks would not be a *niddah* due to *pesichas hakever*. (Nevertheless, in the opinion of some *Poskim* one must be concerned that some blood may be present in the water, see Chapter Twenty-Four, Section D, 8. A Rav should be consulted.)

41. *Shulchan Aruch* (*Y.D.* 188:6) rules that even if the uterus opened to eject an object a bit wider than the thinnest reed, it is considered *pesichas hakever*. See *Biur HaGra* §23 for the source of this ruling.

uterus, we assume that some *dam* was discharged while the uterus was opened, even if no *dam* is visible.[42] This is true even if the physician claims that no *dam* was discharged, and even if the physician is Torah observant.[43]

1. Internally versus externally induced uterine opening:

There is disagreement among *Poskim* whether the ruling regarding *pesichas hakever* is limited to an internally induced opening of the uterus, i.e., a piece of tissue discharged by the body by way of the uterus, or whether even an externally induced opening renders the woman a *niddah*. For example, if an object (e.g., an instrument) is inserted into the uterus, should we assume that some *dam* was discharged since the uterus, in fact, was opened? Perhaps the Talmud was referring only to an internally induced opening. Some opinions rule that only an internally induced opening is assumed to cause a discharge of *dam*.[44] Others do not differentiate between internally and externally induced uterine openings.[45] Common custom is to follow the stricter (latter) opinion.[46]

See note 50 below where we noted the different opinions of *Poskim* regarding the size of the opening. *Poskim* are generally more lenient regarding an externally induced opening.

42. *Y.D.* 188:3.

43. *Igros Moshe, O.C.* 3:100.

44. *Tiferes LeMoshe* 188 (*Maharsham* 4:146, cites *Tiferes LeMoshe's* opinion, extolls his greatness and claims that one may rely upon his opinion). R' Baruch Frenkel, in his comment to *Noda B'Yehudah* 2:120 (see following footnote), explains the concept of *pesichas hakever* in the following manner: One should not imagine the uterus as an organ full of blood and its *pesach* as a plug, which, when opened, releases blood (this seems to be the approach of responsa *Masos Binyamin* 49). This is not so. The uterine blood is held in place by the blood vessels of the uterine lining. However, when the body stimulates the uterus to expel a substance, we assume that the uterine lining is stimulated to expel blood as well. Therefore, if the uterus is induced to open through an external cause, there is no reason to assume that the uterine lining expels any blood. *Chazon Ish, Y.D.* 83:1, also agrees with R' B. Frenkel's approach. However, in §2 he cites *Gra* 188:27 who seems to agree with *Noda B'Yehudah. Chazon Ish,* therefore, leaves the question unresolved.

45. *Noda B'Yehudah* 2:120, cited in *Pischei Teshuvah* 194:4. *Noda B'Yehudah* rules that there is no difference between a minor, a woman after menopause, during pregnancy or while nursing regarding the laws of *pesichas hakever*. See also *Darchei Teshuvah* 188:46. It is not clear how *Noda B'Yehudah* refutes R' Baruch Frenkel's arguments. One could assume that *Noda B'Yehudah* followed the approach of *Masos Binyamin* (see previous footnote). See also *Binas Adam* 13(23), who seems to argue with *Noda B'Yehudah;* however, *Igros Moshe, Y.D.* I:83, notes that *Binas Adam* may actually agree with *Noda B'Yehudah*. In the previous footnote we noted that *Chazon Ish* proves from *Gra* 188:27 that he agrees with *Noda B'Yehudah*.

46. *Aruch HaShulchan* 188:51 warns very forcefully against following the lenient opinion חלילה לומר כן. A similar strict position is also taken by *Avnei Neizer ,Y.D.* 224, *Igros Moshe, Y.D.* I:83,89, and

2. Opening of the cervix versus the uterus:

We noted the disagreement among *Poskim* regarding the cervix. According to the opinion that the cervix is considered part of the *makor*, the opening of the external os would constitute *pesichas hakever*. According to the opinion that the cervix is not part of the *makor*, only the opening of the internal os is *pesichas hakever*. Some contemporary authorities rule that one should follow the stricter opinion.[47] Others follow the lenient view. In their view, if the examination penetrated the external os of the cervix without penetrating the internal os (the entrance to the uterus itself) and no blood appeared, no *halachic* problems exist.[48]

3. The width of the opening:

There is disagreement among *Poskim* as to the width of opening that would constitute *pesichas hakever*.[49] The opinions range from approximately 15 millimeters to one inch (25.4mms).[50] Some authorities rule that if even a narrow

---

Shiurei Sheivet HaLeivi 188:3[4]. One may argue that since, in the opinion of *Rambam* (cited above), *pesichas hakever* does not necessarily cause *dam* to be released, even though we follow the stricter opinion that it does, we should at least be lenient regarding the question of an externally induced opening, since this is a *s'fek s'feika* (a double doubt). However, *Avnei Neizer* (ibid.) rejects this argument. He contends that the issue is essentially reduced to one question: Does this opening of the uterus cause a release of *dam*? See *Igros Moshe*, O.C. 3:100, for another refutation of this argument.

47. *Shiurei Sheivet HaLeivi* ibid.

48. Responsa *Beis Yitzchak* Y.D. 2:14, *Igros Moshe*, Y.D. 1:83, O.C. 3:100, and responsa *Cheisev HaEifod* (R' H. Padwe) 2:7, and *Poseiach Shaar* 6:3. See also *Kitzur Hilchos Niddah* (R' Pfoiffer) 11:8, who contends that even if one concedes that the external os is the *pesach hamakor*, it is nevertheless illogical to suspect that opening it will cause menstrual bleeding since the cervix has no menstrual blood. This argument, while novel, is not convincing since the relationship between opening of the *makor* and *dam niddah* may be a response based on reflex. Perhaps the opening of even the external os causes a release of endometrial blood.

49. The Talmud itself offers no measurement for *pesichas hakever*. *Tosfos* (*Niddah* 22b), *Rosh* (*Niddah* 3:3) and *Rashba* (*Toras HaBayis, Bayis 7*, end of *Shaar* 1) contend that a small opening does not constitute a *pesichah*. *Tur* 188 rules that an opening the size of a reed does not constitute *pesichas hakever*. *Beis Yosef*, end of 188, rules that since no exact measurement is given, we cannot render a woman *tehorah* unless the opening is wider than the thinnest of reeds. This is reflected in *Shulchan Aruch* 188:6. Other *Poskim* try to find other sources to be lenient, even regarding a larger opening. See *Biur HaGra* 188:23, who cites a *Mishnah* (*Ahalos* 7:4) that the size of *pesichas hakever* is the size of a spinner's spool of wool of the warp. See following footnote.

50. *Tiferes Tzvi* 188:9 contends that up to the thickness of a thumb (approximately one inch) is not considered *pesichas hakever* (*Maharsham* 4:146, cites *Tiferes Tzvi* as permitting an opening of up to two inches. *Minchas Yitzchak* 10:31[3] notes that this is a misprint. The correct text should read

instrument penetrated the internal os, she is rendered a *nid-dah*.[51] Many contemporary authorities follow this view. We will note the typical width of many instruments used today in gynecological examinations.

D. A summary of the *halachic* issues

The *halachos* discussed in this chapter revolve around the following four issues:

1. An externally induced opening is considered *pesichas hakever*:

As noted above (C,1), we normally follow the opinions that rule that even an externally induced opening is problematic. Thus, whenever a woman undergoes a gynecological examination, we must be concerned with the question of whether there has been a *pesichas hakever*, even if the examination does not result in bleeding.[52]

2. Penetration of internal or external os:

Any instrument that penetrates the internal os may cause a *niddah* status by two possible means: a) It may constitute

---

"one finger"). Responsa *Divrei Malkiel* 2:56 cites the measurement of a finger. He seems to refer to a regular finger, not the thumb. A similar position is taken by *Igros Moshe, O.C.* 3:100 and *Y.D.* 1:89, who writes that an opening <u>less</u> than the size of the index finger is not considered *pesichas hakever*. He specifies the measurement of three quarters of an inch (19mm). *Pri Deah* on *Taz* 188:13, is stricter yet: He is only lenient with an opening no wider than a little finger. Some consider this to be fifteen millimeters (approximately five eighths of an inch). See *Badei HaShulchan* 194:31 and *Kitzur Hilchos Niddah* (R' Pfoiffer) 10:7. See *Nishmas Avraham* (*Y.D.* 194:2 footnote 55) who notes that most instruments which penetrate the internal os are no wider than 3mm, although some may be as wide as 12mm. He notes that it is impossible to insert an instrument as wide as 20mm. without tearing the cervix and inflicting serious damage. *Be'er Moshe* 3:148, citing responsa *Yeshuos Malko*, notes that penetration of the internal os would cause intense pain. The fact that she felt no such pain is proof that the internal os was not penetrated.

51. *Shiurei Sheivet HaLeivi* 188:3[4]. The reasoning may be that, regarding the internal os, one assumes that even an opening a bit wider than the narrowest reed is considered *pesichas hakever* (as seems from *Shulchan Aruch* 188:6. *Minchas Yitzchak* 10:31[3] maintains that common custom is to consider any opening wider than the narrowest reed a *pesichas hakever*). In addition, if an instrument penetrates the internal os, we are concerned that some uterine blood may be dislodged. However, many *Poskim* rule that even if an instrument penetrated the internal os, the woman is *tehorah* if the opening is less than the prescribed amount. See responsa *Maharsham* 4:146 and *Igros Moshe, Y.D.* 1:89.

52. See responsa *Divrei Malkiel* 2:56, who is very lenient regarding gynecological examinations. He rules that if one does not know the width of the instrument, one may be lenient. In 3:61, he is lenient even if the examination took place during the first three of the seven "clean" days. See other responsa cited in *Darchei Teshuvah* 194:19.

pesichas hakever; depending upon its width (see C,3 above) at the point of penetration, b) whenever an instrument penetrates the internal os, regardless of its width, it may cause trauma to the uterus and cause some of the uterine lining to shed. If bleeding occurs, it may be considered a menstrual flow.[53]

If the instrument only penetrated the external os, the status of the woman would be subject to the disagreement among *Poskim* (cited in C,2 above) as to whether the opening of the external os constitutes a *pesichas hakever*. According to those who rule that it does, the woman's status would depend upon the width of the instrument.

Many gynecological examinations do not even penetrate the external os and clearly present no *halachic* problems. Most examinations do <u>not</u> penetrate beyond the internal os to the uterus. Thus, in the opinion of many authorities, there is no problem of *pesichas hakever*.[54]

3. The source of any bleeding:

If there is bleeding, it is crucial to differentiate between a) vaginal or cervical bleeding induced by the trauma of the examination, and b) uterine bleeding resulting from the examination or from menstruation. Any blood originating from a wound, laceration or abrasion of a non-uterine origin[55] is not *dam niddah* and presents no *halachic* problems. However, <u>one must follow distinct guidelines as to when bleeding may be attributed to such a wound.</u> Any blood originating from the uterus presents serious *halachic* problems since it is difficult to differentiate between menstrual and trauma-induced

---

53. Even though the flow was caused by an external factor, it is not considered a flow caused by a wound. See *Igros Moshe, Y.D.* 2:69. However, if no blood is noticed, one need be concerned about this latter point. See ruling of R' S. Z. Auerbach cited in *Nishmas Avraham, Y.D.* p.103. The issue of *pesichas hakever*, however, is relevant even if no bleeding is noticed.

54. *She'arim Metzuyanim BeHalachah* 153:16 cites responsa *Beis Yitzchak, Y.D.* 2:14, and *Sheilas Shalom* 1:59, who rule that, unless known otherwise, whenever a physician inserts an instrument, we must be concerned that he may have inserted it into the uterus as well. Most other *Poskim* do not accept this opinion. On the contrary, they note that most examinations do not penetrate the uterus. See responsa *Maharsham* 4:146. Nevertheless, one is required to ascertain whether the uterus was penetrated.

55. Essentially, even bleeding caused by an abrasion to the uterine wall itself will not render a woman a *niddah* since it is not menstrual blood. However, it is very difficult to be lenient in this case since it is difficult to determine when such bleeding is *niddah* blood and when it is not.

uterine bleeding. We will, in the following chapter, comment upon the frequency of bleeding resulting from different gynecological procedures.

4. Testimony of the physician:
One cannot always accept, without reservation, statements made by the medical practitioner regarding whether or not a particular procedure causes bleeding or whether that bleeding is uterine or cervical. <u>A Rav must always be consulted.</u>

> A note of caution: These guidelines are meant to enable one to properly present a question to a Rav. A layman should <u>never</u> attempt to reach conclusions based upon the information in this chapter.

III. General guidelines

The following are some general guidelines regarding gynecological examinations:

1. The instrument:
If the physician did not use an instrument during his examination, we assume that the uterus was not opened. Under normal circumstances, the finger cannot reach into the uterus.[56] Often a speculum (an instrument which separates the vaginal walls enabling the physician to examine the vaginal area) is used. This presents no problem.[57] However, if another instrument was used, one must determine both the depth of penetration and the width of the instrument at the point of penetration. This information must be presented to a competent Rav.

Practically, it is rare for a physician to insert an instrument that is 15mm wide even into the external os. It is extremely rare that a physician would insert an instrument of this width into the internal os. Thus, even if one would assume that the external os is the *pesach hamakor*, it would be

---

56. This has been noted by *Binas Adam* 23, responsa *Chasam Sofer, Y.D. 179, Beis Shlomo, Y.D. 39, Maharsham* 2:40. Although a physican can reach the cervix he is unable to penetrate even the external os unless the woman is dilated as in late pregnancy. However, *Minchas Yitzchak* 3:84 notes that while this general assumption is correct, one should inquire whether the physician penetrated the uterus.

57. This is probably similar to the *"mutterspiegel"* cited in *Poskim*. See *Darchei Teshuvah* 194:19.

unusual for the issue of *pesichas hakever* to arise. It would be even more unusual for this issue to arise as a result of penetration by an instrument of the internal os. However, it should be noted that even a narrow instrument which penetrates beyond the internal os may cause trauma to the uterine lining and cause the woman to become a *niddah*.

When a physician wishes to insert a wide instrument, he usually first dilates the opening with a dilator. Thus, when one is concerned about the width of an instrument, one should actually inquire about the width of the dilator. The instrument will usually be narrower than the dilator.

2. The appearance of blood:

If no blood appeared, one may rely upon a physician who states that he did not examine or reach the uterus.[58] However, if any blood appears, the question of *pesichas hakever* is only of secondary importance, for the blood itself may render the patient a *niddah*. Indeed, even if she herself does not notice blood, but the physician informs her that there was blood,[59] she may be a *niddah*. If blood is noticed, the physician should be asked where the blood is uterine or non-uterine. The woman should ascertain whether the procedure she underwent usually causes trauma resulting in bleeding. If the physician claims that the blood is from trauma to the cervix or vaginal canal, she should inquire whether or not he can see the site of bleeding. This information should be forwarded to a Rav who will decide whether or not the woman is *temei'ah*.

3. Consulting a Rav:

As noted earlier, the Rav may wish to discuss the case with the gynecologist. Any responsible gynecologist is cooperative in such matters. However, a woman should not rely upon the physician himself to determine whether or not she is a *niddah*. Often a gynecologist may claim that he has experience with

---

58. *Shiurei Sheivet HaLevi* 188:3[4]. He notes that if the examination reached the uterus itself, the woman would feel excessive pain. It is unclear whether or not this factor is vital to his lenient view. If it is indeed a vital factor, it would seem that if the woman did feel excessive pain, one cannot rely upon the physician's claim that he did not penetrate the uterus.

59. Even if no blood actually left the body, but the physician merely informs her that he saw blood in the vagina, see *Rambam* 5:2,5.

other observant patients, has spoken to Rabbis, and is familiar with the *halachic* guidelines. <u>One may not rely upon such claims.</u> A physician should be respected for his expertise in medical matters. Indeed, a Rav does not and should not make assumptions concerning medical matters without consulting a gynecologist. Similarly, a gynecologist, even if he is learned in *halachah*, should leave *halachic* matters to a Rav who is an expert in this field. All information provided by the physician must be evaluated by a Rav.

4. Things to avoid:

a. One should never tell the physician "don't tell me if you see blood" as this constitutes a willful disregarding of an already known and established fact. However, one is not required to ask the physician whether or not he saw blood.

b. Some authorities advise that a woman do a *bedikah* after a gynecological examination. However, common practice is to avoid *bedikos* after a gynecological examination unless the woman is instructed to do so by a Rav. It is common that examinations cause bruises which, in themselves, may not be problematic. However, if blood is found on a *bedikah* cloth, it may be difficult for a Rav to attribute it to a bruise.[60]

5. In summary, the following factors are essential regarding gynecological procedures:

a. Was an examining instrument (other than a speculum) used?

b. What procedure was performed and what type of instrument was used?

c. What is the woman's menstrual status? Is she currently *tehorah* or *temei'ah*?

---

60. See *Avnei Neizer*, Y.D. 224, who contends that although a small *pesichas hakever* does not <u>necessarily</u> cause a blood flow, it <u>may</u> cause a blood flow. He therefore requires that a *bedikah* be performed. This opinion is not found in earlier *Poskim*. However, *Shiurei Sheivet HaLeivi* 188:3[4] also advises that a *bedikah* be done. Nevertheless, considering the fact that normally there is no *halachic* problem of *pesichas hakever* and considering the frequency of bleeding caused by the trauma of the examination itself to the cervix and vagina, many *Rabbonim* do not advise that a *bedikah* be done. This is the opinion of *Igros Moshe*, O.C. 3:100, and is the common custom.

d. Where does the examining instrument penetrate (vagina, cervix or uterus)? Specifically, does the instrument pass beyond the external or the internal os?

e. To what width was the uterus dilated or how wide is the instrument at the point that it enters the cervix or uterus?

f. How common is it that this examination may cause bleeding? What type of bleeding is caused, uterine or vaginal? If uterine, might it be menstrual bleeding?

g. Can the physician actually see the source of the bleeding?

Practically, if a woman merely establishes the name of the procedure, a Rav will be able to advise her as to her *halachic* status. If bleeding is present, she should inquire as to its source and whether or not the source is visible to the physician. If there is no bleeding at the time of the examination, she should ask whether bleeding is to be expected and from what source.

IV. Scheduling gynecological procedures

Gynecologists prefer to schedule office gynecological procedures post-menstrually. Although the pathology reports resulting from gynecological procedures are not affected by the timing of the procedure, the gynecologist prefers to perform biopsies post-menses, when the pelvis is not congested. Surgical procedures performed pre-menstrually may result in increased bleeding.[61]

The scheduling of gynecological examinations is of particular importance regarding *hilchos niddah*. A woman should try to schedule her appointment so that it will not needlessly cause her to be *temei'ah*. Thus, a post-menstrual examination should, if possible, be scheduled immediately before she begins her seven "clean" days, before her *hefseik taharah*. An examination performed during the seven "clean" days may force her to repeat the *hefseik taharah* and begin the seven "clean" days anew. An examination scheduled after *tevilah* may cause her to become a *niddah* again. However, an examination which may irritate the cervix and make

---

61. A notable exception is the diagnostic laparoscopy performed to rule out endometriosis, which is generally scheduled pre-menstrually since ectopic endometrium is more easily found during this part of the menstrual cycle.

it tender should not be performed immediately before the *hefseik taharah* since it may cause spotting on the *hefseik taharah*.

Another issue to be considered is that the procedure should not be performed on the day of her expected menstruation. Blood found on that day is difficult to attribute to the procedure. In addition, in the opinion of some authorities,[62] even if the procedure is not performed on the actual day of the expected menstruation, but close to the expected day, one should be concerned that any instrument that enters the uterus proper may cause the menstruation to begin earlier. Thus, if any blood appears, it may be menstrual blood. Accordingly, the following guidelines apply:

> 1. A procedure which normally causes cervical or vaginal bleeding, but never causes uterine bleeding or *pesichas hakever*, should preferably be performed after the seven "clean" days have passed. The woman should wear colored garments to avoid any *kesamim* questions. If the procedure must be performed earlier, it should at least be delayed until after the *hefseik taharah* and first day's *bedikah*. If possible, it should be delayed until after the first three of the seven "clean" days.[63] A Rav should be consulted regarding the advisability of performing the other *bedikos* of the seven "clean" days[64] and the permissibility of wearing colored garments.
>
> 2. A procedure which may cause uterine bleeding or *pesichas hakever*, but not lasting irritation to the vagina and cervix, should be performed before the *hefseik taharah*.
>
> 3. If the procedure may cause both uterine bleeding and irritation to the cervix, a Rav should be consulted whether it should be scheduled before or after the *hefseik taharah* and the *bedikah* of the first of the seven "clean" days.
>
> 4. A procedure which may cause any bleeding should not be scheduled on the day of the expected menstruation (i.e. the *vest* day or the *onah beinonis*) unless a woman deems this advantageous. She may feel certain that the period will come on that day anyway; thus, she is not causing additional days of *tumah*.

---

62. See ruling of R' S. Z. Auerbach cited in *Nishmas Avraham*, Y.D. p.103.

63. *Igros Moshe*, O.C. 3:100.

64. *Pischei Teshuvah* 187:32 cites *Chavos Daas* that in a case of an internal wound, only the *hefseik taharah* and *bedikah* of the first day should be performed, not the seventh. This conclusion is accepted by *Igros Moshe*, Y.D. 2:69.

5. A procedure which involves inserting an instrument into the uterus should preferably not be scheduled for the days immediately preceding her expected menstrual period. Bleeding at that time may be difficult to attribute to the procedure.[65] If it must be scheduled at that time (such as an endometrial biopsy), a Rav must be consulted as to whether she is *temei'ah* and when she may begin counting her five preliminary days. A woman may feel that it is advantageous for her to perform the procedure at this time despite the risk of becoming a *niddah* since her menstruation is expected within a few days, regardless.

---

65. See note 10 where we noted that a procedure done in the uterus proper close to the expected period may cause some early menstrual bleeding.

Gynecological procedures

- ☐ Common gynecological procedures.
- ☐ Procedures performed during pregnancy.
- ☐ Hysterectomies.
- ☐ Fertility procedures.
- ☐ Contraception.
- ☐ Gynecological conditions and terms.

Gynecological procedures

The purpose of this chapter is to explain various procedures that are relevant to *hilchos niddah*. We will note which examinations may render a woman a *niddah* and which are usually not problematic. However, the reader should not rely upon this chapter to reach any *halachic* conclusion. These *halachos* are complex and lie entirely in the domain of an experienced Rav. We will often note that a Rav should be consulted. In truth, a Rav should <u>always</u> be consulted.

It is our hope that the information presented below will also broaden the medical background of the Rav and enable him to elicit pertinent medical information more proficiently. A Rav will find this information invaluable in helping him understand the problems involved with individual procedures. This will greatly assist him in reaching *halachic* determinations and recommendations.

A. General considerations

1. Bleeding from an external trauma:
When considering the procedures described below, please note that any bleeding resulting from trauma to the vulva, vagina or outer cervix can be visually verified by the examining physician. Examples of procedures resulting in such trauma include biopsies of the above areas, LEEP, and cryotherapy of the cervix, all of which are described below. Bleeding which is attributed to such sites is not considered *dam niddah*. Nevertheless, a Rav should be consulted.

2. The endocervical canal vs. the uterus:
Procedures involving the endocervical canal (the area between the external and internal os) and beyond may result in bleeding. <u>Such bleeding cannot be visually verified.</u> In such a case, it is important to determine the type of procedure and the type and width of any instrument used, the depth of penetration and the frequency of bleeding. As noted in the previous chapter (II,D,2), penetration beyond the internal os (or, in the opinion of some authorities, even beyond the external os) may cause a *niddah* status by means of *pesichas hakever*. Furthermore, any procedure which involves penetration beyond the internal os may cause uterine bleeding and render the woman a *niddah* by means of uterine bleeding. For example, any bleeding resulting from a routine Pap smear is generally

due to trauma to the outer cervix or the cervical canal only, and generally poses no *halachic* problems. On the other hand, endometrial biopsy penetrates beyond the internal os and generally results in uterine bleeding, which may render the woman a *niddah*. These procedures are described below.

3. Uterine bleeding:

Whenever there is bleeding from the corpus of the uterus, it poses a serious *halachic* problem. There are instances when one may, according to *halachah*, attribute bleeding to a *makkah*, a wound in the uterus. Practically, in the event of uterine bleeding, it becomes very difficult to determine that the bleeding is only from the wound. Some procedures cause bleeding from generalized uterine trauma besides bleeding from the wound itself. There are situations in which it is difficult to establish with certainty whether the trauma of the procedure has resulted in uterine blood being dislodged (which renders her a *niddah*) or whether the bleeding is due only to an actual wound to the uterus (which does not render her a *niddah*). In addition, some types of trauma are difficult to classify as a wound. An instrument that comes into contact with the uterine wall may cause it to shed some of the endometrium. It is unclear if this is considered a *makkah*. In these cases, a Rav may have no choice but to assume that she is a *niddah*.

B. Common gynecological procedures

> Note: the reader is cautioned that modern medicine is ever changing in its techniques. Anything written on the subject may quickly become dated. The information provided herein reflects, to the best of our knowledge, gynecologic practice as of the writing of this work.[1] A Rav

---

1. We have based most of this information upon discussions with practitioners rather than printed matter, so as to keep the information as current as possible. The author is grateful and indebted to the following individuals: Dr. Sidney Jakubovics for his dedicated effort and many hours spent gathering this information and patiently reviewing the manuscript of this chapter countless times. Dr. Solomon Neuhoff for generously making himself available to the author on many occasions to share his expertise and for reviewing and editing this chapter. Dr. Ellen Manos of Lenox Hill Hospital for graciously setting aside time from her busy schedule to discuss and elaborate on these procedures. Dr. Robert Wallach, Director of Gynecologic Oncology, New York University Medical Center for being kind enough to edit and review the final draft of this chapter and make valuable suggestions which contributed to its accuracy.

must keep up to date regarding changes in gynecological practices. A layman should certainly not rely upon the general information being presented to make *halachic* (or medical) decisions.

1. Use of a speculum:

As noted in the introduction, use of a speculum (an instrument used to separate the walls of a cavity) to better examine the vaginal area, without the use of any other instrument, does not constitute a *halachic* problem. There is usually no bleeding. If bleeding occurs, the physician should be asked whether the bleeding was caused by trauma to the vagina or cervix and a Rav should be consulted.[2]

2. Use of a Tenaculum:

The tenaculum is the instrument used by the gynecologist to grasp the cervix and hold it steady in one position. This instrument is used as an adjunct when performing other procedures such as a D&C, hysteroscopy, endometrial biopsy and intrauterine insemination (all of which are described below). Use of the tenaculum usually results in bleeding from the outer surface of the cervix. This bleeding in itself is not a problem *halachically*. However, if the procedure for which the tenaculum is used could potentially cause uterine bleeding, the patient would become a *niddah*. In these cases, it may be *halachically* difficult to attribute all the bleeding to the tenaculum and rule out uterine bleeding.[3] A Rav must always be consulted.

3. Cervical culture:

A sterile cotton swab, less than 5mm in diameter, is inserted into the cervical canal and twirled. This procedure is performed on patients (pregnant or not) to screen for infectious agents (e.g., chlamydia), by brushing the endocervical canal. About half of patients bleed from the endocervical canal due to abrasion. This bleeding would not render the patient a *niddah*. However, as with all gynecological procedures, a Rav should be consulted.

---

2. If the physician's answer is affirmative, the woman is *tehorah* (*Maharsham* 4:146, *Igros Moshe*, O.C. 3:100).

3. Although the trauma caused by the tenaculum certainly qualifies as a *makkah* that is known to bleed, the possibility of uterine bleeding cannot be ruled out.

4. Pap (Papanicolaou) smear:

> Note: A Pap smear is a routine procedure performed at regular intervals as a physician may deem appropriate. It normally presents no *halachic* problems. At times, subsequent to the Pap smear, a physician may decide to perform additional tests such as: a colposcopy with or without biopsy, endocervical curettage (ECC), cryotherapy of the cervix and (or) loop electrosurgical excision procedure LEEP. We will list those procedures often associated with a Pap smear and discuss their *halachic* consequences.

The Pap smear itself: The physician takes a specimen of the cells of the external cervix and the lining of the cervical canal a brushlike instrument (e.g., a cytobrush). Approximately half the patients bleed (depending upon such factors as the patient's age) as a result of trauma to the endocervical canal from the brush. (In the past, a cotton swab was used. Bleeding is perhaps more common today due to use of the brush.) This bleeding usually will not render the patient a *niddah* since the bleeding is generally cervical and it is highly unlikely for the physician to penetrate beyond the internal os.[4] Nevertheless, one should consult a Rav.

5. Colposcopy:

(Gr. *kolpos* — vagina / *skopein* — to look)

This procedure is performed in the event of an abnormal Pap smear. A speculum is placed into the vagina which is rinsed with vinegar to remove cervical mucus. The cervix is then examined with a colposcope (a lighted instrument with lenses for examination of the vagina and cervix). This instrument is not inserted into the uterus and does not cause bleeding unless a biopsy is performed as described below. Therefore, a colposcopy alone presents no *halachic* problems.

6. Colposcopy with biopsy:

If, in the course of the colposcopy (see 5 above), the physician notices abnormal areas, biopsies are taken of those areas. A Rav evaluating the status of a woman who has undergone a

---

4. Some physicians still use a wooden or plastic spatula to scrape the external cervical surface. The external os would then be opened approx. 3mm. This technique is being replaced by a brush as described above.

colposcopy must be aware that biopsies are frequently per-formed. Accordingly, the Rav should ascertain whether a biopsy was performed and determine the site of the biopsy. If, as is generally the case, the biopsies are of lesions external to the uterus, they result in external bleeding only which presents no *halachic* problems.[5]

7. Endocervical curettage (ECC):
(Gr. *endon* — within / cervix / Fr. *curette* — scoop)
Since half the cells from an abnormal Pap smear come from the lining of the endocervical canal, ECC (endocervical curettage) is frequently performed. Accordingly, if a woman informs her Rav that a colposcopy was performed, he should inquire whether an ECC was performed as well and consult with her physician.

ECC can be done at any time during the menstrual cycle. It is performed to evaluate the cells of the endocervical canal (following an abnormal Pap smear). It involves the use of a steel instrument called an endocervical curette to scrape the endocervical canal for the purpose of evaluating the cells microscopically. The resulting bleeding is generally from the endocervical canal from a point between the external and internal os. This bleeding would not render the woman a *niddah*. However, it is possible that the curette may penetrate the internal os and cause uterine bleeding. The woman would then be considered a *niddah*. A Rav would need to discuss the procedure with the physician.[6]

> If the biopsies obtained during colposcopy demon-strate cervical dysplasia (cells that are abnormal in appearance), the physician may choose from a num-ber of different procedures including cryotherapy of the cervix, LEEP, laser vaporization, conization of the cervix, etc. These procedures are described below.

8. Cryotherapy of cervix:
(Gr. *kryos* — cold / *therapeia* — treatment)
Cryotherapy of the cervix is performed to destroy abnormal tissue. This is usually only done if the ECC (endocervical

---

5. There is no reason to suspect uterine bleeding due to trauma to the uterus.

6. If, after discussion with the physician, the Rav is confident that the internal os was not pene-trated and there is no reason to suspect uterine bleeding, the woman is *tehorah*.

curettage) is negative. If ECC is positive, the patient may require further testing and treatment. If the dysplasia is visible and is external only, the cervix can be cryocauterized. An instrument is placed on the cervix to freeze and destroy the area of dysplasia. Actual bleeding is rare but possible. However, this procedure results in a discharge (for some six weeks) which may be slightly blood tinged. As any bleeding that occurs originates from the external cervix, there are no *halachic* problems. The woman should wear colored undergarments during this time to avoid *kesamim* problems.[7]

9. LEEP (Loop Electrosurgical Excision Procedure):
Physicians often prefer to perform a newer procedure, LEEP, instead of cryotherapy of the cervix to treat cervical dysplasia. Anesthesia is injected into the cervix. This results in temporary bleeding from the outer cervical area. An electrical wire loop is then used to remove the dysplastic area. An advantage of this procedure over cryotherapy is that a biopsy is obtained as part of the procedure. The resulting bleeding from the external cervix (which is stopped by means of cauterization) poses no *halachic* problems.

10. Laser vaporization:
Laser vaporization destroys the diseased portion of the cervix by directing high energy light to the area which is vaporized (boiled away). This is done under colposcopic visualization. There is frequently bleeding from the area treated, but this is from the surface of the exocervix (the part of the cervix usually external to the external os) or from the visible endocervix (the part of the cervix just internal to the external os). The bleeding is controlled, usually with a variation of the power intensity and focus of the laser. As this bleeding is from the cervix, it causes no *halachic* problems.

11. Polypectomy:
(Polyp / Gr. *ektome* — excision, removal)
This procedure is done in the office only for cervical polyps. Uterine (endometrial) polyps may require anesthesia and a D & C.
Cervical polypectomy involves removal of the cervical polyp. The base of the polyp may also be scraped. All patients under-

---

7. A Rav should be consulted as to whether or not she should do *bedikos* on her *vest* day which will certainly arrive during these weeks.

going this procedure bleed. Bleeding is due to trauma of the cervical canal. Some gynecologists prefer to schedule this procedure post-menstrually for the patient's convenience. Any bleeding is due to the trauma to the cervical canal and would not render the patient a *niddah*.

Uterine (endometrial) polypectomy involves a D&C and leads to uterine bleeding which would render the woman a *niddah*.

12. Use of endocervical speculum:

The endocervical speculum is a pair of U-shaped wires or two thin metal plates approximately one quarter of an inch wide tapering to a narrow tip. The endocervical speculum is passed through the vagina and into the cervical canal in order to open the canal for improved visualization. Laser treatment can be given into the canal after it has been opened by the endocervical speculum. The use of this instrument sometimes causes small tears in the cervix and results in bleeding. The endocervical speculum does not usually reach the internal os except in a very small uterus. This may occur in post-menopausal women. The endocervical speculum is frequently used to spread the canal of the cervix to a width of one quarter or one half an inch. This would not constitute a *pesichas hakever*[8] and any bleeding would be from a cervical source. However, a Rav should determine whether the instrument penetrated the internal os.

13. Conization of the cervix:

This outpatient procedure is sometimes performed diagnostically to determine the status of the cervical cells in the event of a positive Pap smear. It may also be performed therapeutically to remove abnormal tissue. Under anesthesia, a cone-shaped portion of the cervix is removed. In either case, there will be bleeding which is from the cervix and does not render her a *niddah*. In addition, an ECC is frequently done to assure that no abnormal tissue remains in the endocervical canal. This will also cause bleeding which is cervical. However, as noted in 7 above, if the curette penetrated the internal os the woman will be a *niddah*. At times, in the course of a conization procedure, the physician may wish to perform a D&C (Dilation and

---

8. See Chapter Twenty-Three, note 50.

Curettage, see 14 below) to rule out uterine lining disease. In that case, there is cervical bleeding due to the cone removal and uterine corpus bleeding due to the D&C. This latter bleeding would render a woman a *niddah*.

14. D&C (Dilation and Curettage):
This procedure is performed to determine the cause of abnormal bleeding, e.g., menorrhagia (abnormally heavy or prolonged menstrual bleeding), metrorrhagia (bleeding between periods) or post-menopausal bleeding. This procedure may also be done to remove uterine polyps.

The cervix is grasped with a tenaculum (which may result in cervical bleeding). Generally, the internal os must first be dilated with a dilator usually measuring 7-9mm. A curette of similar width is used to scrape tissue from the uterus. Bleeding which lasts from several hours to two days (or, at times, up to a week) is normal. Although dilation of the internal os is minimal (and hence there is no issue of *pesichas hakever*), and although some of the bleeding may be cervical, this procedure causes uterine corpus bleeding which would render the patient a *niddah*. (Newer instruments which avoid grasping the cervix and forcefully dilating the cervical canal would nevertheless render her a *niddah* due to uterine bleeding.) This procedure is usually scheduled very close to the expected menstruation.

Another type of D&C is called a Suction Curettage. This is performed after a miscarriage. In this case, the internal os may be dilated up to 12-13mm. Suction is used to remove all the uterine lining. Bleeding, in this case, may last up to several weeks due to the miscarriage itself. This would render the woman a *niddah*.

There is an opinion that a woman who has no *vest kavuah* must observe *onah beinonis* on the thirtieth day after a D&C.[9]

15. Endometrial biopsy:
(Gr. *endon* — within / *metra* — womb)
This procedure is used to screen for uterine lining disease (usually in older women) or to determine the hormonal status

---

9. *Kineh Bosem* (R' M. Bransdorfer) on *Shach* 189:48. The logic of an *onah beinonis* is the assumption that a woman will menstruate thirty days after the uterus sheds its lining. The cause of the shedding is irrelevant.

of the uterine lining as part of a fertility workup (in younger women), see section F. It involves removing tissue from the uterine lining for evaluation. All women bleed from this procedure. This bleeding is uterine and the woman should be considered a *niddah*. For further details see Section F,4.

16. Insertion of a pessary:
This procedure is performed in older patients with prolapse (dropping) of either the uterus, vagina or the bladder[10] and for urinary stress incontinence. The purpose of the pessary is to provide support for the uterus, vagina or bladder. Some of the patients undergoing this procedure bleed. A woman who removes the pessary for cleaning purposes may also cause bleeding. Bleeding is from the vagina and the outer cervix only. This would not present a *halachic* problem. Nevertheless, as with all gynecological examinations, one should consult a Rav.

> Note: In the event of any abnormal bleeding (e.g., post-menopausal bleeding), it is likely that before inserting a pessary, the gynecologist would perform an endometrial biopsy (rather than attributing the bleeding to prolapse and then blocking visualization with the pessary). As noted in 15 above, this biopsy would result in uterine bleeding and render the patient a *niddah*.

17. Diagnostic hysteroscopy:
(Gr. *hystera* — womb / *skopein* — to look)
This procedure is performed to rule out fibroids and/or polyps or to find their location and to rule out uterine disease.

Technique: The uterus is dilated with a small dilator and inflated with CO_2, hyskon (a sugar solution) or a salt-water solution. The diagnostic hysteroscope (a thin telescope), which is 5-10mm in diameter, is then inserted. Most patients undergoing this procedure bleed, due either to the trauma of dilation of the cervix (the internal os) or to trauma to the endometrial lining of the uterus from the hysteroscope and are rendered a *niddah*. A Rav must be consulted.[11]

---

10. In *halachic* literature this is called a *"forfall"* — a condition in which the uterine cervix falls into the vagina.

11. While the opening of the internal os may not be of sufficient size to render her a *niddah*, we

18. Operative hysteroscopy:
This outpatient procedure, therapeutic in nature, is per-
formed to remove fibroids, polyps and foreign bodies such as
IUDs.

Technique: The uterine canal is dilated to about 1.5cm and
the operative hysteroscope, which is 1cm in diameter, is
inserted. Resection (removal) of fibroids or polyps is done
with a resectoscope which is passed through the hysteroscope. Uterine bleeding always results due to the dilation and
due to the resection. This dilation of the internal os, which
may constitute *pesichas hakever,* and the uterine bleeding
would render the patient a *niddah.*

19. Hysterogram:
(Gr. *hystera* — womb / *gramma* — record)
A procedure done to take an X-ray image of the uterus. A
catheter 3 or 4mm wide is inserted into the uterus. The uterus
is filled with "dye" (radio-opaque medium) through the
catheter. Patients generally bleed after a hysterogram. This
bleeding may be from the cervix or from the uterus which
may be traumatized if the catheter passes beyond the internal
os. In addition, when the dye leaves the body, it is usually
blood tinged either from contact with the endometrium or
from the cervix. A Rav should be consulted.[12]

Another technique involves a tight application of a rubber
cone to the external os. The dye is then injected into the uterus
through a hole in the cone. This method involves less trauma
to the uterus. With this procedure too, the dye is usually
blood tinged when it leaves the body. A Rav should be consulted.

20. Uterine sounding:
This is a procedure for measurement of the uterus. This is
usually done when there is a question of fibroids or before
insertion of an IUD. An instrument approximately 2-3mm is
inserted to the fundus (the top) of the uterus. Less than half of

noted in A,3 that whenever the possibility of uterine bleeding exists, it is difficult to establish with
certainty whether the bleeding is due to menstrual blood being dislodged through trauma or to
an actual wound to the uterus. It is therefore assumed that if there is bleeding after a hysteroscopy,
the patient is a *niddah.* Some *Rabbonim* require that even if no bleeding is visible, she should do a
bedikah.

12. See A,3 above.

patients bleed as a result of this procedure. This bleeding may be as a result of trauma to the internal os or of trauma to the uterus. Nulliparous women (women who have never given birth and whose internal os is more closed) usually bleed as a result of the opening of the internal os, while multiparous women (women who have previously given birth and whose os is more open) bleed less often as a result of the opening. However, since the instrument touches the endometrium, it may dislodge some blood from the uterine lining. It is usually assumed that the woman is rendered a *niddah*.[13]

21. Saline infusion sonography:
This is a diagnostic procedure in which a catheter (approximately 3mm. wide) is inserted into the uterus past the internal os. Saline is instilled and sonography performed. It is assumed that this trauma to the uterus will cause some uterine bleeding and render the woman a *niddah*.

22. Myomectomy:
(Gr. *mys* — muscle / *oma* — tumor / *ektome* — removal)
Fibroids in the uterus near to its lining (submucosal) can cause heavy and prolonged uterine bleeding. This bleeding is not from the fibroids themselves but from the uterine lining which is affected by the fibroids. This bleeding will render a woman a *niddah*. Fibroids on the external wall of the uterus (subserosal) do not cause uterine bleeding unless the fibroids penetrate the uterus. If a physician decides that surgery is necessary to remove the fibroids, they may be removed either abdominally or vaginally, depending upon the location of the fibroid. External fibroids are usually removed abdominally and cause no uterine bleeding. Internal fibroids may be removed vaginally (see also Hysterectomies E,1). This causes trauma to the adjacent lining and renders the woman a *niddah*. A D&C is usually done in either type of myomectomy and will render the woman a *niddah*.

23. Laparoscopy:
(Gr. *lapara* — loin / *skopein* — to look)
This procedure involves looking into the abdominal cavity through an instrument introduced through the navel. This is sometimes performed by a urologist or general surgeon and

13. See A,3 above.

would not cause any uterine bleeding. If it is performed by a gynecologist, he may use a tenaculum to hold the cervix in place. This would cause bleeding from the external surface of the uterus. He may also hold the uterus through an instrument (e.g., humi, approximately 5mm. wide) inserted into the uterus. The woman may be rendered a *niddah* either by uterine bleeding which may result or by the penetration of the uterus by the instrument. A Rav should be consulted.

24. Laparoscopic ovarian cystectomy or conventional surgical cystectomy:
(Gr. *kystis* — bag, cyst / *ektome* — removal)
Removal of cysts from the ovaries through the abdominal wall. This does not usually cause uterine bleeding. However, in the case of laparoscopic ovarian cystectomy, the gynecologist may hold the uterus through an instrument (e.g., humi) inserted into the uterus. This may render the woman a *niddah* as noted in 23. A Rav should be consulted.

25. Vaginal repair, anterior and posterior:
Plastic surgery done on the vagina as part of treatment for prolapse. This always causes bleeding which is not uterine and does not render a woman a *niddah*.

26. Cystourethroscopy:
(Gr. *kystis* — bag, bladder / ureter / *skopein* — to look)
A urinary tract infection (e.g., cystitis) can cause a woman to find blood in her urine. Indeed, the urine may become heavily tinged with blood. One should consult a Rav. If it can be ascertained that the bleeding is due to a urinary infection, the woman is usually *tehorah*. In addition to urinalysis and urine culture, a cystourethroscopy (performed in the event of hematuria — blood in the urine) is usually performed by a urologist. It involves examining the bladder with a scope. This procedure does not involve the uterus and causes no *halachic* problems.

C. External gynecological procedures

1. Vulvar or vaginal biopsy:
All patients undergoing such biopsies bleed from these external sites. This bleeding would not render a woman a *niddah*.

2. Chemical destruction of vulvar lesions:
This procedure includes removal of such external lesions as warts, skin tags and pigmented lesions from the vulvar area. Some patients bleed from the vulva. There is no reason to suspect uterine bleeding.

3. Cryotherapy of external lesions:
This procedure involves removing external lesions (e.g. warts, skin tags) in the vulvar area through freezing. (It is not to be confused with the cryotherapy described in B,8 above which involves the cervix.) This is performed with an instrument attached to a tank of carbon dioxide, nitrous oxide or liquid nitrogen. Bleeding is rare and always external.

4. Bartholin's abscess — I&D (Incision and Drainage) — Marsupialization:
This procedure involves treatment of inflammation and infection of the vestibular gland at the entrance to the vagina by means of incision and drainage. An alternative procedure, called "Marsupialization," involves stitching the lining to the outside to create a new opening. All patients bleed from the incised area. However, the blood is external, not *dam niddah*, and poses no *halachic* problems.

D. Gynecological procedures performed during pregnancy

In addition to the blood tests and the fetal heartbeat checks performed by the obstetrician, the following procedures may be performed during pregnancy:

1. Pap smear:
This is generally performed during the first prenatal visit which is often between the sixth and twelfth week of pregnancy. This procedure may result in bleeding from the endocervical canal. This bleeding will not usually render the woman a *niddah* (See Section B,4, above).

2. Colposcopy with biopsy:
This procedure is performed in the event of an abnormal Pap smear, and results in bleeding from the biopsy sites (which are external to the cervix). One should note that ECC (endo-

cervical curettage) is rarely performed during pregnancy. See Section B,5,6.

3. Sonogram:

This procedure is used to confirm the EDC (Expected Date of Confinement), to check on the development of the fetus and to evaluate abnormal bleeding (this bleeding renders her a *niddah*). In the event of placenta previa (a condition in which the placenta is implanted abnormally in the uterus so that it covers the internal os and causes painless bleeding) or abruptio placenta (separation of the placenta from the uterine wall which may cause severe and painful uterine bleeding), a sonogram is done for placental localization. The sonogram itself does not cause bleeding.

4. Cervical culture:

As noted in Section C,18 above, this procedure is performed on all pregnant patients to screen for multiple infectious agents (e.g., chlamydia). Most practitioners also perform a Group B Strep culture at approximately thirty-six weeks to ascertain that the mother is not a carrier. Some patients bleed from the cervical canal or from the outer cervix. As noted above, the woman is generally not rendered a *niddah*.

5. Pelvic examination:

This examination is performed on a weekly basis beginning at the thirty-sixth week of pregnancy. Some physicians perform a membrane stripping (to hasten the onset of labor), in which the physician inserts his finger and rotates it between the cervix and the amniotic sac (the bag that contains the fetus and amniotic fluid). Frequently this results in bleeding from the cervix due to local cervical trauma. This alone may not be problematic. However, the finger penetrates the internal os and may be a problem of *pesichas hakever*. A Rav should be consulted. The inclusion of membrane stripping in this work should not suggest that it is an approved procedure. In fact it is controversial. We are merely commenting on the *halachic* status of the woman.

6. Amniocentesis:

(Amniotic / Gr. *kentesis* — pricking)

> Note: There are *hashkafic* as well as *halachic* reservations regarding genetic testing of a fetus. One should

not perform these tests without prior consultation with one's Rav.

Amniocentesis is an outpatient procedure generally performed sixteen to twenty weeks after the first day of the last menstrual period. Early amniocentesis, at less than fifteen weeks' gestation, is sometimes performed. The procedure is used to screen for chromosomal disorders and for neural tube defects. This procedure involves inserting a needle with a stylet through the abdominal wall under the guidance of ultrasonography and withdrawing amniotic fluid for laboratory analysis. In rare instances, this procedure will result in bleeding due to penetration of a uterine blood vessel. Another rare occurrence is penetration of the placenta which may result in bleeding into the amniotic fluid. Premature labor and cervical bleeding may, on rare occasions, result from this procedure. If there is bleeding a Rav should be consulted.

7. CVS (Chorionic Villus Sampling):
Another form of genetic diagnosis is CVS. A bit of placental tissue is extracted either through the abdominal wall or through the cervix. If the procedure is performed through the cervix a catheter (approximately 3mm. wide) is inserted through the cervix into the uterus to remove the placental tissue. This usually results in bleeding which renders her a *niddah*. If the procedure is performed abdominally, there is usually no bleeding through the cervix. However, if bleeding occurs it will render her a *niddah*.

8. Other *halachic* issues arising late in pregnancy:
We noted in Chapter Two, Section V,C the questions of dilation before childbirth, breaking of the water and the mucous plug.

a. Dilation:
When a woman is in the process of childbirth, the uterus opens to a degree that renders her a *niddah*. *Poskim* rule that when a woman is placed upon the travailing chair (or has such contraction pangs that would cause her to be placed on it if it were available[14]), we must be concerned that the uterus has

---

14. See *Sidrei Taharah* ibid. who notes that certainly it is not the travailing chair that causes her to be considered a *niddah,* but her condition. See also *Igros Moshe, Y.D.* 2:75.

opened and caused a discharge of *dam*.[15] Therefore, a woman who has difficulty walking due to her contractions must consider herself a *niddah*.[16] Contemporary authorities rule that neither widely spaced contractions nor the initial dilation of the uterus fall into this category and do not render her a *niddah*.[17]

b. Breakage of the water:
Some *Poskim* rule that if a woman's water breaks, she is not rendered a *niddah* if she can produce a clean *bedikah*.[18] Others consider her a *niddah* if childbirth is imminent since the water may have been accompanied by blood.[19]

c. Mucous plug:
The mucous plug is a collection of thick mucus in the uterine cervix that is often expelled just before labor begins. Some *Rabbonim* rule that when the mucous plug is expelled, the woman becomes a *niddah* since the plug may be streaked with blood. Others contend that the blood associated with the mucous plug is not uterine in origin and does not render her a *niddah*.[20]

E. Hysterectomies

Although the primary focus of this chapter has been the gynecological procedures performed in the practitioner's office or on an out-patient

---

15. The source of this ruling is Responsa *Nachlas Shivah* 9, quoted in *Pischei Teshuvah* 194:8. Indeed, *Nachlas Shivah* contends that even if the contractions stopped completely, the woman has become a *niddah*. In his case, the woman did not actually give birth until four weeks later. Although most *Poskim* reject this view, for they assume that since no birth occurred, the uterus did not open, they accept the basic premise that a woman who is placed upon the travailing chair is considered a *niddah*. See *Chavos Daas* 194:1[b], Responsa *Chasam Sofer* (*Y.D.* 179) and *Sidrei Taharah* 194:25.

16. See *Sidrei Taharah* ibid. citing *Mishnah* (*Oholos* 7:4).

17. See *Igros Moshe*, *Y.D.* 2:76, and *Shiurei Sheivet HaLeivi* 194:2[4]. He notes that dilation begins as early as the sixth month and usually by the beginning of the ninth month. This dilation is not a sign of imminent birth.

18. Responsa of R' S. Z. Auerbach printed in appendix to *sefer Mareh Kohein* p. 184.

19. *Shiurei Sheivet HaLeivi* 194:2[4].

20. Discussions with gynecologists support this latter view which is accepted by many *Rabbonim*.

basis, hysterectomy, the most common major gynecological operation (and the second most common of all major surgical procedures), will be briefly discussed.

1. Abdominal hysterectomy:
(Gr. *hystera* — womb / *ektome* — removal)
Hysterectomy is performed as a result of such acute conditions as severe infection or a pregnancy catastrophe — due to benign diseases such as fibroids, endometriosis and recurrent uterine bleeding — and due to premalignant or malignant disease.

a. Total hysterectomy:
This procedure, which can be done either abdominally or vaginally, involves removal of both the body of the uterus and the cervix. The tubes and ovaries may also be removed (salpingo-oophorectomy, unilateral or bilateral, see c below).

Patients who undergo a total hysterectomy generally experience bleeding from the vaginal vault for two to four weeks. Some *Poskim* rule that the blood which is removed with the uterus in the course of the hysterectomy itself does not render the woman a *niddah*. Only blood that flows from the uterus causes *niddus;* blood that exits with the uterus does not.[21] However, it is possible that due to manipulation of the uterus before the actual surgery, a woman may experience uterine bleeding and becomes a *niddah*. In addition, a D&C is sometimes performed before the hysterectomy. This will certainly render her a *niddah*. A Rav should be consulted in any case.

A woman who had a total hysterectomy and finds blood in the future does not become a *niddah*.[22] If she was in the *niddah* status before the procedure was done, she certainly requires *tevilah*. She may have difficulty completing the *taharah* process due to continual bleeding. A Rav must be consulted.[23]

---

21. See responsa *Har Tzvi*, *Y.D.* 147.

22. *Har Tzvi* ibid., responsa *Chelkas Yaakov* 3:14, *Minchas Yitzchak* 1:125,126, *Sheivet HaLeivi* 2:90.

23. See the responsa cited above.

b. Subtotal hysterectomy (Supracervical Hysterectomy): (L. *supra* — above / cervix)

This procedure, which is done abdominally, involves removing the body of the uterus, leaving the cervix in place attached to the vagina. If there is no bleeding through the cervix, the woman is not rendered a *niddah*.

Patients undergoing subtotal hysterectomy may also experience bleeding for a period of two to four weeks post-operatively. The bleeding is generally from the cervix. In rare cases, a portion of the body of the uterus may remain after a subtotal hysterectomy. In this case, a woman may continue to experience bleeding. This bleeding would render her a *niddah*.[24] Therefore, a woman undergoing a subtotal hysterectomy must inquire whether any portion of the body of the uterus remains.

c. Salpingo-oophorectomy or Bilateral-salpingo-oophorectomy: (Gk. *salpinx* — tube / *oophoron* — ovary / *ektome* — removal) (L. *bis* — two / *latus* — side)

In women who are post-menopausal or approaching menopause, bilateral salpingo-oophorectomy, the removal of the tubes and ovaries, is routinely performed along with abdominal hysterectomy. Rarely, the tubes may be removed without the ovaries; this is called salpingectomy. Neither of these procedures alone (without hysterectomy) would cause uterine bleeding.

2. Vaginal hysterectomy:

This approach, used for hysterectomy, avoids an abdominal scar and minimizes post-operative discomfort. It is most commonly performed for uterine prolapse.

F. Fertility procedures

A couple should note that if faced with infertility problems, they <u>must</u> discuss the matter with their Rav before submitting themselves to tests. There are

---

24. Ibid.

many *halachic* issues involved in both the tests and the methods of treatment (including, but not limited to, artificial insemination). A Rav knows that he must discuss these issues with sensitivity and compassion.

1. Mid-cycle bleeding:
Often a couple may have problems conceiving due to mid-cycle bleeding which delays the woman's *tevilah* past her ovulation. Physicians are able to treat this condition with clomid (which delays ovulation) and estrogen (which shortens the period).

2. Post-coital test (PCT):
This procedure is performed to determine how the husband's sperm reacts with cervical mucous. A glass pipette or a soft catheter which is less than 0.5mm in diameter is inserted into the endocervical canal. This procedure is done mid-cycle when the patient is most fertile and should be done less than 6 hours (preferably less than 4 hours) post-cohabitation. A bulb syringe suctions out the mucous. Some patients bleed due to trauma by the glass pipette to the cervical glands. This bleeding does not render the patient a *niddah*.

3. Injection of dye for hysterosalpingography (HSG):
(Gr. *hystera* — womb / *salpinx* — tube / *gramma* — record)
This procedure is done as an outpatient or in a radiologist's office to determine whether the patient's tubes are patent (open and unblocked). The procedure involves injecting a radiographic dye into the uterine cavity and Fallopian tubes. By observing whether or not the dye spills out of the tubes, the physician can verify whether or not the tubes are patent. Normally, HSG is performed between the end of the menstrual bleeding and the ovulation.
Technique: After inserting a speculum, a catheter (either plastic or metal) which measures 1-3mm in diameter, is inserted into the cervix. The catheter tip may extend beyond the internal os. A balloon is inflated to prevent backflow. Dye is then injected into the uterine cavity which spills into the tubes. Patients generally bleed after hysterosalpingography. This bleeding may be from the cervix or from the uterus which may be traumatized if the catheter passes beyond the internal os. In addition, when the dye leaves the body, it is blood

tinged either from contact with the endometrium or from the cervix. A Rav should be consulted.[25]

Another technique involves a tight application of a rubber cone to the external os. The dye is injected into the uterus through a hole in the cone. This method involves less trauma to the uterus. With this procedure too, the dye is blood tinged when it leaves the body. A Rav should be consulted.

4. Endometrial biopsy:

This procedure may be done as part of fertility work to diagnose ovarian function and the uterine capacity for implantation (it may also be done as a screening procedure, see B,15 above).

Endometrial biopsy involves the use of an endometrial suction curettage instrument. A plastic instrument not measuring more than 5mm may be used (one commonly used model is the Pipelle). Other versions of this instrument are of metal and are also no more than 5mm in diameter.

The instrument is inserted to the fundus (the roof) of the uterus and is twirled as it is removed while suction is applied. All patients undergoing endometrial biopsy bleed. Since this blood is from the uterine lining, one assumes that she is rendered a *niddah*. A Rav should be consulted.

5. Artificial insemination:

Often infertility is treated with artificial insemination. Two techniques are described below.

> Note: There are serious *halachic* issues regarding artificial insemination. These include, but are not limited to, the method of gathering the semen and the concern that another person's semen may be substituted. These issues must be discussed with a Rav who has experience in these matters.

a. Cervical:

This technique involves utilizing a thin pipette (a long thin tube resembling a medicine dropper approximately 10mm in thickness) to squirt sperm at the cervix. On rare occasions, this technique results in bleeding from the cervix. Such bleeding will not render the woman a *niddah*.

---

25. See A,3 above.

b. IUI (intrauterine insemination):
This technique involves inserting an instrument which is 1mm in diameter all the way to the fundus (the roof) of the uterus and then withdrawing slightly. Sperm are then squirted into the uterus. Approximately one third of women bleed due to trauma to the glands of the cervical canal. Bleeding is more common in nulliparous women (women who have never given birth) and rare in multiparous women (women who have previously given birth). The probable source of any bleeding is the endocervix. However, it should be noted that since the instrument touches the uterine fundus, one cannot rule out the possibility of the uterine fundus as a source of bleeding with certainty. Such bleeding may require that we consider the patient a *niddah*. A Rav must be consulted.

G. Contraception

Any method of contraception involves many serious *halachic* and *hashkafic* questions. Some methods are more *halachically* questionable than others. One may not use any contraceptive measure without prior consultation with one's Rav. We will only note those methods which fit into the general subject of *hilchos niddah*.

1. A diaphragm:
If a woman is given *halachic* permission to use a diaphragm, she must undergo a fitting session. This involves fitting different-sized rings into the vagina. The uterus is not involved. There is no bleeding.

It should be noted that when using a diaphragm, a woman may traumatize her vagina or the external portion of the cervix during insertion or removal of the diaphragm. In such cases, she may feel pain or discomfort.[26] If blood is found on the edges of the diaphragm, it is likely attributable to trauma, but if blood is found on the center, it is more difficult to attribute it to trauma. In either case, a Rav must be consulted. A woman is advised to always rinse off the diaphragm after

---

26. See *Igros Moshe, Y.D.* 4:17[16].

use without inspection beforehand, thereby avoiding *halachic* problems.

2. An IUD

Another method of contraception is insertion of an IUD (intrauterine device). There are serious questions regarding the permissibility of its use even when contraception is permitted. These revolve around the question of how this device functions. Medicine itself has not reached a conclusive decision whether the IUD blocks the implantation of the fertilized ovum into the endometrium or whether it prevents the fertilization itself. In the first case, it would present a most serious *halachic* question of abortion. Different *halachic* authorities have different views on the matter.[27] One must consult one's *halachic* authority.

Insertion of the IUD involves grasping the cervix with a tenaculum. The uterus is usually sounded (see sounding of uterus, above). The IUD is inserted with a carrier which is 3-4mm in diameter. Bleeding from the external cervix may be caused by the tenaculum, while bleeding from the internal os or the endometrium may result due to trauma. This is generally not a problem since an IUD is usually inserted while the woman is menstruating.

A woman usually bleeds when the IUD is removed as well. This is done by grabbing the string which is connected to the IUD. One usually finds blood on the IUD after it is removed. This may be from trauma to the uterus or it may be due to uterine blood that is dislodged. If the string is absent, the physician will have to insert IUD hooks or perform a hysteroscopy which causes additional uterine bleeding. A Rav should be consulted.[28]

H. Gynecological Conditions

1. Vaginitis:

An inflammation of the vagina which may cause bleeding. This bleeding is not uterine and causes no *niddus* in itself, but may cause difficulty in producing clean *bedikos*.

---

27. Late medical research seems to indicate that the IUD prevents the fertilization itself.

28. It is usually assumed that a woman is a *niddah* after an IUD is removed.

2. Dysmenorrhea:
Painful periods, often treated with medication.

3. Menorrhagia:
Heavy and/or prolonged menstrual bleeding.

4. Metrorrhagia:
Irregular bleeding, i.e., between periods or in absence of periods.

5. Menometrorrhagia:
Irregular, heavy and/or prolonged bleeding.

6. Dysfunctional bleeding:
Abnormal bleeding due to hormonal imbalance, not to a physical cause in the uterus.

7. Cervical dysplasia:
A condition with abnormal cells in the cervix.

8. Prolapse:
Dropping of either the uterus, vagina or the bladder away from their normal position.

9. Fibroids (Leiomyomata):
Fibroids in the uterus (submucosal) can cause heavy and prolonged uterine bleeding. This bleeding is not from the fibroids themselves but from the uterine lining which is affected by the fibroids. This bleeding will render a woman a *niddah*.

10. Hematuria:
Blood in the urine.

I. Common gynecological terms

Cervical — involving the cervix.
Cystectomy — (Gr. *kystis* — bag, cyst / *ektome* — removal) removal of cyst.
Diagnostic — something done to diagnose a condition.
Endometrial — involving the endometrium (the uterine lining).
Endocervix — the part of the cervix just internal to the external os.
Exocervix — the part of the cervix usually external to the external os.
Fundus of the uterus — the top of the uterus.
Hyster — (Gr. *hystera* — womb) involving the uterus.

Intrauterine — inside the uterus.

Laparoscopic — (Gr. *lapara* — loin / *skopein* — to look) through a small incision in the abdominal wall, using a telescope.

Multiparous women — women who have previously given birth.

Nulliparous women — women who have never given birth.

Therapeutic — something done to treat a condition.

An index of topics discussed in this chapter
(bold conotes where topic is main subject of discussion)

Abdominal hysterectomy — **E1**

Abruptio placenta — D3

Amniocentesis — **D6**

Artificial insemination — **F5**

Bartholin's abscess — **C4**

Bilateral-salpingo-oophorectomy — **E1c**

Breakage of the water — **D8b**

Cervical culture — **B3; D4**

Cervical dysplasia — B7,9; H7

Cervical polypectomy — **B11**

Cervical polyps — **B11**

Chorionic Villus Sampling — **D7**

Colposcope — B5

Colposcopy — B4,**5,6,7**; D2

Colposcopy with biopsy — **B6; D2**

Conization of the cervix — B7,**13**

Cryotherapy — **C3**

Cryotherapy of cervix — A1;B4,7,**8,9**

CVS — **D7**

Cystitis — B26

Cystourethroscopy — **B26**

Cysts (ovarian) — **B24**

Cytobrush — B4

D&C — B2,11,13,**14**,22; E1a

Diagnostic hysteroscopy — **B17**

Diaphragm — **G1**

Dilation — **D8a**

Dilation and Curettage see D&C

Dysfunctional bleeding — **H6**

Dysmenorrhea — **H2**

Endocervical curettage — **B7**

ECC — B4,**7,8**,13; D2

Endocervical curette — B7

Endocervical speculum — **B12**

Endometrial biopsy — B2,**15,16**, **F4**

Endometrial polypectomy — **B11**

Endometrial polyps — **B11**

Fibroids B17,18,20,22; — **E1**: H9

Group B Strep culture — **D4**

Hematuria — B26; H10

HSG — **F3**

Humi — B23,24

Hysterogram — **B19**

Hysterosalpingography — **F3**

Hysteroscope — B17,18

Hysteroscopy — B2,**17,18**; G,2

I&D — **C4**

Incision and Drainage — **C4**

Intrauterine device see "IUD"

Intrauterine insemination — B2; **F5b**

IUD — B18,20; **G2**

IUI see "intrauterine insemination"

Laparoscopic ovarian cystectomy — **B24**

Laparoscopy — **B23**

Laser vaporization — B7,**10**
LEEP — A1,B4,7,**9**
Leiomyomata — **H9**
Loop Electrosurgical Excision Proc.,see LEEP
Marsupialization — **C4**
Membrane stripping — **D5**
Menometrorrhagia — H,5
Menorrhagia — B14; H,3,4
Mid-cycle bleeding — F1
Mucous plug — **D8c**
Myomectomy — **B22**
Operative hysteroscopy — **B18**
Ovarian cystectomy — **B24**
Pap smear — **B4; D1**
PCT — **F2**
Pelvic examination — **D5**
Pessary — **B16**
Pipelle — F4
Placenta previa — D3
Polypectomy — **B11**
Post-coital test — **F2**
Post-menopausal bleeding — B14,16
Prolapse — B16,25; E2; H,8

Resectoscope — B18
Saline sonography — B21
Salpingectomy — **E1c**
Salpingo-oophorectomy — **E1c**
Sonogram — **D3**
Speculum — **B1,12**
Subtotal hysterectomy — **E1b**
Suction Curettage — B14; F4
Supracervical Hysterectomy — **E1b**
Surgical cystectomy — **B24**
Tenaculum — **B2**,14,23; G2
Total hysterectomy — **E1a**
Unilateral salpingo-oophorectomy — **E1c**
Uterine polypectomy — **B11**
Uterine polyps — B11
Uterine sounding — **B20**
Vaginal biopsy — **C1**
Vaginal hysterectomy — **E2**
Vaginal repair — **B25**
Vaginitis — **H1**
Vulvar biopsy — **C1**
Vulvar lesions **C2,3**
X-ray of the uterus **B19**

Appendices

✑ Appendix A

The requirement of *hargashah* — an analysis

Poskim raise a fundamental question regarding the Biblical require-ment of *hargashah*. Is *hagashah* a) an absolute requisite for Biblical *tumas niddah*, or b) is it merely a means by which we verify that the blood was actually discharged from her body? In other words, if there were proof that the blood is from her body, would she be a *niddah* by Torah law, even without *hargashah*? *Poskim* present two applications of this question, in two opposite situations:

> i. The blood certainly came from her body, i.e., she actually observed the discharge of blood from her body, but she felt no *hargashah*. According to position a), she is not a *niddah* by Torah law; according to position b), she is.

> ii. The source of the blood is uncertain. It may be from her body or from another source. She felt a *hargashah* which is attributable to another source, i.e., she felt a sensation which may have been the *hargashah* of *dam* or it may have been caused by something else. If we assume that a *hargashah* in itself is the fundamental requirement (position a), the requirement may have been ful-filled and she may be a *niddah* according to Torah law, even though the source of the *hargashah* is questionable. If, however, the purpose of *hargashah* is to prove that *dam* was expelled from her body (position b), then this *hargashah* alone is not sufficient proof and she is not *temei'ah* according to Torah law.

See *Sidrei Taharah* 190:93, s.v. "וכבר" citing *Maharam Lublin* who was the first to raise this question. *Sidrei Taharah* contends that this is subject to a dispute among *Rishonim*. In the opinion of *Rashi, Tosfos* and possibly *Raavad*, the purpose of *hargashah* is to prove that the blood is from her uterus (this appears to be the opinion of *Tosfos Rid, Niddah* 57b, as well). Thus, if the blood undoubtedly came from her, albeit without *hargashah*, she is a *niddah* by Torah law. Conversely, if there was a doubtful *hargashah*, i.e., she finds a bloodstain after marital relations or after doing a *bedikah* (in either case, the internal sensation may be attributed to a source other than that of a blood flow), she is not *temei'ah* by Torah law since we have no proof that the blood is from her body. *Sidrei Taharah* notes that *Rambam* disagrees. *Rambam* maintains that a *hargashah* is an absolute requisite. Thus, even if the blood certainly came from her uterus, but without *hargashah*, she is *tehorah* according to Torah law.

Other *Poskim* disagree entirely with *Sidrei Taharah's* analysis of *Rashi* and *Tosfos'* position (see *Binas Adam* [9], *Aruch HaShulchan* 183:47-54 and *Pardes Rimonim, Pischei Niddah* p. 11-14). They refute all *Sidrei Taharah's* arguments. In their view, even *Rashi* and *Tosfos* agree that a *hargashah* is an absolute requisite for *tumas niddah*. In the view of these *Poskim*, theoretically, even if the blood certainly came from her body, but without *hargashah*, she is *tehorah* according to Torah law. See *Pardes Rimonim*, ibid. who proves that *Rambam, Ramban, Rashba, Ran* and *Chinuch* all agree on this point. *Daas Torah* 190:1 cites *Or Zarua* who concurs with this position. (Practically, however, even these *Poskim* concede that if the blood certainly came from the woman, and there is reason to suspect that there was *hargashah*, she is a *niddah* according to Torah law. See Chapter Three, Section I, A. Whenever blood certainly flowed from her body we assume that there must have been a *hargashah* as well since a blood flow is usually accompanied by a *hargashah*.)

In conclusion, most *Poskim* maintain that a *hargashah* is an absolute requirement (position a). Therefore, in case i, she is not a *niddah* according to the Torah. It may be that in case ii, she is also not a *niddah* according to Torah law, since the *hargashah* is attributable to another source, unless we have other proof that the blood came from her body.

If the blood certainly came from her body but the woman felt no *hargashah* (and there is no reason to suspect that the was mistaken, see below) she is not *temei'ah* according to Torah law, see *Chochmas Adam* ibid. and *Chasam Sofer, Y.D.* 159. *Chasam Sofer* maintains that even if one actually sees the blood flowing from her vagina she is not a *niddah*, in Torah law, unless she felt a *hargashah*. He adds, however, that in this case we assume that there must have been a *hargashah* unless she claims there was none. In §177 *Chasam Sofer* seems to contend that even if she claims there was no *hargashah*, we assume that there was a *hargashah*.

> An interesting point is noted by R' Akiva Eiger (responsa 62 and 81). He contends that if a minor experiences a blood flow (without *hargashah)* or even finds a *kesem* which certainly came from her body, she is *temei'ah* according to Torah law. A minor is not considered responsible regarding all *halachic* matters. Thus, her claim that she felt no *hargashah* is unacceptable. Accordingly, since blood

which comes from the body is usually accompanied by *hargashah,* we must assume that she actually felt a *hargashah* and is therefore *temei'ah* according to Torah law. A similar point is raised by *Sidrei Taharah* 190 end of 1. He cites the Talmud that a one-day-old girl can become a *niddah;* he proves that this is *deOraisa* even though we have no way of knowing that she felt a *hargashah.*

If the blood certainly came from her body and she claims that she felt no *hargashah,* there is reason to believe that the woman's claim is erroneous, i.e., that there actually was a *hargashah* which she mistakenly attributes to another cause. For example, if she did a *bedikah* and found a bloodstain on the cloth, her claim that she felt no *hargashah* is not accepted. We suspect that she actually felt a *hargashah* but confused it with the sensation of the *bedikah* itself. She is, thus, *temei'ah* according to Torah law (*Chavos Daas* 190:1[b], *Sidrei Taharah* 183:2 and *responsa R' Akiva Eiger* §62).There are, however, opinions (see Chapter 3 note 8) that if a woman who did a *bedikah* is certain that she felt no *hargashah* (i.e., she was aware of the possibility of confusing *hargashah* with the sensation of the *bedikah,* and specifically noted that she felt no other sensation than that of the *bedikah),* she is *tehorah* according to Torah law.

In summary, we have four situations regarding blood which certainly came from the body: a) A child who menstruates is always *temei'ah* by Torah law since we assume that there was a *hargashah.* b) A woman who is certain she felt no *hargashah* and there is no reason to assume she is mistaken is *tehorah* according to Torah law. c) If she claims there was no *hargashah,* but we suspect that she is mistaken — she is *temei'ah* according to Torah law (some *Poskim* contend that this is only a *safek,* a strict ruling based on doubt). d) A case where the woman was aware of the possibility of mistake, but is certain that she is not mistaken, is subject to dispute.

One should note that although the impression may be given that the status of a flow hinges, according to Torah law, entirely upon the issue of *hargashah,* there is another equally important requisite. A woman will not become a *niddah,* according to Torah law, unless the blood certainly came from her body (this is completely unrelated to the question of whether a flow that came from the body is assumed to be accompanied by a *hargashah).* Any blood which may be from another source (even if another possible source has not been identified) is not considered a *re'iyah* but a *kesem* and is *tamei* according to Rabbinic law only. This issue is discussed in *Sidrei Taharah* 190:93 s.v. "ועל פי זה." Therefore, a woman who finds a *kesem* is *tehorah,* according to Torah law, even if there is reason to suspect that there may have been a *hargashah.* The mere fact that the blood may be from another source is sufficient reason to exclude this from the Torah law of *niddah*. Examples of this are the following: A woman did a *bedikah* (which was clear) and immediately afterward found a *kesem*, or a woman found a *kesem* immediately after cohabitation or urination. In each of these cases, there is reason to suspect that the dam was accompanied by a *hargashah* which she assumed was the sensation of the *bedikah*, cohabitation or urination. Nevertheless, she is not subject to the Torah laws of *niddah* since the blood may be from another source.

All of the above applies a situation where the *hargashah* was not definite. If, however, she certainly felt a *hargashah*, she is *temei'ah* even according to Torah law even if the blood may have come from another source. The fact that she felt a *hargashah* is proof that the blood is indeed from her body. Accordingly, a woman who feels a sensation of blood leaving the uterus and subsequently finds a *kesem* must treat that *kesem* as a *re'iyah* not a mere *kesem*. This *halachah* is discussed in Section Chapter Three II,B,3.

The reader should note that this discussion pertains to Torah law only. According to Rabbinic law, any *kesem* renders a woman a *niddah* even though she is certain that she felt no *hargashah* and it is not certain that the *kesem* came from her body. This Rabbinic law of *kesamim* is subject to many limitations, such as its minimum size and the type of garment upon which it is found. These are explained in detail in Book Three. However, a flow which renders her a *niddah* according to Torah law is not subject to any of these limitations.

✑ Appendix B

Is a blood flow without *hargashah* analogous to a *kesem*?

Is a blood flow without *hargashah* analogous to a *kesem*? If a woman knows for certain that the blood came from her body, but she felt no sensation, she is a *niddah*, in the view of most *Poskim*, according to Rabbinic law only. As noted in Appendix A, this is the position taken by most *Poskim*. We noted, too, that *Sidrei Taharah* 190:93 (s.v. "על נחזור") contends that *Rashi, Tosfos* and *Raavad* maintain that if the blood certainly came from her body, she is a *niddah* according to Torah law, even though she felt no *hargashah* (this is also the opinion of *Tosfos Rid*). As noted, this is not the accepted view (as *Sidrei Taharah* himself assumes in 190:61, s.v. "עוד"). Rather, we assume that a *hargashah* is a Biblical requisite for *tumas niddah*. The mere appearance of blood, even visibly flowing from the body, will not bring *niddus* according to Torah law. See *Shiurei Sheivet HaLeivi* 190:1[14]. In this sense, finding blood without a *hargashah* is similar to finding a *kesem*. In either case, she experienced no *hargashah* and is a *niddah* according to Rabbinic law only. However, there is a disagreement among *Poskim* as to whether or not a blood flow without a *hargashah* is completely analogous to and governed by the same rules as a *kesem*. *Poskim* note three applications of this general question:

a) A minor who experiences a blood flow without *hargashah*:
When *Chazal* instituted the laws of *kesamim*, they excluded a minor. Although a minor becomes a *niddah* if she has a menstrual flow, she does not become a *niddah* upon finding a *kesem* (*Y.D.*190:2). However, if blood was certainly discharged from her body (without *hargashah*), some *Poskim* maintain that she is *temei'ah* according to Rabbinic law (*Bach* cited in *Shach* 190:3, *Chavos Daas* 190:4[b]). In their opinion, an appearance of blood without a *hargashah* is not governed by the laws of *kesem*. These authorities differentiate between a *kesem*, which perhaps came from a foreign source (and therefore is not applicable to a minor), and a stain or blood flow that certainly came from the body. Others do not differentiate

and maintain that even a stain that certainly came from the body does not affect a minor. (*Shach* ibid. See *Sidrei Taharah* 190:7, who ties this question to a difference of opinion between *Rashi* and *Tosfos.*) One can further divide the idea of blood without *hargashah* (as opposed to a *kesem*) into two different aspects: i) a *kesem* found on the body that is not attributable to a foreign source and surely came from the body, and ii) an actual blood flow without a *hargashah* (see *responsa R' Akiva Eiger* 1:81.)

b) A blood flow attributable to a wound that is not known to be bleeding:

If a woman has a wound that is not known to be bleeding at the time may attribute a *kesem* to that wound, but not a blood flow (see *Rema* 187:5). *Poskim* note that in regard to this *halachah* a blood flow without *hargashah* is similar to a blood flow with *hargashah* and cannot be attributed to a wound unless it is known to be bleeding (*responsa R' Akiva Eiger* ibid.).

c) A blood flow less than a *gris*:

A woman experiences a blood flow less than a *gris* without a *hargashah* or finds blood less than the size of a *gris* on a garment and the blood is not attributable to any source except herself. If this is considered a case of a *kesem*, she would not be *temei'ah* since the flow is less than a *gris*. If, however, one considers this a blood flow, she is *temei'ah* (albeit by Rabbinic law), since a flow, regardless of size, renders her a *niddah*. See *Pleisi* 183:1, *Sidrei Taharah* 190:61 (s.v. "עוד"), *Binas Adam* 113:[9], *Pri Deah* 183:2[sl] and *Yad Avraham* 183:1, who all contend that this is considered a blood flow, not a *kesem;* accordingly, a *gris* is not required. However, *Toras HaShelamim* 183:1 seems to disagree, as does responsa *Me'il Tzedakah* 59 (cited in *Sidrei Taharah* ibid.). The reader should note that there are several leniencies regarding *kesamim* (all noted in Book Three). One is the leniency of a *kesem* less than a *gris* (Chapter Eight). Another is the leniency that a *kesem* is *tamei* only if it is found on a white garment or object susceptible to *tumah* (Chapter Nine). Our discussion relates only to a stain less than a *gris*, since the leniency of such a stain depends upon the possibility of it being insect blood. Therefore, blood which certainly came from the body cannot be suspected of being insect blood. Apparently, *Toras HaShelamim* considers even the leniency of less than a *gris* absolute, i.e. *Chazal* did not mandate *tumah* on any *dam* less than a *gris*. However, the restriction of *kesem* to a white garment and to an object susceptible to *tumah* is absolute and applies even to blood which certainly came from the body. See *Sidrei Taharah* 190 end of 36. It is questionable whether *Bach* and *Chavos Daas* cited above agree to this.

❧ Appendix C

The *bedikah* after a *hargashah* — its purpose

Poskim raise a fundamental question: Is the purpose of this *bedikah* merely to discover a cause for the *hargashah*, or is it also to ascertain that the *hargashah* was not caused by *dam*? In other words, is it sufficient for the *bedikah* to show that the *hargashah* may have been caused by a clear discharge, or must the *bedikah* prove that no blood appeared?

The difference between these two approaches is illustrated in the following example *(Chavos Daas* 190:37[b], cited in *Pischei Teshuvah* 190:6): A woman does a *bedikah*, but subsequently, half the cloth is lost while the other half shows a clear mucus. If the purpose of the *bedikah* is merely to be able to attribute the *hargashah* to an acceptable discharge, the woman is *tehorah*. If, however, the purpose of the *bedikah* is also to ascertain that no *dam* was present, the woman is *temei'ah* since, in addition to the clear mucus, some *dam* may have appeared on the lost half of the cloth.

Chavos Daas (ibid.) contends that the purpose of the *bedikah* is also to prove that no *dam* was present (the second approach). Thus, in the above-mentioned case, she is *temei'ah*. *Chavos Daas* rules that even if she checked herself with a cloth which was previously soiled with red spots and she finds a clear discharge, she is *temei'ah*, since perhaps one of the red spots was from the *hargashah*. Similarly, even if she checks herself with a clean cloth and finds both a clear stain and a red stain, she is *temei'ah* even if she has a wound to which to attribute the red stain, and even if the red stain is less than a *gris*. His rationale in all these cases is the principle that a *hargashah* is usually caused by *dam*. Thus, unless we can prove that no *dam* appeared, she is *temei'ah*.

Pischei Teshuvah ibid. cites the opposing opinion of responsa *Givas Shaul* 67, regarding a *bedikah* done after a *hargashah* with an unchecked cloth, and a clear stain with a small attached red spot was found on the cloth. *Givas Shaul* rules that the woman is *tehorah* since the small red spot is attributed to lice and the clear stain is attributed to the *hargashah*. Apparently, *Givas Shaul* follows the first approach.

Chasam Sofer also disagrees with *Chavos Daas* (although *Pischei Teshuvah* cites him in agreement) regarding the basic principle that the *bedikah* should prove that no *dam* appeared with the *hargashah*. *Chasam Sofer* contends that it is sufficient that we attribute the *hargashah* to a clear stain. However, *Chasam Sofer* disagrees with *Givas Shaul* as well. *Chasam Sofer* holds that we may only attribute the *hargashah* to the clear stain, rather than the blood stain, if it is logical to assume so. Otherwise, we must attribute the *hargashah* to the bloodstain since most *hargashos* are caused by blood. Thus, *Chasam Sofer* (Y.D. 150) agrees with *Chavos Daas* in the case of a *bedikah* cloth previously stained with red spots, since it is more logical to attribute the *hargashah* to *dam*. However *Chasam Sofer* is not in agreement with *Chavos Daas'* principle that the *bedikah* cloth must prove that no *dam* was present. This is apparent from his position in responsa 180. In that responsa *Chasam Sofer* is lenient regarding a *bedikah* done with a garment that was previously worn and subsequent to the *bedikah* several small red stains and an acceptable stain are found on it. He contends that the small red stains should be attributed to lice since lice commonly cause small bloodstains on garments (we noted elsewhere that *Chasam Sofer* relies on this leniency only in a situation where lice are prevalent) and the acceptable stain must be associated with the *hargashah* since there is no other reasonable source to which to attribute the clear stain. The woman is therefore *tehorah*. Apparently, *Chasam Sofer* is in disagreement with *Chavos Daas* in his basic premise that the *bedikah* must prove that no *dam* was present, since in this case we have no proof that none of the red stains are related to the *hargashah*. Accordingly, *Chasam Sofer* would probably disagree with *Chavos Daas* regarding the case of the half of the *bedikah* cloth that was lost. See *Badei HaShulchan* 188:1, s.v. "ובדקה," who notes that most *Poskim* do not seem to follow the view of *Chavos Daas*.

In regard to the basic case of *Chavos Daas*, it seems odd that he chose the extremely unusual case of a woman who lost half the *bedikah* cloth. A much more common case is that of a woman who lost all of the cloth and subsequently does another *bedikah* and finds a clear mucus.

✎ Appendix D

Vestos regarding a flow immediately following another flow

Although a period may last several days, the *vest* day is determined by the day the menstrual flow begins; the duration of the flow is irrelevant with regard to *vestos*. See *Taz* 184:9 and *Shach* 16, citing *Bach*. There are two approaches in explaining this *halachah:* a) The concept of *vestos* is based upon the assumption that the period will begin again on the same day it began last month. We assume that there is something about that day which activates the period. The residual flow in the following days is merely a continuation of the previous flow and is inconsequential to *vestos*. This is the opinion of *Reah* and *Rosh. Raavad* and *Ramban* maintain that all the days of the duration of the flow are considered days of the *vest. Shulchan Aruch* 184:9 follows the view of *Reah* and *Rosh*. This is the case of a continual flow which we will call case a. b) Even if there was a pause in the flow, i.e., the flow stopped for a day or two and then reappeared within seven days from the original onset, it cannot establish a secondary *vest*. According to the Torah, the *tumah* of *niddus* lasts seven days. *Halachah* considers any additional flow during these seven days a mere continuation of the first flow, not an independent flow. For this reason, the Talmud (*Niddah* 11a) rules that a woman cannot set a *vest* during her seven *niddah* days. For example, if a woman menstruates on the first and the fifth of month A and the fifth of months B and C, she has not established a *vest* for the fifth of the month since the fifth day of month A was one of her *niddah* days (see *Rashi* ad loc.). We will call this case of a pause in the flow, case b.

Accordingly, once a woman menstruates regardless of whether her flow continues without pause (case a) or whether her flow pauses and resumes again during the seven days (case b), her *vest* is based only upon the original onset of the menstruation. The continuation or the new secondary flow are irrelevant.

It would seem at first glance that these *halachos* are related. Each is a case of where the *vest* relates only to the original flow. The difficulty with this approach is that *Tur,* end of 189, citing *Ramban,* rules that since today we are not capable of properly distinguishing between *niddah* and *zivah* days (see Chapter Two), a woman can set a *vest* during her *niddah* days. We cannot be certain that the first flow was a normal *niddah* flow; perhaps it was *zivah* or other fluids irrelevant to the *niddah* process. Although *Shulchan Aruch* does not indicate that he follows this view, it is clear that he does from the fact that he omits all the *halachos* regarding establishing a *vest* on *niddah* and *zivah* days, see *Toras HaShelamim* 189:27. Thus, it appears that the *halachah* in case b should change. A woman whose menstruation begins on day one, stops for a day or two and then resumes on day four must consider both day one and day four as *yemei havest.*

Chavos Daas 184:7[b] finds this contradictory to the ruling of *Tur* and *Shulchan Aruch* 184:6, that *vestos* are determined by the beginning of the menstrual flow only, not the residual flow. If we follow only the original onset, why does *Tur* (and *Shulchan Aruch*) rule in 189 that the resumption of the flow is considered a new *yom havest*? *Chavos Daas* initially attempts to differentiate between these two rulings based on the obvious distinction. *Tur* in 184 is speaking with regard to one continual flow (case a). In this case, he considers the entire flow to be one *vest*. However, in 189 he is referring to two separate flows (case b). In this case, we consider each flow as a separate *vest*. *Chavos Daas* goes on to reject this as the sole distinction since women today do not experience a continual flow throughout their menstruation. A menstrual period reaches a stage where it flows and ebbs only to start again after a short while. Thus, the resumption should be considered a new *vest*. Why, then, do all women consider their entire period as one *vest*?

Chavos Daas concludes by differentiating between a case where the actual beginning of the flow became a *vest kavuah* and where it did not. If the initial flow became a *vest kavuah*, for example, she menstruated on days one and five of months A,B and C, she has a *vest kavuah* for day one only. Since we are faced with two potential *vestos kavuos*, we choose the stronger of the two which is day one, the actual beginning of the flow, as opposed to day five which is the secondary flow.

However, if the initial flow did not become a *vest kavuah* while the secondary flow did become *kavuah*, we choose the secondary flow since that is the stronger of the two. For example, if she menstruated on days one and five of months A and B but only day five of month C, she has a *vest kavuah* for the fifth of the month. The secondary flow of day five is considered the main *vest* because it became a *vest kavuah* as opposed to the initial flow of day one, which did not. Accordingly, *Chavos Daas* rules that if a woman menstruates day one and five of month A and passes day one of month B without incident, she is not required to keep day five as a *vest she'aino kavuah* day since it is a secondary flow that did not yet become *kavuah*.

All of the above relates to a case where both menstruations are separate flows, albeit within the same seven *niddah* days (case b). However, if both menstruations were actually part of one continual flow (case a), the secondary flow is inconsequential. This is the *halachah* related in 184.

In summary, the position of *Chavos Daas* is: The secondary flow is considered a separate *vest* day only if a) it is not a direct continuation of the initial flow, b) the secondary day was established as a *vest kavuah* and c) the primary day was not established as a *vest kavuah*.

Graz 184:21 and 189:112 seems to follow a similar approach. He requires that a) the initial flow stopped completely and continued only the next day and b) the secondary flow became established as a *vest kavuah*. *Shiurei Sheivet HaLeivi* 184:6[3] notes that common custom is to assume that a woman's menstruation was made up of one continual flow and she cannot establish a *vest* during the *niddah* days.

Sidrei Taharah 184:9, s.v. "נחזור לעניננו", is also troubled by the above mentioned apparent contradiction between *Tur* 184 and 189. He resolves the problem by requiring that the date of the secondary flow was the date of an initial flow at least once. For example, a woman menstruated on days one and five of months A and B and day five of month C (in s.v. "ולפ"ז י"ל" he explores the possibility that perhaps day five becomes a *vest kavuah* only if it was the primary day twice, e.g., she menstruated days one and five of month A and only five of months B and C). *Sidrei Taharah* does not reach a positive conclusion to this question.

Pardes Rimonim on *Shach* 184:16 offers a completely different approach. He differentiates between a case where a woman menstruated for several days and one where the menstruation was interrupted with at least one day completely free from any flow. In the first case, the entire period is considered one flow. In the second case, it is considered two separate flows. This is similar to *Chavos Daas'* original approach but he avoids *Chavos Daas'* objection by requiring that the menstruation was interupted for a <u>complete</u> day. This distinction has a basis in *Rashi, Niddah* 11a. *Aruch HaShulchan* 184:32 agrees with *Pardes Rimonim*.

In conclusion, *Pardes Rimonim* disagrees with *Chavos Daas*. According to *Pardes Rimonim*, if a woman menstruated on days one and two of months A and B and on day two of month C, she has not established a *vest kavuah*, even if the flows of days one and two were separate flows (since they were not separated by a complete day). *Badei HaShulchan*

184:6, *Biurim* s.v. וכיין, contends that one may follow the lenient approach of *Pardes Rimonim* in this case. However *Taharas Yisroel*, 184:49 follows an even stricter approach than *Chavos Daas*. The singular case in which all opinions agree that a woman establishes a *vest kavuah* through a secondary flow is the following: A woman menstruated on day three of months A and B and day one and three of month C. In this case, day three was an initial flow day twice. We therefore assume that it was the initial flow day of month C as well. The earlier flow of day one was merely additional blood not relevant to her flow. This principle has a Talmudic source in *Niddah* 39b. If the flows of month C were not separated by a full day, i.e., she menstruated day three of months A and B and days two and three of month C, according to *Pardes Rimonim*, she has no *vest kavuah* and according to *Chavos Daas* she has a *vest kavuah* for day three. However, responsa *Cheishev HaEifod* 1:126 contends that, even according to *Chavos Daas*, day three only becomes established as a *vest kavuah* if there was a break between the flows of day two and three. If the flow continued directly without stop, day three cannot become a *vest kavuah*.

All of the above pertains to two flows that were within the same seven days. However, if a second flow begins eight days after the first flow, it is considered a new *vest* in all cases. See Chapter Thirteen, Section II,B,6.

Bibliography

Index

Index of Primary Sources

✒︎ Bibliography

Achiezer — Responsa of R' Chaim Ozer Grodzinsky, head of Rabbinical Court of Vilna and leader of Lithuanian Jewry (1863-1940).

Aruch HaShulchan — *Halachic* compendium following the order of the *Shulchan Aruch* by R' Yechiel Michel Epstein (1829-1908), Rav of Novardok, Russia.

Aruch LaNer — Commentary on various Talmudic tractates by R' Yaakov Ettlinger, Rav of Altona and other communities, author of responsa *Binyan Tzion* and *Bikurei Yaakov* on the laws of *sukkah* (1798-1871).

Asvan D'Oraisa — Collection of original speculative expositions on Talmudic topics by R' Yosef Engel (1859-1920), Rav of Cracow, Poland.

Avnei Miluim — See *Shev Shmaitisa.*

Avnei Neizer — Responsa by R' Avraham Bornstein, *Rav* and *Rebbe* of Sochaczov, Poland (1839-1910).

Bach — Acronym for *Bayis Chadash*, a commentary on the *Tur* by R' Yoel Sirkis (c. 1561-1640), Rav of Belz, Brest-Litovsk (Brisk) and Cracow, Poland, father-in-law of the *Taz.*

Badei HaShulchan — Commentary to *Shulchan Aruch; Yoreh Deah, Hilchos Basar B'chalav* and *Niddah* by R' Feivel Cohen, contemporary Rav and *halachic* authority in Brooklyn, N.Y.

Baer Heiteiv — Commentary to *Shulchan Aruch: Yoreh Deah* (basically abridged from *Taz* and *Shach*) by R' Zechariah Mendel (d.1706), Rav of Belz, Poland (now Ukraine).

Be'er HaGolah — Short glosses to *Shulchan Aruch*, usually only noting the Talmudic source for each *halachah*, by R' Moshe Ravkas (Rivkas) of Vilna (d. 1671)

Be'er Moshe — Responsa of Rav Moshe Stern, Rav of Debreczin, Hungary, and in Brooklyn, N.Y. (d. 1997).

Bedek HaBayis — Critical notes on *Rashba's Toras Habayis* by R' Aharon HaLevy of Barcelona, see *Re'ah.*

Beis Efraim — Responsa of R' Efraim Zalman Margolies of Brod (1760-1828).

Beis Lechem Yehudah — gloss to *Shulchan Aruch, Yoreh Deah* by R' Tzvi Hirsch of Vilna, first printed in 1733.

Beis Meir — Commentary to *Shulchan Aruch* by R' Meir Posner (early 19th century).

Beis Shlomo — Responsa of R' Shlomo, Rav of Skole, Poland, now Ukraine (mid 19th century).

Beis Shmuel — Commentary to *Shulchan Aruch; Even HoEzer* by R' Shmuel ben Uri Shraga Feivish of Voidislav, disciple of R' Heschel of Cracow (late 17th century).

Beis Yitzchok — Responsa of R' Yitzchok Yehudah Schmelkes, Rav of Lemberg and a leading *halachic* authority in nineteenth century Galicia (1828-1906).

Beis Yosef — Commentary by R' Yosef Caro to the *Tur*, see *Tur* and *Shulchan Aruch*.

BeZeil HaChochmah — Responsa of R' Bezalel Stern, Rav in Hermannstadt, Transylvania, Roumania, Melbourne, Australia, Vienna, and after 1982 in Jerusalem (1910-1989).

Binas Adam — Notes to *Chochmas Adam* by the author, see *Chochmas Adam*.

Biur HaGra — Glosses to the *Shulchan Aruch* by the *Gra*, see *Gra*.

Chasam Sofer — The name of the responsa and principal works of R' Moshe Sofer (1763-1839). Rav of Pressburg and leader of Hungarian Jewry.

Chavos Daas — Commentary to *Shulchan Aruch; Yoreh Deah* by R' Yaakov Lorberbaum, Rav of Lissa, Poland (1760-1832), author of *Nesivos HaMishpat* on *Shulchan Aruch; Chosen Mishpat*.

Chavos Yair — Responsa of R' Yair Chaim Bachrach (1638-1702), Rav of Worms, Germany.

Chazon Ish — *Halachic* work by R' Avraham Yeshayah Karelitz of Bnei Brak (1878-1953).

Cheiker Halachah — Compendium on Talmudic and *halachic* topics by R' Naftali Hertz Landau, Rav of Strelisk (first printed in Lemberg 1888).

Cheishev HaEifod — Responsa of R' Henach Padwe, contemporary *halachic* authority in London.

Chelkas Yaakov — Responsa of R' Mordechai Yaakov Breish, Rav of Zurich (d. 1977).

Chemdas Shlomo — Responsa of R' Shlomo Zalman, first Rav of Warsaw, authored glosses on various tractates of the Talmud (early 17th century).

Chezkas Taharah — Commentary to *Yoreh Deah, Hilchos Niddah* by R' Yechezkel Roth, *halachic* authority and Rav of Kahal Karlsburg, Brooklyn NY.

Chidushim U'Biurim — Talmudic discourses by R' Chaim Shaul Greineman of Bnei Brak.

Chinuch — Compendium on the philosophical and *halachic* aspects of the 613 *mitzvos* by an unknown Spanish author among the *Rishonim* of the 13th century.

Chochmas Adam — *Halachic* work comprising the laws contained in *Shulchan Aruch; Yoreh Deah,* by R' Avraham Danzig of Vilna (1748- 1820).

Chochmas Bezalel (also called *Pischei Niddah*) — Commentary on tractate *Niddah* by R' Bezalel Ransburg, disciple of, and member of *Beis Din* of, the *Noda B'Yehudah.* The author notes in his preface that after completing his work he came upon the *sefer Sidrei Taharah* and noticed that much of what he wrote had been said already by the author of *Sidrei Taharah.* Consequently, he rewrote his work omitting anything that had previously been said by *Sidrei Taharah.*

Daas Torah — Glosses on the *Shulchan Aruch* by R' Sholom Mordechai HaKohen Schwadron, renowned *halachic* authority, author of *Responsa Maharsham,* Rav of Brezan, Galicia (1835-1911).

Dagul Mervavah — Glosses on the *Shulchan Aruch* by R' Yechezkel Landau, author of the classic responsa *Noda B'Yehudah,* Rav of Prague (1713- 1793).

Darchei Moshe — Glosses on the *Tur* by R' Moshe Isserles, see *Rema.*

Darchei Teshuvah — Encyclopedic commentary to *Shulchan Aruch; Yoreh Deah* by R' Tzvi Hirsh Shapira, Rav and *Rebbe* of Munkatch, Hungary, (1850-1913). The last volume on *Hilchos Niddah* was finished by his son and successor R' Chaim Elazar Shapira (1870-1937).

Divrei Chaim — Responsa of R' Chaim Halberstam, Rav of Zanz and important Chassidic leader in Galicia (1793-1876).

Divrei Malkiel — Responsa of R' Malkiel Tzvi Tennenbaum, Rav of Lomza (published 1891-1904).

Divrei Chamudos — Comprehensive commentary to *Rosh* by R' Yom Tov Lipman Heller, the famed author of the *Tosfos Yom Tov,* commentary on the *Mishnah* (1579-1654).

Drishah — Glosses on the *Tur* by R' Yehoshua Falk Katz, *Rosh Yeshivah* in Lemberg (d. 1614).

Eibshutz, R' Yonasan — Rav of Prague and Altona, Hamburg and Wansbeck. Author of *Kreisi U'Pleisi* on *Yoreh Deah, Urim V'Tumim* on *Chosen Mishpat* and many homiletic works (c. 1690-1764).

Eiger, R' Akiva — Author of responsa *Teshuvos R' Akiva Eiger* (1761-1837) and many important *halachic* works including glosses on the *Shulchan Aruch,* Rav of Posen (Prussia / Poland).

Eimek HaTeshuvah — Responsa of R' Yechezkel Roth, see *Chezkas Taharah*.

Elef LaMateh — Source notes to *Mateh Efraim*, both by R' Efraim Zalman Margolies, see *Beis Efraim*.

Eliashiv, R' Yosef Sholom — Leading contemporary *halachic* authority, *Dayan* in Jerusalem.

Frenkel, R' Baruch — See *Imrei Baruch*.

Gilyon Maharsha — Glosses to *Shulchan Aruch*; *Yoreh Deah* by R' Shlomo Eiger (1786-1852), son of and successor to R' Akiva Eiger as Rav of Posen, Poland.

Givas Pinchas — Responsa of R' Pinchas HaLeivi Horowitz, see *Hafla'ah*.

Givas Shaul — Responsa of R' Shaul ben Moshe, Rav of Lomza (published 1774).

Gra — Acronym for *HaGaon Rabbeinu Eliahu*, R' Eliahu ben Shlomo Zalman the famed and revered Gaon of Vilna (1720-1797).

Graz — Acronym for *HaGaon Rabbeinu Zalman*, R' Shneiur Zalman of Liadi, author of the *Shulchan Aruch HaRav* and the *Chasiddic* classic, the *Tanya, Rebbe* in Liozna and Liadi, Lithuania (1745-1813).

HaElef Lecha Shlomo — Short responsa by R' Shlomo Kluger, of Brod (1785- 1869)

Hafla'ah — *Chiddushim* on tractate *Kesubos* by R' Pinchas HaLeivi Horowitz (1730-1805), Rav of Frankfurt–am–Main and mentor of the *Chasam Sofer*. His gloss to *Shulchan Aruch*, called *Chiddushei Hafla'ah*, are printed in the back of many editions of *Shulchan Aruch*.

Hagahos Maimonis — Notes on *Rambam's Mishnah Torah* often citing opinions of the Tosafists, by R' Moshe HaKohen, a disciple of *Maharam* of Rottenburg. R' Moshe and his family perished in the massacres instigated by Rindfleish in 1298.

Har Tzvi — Responsa of R' Tzvi Pesach Frank, Rav of Jerusalem (1874-1960).

Igros Moshe — Responsa of R' Moshe Feinstein of New York, contemporary leading *halachic* authority (1895-1986).

Imrei Baruch — Gloss to *Shulchan Aruch* and to *Chavos Daas* by R' Baruch Teomim Frankel, Rav of Leipnick, Moravia (today Czechoslovakia) and author of *Sefer Baruch Taam* (1760-1828).

Imrei Binah — Responsa of R' Meir Auerbach, Rav of Kalish, Poland before emigrating to Jerusalem (published 1871).

Imrei Yosher — Responsa of R' Meir Eisenstadter, Rav of Ungvar, Hungary, disciple of *Chasam Sofer* (d. 1852).

Kinas Sofrim — Responsa of R' Shlomo Kluger on the laws of *sta"m*, *niddah* and *mikvaos*, (published, Lemberg 1860).

Kineh Bosem — Responsa and commentary to *Yoreh Deah; Hilchos Niddah* by R' Meir Bransdorfer, contemporary *halachic* authority and *Dayan* in the *Eidah HaChareidis* of Jerusalem.

Kitzur Hilchos Niddah — Summary of *Hilchos Niddah* in two volumes by R' Aharon Pfeuffer, Rav in Johannesburg, South Africa.

Kitzur Shulchan Aruch — (an abridged *Shulchan Aruch*) A *halachic* work comprising the laws contained in *Shulchan Aruch* (primarily *Orach Chaim* and parts of *Yoreh Deah* including *Hilchos Niddah*) by R' Shlomo Ganzfried, *Av-Beis-Din* of Ungvar, Hungary (1804-1886).

K'sav Sofer — Responsa by R' Avraham Shmuel Binyamin Sofer, son and successor to his father the *Chasam Sofer* as Rav of Pressburg, Hungary (1815-1871).

Lechem VeSimlah — Commentary by R' Shlomo Ganzfreid on *Yoreh Deah; Hilchos Niddah,* see *Kitzur Shulchan Aruch.*

Leket Yosher — Compendium of *halachos* and *minhagim* by R' Yosef ben Moshe, a disciple of *Terumas HaDeshen* (late 15th Century).

Levushei Sarad — Glosses to *Shulchan Aruch* by R' Dovid Shlomo Eibshitz, Rav of Chorostokov (1765-1814).

Levushei Mordechai — Responsa of R' Mordechai Leib Winkler, Rav of Maad, Hungary (early 20th century).

Maadanei Melech or **Maadanei Yom Tov** — Comprehensive commentary to the *Rosh* by R' Yom Tov Lipman Heller, the famed author of *Tosfos Yom Tov,* Rav in Vienna (1579-1654).

Magid Mishnah — Earliest commentary on *Rambam's Mishneh Torah* by R' Vidal of Tolosa, Spain (late 14th century).

Maharam Lublin — Acronym for *Moreinu HaRav Meir*. Responsa of R' Meir ben Gedaliah, Rav and *Rosh Yeshivah* of Lublin (1558-1616)

Maharam Padua — Acronym for *Moreinu HaRav Meir* Responsa of R' Meir Padua, Rav of Padua, Italy, relative and contemporary of *Rema* (1473- 1565).

Maharam Shick — Acronym for *Moreinu HaRav* Moshe Shick, author of responsa bearing that name, Rav of Chust, Hungary (1807-1879).

Mahari Assad — Acronym for *Moreinu HaRav* Yehudah Assad, author of responsa *Teshuvos Mahariya* (or *Yehudah Yaaleh*). Rav of Semnitz, Hungary. Volumes I and II published 1873 and 1880 respectively (1794-1866).

Mahari Steif — Acronym for *Moreinu HaRav* Yonasan Steif, author of responsa bearing that name. *Dayan* in Budapest, later Rav in Brooklyn N.Y. (1877-1959).

Maharil — Acronym for *Moreinu HaRav Yaakov Leivi*. Responsa and codified customs by R' Yaakov ben Moshe HaLeivi Moellin, *Rosh Yeshivah* in Mainz and leader of Ashkenazic Jewry (c.1360-1427).

Maharil Diskin — Acronym for *Moreinu HaRav Yehoshua Leib* Diskin, Rav of Brisk, Lithuania and from 1877 leader of Ashkenazic Jews in Jerusalem (1817-1898).

Maharshal — Acronym for *Moreinu HaRav Shlomo* Luria (1510-1573). Contemporary of *Rema*. Authored responsa and *sefer Yam Shel Shlomo*, a Talmudic commentary consisting of *halachic* essays on seven tractates.

Maharsham — Acronym for *Moreinu HaRav Shalom Mordechai* Schwadron, author of responsa bearing that name, see *Daas Torah*.

Maharsheishach — Acronym for *Moreinu HaRav Shmuel Shattin Cohen*. Rav and *Rosh Yeshivah* of Frankfurt on Main (d. 1719).

Malbushei Taharah — Commentary on *Yoreh Deah; Hilchos Niddah* by R' Dovid Tzvi Auerbach, Rav of Dubna (first printing, Warsaw 1862).

Masos Binyamin — Responsa of R' Binyomin Aharon Solnik, disciple of *Rema* and *Maharshal* (d. C. 1620).

Mei Niddah — Commentary to *Yoreh Deah; Hilchos Niddah* by R' Shlomo Kluger, see *HaElef Lecha Shlomo*.

Meiri — Commentary to the Talmud by R' Menachem HaMeiri of Perpignan, Southern France (c.1249-c.1306).

Mekor Chaim — Commentary on *Yoreh Deah; Hilchos Niddah*, consisting of two parts: *Mekor Chaim* and *Tiferes Tzvi* (first printing 1798) by R' Shneur Ziskind Gundersheim, *Rosh Beis Din* in Frankfort, Germany.

Minchas Chinuch — *Chiddushim* on the 613 *mitzvos* by R' Yosef Babad (1800- 1875), Rav of Tarnipol, Poland (now Ukraine), based upon *sefer HaChinuch* (Lemberg 1869). See *Chinuch*.

Minchas Yitzchok — Responsa of R' Yitzchak Yaakov Weiss, Rav in Manchester, England and later Rav of the *Eidah HaChareidis* in Jerusalem (d. 1989).

Misgeres HaShulchan — Commentary to the *Kitzur Shulchan Aruch* by R' Chaim Yehshayahu HaCohen of Rachov, Hungary (mid 19th century).

Mishnah Acharonah —Commentary on *Mishnayos Teharos* by R' Efraim Yitzchok *Dayan* in Premishla, Galicia, Poland (1762-1843).

Mishnah B'rurah — Commentary to *Shulchan Aruch Orach Chaim* by R' Yisrael Meir (*HaKohen*) Kagan of Radun, Poland (1839-1933) known by the title of his classical compendium on the laws of *lashon ha'ra* — *Chafetz Chaim*.

Mishnas R' Aharon — Responsa of R' Aharon Kotler, *Rosh Yeshivah* of Kletzk, Lithuania and Lakewood New Jersey (1898-1963).

Mishneh LeMelech — *Chiddushim* on *Rambam's Mishneh Torah* by R' Yehudah Rosanes (1657-1727), Rav in Constantinople, Turkey.

Mordechai — *Halachic* compendium on most tractates of the Talmud by R' Mordechai ben Hillel (born c. 1240) R' Mordechai and his family perished in the massacres instigated by Rindfleish in 1298.

Nachlas Shiva — Responsa of R' Shmuel ben Dovid HaLeivi, Rav in Halberstadt and Bamberg, disciple of *Taz* (d. 1681)

Nekudos Hakesef — Critical notes on *Taz* by R' Shabsai *HaKohen,* see *Shach.*

Nishmas Avraham — Contemporary work on the *halachos* concerning medi cine by Dr. Avraham S. Avraham of Jerusalem.

Noda B'Yehudah — Responsa by R' Yechezkel Landau, Rav of Prague (1713- 1793), see *Dagul Mervavah.*

Or Zarua — R' Yitchak b' Moshe of Vienna (*RIAZ— R' Yitzchak Or Zarua,* d.1260), one of the *Baalei HaTosfos,* disciple of R' Yehudah of Paris and Rav*yah,* Rebbe of *Maharam* of Rottenburg.

Or Zaru,a R' Chaim — Responsa of R' Chaim Or Zarua (late 13th century) son of R' Yitzchok author of *Or Zarua.* Disciple of *Maharam* of Rothenburg.

Orach Chaim — One of the four sections of the *Tur* and *Shulchan Aruch,* dealing with laws of daily practice throughout the year.

Panim Meiros — Responsa of R' Meir Eisenstadt, Rav of Eisenstadt (1670- 1744).

Pardes Rimonim — Commentary to *Yoreh Deah; Hilchos Niddah* in two parts: *Miksheh Zahav* on *Taz* and *Sifsei Chacham* on *Shach,* by R' Moshe Yitzchok Avigdor, Rav of Kovna and Shklov, among other cities (d. 1865). First volume printed in 1869, the last two volumes recently pub lished from manuscript.

Pische Zuta — *Halachic* work on *Hilchos Niddah* by R' Pinchas HaLeivi Horowitz, Rav in Groswardein.

Pischei Migadim — Contemporary *halachic* work on *Hilchos Niddah* by R' Menachem Dan Meisels of Jerusalem.

Pischei Teshuvah — References to responsa works, following the order of *Shulchan Aruch* by R' Tzvi Hirsh Eisenstadt, Rav of Utian, Lithuania (1812-1868).

Pleisi (Kreisi U'pleisi) — Commentary to the first part of *Shulchan Aruch; Yoreh Deah,* by R' Yonasan Eibshutz. The commentary on *Hilchos Niddah* is named *"Tiferes Yisrael"* but most commonly referred to as *"Pleisi".* See R' Yonason Eibshutz.

Poseiach Shaar — contemporary *halachic* work on *Hilchos Niddah* by R' Sholom Friedman, *Dayan* in London (printed, London 1986).

Pri HaSadeh — Responsa of R' Eliezer Deutch, printed 1906.

Pri Migadim — A two part commentary to the *Shulchan Aruch; Yoreh Deah* by R' Yosef Teomim, *maggid* of Lemberg and later Rav of Frankfurt on the Oder (1727-1792).

Pri Deah — Commentary on *Yoreh Deah; Hilchos Niddah* in two parts: *Turei Kesef* on *Taz* and *Sifsei Levi* on *Shach,* by R' Azriel Dov, Rav of Karsan.

Prisha — Glosses on the *Tur* by R' Yehoshua Falk Katz, *Rosh Yeshivah* in Lemberg (d. 1614), see *Drisha.*

Raavad — Acronym of R' Avraham ben David of Posquieres, Talmudist and Halachist, most famous for his *hasagos* (critical comments) on *Rambam's Mishneh Torah* author of *sefer Baalei HaNefesh* on *Hilchos Niddah* (c. 1120-c. 1197)

Rabbeinu Tam — R' Yaakov b' Meir (1100-1171), grandson of *Rashi* and one of the earliest and greatest of the Tosafists.

Rabbeinu Yona — Talmudist, most famous for his classical ethical works including *Sha'arei Teshuvah, Iggeres HaTeshuvah* and his commentary to the *Rif* tractate *B'rachos* (c.1180-1263).

Radvaz — Acronym for R' David ben Zimra author of an extensive responsa bearing that name, Chief Rabbi of Egypt (c.1480-1573).

Rambam — Acronym for R' Moshe ben Maimon, author of the *Mishnah Torah — Yad HaChazakah* (1135-1204). Any reference to *Rambam* is found in *Hilchos Issurei Biah,* unless noted otherwise.

Ramban — Acronym for R' Moshe ben Nachman, author of commentary to the Talmud, to the Torah and codifier of the laws of *Niddah* (d. 1270).

Ran — Acronym for R' Nissim, Halachist and Talmudic commentator (c. 1290 - c. 1375).

Rashba — Acronym for R' Shlomo ben Aderes, Rav of Barcelona, known for his Talmudic commentary, many responsa and *sefer Toras HaBayis,* see *Toras HaBayis* (1235-1310).

Rashi — Acronym for R' Shlomo Yitzchaki, leading commentator on the Torah and the Talmud (1040-1105).

Rav Pealim — Responsa of R' Yosef Chaim of Baghdad, author of *Ben Ish Chai* and leader of Eastern Jewry (c.1835-1909).

Re'ah — Acronym for R' Aharon HaLeivy (1230-1300), Rav of Barcelona, Spain (with *Rashba*). See *Bedek HaBayis.*

Rema — Acronym for R' Moshe Isserles, Rav and *Rosh Yeshiva* of Cracow. Author of *Sefer HaMapah* — annotations to R' Yosef Caro's *Shulchan Aruch* and *Darchei Moshe* to the *Tur;* ultimate *halachic* authority for all of Ashkenazic Jewry (1530-1572).

Reshash — Acronym for R' Shmuel Shtrashun of Vilna (1794-1872), author of supra commentary to Talmud, printed in the back of most editions of the Vilna Talmud.

Rif — Acronym for R' Yitzchak al–Fasi, Talmudist and Codifier (1013-1103).

Ritva — Acronym for R' Yom Tov Ibn Asevili, 14th century Talmudic com mentator and Halachist.

Rivash — Acronym for R' Yitzchok ben Sheshes, born in Barcelona in 1326 and died in Algiers in 1408.

Rosh — Acronym for R' Asher ben Yechiel, Talmudic Commentator and author of Halachic compendium arranged on the tractates of the Talmud, bearing his name (c. 1250-1327)

Rosh Efraim — Commentary to *Shulchan Aruch* by R' Efraim Zalman Margolies, see *Beis Efraim*.

Sefer HaChinuch — See *Chinuch*.

Sefer Hamikneh — Commentary on tractate *Kiddushin* by R' Pinchas HaLeivi Horowitz, see *Givas Pinchas*.

Shaar HaMelech — Glosses on *Rambam's Mishneh Torah* by R' Yitzchok Nunis Bilmunti of Izmir, Turkey (d. 1774).

Shaarei Deah — Commentary on *Shulchan Aruch; Yoreh Deah* by R' Elazor, Rav of Santov, Hungary, author of *Shemen Rokeah*.

Shaarei Taharah — Compendium on *Hilchos Niddah* by R' Yechiel Michel Stern, contemporary Rav in Jerusalem.

Shaarei Tohar — Compendium on *Hilchos Niddah* by R' Avraham Chaim Einhorn from Ober Visheve, Hungary (late 19th century).

Shach — Acronym for *Sifsei Kohen*, classical commentary to *Shulchan Aruch; Yoreh Deah* and *Chosen Mishpat* by R' Shabsai HaKohen of Vilna (1622- 1663).

She'arim M'tzuyanim B'halacha — Glosses to the *Kitzur Shulchan Aruch* by Rav Shlomo Zalman Braun, contemporary *halachic* authority in Brooklyn, New York (d. 1995).

She'ilas Ya'avetz — Responsa by R' Yaakov Emden of Altona, Germany, son of the *Chacham Tzvi* (1698-1776).

Sheivet HaLeivi — Responsa of R' Shmuel HaLeivi Wosner of Bnei Brak, contemporary *halachic* authority, see *Shiurei Sheivet HaLeivi*.

Shev Shemaitisa — Classical Talmudic compendium by R' Aryeh Leib HaCohen Shain, dealing with issues of *safek, chazakah, rov* and *eidus*, author of *K'tzos HaChosen* on *Shulchan Aruch; Chosen Mishpat* and *Avnei Miluim* on *Shulchan Aruch; Even HaEzer*.

Shev Yaakov — responsa of R' Yaakov HaCohen Papirs, Rav in Prague and Frankfurt (d. 1740).

Shevilei Taharah — Compendium on *Hilchos Niddah* by R' Yechiel Michel Stern, contemporary Rav in Jerusalem.

Shiltei Giborim — Glosses to *Rif* by R' Yehoshua Boaz, author of the refer- ences *Mesores HaShas, Torah Or* and *Ein Mishpat,* printed on the margin of every page of the Talmud (1518-1555).

Shiurei Sheivet HaLeivi — Commentary on *Yoreh Deah; Hilchos Niddah* from lectures given by R' Shmuel HaLeivi Wosner Rav of Zichron Meir, Bnei Brak and contemporary *halachic* authority.

Shiyarei Taharah — Notes on *hilchos mikvaos* by R' Meir Arak.

Shoel U'meishiv — Responsa of R' Yosef Shaul Nathanson, Rav of Lemberg (Lvov), Poland (now Ukraine) (1810-1875).

Shulchan Aruch — Universally accepted Halachic compendium encompass ing all facets of practical *halachah,* by R' Yosef Caro (1488-1575).

Shvus Yaakov — Responsa of R' Yaakov Reisher, author of *Minchas Yaakov* on *Toras Chatas* and *Toras HaShelamim* on *Yoreh Deah; Hilchos Niddah,* Rav of Prague, Worms and Metz (c.1670-1733).

Sidei Chemed — *Halachic* encyclopedia of many volumes covering a wide range of subjects by R' Chaim Chizkiyahu Medini, Rav of Karasubazar in Crimea, Russia (1832-1904). We have used the Freidman edition (New York 1962) and used those volume and page numbers for reference.

Sidrei Taharah — Classic commentary on *Yoreh Deah; Hilchos Niddah* by R' Elchonon Ashkenazi, Rav of Shetland (late 18th century).

Smag — Acronym for *Sefer Mitzvos Gadol.* A comprehensive compendi- um of the 613 *mitzvos,* by R' Moshe b' Yaakov of Coucy, an early 13th centu ry Tosafist. Because this compendium is more extensive than that of R' Yitzchok of Corbell, they became known as *"Gadol"* and *"Kattan"* respectively.

Taharas HaBayis — Two volume compendium on *Hilchos Niddah* by Rav Ovadiah Yossef, *halachic* authority and formerly *Rishon L'Tziyon* in Jerusalem.

Taharas Yisroel — Compendium on *Hilchos Niddah* by R' Yisrael Yitzchok (author of *Birchas Yisrael* on *Hilchos B'rachos*), late 19th centu- ry Rav in Praga, Poland.

Tanya — See *Graz.*

Tashbatz — Acronym for *T'shuvos Shimon Ben Tzemach.* Responsa of R' Shimshon Duran (1361-1444).

Taz — Acronym for *Turei Zahav,* classical commentary to all of the *Shulchan Aruch* especially *Orach Chaim* and *Yoreh Deah* by R' David HaLeivi Rav of Ostroh and later in Lemberg (1586-1667).

Terumas HaDeshen — Responsa of R' Yisrael Isserlein, German halachist (c.1390-1460).

TeShuras Shai — Responsa of R' Shlomo Yehudah Tabbak, Rav in Sighet, Roumania (printed in 1905-1910).

Teshuvah MeAhavah — Responsa of R' Eliezer Fleckeles, disciple of *Noda B'Yehudah* and Rav of Prague (1754-1826).

Teshuvos HaRosh — Responsa of *Rosh*, see *Rosh*.

Teshuvos VeHanhogos — Short responsa by R' Moshe Sternbuch, contemporary *halachic* authority and Rav in Johannesburg, South Africa and *Eidah HaChareidis* in *Jerusalem*.

Tevuas Shor — *Halachic* compendium by R' Efraim Shlomo Schor, Rav of Lublin (d. 1633).

Tiferes LeMoshe — Gloss To *Shulchan Aruch; Yoreh Deah* by R' Moshe, Rav of Horodna, grandson and disciple of R' Heschel of Cracow (d. 1681).

Tiferes Tzvi — Responsa on issues of *Shulchan Aruch; Yoreh Deah* by R' Tzadok HaKohen (Rabinowitz) Lithuanian *gadol* who became a *chassid* of R' Mordechai Yosef Leiner of Izbica and eventually a leader of *Chassidim* in Lublin (1823-1900). Authored many works on *Chassidic* thought.

Tiferes Tzvi — Commentary on *Yoreh Deah; Hilchos Niddah*, see *Mekor Chaim*.

Toras HaBayis — Halachic compendium, primarily of dietary laws and *Hilchos Niddah*, composed of the unabridged work (*Toras HaBayis HaAaruch*) and a synopsis (*Toras HaBayis HaKatzer*), and *Mishmeres HaBayis* (a rebuttal of criticisms of *Bedek HaBayis*) by *Rashba*, see *Rashba*.

Toras HaShelamim — Commentary on *Yoreh Deah; Hilchos Niddah* by R' Yaakov Reisher, see *Shvus Yaakov*.

Tosfos — Talmudic commentaries of the Tosafists; the school of French and German Talmudic analysts of 12th and 13th centuries.

Tosfos Rid — Commentary to the Talmud by R' Yeshaya di Trani (c.1200-1260).

Tosfos Yom Tov — Commentary to the Mishnah by R' Yom Tov Lipman Heller, see *Maadanei Yom Tov*.

Toras Chaim — Commentary to *Chullin* and several other tractates, by R' Avraham Chaim Shor, served as Rav in Belz, Kremenitz, Satanov and Lemberg (d. 1632).

Tur — *Halachic* compendium of R' Yaakov *Baal HaTurim*, son of the *Rosh*, upon which the *Shulchan Aruch* is based and patterned (c. 1275-c. 1340).

Tuv Taam Vodaas — Responsa of R' Shlomo Kluger, see *HaElef Lecha Shlomo*.

Tzemach Tzedek — Responsa and commentaries to *Shulchan Aruch* of R' Menachem Mendel, grandson of the *Graz* and leader of *Chabad* Chassidim (1784-1866).

Tzitz Eliezer — Contemporary responsa by R' Eliezer Yehudah Waldenberg, *halachic* authority and member of the *Beis Din* in Jerusalem.

Waldenberg, R' Eliezer — See *Tzitz Eliezer*

Yabia Omer — Responsa by Rav Ovadiah Yossef, see *Yechaveh Daas.*

Yad Avraham — Gloss to *Shulchan Aruch; Yoreh Deah* by R' Avraham Maskil Le'aison of Minsk, Russia (1788-1848).

Yad Yosef — Halachic work by R' Yosef Yehudah Strasburg, Rav of Kosov, Jerusalem 1898. According to the title page, the work met the approval of R' Yehoshua Leib Diskin and R' Yosef Chaim Sonnenfeld.

Yechaveh Daas — Contemporary responsa by Rav Ovadiah Yossef, *halachic* authority and formerly *Rishon L'Tziyon* in Jerusalem.

Yeshuos Yaakov — Commentary to *Shulchan Aruch* by R' Yaakov Meshulem Orenstein, Rav of Lemberg (early 19th century).

Yoreh Deah — One of the four sections of the *Tur* and *Shulchan Aruch,* deal ing primarily with the laws of kashrus, purity and other subjects.

✎ Index

abdominal hysterectomy 466
abruptio placenta
  definition of 463
aches
  as vest haguf 338
akiras vest
  definition of 266
  through hormonal therapy 368
  vest hachodesh 326, 335, 386
  vest haflagah 326, 327, 329, 387
  vest haguf 353
  vest hamurkav 354
  vest haones 361
  vest kavuah 276, 324, 327, 328, 333
    only with bedikah 276
  vest she'aino kavuah 325, 330
amasla 93, 94, 103–106
  accepting on the day of her expected
    period 103, 106
  cannot establish a fact 105
  caution in resolving questions of 106
  choosing not to accept 106
  encouraging a retraction 106
  if announced niddus publicly104
  if displayed niddus publicly 104
  retained niddah status for a long
    period 104
  regarding tevilah 105
  when suspicion is justified 106
amniocentesis
  consultation with Rav beforehand 463
  description of 464
  status in halachah 464
amniotic fluid
  removal of 464
anatomical terms
  our inability to properly identify 424
  regarding hilchos niddah 423
anovulation 364
artificial insemination
  cervical 469
  consultation with Rav beforehand 469
  intrauterine 470

asking a second opinion
  regarding a bedikah cloth 152
Aviasaf's view
  regarding onas havest 404
avoiding kesamim problems 173, 214
  by wearing colored garments 207
  by wearing very dark undergarments
    184
  should or may, wear colored garments
    208
Bartholin's abscess treatment of 462
bathing
  during the onas havest 398
bedikah
  after a gynecological examination 138,
    422, 444
  after finding a kesem 175, 183
  after hargashah, its purpose 483
  assumed accompanied by hargashah
    50, 73, 123
  attributing a stain to a wound 286,
    433, 434
  bedikah afterwards with unchecked
    cloth 81
  before cohabitation after onas havest
    passes 413
  blood on, the equivalent of a blood
    flow 124
  checking hands before 130
  depth to which must be inserted 131
  doing unnecessary 146
  done immediately before cohabiting
    278, 396
  done with
    colored cloth 127
    large garment 128
    tampon 129
    paper 130
    raw cotton 129
    finger 133
  douching beforehand 130, 134
  during the onas havest 136, 395
    number of bedikos required 397

bedikah (continued)
  during onah beinonis 137
  during the seven clean days 136
  during vest kavuah 395
  excessive bedikos 183
  experiences pain at the time of 434
  first three times of cohabitation 281
  following a hargashah 137
  how differs from kesem 123
  if painful 133
  if required before or after cohabitation
    280, 281, 285
  judged more cautiously than a kesem
    124
  manner in which performed 131
  on day of expected vest 136
  on onas havest, whether Biblically
    required 259
  position during 131
  proper cloth to be used 127
  purpose 122
  repeating immediately 165
  required on the onah of the vest 277
  requirement of, after hargashah 78
  upon finding a kesem 138
  using a pre-checked cloth 125, 130
  using a washed cloth 125
  washing the external area before 130
  when required 135
  whether certainly accompanied by
    hargashah 123
  woman insists that she felt no
    hargashah 73, 479
bedikah cloth
  being needlessly strict regarding 146
  black specks or granules on 143
  blood found on, after hargashah 78
  blood on, attributable to hymenal
  bleeding 133
  cleanliness 127
  clear mucous on 156
  dampening 133
  discarding after inspection 142, 144
    if usually changes color 164
  if lost 109, 139
  if not checked thoroughly before
    insertion 150
  if required to show to husband 144
  inspecting a thin cloth 128
  inspection
    by night 144–146, 162
    by day 144
    in direct sunlight 146

bedikah cloth,
  inspection (continued)
    of attached string 143
    while still damp 142
    with magnifying glass 142, 159
  keeping for an extended period 148
  left laying in the open 125
  made of
    cotton 129
    linen 129
    synthetic material 129
    wool 128
  marking and identifying 37
  method of
    inspection 142
    marking 148
    storing 147
  must be white 127
  not checked thoroughly before
    125,130
  red thread on 159
  reddish tinge on, if safek deoraisa
    154
  ruling on those of of one's wife 110
  size 128
  smallest red or black speck on 142,
    143, 159
  stain during first three of the seven
    clean days 249
  stain on
    beeswax color 158
    black 155, 156
    brown 157
    egg yolk color 158
    esrog color 158
    gold color 158
    grey 156
    light grey 156
    orange color 159
    surrounded by thin red edge 143,
      159, 160, 162
    yellow 158
  storing for a longer period 37, 160
  storing properly 37
  tampering with 159
  texture 127
  thickness 128
  tiny red spot on 159
  translucent, inspection of 143
  treating with vaseline 134
  why must be clean 127
bedikah cloth, questionable
  a color chart 154

bedikah cloth, questionable (continued)
a woman evaluating the color of a
stain 107
a woman undergoing fertility
treatment 152
asking a second opinion 152
attributing to an external source 159,
166
before the onset of menstruation 273
being improperly lenient 147
changes of color 160, 162–164
informing Rav of 160
overturning lenient ruling 160
possibility of 160
if usually changes color 164
conduct in the interim 148
from a bride 152
if felt pain at the time 151
importance of showing to a Rav 146,
155
marking small spot 150
may be accompanied by hargashah
186
not accepting lenient ruling of a Rav
147
of a pregnant or nursing woman 151
possibility of attributing stain to
another source 151
preference of asking a sheilah personally 149
providing the Rav with all relevant
information 149
reddishness disappears when dry 162
regarding vestos 268
renders a woman niddah according to
Torah law 186
repeating immediately 165
repeating the bedikah 164, 165
repeating the hefseik taharah 148, 164,
165
repeating the moch dachuk 148
showing a stain to another woman 108
teliyah 159, 166
waiting until it dries 160
whether to note on the calendar 269
woman insists that originally was red
163
woman insists that she felt no hargashah 186
woman who has a vaginal irritation
152
bedikah, first three cohabiations
a woman with a negative vest 283

bedikah, first three cohabiations
(continued)
churin u'sedakin, or only kinuach 281
examining the cloth the following day
281
how early before 281
how late after 282
if not done 282
if required 281
if valid on one night 281
number of bedikos 281
should be consecutive 282
when dam besulim is possible 282
women who are exempt 282
bedikos
doing additional 135
limiting the number of 134
prior to cohabitation 137
three preliminary 137
beeswax color
stain found upon a bedikah cloth 158
bein hashinayim, definition of 425, 426
beis hachitzon, definition of 423, 426
belching spell as vest haguf 338
besulah 117, 132, 247, 370, 380, 381
definition of 370
manner in which to do bedikah 132
regarding vest she'aino kavuah 381
regarding vestos 370
bilateral-salpingo-oophorectomy
description of 467
biopsies 450
birth of a female
regarding niddus 64, 65
birth of a male, regarding niddus 63, 64
bitul, regarding yom havest 414, 416
black or navy blue garments wearing
to avoid kesamin 173, 184, 204
bleeding caused by external trauma 450
blood flow
due to wound 59, 66, 428-434
minute amount 58
of minor, without hargashah 478
result of gynecological examinations
59, 428-434
that does not leave the body 58
without hargashah 72, 123, 477, 478
during seven clean days 72
if analogous to kesem 72, 481
blue and green stain on bedikah cloth
158
bodily tremble
as hargashah 75

bodily tremble (continued)
    without appearance of blood 78
breakage of the water during childbirth
    465
bride, stain found upon a bedikah cloth
    152
brown stain on bedikah cloth 157
caesarean section
    regarding niddus 64
    regarding vestos 375
calendar
    if lost 413
    importance of keeping record 260
    marking immediately 386
    to note whether period began by day
        or night 271
    whether to note bedikah stains on 269
candle lighting time, as relates to onas
    havest 384
causative and symptomatic vestos 263
cervical bleeding 441
    status in halachah 425
cervical culture
    description of 452
    status in halachah 463
cervical dysplasia 454
    definition of 472
    description of 455
cervical erosion 428
cervicitis 428
cervix, status in halachah 424, 439
chaluk habaduk
    definition of 215
    garment previously worn during
        niddus 216
    garment taken from the clothes-dryer
        216
    pre-washed garments 216
chaluk she'aino baduk
    definition of 215
    stain seems to be actual blood 216
changing time-zones
    regarding onas havest 404
    regarding seven clean days 404
chibuk v'nishuk 396
    during the onas havest 394
    during the Or Zarua vest 403
    if bedikah omitted on onas havest 278
    on onas havest prior to journey 406
childbirth
    breakage of the water 465
    contractions during 465
    dilation during 464

childbirth (continued)
    flow accompanying, regarding vestos
        376
    mucous plug is expelled 465
childbirth, twenty four months after,
    regarding the problematic days 412
chlamydia 452, 463
Chorionic Villus Sampling
    consultation with Rav beforehand 464
    description of 464
    status in halachah 464
churin u'sedakim 132, 395
clomid 468
Clomiphene 365
cohabitation
    bedikah if required before and after
        280, 281
    before one embarks on a journey 405
    blood flow during 67
    blood found afterwards 285
    kesem found afterwards 185
    kinuach afterwards 73
    may cause menstruation 258, 280
    may cause the flow to come earlier
        347
    may mask a hargashah 50
colored garments 71, 80, 87, 91, 151,
    172-174, 183-185, 192, 194, 196, 197,
    202-207, 209-211, 237, 245, 273
colored garments
    black undergarments 208
    during her vest day 208
    during the seven clean days 208
    garment with a white lining 208
    if certainly originated from her body
        207
    if obviously blood 207
    kesem found upon 172
    light beige 208
    off-white 208
    should or may, wear 208
    wearing to avoid kesamim problems
        172, 207
colposcopy 453
    description of 453
    status in halachah 453, 454
    with biopsy 453, 462
common gynecological terms 472
contraception
    consultation with Rav beforehand 470
    permissibility of 198
contractions during childbirth 63, 465
contradicting the ruling of another Rav 152

cotton
kesem found upon 214
cramps
as vest haguf 338
cryotherapy
of the cervix 450, 453, 454
description of 454
status in halachah 455
cryotherapy of external lesions
status in halachah 462
curette 456, 457
CVS see "Chorionic Villus Sampling"
cystitis 461
cystourethroscopy
description of 461
cytobrush 453
D&C 452, 456, 466
description of 457
if must observe onah beinonis after
457
dam besulim 67, 247, 282
first three of the seven clean days after
247
dam chimud 247
first three of the seven clean days after
247
dam makkah
definition of 428
dam niddah
black 57, 153, 155
where turns black 155
dry 59, 61
esrog color 153
four shades of red 57, 153
light black 154
not to differentiate between shades of
red 57
the subtlety of the different shades
203
dam tohar
practical halachah 65
Torah law 63
dampness, sensation of
as hargashah 76
finds a stain afterwards 91
whether requires bedikah 91
day, definition of 261, 263
diagnostic hysteroscopy
description of 458
status in halachah 458
diaphragm
blood found on 470
fitting session 470

diaphragm (continued)
rinse off after use 471
dilation before childbirth 63
dilator 457
douching
before a bedikah 130, 134
during the onas havest 398
during the seven "clean" days 131, 134
dysfunctional bleeding
definition of 472
dysmenorrhea
description of 472
ECC 453, 456
EDC, definition of 463
egg yolk color stain found upon a
bedikah cloth 158
eid b'chezkas meluchlach, definition
125, 126
eid beinoni, definition of 126, 215
eid habaduk 115, 124–127, 215
definition of 125, 215
eid she'aino baduk, definition of
125, 126, 215
endocervical canal
bleeding from 450
definition of 450
endocervical curettage 453
description of 454
status in halachah 454
endocervix, definition of 455
endometrial biopsy 451, 452
definition of 457
description of 469
status in halachah 458, 469
endometriosis 466
esrog color stain found on a bedikah
cloth 158
estrogen 468
regarding vestos 365
estrogen/progesterone pills 365
regarding vestos 365
exocervix, definition of 455
external flow, sensation of
as hargashah 76, 87
if usually finds clear discharges 88
stain found afterwards 88
less than a gris 87
on a colored garment 87
external os 424
Factrel 365
fallopian tubes 424
fecal matter, attributing stain to 159
fertility problems 364

fertility treatment
    notifying the Rav 152
    consulting a Rav beforehand 363, 467
fibroids 459, 460, 466, 472
    removal of 460
finger, bedikah done with 133
finger-width, measurement of 212
first day of Rosh Chodesh regarding
    vestos 301
first three months of pregnancy
    see "pregnancy, first three months"
first three of the seven clean days
    see "seven clean days, first three days"
flatulence, as vest haguf 338
fluorescent light, inspection of bedikah
    with 144, 162
forfall 458
fright, inhibits the onset of menstruation
    370
fundus, definition of 459
garment worn during niddus period
    attributing a kesem found on 242
garment not previously checked for
        cleanliness, kesem found upon 172
garment taken from clothes-dryer, kesem
    found upon 172
garment taken from the drawer, kesem
    found upon 172
garment with a white lining, kesem
    found upon 173
gilui arayos 48
    severity of 48
gold color, stain found on bedikah cloth
    158
grey stain found on bedikah cloth 156
gris, kesem smaller than
    see "kesem, smaller than gris"
gynecological examination 61
gynecological procedures
    doing a bedikah afterwards 138
    during the seven clean days 433, 445,
        446
    during the time of her vest 446
    on day of her expected menstruation
        446
    performed during pregnancy 462
    resulting in bleeding 443
    scheduling of 445
gynecological terms 472
halachic decisions regarding one's wife
    110
halachic ruling
    asking a second opinion 38

halachic ruling (continued)
    contradicted by the Rav himself 110
    contradicting the ruling of another
        Rav 152
    whether overturned if color changes
        160
handshaking between men and women
    47
harchakos 34, 105, 210
    during the onas havest 395
hargashah
    accustomed to feeling hargashos
        discharge during her seven clean
            days 90
        if requires bedikah 84, 88
        regarding a pregnant or nursing
            woman 90
        sensation occurred on the day of
            her veset 89
    as opposed to vest haguf 75, 338
    associated with kesem 184
    assumed to accompany menstruation
        49, 176
    bedikah afterwards 137
        external, if sufficient 80
        if half the cloth is lost 483
        if immediate 81
        if not immediate 78
        no blood found 81
        only a light fluid found 79
        purpose of 78–81, 483
        required, or merely chumra 81
        with unchecked cloth 81, 483
    Biblical source 72
    blood flow without, during seven
        clean days 176
    definite and possible 184
    definition of 75
    during the onas havest 401
    if absolute requirment according to
        Torah law 72, 175, 176, 477
    if not completely certain that felt
        hargashah 82
    if not during time of expected period 81
    of fluid leaving her body 401
    of vaginal flow 401
    regarding pregnant or nursing woman
        81
    requirement of 49
    sensation of during cohabitation 77
    stain on garment found afterwards 79
        if attributable 80
    usually finds clear discharges 84

hargashah (continued)
    without appearance of blood 77
    woman unduly nervous about 81
headache
    as vest haguf 339
hefseik taharah
    attributing stain on to a wound 432
    done before the end of five days 246
    purpose of 130, 136
    repeating if questionable 165
    repeating immediately 165
    that was lost 109
    with the smallest red or black speck 143
hematuria
    definition of 461, 472
hemorrhoids
    attributing a kesem to 151, 159, 166,
        174, 233, 240
    attributing a kesem to during first
        three days 248
hilchos niddah
    being inappropriately lenient or strict 35
    importance of studying and reviewing
        34
hormonal therapy 36, 59, 363–368
    akirah of vest through 368
    establishing a vest through 368
    must discuss with Rav 363
    reasons for 363
    regarding vestos 363, 366
    reservations about 364
hot flashes,
    as vest haguf 339
hugging or kissing
    see "chibuk v'nishuk"
humi 461
hymenal bleeding
    see "dam besulim"
hysterectomy
    abdominal 466
    if finds blood in the future 466
    subtotal 467
    total 466
    vaginal 467
hysterogram
    description of 459
    status in halachah 459
hysterosalpingography
    description of 468
    status in halachah 469
hysteroscopy 452, 471
    diagnostic 458
    operative 459

I&D 462
immediate, definition of 73, 78
immediate retraction of self declared
    niddah status 102
incandescent bulbs, inspection of
    bedikah with 144, 162
incontinence 458
inflammations 428
inspection of bedikah cloth
    at night 144–146
    difficulty of 146
    during the day 144
    entire surface of the cloth 143
    in direct sunlight 146
    in sunlight 144
    including attached string 143
    tiny black specks 143
    tiny red specks 143
    translucent cloth 143
    while still damp 142
    with electric light 144, 162
internal flow
    sensation of, as hargashah 76
internal os 424
intimate talk, during the onas havest 394,
    406
Intrauterine device see "IUD"
intrauterine insemination 452
    description of 470
    status in halachah 470
issur niddah
    punishment 46
    whether tumah or issur 46
IUD 459
    insertion of 471
    permissibility of 471
    removal of 471
IUI, description of 470
kever (uterus)
    definition of 424
kinuach 395, 412
joking
    regarding self declared niddah staus
        103
    impropriety of jesting regarding
        niddah status 107
journey
    chibuk v'nishuk on onas havest 406
    cohabitation before 405
    embarking on prior to onas havest 405
    Or Zarua's vest 406
judging colors on a bedikah cloth,
    difficulty of 107

kallah
  bedikah the first three times of cohabi-
      tation 282
  manner in which to do bedikah 132
  regarding kesamim 170, 181
  using hormonal treatment 364
kareis
  definition of 47
kesamim
  as a vest haguf   210, 339, 400
  avoiding
      by wearing colored garments 173,
          184, 207, 214
      by wearing very dark
          undergarments 184
      should or may, wear colored
          garments 208
  originally established regarding tumas
      niddah 190
kesem
  a black stain 194
  a very large stain 204, 215
  abstaining from cohabitation when
      finding 173, 184
  accompanied by a hargashah 151, 211
  after menopause 170, 181
  appears to have fallen from the
      ground upwards 200
  as opposed to a reiyah 170, 175
  associated with a hargashah 184
  assuming indirect contact 227
  attributing to
      her niddus days 250
      external source 124, 174
      hemorrhoids 174
      nose-bleed 174
      partially healed wound 174
      wound 431, 432
  avoiding 172, 183
  before the onset of menstruation 273
  black stain 199
  color different from menstrual blood
      199
  definition of 176
  dependent upon being found 179
  difference between it and reiyah 170
  difficulty in measuring 180
  doing a bedikah after finding 138, 175,
      183
  first three of the seven clean days after
      a 246
  found after
      cohabitation 174, 185, 186, 480

kesem (continued)
      hargashah 184, 196
      urination 185
  found close to expected period 173
  found during the onas havest 400
  found in
      shower stall 211
      urine or stool 215
      water 211
  found on
      back of the hand 225
      body and garment 196
      body only 195, 224
      both white sides of a colored area
          206
      calf 226
      cloth used to wipe the vaginal
          opening 197
      colored garment 172
      cotton 214
      diaphragm 198
      fingers 224
      foot 226
      garment not checked for cleanliness
          172, 215
      garment taken from the clothes-
          dryer 172
      garment that is pulled upwards 221
      garment used as covering during
          daytime nap 222
      garment used as covering at night
          174, 222
      garment with a white lining 173
      ground or anything attached to it
          211
      hand 196, 224
      heel 226
      husband 227
      kerchief 223
      leg 226
      loose fitting robe 221
      mattress 222
      nylon 214
      object that is not mekabel tumah
          173, 210
      outer garment 223
      outer surface of a garment 223
      palm 224
      paper 212
      partially colored garment 172, 192
      parts of body that are far from one
          another 195
      plastic toilet seat 173

kesem, found on (continued)
    pleated garment 193
    quilt 174, 222
    robe or dress 220
    robe used as covering during sleep 174
    sanitary napkin 214
    sheet 174, 222
    shoulder 220
    sleeve 221
    slip 223
    small piece of cloth 211
    stretchable garment 193
    synthetic materials 214
    tampon 214
    thick, absorbent garment 194
    thigh 226
    toes 226
    toilet fixture 173
    toilet seat 186, 211
    toilet tissue 173, 185, 212–214
    top of blouse 220
    wall in Eretz Yisrael 211
    water 186
    wrist or fore-arm 225
  garment was lost or washed 172, 180
  how differs from bedikah 123
  if certain that she felt no hargashah 178
  if certainly originated from the body 197
  if felt external sensation of a flow 173, 185
  if tahor, may be washed immediately 180
  if the tampon is clean 223
  its color 199
  its shape 200
  keeping for an extended period 171, 180
  laws of, reason established 177
  location 173
  may be from external source 170, 175, 176
  measurement of 171
  minimum size 171
  niddah according to Rabbinic law only 170, 175
  not required to check her garments for 170, 179
  on garment taken from the drawer 172
  partially on white and partially on colored 205
  perhaps instituted only regarding laws of tumah 177

kesem, found on (continued)
  practical difference between it and a reiyah 178
  practically the equivalent of a reiyas dam 179
  preceding a menstrual period 183
  preventing from reaching a gris 199
  reciting b'rachah on tevilah 178
  regarding
    kallah 170, 181
    minor 181
    pregnant or nursing women 170, 181
    tightly fitting undergarments 225
    unmarried woman 170, 181
    vestos 170, 175, 179, 267
  requires same taharah procedure as reiyah 170, 178
  shape of 171
  showing to a Rav 171, 180
  smaller than a gris 188
  surrounded by a red edge 192
  teliyah 174
  that is certainly blood 400
  that passes through two garments 194
  two small separate stains on the body 195, 224
  two smaller stains 171, 193
  whether to abstain until the staining stops 273
  which may be from the first three days 249
  why not s'fek s'feika 177
  why not safek deoraisa 176
  with several shades 192
  without hargashah 170, 175
kesem, on body
  measurement of 171
  smaller than a gris 171, 224
  two separate spots 171
kesem, on colored
  a sensation of a flow 209
  a stain partially on the white and partially on colored 205
  accompanied by a hargashah 211
  found after a hargashah 209
  found after cohabitation 209
  found immediately after urination 209
  close to the expected arrival of period 209
  during the first three of the seven clean days 203

kesem, on color (continued)
if almost certainly came from body
203, 211
if obviously blood 203
larger than a gris 203
logic of the exemption today 204
on colored fingernail 202
on colored ground 202
on colored skin 202
on object other than garment 202
on the day of her expected period 203
reason for exclusion 203
type of color
color only noticeable when
compared to white 205
colors other than red 202
extremely light shaded fabrics 205
depth of the fabric color 204
light beige 205
light pastel colors 205
off-white 205
type of garment
black undergarments 204
leather garment 207
naturally colored garment 206
naturally colored but dyed white
202
non-absorbent materials 202, 206
pale yellow garment 204
partially colored garment 205
treated white garment 207
white woof and colored warp 206
worn close to the body 207
type of stain
a dry piece of blood 207
a thick kesem 207
a very large stain 204, 210
wiped onto white garment 202
kesem, on object not mekabel tumah
a piece of dried blood 210
accompanied by a hargashah 211, 215
during the first three of the seven
clean days 211
held by something that is mekabel
tumah 210, 213
if almost certainly came from body 210
if found on the day of expected vest 211
if mekabel tumah only according to
Rabbinic law 210
if susceptible to tumas negaim only 210
reason exempted 210
very large kesem 215
kesem, smaller than a gris

a black stain 194
a stain that spread 192
a thick stain 194
an oblong kesem 191
difficulty relating the halachah to
modern times 190, 244
found after a hargashah 189, 196
found on
cloth used to wipe the vaginal
opening 197
diaphragm 198
garment and the body 196
only upon the body 195
pleated garment 193
stretchable garment 193
thick, absorbent garment 194
the body 171, 213, 224
the hand 196, 225
if certainly originated from the body
189, 197
if dependent upon the prevalence of
lice 190, 191
if excluded because of teliyah 189, 245
measurement of 189, 191
passed through two garments 194
two small separate stains on the body
195
two small stains 171, 193
why excluded 188
with several shades 192
kinuach 73, 132, 213, 281, 285
after cohabitation 73
definition of 73
Lacerations 428
laparoscopic ovarian cystectomy
description of 461
laparoscopy 445
description of 460
laser vaporization 454
description of 455
status in halachah 455
leap year
regarding meinekes 375
LEEP 450, 453, 454
description of 455
status in halachah 455
Leiomyomata, definition of 472
light beige, kesem found upon 173
light pastel colored garments, kesem
found upon 172
lipstick, attributing stain to 159
lost
garment with kesem 172, 180

lost (continued)
  bedikah cloth 109
  hefseik taharah 109
  vestos calendar 413
Lutrepulse 365
makor, definition of 424
Marsupialization, status in halachah 462
meinekes 59
  after caesarean section 375
  bedikah the first three times of
    cohabitation 283
  definition of 375
  establishing a vest during 376
  if forgot the exact date of vest 416
  onah beinonis 375
  pre-existing vestos 376
  regarding
    a leap year 375
    pesichas hakever 438
    teliyah b'makkah 429
    thirty-first onah beinonis 375
    vest hadilug 312
    vest she'aino kavuah 381
  required term of pregnancy 375
  the halachah today 283, 376
  when the twenty-four months pass 377
  why exempt from vestos 375
mekabel tumah 51, 116, 173, 186, 199,
  202, 210–215
membrane stripping, status in halachah
  463
menopause, after 378
  regarding kesem found 170, 181
  regarding pesichas hakever 438
  regarding teliyah b'makkah 429
  regarding vestos 381
menorrhagia, definition of 457, 472
menstrual anatomy 45
menstrual flow
  presumed accompanied by hargashah
    74
  usually begins with staining 184
menstrual process 45
menstruation
  brought on by cohabitation 394
  usually not a small spot 400
Metrodin 365
metrorrhagia, definition of 457, 472
mid-cycle bleeding 59, 364, 365, 468
migo, to retract self made niddah status
  101
miktzas hayom k'kulo 54
mikveh, for unmarried women 58

minor
  claims that she felt no hargashah 478
  definition of 181
  kesem of, if blood was certainly
    discharged from her body 481
  regarding a blood flow 182
  regarding kesamim 181
    if unattributable to any other source
    182
  regarding pesichas hakever 438
miscarriage 44, 66, 283, 375, 376
  regarding vestos 375, 376
moch dachuk 37, 107, 119–121, 132, 135,
  136, 145, 148–150, 152, 158, 166
  when performed 136
month, regarding vestos, exclusively to
  the Hebrew month 261
mood changes, not considered a vest
  haguf 340
mucous plug 63
  when expelled 465
multiparous women, definition of 460
myomectomy, description of 460
nausea, as vest haguf 339
negiah with an ervah 58
  whether Biblically prohibited 47
newlyweds, onah over a span of several
  days 411
niddah
  if difficult to ask her whether she
    immersed 100
  physical contact with 47
  remains so until she states that
    immersed 99
  tevilah on the seventh day 54
niddah and zivah, difference between
  the two 52
niddah status, using in jest or quarrel 107
niddus caused by a kesem, regarding the
  first three of the seven clean days 247
niddus caused by a small speck,
  regarding the first three of the seven
  clean days 249
night, definition of 261, 263
nishtanu hativim 371, 376, 377
non-Jewish physician, relying upon 435
non-observant Jewish physician, relying
  upon 435
nose-bleed, attributing kesem to 174
nursing woman, see "meinekes"
nulliparous women, definition of
  460
nylon, kesem found upon 214

object that is not mekabel tumah
  see "kesem, on object not mekabel
    tumah"
off-white, kesem found upon 173
off-white or light beige garment, kesem
  found upon 172
oligo-ovulation 364
onah, definition of 261
onah beinonis
  a woman with vest kavuah exempt
    from 277, 388
  after twenty-four months after child
    birth 378
  always calculated from the last
    menstruation 303
  an onah beinonis kavuah 305
  bedikah during 137
  bedikah, if omitted 278
  computation of 255, 385, 303
  length of menstruation irrelevant 293
  definition of 262
  duration of 305
  explanation of Shach's position 304
  if forgot the exact date 415
  if never menstruates before the thirty-
    first 309
  if passes the vest kavuah day 308
  logic of 265
  number of bedikos required 398
  Or Zarua vest on night of thirty-first
    403
  regarding
    a pregnant woman 373
    a vest haguf 342, 352
    a woman on hormonal therapy 367
    meinekes 375
    the Or Zaruah's vest 306
    vest haones 359
    yemei tohar 375
  tevilah night coincides with 308
  thirtieth or thirty-first day 304, 385
  treated as a vest kavuah 303
  underlying logic 302
  whether a full twenty-four hours 305
onas havest
  a change in time-zones 404
  about to embark on a journey 405
  alternates between day and night 410
  Aviasaf's view 404
  bathing during 398
  bedikah cloth is lost 395
  bedikah done at a later time 396
  bedikah omitted 395

onas havest (continued)
  bedikah required 258
  bedikos during 395
  chibuk v'nishuk during 394
  cohabitation during 394
  coincides with both a tevilah night
    and journey 408
  definition of 258
  douching during 399
  harchakos during 395
  hargashah during 401
  if forgot the exact date 414
  importance of identifying 258
  intimate talk during 395, 406
  kesem found during 400
  number of bedikos required 397
  Or Zarua's vest 402
  over a span of several days 408
    see "the problematic days"
  perishah, duration of 401
  perishah, whether Biblical requirement
    393
  sharing a bed during 394
  showering during 399
  swimming during 398
  the problematic days 408
  to don white during 400
  two steps to be taken 258, 392
  wearing colored garments during
    400
  wearing very dark undergarments
    during 400
  when passes 413
    must assume that she is temeah
      287
  whether abstaining is Biblically
    required 259
  whether bedikah is Biblically required
    259
opening of the uterus
  as hargashah 75
  without appearance of blood 78
operative hysteroscopy
  description of 459
  status in halachah 459
Or Zarua's vest
  chibuk v'nishuk during 403
  chumra or halachah 402
  coincides with tevilah 407
  coincides with wedding night 408
  husband is leaving on a trip 403
  if usually alternates her period
    between day and night 402

Or Zarua's vest (continued)
    if usually menstruates within a span of
        a few days 403
    if vest uprooted by shorter interval 403
    in situation of doubt 402
    night of the thirty-first day 404
    on the thirty-first day 306
    on the evening of a tevilah 403
    perishah, whether required 402
    rationale of 402
    regarding
        a pregnant woman 374
        onah beinonis 306
        vest hamurkav 344
        vest she'aino kavuah 288, 403
    the problematic days 411
    when may be lenient 402
orange color, stain found upon a bedikah
    cloth 159
ovarian cystectomy, description of 461
pap smear
    bleeding caused by 450
    description of 453
    status in halachah 453, 462
paper
    kesem found upon 212
partially white garment
    kesem found upon 172
PCT, description of 468
pelvic examination, status in halachah
    463
Pergonal 365
period induced by the pill, regarding
    vestos 367
perishah, during the onas havest 393
pesichas hakever 39, 43, 44, 59–61, 138
    an instrument that penetrates the
        external os 439, 441
    an instrument that penetrates the
        internal os 440, 441
    definition of 437
    during pregnancy 438
    during the first three of the seven
        clean days 440
    external or internal os 425, 438, 439
    externally induced 61, 425, 440
    if fluid is discharged 437
    regarding a minor 438
    regarding a nursing woman 438
    regarding a woman after menopause
        438
    size of the opening 437
    the cervix or the uterus 439

pesichas hakever (continued)
    the width of opening 439
    use of a speculum 442
    use of an instrument 442
    use of the finger 442
    without discharging anything 437
pessary
    insertion of 458
    removal of 458
physical contact between a niddah and
    any man 394
physician
    asking whether he saw blood 422, 444
    examining a female 47
    non-Jew or a non-observant Jew, rely-
        ing on 435
    preferably an observant Jew 422, 437
    relying upon 60, 62, 422, 429, 435, 436,
        442, 443
pigmented lesions 462
pink stain on bedikah cloth 156
placenta previa definition of 463
polypectomy
    cervical 455
    description of 455
    status in halachah 456
    uterine (endometrial) 456
polyps 428, 459
post coital test, description of 468
post-menopause see "zekeinah"
post-menopausal bleeding 59, 458
post-partem 283, 374–377
    see "meinekes"
pre-menstrual staining 364
pre-washed garments
    if considered chaluk habaduk 216
    if hung outdoors to dry 216
pregnant or nursing woman
    bedikah after hargashah 90
    regarding kesamim 170, 181
    stain found upon a bedikah cloth
        151
pregnant woman
    regarding pesichas hakever 438
pregnancy 59
    bedikah the first three times of
        cohabitation 283
    determining when began 371
    dilation at end of 464
    establishing a vest during 374
    first three months
        if pregnancy is medically confirmed
            371

pregnancy (continued)
    menstruation during 373
    regarding vestos 371
    the halachah today 371
  gynecological procedures performed
    during 462
  pre-existing vestos 372
  regarding
    bedikos before and after first three
      cohabitations. 371
    Or Zarua vest 374
    vest hadilug 377
    vest haseirug 377
    vest she'aino kavuah 374, 381
    vestos 371–373
  shorter interval uprooting a longer
    interval 331
  the halachah today 373
  when considered pregnant 283
progesterone injections
  regarding vestos 365
prolapse 458
prozdor definition of 45, 423, 426
public display of her niddus, regarding
  amasla 104
quilt, kesem found upon 174
Rav
  asking a second opinion 38
  asking sheilos anonymously 35
  asking sheilos personally as opposed
    to over the phone 384
  consulting regarding scheduling a
    procedure 422, 444
  consulting regarding gynecological
    procedures 450
  contradicting own decision 110
  contradicting the ruling of another
    Rav 152
  divulging personal information to 35
  for advice in organizing a vest
    calendar 384
  hesitancy to disturb 37
  indispensable regarding hilchos
    niddah 34
  relating information about
    gynecological procedure 422
  showing vestos calendar to 38
red edge on bedikah cloth 159
reiyah
  absolute and cannot be limited
    178
  practical difference between it and
    kesem 178

repeating bedikah immediately 165
resectoscope 459
Rosh Chodesh
  the first day of 301
  vest for 301
s'fek-s'feika 99
safek chisaron yediah 180
safek deoraisa lechumra 176
safek derabanan lehakel 313
saline infusion sonography, description
  of 460
salpingo-oophorectomy, description of
  467
sanitary napkin, kesem found upon 214
self declared niddah status
  an immediate retraction 102
  encouraging a retraction 106
  how functions 101
  if obviously untrue 102
  made in jest 102
  provoked by anger 103, 104, 107
  reciting a b'rachah over the tevilah
    102, 106
  retained niddah status for a long
    period 104
  retraction of claim 101
  retraction through migo 101
  retraction through witnesses 101
  when displayed niddus publicly 104
  when told several people 104
  whether requires seven clean days 102
sensation of a flow
  as hargashah 76
  when finding kesem 173
sensation of fluid leaving the body
  accustomed to feeling such discharges
    401
  bedikah, if required 401
  during the onas havest 401
sensation of vaginal flow
  during the onas havest 401
seven clean days
  attributing to a wound on husband 241
  bedikos during 136, 170
  blood flow without hargashah, during
    72, 176
  douching during 131
  first three days 90, 143, 216, 243,
    245–250
    a kesem attributable to her
      niddus days 250
    a stain attributable to a wound
      248

seven clean days, first three days
    (continued)
    a stain found during 244
    a stain found on a bedikah cloth
      249
    a stain found on colored during 245
    a stain less than gris found during
      245
    after niddus caused by a small
      speck 249
    following a kesem 246
    following dam besulim 247
    following dam chimud 247
    kesem which may or may not be
      from 249
    regarding teliyah b'makkah 433
    when are telios possible 246
    when begin 245
  repeating a bedikah 166
  repeating the hefseik taharah 166
  repeating the moch dachuk 166
  required to check her garments for
    kesamim 179
  wearing colored garments during 209
  wearing white garments during 170,
    179
  why required of a niddah 56
sharp foods, vest for eating 362
shaviah anafshei
  refuted by witnesses 101
  whether Biblical precept 101
sheet, kesem found upon 174
sheilos, asking anonymously 35
shimush 155
shivering spell as vest haguf 339
shomeres yom k'neged yom 53
shower during the onas havest 399
single witness when believed 96
skin tags 462
small speck of blood, first three of the
  seven clean days after 249
sneezing spell as vest haguf 338
sonogram status in halachah 463
sounding of uterus 459, 471
speculum
  endocervical, use of 456
  use of 452
stain on a bedikah cloth during first
  three of the seven clean days 249
staining, usually preceedes menstruation
  184
stains as vest haguf 339
stretching spell as vest haguf 338

Suction Curettage, definition of 457
supracervical hysterectomy
  description of 467
  if finds blood in the future 467
suspicion that wife was not tovel 101
swimming during the onas havest 398
synthetic materials kesem found upon 214
tampon
  inserted while garment was worn 223
  stain found upon 214
teliyah
  comparison, if required 231
  if the shades are slightly different 231
  indication that the kesem came from
    the body 232
  indirect 237
  governed by specific regulations 230
  must be definitive 232
  must be direct 236
  must be logical 234
  of kesem 174
  only identifiable source 176
  only if colors are similar 230
  regarding a bedikah cloth 286
  regarding a Torah prohibition 230
  retroactive 233
  straining while relieving herself 240
  to a less probable source 230
  to purposely cause a teliyah 237
  to several sources 233
  two sources combined to form one
    stain 234
  was painting with red paint 238
  was salting meat 238
  wound noticed only later 233
teliyah b'makah 428
  a wound not known to be bleeding
    429
  after menopause 429
  determining presence of makkah
    432
  during the first three of the seven
    clean days 433
  during the Or Zarua's vest 432
  during the time of her vest 431, 432
  for a nursing woman 429
  if woman has no veset kavuah
    429, 431
  on (or after) the thirtieth day 431, 432
  on a hefseik taharah 432
  on the day of her veset 431
  on the day of veset she'aino kavuah 432
  regarding a kesem 431, 432

teliyah b'makah (continued)
  regarding first bedikah of the seven
    clean days 433
  regarding uterine bleeding 451
teliyah of
  kesem found
    during the first three of the seven
      clean days 244
    on expected vest day 230
    on her hand or foot 235
    on the body and a garment 235
    on the outside of the inner garment
      235
    only on the body 234
    upon an inner garment 234
  kesem that looks like actual blood 230
  yellow discharge, surrounded by a red
    edge 232
  black to red 230
  completely dissimilar shades of red
    230
teliyah to
  nose-bleed 239
  hand that touched a wound 237
  husband or child 240, 241
  partially healed wound 238
  slaughtering market 238
  source incapable of producing a stain
    the size of the kesem 231
  source of uncertain color 231
  source which is itself dependent upon
    a teliyah 234
  wound 238
    on husband during seven clean
      days 241
    on husband or child 241, 242
    on older son 241
    on the neck 239
    which is not similar to uterine
      blood 230
  unknown source 243, 244
  another woman 242
  hemorrhoids 233, 240
  niddus period 242
tenaculum 471
  description of 457
  use of 452, 461
Terumas HaDeshen's vest 284, 409
testimony pertaining to matters of
  halachah 95
tevilah
  amasla regarding 105
  during the Or Zarua vest 407

tevilah (continued)
  during the problematic days 412
  for kesem, reciting b'rachah 178
  on the thirty-first night 308
  reciting a b'rachah over questionable
    147
  ruling on that of of one's wife 111
the problematic days
  perishah, whether required 408, 411
  regarding a tevilah night 412
  regarding newlyweds 411
  regarding Or Zarua's vest 411
  the twenty-four months following
    childbirth 412
  uprooting some days 412
  whether a span of, three, four or seven
    410
thirtieth of the month
  vest for 299, 300
  regarding vest hachodesh bedilug 315
thirty-first day of the month
  regarding the Or Zaruah's vest 306
  whether considered onah beinonis 304
thread, on bedikah cloth 159
tightly fitting garment,
  if analagous to a bedikah 80, 81, 87
tiny red spot on bedikah cloth 159
tissue
  a stain found on 138, 212, 214
  if mekabel tumah 212
  inspecting 138
  kesem found upon 173, 185
  looking at 173, 212
toilet seat, kesem found upon 186
total hysterectomy 466
tovel v'sheretz b'yado 53
trust
  in halachah not a matter of believa-
    bility 96
  pertaining to matters of halachah 95
  the Torah accords a woman 97
tumah,
  active and residual 53
tumas niddah,
  ramifications of 46, 54
twelve year old girl,
  assumed to be a niddah 58
twenty-four months after pregnancy
  see "meinekes"
  regarding vestos 377
  when pass
    regarding onah beinonis 378
    regarding vest hachodesh 377

twenty-four months after pregnancy,
  when pass (continued)
    regarding vest haflagah 378
    regarding vest she'aino kavuah 378
tzavar harechem 45
  definition of 424
ulcerations 428
unmarried woman
  physical contact with 58
  regarding kesamim 170, 181
  regarding niddus 58
uprooting vest, see "akiras vest"
urination
  blood found afterwards 74
  kesem found afterwards 185
  may mask a hargashah 50
urine, if mekabel tumah 215
urine or stool, kesem found upon 215
uterine bleeding 441
  attributing to a makkah 451
  due to an injury 428
uterine blood, extracted in an unnatural
  manner 178
uterine flow
  sensation of, as hargashah 77
  sensation of, whether possible 76
uterine sounding
  description of 459
  status in halachah 460
uterine wound 429
  bleeding from, whether render a
    woman a niddah 178
  definition of 430
vaginal biopsy, status in halachah 461
vaginal bleeding 441
vaginal flow, sensation of
  as hargashah 76
  bedikah afterwards
    if no blood found 86
    requirement of 85
  if not certain that felt 86
  if usually finds clear discharges 88
  stain less than a gris found afterwards
    87
  stain on garment found afterwards 87
vaginal irritation
  attributing stain to 160
  notifying the Rav 152
vaginal hysterectomy 467
vaginal repair, status in halachah 461
vaginitis 428
  definition of 471
vaseline

treating bedikah cloth with 134
treating vaginal area with 134
very dark undergarments, wearing,
  when menstruation is expected 400
vest
  abstaining on the onas havest,
    deoraisa or derabanan 260
  according to the onset or the duration
    269
  as relates to candle lighting time 384
  based on a flow without a hargashah
    268
  based on a stained bedikah cloth 268
  based on Hebrew calendar 384
  based on kesamim 267
  calculation of 384
  day, when begins 384
  definition of 258
  determined by the day and the onah
    270
  determined by the day the flow begins
    269, 270
  dormant vest 326, 327
    if when reactivated can uproot
      another vest 333
    regarding a vest hadilug 316
  duration of 263
  establishing during pregnancy 374
  flow continues for a short while into
    the next onah 270
  from a period induced by the pill 366
  length of the flow 384
  logic of 263
  longer interval
    if ever uprooted by shorter
      intervals 331
    uprooted by a shorter interval 330,
      387
  minutest amount of dam 266
  negative vest, regarding first three
    times of cohabitation 284
  only from a menstrual flow 266
  preceded by a stained bedikah cloth
    273
  regarding meinekes 375
  shorter interval, uprooting a longer
    interval 330, 387
  to note whether period began by day
    or night 271
  uprooting, see "akiras vest"
  when flow is considered a
    continuation of previous flow
    269

vest (continued)
   when the vest day passes 274
vest day
   relations after the day has passed 98
   relations during 98
vest haachilos
   compared to vest haguf or vest haones
     362
   definition of 362
   if becomes vest kavuah by itself 363
   more natural than vest haones 363
   three different foods of similar type
     362
vest hachodesh
   a flow that continues on the vest day
     335, 336
   a menstruation on the night before the
     vest day 335
   after twenty-four months 377
   akirah of 326, 335, 386
   all menstrations must begin in same
     onah 298
   alternates between day and night 299
   bedilug 315
   beseirug 317
   calculation of 254, 385
   definition of 262, 297
   differences between it and vest
     haflagah 302
   established with only three periods
     297, 302
   even if interval of days are unequal
     297
   even if skipped a period 302
   for the last day of the month 300
   if forgot the exact date 415
   logic of 264
   on alternating months 298
   one onah later each month 299
   regarding a pregnant woman 373
   regarding vest haones 359
   the thirtieth of the month 299, 300
   two independent vestos 298, 302
   unaffected by any menstruation on
     another day 297
   vest kavuah for Rosh Chodesh 301
   whether can uproot another vest
     hachodesh 329
vest hachodesh bedilug
   a recurring cycle 316
   amount of periods required 315
   regarding the thirtieth of the month
     315

vest hadilug
   a decreasing vest 317
   amount of periods required 313
   definition of 312
   dispute of Rav and Shmuel regarding
     313
   how differs from other vestos 312
   if follows predetermined system 314
   increments in the amount of
     increments 312
   logic of 265
   only if established 287
   regarding a pregnant woman 377
   regarding nursing woman 312
   significant only if vest kavuah 312
   whether remains dormant 316
vest haflagah
   a flow that continues on the vest day
     335
   after twenty-four months 378
   akirah of 326, 329, 387
   all menstrations must begin in same
     onah 294
   bedilug 313
   computation of 255, 292, 386
     according to Graz 293, 294
     from days, not onos 294, 295
     from immediately preceding flow
       293, 334
     length of menstruation irrelevant
       293
     not from an expected flow 295, 302
   cannot have two vestos 302
   definition of 262, 292
   difference between it and a vest
     hashavuah 320
   differences between it and vest
     hachodesh 302
   for the sixtieth interval day 299
   if forgot the exact date 415
   if skips three menstrual periods 327
   intervals must be free of intermediate
     menstrual flow 292
   logic of 264
   not possible beseirug 318
   readjusting calendar to latest
     menstruation 296, 302
   regarding vest haones 359
   requires four periods to establish vest
     kavuah 292, 302
   sequence of intervals, ten, ten, twenty
     and twenty 296
   when a woman becomes pregnant 373

vest haflagah bedilug
  a recurring cycle 317
  amount of periods required 314
vest haguf 69, 70, 75, 184
  a feeling that the period is imminent
    340
  a flow limited to the duration of the
    cramps 348
  a flow preceded by kesamim 273
  a symptomatic vest 338
  abstaining after the cramps stop 345
  akirah of 353
    without bedikah 280
  arrival of the day alone 347
  as opposed to hargashah 338
  bedikah on the onas havest, if omitted
    279, 341, 353
  definition of 262, 265, 338
  duration of sneezing spell 339
  duration of the onas havest 346
  flow usually
    begins after the cramps end 349
    begins before the cramps 350
    begins immediately with the onset
      of the cramps, 348
    begins on the following onah 349
    begins some time after the cramps
      348
    continues after the cramps subside
      349
    is delayed for more than a day 349
  how differs from hargashah 75
  how differs from other vestos 341
  how similar to other vestos 340
  if the symptom appears on a different
    day 347
  if the three periods occurred in differ-
    ent onos 341
  kesamim as 400
  mood changes 340
  only unusual symptoms 339
  physical manifestations not noted by
    Chazal 338
  regarding onah beinonis 342, 352
  similarity of the symptoms 339
vest haguf murkav see "vest hamurkav"
vest haguf, a woman with
  regarding bedikah the first three times
    of cohabitation 283
vest hakefitzos see "vest haones" 358
vest hamurkav
  a causative vest 342
  akirah of 354

vest hamurkav (continued)
  altering the nature of the vest 352
  arrival of the day alone 344–346
  definition of 265
  if concludes as a simple vest 352
  if day passes without cramps 344
  if symptom appears on a different day
    343, 345
  if three occasions must be consecutive
    345
  menstrual bleeding that occurs
    between the three occasions 343
  must abstain the entire day 344
  on the day following the cramps. 342
  positive vest hamurkav
    definition of 343
  possible vest hamurkav
    definition of 345
  reestablishing 355
  regarding onah beinonis 346
  she'aino kavuah
    if bedikah is not done on onas
      havest 351
    must abstain on all the vest possi-
      bilities 351
  when bedikah is required 344
  with a combination of two physical
    manifestations 342
vest haones
  a causative vest 358
  after three different physical exertions
    358
  akirah of 361
  both periods of interval associated
    with jump 359
  definition of 358
  if menstruated on the day following
    the jump 360
  if required to observe vest hachodesh
    359
  if she jumps again on a different day
    359
  if she jumps again on same day 359
  menstruated two days after the jump
    360
  must observe onah beinonis 359
  only if established 287
  somewhat illogical 358
  when becomes a vest kavuah 360, 361
  when becomes a vest she'aino kavuah
    361
vest haseirug
  amount of periods required 318

vest haseirug (continued)
definition of 317
regarding a pregnant woman 377
vest hashaos
definition of 288
parameters of the hour 290
vest hashavuah
bedilug 319
definition of 319
difference between it and a vest
haflagah 320
significant only if vest kavuah 322
two types 319
unique nature of 321
when transformed into a regular vest
haflagah 322
vest kavuah
a dormant vest 326, 327, 388
akirah of 276, 324, 388
if bedikah done next day 278
only with bedikah 276, 325
bedikah delayed for a long time 278
bedikah on the onas havest
cloth if lost 279
if omitted 278
regarding chibuk v'nishuk 278
required 278
definition of 261
establishing 387
followed by a vest she'aino kavuah
329
if forgot the exact date 415
if passed, must ask whether did
bedikah 287, 397
never becomes uprooted 325
reactivation 326
uproots all other vestos 286
when passed 98
vest kavuah, shorter, whether uproots a
longer vest kavuah 334
vest kavuah, a woman with
if bedikah required before or after
cohabitation 280
if menstruates on another day 290
vest she'aino kavuah
after twenty-four months after child
birth 378
akirah of 277, 325, 330
akirah of, even without bedikah 277,
280, 325
bedikah if required on the onah of the
vest 279, 397
bedikah, if omitted 279, 397

vest she'aino kavuah (continued)
definition of 262
if must abstain on Or Zarua's onah 288
if passed, if must ask whether menstruated 287
rationale of 263
uprooting through vest kavuah 328
when passed 99
vest she'aino kavuah, a woman with
after the three bedikos 285
if bedikah required before or after
cohabitation 281
vestos
a flow preceded by kesamim 272
causative and symptomatic 263
deOraisa or deRabanan 260, 393
depend upon sunrise and sunset 270
dependent upon the deliberations of
Beis Din 264
doubt whether before or after sunrise
271
established before conversion 261
importance of familiarity with the
laws of 260
logic of 261, 263
not a simple matter of probability 261
regarding a flow following another
flow 485
regarding kesamim 170, 175, 179
regarding kesamim that precede a
menstruation 183
to keep a written record of 260
two close consecutive flows 274
why deRabanan 260
vestos calendar, showing to Rav 38
vulvar biopsy, status in halachah 461
vulvar lesions, removal of 462
washed garment with kesem 172
washed cloth, if considered eid habaduk
125
washed garment, kesem found upon 172
warts 462
water, kesem found in 186
water breakage before childbirth 63
wearing colored garments during the
onas havest 400
wedding night during the Or Zarua vest
408
witnesses to retract self made niddah
status 101
woman
assuming that she is tehorah 98
evaluating the color of a stain 107

woman (continued)
    relating a halachic decision 108, 110
    relations with when sleepy 98, 99
    showing a stain to another woman
        108
    suspected claim that she was tovel 100
    trust that the Torah accords to 97
    when relied upon less than a man 97
    who misleads husband, relying on in
        future 98
wound
    attributing a kesem to during first
        three days 248
    determining presence of makkah 431
yawning spell as vest haguf 338
yemei niddah 52
yemei tohar
    after childbirth 63
    regarding onah beinonis 375

yemei tumah
    after childbirth 63
yemei zivah 52
    Rambam's view 52
yoledes
    Rabbinic law 65
    regarding a miscarriage 66
    Torah law 63
young couples
    following lenient opinion 331
zavah 51–56, 64, 65, 97
zavah ketanah 53, 54
zekeinah
    definition of 378, 379
    how differes from besulah 381
    how halachah differs from regular
        akiras vest 379
    regarding vest she'aino kavuah 381
    regarding vestos 378

❧ Hebrew Concepts Discussed

achar kach — אחר כך definition of 73
eid echad ne'eman b'issurin — עד אחד נאמן באיסורין 96
miktzas hayom k'kulo — מקצת היום ככלו 54
nishtanu hativim — נשתנו הטבעים 371, 376, 377
safek chisaron yediah — ספק חסרון ידיעה 180
safek deOraisa lechumra — ספק דאורייתא לחומרא 176
safek deRabanan lehakel — ספק דרבנן להקל 313
shaviah anafshei — שויא אנפשיה 101
tovel v'sheretz b'yado — טובל ושרץ בידו 53

♆ Index of Primary Sources

TALMUD NIDDAH

3a	221
5a	181, 182
7a	370
7b	370
9a	259, 371
9b	52, 303
11a	359, 485
12b	281
13a	135, 137
14a	73
15a	259, 260
16a	210, 278, 396
17a	125, 128, 129
17b	424
19a	57, 153
19b	188, 203
20b	107, 144, 154, 162
21b	60, 437
22b	439
32a	182
37a	64
39a	370
40a	58, 64, 424-426
41b	64, 426
53b	272
57b	72, 74, 176, 185, 202, 211, 235, 426
58a	74, 178, 200, 219, 226
58b	176, 223
60b	202
61b	204, 207, 208
63a	338, 339
63b	258, 263, 338, 339 347, 362, 363
64a	313
66a	56
67b	54

SHULCHAN ARUCH, YOREH DEAH

98:3	180
127:1	96
183	58, 59
184:1	98, 135, 183
184:2	394, 401, 402
184:3	394
184:4	271
184:5	270
184:6	269, 486
184:9	136, 137, 278, 279, 396 406, 485
184:11	98, 99, 287, 397
184:12	98, 359
185:1	100
185:3	67, 101, 103
185:4	67, 77, 258
186:1	280
186:2	137, 281, 285
186:3	283, 409
187:1	73
187:5	178
187:7	431, 434
188:1	78, 79, 154, 158
188:2	108, 109
188:3	60, 178, 437, 438
188:4-6	59
188:6	437, 439, 440
189:1	277, 303, 309
189:2	276, 297, 324, 325
189:3	288, 290
189:4	137, 278, 279, 303 396, 406
189:5	287
189:6	297, 319
189:7	313
189:8	316

189:9	318
189:10	314, 315
189:11	287, 312
189:12	298, 309, 319
189:13	299
189:13-16	324
189:14	290, 318, 329
189:15	326, 327
189:17	359-361
189:19	338-340, 343, 345
189:20	352
189:21	351
189:22	342, 351
189:23	339
189:24	348, 349
189:25	345, 346
189:26	340, 353, 354
189:27	370, 381
189:28	381
189:29	379
189:30	380, 381
189:31	381
189:32	298
189:33	372, 374, 375, 381
189:34	372, 374, 377
190:1	51, 81, 176, 178 183
190:2	181, 182
190:3	182
190:4	182
190:5	189
190:6	195, 224
190:8	193, 196, 224
190:9	200
190:10	202
190:11	222, 224, 226, 227, 234, 236, 238, 239
190:12	220, 223, 236

190:14 222, 223
190:15 242
190:17 243, 244
190:18 88, 230, 234, 235, 238, 239, 432
190:19 240, 241
190:22 232
190:23 230
190:26 231
190:30 231
190:33-37 126
190:35 189
190:36 81, 126, 189
190:37 126
190:39 215
190:41 242
190:42 242
190:44 216, 243, 250
190:46 125
190:48 242
190:49 242
190:50 242
190:51 242
190:52 181, 242
190:54 124, 179, 267
194:1 63, 65
194:14 64
195 148
196:1 136
196:2 246
196:4 136
196:5 136
196:6 129, 132
196:9 135, 183

REMA
127:3 96, 97
184:1 280
184:2 409
184:32 367
185:1 100, 101
185:3 102, 103, 106, 110
185:4 47
186:2 281
187:5 328, 429, 431, 432
188:1 158
188:4 145
189:13 286, 296, 303

328-330, 334
189:14 286
189:23 362
190:10 208
190:11 226
190:12 221
190:13 221
190:27 232
190:33 125
190:41 245
194:1 66
196:6 132
196:10 245, 248, 249
196:11 246
242:31 152

TAZ
184:1 98
184:2 263, 402, 404
184:9 269, 485
184:16 99
185:1 100, 101
185:2 104, 105
185:3 110
187:10 431
188:1 142, 143, 162
189:5 309
189:10 317
189:12 318, 319
189:14 304
189:17 303, 304
189:18 295, 296, 303, 330, 334
189:28 329, 332
189:30 295
189:31 295, 309, 327
189:33 338
189:36 343
189:38 279, 325, 341, 351, 353, 367
189:39 344, 346
189:46 379
190:2 177
190:10 226
190:11 226
190:12 227
190:14 237
190:19 227

190:37 222
190:41 88, 192, 230, 232
191:4 143
194:1 65
196:4 248

SHACH
127:30 97
157:10 47
183:3 58
184:7 402
184:13 271
184:14 271
184:16 269, 485
184:18 375
184:23 278, 396
184:25 405
184:27 406
184:31 98
184:32 353
184:34 98
185:1 100, 101
185:2 67, 102
185:3 103
185:5 104,105
186:1 281
187:1 73
187:17 428
187:19 432
187:20 429
187:24 431
187:26 431, 432
187:27 238, 431, 432
188:2 156
188:3 142,143
188:4 158
188:5 158
188:7 108, 110
189:1 304, 309
189:9 317
189:13 297
189:14 320
189:15 313
189:20 316
189:21 317
189:30 304, 305, 308, 310
189:31 296, 330, 334
189:32 334

189:39	409, 410	189:73	374	190:58	221
189:40	296, 329, 330	189:75	377	190:60	216
	332, 334	190:3	182	190:68	222
189:41	328	190:10	195	195:20	47
189:48	359, 361	190:13	196, 224	196:13	248
189:50	360, 361	190:16	212	242:54	153
189:52	338	190:17	226		
189:53	338	190:18	225	**NEKUDOS HAKESEF**	
189:54	339	190:19	224	189:18	296
189:57	352	190:29	239	189:38	279, 325, 341,
189:58	352	190:31	244		351
189:61	351	190:33	240	189:39	344, 346
189:65	327, 380	190:51	248, 250	190:41	232